AN INTRODUCTION TO THE STUDY OF INSECTS

DONALD J. BORROR
Professor of Entomology
The Ohio State University

DWIGHT M. DeLONG
Emeritus Professor of Entomology
The Ohio State University

HOLT, RINEHART AND WINSTON

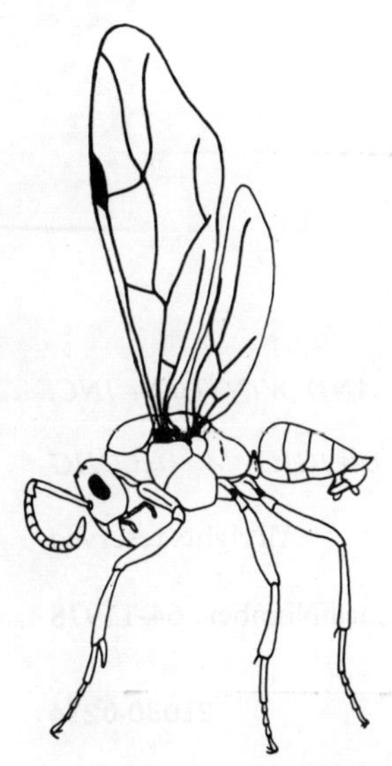

AN INTRODUCTION TO THE STUDY OF INSECTS

REVISED EDITION

NEW YORK • CHICAGO • SAN FRANCISCO • TORONTO • LONDON

Library of Congress Catalog Card Number: 64-11978

21030-0214

Printed in the United States of America

THIRD PRINTING

Preface to the Revised Edition

Since the first appearance of this book in 1954 a number of studies have been made on the taxonomy of insects, and these studies have altered our concept of the subordinal groupings in many orders; in addition, many new genera and species have been described, and these, together with the discovery of forms hitherto unrecorded for the United States, have necessitated a revision of our outline and account of several orders. The several years of student use of the keys in the first edition have revealed some weak points.

The major changes in this edition consist of a bringing up to date of the classification of several orders, and a revision of most of the keys. A few new illustrations have been added, and a few of the old ones have been changed. The bibliographies of most chapters have been brought up to date by the addition of recent references. The discussions of a number of topics throughout the book have been expanded. The chapter on insect control in the first edition has been deleted, as the authors feel that this subject is somewhat out of place in a book of this type.

A great many people have made valuable suggestions and criticisms regarding specific portions of this book, but we are particularly indebted to the following for assistance in this revision: Richard D. Alexander, Ross H. Arnett, Jr., Arthur C. Borror, Osmond P. Breland, Theodore J. Cohn, Paul H. Freytag, Theodore H. Hubbell, F. P. Ide, D. E. Johnston, Josef N. Knull, Michael Kosztarab, Alan Stone, Charles A. Triplehorn, Barry Valentine, and Richard E. White. The following have assisted with the loan of illustrations or permission to use illustrations previously printed in their publications: Richard D. Alexander, Arthur C. Borror, Adrien Robert, Charles A. Triplehorn, and Richard E. White.

Columbus, Ohio
November, 1963

D.J.B.
D.M.DeL.

Preface to the First Edition

The importance of the role played by insects in the world of living things is becoming more appreciated each year, not only because of the attention given to the species which act as pests, but because of the increasing realization that many species are extremely valuable to man. The study of insects is an important part of the training of every agriculturist, biology teacher, and student of nature.

Many books are already available to the student or teacher interested in insects; some give special emphasis to the biological or economic aspects, and others emphasize the taxonomic phase of entomology, but few combine emphasis on both insect study—actually working with insects—and identification. This book is intended to serve as a text for a beginning course in college entomology, and as a guide for teachers and others interested in the study of insects. Since most of the keys are complete for all the families occurring in the United States, this book could serve as a text for an advanced course in insect classification.

The discussions of morphology and physiology have been kept to a minimum, the aim being to present enough material on these phases of entomology to enable the student to use the keys and understand something of the general biology of the insects he encounters. An attempt has been made to make the keys as workable as possible by illustrating most of the key characters. No attempt has been made to present keys to larval forms.

Insects should be observed and studied in the field as well as in the classroom and laboratory, and this book is designed to serve as a text for entomology courses which involve field and laboratory work. We realize that field work is difficult or impossible in some courses, due to the season in which the course is given, the location of the school, or other factors, but many insects can be maintained indoors in cages or aquaria, and the study of such living material can be substituted for field observations.

We have drawn on many sources of information in the preparation of this book, some of which are listed in the bibliographies at the end of each chapter. These bibliographies are far from complete; rather than striving for completeness, we have tried to list references which can serve as a starting point for the student interested in going further. In our treatment of the various orders we have generally followed the most recent or accepted classification; in some cases we have used a somewhat simplified classification because it seemed more suitable in a book of this type. Concepts of insect relationships and classification change as our knowledge of insects increases, and no arrangement of orders and families is likely to be permanent.

We are greatly indebted to a number of persons who have read portions of the manuscript and have made valuable suggestions and criticisms, particularly to J. Gordon Edwards, T. H. Hubbell, Maurice T. James, Clarence H. Kennedy, Josef N. Knull, Karl V. Krombein, John E. Lane, A. W. Lindsey, Harlow B. Mills, C. F. W. Muesebeck, Alvah Peterson, E. S. Ross, H. H. Ross, Marion R. Smith, Kathryn M. Sommerman, Louis J. Stannard, Edward S. Thomas, and E. M. Walker.

The majority of the original drawings in this book was made by or under the direction of the senior author. The following persons have assisted in the preparation of these drawings: Richard D. Alexander, Calvin E. Beckelheimer, Arthur C. Borror, G. Mallory Boush, William C. Costello, Edward W. Huffman, John E.

Lane, Paul D. Ludwig, George W. Murphy, Robert F. Ruppel, and Celeste W. Taft. The original photographs were made principally by the junior author, assisted by Oscar Metze.

Many entomologists and a few editors have assisted with the loan of illustrations or permission to use certain illustrations previously printed in their publications. In each case where a borrowed illustration is used its source is indicated. Special credit, we believe, should be given the following persons: James S. Ayars, Stanley F. Bailey, Richard M. Bohart, Hazel E. Branch, A. W. A. Brown, H. E. Burke, Barnard D. Burks, R. W. Burrell, C. P. Clausen, Ralph H. Davidson, Donald DeLeon, Lafe R. Edmunds, Richard C. Froeschner, B. B. Fulton, Robert Glenn, Ashley B. Gurney, David G. Hall, Philip H. Harden, M. J. Hayell, William R. Horsfall, H. B. Hungerford, Maurice T. James, B. J. Kaston, George F. Knowlton, J. N. Knull, J. W. Leonard, Philip Luginbill, E. A. McGregor, Luis F. Martorell, John Moser, Claud R. Neiswander, Harry L. Parker, Alvah Peterson, Edward S. Ross, Herbert H. Ross, John G. Shaw, Herbert H. Smith, Kathryn M. Sommerman, R. W. Strandtmann, George R. Struble, Edwin Way Teale, C. A. Triplehorn, G. Stuart Walley, E. M. Walker, and Mrs. Blanche P. Young. To all organizations and individuals who have loaned illustrations, we wish to express our sincere thanks for permission to use their material.

The Ohio State University
January, 1954

DONALD J. BORROR
DWIGHT M. DELONG

Contents

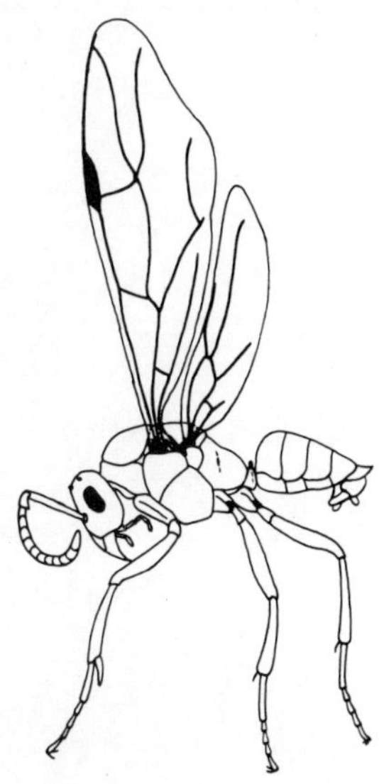

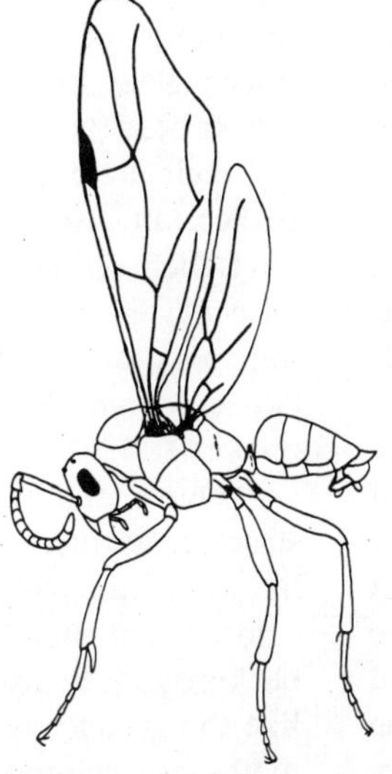

1

Insects and Their Ways

The insects are the dominant group of animals on the earth today. They far surpass all other terrestrial animals in number, and they occur practically everywhere. Several hundred thousand different kinds have been described—three times as many as there are in the rest of the animal kingdom—and over a thousand kinds may occur in a fair-sized backyard. Their populations often number many millions to the acre.

The world of insects abounds in the picturesque, the unusual, and even the fantastic. An almost endless variety of structural and physiological peculiarities and adaptations to different living conditions is to be found among these animals. A great many insects are extremely valuable to man, and human society could not exist in its present form without them: by their pollinating activities they make possible the production of many agricultural crops, including most orchard fruits, clovers, many vegetables, cotton, and tobacco; they provide us with honey, beeswax, silk, and other products of commercial value; they serve as the food of many birds, fish, and other useful animals; they perform services as scavengers; they help to keep harmful animals and plants in check; they have been useful in medicine and in scientific research and they are looked upon as interesting animals by people in all walks of life. A few insects are harmful and cause enormous losses each year in agricultural crops, stored products, and the health of man and animals.

Let us examine briefly some of the ways insects are fitted for life in the world about us. These ways, or adaptations, are the factors responsible for the present dominance of the insect group.

Insects have lived on the earth for about 300 million years—compared with less than 1 million for man—and during this time they have evolved in many directions to become adapted for life in almost every type of habitat. In their evolution they have "solved" in many ways the various problems with which man still struggles—the problems of food supply, protection against enemies, adaptation to specific environmental conditions, and social organization.

Some insects have structures that are amazing when we consider them in relation to the structures possessed by vertebrates. The bees and wasps and some of the ants have their ovipositor or egg-laying organ developed into a poisoned dagger (sting), which serves as an excellent means of offense and defense. Some ichneumons have a hairlike ovipositor 4 inches long that can penetrate wood. Some snout beetles have the front of the head drawn out into a slender affair longer than the rest of the body, with tiny jaws at the end; some stalk-eyed flies have their eyes situated at the ends of long slender stalks, which in one South American species are as long as the wings. Certain individuals in some of the honey ants become so engorged with food that their abdomens become greatly distended, and they become living storehouses of food which they regurgitate "on demand" to other ants in the colony. Some of the stag beetles have jaws half as long as the body and branched like the antlers of a stag.

Compared with ourselves, insects are peculiarly constructed animals. They might be said to be inside out because their skeleton is on the outside, or upside down because their nerve cord extends along the lower side of the body and the heart lies above the alimentary canal. They have no lungs, but breathe through a number of tiny holes in the body wall—all behind the head; the air entering these holes is distributed over the body directly to the body tissues through a multitude of tiny branching tubes.

Insect sense organs are often peculiar compared with those of man and other vertebrates. Most insects have two kinds of eyes—two or three simple eyes located on the upper part of the face, and a pair of compound eyes on the sides of the head; the compound eyes are often very large, occupying most of the head, and may consist of thousands of individual eye units. Some insects hear by means of eardrums, while others hear by means of very sensitive hairs on their antennae or elsewhere on their bodies; an insect possessing eardrums may have them on the sides of the body at the base of the abdomen (short-horned grasshoppers), or on the front legs below the "knee" (long-horned grasshoppers and crickets).

One of the interesting features of insect structure is the way so many insects look like or mimic something else. Many are so colored that they blend perfectly with their background; many grasshoppers are colored like the ground on which they alight; many moths are colored like the bark of a tree; and many beetles, bugs, flies, and bees are colored like the flowers they visit. This color resemblance makes the insect very inconspicuous and probably serves to protect it against attack by enemies.

Many insects strikingly resemble objects in their environment—in both color and shape. Walking sticks and inchworms resemble twigs, so much so that it sometimes takes a keen eye to detect them when they remain motionless. Certain treehoppers resemble thorns, some of the butterflies resemble dead leaves, some of the beetles resemble bits of bark, and some scale insects resemble galls.

Some insects are rendered inconspicuous by covering themselves with debris or excrement, and others build cases over themselves. The larvae of tortoise beetles attach bits of debris and excrement to a pair of spines at the posterior end of their body and hold this material over their body like a parasol. Many dragonfly nymphs become covered with silt and debris as they rest on the bottom of a pond waiting for prey. The larvae of some of the lacewings cover themselves with debris, which offers them concealment as they wait or forage for prey. The larvae of many caddisflies and a few moths live in cases constructed of materials from their environment; caddisfly larvae construct cases of sand grains, pebbles, twigs, or leaves, and they live and pupate in these cases. The larvae of bagworms live in cases made of leaves or twigs.

One of the most remarkable types of mimicry to be found in insects is that in which an insect without special means of defense resembles another that has a sting or some other effective defensive mechanism. This resemblance may be in size, shape, and behavior, as well as in color. The nymphs of some of the broad-headed bugs resemble ants, and the adults resemble spider wasps. Some of the robber flies, hawk moths, and syrphid flies mimic bumble bees, and many syrphid flies, thick-headed flies, clear-winged moths, and beetles mimic wasps; this mimicry is often very striking, and only a trained observer will notice that these insects are not wasps and will neither bite nor sting. The art of camouflage is indeed highly developed in insects.

Insects sometimes exhibit unusual physiological characteristics. Some of them may be frozen solid at temperatures of 30 or more degrees below zero Fahrenheit, and still be revived. Some can be exposed to as great a vacuum as man can obtain, and then be instantly changed to normal air pressure (by breaking the vacuum chamber) without serious effects.

One may find many instances where the behavior of insects seems to surpass in intelligence the behavior of man. Some insects seem to show an amazing foresight, especially as regards egg laying with a view to the future needs of the young. Many species have a social organization that is often more efficient than that of man; some social insects have mastered the art of sex control, and most of them have solved problems of food storage that are not yet completely solved by man. Indeed, man can learn much about social organization by studying the ant or the termite.

In the nature of their development and life cycle, insects run the gamut from the very simple to the complex and even amazing. Many undergo relatively little change as they develop; the young differ from the adults principally in size, and the young and adults have similar habits. The vast majority, however, undergo in their development rather remarkable changes, both in appearance and in habits. Most people are familiar with the metamorphosis of insects and possibly think of it as commonplace—which, as a matter of fact, it is—but in comparison with the development of a vertebrate, it is indeed fantastic. Consider the development of a butterfly: an egg hatches into a wormlike caterpillar; this caterpillar eats ravenously and every week or so sheds its skin and the lining of its "lungs" and intestine; after a time it becomes a pupa hung on a branch or leaf like a ham in a meat shop; after a while a beautiful winged butterfly emerges from this "ham." If this sort of thing happened in the vertebrates, it would be like an eagle developing from a snake—an event which would indeed be fantastic.

The majority of insects have a life cycle like that of a butterfly; the eggs hatch into wormlike larvae, which grow by periodically shedding their outer skin (together with the linings of their foregut, hindgut, and breathing tubes), finally transforming into an inactive pupal stage from which the winged adult emerges. A fly grows from a maggot; a beetle grows from a grub; and a bee, wasp, or ant grows from a maggotlike grub. When these insects become adult, they stop growing; a little fly (in the winged stage) does not grow into a bigger one.

An insect with this sort of development (complete metamorphosis) may live as a larva in a very different sort of place than it lives in as an adult. One fly that is a common household pest spends its larval life in garbage or some other filth; another very similar fly may have spent its larval life eating the insides out of a grub or caterpillar; the junebug or may beetle that beats against the screens at night spent its larval life in the ground; a long-horned beetle one may see on a flower spent its larval life in the wood of a tree or log.

Insects feed on an almost endless variety of foods. Thousands feed upon plants and practically every plant is fed upon by some kind of insect. The plant feeders may feed on almost any part of the plant; caterpillars, leaf beetles, and leafhoppers feed on the leaves, aphids feed on the stems, white grubs feed on the roots, certain weevil and moth larvae feed on the fruits, and so on; many of these insects burrow into the plant and feed inside it. Thousands of insects are carnivorous, feeding on both vertebrate animals and other insects; some are predators, some are parasites, and some are blood-sucking. Some of the blood-sucking types, such as the mosquitoes, lice, and fleas, are disease vectors and cause untold injury to man and other animals. Some species feed in dead wood; others feed on stored foods of all types; some feed on various fabrics; and many feed on decaying materials. Drugstore beetles are capable of feeding on almost everything from face powder to mustard plasters.

Insects often have interesting and effective means of defense against intruders or enemies. Most insects when disturbed will attempt escape, and many are extremely quick; on the other hand, many beetles and caterpillars "play dead" when disturbed. Some beetles fold up their legs and fall to the ground and remain motionless, often resembling a bit of dirt. Many caterpillars will "freeze" and remain motionless, often in a peculiar position; some of the inch worms hold the body out like a twig, holding on by means of prolegs at the posterior end of the body; some hawk-moth larvae elevate the front part of the body and assume a sphinxlike position (it is because of this behavior that the hawk moths are often called sphinx moths); the larvae of the handmaid moths elevate both ends of the body when disturbed, holding on with the prolegs in the middle of the body.

Some insects give off foul-smelling liquids when disturbed. Stink bugs, broad-headed bugs, lacewings, and others might well be called the skunks of the insect world; some of them have an extremely disagreeable odor. A few insects have very pleasant odors; whirligig beetles give off a liquid that smells like pineapples; bumble bees give off an odor that is not unpleasant. Bombardier beetles give off from the anus a liquid that quickly volatilizes and looks like a puff of smoke; some ants eject from their anus a very irritating liquid.

Many insects will inflict a painful bite when handled—and some will bite if given the opportunity, whether handled or not. The bite may be simply a severe pinch by means of powerful jaws, as in certain ants, stag beetles (or pinchingbugs), and others, or it may be a piercing by needlelike mouth parts. The bites of mosquitoes, fleas, horse flies, black flies, and bed bugs are very much like a hypodermic injection, and the irritation they cause is due to the saliva injected by the insect. Centipedes, spiders, and ticks (which are not insects but are closely related to them) inject venom when they bite.

Everyone is familiar with the stinging habits of wasps and bees. Since a sting of an insect is a modified egg-laying organ, only females sting; and since the sting is posteriorly located on the body, the "business" end of a bee or wasp is the rear. A few caterpillars, such as the saddleback and the larva of the io moth, have stinging hairs; these hairs are hollow and contain a substance that is irritating to the skin, and the effect of handling such a caterpillar is much like that produced by nettles.

Many insects live in curious habitats. The larva of the petroleum fly lives in pools of petroleum around oil wells in California; other fly larvae breed by the millions in Great Salt Lake; a few flies have been found breeding in the medical-school brine vats in which human cadavers are preserved; and one beetle in the West—often called the "short-circuit" beetle—bores into lead cables. A few insects live in hot springs where the temperatures go as high as 120 degrees Fahrenheit.

Most insects are relatively small; probably three-fourths to nine-tenths of them are less than $\frac{1}{4}$ inch in length. Their small size enables them to live in places that would not be available to larger animals. This fact, plus the fact that there are a great many different kinds of places where they can live, is in part responsible for the large number of different kinds of insects.

They range in size from about $\frac{1}{100}$ of an inch to over 8 inches in length, and from about $\frac{1}{50}$ of an inch to nearly a foot in wingspread. (One fossil dragonfly had a wingspread of over 2 feet!) Some of the largest insects are very slender, but some beetles have a body nearly as large as one's fist. The largest insects in the United States are some of the moths (with a wingspread of 6 inches or more), and the walking sticks (with a body length up to about 6 inches).

The reproductive powers of insects are often tremendous; most people do not realize just how great they are. The capacity of any animal to build up its numbers through reproduction depends on three characteristics of that animal—the number of eggs laid by each female (which in insects may vary from a few dozen to many thousands), the length of a generation (which may vary from a few days to several years), and the proportion of each generation that are females and will produce the next generation. (Among some insects there are no males!) It might be illuminating to cite an example of how great the reproductive capacity of an insect may be; those who do not believe what follows may figure it out for themselves.

Most people have heard of *Drosóphila*, the pomace flies that have been studied so much by geneticists. These flies develop rapidly, and under ideal conditions, may produce 25 generations a year. Each female will lay up to 100 eggs, of which about half will hatch into males and half into females. Now, suppose we started with a pair of these flies and allowed them to reproduce under ideal conditions for a year—with the original and each succeeding female laying 100 eggs before she dies, and each egg hatching and the young growing to maturity and reproducing again. The number of flies that would be produced in the twenty-fifth generation is fantastic; if the flies of this generation were packed tightly together, 1000 to a cubic inch, they would form a ball of flies *96 million miles* in diameter, or a ball extending nearly from the earth to the sun!

These are only a few of the many ways in which insects have become adapted to life in the world about us. Some of the detailed stories about these animals are fantastic and almost incredible. In the succeeding chapters, we have tried to point out in a scientific way interesting and often unique features of insect biology—methods of reproduction, obtaining food, depositing eggs, and rearing young—as well as the more technical phases that deal with morphology and taxonomy.

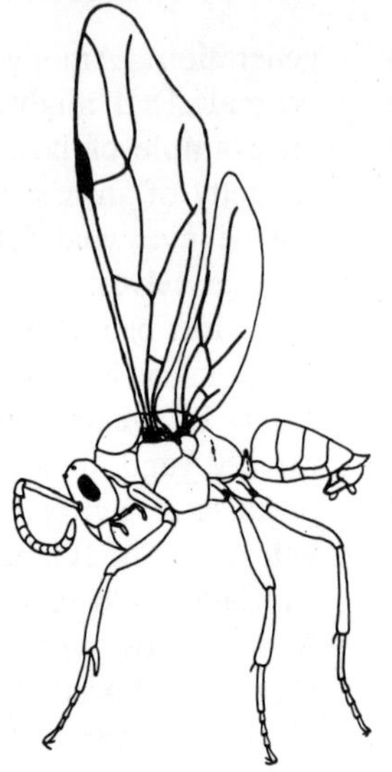

2

The Anatomy and Physiology of Insects

THE GENERAL STRUCTURE OF AN INSECT

A knowledge of the anatomy of insects is essential to an understanding of how insects live and how they can be distinguished from one another and from other animals.

BODY FORM

Insects are generally more or less elongate and cylindrical in form and are bilaterally symmetrical; that is, the right and left sides of the body are essentially alike. The body is segmented, and the segments are grouped into three distinct regions, the head, thorax, and abdomen (Figure 2-1). The head bears the eyes. antennae, and mouth parts; the thorax bears the legs and wings (when these are present); the abdomen usually bears no locomotor appendages, but often has some appendages at its apex. Most of the appendages of an insect are segmented.

THE BODY WALL

In man and other vertebrates the skeleton or supporting framework is on the inside of the body and is spoken of as an endoskeleton; in insects and some other animals the skeleton is for the most part on the outside and is spoken of as an exoskeleton. The insect's body wall thus serves not only as the outer covering of the body but also as a supporting structure, and it is to the body wall that muscles are attached.

The body wall of an insect (Figure 2-2) is composed of three principal layers: an outer cuticula, which contains pigment and other substances, including a characteristic chemical compound called chitin; a cellular layer, the epidermis, which lies beneath and secretes the cuticula; and a thin noncellular layer beneath the epidermis, called the basement membrane. The body wall completely covers the insect and bends inward at various points to form supporting ridges and

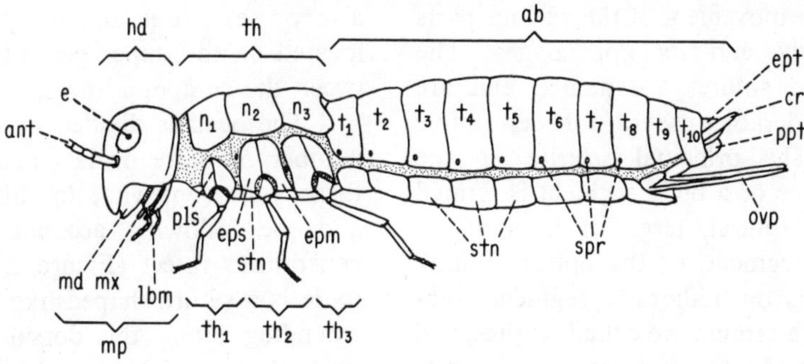

Fig. 2-1. The general structure of an insect. *ab*, abdomen; *ant*, antenna; *cr*, cercus; *e*, compound eye; *epm*, epimeron; *eps*, episternum; *ept*, epiproct; *hd*, head; *lbm*, labium; *md*, mandible; *mp*, mouth parts; *mx*, maxilla; *n*, nota of thorax; *ovp*, ovipositor; *pls*, pleural suture; *ppt*, paraproct; *spr*, spiracles; *stn*, sterna; t_{1-10}, tergites; *th*, thorax; th_1, prothorax; th_2, mesothorax; th_3, metathorax. (Modified from Snodgrass by permission of McGraw-Hill Book Company.)

braces. The tracheae (breathing tubes) and the anterior and posterior ends of the digestive tract are lined with cuticula.

The cuticula is made up of three fairly distinct layers, epicuticula, exocuticula, and endocuticula. The epicuticula is a thin outer layer, about one micron thick, and contains no chitin; the exocuticula and endocuticula are thicker layers and contain chitin. The exocuticula, which lies immediately beneath the epicuticula, is denser, harder, and more pigmented than the endocuticula.

Chitin is a nitrogenous polysaccharide with the formula $(C_{32}H_{54}N_4O_{21})_x$; it is a very resistant substance and is insoluble in water, alcohol, dilute acids, and alkalis; it is not attacked by the digestive enzymes of mammals, but is broken down by certain bacteria. Clearing with alkali removes the coloring and hardening substances, but produces no visible change in the essential structure of the cuticula. The hardness of the cuticula is due to nonchitinous substances, the chemistry of which is not definitely known; the endocuticula and the softer parts of the cuticula usually contain more chitin than the harder parts. The hardening of the cuticula is spoken of as sclerotization.

The surface of the insect body consists of a number of hardened plates or sclerites, which are separated by sutures or membranous areas. Sutures[1] are seamlike lines marking an infolding of the body wall (the suture at the left in Figure 2-2) or lines of softer cuticula (the suture at the right in Figure 2-2). The membranous lines and

[1] Snodgrass (1962) has proposed that these lines be called sulci (singular, sulcus), rather than sutures.

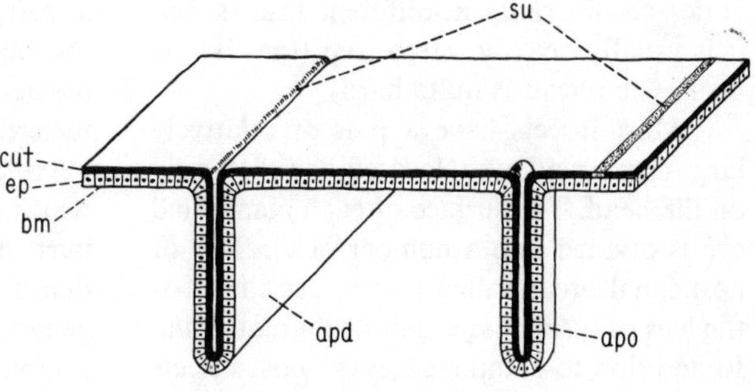

Fig. 2-2. Diagram of the insect body wall. *apd*, apodeme; *apo*, apophysis; *bm*, basement membrane; *cut*, cuticula; *ep*, epidermis; *su*, sutures. (Redrawn from various sources.)

areas permit movement of the various parts of the body and its appendages. The sclerites and sutures are named and are made considerable use of for descriptive purposes. The principal sclerite on the dorsal surface of a body segment is termed the tergum (plural, terga) if it is on an abdominal segment, or the notum (plural, nota) if it is on a thoracic segment; subdivisions of a tergum are called tergites, and subdivisions of a notum have special names (see below, under "The Thorax"). The principal sclerite on the ventral surface of a body segment is called the sternum (plural, sterna), and subdivisions of it are called sternites. If sclerites are present between the dorsal and ventral sclerites (such sclerites are usually present only on the thorax), they are called pleurites; the lateral area of a segment is often called the pleuron (plural, pleura).

The body wall bears numerous external and internal processes. The external processes include setae, spines, scales, and the like; some of these are solid cuticula, while others contain all three body-wall layers. Some external processes, such as setae, are outgrowths of individual epidermal cells. The internal processes of the body wall may be ridgelike (Figure 2-2, *apd*) or spinelike (Figure 2-2, *apo*); these infoldings strengthen the body wall and serve as the place of attachment of muscles.

THE HEAD

The head is the anterior capsulelike body region that bears the eyes, antennae, and mouth parts. The shape of the head varies considerably in different insects, but it is usually heavily sclerotized (that is, the wall of the head is quite hard).

Most insects have a pair of relatively large compound eyes, located dorsolaterally on the head. The surface of each compound eye is divided into a number of circular or hexagonal areas called facets; each facet is the lens of a single eye unit or ommatidium. In addition to compound eyes, most insects also possess three simple eyes, the ocelli, located on the upper part of the head between the compound eyes.

The head is divided by sutures into a number of more or less distinct sclerites; these vary somewhat in different insects, and the following account applies to a generalized insect (Figure 2-3). Typically, there is a suture shaped like an inverted **Y** extending along the dorsal and anterior part of the head; just above the median ocellus this suture forks to form two diverging sutures, which extend down the anterior side of the head. The dorsal part of this suture (the base of the **Y**) is called the coronal suture (*cs*), and the two anterior branches are called the frontal sutures (*fs*), At the lower end of the frontal sutures is a transverse suture, which extends across the face just above the base of the mouth parts; the medial or anterior part of this suture is called the epistomal suture (*es*), and the lateral portions, above the mandibles and maxillae, the subgenal sutures (*sgs*). The anterior sclerite of the head, between the frontal and epistomal sutures and including the median ocellus, is the frons (*fr*). The area above the frons on the dorsal part of the head between the compound eyes is the vertex (*ver*). The area on each side of the head, laterad of the frontal sutures and between the compound eye and the subgenal suture, is the gena (*ge*). Below the epistomal suture is a flaplike structure composed of two sclerites; the upper sclerite is the clypeus (*clp*), and the lower one is the labrum, or upper lip (*lbr*). Behind the labrum are the mandibles (*md*), a pair of heavily sclerotized jaws; behind the mandibles are the maxillae (*mx*), segmented mouth-part structures that bear feelerlike palpi (*p*); and behind the maxillae is the lower lip, or labium (*lbm*), which also bears palpi. These mouth-part structures will be discussed in more detail later. Typically, the vertex and genae are limited posteriorly by the occipital suture (*os*); behind the occipital

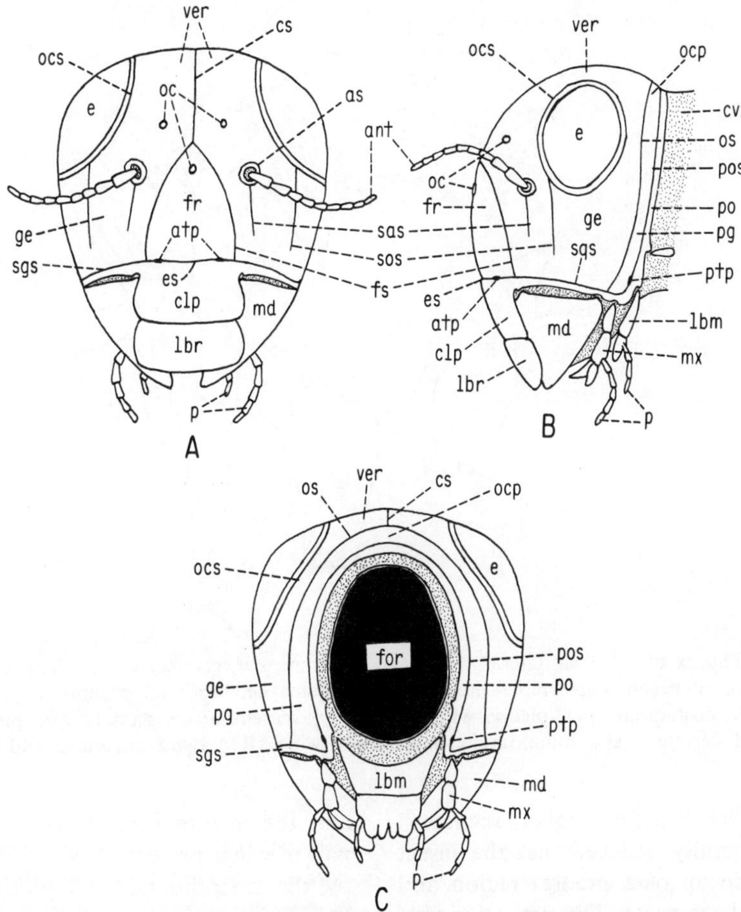

Fig. 2-3. Typical structure of the insect head. A, anterior view; B, lateral view; C, posterior view. *ant*, antenna; *as*, antennal suture; *atp*, anterior tentorial pit; *clp*, clypeus; *cs*, coronal suture; *cvx*, cervix; *e*, compound eye; *es*, epistomal suture; *for*, foramen magnum; *fr*, frons; *fs*, frontal suture; *ge*, gena; *lbm*, labium; *lbr*, labrum; *md*, mandible; *mx*, maxilla; *oc*, ocelli; *ocp*, occiput; *ocs*, ocular suture; *os*, occipital suture; *p*, palpi; *pg*, postgena; *po*, postocciput; *pos*, postoccipital suture; *ptp*, posterior tentorial pit; *sas*, subantennal suture; *sgs*, subgenal suture; *sos*, subocular suture; *ver*, vertex. (Modified from Snodgrass by permission of McGraw-Hill Book Company.)

suture dorsally is the occiput (*ocp*), and behind it on the sides of the head are the postgenae (*pg*). The occiput and postgenae are limited posteriorly by the postoccipital suture (*pos*), behind which is a narrow ringlike sclerite, the postocciput (*po*), which forms the posterior rim of the head and surrounds the foramen magnum (*for*).

There is considerable variation in the development of the head sutures and the shape of the head sclerites. The frontal sutures are often short or poorly developed, and there may be sutures extending ventrally from the compound eyes (*sos*) or the antennae (*sas*). There are usually sutures closely paralleling the compound eyes (*ocs*) and surrounding the bases of the antennae (*as*). The head sclerites posterior to the occipital suture are often on the posterior surface of the head.

The number of segments making up the head is not apparent in the adult insect, as the head sutures rarely coincide with

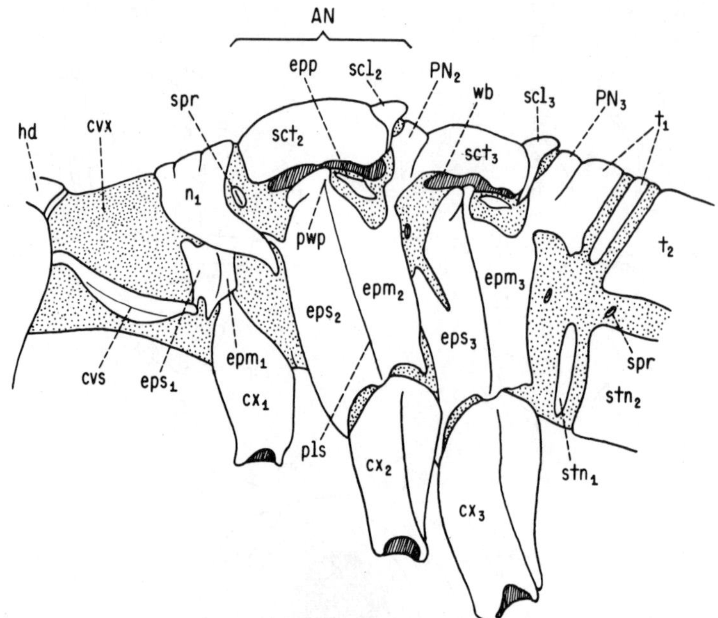

Fig. 2-4. Thorax of *Panórpa,* lateral view. *AN,* alinotum; *cvs,* cervical sclerite; *cvx,* cervix; *cx,* coxa; *epm,* epimeron; *epp,* epipleurite; *eps,* episternum; *hd,* head; n_1, pronotum; *pls,* pleural suture; *PN,* postnotum; *pwp,* pleural wing process; *scl,* scutellum; *sct,* scutum; *spr,* spiracle; *stn,* abdominal sternite; *t,* abdominal tergite; *wb,* base of wing. (Redrawn from Ferris and Rees.)

the sutures between the original segments, but it is generally believed that the insect head is made up of a preoral region and four postoral segments. The preoral region bears the compound eyes, ocelli, antennae, and the facial areas (including the labrum); the first postoral segment is greatly reduced and bears no appendages (this segment bears the chelicerae in the chelicerate arthropods); the second, third, and fourth postoral segments bear the mandibles, maxillae, and labium, respectively.

THE THORAX

The thorax is the middle region of the body and bears the legs and wings (in some adult insects there are no wings, and in many immature and a few adult insects there are no legs). The thorax is composed of three segments, the prothorax, mesothorax, and metathorax. Each thoracic segment typically bears a pair of legs, and the wings (when present) are borne by the mesothorax and the metathorax. If there is only one pair of wings present, they are usually borne by the mesothorax. The prothorax never bears wings.

The thorax is connected to the head by a membranous neck region, the cervix (Figure 2-4, *cvx*). There are usually one or two small sclerites (*cvs*) on each side of the neck, which link the head with the episterna of the prothorax.

Each thoracic segment is composed of four groups of sclerites: the notum dorsally, the pleura laterally, and the sternum ventrally. Any thoracic sclerite may be located on a particular segment by using the appropriate prefix, either pro-, meso-, or meta; for example, the notum of the prothorax, which in insects such as a grasshopper or cricket is a large and conspicuous saddle-like plate between the head and the base of the wings, is called the pronotum. The thoracic segment of any given sclerite is indicated in our illustrations by a subscript numeral; for example, the pronotum is indicated by n_1, the episternum of the mesothorax by eps_2, and the epimeron of the metathorax by epm_3.

The nota of the mesothorax and metathorax are often divided by sutures into two or more sclerites each. In a rather generalized winged insect there are two principal notal sclerites, the alinotum (*AN*), which occupies most of the notum, and the postnotum (*PN*), at the posterior margin of the notum. The alinotum is often divided into two sclerites, an anterior scutum (*sct*) and a posterior scutellum (*scl*); in some insects there are additional sutures on the alinotum. Each pleuron is typically divided into two sclerites by a pleural suture (*pls*) which extends dorsoventrally between the base of the leg and the base of the wing; the anterior sclerite is the episternum (*eps*), and the posterior sclerite is the epimeron (*epm*). The pleuron in a wing-bearing segment is produced into a pleural wing process (*pwp*) at the upper end of the pleural suture; this process serves as a fulcrum for the movement of the wing. There are usually one or two small sclerites, the epipleurites (*epp*), in the membranous area between the pleuron and the base of the wing; these are important to the wing movements, for certain muscles that move the wings are attached to them. Each sternum may be divided into two or more sclerites.

On each side of the thorax are two slit-like openings, one between the prothorax and mesothorax, and the other between the mesothorax and metathorax. These are the spiracles (*spr*), the external openings of the respiratory system (which will be discussed later).

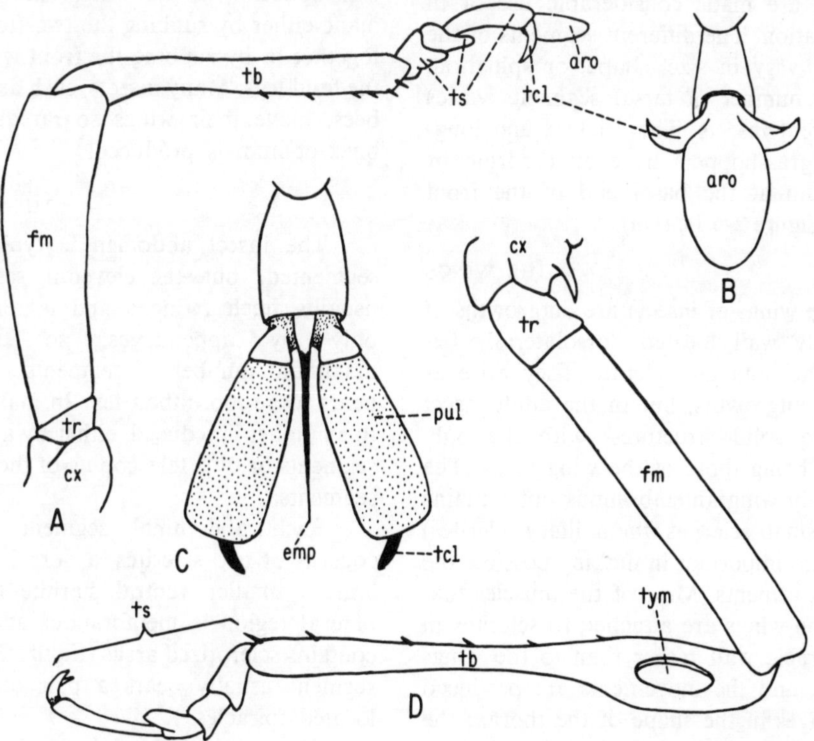

Fig. 2-5. Leg structure in insects. A, middle leg of a short-horned grasshopper (*Melánoplus*); B, apex of tarsus of *Melánoplus*; C, apex of tarsus of a robber fly; D, front leg of a long-horned grasshopper (*Scuddèria*). *aro*, arolium; *cx*, coxa; *emp*, empodium; *fm*, femur; *pul*, pulvillus; *tb*, tibia; *tcl*, tarsal claw; *tr*, trochanter; *ts*, tarsus; *tym*, tympanum.

THE LEGS

The legs of insects (Figure 2-5) typically consist of the following segments: the coxa (*cx*), the basal segment; the trochanter (*tr*), a small segment (rarely two segments) following the coxa; the femur (*fm*), the first long segment of the leg; the tibia (*tb*), the second long segment of the leg; and the tarsus (*ts*), a series of small segments beyond the tibia. The number of tarsal segments in different insects varies from one to five. The last tarsal segment generally bears a pair of claws (*tcl*) and often one or more padlike structures between or at the base of the claws; a pad or lobe between the claws is usually called an arolium (*aro*), and pads located at the base of the claws are called pulvilli (*pul*).

The legs may be variously modified in different insects, and the characters of the legs are made considerable use of in identification. The different segments of the leg may vary in size, shape, or spination, and the number of tarsal segments varies in different insects. The crickets and long-horned grasshoppers have an eardrum or tympanum at the basal end of the front tibiae (Figure 2-5 D, *tym*).

THE WINGS

The wings of insects are outgrowths of the body wall located dorsolaterally between the nota and pleura. They arise as saclike outgrowths, but in the adult insect they are solid structures, with the only cavities being those of the wing veins. The base of the wing is membranous, but contains certain small sclerites (the axillary sclerites) which are important in making possible the wing movements. Most of the muscles that move the wings are attached to sclerites in the thoracic wall rather than to the wings directly, and the movements are produced by changes in the shape of the thorax; the only muscle attached to the wing directly (at least in most insects) is attached to one of the sclerites in the membranous wing base.

The wings of insects vary in number, size, shape, texture, venation, and in the position at which they are held at rest. Most adult insects have two pairs of wings, borne by the mesothorax and metathorax, but some have only one pair (usually borne by the mesothorax), and some are wingless. In most insects the wings are membranous and may bear tiny hairs or scales; in some insects the front wings are thickened, leathery, or hard and sheathlike. Most insects are able to fold the wings over the abdomen when at rest, but the dragonflies, damselflies, and mayflies cannot do this and hold the wings either outstretched or together above the body when at rest.

The wing venation is discussed in greater detail below.

Some insects, such as male crickets and grasshoppers, are able to make a characteristic sound with the wings; the sound is made either by rubbing the two front wings together or by rubbing the front wings with the hind legs. Many insects, such as flies and bees, move their wings so rapidly that a buzz or hum is produced.

THE ABDOMEN

The insect abdomen is typically 11-segmented, but the eleventh segment is usually much reduced and is represented only by appendages, so that the maximum number of segments rarely appears to be more than ten. In many insects this number is reduced, either by a fusion of segments or by a telescoping of the terminal segments.

Each abdominal segment generally consists of two sclerites, a dorsal tergite (*t*) and a smaller ventral sternite (*stn*); the pleural region is membranous and seldom contains sclerotized areas (Figure 2-1). Each segment usually bears a pair of laterally located spiracles.

The pregenital abdominal segments (segments 1-7) bear appendages in various immature insects and in adult Apterygota and male Odonata. The abdominal appendages of immature insects may consist of gills (for example, in mayfly nymphs, Figure 7-2), lateral filaments (for example, in certain Neuroptera larvae, Figure 21-7), or prolegs (for example, in Lepidoptera larvae, Figure 26-3). The abdominal appendages in Apterygota consist of styli or other appendages (see Chapter 6), and in male Odonata they consist of the copulatory structures (Figure 8-1 A, *gen*).

The genital segments (8 and 9, Figure 2-6) may bear structures associated with the external openings of the genital ducts; in the male these structures have to do with copulation and the transfer of sperm to the female, and in the female they are concerned with oviposition. These structures are the external genitalia, though they may be partly or entirely withdrawn into the abdomen when not in use, and are often (especially in the male) not visible without dissection.

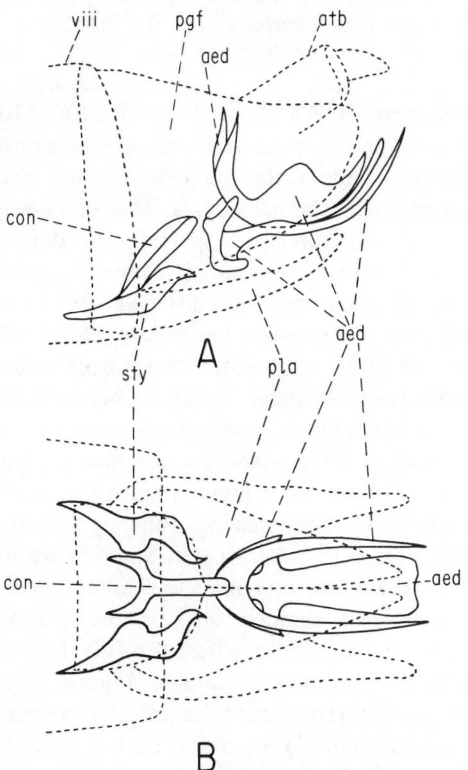

Fig. 2-6. The male genitalia of a leafhopper, *Draeculacéphala ántica* (Walker). A, lateral view; B, ventral view. The external structures are shown by dotted lines, and the internal structures by solid lines. *aed*, aedeagus; *atb*, anal tube; *con*, connective; *pgf*, pygofer; *pla*, plate; *sty*, style; *va*, valve; *VIII*, eighth abdominal segment.

The external genitalia of the male are extremely variable, and are often quite complex; they are frequently of considerable taxonomic value. In a leafhopper (Figure 2-6) they are contained in a genital chamber that is formed by a dorsolaterally located pygofer (*pgf*) and a pair of ventrally located plates (*pla*); these structures are portions of the ninth segment. The genitalia within this chamber consist of a pair of lateroventral processes, the styles (*sty*), a median basal connective (*con*), and a central structure, the aedeagus (*aed*). The aedeagus, through which the sperms are discharged during mating, is often provided with various processes. When the male leafhopper mates, the genital chamber is completely opened; the pygofers are pushed dorsally and the plates are deflected, and the aedeagus and styles are exposed directly to the base of the female ovipositor.

The female genitalia consist of an ovipositor, which is formed by the appendages (gonopods) of segments 8 and 9 (Figure 2-7). A gonopod characteristically consists of a basal portion (the coxopodite) that bears a more or less elongate process (the gonapophysis), and sometimes also a style, posteriorly. The ovipositor consists of a pair of basal plates, the valvifers (*vf*), and three pairs of elongate structures, the valvulae (*vlv*); the valvifers are formed by the coxopodites of the gonopods of segments 8 and 9, and the valvulae are formed by the gonapophyses of these gonopods (the first and second valvulae) and by a posterior prolongation of the ninth coxopodite (the third valvulae). The ovipositor is generally used to pierce and insert the eggs into something, such as plant or animal tissue; one or more of the pairs of valvulae serve as the shaft

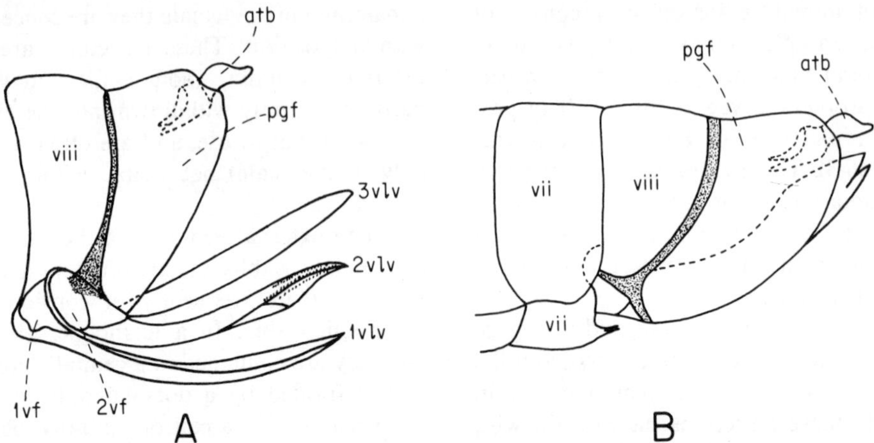

Fig. 2-7. The ovipositor of a leafhopper. A, lateral view, with the parts of the ovipositor spread out; B, lateral view of the terminal segments of the abdomen, with the ovipositor in a normal or resting position. *atb*, anal tube; *ovp*, ovipositor; *1 vf, 2 vf*, first and second valvifers; *1 vlv, 2 vlv, 3 vlv*, first, second, and third valvulae. The first and second valvulae form the shaft, or piercing part of the ovipositor, and the third valvulae serves as a sheath for the shaft.

of the ovipositor, and do the actual piercing; one of the pairs of valvulae, usually the third, may serve as a sheath for the shaft and may not function as piercing structures.

An ovipositor is present only in the Thysanura (suborder Ectognatha; Figure 6-2, *ovp*), Thysanoptera (suborder Terebrantia), Odonata (except the Gomphidae and Libelluloidea), Orthoptera, Homoptera (suborder Auchenorrhyncha) and the Hymenoptera. The ovipositor varies considerably in form in different insects; in a damselfly it is located on the ventral side of segments 9 and 10, and gives the abdomen a swollen appearance (Figures 8-1 E, 8-13 D); in a long-horned grasshopper it is a long sword-shaped structure (Figures 9-11 C, 9-12 B, 9-13); in ichneumons (Figure 29-38 A) it appears as three long hairlike structures, often as long as or longer than the body (the median structure here is the shaft and consists of the first two pairs of valvulae fused together; the lateral structures are the third valvulae, which function as a sheath for the shaft); in bees and wasps the ovipositor is modified into a sting, and is withdrawn into the abdomen when not in use.

The appendages at the apex of the abdomen, which arise from segment 10 (when ten complete segments are present), consist of the cerci (singular, cercus), the epiproct, and the paraprocts. The cerci are a pair of structures arising from the dorsal part of the last abdominal segment (Figure 2-1, *cr*); they may be clasperlike (Figures 8-1 and 12-2), feelerlike (Figures 9-16 and 11-1 to 11-3), or absent. The epiproct arises just above the anus; it may be filamentous (the median filament of mayflies, Figure 7-2), somewhat clasperlike (the inferior appendage of male Anisoptera, Figure 8-1, *ept*), a small and inconspicuous lobe, or lacking. The paraprocts are located ventrolaterally from the anus, and may appear as small, more or less rounded lobes (Figures 8-1 A, B, E, *ppt*), leaflike structures (the lateral gills of Zygoptera nymphs, Figure 8-7), clasperlike structures (the inferior appendages of male Zygoptera, Figure 8-1 C, D, *iap*), or lacking.

THE WING VENATION OF INSECTS

The wings of most insects are membranous and bear a framework of thickened ridges, the veins. The number and arrangement of the veins is of great value in identi-

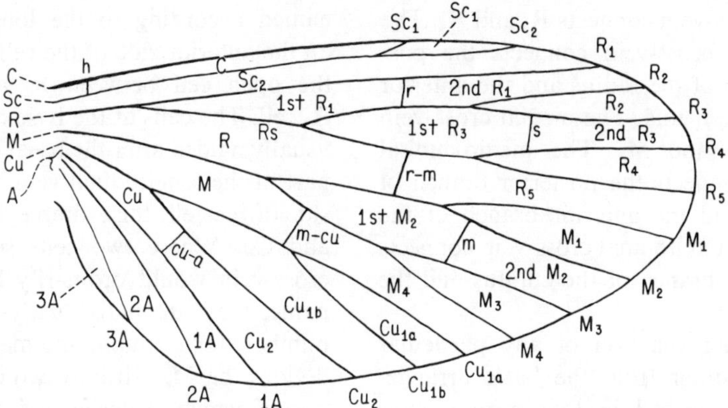

Fig. 2-8. Generalized wing venation. (For key to lettering, see accompanying text.)

fication, particularly in those groups of insects that have membranous wings. There is a great deal of variation in the wing venation of different insects, but it is possible to homologize the veins and to use a system of terminology applicable to all insects. This system is called the Comstock-Needham system and is outlined below. For the most part, it is used in this book. In a few cases, where it appears more convenient, or where subsequent studies have shown that the Comstock-Needham interpretation was not entirely correct, we have departed from this system.

The principal veins of the insect wing (with their abbreviations in parentheses) are as follows:

Longitudinal veins
- Costa (C)
- Subcosta (Sc)
- Radius (R)
- Radial Sector (Rs)
- Media (M)
- Cubitus (Cu)
- Anal veins (A)

Cross-veins
- humeral (h)
- radial (r)
- sectorial (s)
- radio-medial (r-m)
- medial (m)
- medio-cubital (m-cu)
- cubito-anal (cu-a)

The longitudinal veins vary somewhat in their method of branching in different insects, but the basic or hypothetical primitive arrangement is as follows (Figure 2-8): The costa is an unbranched vein that usually forms the anterior (or costal) margin of the wing. The subcosta is forked distally. The branches of the longitudinal veins are numbered from anterior to posterior around the wing by means of subscript numerals; the two branches of the subcosta are designated Sc_1 and Sc_2. The radius gives off a posterior branch, the radial sector, usually near the base of the wing; the anterior branch of the radius is R_1; the radial sector forks twice, with four branches reaching the wing margin. The media forks twice, with four branches reaching the wing margin. The cubitus, according to the Comstock-Needham system, forks once, the two branches being Cu_1 and Cu_2; according to some other authorities, Cu_1 forks again distally, the two branches being Cu_{1a} and Cu_{1b}. The anal veins, which are typically unbranched, are designated from anterior to posterior as the first anal (1A), second anal (2A), and so on.

The cross-veins are named according to their location in the wing or the longitudinal veins they connect. The humeral cross-vein is located near the base of the wing, between the costa and the subcosta. The radial cross-vein connects R_1 and the anterior branch of the radial sector. The sectorial cross-vein connects R_3 and R_4. The radio-medial cross-vein connects the posterior branch of the radius and the anterior branch of the media. The medial cross-vein connects M_2 and M_3. The medio-cubital cross-vein connects the posterior branch of the media and the anterior branch of the cubitus. The cubito-anal cross-vein connects the posterior branch of the cubitus and the first anal vein.

The wing venation of any particular insect may differ from the basic arrangement just described in that it may have fewer veins or more veins. If the venation is reduced, either one or more veins are lacking, two or more veins are fused, or one or more veins fail to branch. A fused or unbranched vein is named on the basis of its component parts; for example, the anterior branch of the radial sector is R_{2+3}, and it sometimes fails to branch. Other similar veins are R_{4+5}, M_{1+2}, and Cu + 2A. Extra veins may be either extra cross-veins or extra branches of the longitudinal veins. Extra cross-veins may be designated by number (for example, first radial and second radial) if they are not too numerous, or they may have special names based on their location (for example, the antenodal cross-veins in the Odonata), or they may be unnamed. Extra longitudinal veins are usually additional branches of the principal veins, called accessory veins; such veins, if they are not too numerous and are constant in number and position, are named after the vein from which they branch; a single accessory vein branching from M_1, for example, is designated as M_{1a}. If there are two or more accessory veins branching from M_1 (or any other principal vein), they are usually simply called M_1 accessories. Other types of extra longitudinal veins may have special names, such as the intercalary veins of mayflies and the supplements of dragonflies.

The spaces in the wing between the veins are called cells. Cells may be open (extending to the wing margin) or closed (completely surrounded by veins). The cells are named according to the longitudinal vein on the anterior side of the cell; for example, the open cell between R_2 and R_3 is the R_2 cell. The cells at the base of the wing are usually named after the basal or unbranched part of the longitudinal vein on the anterior side of the cell; for example, the cells R, M, and Cu. Where two cells separated by a cross-vein would ordinarily have the same name, they are individually designated by number; for example, the medial cross-vein divides the M_2 cell into two cells, the basal one of which is designated as the first M_2 cell and the distal one as the second M_2 cell. Where a cell is bordered anteriorly by a fused vein (for example, R_{2+3}), it is named after the posterior component of that fused vein (cell R_3). In some insects certain cells may have special names; for example, the triangles of the dragonfly wing and the discal cell of Lepidoptera.

THE ANTENNAE OF INSECTS

The antennae of insects vary greatly in size and form and are much used in classification. They are sensory in function and act as tactile organs, organs of smell, and in some cases, organs of hearing. They are usually located between or below the compound eyes. The first segment is called the scape; the second segment, the pedicel; and the remaining segments, the flagellum.

The following terms are used in describing the form of the antennae:

Setaceous—bristlelike, the segments becoming more slender distally; for example, dragonfly (Figure 2-9 A), damselfly, leafhopper

Filiform—threadlike, the segments nearly uniform in size, and usually cylindrical; for example, ground beetle (Figure 2-9 B), tiger beetle

Moniliform—like a string of beads, the segments similar in size and more or less spherical in shape; for example, rhysodid beetle (Figure 2-9 C)

Serrate—sawlike, the segments, par-

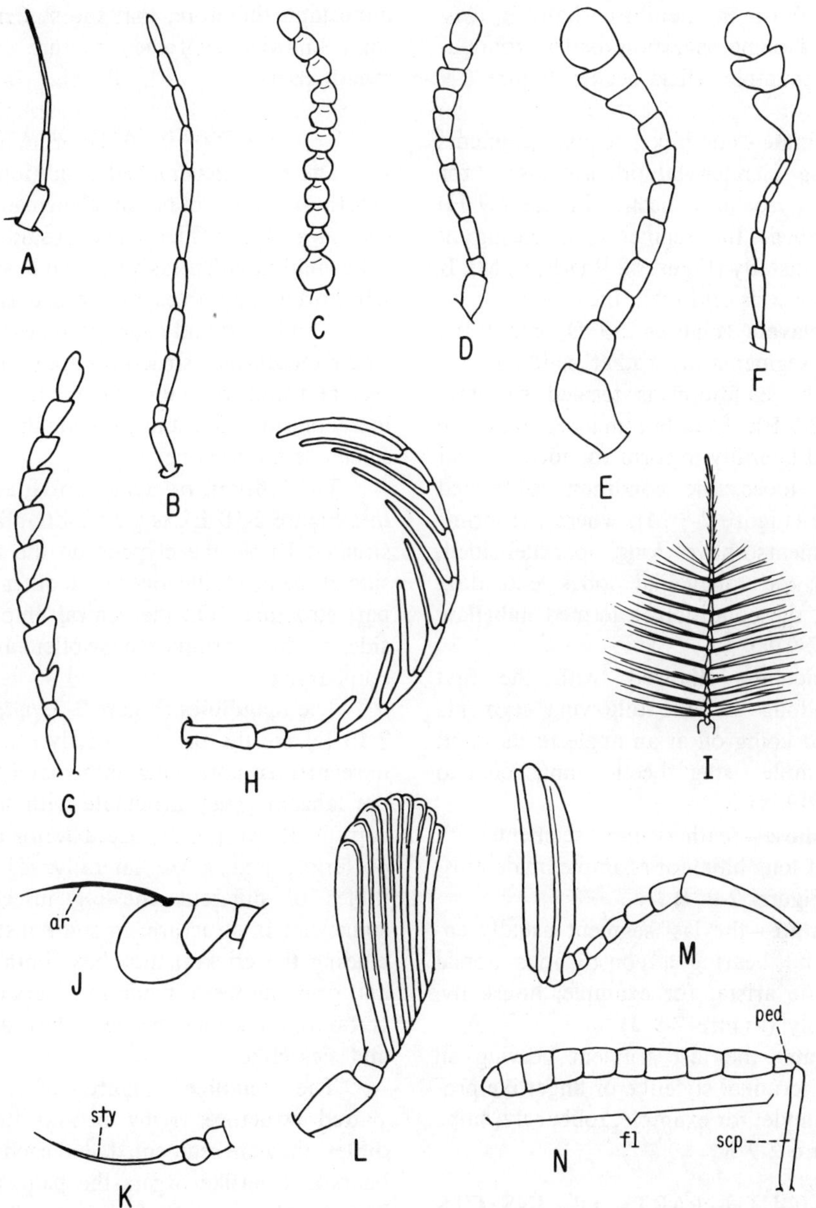

Fig. 2-9. Types of antennae. A, setaceous (dragonfly); B, filiform (ground beetle); C, moniliform (rhysodid beetle); D, clavate (darkling beetle); E, clavate (ladybird beetle); F, capitate (nitidulid beetle); G, serrate (click beetle); H, pectinate (pyrochroid beetle); I, plumose (male mosquito); J, aristate (syrphid fly); K, stylate (snipe fly); L, flabellate (sandalid beetle); M, lamellate (June beetle); N, geniculate (chalcid). Antennae such as those in D-F, L, and M are also called clubbed. *ar,* arista; *fl,* flagellum; *ped,* pedicel; *scp,* scape; *sty,* style.

ticularly those in the distal half or two-thirds of the antenna, more or less triangular; for example, click beetle (Figure 2-9 G)

Pectinate—comblike, most segments with long slender lateral processes; for example, pyrochroid beetle (Figure 2-9 H)

Clubbed—the segments increasing in diameter distally (Figures 2-9 D-F, L, M). If the increase is gradual, the condition is termed **clavate** (Figures 2-9 D, E); if the terminal segments are rather suddenly enlarged, the condition is termed **captitate** (Figure 2-9 F); if the terminal segments are expanded laterally to form rounded or oval sheetlike lobes, the condition is termed **lamellate** (Figure 2-9 M); where the terminal segments have long, parallel-sided, sheetlike, or tonguelike lobes extending laterally, the condition is termed **flabellate** (Figure 2-9 L)

Geniculate—elbowed, with the first segment long and the following segments small and going off at an angle to the first; for example, stag beetle, ant, chalcid (Figure 2-9 N)

Plumose—feathery, most segments with whorls of long hair; for example, male mosquito (Figure 2-9 I)

Aristate—the last segment usually enlarged and bearing a conspicuous dorsal bristle, the arista; for example, house fly, syrphid fly (Figure 2-9 J)

Stylate—the last segment bearing an elongate terminal stylelike or fingerlike process, the style; for example, robber fly, snipe fly (Figure 2-9 K)

THE MOUTH PARTS OF INSECTS

Insect mouth parts typically consist of a labrum, a pair each of mandibles and maxillae, a labium, and a hypopharynx. These structures are variously modified in different insect groups and are often used in classification and identification. The type of mouth parts an insect has determines how it feeds and (in the case of most injurious species) what sort of damage it does. It is important, therefore, that the student have some knowledge of the structure of insect mouth parts.

THE MOUTH PARTS OF A CRICKET

The most generalized condition of the mouth parts is found in chewing insects, such as a cricket. The cricket is said to have "chewing" mouth parts because it has heavily sclerotized mandibles that move sideways and can bite off and chew particles of food. These mouth-part structures are most easily seen and studied by removing them from the insect one at a time and studying them under a lens or microscope.

The **labrum,** or upper lip (Figure 2-3, *lbr;* Figure 2-10 E), is a broad flaplike lobe situated below the clypeus on the anterior side of the head, in front of the other mouth-part structures. On the ventral or posterior side of the labrum is a swollen area, the epipharynx.

The **mandibles** (Figure 2-3, *md;* Figure 2-10 D) are the paired, heavily sclerotized, unsegmented jaws lying immediately behind the labrum. They articulate with the head capsule at two points, one anterior and one posterior, and move laterally. The mandibles of different chewing insects vary somewhat in structure; in some insects (including the cricket) they bear both cutting and grinding teeth, while in others (such as certain predaceous beetles) they are long and sicklelike.

The **maxillae** (Figure 2-10 A) are paired structures lying behind the mandibles; they are segmented, and each maxilla bears a feelerlike organ, the palpus (*mxp*). The basal segment of the maxilla is the cardo (*cd*); the second segment is the stipes (*stp*). The palpus is borne on a lobe of the stipes called the palpifer (*plf*). The stipes bears at its apex two lobelike structures: the lacinia (*lc*), an elongate jawlike structure, and the galea (*g*), a lobelike structure. Variations in the maxillae in different chewing insects involve chiefly the palpi and the terminal lobes.

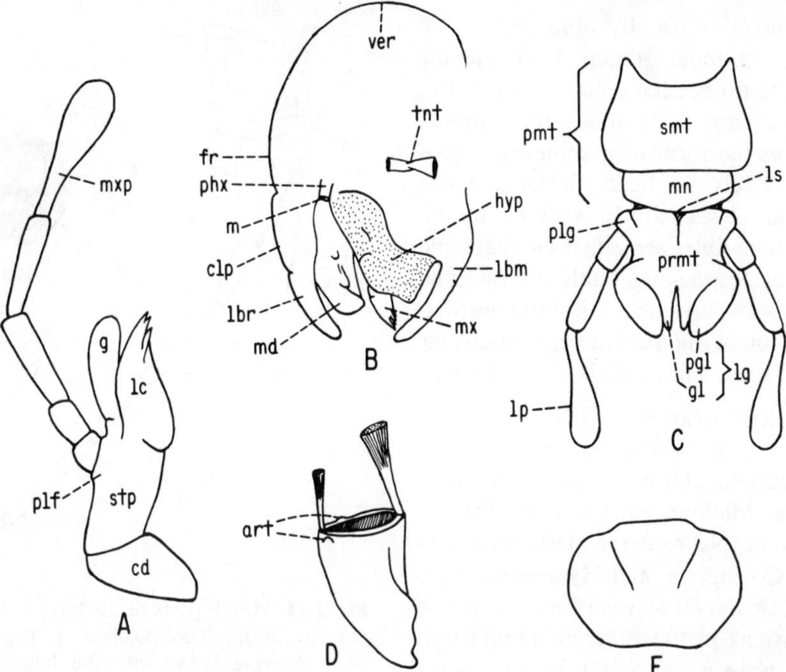

Fig. 2-10. Mouth parts of a cricket (*Grýllus*). A, maxilla; B, median vertical section of head showing relation of hypopharynx (*hyp*) to other mouth parts (somewhat diagrammatic); C, labium; D, mandible, showing muscle attachments and points of articulations; E, labrum. *art*, points of articulation of mandible; *cd*, cardo; *clp*, clypeus; *fr*, frons; *g*, galea; *gl*, glossa; *hyp*, hypopharynx; *lbm*, labium; *lbr*, labrum; *lc*, lacinia; *lg*, ligula; *lp*, labial palpus; *ls*, labial suture; *m*, mouth; *md*, mandible; *mn*, mentum; *mx*, maxilla; *mxp*, maxillary palpus; *pgl*, paraglossa; *phx*, pharynx; *plf*, palpifer; *plg*, palpiger; *pmt*, postmentum; *prmt*, prementum; *smt*, submentum; *stp*, stipes; *tnt*, tentorium; *ver*, vertex.

The **labium**, or lower lip (Figure 2-3, *lbm;* Figure 2-10 C), is a single structure (though it probably evolved from two maxillalike structures fusing along the midline) lying behind the maxillae. It is divided by a transverse suture (*ls*) into two portions, a basal postmentum (*pmt*), and a distal prementum (*prmt*). The postmentum in the cricket is divided into a basal submentum (*smt*) and a distal mentum (*mn*). The prementum bears a pair of palpi (*lp*) and a group of apical lobes which constitute the ligula (*lg*). All the muscles of the labium have their insertions distad of the labial suture. The labial palpi are borne on lateral lobes of the prementum, called palpigers (*plg*). The ligula consists of a pair of small lobes mesally, the glossae (*gl*), and a pair of larger lobes laterally, the paraglossae (*pgl*). The variations in labial structure in chewing insects involve principally the structure of the ligula and the sclerotization of the basal portion of the labium.

If the mandible and maxilla on one side are removed, one may see the **hypopharynx** (Figure 2-10 B, *hyp*), a short tonguelike structure located immediately in front of or above the labium and between the maxillae. In most insects the ducts from the salivary glands open on or near the hypopharynx. Between the hypopharynx, mandibles, and labrum lies the preoral food cavity, which leads dorsally to the mouth (*m*).

VARIATIONS IN INSECT MOUTH PARTS

Insect mouth parts are of two general types, chewing and sucking. In chewing mouth parts, the mandibles move sideways, and the insect is usually able to bite off and chew its food. Insects with sucking mouth parts do not have mandibles of this type and cannot chew food; their mouth parts are in the form of a somewhat elongated proboscis or beak through which liquid food is sucked. In sucking mouth parts, the mandibles are either elongate and styletlike or are lacking. Both chewing and sucking mouth parts are subject to considerable variation in different insects; an outline of some of these variations is given below.

CHEWING MOUTH PARTS: This is the more primitive type and occurs in adult Thysanura, Collembola, Orthoptera, Dermaptera, Psocoptera, Mallophaga, Odonata, Plecoptera, Isoptera, Neuroptera, Mecoptera, Trichoptera, Coleoptera, and Hymenoptera, as well as in the larval stages of many insects. The variations in the different mouth-part structures were noted briefly in the discussion of the mouth parts of a cricket.

SUCKING MOUTH PARTS: In these mouth parts, some of or all the various parts are elongate or styletlike. There are eight principal types of sucking mouth parts: those occurring in (1) thrips, (2) Hemiptera and Homoptera, (3) "lower" Diptera, (4) robber flies, (5) "higher" Diptera, (6) fleas, (7) sucking lice, and (8) Lepidoptera. A few insects have mouth parts that are somewhat intermediate between chewing and sucking.

—The Mouth Parts of Thrips— The proboscis in thrips is a short, stout, asymmetrical, conical structure located ventrally at the rear of the head. The stylets usually function by rasping the tissues fed upon, and this type of mouth-part structure is often called rasping-sucking. The labrum forms the front of the proboscis, the basal portions of the maxillae form the sides, and the labium forms the rear. There are three stylets, the left mandible (the right mandible is rudimentary) and two maxillary stylets. Both maxillary and labial palpi are present, but short. The hypopharynx is a small median lobe in the proboscis.

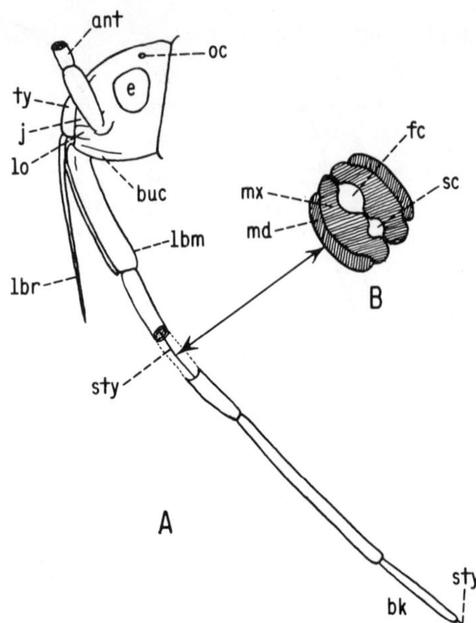

Fig. 2-11. Mouth parts of the large milkweed bug, *Oncopéltus fasciàtus* (Dallas). A, lateral view of head showing beak, with the labrum detached from the front of the beak; B cross-section of stylets (somewhat diagrammatic). *ant*, antenna; *bk*, beak; *buc*, buccula; *e*, compound eye; *fc*, food channel; *j*, jugum; *lbm*, labium; *lbr*, labrum; *lo*, lorum; *md*, mandible; *mx*, maxilla; *oc*, ocellus; *sc*, salivary channel; *sty*, stylets; *ty*, tylus.

—The Mouth Parts of the Hemiptera and Homoptera (Figure 2-11)— The beak is elongate, usually segmented, and arises from the front (Hemiptera) or rear (Homoptera) of the head. The external segmented structure of the beak is the labium, which is sheathlike and encloses four piercing stylets, the two mandibles and the two maxillae. The labrum is a short lobe at the base of the beak on the anterior (or ventral) side, and the hypopharynx is a short lobe within the base of the beak. The labium does no piercing, but folds up as the stylets enter the tissue fed upon. The inner stylets in the beak, the maxillae, fit together in such a way as to form two channels, a food channel and a salivary channel. The palpi are lacking.

—The Mouth Parts of the Biting Lower Diptera— The biting lower Diptera include the mosquitoes (Figure 2-12), sand flies, punkies, black flies, horse flies, and snipe flies. These insects have six piercing stylets: the labrum,[2] the mandibles, the maxillae, and the hypopharynx; the labium usually serves as a sheath for the stylets. The stylets may be very slender and needle-like (mosquitoes) or broader and knife-like (the other groups). The maxillary palpi are well developed, but labial palpi are lacking. The salivary channel is in the hypopharynx, and the food channel is between the grooved labrum and the hypopharynx (for example, mosquitoes) or between the labrum and the mandibles (for example, punkies and horse flies). The labium does no piercing and folds up or back as the stylets enter the tissue pierced.

[2] The labrum in the Diptera is sometimes called the labrum-epipharynx.

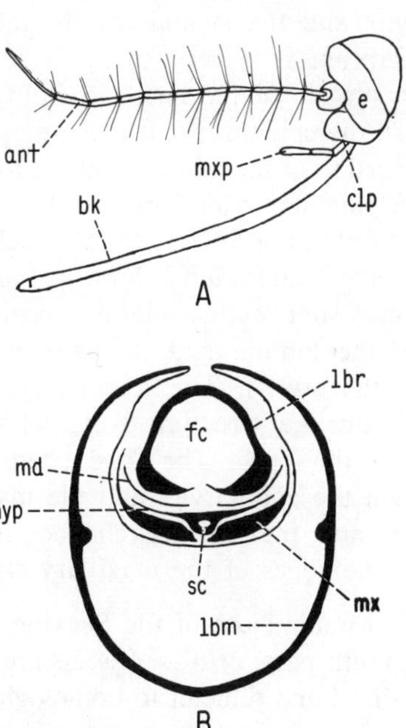

Fig. 2-12. Mouth parts of a mosquito. A, head of *Aèdes*, lateral view; B, cross-section of proboscis of *Anópheles*. *ant*, antenna; *bk*, proboscis; *clp*, clypeus; *e*, compound eye; *fc*, food channel; *hyp*, hypopharynx; *lbm*, labium; *lbr*, labrum; *md*, mandible; *mx*, maxilla; *mxp*, maxillary palpus; *sc*, salivary channel. (B redrawn from Snodgrass, after Vogel.)

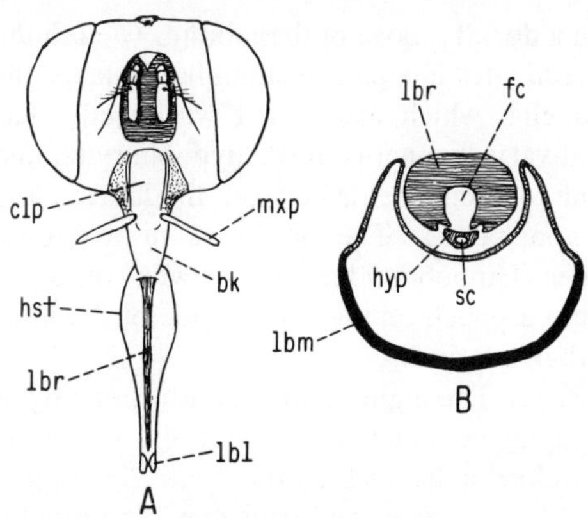

Fig. 2-13. Mouth parts of the stable fly, *Stomóxys cáclcitrans* (Linn.). A, anterior view of head; B, cross-section through haustellum. *bk*, rostrum; *clp*, clypeus; *fc*, food channel; *hst*, haustellum; *hyp*, hypopharynx; *lbl*, labellum; *lbm*, labium; *lbr*, labrum; *mxp*, maxillary palpus; *sc*, salivary channel. (Redrawn from various sources; somewhat diagrammatic.)

—The Mouth Parts of Robber Flies (Asílidae)— The mouth parts of these insects are similar to those of the preceding group, but there are no mandibles and the principal piercing organ is the hypopharynx. There are four stylets: the labrum, maxillae, and hypopharynx. The salivary channel is in the hypopharynx, and the food channel is between the labrum and the hypopharynx. The robber flies feed on other insects or spiders, and only rarely bite man.

—The Mouth Parts of the Higher Diptera— By "higher" Diptera is meant the flies belonging to the Cyclórrhapha (see pages 438-440). The mandibles in these flies are lacking, and the maxillae are represented by the palpi (maxillary stylets are usually lacking). The proboscis consists of the labrum, hypopharynx, and labium. There are two modifications of the mouth parts in these flies: (1) a piercing type, and (2) a sponging or lapping type.

1. The higher Diptera with piercing mouth parts include the stable fly (Figure 2-13), tsetse fly, horn fly, and the louse flies. The principal piercing structure in these flies is the labium; the labrum and hypopharynx are slender and styletlike and lie

in a dorsal groove of the labium. The labium terminates in a pair of small hard plates, the labella, which are armed with teeth. The salivary channel is in the hypopharynx, and the food channel is between the labrum and hypopharynx. The proboscis in the louse flies (Hippobóscidae) is somewhat retracted into a pouch on the ventral side of the head when not in use.

2. The higher Diptera with sponging or lapping mouth parts include the nonbiting Cyclórrhapha such as the house fly (Figure 2-14), blow flies, and fruit flies. The mouth-part structures are suspended from a conical membranous projection of the lower part of the head called the rostrum. The maxillary palpi arise at the distal end of the rostrum, and that part of the proboscis beyond the palpi is termed the haustellum. The labrum and hypopharynx are slender and lie in an anterior groove of the labium, which forms the bulk of the haustellum. The salivary channel is in the hypopharynx, and the food channel lies between the labrum and the hypopharynx. At the apex of the labium are the labella, a pair of large, soft, oval lobes. The lower surface of these lobes bears numerous transverse grooves, which serve as food channels. The proboscis can usually be folded up against the lower side of the head, or into a cavity on the lower side of the head. These flies lap up liquid food; this food may be already in liquid form, or it may first be liquefied by salivary secretions of the fly.

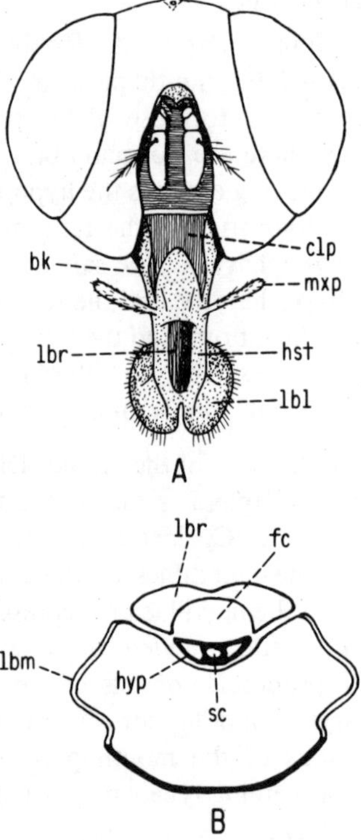

Fig. 2-14. Mouth parts of the house fly, *Músca doméstica* (Linn.). A, anterior view of head; B, cross-section through haustellum. *bk,* rostrum; *clp,* clypeus; *fc,* food channel; *hst,* haustellum; *hyp,* hypopharynx; *lbl,* labellum; *lbm,* labium; *lbr,* labrum; *mxp,* maxillary palpus; *sc,* salivary channel. (Redrawn from Snodgrass.)

—The Mouth Parts of Fleas (Figure 2-15)— Adult fleas feed on blood, and their mouth parts contain three piercing stylets, the epipharynx and the laciniae of the maxillae. The labrum is a very small lobe on the lower surface of the head, in front of the base of the epipharynx; it is the epipharyngeal portion of the labrum that is prolonged into a piercing stylet. The maxillae consist of large plates or lobes, each of which bears a piercing lacinia and a large palpus. The labium is short and slender and bears short palpi; the labium and its palpi serve to guide the stylets. The hypopharynx is a small lobelike structure lying within the base of the beak. The food channel lies between the epipharynx and the maxillary stylets, and the salivary channel lies between the edges of the maxillary stylets.

—The Mouth Parts of the Sucking Lice— The mouth parts of these insects are highly specialized and difficult to homologize with those of other sucking insects. There is a short rostrum (probably the labrum) at the anterior end of the head, from which the three piercing stylets are protruded; the rostrum is eversible and is armed internally with small recurved teeth. The stylets are about as long as the head and, when not in use, are withdrawn into a long saclike struc-

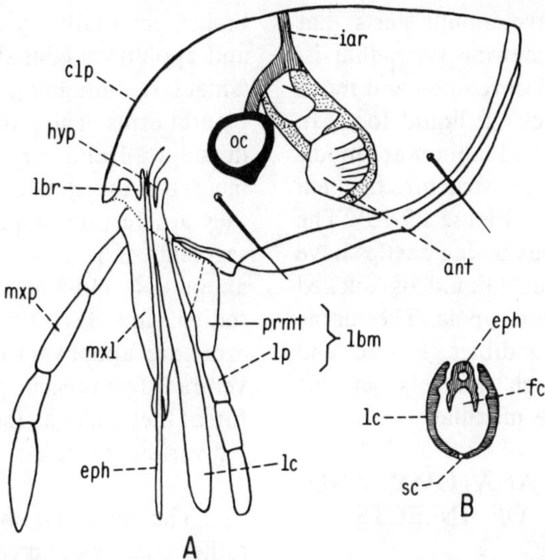

Fig. 2-15. Mouth parts of a flea. A, lateral view of head, somewhat diagrammatic, with stylets separated and the left maxilla not shown; B, cross-section through stylets; *ant,* antenna; *clp,* clypeus; *eph,* epipharynx; *fc,* food channel; *hyp,* hypopharynx; *iar,* interantennal ridge; *lbm,* labium; *lbr,* labrum; *lc,* lacinia; *lp,* labial palpus; *mxl,* maxillary lobe; *mxp,* maxillary palpus; *oc,* ocellus; *prmt,* prementum; *sc,* salivary channel. (A modified from Snodgrass; B redrawn from Matheson by permission of Comstock Publishing Associates.)

ture lying below the alimentary tract. The dorsal stylet probably represents the fused maxillae; its edges are curved upward and inward to form a tube that serves as a food channel. The intermediate stylet is very slender and contains the salivary channel; this stylet is probably the hypopharynx. The ventral stylet is the principal piercing organ; it is a trough-shaped structure, and is probably the labium. There are no palpi.

—The Mouth Parts of Lepidoptera (Figure 2-16)— The proboscis of adult Lepidoptera is usually long and coiled and is formed of the two galeae of the maxillae; the food channel is between the galeae. The labrum is reduced to a narrow transverse band across the lower margin of the face, and the mandibles and hypopharynx are lacking. The maxillary palpi are usually reduced or absent, but the labial palpi are usually well developed. There is no special salivary channel. This type of mouth-part structure is sometimes called siphoning-sucking, for there is no piercing, and the insect merely sucks or siphons liquids up through the proboscis. When used, the proboscis is uncoiled by blood pressure; it recoils by its own elasticity.

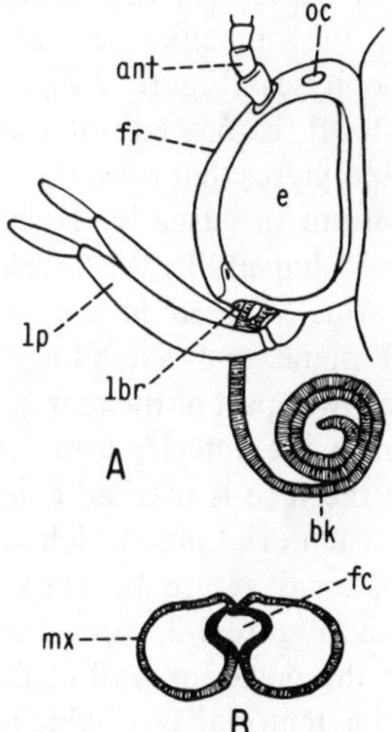

Fig. 2-16. Mouth parts of a moth. A, lateral view of head; B, cross-section through proboscis. *ant,* antenna; *bk,* proboscis; *e,* compound eye; *fc,* food channel; *fr,* frons; *lbr,* labrum; *lp,* labial palpus; *mx,* maxilla (galea); *oc,* ocellus. (Redrawn from Snodgrass.)

A few insects have mouth parts that appear to be of the chewing type; that is, the mandibles are well developed and move sideways, but they suck up liquid food. In the bees, the maxillae and labium are modified into a long tonguelike structure through which liquid is sucked (Figure 29-15). The larvae of the predaceous diving beetles have tubular mandibles, and liquid is sucked through the mandibular canals. The larvae of antlions have the mandibles grooved, and liquid is sucked through channels between the mandibles and the maxillae.

THE INTERNAL ANATOMY AND PHYSIOLOGY OF INSECTS

ENDOSKELETON

The principal skeleton of an insect is an exoskeleton located on the outside of the body, but there are various invaginations of the exoskeleton that serve to strengthen the body wall and provide points for the attachment of muscles; these invaginations constitute an endoskeleton. The elements of the endoskeleton may take various forms; the ridgelike invaginations are usually called apodemes; the spinelike or armlike processes, apophyses (Figure 2-2).

The head is braced internally by a group of apophyses that form the tentorium. The tentorium is usually **H**-shaped, **X**-shaped, or is shaped like the Greek letter *pi*, with the arms situated in a more or less horizontal plane and extending from the face to the lower part of the rear of the head. The origin of the anterior arms of the tentorium on the face is marked externally by the anterior tentorial pits, which are located in the epistomal suture between the frons and clypeus (Figure 2-3, *atp*); the posterior arms meet the posterior wall of the head at the posterior tentorial pits, which are located at the lower end of the postoccipital sutures (Figure 2-3, *ptp*). Some insects have dorsal arms on the tentorium, which extend to the upper part of the face.

Each thoracic segment is usually braced internally by a group of apodemes and apophyses consisting of the phragmata (singular, phragma), the furca, and the pleural arms. The phragmata arise from the dorsal wall and serve as points of attachment for the dorsal longitudinal muscles; they are best developed in the wing-bearing segments. The furca is a **Y**-shaped sternal apophysis, and most of the ventral longitudinal muscles attach to it. The pleural arms are apophyses extending inward and ventrad from each pleural suture to the furca; they serve as the points of attachment for various muscles.

MUSCULAR SYSTEM

The muscular system of an insect is rather complex and consists of from several hundred to a few thousand individual muscles. The muscles are distinctly cross-striated, very strong, and often are capable of extremely rapid action. Many insects can lift 20 or more times their body weight, while man can rarely lift more than his body weight.

The wings of most insects are moved by five groups of muscles: (1) dorsal longitudinal muscles extending between the phragmata, (2) tergosternal muscles extending from the tergum to the sternum, (3) axillary muscles arising on the pleuron and inserted on the first and third axillary sclerites, (4) basalar muscles arising on the episternum and inserted on the basalare, and (5) subalar muscles arising on the epimeron and inserted on the subalare. The wing movements in flight consist of an upstroke, a downstroke, forward and rearward movements, and a partial rotation of the wing on its long axis; most insects can flex their wings, that is, fold them back over the abdomen. The upstroke and downstroke are produced by changes in the shape of the thorax; the tergosternal muscles produce the upstroke, and the dorsal muscles produce the downstroke. The wings are flexed by the axillary muscles. Rotating and forward and rearward movements of the wings are brought about by the basalar and subalar muscles; the basalar muscles also function in extending the flexed wings.

When an insect is held so that its feet are in contact with a resting surface, it will usually remain quiet; if this surface is removed, the insect usually moves its wings as in flight, and studies of the wing movements in flight can be made while the insect is held suspended. By attaching a tiny metallic object such as a piece of tin foil or gold leaf to the wing tip, one may follow the movements of the wing. A graphic record of the wing movements can be made by attaching a tiny bristle to the wing tip and allowing it to make a line on a moving drum as the wings are moved. Wing movements are probably best studied by means of high-speed moving pictures, but the rate of wing movement can often be determined by means of a stroboscope or by measuring the pitch of the sound produced by the beating wings. The rate of wing movement in insects varies considerably; some butterflies move their wings only a few times a second, while some midges can beat their wings nearly 1000 times a second; the wing beat in many flies is 200 to 400 beats per second.

DIGESTIVE SYSTEM

The alimentary canal is a tube, usually somewhat coiled, which extends from the mouth to the anus (see Figure 2-17). It is differentiated into three main regions: the foregut or stomodaeum, the midgut or mesenteron, and the hindgut or proctodaeum. The foregut is usually differentiated into pharynx, esophagus, crop, and proventriculus; the salivary glands arise as evaginations of the foregut. The midgut is usually undifferentiated except for evaginations called gastric caeca. The hindgut may be differentiated into the small intestine or ileum, the large intestine or colon, and the rectum. The malpighian tubules connect with the alimentary canal at the point of union of the midgut and hindgut. Valves between the three main divisions of the alimentary canal regulate the passage of food from one region to another.

The major functions of the digestive system are the ingesting and digesting of food. Digestion is the process of changing food chemically so that it may be taken into the blood and supply nutriment to various parts of the body.

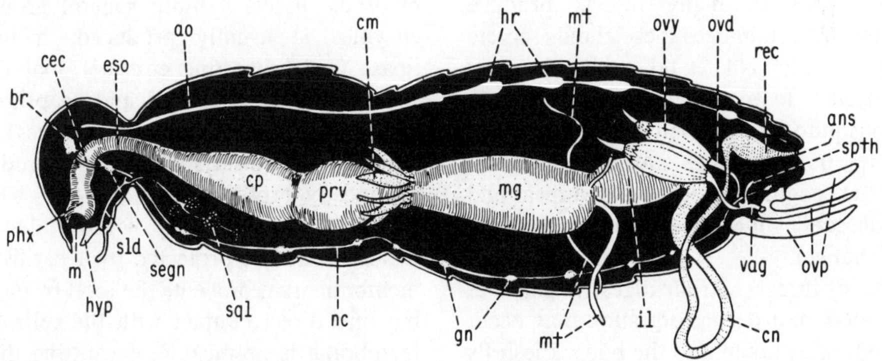

Fig. 2-17. The internal organs of an insect, lateral view (somewhat diagrammatic). *ans,* anus; *ao,* dorsal aorta; *br,* brain; *cec,* circumesophageal connective; *cm,* gastric caeca; *cn,* colon; *cp,* crop; *eso,* esophagus; *gn,* ganglia of the ventral nerve cord; *hr,* heart; *hyp,* hypopharynx; *il,* ileum; *m,* mouth; *mg,* midgut or mesenteron; *mt,* malpighian tubules; *nc,* ventral nerve cord; *ovd,* oviduct; *ovp,* valvulae of ovipositor; *ovy,* ovary; *phx,* pharynx; *prv,* proventriculus; *rec,* rectum; *segn,* subesophageal ganglion; *sgl,* salivary gland; *sld,* salivary duct; *spth,* spermatheca; *vag,* vagina.

Most insects take their food into the body through the mouth. Some internal parasitic larvae are able to absorb their food through the surface of their bodies from host tissues. Many insects have chewing mouth parts fitted with mandibles and maxillae which cut, crush, or macerate food materials and force them into the pharynx. The pharynx of insects with sucking mouth parts functions as a bulblike pump that brings liquid foods through the beak and into the esophagus. Food is moved along the alimentary canal by peristaltic action.

Insects feed upon a great variety of living, dead, and decomposing animals and plants, as well as plant and animal products; in some cases, blood or plant juices may constitute their entire food supply. The digestive system varies considerably with the different kinds of foods utilized. The food habits may vary greatly in a given order; larvae and adults usually have entirely different food habits and different types of digestive systems.

Saliva is usually added to the food, either as it enters the alimentary canal, or before, as in the case of many sucking insects which inject it into the fluids they siphon up as foods. Saliva is usually produced by labial or salivary glands. The labial glands of many insects produce amylase; in certain bees these glands secrete invertase, which is later taken into the body with nectar. In blood-sucking insects such as mosquitoes the saliva contains no enzymes, but contains a substance that prevents the coagulation of the blood meal and the consequent mechanical plugging of the food channel.

Many insects extrude digestive enzymes upon food, and partial digestion may occur before food is taken into the body. Flesh fly larvae discharge proteolytic enzymes onto their food, and plant lice inject amylase into the plant tissues and thus digest starch in the food plant. Extraintestinal digestion also occurs in the larvae of antlions and predaceous diving beetles.

After ingestion the food passes through the esophagus into the posterior part of the foregut; this latter region often serves as a crop where food is stored and in which partial digestion may take place. The foregut is lined with cuticle, and very little absorption (except possibly of fats) takes place in this portion of the alimentary tract. The proventriculus, at the end of the foregut and the entrance to the midgut, may be supplied with large or sharp needlelike teeth; when the food consists of coarse particles, these teeth serve as separators or may even break up the particles into smaller pieces.

The midgut is lined with epithelial cells; no cuticle is present in this portion of the alimentary tract. Some of the epithelial cells produce enzymes, and others absorb digested food. Two methods of enzyme secretion occur here: holocrine secretion, in which the cells disintegrate, and merocrine secretion, in which the enzymes diffuse through the cell membrane into the lumen. Most of the absorption takes place in the midgut.

The insect's food habits determine to a large degree the types of enzymes produced in the midgut; in some cases, such as the clothes moth that digests keratin or hair, the enzymes produced are very specific. In omnivorous insects a more general group of enzymes is usually produced, including lipase (a fat-digesting enzyme), maltase (a sugar-digesting enzyme), and trypsin and pepsin (protein-digesting enzymes). In blood-sucking insects the enzymes produced are mostly proteolytic.

The epithelial cells of the midgut are delicate, and are protected by a peritrophic membrane that prevents the food from coming into direct contact with the cells. This membrane is permeable, permitting the interchange of both digestive enzymes and the digestive products that are ready for absorption. The peritrophic membrane is secreted by the epithelial cells of the midgut. It often pulls loose, stays around the food, and is voided with the excrement.

After food is digested and for the most part absorbed, the residue passes into the hindgut, where some slight absorption may take place, though the epithelial cells here too are lined with cuticle. Water absorption occurs in the hindgut, especially in insects feeding on stored grain, where water is conserved and reused by the insect. In such cases the fecal pellets are dry and are compressed and expelled by the heavy muscles of the rectum.

A fauna of symbiotic microorganisms is sometimes necessary to accomplish the digestion, especially in insects such as termites and other cellulose-feeding species which do not produce enzymes that will break down cellulose. Such microorganisms occur in the hindgut, and absorption apparently takes place in that portion of the alimentary tract.

Insects feeding on blood, plant juices, or other liquid foods are equipped with various specialized arrangements for extracting a large percentage of the water from the food before it comes in contact with the digestive enzymes. In the blood-sucking Hemiptera the blood meal is temporarily stored in the crop; the water is absorbed through the crop wall into the blood, and passes to the hindgut by way of the malpighian tubules. In the case of the Homoptera, where enormous quantities of plant juices are taken into the body, the excess water is extracted by a filter chamber which is so constructed that a great amount of excess water is absorbed through the walls of the anterior part of the mesenteron and passes to the proctodaeum, which is looped close to it. This concentrates the food material, and the excess water is passed to the rectum and excreted as honeydew. The presence of this filter chamber is one feature that distinguishes the Homoptera from the Hemiptera.

The vitamin requirements of insects are not fully known, but most insects require cholesterol and several vitamins of the B group (for example, thiamin, riboflavin, pyridoxine, and nicotinic acid). In some cases certain essential vitamins are furnished by symbiotic microorganisms. The quantity and quality of the food has considerable effect on the growth rate of the insect and sometimes also on reproductive processes.

The water requirements are very different in different types of insects. Leaf-feeding insects obtain great quantities of water with their food, and the body water loss is usually high. On the other hand, insects feeding on stored grain obtain little water with their food and conserve practically all of it. In insects that conserve water to a high degree, water is absorbed from the proctodaeum and eventually returned to the body cells. In some cases the water is so completely extracted in the rectum that the excrement consists of dry pellets. Water in some cases may be obtained chiefly through metabolic processes such as the oxidation of foods. Insects such as the mealworm are able under conditions of high humidity to absorb moisture from the air.

CIRCULATORY SYSTEM

The circulatory system of an insect is an open one, as compared with the closed system of a vertebrate. The only blood vessel is a tube located dorsal to the alimentary tract and extending through the thorax and abdomen. The posterior portion of this tube, the heart (Figure 2-17, *hr*), is divided by valves into a series of chambers, each of which has a pair of lateral openings called ostia. The number of ostia varies in different species; in some cases there are as few as two pairs. The anterior part of the tube, which lacks ostia, is called the dorsal aorta (Figure 2-17, *ao*).

Pulsations of the heart produce the circulation by pumping the blood forward and out of the aorta in the neck region; the increased pressure here causes the blood to move posteriorly through the body cavity. The body cavity of an insect lacks the epithelial lining of a true coelom and serves as a chamber for circulating blood. The organs

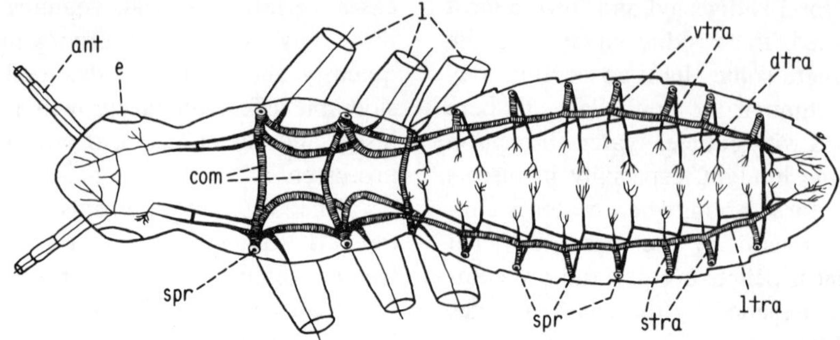

Fig. 2-18. Diagram of a horizontal section of an insect showing the arrangement of the principal tracheae. *ant,* antenna; *com,* commissural tracheae; *dtra,* dorsal trachea; *e,* compound eye; *l,* legs; *ltra,* main longitudinal tracheal trunk; *spr,* spiracles; *stra,* spiracular tracheae; *vtra,* ventral tracheae. (Modified from Fernald and Shepard, after Kolbe, by permission of McGraw-Hill Book Company.)

and tissues of the insect are thus exposed to and bathed by the circulating blood. The appendages are usually irrigated by special arrangements, but rarely through closed vessels; as a rule, independent pumps or pulsating organs serve to supply the appendages with blood. Respiratory movements may also influence the circulation of the blood.

The blood, or haemolymph, is usually a clear fluid, often greenish or yellowish in color, seldom red. It makes up from 5 to 40 percent of the body weight (usually 25 percent or less), and serves as a medium for the chemical exchanges that are necessary for the proper functioning of the tissues and organs. It transports food from the alimentary tract and waste products to the excretory organs, and it also functions in the transport of hormones. The transport of oxygen and carbon dioxide is not a basic function of the blood, but the blood may serve in the exchanges of these gases in the case of cells that are not reached by the tracheoles.

GASEOUS EXCHANGE SYSTEM

The intake of oxygen, its distribution to the tissues, and the removal of carbon dioxide are accomplished by means of an intricate system of tubes called the tracheal system (Figure 2-18). The principal tubes of this system, the tracheae, open externally at the spiracles (*spr*); internally they branch variously, extend throughout the body, and terminate in very fine branches called tracheoles, which permeate the various tissues. The tracheae are lined with a thin layer of cuticle, which is thickened to form spiral rings that give the tracheae rigidity. The tracheoles are simple cells with thin walls and often contain liquid.

The spiracles are located laterally and vary in number from one to about nine or ten pairs. There is typically a pair on the anterior margin of the mesothorax, another pair on the anterior margin of the metathorax, and a pair on each of the first seven or eight abdominal segments.

The oxygen enters through the spiracles, is conveyed through the tracheae to the tracheoles, and the carbon dioxide is eliminated principally through these same spiracles; probably one fourth of the carbon dioxide is carried by the blood and eliminated through the body wall. In certain insects, such as the grasshopper, it has been demonstrated that there is a type of ventilation in which air is taken into the body through the thoracic spiracles and is exhaled through the abdominal spiracles. In some cases portions of the tracheae may be flattened and serve as reservoir sacs (or miniature lungs). The spiracles may be partially or completely closed for extended periods by some insects; water loss may be partially controlled in this way.

The control of gaseous exchange is apparently through the nervous system, and each ganglion seems to control only its own segment. External and internal stimuli affect the respiratory rate.

Various respiratory adaptations occur in insects that are aquatic or parasitic. Many small, soft-bodied, aquatic or parasitic insects breathe directly through the body wall. Many aquatic insects have gills, evaginations of the body wall which are usually provided with a system of tracheae. These tracheal gills vary in shape and location in different insects; in stonefly nymphs they are fingerlike or branched and are located around the bases of the legs or on the basal abdominal segments; in mayfly nymphs they are leaflike and located along the sides of the abdomen; in damselfly nymphs they are leaflike but are located at the tip of the abdomen; in dragonfly nymphs they are located in the rectum. In each case the gases are exchanged through the membrane separating the tracheae from the water. Some aquatic (and a few parasitic) insects have a respiratory tube at the posterior end of the body and may live submerged and obtain air through this tube, which is extended to the surface of the water or into the air spaces of an aquatic plant; waterscorpions and such aquatic ditperous larvae as mosquito larvae and rat-tailed maggots are equipped with tubes of this sort.

Certain adult aquatic insects that have normal tracheal systems with active spiracles are able to go beneath the water and remain for extended periods by carrying with them a film of air on the surface of the body. By means of such a reservoir of air, water boatmen, backswimmers, and diving beetles are able to remain under water and obtain up to 13 times as much oxygen from this reservoir—due to gaseous exchanges between the reservoir and the water —as was originally in it.

EXCRETORY SYSTEM

The excretory system consists of a group of tubes, the malpighian tubules (Figure 2-17, *mt*), which arise as evaginations at the anterior end of the hindgut. These tubules vary in number from one or two to over a hundred, and their distal ends are closed. Various waste products are taken up from the blood by these tubules and passed out by way of the hindgut and anus.

The waste products consist chiefly of nitrogenous wastes, salts, and excess water; uric acid is probably the main waste product. Water is apparently necessary for the excretory process and is circulated through the blood that surrounds the malpighian tubules. The cells of these tubules absorb the aqueous form of uric acid, condense it in the proximal end of the tubules, and discharge it into the hindgut where it mixes with the fecal materials and passes out through the anus. The use and conservation of water is necessary in this process, and water is apparently often absorbed almost directly through the cells of the malpighian tubules, where they come in contact with the walls of the hindgut, and may even be held there by a surrounding membrane.

Excretory products are often deposited in the form of pigments or other materials in cuticular or other structures.

NERVOUS SYSTEM

The nervous system of an insect consists of a brain located in the head above the esophagus, a subesophageal ganglion[3] connected to the brain by two commisures that extend around either side of the esophagus (Figure 2-17, *cec*), and a ventral nerve cord extending posteriorly from the subesophageal ganglion. The ventral nerve cord is typically double and contains segmentally located ganglia; occasionally some of these ganglia fuse, and there may be fewer ganglia than segments.

[3] This ganglion is usually called the subesophageal ganglion, though it may sometimes be below the pharynx.

The cells of the nervous system consist of more or less rounded cell bodies provided with various branching processes; at least one of these processes (the axon) is sometimes very much elongated. The nerve cells function in transmitting impulses from one part of the body to another. The impulse originates at a sense organ and travels over sensory nerve cells to the central nervous system; there it passes over association cells to motor cells, over which it travels to a muscle or gland. In passing from one nerve cell to another, the impulse passes across a synapse, a point where the branching processes of one nerve cell lie adjacent to those of another cell; nerve cells are not directly connected. The cell bodies of motor and association nerve cells lie in the central nervous system (brain and nerve cord), and the cell bodies of sensory nerve cells are usually located in the insect's integument. The nerves, which extend from the central nervous system to the periphery of the body, consist of bundles of axons.

REPRODUCTIVE SYSTEM

Reproduction in insects is nearly always sexual, and the sexes are separate.[4] Variations from the usual reproductive pattern occur occasionally; in many social insects, such as the ants and bees, certain females (the workers) may be unable to reproduce because their sex organs are undeveloped; in some insects, individuals occasionally occur that have characters of both sexes (gynandromorphs). The gonads of insects—ovaries in the female, testes in the male—are located in the abdomen, and the ducts from the gonads open to the outside near the posterior end of the abdomen.

In the female (Figure 2-17) the oviducts usually unite posteriorly to form a vagina which leads to the outside. Associated with the vagina, or with a genital chamber at the posterior end of the vagina, there is usually a saclike structure called the spermatheca (in which sperm are stored) and often also various accessory glands.

In the male the ducts from the testes, the vasa deferentia, usually unite posteriorly to form the ejaculatory duct which extends to the outside. Each vas deferens usually contains an enlarged portion, the seminal vesicle, which serves as a reservoir for sperm. There are often various accessory glands associated with the ejaculatory duct. This duct usually terminates in an intromittent organ, the aedeagus.

In addition to the structures mentioned above, there are frequently various structures associated with the external openings of the genital ducts; these are the external genitalia (though some of them may be withdrawn into the abdomen when not in use), which in the male are concerned with copulation and the transferral of sperm to the female, and in the female are concerned with oviposition. The external genitalia have been discussed above (see page 13).

SENSE ORGANS

The sense organs of insects are located mainly in the body wall, and most of them are microscopic in size; each is usually excited only by a certain type of stimulus. Insects have sense organs receptive to mechanical, chemical, visual, auditory, or other types of stimuli.

THE MECHANICAL SENSES: The sense organs receptive to mechanical stimuli are of three principal types: tactile spines and hairs, campaniform sensilla, and chordotonal sensilla. Many, perhaps most, of the movable spines and hairs on the insect's body are provided with sensory cells which give the insect the sense of touch. In a campaniform sensillum there is no outgrowth of the cuticula like a hair or spine; the terminal filament of the sensory cell is inserted in a dome-shaped area of the cuticula. Campaniform sensilla are widely distributed over the body and are sensitive to pressure or a bending of the cuticula. In a chordotonal sensillum the sensory cell ends in the

[4] The cottony cushion scale, *Icérya púrchasi* Maskell, is normally hermaphroditic; that is, both sexes are present in one individual.

axis of an elastic strand stretched between two points on the body wall, one of which is usually more or less movable. These sensilla are widely distributed and are sensitive to body movements. In the second antennal segment of most insects there is a sense organ similar to a chordotonal sensillum, called Johnston's organ; this organ is sensitive to movements of the antenna.

THE CHEMICAL SENSES: The chemical senses are those of taste and smell; the principal difference between these two is that taste is detected by contact and smells are detected from a distance. The organs of taste are located principally on the mouth parts, but some insects (for example, ants, bees, and wasps) also have taste organs on the antennae, and some (for example, butterflies, moths, and flies) have taste organs on the tarsi. The organs of smell are located principally on the antennae (in some cases also on the palpi, and possibly the tarsi). The chemical senses of insects are often extremely keen, much more so than those of man; many insects can detect odors at very great distances (often several miles).

ORGANS OF VISION: Insects possess two types of eyes, simple and compound. Simple eyes, or ocelli, are present in many larvae and nymphs and in a great many adults; most adults have compound eyes.

Each compound eye is composed of many (up to several thousand) individual units called ommatidia, each of which is marked externally by a hexagonal area called a facet. The facet is a cuticular lens secreted by two epidermal cells, which lie beneath it and which are usually pigmented; these epidermal cells surround a crystalline cone made up of four cells. The sensory part of the eye extends from the apex of the cone to the basement membrane and consists of a bundle of several elongate cells, the inner surfaces of which form an axial rod called the rhabdom; visual stimuli are picked up by the rhabdoms.

There are two principal types of ommatidia in the compound eyes of insects. In most diurnal insects the ommatidia are relatively short and each forms its own image, so that the picture obtained by an insect is probably a sort of mosaic. In most nocturnal insects the ommatidia are more elongated and the image of a single rhabdom is formed by several ommatidia. Both types of ommatidia may be present in the same compound eye.

The ocelli are somewhat simpler in structure than the compound eyes. Each ocellus consists of an external facet or cornea, a layer of epidermal cells beneath and secreting the cornea, and underneath the epidermis is a layer of sensory cells forming a retina. The function of the ocelli is not too well understood; in many adult insects they function as supplementary light perception organs, but do not perceive images; the ocelli of many larvae perceive images.

An insect probably does not get so clear an image of objects as do vertebrates, and its ability to distinguish form is not very well developed. It is usually very sensitive to motion. The insect's visible spectrum is usually not the same as that of man; insects see farther into the ultraviolet than we do, in some cases to wavelengths as short as 0.257 micron (the limit in man is about 0.400 micron), and do not see as far into the red (the limit is about 0.690 micron for insects, and 0.800 micron for man).

AUDITORY ORGANS: Insects hear by means of two sorts of sense organs, delicate tactile hairs sensitive to sound waves, and tympanal organs. Some insects, such as male mosquitoes, detect sound by means of the antennal hairs; many insects are able to detect sounds by means of their body hairs. Tympanal organs (eardrums) are present in certain Lepidoptera and Orthoptera. Some moths have tympana on the dorsal surface of the metathorax. In the short-horned grasshoppers (Tetrígidae and Acrídidae) the tympana are located on the sides of the first abdominal segment; in the long-horned grasshoppers (Tettigonìidae) and crickets (Grýllidae) the tympana, when present, are located at the proximal end of the front tibiae. Some Orthoptera are sensitive to much higher frequencies than man can hear; the upper limit of human hearing is usually between 15,000 and 20,000 vibrations per second, but some Orthoptera are sensitive to frequencies as high as 100,000.

OTHER SENSE ORGANS: Insects usually have a well-developed temperature sense; the sense organs involved are distributed all over the body, but are more numerous on the antennae and legs. It is probable that these organs are specialized thermal receptors. Insects usually also have a well-developed humidity sense, but little is known of the sensory mechanism involved.

HORMONES

Hormones are chemical substances produced in some body organ and introduced into the blood stream, which carries them to other parts of the body to produce some effect on physiological processes. Several organs in an insect are known to produce hormones, the principal functions of which are the control of molting and metamorphosis.

The hormones involved in metamorphosis have been studied in some detail in the cecropia moth. This insect (and probably also other insects with complete metamorphosis) has three hormones controlling metamorphosis: a brain hormone, a prothoracic gland hormone, and a corpus allatum hormone. The brain hormone, produced after the low temperature of hibernation (as a pupa in the cecropia), stimulates the production of the prothoracic gland hormone, which promotes metamorphosis. If the brain is removed from a hibernating pupa, the pupa will not metamorphose to the adult, but the implantation of a brain from a chilled pupa into such a brainless pupa will bring about normal development. If a larva nearly ready to pupate is divided in the middle of the body by a tight ligature, only the anterior half will pupate, although the posterior half will remain alive for several days. Similarly, if a pupa is cut in two parts and the cut ends are sealed, the anterior half will transform to the adult, but the posterior half will not. The corpus allatum hormone apparently functions in inhibiting metamorphosis; the removal of the corpora allata (a pair of structures lying immediately behind the brain) during the larval stage will result in pupation.

Metamorphosis in the assassin bug *Rhódnius* (and probably also in other insects with simple metamorphosis) is controlled by hormones in much the same way as in the cecropia. The brain hormone is produced under the stimulus of the stretched abdomen after feeding and, through the prothoracic gland hormone, promotes metamorphosis and molting and stimulates the secretion of the corpus allatum hormone. Injection of the brain hormone into an adult causes molting to occur. The corpus allatum hormone inhibits metamorphosis and brings about nymphal characters after the molt; its removal causes premature metamorphosis, and its injection into last-instar nymphs produces another nymphal instar; this hormone is normally inactive during the last instar.

PHEROMONES: Pheromones are substances that are secreted to the outside, where they cause a specific reaction by other individuals of the same species. They are not true hormones in the sense that the term is defined above; they have sometimes been called "social hormones." Pheromones include such things as sex attractants (produced by the females of many moths and other insects, attracting the males, often from considerable distances) and the queen substances produced by such social insects as the honey bee, ants, and termites, which influence the behavior of other individuals. Pheromones do not include repellents.

INSECT BEHAVIOR

The behavior of insects consists of responses to stimuli. A response is the result of impulses that are set up by the stimuli and which travel over the nervous system to effectors. The way an insect responds is determined by the pattern of pathways over which the impulses travel. The fact that the response may be advantageous to the insect does not indicate that any thinking or reasoning is involved; it is unsafe to assume that a mental reaction such as liking or disliking something has anything to do with the insect's responses. The nerve pathways involved in insect behavior are largely hereditary, hence the responses are largely automatic.

DIRECTED RESPONSES: Many of an insect's responses to stimuli consist of orientation and movement toward or away from the stimulus. These directed responses may be positive (toward the stimulus) or negative (away from the stimulus); responses consisting of orientation with respect to the stimulus are usually called tropisms, and movements toward or away from the stimulus are called taxes. The stimulus producing a directed response may be light, temperature, water, chemicals, touch or contact, the force of gravity, or currents of air or water.

Many insects have very definite responses to light; some, such as house flies, go toward a light whereas others, such as bed bugs, avoid it. Night-flying insects respond positively to a source of light but not to a diffuse light, especially one of high intensity. The intensity, duration, or wavelength (color) of the light may influence the response. Positive responses to certain chemicals often result in the insect's locating its food or a site for oviposition; a chemical producing a negative response is called a repellent. Insects react negatively to many tactile stimuli; for example, they move away when touched; on the other hand, a positive response to certain tactile stimuli may result in an insect like a cockroach squeezing into a small opening or crevice. A group of dragonflies sitting on a fence, all headed into the wind, show a positive orientation response to air currents. Many aquatic insects head or swim upstream, thus exhibiting a positive response to water currents.

The nature of an insect's response to a specific stimulus is often modified by other stimuli. Honey bees respond positively to a bright light at high temperatures (for example, they leave the hive), but respond negatively to the same light intensity at low temperatures (for example, they remain in the hive). House flies move upward at night, but do not exhibit this response (to gravity) during the day. The responses of many insects to gravity are influenced by temperature, being negative at high temperatures (that is, the insects move upward) and positive at low temperatures. The physiological state of the insect, as affected by its food or its state of development or by other factors, often influences its response to a given stimulus; an insect that is well fed often does not respond to a chemical stimulus to which it will respond when it is not well fed; the larval and adult stages of the same species often react differently to a given stimulus.

A knowledge of insect responses has many practical applications. Such knowledge may be used to locate insects or to predict where they will go under certain conditions. Directed responses make it possible to trap and destroy undesirable insects or to avoid the damage they do by repelling them. Many control measures depend for their effectiveness upon the reaction of the insect to particular stimuli.

COMPLEX BEHAVIOR: Much of the behavior of insects involves more than orientation or movement with respect to a particular stimulus. Egg laying, capturing prey, nest building, cocoon making, and other activities involve a number of different movements and responses. Many insects have rather elaborate egg-laying habits; the cicada slits the bark of a twig and lays its eggs in this slit; lacewings lay their eggs at the ends of long slender stalks; certain carrion beetles excavate beneath carcasses and bury them, and lay their eggs in them; most parasitic insects lay their eggs in or on the body of their host. Much of this behavior appears purposive and intelligent; for example, the activities of a wasp in building a nest, capturing and stinging prey, storing that prey in a cell in the nest, laying an egg in the cell, and then sealing up the cell seem to show a remarkable foresight on the part of the wasp. When carefully examined, however, this behavior is generally found to be automatic. These activities are performed in a characteristic manner by all the members of a species; they do not have to be learned and are performed about as well the first time as after practice, and the various individual acts involved are performed in a characteristic sequence. This type of behavior is generally spoken of as instinctive and does not involve volition or learning.

Instinctive behavior is usually valuable to the species and has persisted during the course of evolution because of its survival value. Individuals whose behavior pattern is not beneficial tend to die out, whereas those whose behavior favors survival persist in greater numbers and pass the hereditary elements of this behavior to their offspring.

Whether or not insects can be said to be intelligent depends on how intelligence is defined. There is some difference of opinion as to just what intelligence is, but the term usually implies a capacity to modify behavior as a result of experience (that is, the capacity to learn), and possibly the ability to think or reason. There is abundant evidence that insects possess some capacity to learn, but little or no positive evidence that they can think. A honey bee can learn to recognize certain surroundings and use these for orientation in flight. It can learn to associate a color with food, and such conditioning helps the bee to locate food; if the color is changed, the bee must learn the association again. The ability of nest-building insects like bees and wasps to return to their nests from a distance involves some sort of sensory memory of visual, chemical, or tactile stimuli. Whether or not such learning involves any thinking or reasoning, it is impossible to say. Entomological literature abounds in descriptions of insect behavior that appears intelligent, especially in the social insects, but a careful study of such behavior shows it to be largely automatic. Insects might be said to possess a certain amount of intelligence, but the gap between the intelligence of insects and that of man is enormous.

ACOUSTICAL BEHAVIOR: One of the most interesting types of behavior in insects is that which occurs in relation to sound. A great many insects—probably as many as all other animals combined—produce sounds by means of special structures, but only a few, such as the crickets, grasshoppers, and cicadas, are heard by most people. The sounds produced by many insects are very soft, or very high-pitched, and are seldom if ever heard. Sound in many insects plays an important role in behavior.

Sounds are produced by insects in about five principal ways: (1) by stridulation, that is, by rubbing one body part against another (grasshoppers, crickets, bugs, beetles, and others); (2) by striking some body part, such as the feet (band-winged grasshoppers), the tip of the abdomen (cockroaches), or the head (deathwatch beetles) against the substrate; (3) by vibrating some body part, such as the wings, in the air (flies, bees, and others); (4) by vibrating drumlike membranes called tymbals (cicadas and some hoppers); and (5) by forcibly ejecting air or fluid (some short-horned grasshoppers, bombardier beetles).

The auditory organs of insects are usually tympanal organs or hair sensilla. They are generally not very sensitive to changes in frequency (or pitch), but are capable of responding to rapid fluctuations in intensity. The auditory organs of some insects are capable of detecting frequencies much higher than can be detected by the best human ears (up to 100,000 cycles per second); for example, the noctuid moths have tympanal auditory organs capable of detecting the supersonic sounds emitted by bats.

The principal differences in the sounds produced by different species, or by a given species under different circumstances, are in rhythm; the rhythm of a sound is much more important to an insect than its pitch.

Many insects, such as the crickets, grasshoppers, and cicadas, produce sounds more or less continuously through certain daily periods; these periods are probably determined largely by light intensity, temperature, and (or) humidity. Such sounds are the best known of those produced by insects, and are commonly called "songs." They are usually produced only by the male. They appear to function in (1) attracting a female, (2) causing the female to produce a sound that enables the male to locate her, and (or) (3) causing the congregation of large numbers of individuals (for example, in cicadas).

In many species of singing insects, neighboring males synchronize their songs. When the first individual begins to sing, others nearby chime in very quickly, their pulses or chirps synchronized. This synchronization of singing occurs in spite of other species singing in the same area; hence the individuals involved must be able to recognize the song of their own species very quickly.

Some insect sounds are produced in response to the presence or activities of other organisms. Many insects produce what might be called a disturbance call when disturbed, captured, or handled. Some insects produce a special type of sound, often called a courtship song, only in the presence of a female of the same species. The males of many crickets and other insects produce what might be called warning sounds in the presence of another male of the same species. The females of some species produce a special sound in the presence of a male of the same species.

REFERENCES ON THE ANATOMY AND PHYSIOLOGY OF INSECTS

Alexander, Richard D. 1957. Sound production and associated behavior in insects. Ohio J. Sci., 57(2):101-113; 13 f.

Comstock, John H. 1940 (9th ed.). An introduction to entomology. Ithaca, N.Y.: Comstock Publishing Associates. xix + 1064 pp., 1228 f. Especially Chaps. 2 and 3.

Craig, Roderick. 1960. The physiology of excretion in the insect. Ann. Rev. Entomol., 5:53-68.

Essig, E. O. 1942. College entomology. New York: The Macmillan Company. vii + 900 pp., 305 f. Especially Chap. 2.

House, H. L. 1961. Insect nutrition. Ann. Rev. Entomol., 6:13-26.

Imms, A. D. 1957 (9th ed., revised by O. W. Richards and R. G. Davies). A general textbook of entomology. New York: E. P. Dutton & Co., Inc. x + 886 pp., 609 f.

Lipke, H., and G. Fraenkel. 1956. Insect nutrition. Ann. Rev. Entomol., 1:17-44.

Matheson, Robert. 1951 (2nd ed.). Entomology for introductory courses. Ithaca, N.Y.: Comstock Publishing Associates. xiv + 629 pp., 500 f. Especially Chaps. 3 and 4.

Metcalf, C. L., and W. P. Flint. 1962 (4th ed., revised by R. L. Metcalf). Destructive and useful insects. New York: McGraw-Hill Book Company, Inc. xii + 1087 pp.; illus. Especially Chaps. 3-5.

Roeder, Kenneth D. (ed.) 1953. Insect physiology. New York: John Wiley & Sons, Inc. xiv + 1100 pp., 257 f.

Ross, Herbert H. 1956 (2nd ed.). A textbook of entomology. New York: John Wiley & Sons, Inc. xi+519 pp., 402 f.

Schmitt, J. B. 1962. The comparative anatomy of the insect nervous system. Ann. Rev. Entomol., 7:137-156; 1 f.

Snodgrass, R. E. 1935. Principles of insect morphology. New York: McGraw-Hill Book Company, Inc. x+667 pp., 319 f.

Snodgrass, R. E. 1952. A textbook of arthropod anatomy. Ithaca, N.Y.: Comstock Publishing Associates. viii+363 pp., 88 f.

Snodgrass, R. E. 1962. Suture or sulcus? Proc. Entomol. Soc. Wash., 64(4):222-223.

Waterhouse, D. F. 1957. Digestion in insects. Ann. Rev. Entomol., 2:1-18.

Wigglesworth, V. B. 1950 (4th ed.). The principles of insect physiology. London: Methuen & Co., Ltd. viii+544 pp., 355 f.

Wigglesworth, V. B. 1954. The physiology of insect metamorphosis. Cambridge: Cambridge University Press. vii+151 pp., illus.

Wigglesworth, V. B. 1956 (5th ed.). Insect physiology. London: Methuen & Co., Ltd. x+130 pp., 12 f.

Wigglesworth, V. B. 1959. The control of growth and form. Ithaca, N.Y.: Cornell University Press. 140 pp., illus.

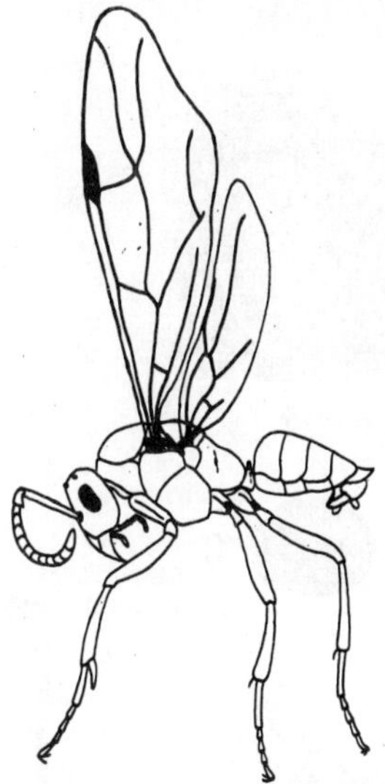

3

The Development and Metamorphosis of Insects

All insects develop from eggs. Most insects are oviparous, that is, the young hatch from the eggs after they have been laid; in a few insects the eggs develop within the body of the female, and living young are produced.

INSECT EGGS

Most insect eggs develop only if they are fertilized, the fertilization occurring before the eggs are laid. In some insects, however, parthenogenesis occurs, that is, the eggs develop without being fertilized. Parthenogenesis occurs sporadically in many species and is a regular feature of the life cycle in others. In the aphids and gall wasps, for example, parthenogenesis alternates during the year with bisexual reproduction; in insects such as the honey bee the fertilization of the egg determines the sex, with fertilized eggs developing into females and unfertilized eggs into males.

In a few of the parasitic Hymenoptera a single egg develops into more than one young; this phenomenon is known as polyembryony. The number of young developing from a single egg in such insects may vary from two to over a thousand.

The eggs of different insects vary greatly in appearance (Figures 3-1, 3-2). Most eggs are spherical, oval, or elongate (Figure 3-1 B, C, G), but some are barrel-shaped (Figure 3-2), some are disc-shaped, and others are of other shapes. The egg is covered with a shell that varies in thickness, sculpturing, and color; many eggs are provided with characteristic ridges, spines, or other processes, and some are brightly colored.

Most insect eggs are laid in a situation where they are afforded some protection, or where the young on hatching will have suitable conditions for development. Many insects enclose their eggs in some sort of pro-

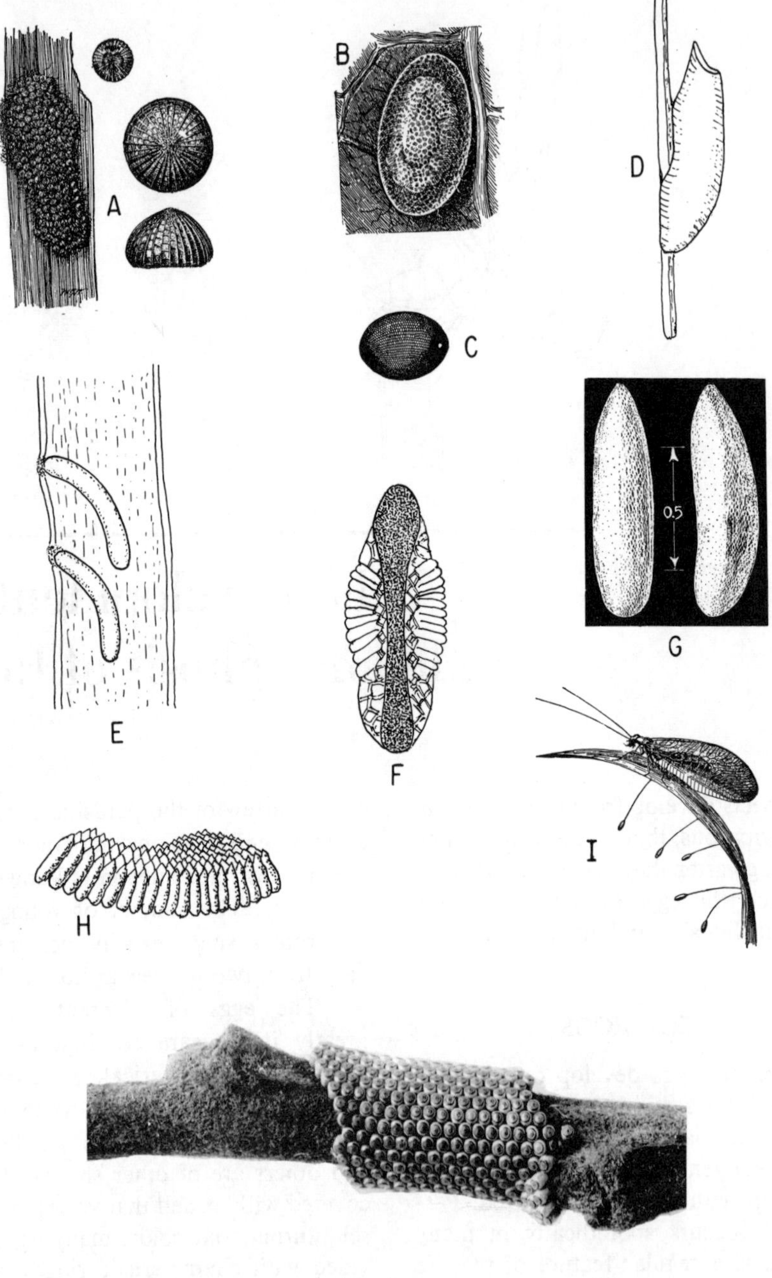

Fig. 3-1. Insect eggs. A, fall armyworm, *Laphýgma frugipérda* (Abbott and Smith); B, grape-leaf folder, *Désmia funeràlis* (Hübner); C, southern corn rootworm, *Diabrótica undécimpunctàta howardi* (Baker); D, horse bot fly, *Gasteróphilus intestinàlis* (DeGeer); E, snowy tree cricket *Oecánthus fúltoni* Walker; F, *Anópheles* mosquito; G, seed-corn maggot, *Hylemỳa cilcrùra* (Rondani); H, *Culex* mosquito, egg raft; I, lacewing, *Chrysòpa* sp.; J, fall cankerworm, *Alsóphila pometaria* (Harris). (A-C, G, and I, courtesy of USDA; J, courtesy of the Ohio Agricultural Experiment Station.)

Fig. 3-2. Eggs of a stink bug. (Courtesy of the Ohio Agricultural Experiment Station.)

tective material; cockroaches, mantids, and other insects enclose their eggs in an egg case or capsule; the tent caterpillar covers its eggs with a shellaclike material; the gypsy moth lays its eggs in a mass of its body hairs. Grasshoppers, June beetles, and other insects lay their eggs in the ground; tree crickets insert their eggs in plant tissues (Figure 3-1 E). Most plant feeding insects lay their eggs on the food plant of the young. Insects whose immature stages are aquatic usually lay their eggs in water, often attaching them to objects in the water. Parasitic insects usually lay their eggs in or on the body of the host. Some insects deposit their eggs singly, while others lay their eggs in characteristic groups or masses (Figures 3-1 H, J, 3-2). The number laid varies from one in certain aphids to many thousands in some of the social insects; most insects lay from fifty to a few hundred eggs.

Hatching young escape from the egg in various ways. The young of most insects with chewing mouth parts chew their way out of the egg. Many insects possess what are called egg-bursters—spinelike, knifelike, or sawlike processes on the dorsal surface of the head—which are used in breaking through the egg shell. The egg shell is sometimes broken along weakened lines, either by the wriggling of the insect within or by the insect taking in air and rupturing the shell by internal pressure.

GROWTH AND METAMORPHOSIS

The growth of an insect is accompanied by a series of molts or ecdyses, in which the cuticle is shed and renewed. The molt involves not only the external layers of the body wall (cuticula), but also the cuticular linings of the tracheae, foregut, and hindgut; the cast skins (exuviae) often retain the shape of the insects from which they were shed.

Prior to the actual shedding process, a new cuticular layer is secreted by the epidermal cells beneath the old layer, and a molting fluid is secreted which separates the new cuticle from the old. The shedding process begins with a splitting of the old cuticle, usually along the midline on the dorsal side of the thorax; this split grows, and the insect eventually wriggles out of the old cuticle.

The number of molts varies in most insects from 4 to 8; however, some of the Odonata undergo 10 or 12 molts, and some of the Ephemeroptera may undergo as many as 20 or more molts. A few insects, such as

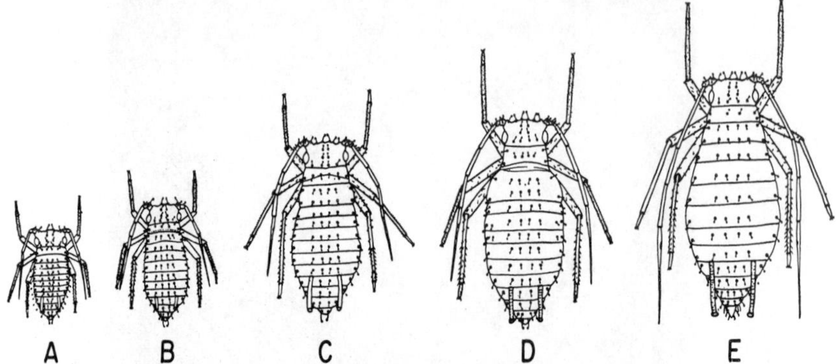

Fig. 3-3. Stages in the development of the strawberry aphid, *Capitóphorus fragaefòlii* (Cockerell). A, first instar; B, second instar; C, third instar; D, fourth instar; E, adult female. (Courtesy of Baerg and the Arkansas Agricultural Experiment Station.)

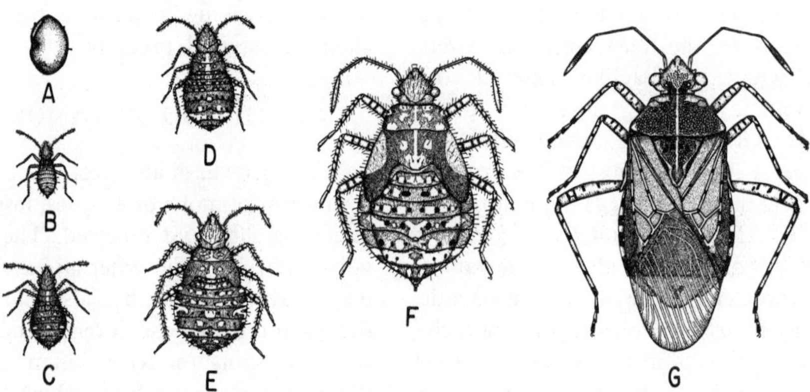

Fig. 3-4. Stages in the development of the grass bug, *Corìzus sidae* (Fabricius). A, egg; B, first instar; C, second instar; D, third instar; E, fourth instar; F, fifth instar; G, adult female. (Courtesy of Readio and the Entomological Society of America.)

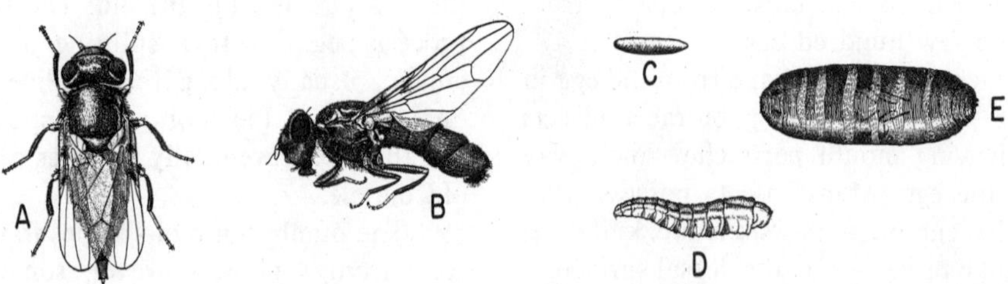

Fig. 3-5. Stages in the development of the sugar-beet root maggot, *Tétanops myopaefórmis* (Röder). A, adult female; B, adult male; C, egg; D, larva; E, puparium (pupa inside). (Courtesy of Knowlton and the Utah Agricultural Experiment Station.)

the bristletails, may continue to molt after reaching the adult stage, but most insects neither molt nor increase in size once the adult stage is reached.

The form of the insect between molts is called an instar; the first instar is between hatching and the first molt; the second instar is between the first and second molts, and so on. The interval of time between successive molts is called a stadium (plural, stadia).

Most insects change in form during development, and the different instars are not all alike; this change is called metamorphosis. Some insects undergo very little change in form, and the young and adults are very similar except for size (Figure 3-3); in other cases the young and adults are quite different—in habits as well as in form (Figure 3-5).

There are two principal types of metamorphosis in insects. In one type, called simple metamorphosis, the wings (if any) develop externally during the immature stages, and there is ordinarily no prolonged resting stage preceding the last molt (Figures 3-3, 3-4); in the other type, called complete metamorphosis, the wings (if any) develop internally during the immature stages, and there is a resting or pupal stage preceding the last molt (Figure 3-5).

SIMPLE METAMORPHOSIS: The young of insects with this type of metamorphosis are called nymphs and are usually very similar to the adults. Compound eyes are present in the nymph if they are present in the adult. If the adults are wingless, the nymphs differ from them principally in size (Figure 3-3), and such insects are sometimes said to have no metamorphosis. If the adults are winged, the wings appear as budlike outgrowths in the early instars (Figure 3-4) and increase in size only slightly up to the last molt; after the last molt, the wings expand to their full adult size. In the Odonata, Plecoptera, and Ephemeroptera, the nymphs are aquatic and breathe by means of gills, while the adults are winged and aerial. In most other insects with simple metamorphosis, both nymphs and adults live in the same habitat. The principal changes during growth are in size, body proportions, the development of the ocelli, the size of the wings, and occasionally in the form of the antennae, mouth parts, abdomen, or other structures. Simple metamorphosis occurs in orders 1-17 (see list, page 56).

COMPLETE METAMORPHOSIS: The immature and adult stages of insects that undergo complete metamorphosis are usually quite different in form, and often live in different habitats and have very different habits. The early instars are more or less wormlike, and the young in this stage are called larvae (Figures 3-5 D, 3-6). The different larval instars are usually similar in form but differ in size. The wings, when they are present in the adult, develop internally during the larval stage and are not everted until the end of the last larval instar. Larvae do not have compound eyes; they may or may not have thoracic legs, and they sometimes possess leglike appendages (the prolegs) on the abdomen. Larvae generally have chewing mouth parts, even in those orders in which the adults have sucking mouth parts.

Following the molt of the last larval instar, the insect transforms into a stage called the pupa (Figures 3-5 E, 3-7). The insect does not feed in this stage and is usually inactive. Pupae are often covered

[1] Many authors distinguish three types of development in these orders: ametabolous (no metamorphosis), paurometabolous (gradual metamorphosis), and hemimetabolous (incomplete metamorphosis). These authors classify the metamorphosis of the Protura, Thysanura, and Collembola as ametamolous, that of the Odonata, Ephemeroptera, and Plecoptera as hemimetabolous, and that of the remaining exopterygote orders as paurometabolous. Since the development of the wingless species in these groups is essentially similar, whether they be in an apterygote or pterygote order, and since the development of the Odonata, Ephemeroptera, and Plecoptera is fundamentally similar to that of other winged forms in the exopterygote orders, it seems best to group these types of development into a single category, simple metamorphosis.

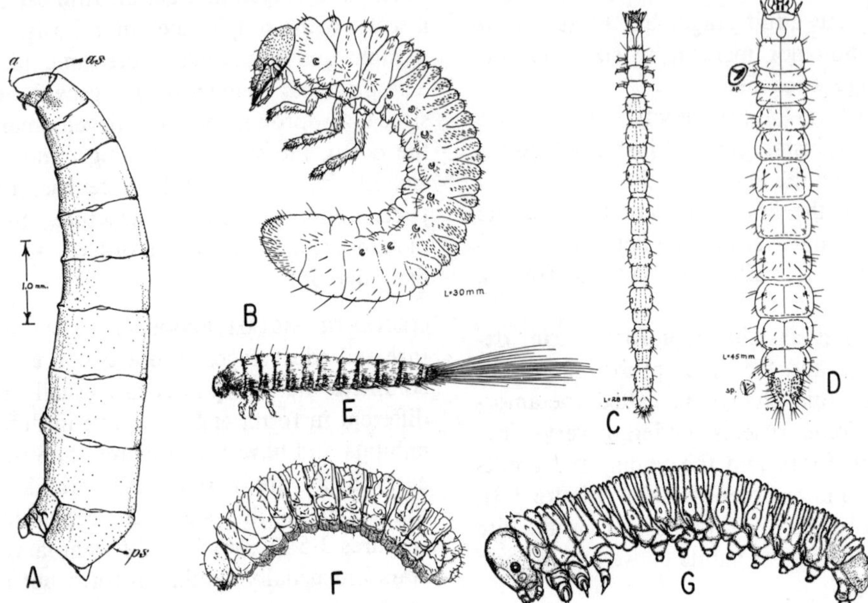

Fig. 3-6. Insect larvae. A, maggot or vermiform larva or *Hylemỳa cilicrùra* (Rondani) (Diptera, Anthomyìidae); B, grub or scarabaeiform larva of *Phyllóphaga rugòsa* (Melsheimer) (Coleoptera, Scarabaèidae); C, elateriform larva of *Cardióphorus* sp. (Coleoptera, Elatéridae); D, elateriform larva of *Álaus oculàtus* (Linn.) (Coleoptera, Elatéridae); E, larva of *Attágenus pìceus* (Olivier) (Coleoptera, Derméstidae); F, vermiform larva of *Cỳlas formicàrius elagántulus* (Summers) (Coleoptera, Curculiónidae); G, eruciform larva of *Caliròa aèthiops* (Fabricius) (Hymenoptera, Tenthredínidae). *a*, antenna; *as*, anterior spiracle; *L*, length; *ps*, posterior spiracle; *sp*, spiracle. (A and E-G, courtesy of USDA; B-D, courtesy of Peterson. Reprinted by permission.)

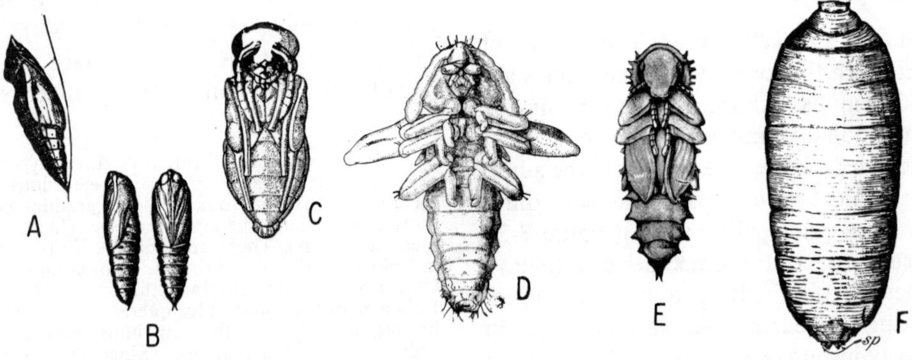

Fig. 3-7. Insect pupae. A, chysalis of the sulfur butterfly, *Còlias eurýtheme* (Boisduval) (Lepidoptera. Piéridae); B, fall armyworm, *Laphýgma frugipérda* (Abbott and Smith) (Lepidoptera, Noctùidae); C, clover-seed chalcid, *Bruchóphagus gíbbus* (Boheman) (Hymenoptera Eurytómidae); D, sweetpotato weevil *Cỳlas formicàrius elegántulus* (Summers) (Coleoptera, Curculiónidae); E, saw-toothed grain beetle, *Orzaéphilus surinaménsis* (Linn.) (Coleoptera, Silvánidae); F, seed-corn maggot, *Hylemỳa cilicrùra* (Rondani) (Diptera, Anthomyìidae). A and B are obtect pupae, C-E are exarate pupae, and F is a coarctate pupa. *sp. spiracle.* (Courtesy of USDA.)

by a cocoon or some other protective material, and many insects pass the winter in the pupal stage. The final molt occurs at the end of the pupal stage, and the last stage is the adult. The adult is usually pale in color when it first emerges from the pupa, and its wings are short, soft, and wrinkled. In a short time, from a few minutes to several hours or more, depending on the species, the wings expand and harden, the pigmentation develops, and the insect is ready to go on its way. This type of metamorphosis occurs in orders 18-26 (see list, page 57).

INTERMEDIATE TYPES OF METAMORPHOSIS: Insects with simple metamorphosis have the wings (if present) developing externally, they have compound eyes in the nymphal stages if such eyes are present in the adult, and although the insect may be quiescent prior to the final molt, this quiescence usually does not last through the entire penultimate instar; this instar is generally not referred to as a pupa. Insects with complete metamorphosis have the wings (if present) developing internally during the early (larval) instars, and the wings do not appear externally until the penultimate instar, which is usually quiescent and is called a pupa; the larva lacks compound eyes and is usually quite different from the adult in body form and habits.

Not all insects have a type of metamorphosis that can be readily classified as simple or complete; some have a metamorphosis that is somewhat intermediate between these two types. Such intermediate metamorphosis is found in thrips (page 157), whiteflies (page 213), and in male scale insects (page 219).

—Metamorphosis in Thrips— The first two instars are wingless and active, and are usually called larvae. The next two instars (the next three in the suborder Tubulifera) are inactive, with external wings; the first of these (the first two in the Tubulifera) is called a prepupa and the second a pupa; the final instar is the adult. Apparently at least some of the wing development is internal during the first two instars. This metamorphosis resembles complete metamorphosis in that at least some of the wing development is internal, and an inactive ("pupa") stage precedes the adult; it is similar to simple metamorphosis in that the early instars have compound eyes, and external wings are present in more than one preadult instar.

—Metamorphosis in Whiteflies— These insects have five instars, the last of which is the adult. The first instar is active and wingless, while the next three instars are inactive, sessile, and scalelike, with the wings developing internally. The fourth instar is called the pupa, and it has external wings. The first three instars are usually called larvae. The molt from the last larval instar to the pupa takes place inside the last larval skin, which forms a puparium. This metamorphosis is essentially complete, though most other members of this order (Homoptera) have simple metamorphosis.

—Metamorphosis in Male Scale Insects— These insects have a type of metamorphosis that is very similar to that in whiteflies. The first instar (Figure 20-28 B), the "crawler," is active and wingless, but the remaining preadult instars are sessile and inactive; the last preadult instar, which has external wings, is called the pupa. The development of the wings is at least partly internal.

TYPES OF LARVAE

The larvae of the various insects that undergo complete metamorphosis differ considerably in form, and several types may be recognized:

Eruciform—caterpillarlike (Figure 3-6 G); body cylindrical, the head well developed but with very short antennae, and with both thoracic legs and abdominal prolegs. This type occurs in the Lepidoptera, Mecoptera, and some Hymenoptera (suborder Sýmphyta).

Scarabaeiform—grublike (Figure 3-6 B); usually curved, the head well developed, with thoracic legs but without abdominal prolegs, and relatively inactive and sluggish. This type occurs in certain Coleoptera (for example, Scarabaèidae).

Campodeiform—resembling bristletails in the genus *Campòdea*; body elongate and somewhat flattened, the cerci and antennae usually well developed, the thoracic legs well developed, and the larvae usually active. This type occurs in the Neuroptera, Trichoptera, and many Coleoptera.

Elateriform—wirewormlike (Figure 3-6 C, D); body elongate, cylindrical, and hard-shelled, the legs short, and the body bristles reduced. This type occurs in certain Coleoptera (for example, Elatéridae).

Vermiform—maggotlike (Figure 3-6 A, F); body elongate and wormlike, legless, and with or without a well-developed head. This type occurs in the Diptera, Siphonaptera, most Hymenoptera (suborder Apócrita), and in some Coleoptera and Lepidoptera.

TYPES OF PUPAE

The pupae of insects with complete metamorphosis vary, and three principal types may be recognized:

Obtect—with the appendages more or less glued to the body (Figure 3-7 A-B). This type occurs in the Lepidoptera and some Diptera (suborder Nematócera). The pupa in many Lepidoptera is covered by a silken cocoon formed by the larva before it molts to the pupal stage.

Exarate—with the appendages free and not glued to the body (Figure 3-7 C-E). Such a pupa looks much like a pale mummified adult, and is usually not covered by a cocoon. This type occurs in most insects with complete metamorphosis, except the Diptera and most Lepidoptera.

Coarctate—essentially like an exarate pupa, but remaining covered by the hardened exuviae of the next to the last larval instar, which is called a puparium (Figure 3-7 F). This type occurs in the Diptera (suborders Brachýcera and Cyclórrhapha).

HYPERMETAMORPHOSIS

Hypermetamorphosis is a type of complete metamorphosis in which the different larval instars are not of the same type; the first instar is active and usually campodeiform, and the subsequent larval instars are vermiform or scarabaeiform. Hypermetamorphosis occurs in parasitic insects; the first instar seeks out the host, and once in the host, molts into a less active type of larva. This type of complete metamorphosis occurs in the Melòidae (Figure 22-45) and Rhipiphóridae (Coleoptera), the Mantíspidae (Neuroptera), the Strepsiptera, and in a few Diptera and Hymenoptera.

VARIATIONS IN LIFE HISTORY

The length of a generation and the way it is fitted to the different seasons vary quite a bit in different insects. Most insects in temperate regions have what is called a heterodynamic life cycle; that is, the adults appear for a limited time during a particular season, and some life stage passes the winter in a state of dormancy. The overwintering stage may be the egg (for example, most Orthoptera and Homoptera), nymph (for example, most Odonata and many Orthoptera), larva (for example, many Lepidoptera), or adult (for example, most Hemiptera and many Coleoptera). Many insects, particularly those living in the tropics, have a homodynamic life cycle; that is, development is continuous and there is no regular period of dormancy.

Most insects in the United States have a single generation a year. Some require two or more years to complete their life cycle; this is usually the case with large insects occurring in the northern part of the country. Some of the larger beetles, dragonflies, and moths in the Northern states and Canada regularly require two or three years to complete their development. Perhaps the longest life cycle of any insect is that of some of the periodical cicadas (*Magicicàda* spp.), which lasts 17 years (see page 204).

Many insects have more than one

generation a year. In some cases the number of generations in a year is constant throughout the range of the species; in other cases the species may have more generations per year in the southern part of its range. A few insects, usually rather small species that can complete their life cycle in a few weeks, have many generations a year; such insects continue to reproduce through the season as long as weather conditions are favorable. Insects of tropical origin, such as those of the household and those which attack stored products, may continue breeding throughout the entire 12 months.

Many of the insects that regularly have one or two generations a year cannot be forced to produce more unless they are subjected to a period of dormancy at low temperatures. Such a period of dormancy is apparently an essential feature of the life history of these insects.

Most birds and mammals, as well as many other vertebrates, have a type of life history sometimes spoken of as iteroparous; that is, they reproduce two or more times during their lifetime—once or more each year—and adults may live several years, or (for example, some rodents) at fairly regular intervals through a year. Natural populations of such animals normally contain individuals of different age. Insects, on the other hand, are generally semelparous; that is, they reproduce only once during their lifetime. Natural populations of such animals usually consist of individuals about the same age, and there is little or no overlapping of successive generations.

A number of insects reproduce parthenogenetically (see page 37), and in some of these the life cycle involves an alternation of bisexual and parthenogenetic reproduction; this is the case, for example, in many aphids (see pages 214-218) and gall wasps (see page 569). The adults of the bisexual and parthenogenetic generations of such insects may be different in appearance and may occur on different host plants. Males are unknown in some insects, and parthenogenesis is the only known type of reproduction; this is the case, for example, in the white-fringed beetle, *Graphógnathus leucolóma* (Boheman) (see page 336).

Paedogenesis, or reproduction by larval stages, occurs in a few insects; such insects may produce a series of generations in this way, or paedogenesis may alternate with normal reproduction. Paedogenesis occurs in the beetle *Micromálthus débilis* LeConte (see page 275) and in the gall gnat *Miástor americàna* Felt (see page 479).

REFERENCES ON DEVELOPMENT AND METAMORPHOSIS

Comstock, John H. 1940 (9th ed.). An introduction to entomology. Ithaca, N.Y.: Comstock Publishing Associates. xix + 1064 pp., 1228 f. Especially Chap. 4.

Essig, E. O. 1942. College entomology. New York: The Macmillan Company. vii + 900 pp., 305 f. Especially Chap. 1.

Imms, A. D. 1957 (9th ed., revised by O. W. Richards and R. G. Davies). A general textbook of entomology. New York: E. P. Dutton & Co., Inc. x + 886 pp., 609 f. Especially Part II.

Matheson, Robert. 1951 (2nd ed.). Entomology for introductory courses. Ithaca, N.Y.: Comstock Publishing Associates. xiv + 629 pp., 500 f. Especially Chap. 5.

Metcalf, C. L., and W. P. Flint. 1962 (4th ed., revised by R. L. Metcalf). Destructive and useful insects. New York: McGraw-Hill Book Company, Inc. xii + 1087 pp.; illus.

Peterson, Alvah. 1948. Larvae of insects. Part I. Lepidoptera and Hymenoptera. Ann Arbor, Mich.: Edwards Bros., Inc. 315 pp., 84 f.

Peterson, Alvah. 1951. Larvae of insects. Part II. Coleoptera, Diptera, Neuroptera, Siphonaptera, Mecoptera, Trichoptera. Ann Arbor, Mich.: Edwards Bros., Inc. v + 416 pp., 104 f.

Snodgrass, R. E. 1954. Insect metamorphosis. Smithsonian Misc. Collections, 122(9): iii + 1-124 pp.; 17 f.

Wigglesworth, V. B. 1954. The physiology of insect metamorphosis. Cambridge: Cambridge University Press. vii + 151 pp.; illus.

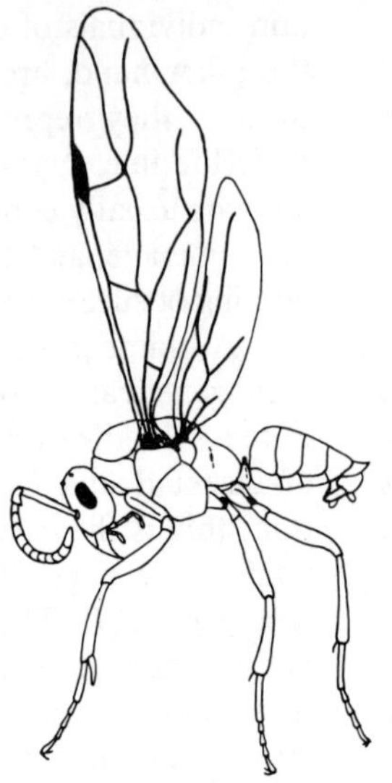

4

Classification, Nomenclature, and Identification

CLASSIFICATION

Living things, which feed, grow, respond to stimuli, and reproduce, may be divided into two big groups or kingdoms, plants and animals. In general, plants are more or less sessile organisms that utilize inorganic materials as food, and animals are more or less motile organisms that take in organic materials as food; a few organisms, like the spirochaetes, viruses, and others, do not fall readily into either kingdom and are somewhat intermediate in character between the two.

There are upwards of a million different kinds of animals in the world, and a systematic study of the animal kingdom necessitates some scheme of arranging them into groups, or classifying them. Animals might be classified in various ways, but the classification followed by zoologists is one based primarily on *structural* characters; those animals with certain structures in common are classified into one group, and those with other structures into other groups. Thus, the animal kingdom is divided into a dozen or so major groups called *phyla* (singular, *phylum*); each phylum has a name, and its members have certain structural characters in common. The characters used to distinguish phyla include the number of cells, symmetry, body form and segmentation, the nature of the appendages, and the arrangement of the internal órgans.

On the basis of degree of complexity, and probable evolutionary sequence, the animal phyla are usually arranged in a series from the "lower" phyla to the "higher" ones. The principal phyla of the animal kingdom are as follows:

Phylum **Protozòa**—single-celled animals
Phylum **Porífera**—sponges
Phylum **Coelenteràta**—jellyfish, hydroids, corals, sea anemones

Phylum **Platyhelmínthes**—flatworms: planarians, flukes, tapeworms
Phylum **Nemathelmínthes**—roundworms
Phylum **Trochelmínthes (Rotatòria)**—rotifers
Phylum **Brachiópoda**—brachipods
Phylum **Bryozòa**—moss animals
Phylum **Mollúsca**—molluscs: clams, snails, octopi
Phylum **Echinodérmata**—starfish, sea urchins, crinoids, sea cucumbers
Phylum **Annélida**—earthworms, marine worms, leeches
Phylum **Onychóphora**—onychophorans: *Perípatus* and its allies
Phylum **Arthrópoda**—crayfish, millipedes, spiders, INSECTS, centipedes
Phylum **Chordàta**—fish, amphibians, reptiles, birds, mammals

The characters of the phylum ARTHROPODA,[1] to which the insects belong, may be listed briefly as follows:

1. Body segmented, the segments usually grouped into two or three rather distinct regions
2. Paired segmented appendages. It is from this character that the phylum gets its name
3. Bilateral symmetry
4. An exoskeleton, which is periodically shed and renewed as the animal grows
5. A tubular alimentary canal, with mouth and anus
6. The circulatory system an open one, the only blood vessel usually being a tubular structure dorsal to the alimentary canal, with lateral openings in the abdominal region
7. The body cavity a blood cavity or haemocoele, the coelom reduced
8. The nervous system consisting of an anterior ganglion or brain located dorsally to the alimentary canal, two connectives extending ventrally from the brain around the alimentary canal, and paired ventral ganglionated nerve cords
9. Excretion by means of tubes, the malpighian tubules, which empty into the alimentary canal (except in crustaceans, king crabs, and some others)
10. Respiration by means of tracheae and spiracles (except in some crustaceans and arachnids)

[1] Arthropoda: *arthro,* joint or segment; *poda,* foot or appendage.

The classification of animals does not stop with phyla; each phylum is further subdivided, on the basis of structural characters, into groups called *classes.* Each class has a name and certain structural characters in common. The classes of the phylum Arthropoda are as follows:

Class **Trilóbita**—trilobites (fossil)
Class **Crustàcea**—crustaceans: crabs, crayfish, shrimp, water fleas, and so forth
Class **Diplópoda**—millipedes
Class **Chilópoda**—centipedes
Class **Paurópoda**—pauropods
Class **Sýmphyla**—symphylids
Class **Insécta (Hexápoda)**—INSECTS
Class **Xiphosùra**—king crabs or horseshoe crabs
Class **Pycnogónida**—sea spiders
Class **Tardigràda**—water bears
Class **Lingulatùlida (Pentastómida)**—tongueworms
Class **Aráchnida**—spiders, mites, ticks, scorpions, harvestmen, and so forth

It will be seen that the insects with which we are concerned constitute one *class* of the animal kingdom; the insects have the characters of the arthropods listed above, and are further characterized by having three body regions (head, thorax, and abdomen), one pair of antennae, nearly always three pairs of legs, and usually one or two pairs of wings.

Classes of animals are further subdivided into *orders,* the orders into *families,* the families into *genera* (singular, *genus*), and genera into *species.* The main categories in animal classification are phylum, class, order, family, genus, and species, but frequently intermediate categories may be used; the principal categories used in classification, arranged in order of rank, may be listed as follows:

PHYLUM
  SUBPHYLUM
    CLASS
      SUBCLASS
        ORDER
          SUBORDER
            SUPERFAMILY
              FAMILY
                SUBFAMILY
                  TRIBE
                    GENUS
                      SUBGENUS
                        SPECIES
                          SUBSPECIES

The arrangement of animals into these various systematic categories is more or less arbitrary, but it is nevertheless of value in indicating relationships. Because animals have been (and still are) evolving, and different groups have been evolving at different rates, some groups are more distinct than others, and there are frequently differences of opinion among zoologists regarding the systematic category to be used in particular cases.

The basic category in this scheme of classification is the *species*. The species is not easy to define because different species are in different stages of evolutionary development; this classification often represents the relationships of animals as simpler than they actually are. A species is usually looked upon as a group of individuals or populations in nature that are (1) fundamentally similar in structure, (2) capable of interbreeding and producing fertile offspring, and (3) reproductively isolated from (that is, ordinarily not interbreeding with) other such groups. A subspecies is a geographic race of a species. The differences between the subspecies of a given species are usually not clear-cut, but are intergrading, particularly where adjacent races come in contact; where adjacent races come in contact, they may intergrade so that it is impossible to assign a given individual to either race. Since it is often impossible to determine by experiment whether or not two geographic groups will interbreed, it is often a matter of opinion whether such groups should be considered as species or subspecies.

SCIENTIFIC NOMENCLATURE

The scientific naming of animals follows certain definite rules, which are outlined in the International Code of Zoological Nomenclature (Stoll *et al.*, 1961). Scientific names are Latinized, but may be derived from any language or from the names of people or places; most names are derived from Latin or Greek words, and usually refer to some characteristic of the animal or group named.

The names of genera and subgenera are Latinized nouns in the nominative singular; names of higher categories are Latinized nouns in the nominative plural. Specific and subspecific names may be adjectives, the present or past participles of verbs, or nouns; adjectives and participles must agree in gender with the genus name, and nouns are either in the nominative or genitive case.

The names of some of the higher systematic categories have standard endings, and hence can always be recognized as referring to a particular category. These are as follows:

Superfamily names end in *-oidea*; for example, *Papilionòidea,* butterflies

Family names end in *-idae*; for example, *Papiliónidae,* swallowtails and parnassians

Subfamily names end in *-inae*; for example, *Papilionìnae,* swallowtails

Tribe names end in *-ini*; for example, *Crabronìni,* square-headed wasps

All the above-named categories have, for nomenclatural purposes, a *type genus*; the category names are formulated by adding the appropriate ending to the stem of the name of the type genus (for example, for the type genus *Papílio,* the stem is *Papilion-*).

A species or subspecies is usually referred to by a *scientific name*. The scientific name of a species consists of the genus and species names, and that of a subspecies consists of the genus, species, and subspecies names; thus the scientific name of a species is a binomial, and that of a subspecies is a trinomial. Scientific names are always printed in *italics* (if written or typewritten, italics are indicated by underlining). Scientific names are followed by the name of the author—the person who described the species or subspecies; authors' names are not italicized. The genus name always begins with a capital letter; species and subspecies names do not. If the author's name is in parentheses, it means that he described the species (or subspecies, in the case of a trinomial) in some genus other than the one in which it is now placed. For example:

Papílio glaùcus Linnaeus[2]—the tiger swallowtail. The species *glaùcus* was described by Linnaeus, who described it in the genus *Papílio.*

Leptinotársa décimlineàta (Say)—the Colorado potato beetle. The species *décimlineàta* was described by Say, who described it in some genus other than *Leptinotársa,* and this species has since been transferred to the genus *Leptinotársa.*

Tetragoneùria cynosùra (Say)—the dogtail dragonfly. The species *cynosùra* was described by Say, in a genus other than *Teragoneùria.* There are two geographic races (subspecies) of this species: a northern and eastern race (*símulans*), and a southern and western race (*cynosùra*). These two subspecies are indicated as follows:

Tetragoneùria cynosùra cynosùra (Say)

Tetragoneùria cynosùra símulans Muttkowski[3]

[2] Throughout this book Linnaeus is abbreviated "Linn."

A species referred to but not named is often designated simply by "sp." For example, "*Gómphus* sp." refers to a species of *Gómphus.* More than one species may be designated by "spp."; for example, "*Gómphus* spp." refers to two or more species of *Gómphus.*

Some entomologists, contrary to present nomenclatorial practice, have used trinomials for other things besides geographic races, which they have called "varieties." Many such varieties are merely individual variants, due to food or climatic conditions, or seasonal or color forms, which should not have been designated by a trinomial. Present practice in zoological nomenclature is to use a trinomial only for a geographic race.

TYPES: Whenever a new species or other group is described, the describer is supposed to designate a *type,* which is used as a reference if there is ever any question what that species or group includes. The type of a species or subspecies is a specimen (the *holotype*), the type of a genus or subgenus is a species (the *type-species*), and the type of a family or subfamily is a genus (the *type-genus*). Family and subfamily names are formed by adding *-idae* or *-inae* to the root of the name of the type-genus (for example, the type-genus of the swallowtail family is *Papílio*; the family name is *Papiliónidae*). If a species is divided into subspecies, the particular subspecies that includes the holotype of the species has the same subspecies name as species name (for example, *Tetragoneùria cynosùra cynosùra*); similarly, if a genus is divided into subgenera, the subgenus that contains the type-species of the genus has the same subgenus name as genus name [for example, *Formìca* (*Formìca*) *rùfa* Linn. (the name in parentheses is the subgenus)].

[3] Since Muttkowski's name is not in parenthesis, it indicates that he described *símulans* in the genus *Tetragoneùria;* there is no way of knowing from this scientific name whether *símulans* was originally described as a subspecies of *cynosùra,* as a subspecies of another species of *Tetragoneùria,* or as a species of *Tetragoneùria.*

PRIORITY: It often happens that the same species, genus, family, or other group is described independently by two or more people; hence there may be more than one name for the same species or group. In such cases the first name to be used (provided the describer has followed certain rules) is the correct name, and any other names are relegated to synonymy. Often a particular name will be used for a long time before it is discovered that another name has priority over it. If a person gives a new genus a name that has previously been used for some other genus, his name is invalid (as a homonym) and his genus must be renamed. The same rule applies to species: there cannot be two species in the same genus with the same name. Because of the large number of species and genera of animals, and the vast amount of zoological literature, errors in naming such as those just described are not easy to discover; as they are discovered, it becomes necessary to change names, not only of genera and species, but of families and even orders. The problems of scientific nomenclature are often very intricate, and it is sometimes difficult to determine just what name is the correct one; as a result two or more names for the same species or group may be equally widely used.

In cases where two or more names for a group have been in fairly wide use, we have listed first in this book what we believe to be the correct name, and have listed the synonyms in parentheses.

PRONUNCIATION

The correct pronunciation of some of the technical names and terms used in entomology may be found in a good dictionary or glossary, but very few texts or references give the pronunciation of the vast bulk of technical names (genera and species). Since there are often differences of opinion as to how certain names are pronounced, it seems appropriate to list here a few of the general rules for the pronunciation of the technical names and terms used in zoology.

VOWELS: All vowels in scientific names are pronounced. Vowels are generally either long or short, and in the examples that follow (and elsewhere in this book), a long vowel sound is indicated by a grave accent (`) and a short vowel sound by an acute accent (´); for example, *màte, mát, mète, mét, bìte, bít, ròpe, rót, cùte, cút, bỳ, sýmmetry*. A vowel at the end of a word has the long sound, except when it is *a*; a final *a* has the *uh* sound, as in *idea.* The vowel in the final syllable of a word has the short sound, except *es,* which is pronounced *ease*.

DIPHTHONGS: A diphthong consists of two vowels written together and pronounced as a single vowel. The diphthongs are *ae* (pronounced *è*), *oe* (usually pronounced *è*, rarely *é*), *oi* (pronounced as in *oil*), *eu* (pronounced *ù*), *ei* (pronounced *ì*), *ai* (pronounced *à*), and *au* (pronounced as in *August*).

CONSONANTS: *Ch* has the *k* sound, except in words derived from a language other than Greek. When *c* is followed by *ae, e, oe, i,* or y, it has the soft (*j*) sound; when it is followed by *a, o, oi,* or *u,* it has the hard (*k*) sound. When *g* is followed by *ae, e, i, oe,* or *y,* it has the soft (*j*) sound; when it is followed by *a, o, oi,* or *u,* it has the hard sound (as as *go*). In words beginning with *ps, pt, ct, cn, gn,* or *mn,* the initial letter is not pronounced, but when these letters appear together in the middle of a word the first letter is pronounced (for example, the *p* is not pronounced in the word *pteromorph,* but it is pronounced in the word *Orthoptera*). An *x* at the beginning of a word is pronounced as *z,* but as *ks* when it appears elsewhere in a word. When a double *c* is followed by *i* or *y*, it is pronounced as *ks.*

ACCENT: The pronunciation of technical names and terms in this book is indicated by a grave or acute accent on the vowel of the accented syllable. When the accented syllable contains a diphthong, the accent mark is placed over the vowel that gives the diphthong its sound (for example, *aè, oè, eù, eì, ài*), or over the first vowel of the diphthong (for example, *òi, àu*). The accented syllable is either the penult or the antepenult (in very long words there may be a secondary accent on a syllable near the beginning of the word). The principal rules governing the syllable accented and the vowel sound (whether long or short) are as follows:

1. The accent is on the penult syllable in the following cases:
   a. When the name contains only two syllables; for example, *Àpis, Bómbus*
   b. When the penult contains a diphthong; for example, *Culicòides, Hemileùca, Lygaèus*
   c. When the vowel in the penult is followed by *x* or *z;* for example, *Agromỳza, Coríxa, Prodóxus*
   d. When the vowel of the penult is long. Whether the penult vowel is long or short often depends on the derivation of the word and the vowel sound in the source language. For example, in words derived from the Greek μηρος, meaning *thigh,* the *e* is long (for example, *Diáphero-mèra, epimèron*), while in those derived from the Greek μερος, meaning *part,* the *e* is short (for example, *Heterómera*). The penult vowel is long in subfamily names (for example, *Sphecìnae*) and tribe names (for example, *Sphecìni*); in tribe names, the final *i* is also long. The penult vowel is usually long in the following cases:
      (1) Words derived from the Latin past participle and ending in *-ata, -atus* or *-atum;* for example, *maculàta.* (The penult vowel is short in such Greek plurals as *Echinodérmata*).
      (2) Latin adjectives ending in *-alis*; for example, *orientàlis, verticàlis*
      (3) Words ending in *-ina*; for example, *carolìna, Glossìna, Hetaerìna*
      (4) Words ending in *-ica*; for example, *Formìca, Myrmìca*
      (5) Words ending in *-ana, -anus,* or *-anum*; for example, *americàna, Tabànus, mexicànum*
      (6) Words ending in *-ura*; for *example, Thysanùra, Xíphosùra*
      (7) Words ending in *-odes*; for example, *Sabulòdes, Sphecòdes*
      (8) Words ending in *-otes*; for example, *Epiròtes*
      (9) Words ending in *-ates*; for example, *Aceràtes, Hippelàtes*
      (10) Words ending in *-ales*; for example, the names of plant orders (for example, *Graminàles*)
      (11) Words ending in *-osis*; for example, *pediculòsis, trichinòsis*; there are a few exceptions in modern usage, for example, *metamórphosis*
      (12) Words ending in *-soma*; for example, *Calosòma, Eriosòma*
      (13) Words ending in *-pogon*; for example, *Heteropògon, Lasiopògon*
      (14) Words ending in *-chlora*; for example, *Augochlòra*
      (15) Words in which the vowel of the penult is *u*, except when the *u* is followed by *l*; for example, *Fenùsa, Ctenùcha*; exceptions, *Libéllula, Bétula*
      (16) When the vowel is followed by *z*; for example, *Agromỳza, Triòza*
   e. When the vowel of the penult is short and followed by two consonants, except a mute followed by *l* or *r*; for example, *Pseudocóccus, pulchélla, Pterophýlla, Vanéssa, Chlorotéttix, Latrodéctus, Enallágma, Gryllotálpa, Adélges, Hemerocámpa, Microbémbex, Philánthus,*

Monárthrum, Leptinotársa, Schistocérca, Sapérda, Polyérgus, Osmodérma, Panórpa, Pyromórpha, Chionáspis, Cordulegáster, Derméstes, Mantíspa, Prionoxýstus, Carpocápsa, Macrópsis

When the vowel of the penult is followed by a mute (*b*, hard *c*, *d*, *g*, *k*, *p*, *q*, *t*, *ch*, *ph*, or *th*) and *l* or *r*, the accent is on the antepenult; for example, *Cutérebra, Geómetra, Ánabrus, Ránatra, Éphydra, Grýllacris, Melánoplus, Stenóbothrus, élytra.*

2. In other cases the antepenult is accented.
   a. The vowel of the antepenult is long in the following cases:
      (1) When it is followed by another vowel; for example, *Epèolus, Llavèia, Hepìalus, Pìeris, Síalus.* This includes family names that have a vowel immediately preceding the *-idae*; for example, *Danàidae, Trupanèidae, Citheroǹiidae, Melòidae, Melandrỳidae*
      (2) When it is *a, e, o,* or *u*, followed by a single consonant and two vowels, the first of which is *e, i,* or *y*; for example, *Aràneus, Callosàmia, Climàcia, Lecànium, Làsius, Rhàgium, Tèlea, Celèrio, Orthèzia, Nemòbius, Plòdia, Citherònia*
      (3) When it is *u* and followed by a single consonant; for example, *Cordùlia, Redùvius, Libellùlidae, Linguatùlida*
   b. The vowel of the antepenult is short in other cases. This includes all family names in which the antepenult vowel is followed by a consonant (except when the vowel is *u* followed by a single consonant); for example, *Belostomátidae, Elatéridae, Asílidae, Chrysópidae, Agromýzidae.* The following names, and others with similar endings, have the antepenult vowel short: *Heterócera, Geócoris, Conocéphalus, Tiphódytes, Chauliógnathus, Pantógrapha, Chirónomus, Mallóphaga, Drosóphila, Anthóphora, Orthóptera, Micrópteryx, Chilópoda, Triátoma.*

COMMON NAMES OF INSECTS

Because there are so many species of insects, and because so many of them are small or little known, relatively few have common names. Those that do are either particularly showy insects, such as the luna moth, *Áctias lùna* (Linn.), the tiger swallowtail, *Papílio glàucus* Linn., and the black-winged damselfly, *Ágrion maculàtum* Beauvais, or they are economically important species, such as the honey bee, *Àpis mellífera* Linn., the spruce budworm, *Choristoneùra fumiferàna* (Clemens), the Colorado potato beetle, *Leptinotársa décimlineàta* (Say), and the chinch bug, *Blíssus leucópterus* (Say).

Most common names of insects refer to large groups, such as subfamilies, families, suborders, or orders, rather than to individual species. The names "tortoise beetle," for example, refers to the species in the subfamily Cassidìnae of the family Chrysomélidae; the term "leaf beetle" applies to all the species in the family Chrysomélidae (of which there are hundreds); the term "beetle" refers to the entire order Coleoptera, of which there are thousands of species. The term "damselfly" refers to the entire suborder Zygoptera of the Odonata, of which there are hundreds of species; the term "narrow-winged damselfy" refers to the species in the family Coenagriónidae, of which there are dozens of species.

The names "fly" and "bug" are used for insects in more than one order. When the "fly" of an insect's name is written separately (for example, black fly, blow fly, or horse fly), that insect belongs to the order

Diptera, which are often spoken of as the "true" flies. When the "fly" of the name is written together with the descriptive word (for example, dragonfly, scorpionfly, sawfly, or stonefly), the insect is in some other order. Similarly, the "true" bugs of the order Hemiptera are named with the "bug" as a separate word (for example, damsel bug, stink bug, water bug, or lace bug), while for insects in other orders, the "bug" of the name is written together with the descriptive word (for example, mealybug, sowbug, or ladybug).

Families are often referred to by means of the root of the family name; for example, the Anthomýzidae are called the anthomyzid flies, and the Tiphìidae are called the tiphiid wasps. A few families are named from one well-known species in the family; for example, the family Lygaèidae is often called the chinch bug family, and the Corèidae the squash bug family. This method of naming families is sometimes misleading to the student, as the other members of such a family may not always look much like the species after which the family is named; most lygaeid bugs, for example, do not look much like the chinch bug.

THE IDENTIFICATION OF INSECTS

When one encounters an insect, one of the first questions that will be asked is, "What kind of insect is it?" One of the principal aims of the beginning student in any field of biology is to become able to identify the organisms he is studying. The identification of insects differs from the identification of other types of organisms only in that it is likely to be somewhat more difficult, for there are more kinds of insects than anything else.

Four things complicate the problem of insect identification. In the first place, there are so many different kinds (species) of insects that the beginner may be discouraged at the outset at ever becoming proficient in insect identification. In the second place, most insects are small, and the identifying characters are often difficult to see. In the third place, many insects are little known, and when finally identified, the student may have only a technical name (which he may not understand) and no very specific common name. In the fourth place, many insects go through very different stages in their life history, and one may come to know insects in one stage of their life cycle and still know very little about those same insects in another stage.

As a general rule in this book, identification will be carried only to family. To go further usually requires specialized knowledge and is beyond the scope of this book. Identifying insects only to family, rather than to species, reduces the number of names with which we shall be concerned from many thousand to several hundred,[4] and of these probably only two hundred or less are likely to be encountered by the average student. Thus, insect identification becomes much less formidable.

There are about six ways a student may identify an unknown insect: (1) by having it identified for him by an expert, (2) by comparing it with labeled specimens in a collection, (3) by comparing it with pictures, (4) by comparing it with descriptions, (5) by the use of an analytical key, or (6) by a combination of two or more of these procedures. Of these six methods, obviously the first is the simplest, but this method is not always available; similarly, the second method may not always be available. In the absence of an expert or a labeled collection, the next best method is usually the use of a key. In the case of particularly striking or well-known insects, the identification can often be made by the third method mentioned above, but in many groups this method is unsatisfactory. No book can illustrate all kinds of insects and still sell for a price a student can afford to pay. Where

[4] The total number of insect families recognized and keyed out in this book is 579.

an unknown insect cannot be definitely identified by means of illustrations, the best procedure is to use an analytical key, and then to check the identification by as many of the other methods mentioned as possible. Identification from pictures is often unsafe, as there are many instances in the insect world where one type of insect looks a great deal like another.

ANALYTICAL KEYS: Analytical keys are devices used to identify all sorts of things, plants as well as animals. Different keys may be arranged somewhat differently, but all involve the same general principles. One runs an insect (or other organism) through a key in steps; at each step he is faced with two (rarely more) alternatives, one of which should apply to the specimen at hand. In our keys there is either a number or a name following the alternative that fits the specimen; if a number, the next step is the couplet with this number. Thus each step leads to another step and its alternatives, until a name is reached.

The couplets of alternatives are numbered 1 and 1′, 2 and 2′, and so on. In each couplet after the first is a number in parentheses; this is the number of the couplet from which that couplet is reached, and enables the student to work backward in the key if he discovers he has made a mistake somewhere along the line. This method of numbering also serves as a check on the accuracy of the organization of the key.

No analytical key, unless it is very long and cumbersome and difficult to work, is ever perfect. There are species or specimens in every group that are erratic in their characters, and to include such forms in the key would only serve to complicate it. The keys in this book should work for at least 95 percent of the material that the beginning student is likely to collect. When a determination is reached in the key, the student should check the specimen against any illustrations or descriptions available; if these do not fit the specimen, then he has either made a mistake somewhere in the key, or the specimen is one that will not work out correctly in the key. In the latter event, the specimen should be saved until it can be shown to an expert; it may be something rare or unusual.

One's success in running an insect through a key depends largely on an understanding of the characters used. In many cases in this book the key characters are illustrated. Often several characters are given in each alternative; in case one character cannot be seen or interpreted, the student can use the other characters. If at any point in the key the student cannot decide which way to go, he should try following up both alternatives, and then check further with illustrations and descriptions when he reaches a name.

It should be understood that analytical keys are made for people who do not know the identity of a specimen they have. Once a specimen has been identified with a key, subsequent identifications of this same insect may often be based on such characters as general appearance, size, shape, and color, without reference to minute characters.

It will be apparent very early in the student's work in identifying insects that a good hand lens, and preferably a binocular microscope, is necessary to see many of the characters of the insect. Most insects, once the student knows what to look for, can be identified by means of a good hand lens (about 10 ×).

The mere identification and naming of insects should not be the student's final objective in insect study; there is much more of interest in insects than just identifying them. The student should go further and learn something of the habits, distribution, and importance of insects.

REFERENCES ON CLASSIFICATION, NOMENCLATURE, AND IDENTIFICATION

Borror, Donald J. 1960. Dictionary of word roots and combining forms. Palo Alto, Calif.: National Press Publications. v+134 pp.

Calman, W. T. 1949. The classification of animals. London: Methuen & Co., Ltd. vii+54 pp.

Chamberlin, W. J. 1946 (2nd ed.). Entomological nomenclature and literature. Ann Arbor, Mich.: J. W. Edwards, Publisher, Inc. xvi+135 pp.

Ferris, Gordon F. 1928. The principles of systematic entomology. Stanford University, Calif.: Stanford University Press. 169 pp., 11 f.

Laffoon, Jean L. 1960. Common names of insects. Entomol. Soc. Am. Bul., 6(4):175-211.

Mayr, Ernst, E. Gorton Linsley, and Robert L. Usinger. 1953. Methods and principles of systematic zoology. New York: McGraw-Hill Book Company, Inc. ix+328 pp., 45 f.

Melander, A. L. 1940. Source book of biological terms. New York: Dept. Biol., City College of New York. vi+157 pp.

Schenk, Edward T., and John H. McMasters. 1956 (3rd ed.). Procedure in taxonomy. Stanford University, Calif.: Stanford University Press. vii+119 pp.

Simpson, George Gaylord. 1961. Principles of animal taxonomy. New York: Columbia University Press. 247 pp., illus.

Stoll, N. R., R. Ph. Dollfus, J. Forest, N. D. Riley, C. W. Sabrosky, C. W. Wright, and R. V. Melville (Editorial Committee). 1961. International Code of Zoological Nomenclature adopted by the XV International Congress of Zoology. London: International Trust for Zoological Nomenclature. xviii+176 pp.

5

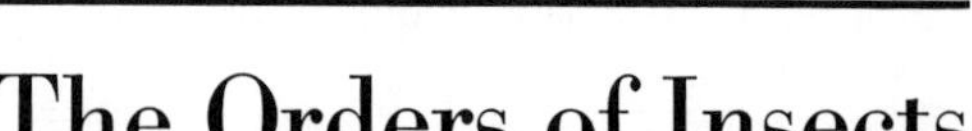

The Orders of Insects

The class Insecta is divided into orders on the basis of the structure of the wings and mouth parts, the metamorphosis, and on various other characters. There are differences of opinion among entomologists as to the limits of some of the orders; a few of the groups here treated as a single order have been divided into two or more orders by some entomologists. The orders of insects are as follows:

Subclass Apterygòta

1. Order Protùra (Myrienómata) —telsontails
2. Order Thysanùra—bristletails, silverfish, firebrats
3. Order Collémbola—springtails

Subclass Pterygòta

Exopterygòta—insects with simple metamorphosis

4. Order Ephemeróptera (Ephemérida, Plectóptera)—mayflies
5. Order Odonàta—dragonflies and damselflies
6. Order Orthóptera—grasshoppers, katydids, crickets, walking sticks, cockroaches, and mantids
7. Order Isóptera—termites
8. Order Plecóptera—stoneflies
9. Order Dermáptera (Euplexóptera)—earwigs
10. Order Embióptera (Embiidìna)—webspinners
11. Order Psocóptera (Corrodéntia)—psocids
12. Order Zoráptera—zorapterans
13. Order Mallóphaga—chewing lice
14. Order Anoplùra (Siphunculàta)—sucking lice
15. Order Thysanóptera (Physópoda)—thrips[1]
16. Order Hemíptera (Heteróptera)—bugs
17. Order Homóptera—cicadas, hoppers, aphids, whiteflies, scale insects[2]

[1] The metamorphosis in this order is intermediate between simple and complete.

[2] The metamorphosis of a few forms in this order is intermediate between simple and complete.

Endopterygòta—insects with complete metamorphosis

18. Order Neuróptera—dobsonflies, fishflies, snakeflies, lacewings, antlions
19. Order Coleóptera—beetles
20. Order Strepsíptera—stylopids or twisted-wing parasites
21. Order Mecóptera—scorpionflies
22. Order Trichóptera—caddisflies
23. Order Lepidóptera—butterflies and moths
24. Order Díptera—true flies
25. Order Siphonáptera—fleas
26. Order Hymenóptera—sawflies, ichneumons, chalcids, wasps, ants, bees

The relative size of the various insect orders is shown by Table 5-1.

TABLE 5-1 RELATIVE SIZE OF THE VARIOUS INSECT ORDERS AS SHOWN BY THE NUMBER OF SPECIES AND FAMILIES OCCURRING IN DIFFERENT GEOGRAPHIC AREAS

	SPECIES					FAMILIES IN
ORDER	NORTH CAROLINA[a]	MT. DESERT MAINE[b]	NEW YORK[c]	N. A. NORTH OF MEXICO[d]	WORLD[d]	N.A. NORTH OF MEXICO[e]
Protura	0	0	1	20	90	4
Thysanura	7	2	7	50	700	6
Collembola	105	1	71	314	2,000	3
Ephemeroptera	116	44	61	550	1,500	3
Odonata	146	81	159	412	4,870	10
Orthoptera	243	50	136	1,015	22,500	12
Isoptera	3	0	1	41	1,717	4
Plecoptera	53	31	59	400	1,550	10
Dermaptera	7	0	4	18	1,100	4
Embioptera	0	0	0	9	149	3
Psocoptera	34	25	36	143	1,100	11
Zoraptera	1	0	0	2	19	1
Mallophaga	161	180	53	318	2,675	6
Anoplura	8	6	11	62	250	4
Thysanoptera	64	9	71	606	3,170	5
Hemiptera	548	179	727	4,500	23,000	42
Homoptera	707	224	864	5,700	32,000	32
Neuroptera	64	35	61	338	4,670	14
Coleoptera	3,155	1,175	4,546	26,576	276,700	120
Strepsiptera	11	2	2	60	300	4
Mecoptera	27	5	20	66	350	4
Trichoptera	144	96	174	975	4,450	17
Lepidoptera	1,384	1,479	2,439	10,300	112,000	77
Diptera	2,111	1,626	3,615	16,700	85,000	105
Siphonaptera	14	10	26	238	1,100	7
Hymenoptera	1,981	1,107	2,300	15,218	103,000	71
Total	11,094	6,367	15,450	84,631	685,963	579

[a] From Wray, David L. 1950. Insects of North Carolina, Second Supplement. North Carolina Department of Agriculture, Division of Entomology. 59 p.

[b] From Procter, William. 1946. Biological Survey of the Mt. Desert Region, Part VIII. The Insect Fauna. Wistar Institute Press. 566 p.

[c] From Leonard, M. D. 1928. A List of the Insects of New York, Cornell University Agricultural Experiment Station. Mem. 101. 1121 p.

[d] From various sources, chiefly the U.S.D.A. Yearbook for 1952, p. 6; the figures in most cases are approximate.

[e] The number recognized in this book.

The following key to the orders of insects is based on adults, but will work with some nymphs. The orders marked with an asterisk are unlikely to be encountered by the general collector.

KEY TO THE ORDERS OF INSECTS

1. With well-developed wings 2

1′. Wingless, or with vestigial or rudimentary wings 30

2(1). Front wings horny, leathery, or parchmentlike, at least at base (Figure 5-2); hind wings, if present, membranous 3

2′. Wings entirely membranous 8

3(2). Front wings minute and club-shaped, hind wings fanlike (Figure 23-1 A-D); antennae with at least one segment bearing a long lateral process; minute insects (male twisted-winged parasites) . . . . **Strepsíptera*** p. 342

3′. Not exactly fitting the above description 4

4(3′). Mouth parts sucking, the beak elongate and usually segmented (Figure 5-1) 5

4′. Mouth parts chewing 6

5(4). Beak arising from front of head (Figure 5-1 A); front wings usually leathery at base and membranous at tip, the tips generally overlapping when at rest (Figure 5-2 C) (bugs) . . . . **Hemíptera** p. 163

5′. Beak arising from hind part of head, often appearing to arise at base of front legs (Figure 5-1 B); front wings of uniform texture throughout, the tips not or but slightly overlapping when at rest (hoppers). . **Homóptera** p. 195

6(4′). Abdomen with forcepslike cerci (Figure 5-2 D); elytra short, leaving most of abdomen exposed; tarsi 3-segmented (earwigs) . . . . **Dermáptera** p. 132

6′. Abdomen without forcepslike cerci, or if cerci appear forcepslike, then wings cover most of abdomen; tarsi variable 7

7(6′). Front wings without veins, and usually meeting in a straight line down middle of back; antennae usually with 11 or fewer segments; hind wings narrow, usually longer than front wings when unfolded, and with few veins (Figure 5-2 E) (beetles) . . . . **Coleóptera** p. 239

7′. Front wings with veins, and either held rooflike over abdomen or overlapping over abdomen when at rest; antennae usually with more than 12 segments; hind wings broad, usually shorter than front wings, and

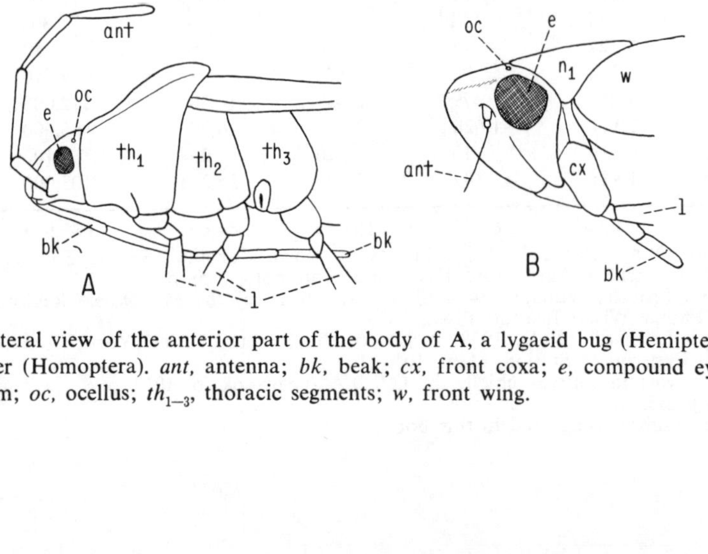

Fig. 5-1. Lateral view of the anterior part of the body of A, a lygaeid bug (Hemiptera) and B, a froghopper (Homoptera). *ant*, antenna; *bk*, beak; *cx*, front coxa; *e*, compound eye; *l*, legs; n_1, pronotum; *oc*, ocellus; th_{1-3}, thoracic segments; *w*, front wing.

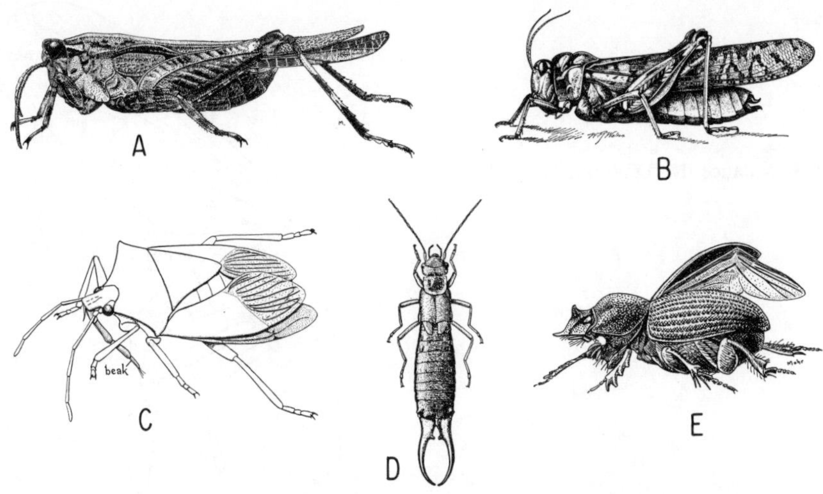

Fig. 5-2. Insects with the front wings thickened and the hind wings membranous. A, a pygmy locust (Orthoptera); B, a band-winged grasshopper (Orthoptera); C, a stink bug (Hemiptera); D, an earwig (Dermaptera); E, a dung beetle (Coleoptera). (A, C, and E, courtesy of Illinois Natural History Survey; B, courtesy of USDA; D, courtesy of Knowlton and the Utah Agricultural Experiment Station.)

with many veins (Figure 9-9 B) (grasshoppers, crickets, cockroaches, and mantids) .... **Orthóptera** p. 96

8(2′). With 2 wings 9

8′. With 4 wings 13

9(8). Body grasshopperlike; pronotum extending back over abdomen, and pointed apically; hind legs enlarged (Figures 5-2 A and 9-6) (grouse or pygmy grasshoppers, family Tetrígidae) .... **Orthóptera** p. 103

9′. Body not grasshopperlike; pronotum not as above; hind legs not so enlarged 10

10(9′). Antennae with at least one segment bearing a long lateral process; front wings minute, the hind wings fanlike (Figure 23-1 A-D); minute insects (male twisted-winged parasites) .... **Strepsíptera*** p. 342

10′. Not exactly fitting the above description 11

11(10′). Abdomen with threadlike or stylelike tails; mouth parts vestigial; halteres present or absent 12

11′. Abdomen without threadlike or stylelike tails; mouth parts usually well developed and forming a sucking proboscis; halteres present (Figure 5-3) (true flies) .... **Díptera** p. 436

12(11). Antennae long and conspicuous; abdomen terminating in a long style; wings with only a single forked vein (Figure 20-28 A); halteres present and hooklike; minute insects, usually less than 5 mm in length (male scale insects) .... **Homóptera*** p. 219

12′. Antennae short, bristlelike, and inconspicuous; abdomen terminating in 2 or 3 threadlike tails; wings with numerous veins and cross veins; halteres absent; usually over 5 mm in length (mayflies) .... **Ephemeróptera** p. 75

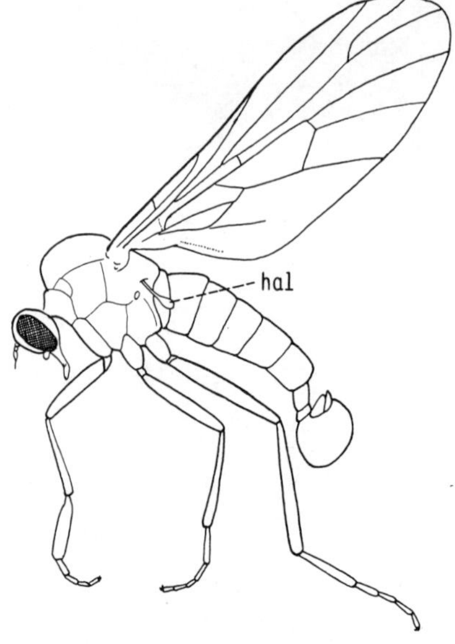

Fig. 5-3. A dance fly (Diptera), *hal,* haltere.

13(8′). Wings largely or entirely covered with scales; mouth parts usually in the form of a coiled proboscis; antennae many-segmented (Figure 5-5) (butterflies and moths) .... **Lepidóptera** p. 362

13′. Wings not covered with scales, though they may be hairy; mouth parts not in the form of a coiled proboscis; antennae variable 14

14(13′). Wings long and narrow, veinless or with only 1 or 2 veins, and fringed with long hairs (Figure 5-6); tarsi with only 1 or 2 segments, the last segment swollen; minute insects, usually less than 5 mm in length (thrips) .... **Thysanóptera** p. 157

14′. Wings not as above; if wings are somewhat linear, then the tarsi have more than 2 segments 15

15(14′). Hind wings shorter than front wings, and usually with fewer veins....16

15′. Hind wings as long as or longer than front wings, and with as many or more veins 25

16(15). Front wings with many cross veins and cells; antennae short, bristlelike, and inconspicuous; abdomen with 2 or 3 long threadlike tails (Figure 5-4); delicate, soft-bodied insects (mayflies) ....**Ephemeróptera** p. 75

16′. Front wings variable, but usually with few cross veins and cells; antennae fairly long and conspicuous, or if short and bristlelike, then there are no threadlike tails 17

17(16′). Tarsi 2- or 3-segmented 18

17′. Tarsi 4- or 5-segmented (usually 5-segmented) 23

18(17). Mouth parts sucking, the beak arising at rear of head (Figure 5-1 B) (cicadas, aphids, and hoppers).........................**Homóptera** p. 195

18′. Mouth parts chewing 19

19(18′). Minute insects, with venation greatly reduced (Figure 29-16 B), the hairs of the wings often arranged in rows; abdomen constricted at base (family Trichogrammátidae) ....**Hymenóptera*** p. 517

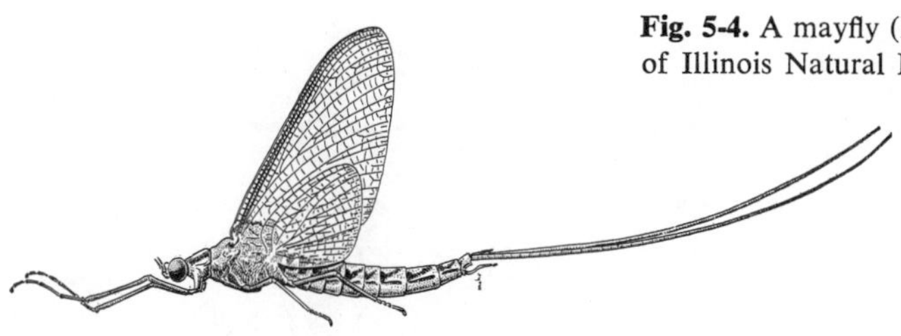

Fig. 5-4. A mayfly (Ephemeroptera). (Courtesy of Illinois Natural History Survey.)

19′. Size variable; abdomen not constricted at base 20

20(19′). Basal segment of front tarsi swollen (Figure 13-1); tarsi 3-segmented; southern United States (webspinners) .... **Embióptera*** p. 136

20′. Basal segment of front tarsi not swollen; tarsi 2- or 3-segmented 21

21(20′). Hind wings with anal area enlarged and folded fanwise at rest (Figure 5-7); cerci present and usually elongate; mostly 15 to 20 mm in length (stoneflies) .... **Plecóptera** p. 125

21′. Front and hind wings similar in shape, the hind wings without an enlarged anal lobe; usually less than 15 mm in length 22

22(21′). Cerci present; tarsi 2-segmented; wing venation greatly reduced (Figure 15-1 A) (zorapterans) .... **Zoráptera*** p. 147

22′. Cerci absent; tarsi 2- or 3-segmented; wing venation not greatly reduced (Figure 14-3 A-E) (psocids) .... **Psocóptera** p. 139

23(17′). Wings noticeably hairy; mouth parts usually much reduced except for the palpi; antennae usually as long as body or longer; venation in front and hind wings similar; abdomen not constricted at base; rather soft-bodied insects, not wasplike (caddisflies) .... **Trichóptera** p. 350

23′. Wings not hairy, or with only microscopic hairs: mandibles well developed; antennae shorter than body; usually fewer veins and cells in hind wing than in front wing; abdomen often constricted at base .. 24

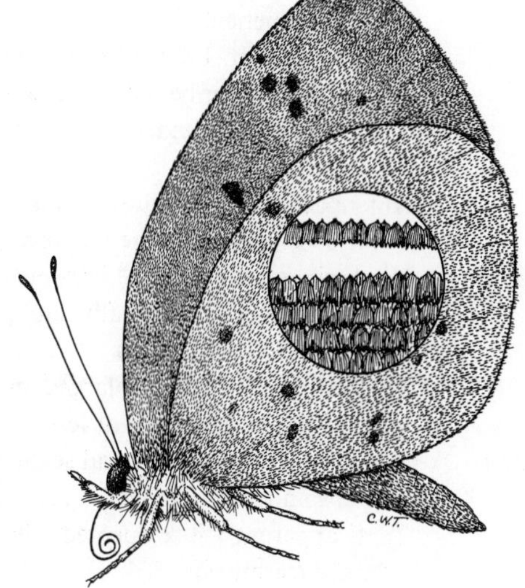

Fig. 5-5. A butterfly (Lepidoptera), with a section of the wing enlarged to show the scales.

Fig. 5-6. (*left*). A thrips (Thysanoptera). (Courtesy of Illinois Natural History Survey.) **Fig. 5-7** (*right*). A stonefly (Plecoptera). (Courtesy of USDA.)

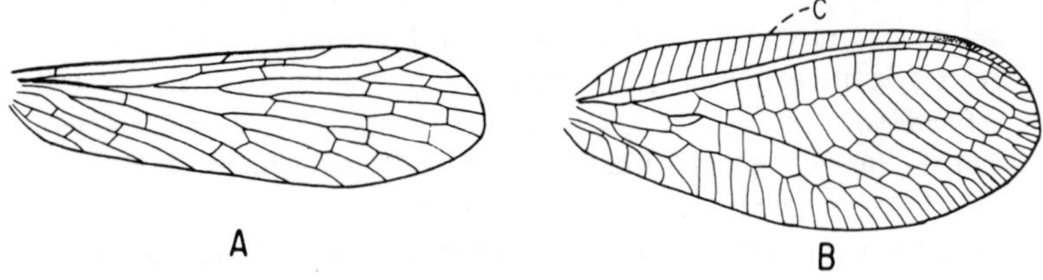

Fig. 5-8. A, front wing of a scorpionfly (Mecoptera); B, front wing of a lacewing (Neuroptera).

24(23′). Rather hard-bodied, wasplike insects; costal area of front wings with few or no cross-veins; front wings with 20 or fewer cells (sawflies, ichneumons, chalcids, ants, wasps, and bees) .... **Hymenóptera** p. 517

24′. Soft-bodied insects, not wasplike; costal area of front wings usually with numerous cross-veins (Figure 5-8 B); front wings usually with more than 20 cells (fishflies, dobsonflies, lacewings, and antlions). . **Neuróptera** p. 229

25(15′). Tarsi 3- or 4-segmented 26

25′. Tarsi 5-segmented 29

26(25). Antennae short, bristlelike, and inconspicuous; wings with many cross-veins, and never held flat over abdomen when at rest; tarsi 3-segmented; body long and slender, ¾ to 3½ in. in length (Figure 5-9) (dragonflies and damselflies) .... **Odonàta** p. 80

26′. Antennae long and conspicuous; venation variable; wings usually held flat over abdomen when at rest; 1½ in. in length or less 27

27(26′). Hind wings with the anal area enlarged and folded fanwise when at rest; cerci present and usually elongate; mostly 15 to 20 mm in length (Figure 5-7) (stoneflies) .... **Plecóptera** p. 125

27′. Hind wings without an enlarged anal area; cerci usually present but small; body 10 mm in length or less 28

28(27′). Tarsi 3-segmented, the basal segment of front tarsi enlarged (Figure 13-1) (webspinners) .... **Embióptera*** p. 136

28′. Tarsi apparently 4-segmented, the basal segment of front tarsi not enlarged (termites) .... **Isóptera** p. 118

29(25′). Costal area of front wings with numerous cross-veins (Figure 5-8 B); mouth parts not prolonged into a beak (fishflies, dobsonflies, lacewings, and antlions) . . . . **Neuróptera** p. 229

29′. Costal area of front wings with not more than 1 or 2 cross-veins (Figure 5-8 A); mouth parts prolonged ventrally to form a beaklike structure (Figures 24-1 and 24-2) (scorpionflies) . . . . **Mecóptera** p. 345

30(1′). Body insectlike, with a more or less distinct head and segmented legs . . 31

30′. Body not insectlike, without a distinct head or legs, and usually incapable of locomotion 54

31(30). Usually ectoparasites of birds or mammals; body more or less leathery and flattened dorsoventrally or laterally 32

31′. Free-living, not ectoparasites; body usually not flattened or leathery . . 36

32(31). Body flattened laterally; jumping insects; tarsi 5-segmented (Figure 5-10 A) (fleas) . . . . **Siphonáptera** p. 510

32′. Body flattened dorsoventrally; not jumping insects; tarsi variable 33

33(32′). Mouth parts chewing; tarsi with 1 (parasites of mammals) or 2 (parasites of birds) claws (chewing lice) . . . . **Mallóphaga** p. 149

33′. Mouth parts sucking (sometimes the stylets are withdrawn into the head and are not visible); usually 2 tarsal claws 34

34(33′). Antennae concealed in grooves beneath head; tarsi 5-segmented (louse flies) . . . . **Díptera*** p. 436

34′. Antennae not concealed, usually conspicuous; tarsi 1- to 3-segmented . . 35

35(34′). Beak elongate, 4-segmented, and extending back below body; tarsi with 2 small claws (wingless bugs) . . . . **Hemíptera** p. 163

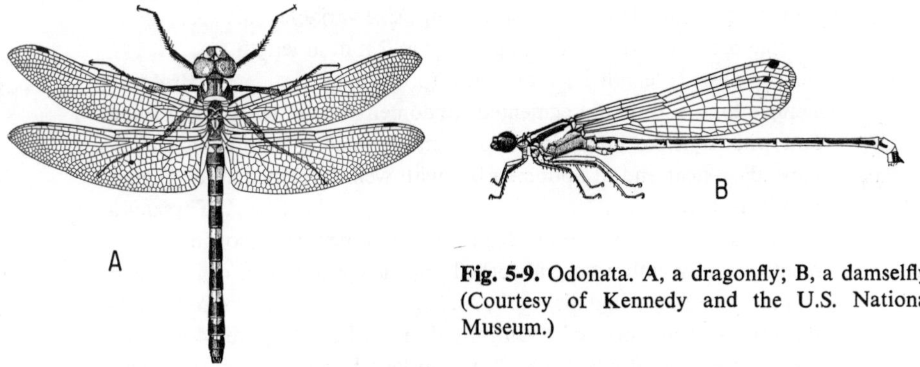

A

B

Fig. 5-9. Odonata. A, a dragonfly; B, a damselfly. (Courtesy of Kennedy and the U.S. National Museum.)

35′. Head with only a short snout anteriorly, the stylets withdrawn into head when not in use; tarsi with 1 very large claw (sucking lice) . . . . **Anoplùra** p. 153

36(31′). Abdomen distinctly constricted at base; antennae usually elbowed; hard-bodied, antlike insects (ants and wingless wasps) . . . . . . **Hymenóptera** p. 517

36′. Abdomen not particularly constricted at base; antennae not elbowed . . 37

37(36′). Body covered with scales 38

37′. Body not covered with scales 39

38(37). Abdomen with 3 long threadlike tails, and with stylelike appendages on some abdominal segments (Figure 5-10 D); mouth parts chewing (bristletails) . . . . **Thysanùra** p. 69

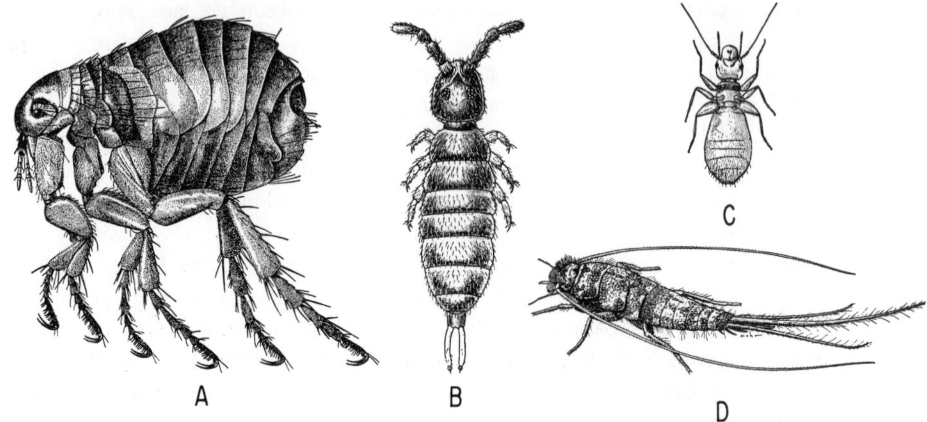

Fig. 5-10. Wingless insects. A, human flea (Siphonaptera); B, springtail (Collembola); C, psocid (Psocoptera); D, bristletail (Thysanura). (A and C, courtesy of USDA; B, courtesy of Folsom and the U.S. National Museum; D, courtesy of Illinois Natural History Survey.)

38′. Abdomen without such tails or stylelike appendages; mouth parts sucking, and usually in the form of a coiled proboscis (wingless moths)... **Lepidóptera** p. 362

39(37′). Mouth parts usually drawn into head and not apparent; abdomen with stylelike appendages on some segments, or with a forked appendage near end of abdomen; usually less than 7 mm in length................40

39′. Mouth parts distinctly chewing or sucking; size variable 42

40(39). Antennae present; size variable, up to about 7 mm in length 41

40′. Antennae absent; length 1.5 mm or less (proturans) ....**Protùra*** p. 68

41(40). Antennae long and many-segmented; abdomen with at least 9 segments, and with stylelike appendages on some segments; without a forked appendage near end of abdomen but with well-developed cerci (Figure 6-4) (bristletails) ....**Thysanùra** p. 69

41′. Antennae short, with 6 or fewer segments; abdomen with 6 or fewer segments, usually with a ventral forked appendage near end of abdomen (Figure 5-10 B) (springtails) ....**Collémbola** p. 71

42(39′). Mouth parts in the form of a ventrally directed beak (Figure 24-6); tarsi 5-segmented; usually less than 8 mm in length (wingless scorpionflies) ....**Mecóptera*** p. 345

42′. Mouth parts not as above; tarsi and size variable 43

43(42′). Cerci forcepslike; tarsi 3-segmented 44

43′. Cerci absent, or if present, not forcepslike; tarsi variable 45

44(43). Antennae more than half as long as body; western United States (*Tímema*, family Phásmidae) ....**Orthóptera*** p. 114

44′. Antennae usually less than half as long as body; widely distributed (earwigs)...**Dermáptera** p. 132

45(43′). Mouth parts sucking, with beak elongate and extending backward from head, or cone-shaped and directed ventrad 46

45′. Mouth parts chewing 48

46(45). Body long and narrow; tarsi with 1 or 2 segments and often without claws; beak cone-shaped; minute insects, usually less than 5 mm in length (thrips) .... **Thysanóptera** p. 157

46′. Body usually more or less oval; tarsi usually 3-segmented, and with well-developed claws; size variable 47

47(46′). Beak arising from front part of head; abdomen without cornicles (wingless bugs) .... **Hemíptera** p. 163

47′. Beak arising from hind part of head; abdomen often with a pair of cornicles (Figure 20-3) (aphids and others) .... **Homóptera** p. 195

48(45′). Tarsi 5-segmented; body larviform (some beetles) .... **Coleóptera*** p. 239

48′. Tarsi with 4 or fewer segments, or if tarsi are 5-segmented, then body is not larviform 49

49(48′). Tarsi 3-segmented, the basal segment of front tarsi enlarged (Figure 13-1) (webspinners) .... **Embióptera*** p. 136

49′. Tarsi with 2 to 5 segments, the basal segment of front tarsi not enlarged. 50

50(49′). Small, more or less louselike insects, less than 5 mm in length; tarsi 2- or 3-segmented; prothorax small.................................. 51

50′. Not louselike, and usually over 5 mm in length; tarsi variable; prothorax large 53

51(50). Tarsi 4-segmented; whitish, soft-bodied, wood- or ground-inhabiting insects, 8 mm in length or less (termites) .... **Isóptera** p. 118

51′. Tarsi 2- or 3-segmented; color, habits, and size variable 52

52(51′). Cerci present, 1-segmented; antennae 9-segmented and moniliform; compound eyes and ocelli absent; tarsi 2-segmented (zorapterans)........ .... **Zoráptera*** p. 147

52′. Cerci absent; antennae with 13 or more segments, and usually filiform; compound eyes and 3 ocelli usually present; tarsi 2- or 3-segmented (psocids) .... **Psocóptera** p. 139

53(50′). Tarsi 3- to 5-segmented, if 3-segmented, the hind legs are enlarged and fitted for jumping .... **Orthóptera** p. 96

53′. Tarsi 3-segmented; hind legs not enlarged or modified for jumping (wingless stoneflies) .... **Plecóptera** p. 125

54(30′). Sessile, plant-feeding; body covered by a scale or waxy material; mouth parts sucking, long and threadlike (scale insects) .... **Homóptera** p. 219

54′. Endoparasites of other insects; body not covered by a scale or waxy material; mouth parts not as above (twisted-winged parasites)........ .... **Strepsíptera*** p. 342

REFERENCES ON THE ORDERS OF INSECTS

Brues, Charles T., A. L. Melander, and F. M. Carpenter. 1954. Classification of insects. Harvard Univ., Mus. Compar. Zool., Bull. 73: v+1-917, 1219 f.

Comstock, John H. 1940 (9th ed.). An introduction to entomology. Ithaca, N.Y.: Comstock Publishing Associates. xix+1064 pp., 1228 f.

Craighead, F. C. 1950. Insect enemies of Eastern forests. U.S. Dep. Ag. Misc. Pub. 657; 679 pp., 197 f.

Essig, E. O. 1942. College entomology. New York: The Macmillan Company. vii+900 pp., 305 f.

Essig, E. O. 1958. Insects and mites of Western North America. New York: The

Macmillan Company. xiii+1050 pp., 766 f.

Imms, A. D. 1947. Insect natural history. New York: William Collins Sons & Co., Ltd. xviii+317 pp, 40 text f., 32 pl. in black and white, 40 pl. in color.

Imms, A. D. 1957 (9th ed., revised by O. W. Richards and R. G. Davies). A general textbook of entomology. New York: E. P. Dutton & Co., Inc. x+886 pp., 609 f.

Jaques, H. E. 1947 (2nd ed.). How to know the insects. Dubuque, Iowa: Wm. C. Brown Company, Publishers. 205 pp., 411 f.

Little, V. A. 1963 (rev. ed.). General and applied entomology. New York: Harper & Row, Publishers. viii+543 pp., 326 f.

Lutz, F. E. 1935. Field book of insects. New York: G. P. Putnam's Sons. ix+510 pp., 100 pl.

Matheson, Robert. 1951 (2nd ed.). Entomology for introductory courses. Ithaca, N.Y.: Comstock Publishing Associates. xiv+629 pp., 500 f.

Pennak, Robert W. 1953. Fresh-water invertebrates of the United States. New York: The Ronald Press Company. ix+769 pp., 470 f.

Peterson, Alvah. 1939. Keys to the orders of immature stages (exclusive of eggs and pronymphs) of North American insects. Ann. Entomol. Soc. Am., 32(2):267-278.

Peterson, Alvah. 1948. Larvae of insects. Part I. Lepidoptera and Hymenoptera. Ann Arbor, Mich.: Edwards Bros., Inc. 315 pp., 84 f.

Peterson, Alvah. 1951. Larvae of insects. Part II. Coleoptera, Diptera, Neuroptera, Siphonaptera, Mecoptera, Trichoptera. Ann Arbor, Mich.: Edwards Bros., Inc. v+416 pp., 104 f.

Ross, Herbert H. 1956 (2nd ed.). A textbook of entomology. New York: John Wiley & Sons, Inc. xi+519 pp., 402 f.

Swain, Ralph B. 1948. The insect guide. New York: Doubleday & Company, Inc. xlvi+261 pp., illus.

Usinger, Robert L. (Ed.) 1956. Aquatic insects of California, with keys to North American genera and California species. Berkeley, Calif.: University of California Press. ix+508 pp., illus.

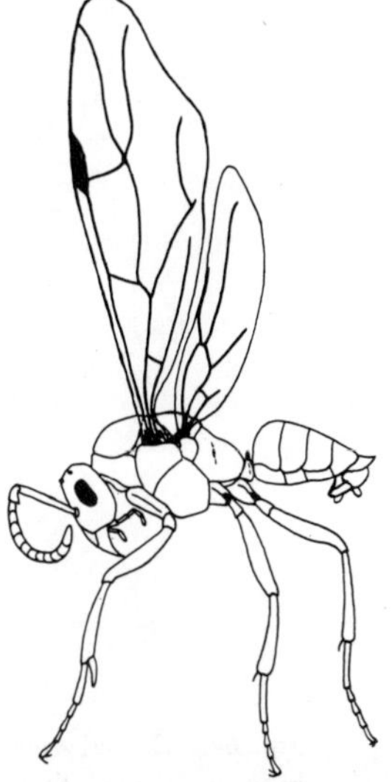

6

Subclass Apterygota

Protura, Thysanura, and Collembola

The subclass Apterygòta contains small, primitive, wingless insects with simple metamorphosis. Some of the Pterygòta lack wings, but this wingless condition is a secondary one; the wingless Pterygòta are thought to have evolved from winged ancestors.

The two subclasses of insects differ in the structure of the thorax and in the development of abdominal appendages; certain features of thoracic structure in the Pterygòta are correlated with the development of wings and are present even in the wingless members of this subclass. In the Pterygòta, each thoracic pleuron (with rare exceptions) is divided by a pleural suture into an episternum and an epimeron, and the thoracic wall is strengthened internally by furcae and phragmata; in the Apterygòta, there is no pleural suture, and furcae and phragmata are not developed. The Apterygòta usually have stylelike appendages on some of the pregenital abdominal segments; such appendages are lacking in adult Pterygòta.

There are differences of opinion regarding the status of the groups of apterygote insects; our arrangement is outlined below.

Order Protùra—proturans
- Eosentómidae
- Hesperentómidae
- Acerentómidae
- Protentómidae

Order Thysanùra—bristletails and diplurans
- Suborder Ectógnatha (Ectótrophi)—bristletails
  - Lepidotríchidae—primitive bristletails
  - Lepismátidae—silverfish
  - Machílidae—jumping bristletails

Suborder Entógnatha (Entótrophi, Diplùra, Áptera)—diplurans
Japýgidae
Campodèidae
Anajapýgidae
Order Collémbola—springtails
Suborder Arthroplèona—elongate springtails
Podùridae (including Podurìnae, Onychiurìnae, Hypogastrurìnae, and Neanurìnae)
Entomobrỳidae (including Entomobryìnae, Isotomìnae, and Tomocerìnae)
Suborder Symphyplèona—oval-bodied springtails
Sminthùridae (including Neelìnae, Dicyrtomìnae, Sminthuridìnae, and Sminthurìnae)

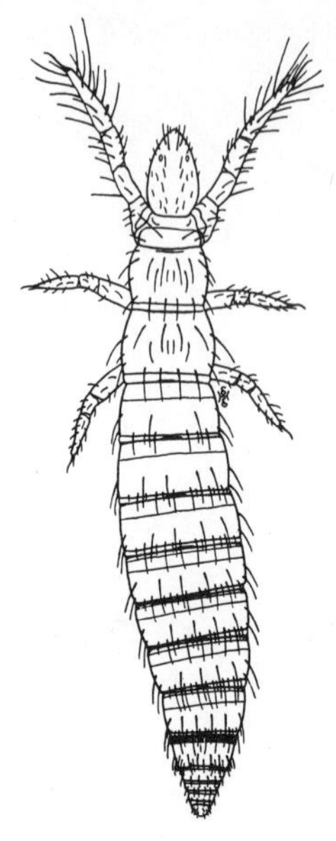

Fig. 6-1. Dorsal view of a proturan, *Aceréntulus bárberi bárberi* Ewing. (Courtesy of Ewing and the Entomological Society of America.)

ORDER PROTURA[1]—PROTURANS

The proturans are minute whitish insects, 0.6 to 1.5 millimeters in length. The head is somewhat cone-shaped, with the mouth parts suctorial and largely withdrawn into the head, and there are no eyes or antennae (Figure 6-1). The first pair of legs is principally sensory in function, and is carried in an elevated position like antennae. Styli are present on the 3 basal abdominal segments. The proturans undergo only 3 molts; at hatching there are 9 abdominal segments, and another is added at each molt; the abdomen of the adult contains 12 segments.

These insects live in moist soil or humus, in leaf mold, under bark, and in decomposing logs; they feed on decomposing organic matter.

The order Protura is divided into four families, which may be separated by the following key.

[1] Protura: *prot*, first; *ura*, tail.

KEY TO THE FAMILIES OF PROTURA

1. Tracheae present, with 2 pairs of spiracles on thorax; abdominal appendages 2-segmented .... **Eosentómidae** p. 69

1′. Tracheae and spiracles absent; abdominal appendages 1- or 2-segmented 2

2(1′). Appendages on segments 1-3 of abdomen 2-segmented; abdominal terga 3-6 with 2 complete transverse rows of setae; California .... **Hesperentómidae** p. 69

2′. Appendages on segment 3 of abdomen 1-segmented; those on segment 2, 1- or 2-segmented; abdominal terga 3-6 with 1 or 2 transverse rows of setae; widely distributed 3

3(2′). Typical abdominal terga with 1 to 3 transverse sutures and a pair of laterotergites, and with 2 transverse rows of setae...... **Acerentómidae** p. 69

3′. Abdominal terga without transverse sutures and laterotergites, and usually with only a single transverse row of setae...... **Protentómidae** p. 69

The **Eosentómidae** contains 6 North American species, all belonging to the genus *Eoséntomon.* The **Protentómidae** contains 3 small (0.58 to 0.73 millimeters in length) rare species, one known from Iowa and the other 2 from Maryland. The **Acerentómidae** contains 11 North American species, 5 in the genus *Aceréntomon* and 6 in the genus *Aceréntulus.* The **Hesperentómidae** contains a single species, *Hespérentomon macswàini* Price, known only from California.

ORDER THYSANURA[2]—BRISTLETAILS

The bristletails are moderate-sized to small insects, usually elongate in shape, with two or three tail-like appendages at the posterior end of the abdomen and with stylelike appendages on some of the abdominal segments. The paired caudal appendages are the cerci, and the third (when present) is the median caudal filament. The abdomen is 11-segmented, but the last segment is often much reduced. The mouth parts are of the chewing type, and in some members of the order are withdrawn into the head. The body in many bristletails is covered with scales.

[2] Thysanura: *thysan,* bristle or fringe; *ura,* tail.

The families of Thysanura may be separated by the following key.

KEY TO THE FAMILIES OF THYSANURA

1.	Three caudal filaments, the cerci and a median caudal filament (Figures 6-2 and 6-3); body usually covered with scales; compound eyes usually present; tarsi 3- to 5-segmented (suborder Ectógnatha) 2	
1′.	Only 2 caudal filaments or appendages (the cerci) (Figure 6-4); body not covered with scales; compound eyes absent; tarsi 1-segmented (suborder Entógnatha) 4	
2(1).	Compound eyes large and usually contiguous; middle and hind coxae with styli; abdominal styli on segments 2-9; tarsi 3-segmented; jumping insects (Figure 6-2) .... **Machílidae**	p. 71
2′.	Compound eyes small and widely separated, or absent; middle and hind coxae without styli; abdominal styli variable; tarsi 3- to 5-segmented; running insects 3	
3(2′).	Body covered with scales (Figure 6-3); ocelli absent; tarsi 3- or 4-segmented; widely distributed .... **Lepismátidae**	p. 70
3′.	Body not covered with scales; ocelli present; tarsi 5-segmented; northern California .... **Lepidotríchidae**	p. 69
4(1′).	Cerci 1-segmented and forcepslike (in adults) (Figure 6-4 C) .. **Japỳgidae**	p. 71
4′.	Cerci with more than 1 segment, and not forcepslike (Figure 6-4 A, B) .. 5	
5(4′).	Cerci as long as antennae, and many-segmented (Figure 6-4 A); styli on abdominal segments 2-7; palpi absent; 4 mm or more in length .... **Campodèidae**	p. 71
5′.	Cerci shorter than antennae and fewer-segmented (Figure 6-4 B); styli on abdominal segments 1-7; palpi present; less than 4 mm in length .... **Anajapýgidae**	p. 71

FAMILY **Lepidotríchidae**—Primitive Bristletails: This family is represented in the United States by a single species, *Tricholepídion gértschi* Wygodzinsky, recently discovered under decaying bark and in rotten wood of fallen Douglas firs in northern California (Wygodzinsky, 1961); the family was previously known only from fossils. This species has a maximum body length of 12 millimeters, with the antennae reaching to a length of 9 millimeters and the caudal appendages to 14 millimeters.

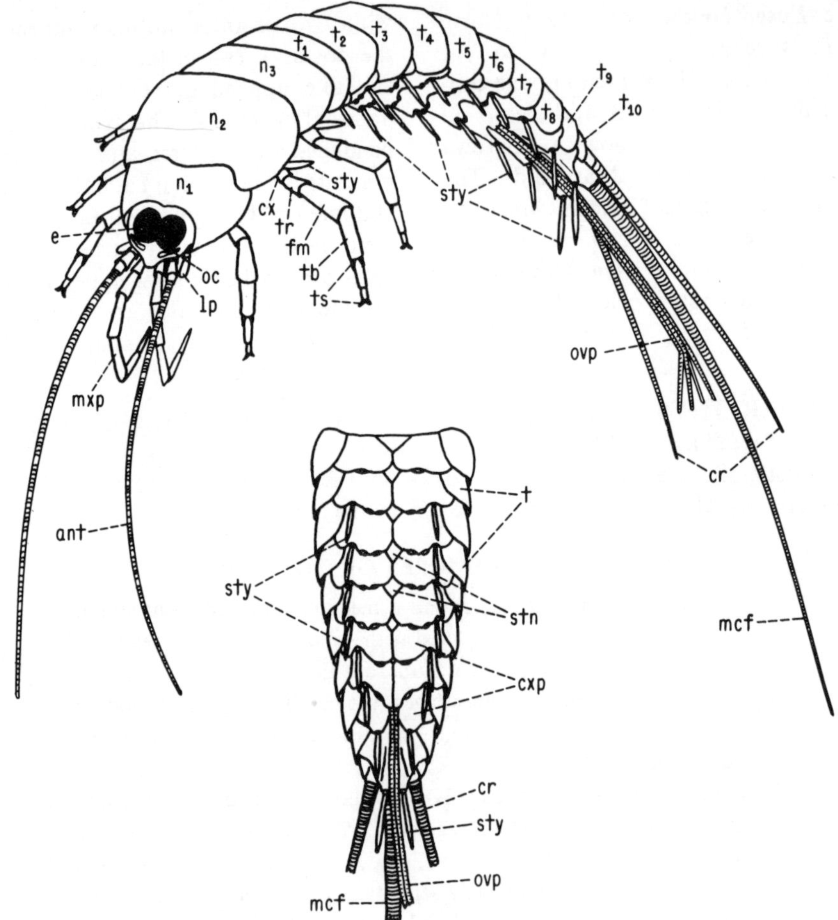

Fig. 6-2. A jumping bristletail, *Máchilis* sp., female. Lower figure, ventral view of abdomen. *ant,* antenna; *cr,* cerci; *cx,* coxa; *cxp,* coxopodite of abdominal appendages; *e,* compound eye; *fm,* femur; *lp,* labial palpus; *mcf,* median caudal filament; *mxp,* maxillary palpus; n_{1-3}, thoracic nota; *oc,* occellus; *ovp,* ovipositor (in the upper figure the gonapophyses forming the ovipositor are shown separated at the apex); *stn,* abdominal sternites; *sty,* styli; *t,* tergites; *tb,* tibia; *tr,* trochanter; *ts,* tarsus.

FAMILY **Lepismátidae:** The best-known members of this family are the silverfish, *Lepísma saccharìna* Linn., and the firebrat, *Thermòbia doméstica* (Packard), which are domestic species inhabiting buildings. They feed on all sorts of starchy substances and frequently become pests. In libraries they feed on the starch of books, bindings, and labels; in dwellings they feed on starched clothing, curtains, linens, silks, and the starch paste in wallpaper; in stores they feed on paper, vegetables, and foods that contain starch. The silverfish is gray in color, a little less than half an inch in length, and is found in cool damp situations. The firebrat (Figure 6-3) is tan or brown in color, about the same

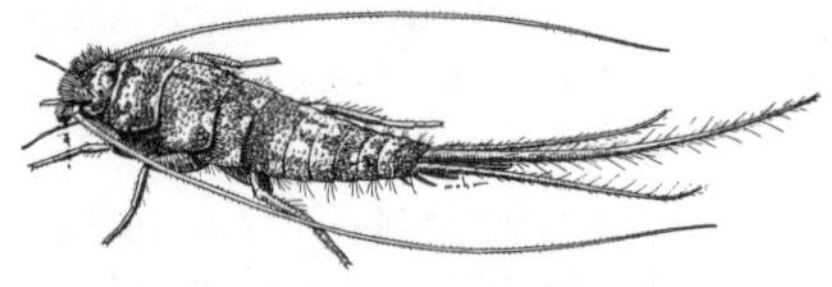

Fig. 6-3. The firebrat, *Thermòbia doméstica* (Packard). (Courtesy of the Illinois Natural History Survey.)

size as the silverfish, and frequents the warm situations around furnaces, boilers, and steampipes. Both species are quite active and can run rapidly. The lepismatids that occur outside of buildings are found in caves, debris, under stones and leaves, or in ant nests.

FAMILY **Machílidae**—Jumping Bristletails: These insects live in grassy and wooded areas among leaves, under bark or stones, in dead wood, and in similar habitats. The largest members of the group are a little over ½ inch in length. These insects are more cylindrical than the Lepismátidae. They are quite active and jump when disturbed. The North American species belong to the genus *Máchilis.*

FAMILIES **Campodèidae, Japýgidae,** AND **Anajapýgidae**—Diplurans: The members of these families lack a median caudal filament; they are light-colored, about ¼ inch in length or less, and are found in damp places under bark, under stones or logs, in rotting wood, in debris, and in similar situations. A fairly common member of the Campodèidae is *Campòdea staphylìnus* Westwood. The family Anajapýgidae is represented by a single rare species, *Anajápyx hermòsus* Smith, known only from California. A fourth family in this group, the Projapýgidae, is known from Mexico, but not from the United States.

ORDER COLLEMBOLA[3]—SPRINGTAILS

The springtails are minute insects with chewing or piercing mouth parts. The name "springtail" refers to the fact that most of these insects have a forked structure or furcula with which they jump. The furcula arises on the ventral side of the fourth abdominal segment, and at rest is folded for-

[3] Collembola: *coll,* glue; *embola,* a bolt or wedge (referring to the collophore).

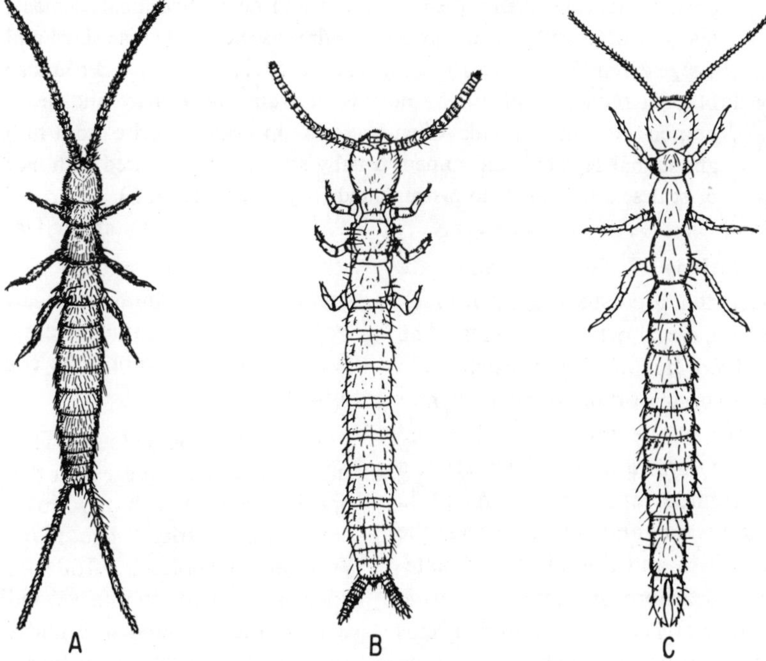

Fig. 6-4. Two-tailed Thysanura (suborder Entógnatha). A, *Campòdea fòlsomi* Silvestri (Campodèidae); B, *Anajápyx vesiculòsus* Silvestri (Anajapýgidae); C, *Jápyx diversiúngis* Silvestri (Japýgidae). (Redrawn from E. O. Essig, *College Entomolgy,* copyright, 1942, by permission of The Macmillan Company.)

ward under the abdomen where it is held in place by a clasplike structure on the third abdominal segment called the tenaculum. The insect jumps by extending the furcula ventrally and posteriorly; a springtail 5 or 6 millimeters in length may be able to jump 3 or 4 inches. The mouth part structures are somewhat elongated and styletlike and are concealed within the head. The Collembola possess a tubelike or tuberclelike structure, the collophore, on the ventral side of the first abdominal segment; at the apex of the collophore is a bilobed eversible vesicle. Most springtails are yellowish, whitish, or brownish in color; some are gray or black, and a few are mottled.

The springtails are usually very common and abundant insects, but they are seldom observed because of their small size and the fact that most of them are found in concealed situations. They occur in leaf mold, in damp soil, under bark, in decaying logs, in fungi, and a few species may be found on the surface of freshwater pools or along the seashore. A few species occur on vegetation. Some species may occasionally cause damage in gardens, greenhouses, or mushroom cellars.

The families of springtails may be separated by the following key.

KEY TO THE FAMILIES OF COLLEMBOLA

1. Body elongate (Figure 6-5 A, D-F), the abdomen with 6 distinct segments (suborder Arthroplèona) 2

1′. Body oval or globular (Figure 6-5, B, C), the abdomen with the 4 basal segments fused and segments 5 and 6 forming a small apical papilla (suborder Symphyplèona) .... **Sminthùridae** p. 73

2(1). Prothorax well developed and visible from above, and with bristles dorsally; furcula when present arising from fourth abdominal segment; integument granular or tuberculate, without scales; antennae short and 4-segmented (Figure 6-5 F) .... **Podùridae** p. 72

2′. Prothorax reduced and usually not visible from above, bare and membranous dorsally; furcula when present appearing to arise from fifth abdominal segment; integument usually smooth and covered with hair or scales; antennae 4- to 6-segmented (Figure 6-5 A, D, E).......... .... **Entomobrỳidae** p. 72

FAMILY **Podùridae:** The Podùridae are minute insects that are usually gray or black in color and have short appendages. The snow flea, *Achorùtes nivícolus* (Fitch), is a dark-colored species often found in winter on the surface of the snow. The armored springtail, *Achorùtes armàtus* (Nicolet), is a widely distributed species occurring in leaves, rotting wood, and similar places; the young are whitish and the adults are slate-colored. The seashore springtail, *Anùrida maritíma* (Guerin), is a slate-colored species that is sometimes extremely abundant along the seashore between the tide marks, where it is found on the surface of small pools, under stones, and crawling over the shore; it feeds on dead animal matter and on organic debris. Another aquatic springtail, *Podùra aquática* Linn., occurs on the surface of the water along the edges of ponds and streams.

FAMILY **Entomobrỳidae:** The family Entomobrỳidae is the largest in the order. Most species are brownish or whitish in color, but some are mottled. The marsh springtail, *Isotomùrus palústris* (Müller), is a common species occurring in moist woodlands, under leaves, and in moist soil, and it may sometimes be found on the surface of freshwater pools. Other species are found in leaf litter, in the soil, in fungi, under bark, and in similar situations. These springtails are

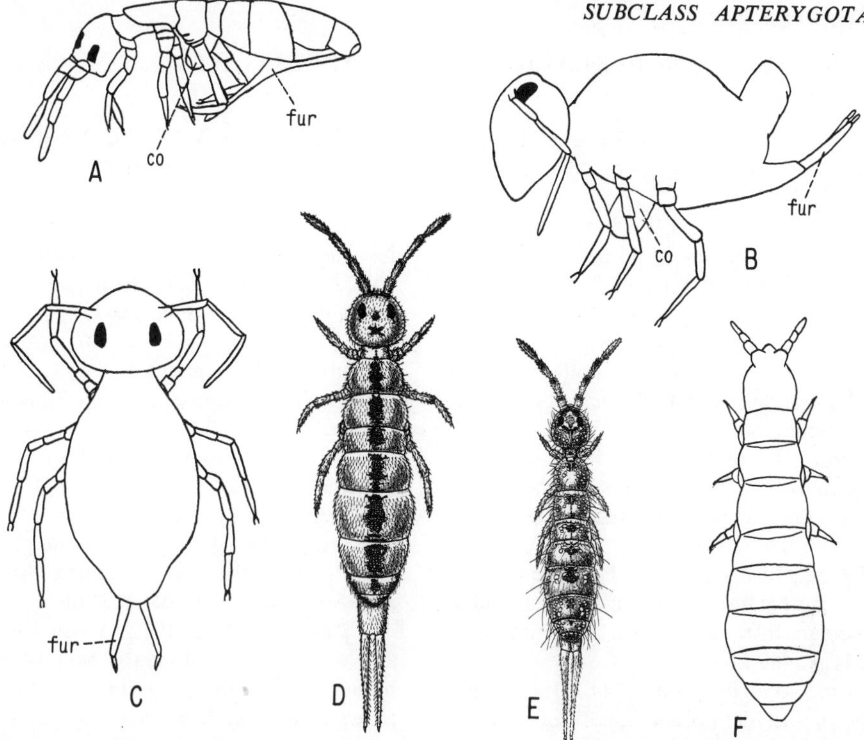

Fig. 6-5. Springtails (Collembola). A, *Orchesélla* (Entomobrỳidae); B, *Bourletiélla* (Sminthùridae), lateral view; C, same, dorsal view; D, *Isotomùrus palústris* (Müller) (Entomobrỳidae); E, *Isótoma víridis* (Bourlet) (Entomobrỳidae); F, *Anùrida maritíma* (Guerin) (Podùridae). *co,* collophore; *fur,* furcula. (A-C redrawn from Maynard by permission of Comstock Publishing Associates; D and E, courtesy of Folsom and the U.S. National Museum; F redrawn from Lubbock.)

often extremely abundant, and in some woodland areas their populations may be as high as 10 or 15 million individuals per acre.

FAMILY **Sminthùridae:** The Sminthùridae, or globular springtails, are minute, oval-bodied, usually yellowish insects with black eyes. They commonly occur on vegetation and are sometimes quite abundant. The garden springtail, *Bourletiélla horténsis* (Fitch), is a common species occurring on various flowers and vegetables and may cause considerable damage.

COLLECTING AND PRESERVING APTERYGOTA[4]

Indoor species like the silverfish and firebrat can be trapped (see page 682), or they may be collected with forceps or with a moistened brush. Most outdoor species can be collected by sifting debris or by looking under bark or stones and in fungi. Soil, leaf litter, or other material that may contain these insects can be sifted onto a white surface and the insects can be picked up with a moistened brush or an aspirator; many forms are easily collected by means of a Berlese funnel. The springtails that occur on vegetation can be collected by "sweeping" the vegetation with a white enameled pan held at about a 30-degree angle to the ground; the insects falling or jumping into the pan can be easily seen and collected. The aquatic springtails can be collected with a dipper or tea strainer.

These insects should be preserved in 80 to 95 percent alcohol; it is necessary to mount the smaller forms on microscope slides for detailed study.

[4] See also Chap. 32.

REFERENCES ON THE APTERYGOTA

Ewing, H. E. 1940. The Protura of North America. Ann. Entomol. Soc. Amer., 33(3): 495-551; 32 f.

Folsom, Justus W. 1913. North American springtails of the subfamily Tomocerinae. Proc. U.S. Natl. Museum, 46(2037):451-472; pl. 40-41.

Folsom, Justus W. 1916. North American collembolous insects of the subfamilies Achorutinae, Neanurinae, and Podurinae. Proc. U.S. Natl. Museum, 50(2134):477-525; pl. 7-25.

Folsom, Justus W. 1917. North American collembolous insects of the subfamily Onychiurinae. Proc. U.S. Natl. Museum, 53(2222): 637-659; pl. 68-79.

Folsom, Justus W. 1937. Nearctic Collembola, or springtails, of the family Isotomidae. Smithsonian Inst., U.S. Natl. Museum, Bull. 168; 144 p., 460 f.

Gisin, von Hermann. 1944. Hilfstabellen zum Bestimmen der holarktischen Collembolen. Verhandl. der naturforsch. Ges. Basel, 55:1-130.

Guthrie, J. E. 1903. The Collembola of Minnesota. Minn. Geol. and Nat. Hist. Survey, Ser. 4; 110 pp., 16 pl.

Lubbock, J. 1873. Monograph of the Collembola and Thysanura. Roy. Soc., London. x+276 pp., 78 pl.

MacGillivray, A. D. 1893. North American Thysanura. Can. Entomologist, 25(5, 7, 9, 12): 127-128, 173-174, 218-220, 313-318.

Maynard, Elliott A. 1951. A monograph of the Collembola or springtail insects of New York state. Ithaca, N.Y.: Comstock Publishing Associates. xxiv+339 pp., 669 f.

Mills, H. B. 1934. A monograph of the Collembola of Iowa. Ames, Iowa: Iowa State College Press. Monog. 3, Iowa State College; 143 pp., 12 pl., 183 f.

Price, Douglas W. 1960. A new family of Protura from California. Ann. Entomol. Soc. Am., 53(5):675-678; 4 f.

Scott, Harold G. 1961. Collembola: pictorial keys to the nearctic genera. Ann. Entomol. Soc. Am., 54(1):104-113: illus.

Slabaugh, R. E. 1940. A new thysanuran, and a key to the domestic species of Lepismatidae (Thysanura) found in the United States. Entomol. News, 51(4):95-98; 1 pl.

Smith, Leslie M. 1960. The family Projapygidae and Anajapygidae (Diplura) in North America. Ann. Entomol. Soc. Am., 53(5):575-583; 25 f.

Wygodzinsky, Pedro. 1961. On a surviving representative of the Lepidotrichidae (Thysanura). Ann. Entomol. Soc. Am., 54(5):621-627; 54 f.

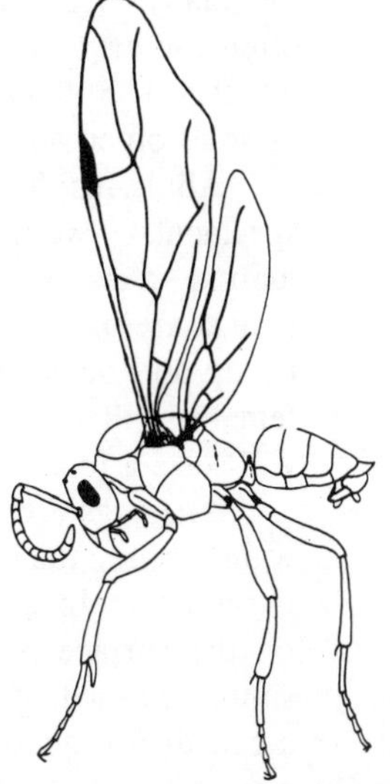

7

Order Ephemeroptera[1]: Mayflies

Mayflies are small to medium-sized, elongate, very soft-bodied insects with two or three long threadlike tails; they are often very common about ponds or streams. The adults (Figure 7-1) have membranous wings with numerous veins; the front wings are large and triangular, and the hind wings are small and rounded; in some species the hind wings are vestigial or absent. The wings at rest are held together above the body. The antennae are small, bristlelike, and inconspicuous. The immature stages are aquatic, and the metamorphosis is simple.

Mayfly nymphs may be found in a variety of aquatic habitats. Some are streamlined in form and very active; others are burrowing in habit. They can usually be recognized by the leaflike gills along the sides of the abdomen and the three long tails (Figure 7-2); stonefly nymphs are similar (Figures 11-2 and 11-3), but have only two tails (the cerci), and the gills are on the thorax (only rarely on the abdomen) and are not leaflike. When ready to transform to the winged stage, the nymph rises to the surface of the water, molts, and the winged form flies a short distance to the shore where it usually alights on the vegetation. This insect, which is usually dull in appearance and more or less pubescent, is not the adult stage, and is called a subimago; it molts once more, usually the next day, to become the adult. The adult is usually smooth and shining, and has longer tails and legs than the subimago. The mayflies are the only insects that molt after the wings become functional.

Mayflies often emerge in enormous numbers from lakes and rivers, and sometimes may literally pile up along the shore or in the streets of a nearby town. Up until about

[1] Ephemeroptera: *ephemero*, for a day, short-lived; *ptera*, wings (referring to the short life of the adults).

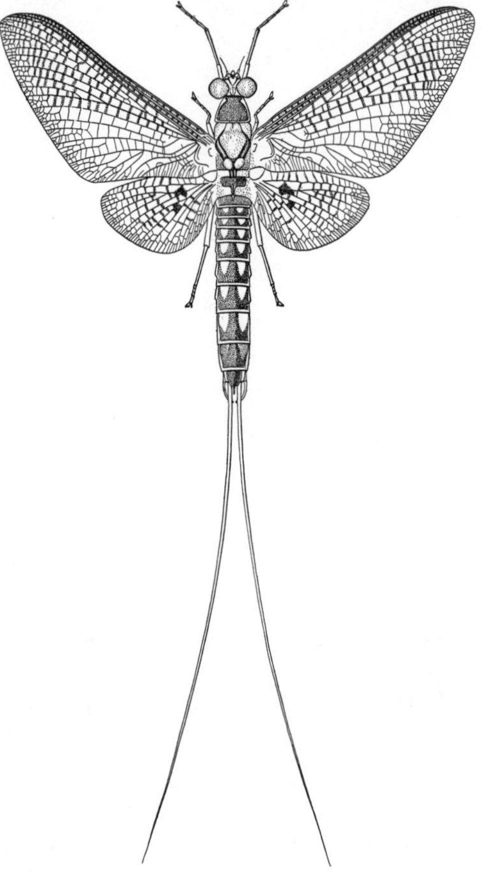

Fig. 7-1. A mayfly, *Hexagènia bilineàta* (Say) (Ephemériidae). (Courtesy of Needham and the Bureau of Fisheries.)

ten years ago, this frequently happened along the shores of Lake Erie (Figure 7-3), but changes in the lake have reduced the number of these insects (and also the numbers of many fish), and their emergences are no longer as striking as they used to be.

The aquatic stages require a year or more to develop, but the adults, which have vestigial mouth parts and do not feed, seldom live more than a day or two. Both young and adults serve as an important food for many freshwater fish, and fishermen often use artificial flies modeled after these insects. The nymphs feed on algae and various other aquatic plants.

Adult mayflies often engage in rather spectacular swarming flights during which mating takes place. The individuals in a swarm are usually all males, and they often fly up and down in unison. Sooner or later females will enter the swarm, and a male will seize a female and fly away with her.

The eggs are laid on the surface of the water or are attached to vegetation or stones in the water. In cases where the eggs are laid on the surface of the water, they may be simply washed off the end of the abdomen a few at a time, or they may all be laid in one clump. Each species has characteristic egg-laying habits.

CLASSIFICATION OF THE EPHEMEROPTERA

Different authorities differ in their division of this order into families; we follow the classification of Needham, Traver, and Hsu (1935), who recognize three families, as follows:

Epheméridae (including Neoepheméridae)—burrowing mayflies
Heptageniidae—stream mayflies
Baètidae (including Caènidae, Oligoneùridae, Baetíscidae, Ephemeréllidae, Leptophlebiidae, and Ametrópidae)—small mayflies

These three families may be separated by the following key. The venational terminology used is that of Needham, Traver, and Hsu (1935), which is illustrated in Figures 7-4 and 7-5.

KEY TO THE FAMILIES OF EPHEMEROPTERA

1. Veins M and Cu_1 in front wing strongly divergent at base, with M_2 bent strongly toward Cu_1 basally (Figure 7-4); outer fork in hind wing lacking; hind tarsi 4-segmented .... **Epheméridae** p. 78

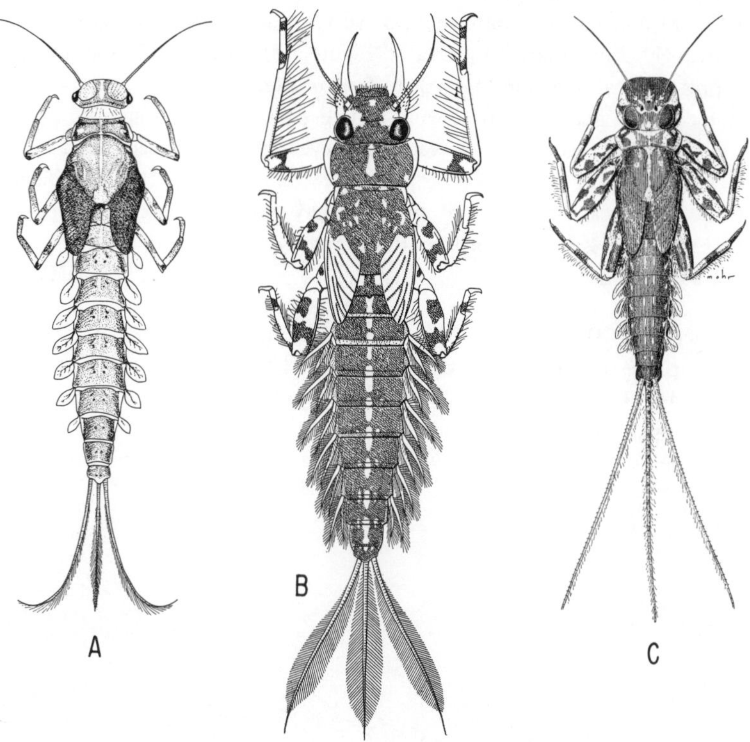

Fig. 7-2. Mayfly nymphs. A, *Baètis hiemàlis* Leonard (Baètidae); B, *Polymitárcys álbus* Say (Epheméridae); C, *Heptagènia diabàsia* Burks (Heptagenìidae). (A, courtesy of Leonard and the Entomological Society of America; B, courtesy of Needham and the Bureau of Fisheries; C, courtesy of Burks and the Entomological Society of America.)

Fig. 7-3. Mayflies (*Hexagènia*, sp., family Epheméridae) in front of a store in Put-in-Bay, Ohio. (Courtesy of T. H. Langlois.)

1′. Veins M and Cu_1 in front wing not very divergent at base and M_2 not strongly bent toward Cu_1 basally (Figure 7-5); outer fork in hind wing present or absent; hind tarsi 3- to 5-segmented 2

2(1′). Cubital intercalaries in front wing in two parallel pairs, long and short alternately (Figure 7-5 A); venation never greatly reduced; hind tarsi 5-segmented .... **Heptageniidae** p. 79

2′. Cubital intercalaries in front wing usually not in two parallel pairs (Figure 7-5 B); venation sometimes greatly reduced; hind tarsi 3- or 4-segmented .... **Baètidae** p. 79

FAMILY **Epheméridae**—Burrowing Mayflies: The nymphs of these mayflies (Figure 7-2 B) have long mandibles and plumose gills and are usually burrowing in habit; the adults are fairly large insects with numerous cross veins in the wings (Figure 7-1). The adult has two or three tails, the number varying in different species and between the sexes in some species. Many adults have the wings spotted or mottled.

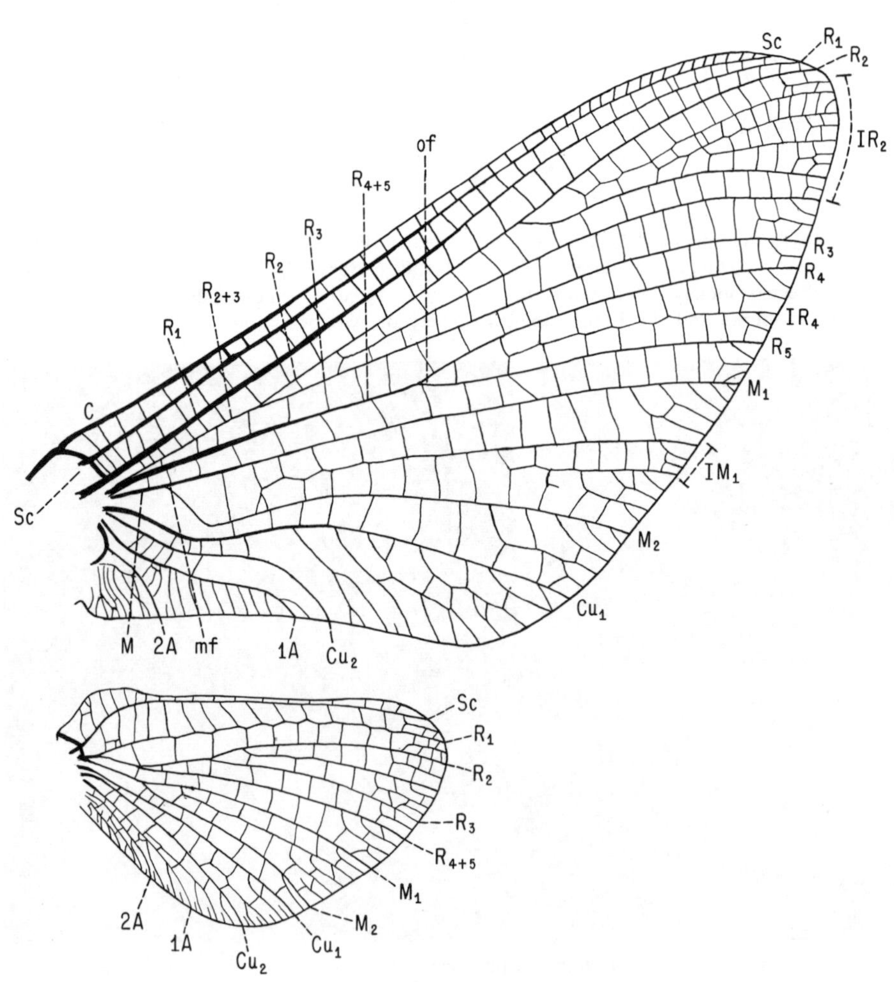

Fig. 7-4. Wings of *Pentagènia* (Epheméridae). *mf,* fork of M; *of,* outer fork.

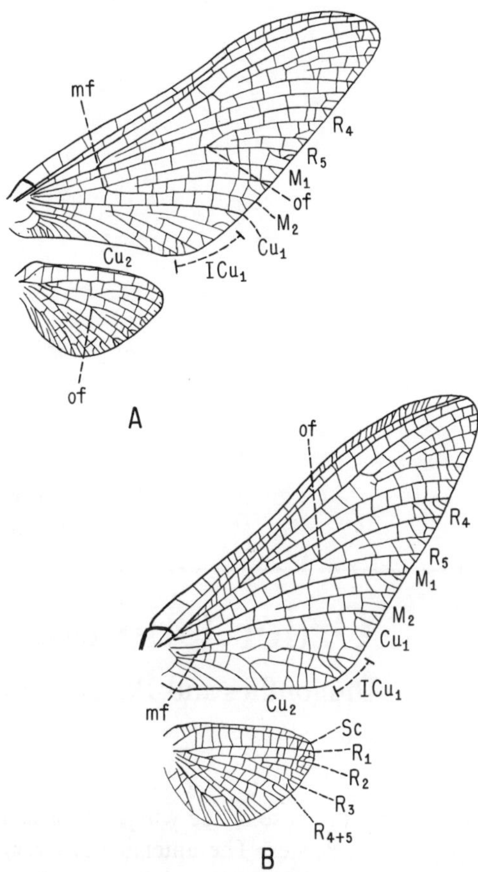

Fig. 7-5. A, wings of a heptageniid; B, wings of a baetid, ICu_1, cubital intercalaries; *mf*, fork of M; *of*, outer fork.

The common genera in this family are *Ephémera* (wings spotted), and *Hexagènia* and *Pentagènia* (wings not spotted).

FAMILY **Heptageniidae**—Stream Mayflies: The nymphs of this family are sprawling forms, usually dark-colored with the head and body flattened (Figure 7-2 C); they are found on the under side of stones in streams. The adults are medium-sized insects, usually without spots on the wings.

FAMILY **Baètidae**—Small Mayflies: The nymphs of this group (Figure 7-2 A) are more cylindrical than heptageniids and occur in a variety of habitats. The adults vary considerably in size and appearance, but many are small, with reduced venation, and in some genera the hind wings are entirely absent.

COLLECTING AND PRESERVING EPHEMEROPTERA

Adult mayflies may be captured by simply picking them up with the fingers, or they may be collected with a net. Nets are useful in capturing mayflies from swarms and in sweeping vegetation for them. The adults are extremely fragile and must be handled with considerable care. They should be preserved in 70 or 80 percent alcohol; specimens that are pinned or in envelopes often shrivel and are easily broken.

Nymphs may be collected in various types of aquatic habitats by the usual methods of collecting aquatic animals. They should be preserved in 70 or 80 percent alcohol.

REFERENCES ON MAYFLIES

Berner, L. 1950. The mayflies of Florida. Gainesville: University of Florida Press. xii+267 pp., 24 pl., 88 f., 19 maps.

Burks, B. D. 1953. The mayflies, or Ephemeroptera, of Illinois. Illinois Nat. Hist. Survey, Bull., 26(1):1-216, 395 f.

Day, Willis C. 1956. Ephemeroptera. In Aquatic insects of California, edited by Robert L. Usinger. Berkeley: University of California Press. Pp. 79-105; 28 f.

Edmunds, George F., Jr. 1959. Ephemeroptera. In: Fresh-water biology, edited by W. T. Edmondson. New York: John Wiley & Sons, Inc. Pp. 908-916, 39 f.

Needham, J. G., J. R. Traver, and Yin-Chi Hsu. 1935. The biology of mayflies. Ithaca, N.Y.: Comstock Publishing Associates. xiv+759 pp., 168 f., 40 pl.

Pennak, Robert W. 1953. Fresh-water invertebrates of the United States. New York: The Ronald Press Company. ix+769 pp., 470 f.

Traver, Jay R. 1932-1933. Mayflies of North Carolina. J. Elisha Mitchell Sci. Soc., 47(1);85-161, pl. 5-12 (1932); 47(2):163-236 (1932); 48(2):141-206, pl. 15 (1933).

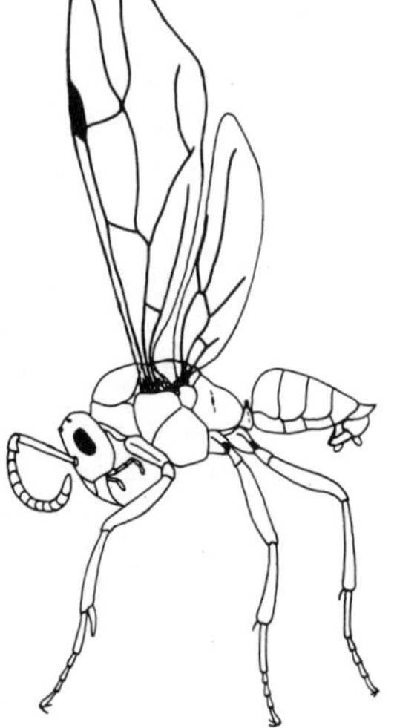

8

Order Odonata[1]

Dragonflies and Damselflies

The Odonata are relatively large and often beautifully colored insects that spend a large part of their time on the wing. The immature stages are aquatic, and the adults are usually found near water. All stages are predaceous and feed on various insects and other organisms, and from man's point of view, are generally very beneficial; the adults are harmless to man; that is, they do not bite or sting.

Adult dragonflies and damselflies are easily recognized (Figures 8-11 to 8-14). The four wings are elongate, many-veined, and membranous; the compound eyes are large and many-faceted, and often occupy most of the head; the thorax is relatively small and compact (the prothorax is always small, and the other two thoracic segments make up most of the thorax), and the dorsal surface of the pterothorax, between the pronotum and the base of the wings, is formed by pleural sclerites. The antennae are very small and bristlelike. The abdomen is long and slender; the cerci are 1-segmented and function as clasping organs in the male. The mouth parts are of the chewing type, and the metamorphosis is simple.

Present-day Odonata vary in length from about $\frac{3}{4}$ inch to over 5 inches; the largest dragonfly known, which lived about 250 million years ago and is known only from fossils, had a wing spread of about 27 inches! The largest dragonflies in this country are about $3\frac{1}{4}$ inches in length, though they often look much larger when seen on the wing.

Odonata nymphs are aquatic and breathe by means of gills. The gills of damselfly nymphs (Zygóptera) are in the form of three leaflike structures at the end of the abdomen (Figure 8-7); these nymphs swim by body undulations, the gills func-

[1] Odonata: from a Greek word meaning tooth (referring to the teeth on the mandibles).

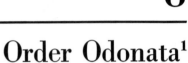

tioning like the tail of a fish. The gills of dragonfly nymphs (Anisóptera) (Figures 8-9 and 8-10) are in the form of ridges in the rectum; when a dragonfly nymph breathes, it draws water into the rectum through the anus and then expels it. If the insect is "in a hurry," this expulsion of water from the anus is the chief means of locomotion, and the insect moves by "jet" propulsion.

The nymphs vary somewhat in habits, but all are aquatic and feed on various sorts of small aquatic organisms. They usually lie in wait for their prey, either on a plant or more or less buried in the mud. The prey is generally small, but some of the larger nymphs (particularly Aéshnidae) occasionally attack tadpoles and small fish. The nymphs have the labium modified into a peculiar segmented structure with which the prey is captured. The labium is folded under the head when not in use; when used, it is thrust forward, usually very quickly, and the prey is grabbed by two movable clawlike lobes (the lateral lobes or palpi) at the tip of the labium (Figure 8-8). The labium, when extended, is usually at least a third as long as the body (Figure 8-10 B).

When a nymph is fully grown, it crawls up out of the water, usually on a plant stem or rock (and usually early in the morning), and undergoes its final molt; the nymphs of some species wander many yards from the water before molting. Once out of the last nymphal skin, the adult expands to its full size in about half an hour. The flight of newly emerged adults is relatively feeble and they are very easy to catch, but they make poor specimens. They are not yet fully colored, and they are very soft-bodied. It is usually a few days before the insect's full powers of flight are developed, and it may be a week or two before the color pattern is fully developed. Many Odonata have quite a different color or color pattern the first few days of their adult life than they will have after a week or two. Newly emerged, pale, soft-bodied adults are usually spoken of as *teneral* individuals.

The two sexes in the suborder Anisóptera are usually similarly colored, though the colors of the male are frequently brighter. In some of the Libellùlidae the two sexes differ in the color pattern on the wings. The two sexes are differently colored in most of the Zygóptera and the male is usually the more brightly colored. In most of the Coenagriónidae the two sexes have a different color pattern. Some damselflies have two or more different color phases in the female; for example, most females of *Ischnùra verticàlis* (Say) have a color pattern that is different from that of the male, and are either orange and black (newly emerged) or rather uniformly bluish (older individuals), but a few females have a color pattern that is similar to that of the male.

Some species of Odonata are on the wing for only a few weeks each year, whereas others may be seen throughout the summer or over a period of several months. Observations of marked individuals indicate that the average damselfly probably has a maximum adult life of three or four weeks, and some dragonflies may live six or eight weeks. Most species have a single generation a year, with the egg or nymph (usually the nymph) overwintering; a few of the larger darners are known to spend two or three years in the nymphal stage.

Dragonflies and damselflies are peculiar among insects in having the copulatory organs of the male located at the anterior end of the abdomen, on the ventral side of the second abdominal segment; the male genitalia of other insects are located at the posterior end of the abdomen. Before mating, the male dragonfly must transfer sperm from the genital opening on the ninth segment to the structures on the second segment; this is done by bending the abdomen downward and forward.

The two sexes frequently spend considerable time "in tandem," with the male clasping the female by the back of the head or the prothorax with the appendages at the

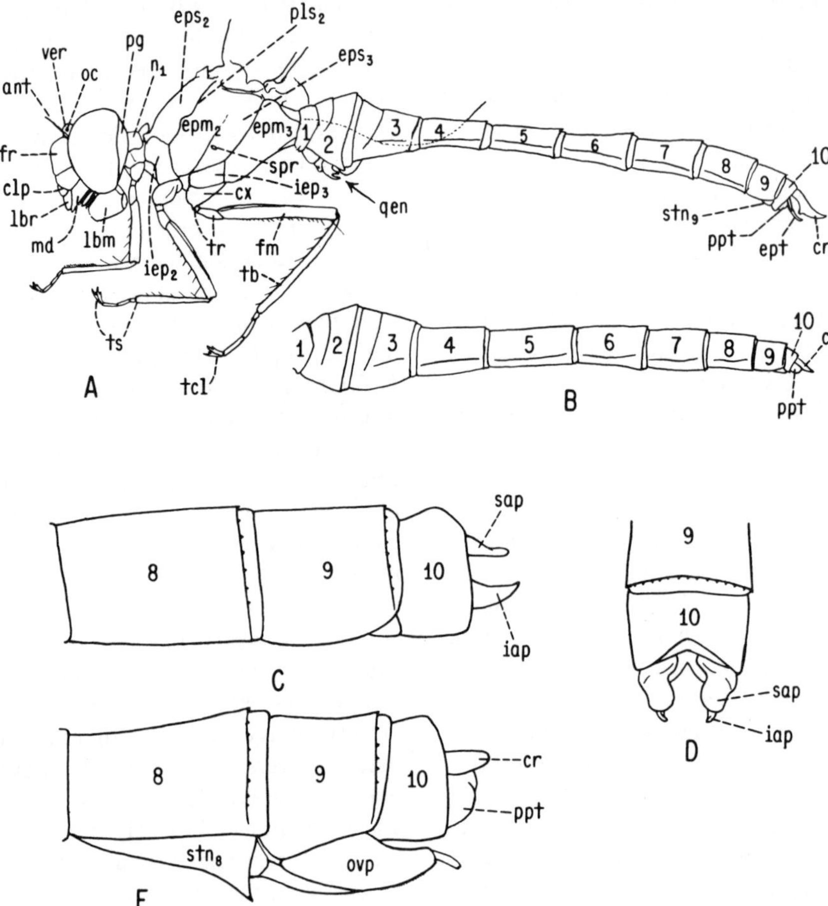

Fig. 8-1. Structural characters of Odonata. A, lateral view of *Sympètrum intérnum* Montgomery, male; B, lateral view of abdomen of *S. intérnum,* female; C, terminal abdominal segments of *Enallágma hágeni* (Walsh), male, lateral view; D, same, dorsal view; E, terminal abdominal segments of *E. hágeni,* female, lateral view. *ant,* antenna; *clp,* clypeus; *cr,* cerci or superior appendages; *cx,* coxa; *e,* compound eye; epm_2, mesepimeron; epm_3 metepimeron; eps_2, mesepisternum; eps_3, metepisternum, *ept,* epiproct or inferior appendage; *fm,* femur; *fr,* frons; *gen,* male copulatory apparatus; *iap,* inferior appendage; iep_2, mesinfraepisternum; iep_3, metinfraepisternum; *lbm,* labium; *lbr,* labrum; *md,* mandible; n_1, pronotum; *oc,* ocellus; *ovp,* ovipositor; *pg,* postgena; pls_2, mesopleural or humeral suture; *ppt,* paraproct; *sap,* superior appendage or cercus; *spr,* spiracle; *stn,* sternite; *tb,* tibia; *tcl,* tarsal claws; *tr,* trochanter; *ts,* tarsus; *ver,* vertex; 1-10, abdominal segments.

end of his abdomen. Copulation, with the female bending its abdomen downward and forward and contacting the second segment genitalia of the male, usually occurs in flight.

Odonata lay their eggs in or near water, and may do so while in tandem or when alone. In some species where the female detaches from the male before beginning oviposition, the male will remain nearby—"on guard"—while the female is ovipositing, and will chase off other males that come near. An unprotected female, after she begins ovipositing, may be interrupted by another male, who may grab her and fly off in tandem with her.

Females of the Gómphidae, Macromìidae, Cordulìidae, and Libellùlidae do not have an ovipositor, and the eggs are generally laid on the surface of the water by the female flying low and dipping its abdomen in the water and washing off the eggs; the females of most species in these groups are alone when ovipositing. A somewhat rudimentary ovipositor is developed in the Cordulegástridae, which oviposit by hovering above shallow water with the body in a more or less vertical position, and repeatedly jabbing the abdomen into the water and laying the eggs in the bottom. The females of the other groups (Aéshnidae, Petalùridae, and all Zygóptera) have a well-developed ovipositor (Figure 8-1 E), and insert their eggs in plant tissues (in many species while still in tandem with the male). The eggs are usually inserted just below the surface of the water, no farther than the female can reach, but in a few cases (for example, some species of *Léstes*) the eggs are laid in plant stems above the water line, and in a few other cases (for example, some species of *Enallágma*) the female may climb down a plant stem and insert her eggs into the plant a foot or more below the surface of the water. The eggs usually hatch in one to three weeks, but in some species (for example, *Léstes*) overwinter and hatch the following spring.

Most species of Odonata have characteristic habits of flight. The flight of most common skimmers (Libellùlidae) is very erratic; they fly this way and that, often hovering in one spot for a few moments, and they seldom fly very far in a straight line. Many stream species fly relatively slowly up and down the stream, often patrolling a stretch of a hundred yards or more; these dragonflies fly at a height and speed that is characteristic for the species. Some of the gomphids, when flying over open land areas, fly with a very undulating flight, each undulation covering 4 to 6 feet vertically and 2 to 3 feet horizontally. Many of the corduliids and aeshnids fly from 6 to 20 or more feet above the ground, and their flight seems tireless; many of the smaller damselflies fly only an inch or two above the surface of the water.

Most dragonflies feed on a variety of small insects that are caught on the wing in a basketlike arrangement of the legs. The dragonfly may alight and eat its prey or may eat it on the wing. The prey is chiefly small flying insects such as midges, mosquitoes, and small moths, but the larger dragonflies often capture bees, butterflies, or other dragonflies. Odonata normally take only moving prey, but if captured will eat or chew on almost anything that is put into their mouth—even their own abdomen!

Many pond species are frequently found with large numbers of small, rounded, usually reddish bodies attached to the under side of the thorax or abdomen; these bodies are larval water mites. The mite larvae attach to the dragonfly nymph, and when the nymph emerges, move onto the adult. The mites spend two or three weeks on the dragonfly, feeding on its blood and increasing in size, and eventually leave it; if they get back into water, they develop into adult mites, which are free-living and predaceous. The mite larvae do not appear to do a great deal of damage to the dragonflies; it is not unusual to find dragonflies with dozens of mite larvae on them.

CLASSIFICATION OF THE ODONATA

A synopsis of the Odonata occurring in the United States is given below; synonyms and alternate spellings are given in parentheses.

Suborder Anisóptera—dragonflies
- Superfamily Aeshnòidea
  - Petalùridae—graybacks
  - Aéshnidae (Aéschnidae)—darners
  - Gómphidae—clubtails
  - Cordulegástridae (Cordulegastéridae)—biddies
- Superfamily Libellulòidea
  - Macromìidae—belted skimmers and river skimmers

Corduliidae—green-eyed skimmers
Libellùlidae—common skimmers
Suborder Zygóptera—damselflies
Agriónidae (Agrìidae, Calopterýgidae) —broad-winged damselflies
Léstidae—spread-winged damselflies
Coenagriónidae (Coenagrìidae, Agriónidae)—narrow-winged damselflies

The separation of the various groups of Odonata is based primarily on characters of the wings. There are two major interpretations of the wing venation in this order; we use the Comstock-Needham interpretation, illustrated in Figures 8-2 and 8-3. Within each family the separation of genera and species is based on wing venation, color pattern, the structure of the genitalia, and other characters. Many species of Odonata can be recognized in the field by their characteristic size, shape, color, or manner of flight.

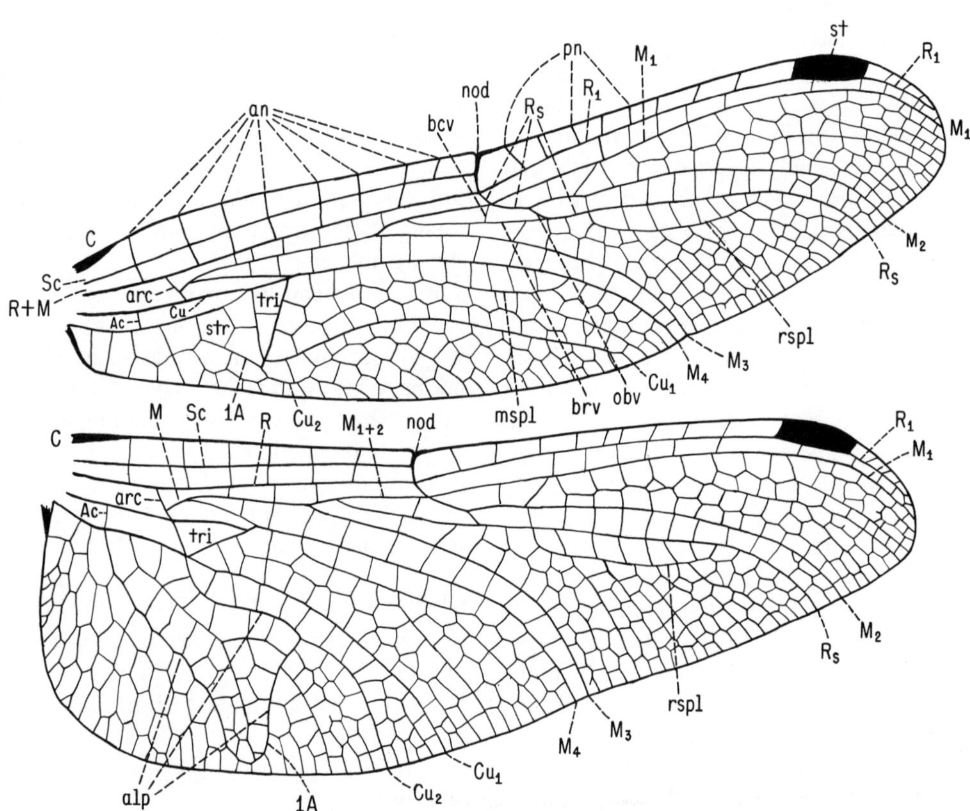

Fig. 8-2. Wings of *Sympètrum rubicúndulum* (Say) (Libellùlidae), showing the Comstock-Needham system of terminology. *Ac,* anal crossing (A branching posteriorly from Cu; often called the cubito-anal cross-vein); *alp,* anal loop (foot-shaped in this species); *an,* antenodal cross-veins; *arc,* arculus (the upper part is M, the lower part is a cross-vein); *bcv,* bridge cross-vein; *brv,* bridge vein; *mspl,* median supplement; *nod,* nodus; *obv,* oblique vein; *pn,* postnodal cross-veins; *rspl,* radial supplement; *st,* stigma; *str,* subtriangle (3-celled in this wing); *tri,* triangle (2-celled in the front wing, 1-celled in the hind wing). The usual symbols are used for other venational characters.

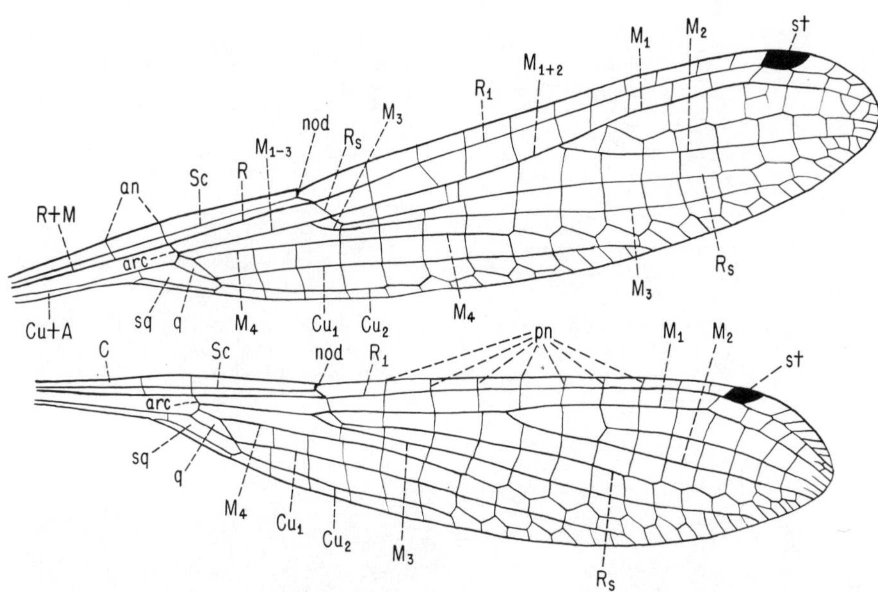

Fig. 8-3. Wings of *Enallágma hágeni* (Walsh) (Coenagriónidae), showing the Comstock-Needham system of terminology. *an*, antenodal cross-veins; *arc*, arculus; *nod*, nodus; *pn*, postnodal cross-veins; *q*, quadrangle; *sq*, subquadrangle; *st*, stigma. The usual symbols are used for the other venational characters.

KEY TO THE FAMILIES OF ODONATA

1. Front and hind wings similar in shape and both narrowed at base (Figures 8-3 and 8-4 D, E); wings usually held together above body when at rest (Figure 8-13 B, D); head transversely elongate; males with 4 appendages at end of abdomen (Figure 8-1 C, D) (damselflies, suborder Zygóptera) 2

1′. Hind wings wider at base than front wings (Figures 8-2 and 8-4 A-C); wings held horizontal when at rest; head usually not transversely elongate, but more rounded; males with 3 appendages at end of abdomen (dragonflies, suborder Anisóptera) 4

2(1). Ten or more antenodal cross-veins (Figure 8-4 D); wings not stalked, and often with black or red markings .... **Agriónidae** p. 91

2′. Two (rarely 3) antenodal cross-veins (Figures 8-3, 8-4 E); wings stalked at base, and either hyaline or lightly tinged with brownish (only rarely blackish) 3

3(2′). M_3 arising nearer arculus than nodus (Figure 8-4 E); wings usually divergent above body when at rest .... **Léstidae** p. 92

3′. M_3 arising nearer nodus than arculus, usually arising below nodus (Figure 8-3); wings usually held together above body when at rest (Figure 8-13 B, D) .... **Coenagriónidae** p. 92

4(1′). Triangles in front and hind wings similar in shape and about equidistant from arculus (Figure 8-4 A); most of costal and subcostal cross-veins not in line; usually a brace vein (an oblique cross-vein, Figure 8-4 F, *bvn*) behind proximal end of stigma (superfamily Aeshnòidea) 5

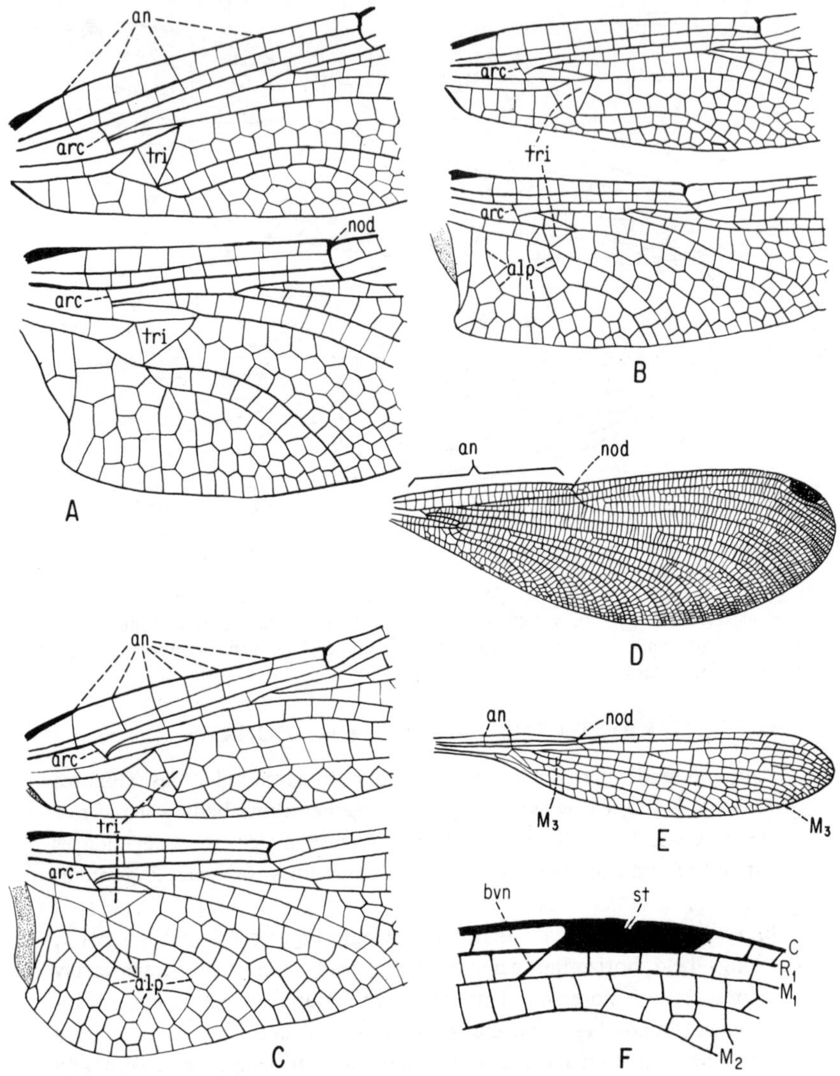

Fig. 8-4. Wings of Odonata. A, base of wings of *Gómphus* (Gómphidae); B, base of wings of *Dídymops* (Macromìidae); C, base of wings of *Tetragoneùria* (Cordulìidae); D, front wing of *Ágrion* (Agriónidae); E, front wing of *Léstes* (Léstidae); F, wing tip of *Aéshna* (Aéshnidae). *alp,* anal loop; *an,* antenodal cross-veins; *arc,* arculus; *bvn,* brace vein; *nod,* nodus; *st,* stigma; *tri,* triangle.

4′. Triangles in front and hind wings usually not similar in shape, the triangle in front wing farther beyond arculus than triangle in hind wing (Figures 8-2 and 8-4 B, C); most of costal and subcostal cross-veins in line; no brace vein behind proximal end of stigma (superfamily Libellulòidea) 8

5(4). A brace vein behind proximal end of stigma (Figure 8-4 F, *bvn*)......6

5′. No brace vein behind proximal end of stigma..........**Cordulegástridae** p. 88

6(5). Compound eyes in contact for a considerable distance on dorsal side of head (Figure 8-6 B) ....**Aéshnidae** p. 87

6′. Compound eyes separated on dorsal side of head (Figure 8-6 A) or meeting at a single point only 7

7(6′). Median lobe of labium notched (Figure 8-5 A); stigma at least 8 mm in length . . . . **Petalùridae** p. 87

7′. Median lobe of labium not notched (Figure 8-5 B); stigma less than 8 mm in length . . . . **Gómphidae** p. 87

8(4′). Hind margin of compound eyes slightly lobed (Figure 8-6 D); males with a small lobe on each side of second abdominal segment, and with inner margin of hind wing somewhat notched; anal loop rounded (Figure 8-4 B) or elongate (Figure 8-4 C), if foot-shaped, with little development of "toe" 9

8′. Hind margin of compound eyes straight or with a very small lobe (Figure 8-6 C); males without a small lobe on side of second abdominal segment, and with inner margin of hind wing rounded; anal loop usually foot-shaped, with "toe" well developed (Figure 8-2) . . . . . . **Libellùlidae** p. 90

9(8). Anal loop rounded, without a bisector (Figure 8-4 B); triangle in hind wing distad of arculus; 3 or more cu-a cross-veins in hind wing . . . . **Macromìidae** p. 88

9′. Anal loop elongate, with a bisector (Figure 8-4 C); triangle in hind wing opposite arculus or nearly so; 1 to 2 cu-a cross-veins in hind wing . . . . **Corduliidae** p. 89

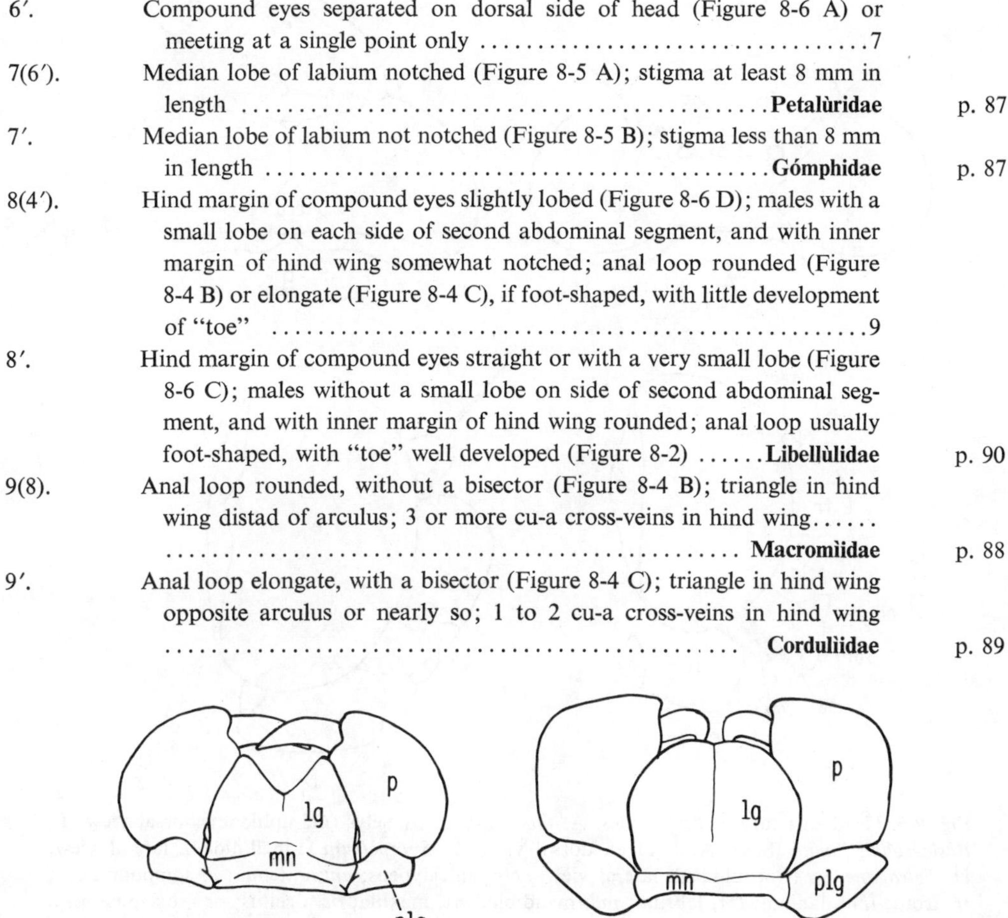

Fig. 8-5. Labia of adult dragonflies. A, *Tachópteryx* (Petalùridae); B, *Aéshna* (Aéshnidae). *lg*, ligula or median lobe; *mn*, mentum; *p*, palpus or lateral lobe; *plg*, palpiger or squama.

FAMILY **Petalùridae**—Graybacks: Two species in this group occur in the United States: *Tachópteryx thòreyi* (Hagen) in the eastern states, and *Tanýpteryx hágeni* (Selys) in the West. These dragonflies are large grayish brown (*Tachópteryx*) or blackish (*Tanýpteryx*) insects about 3 inches in length, and they usually occur along small streams in wooded valleys; the adults frequently alight on tree trunks, where their color blends with that of the bark.

FAMILY **Gómphidae**—Clubtails: This is a fairly large group, and most of its members occur along streams or lake shores. The clubtails are 2 to 3 inches in length, dark-colored, usually with yellowish or greenish markings. They generally alight on a bare flat surface. Many species have the terminal abdominal segments swollen; hence the common name for the group. The largest genus in the family is *Gómphus.*

FAMILY **Aéshnidae**—Darners: This group includes the largest and most powerful of the dragonflies; most of them are about 3 inches in length. The green darner, *Anax jùnius* (Drury), a common and widely distributed species that occurs about ponds, has a greenish thorax and a bluish abdomen,

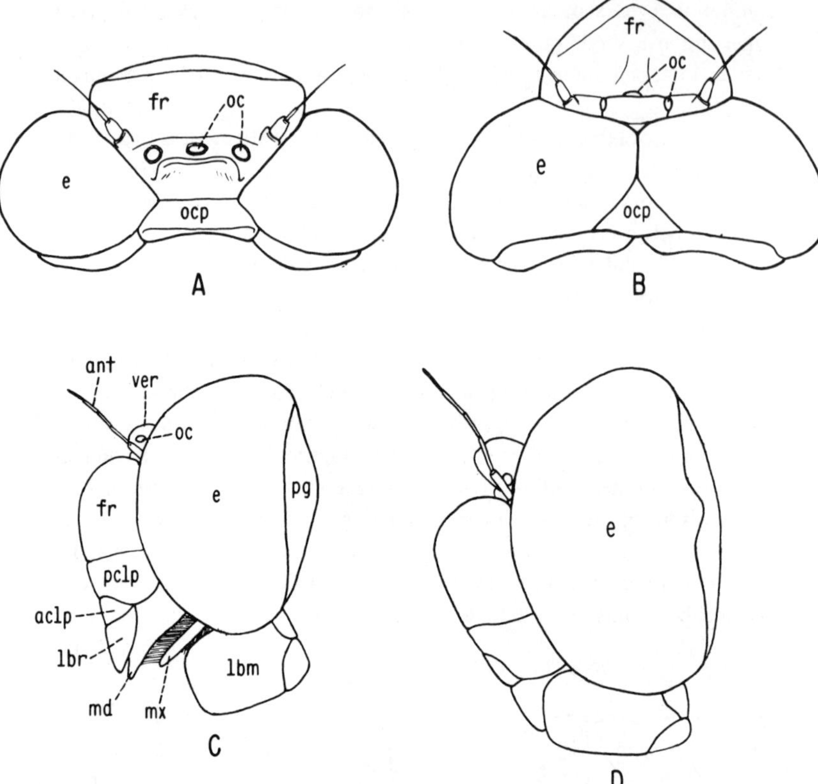

Fig. 8-6. Head structure in dragonflies. A, *Gómphus éxilis* Selys (Gómphidae), dorsal view; B, *Basiaéschna janàta* (Say) (Aéshnidae), dorsal view; C, *Sympètrum* (Libellùlidae), lateral view; D, *Tetragoneùria* (Cordulìidae), lateral view. *aclp,* anteclypeus; *ant,* antenna; *e,* compound eye; *fr,* frons; *lbm,* labium; *lbr,* labrum; *md,* mandible; *mx,* maxilla; *oc,* ocellus; *ocp,* occiput; *pclp,* postclypeus; *pg,* postgena; *ver,* vertex.

and a targetlike mark on the upper part of the face. The genus *Aéshna* contains a number of species, most of which are to be found near marshes in the latter part of the summer; they are dark-colored with blue or greenish markings on the thorax and abdomen. One of the largest species in this family is *Epiaéschna hèros* (Fabricius), an early-summer species about $3\frac{1}{4}$ inches in length, and dark brown with indistinct greenish markings on the thorax and abdomen.

FAMILY **Cordulegástridae**—Biddies: The biddies are large, brownish black dragonflies with yellow markings; they differ from the other Aeshnòidea in lacking a brace vein at the proximal end of the stigma. These dragonflies are usually found along small, clear, woodland streams. The adults fly slowly up and down the stream, a foot or two above the water, but if disturbed can fly very rapidly. The group is a small one, and all the species in this country belong to the genus *Cordulegáster*.

FAMILY **Macromìidae**—Belted Skimmers and River Skimmers: The members of this group can be distinguished from the Cordulìidae, with which they were formerly classified, by the rounded anal loop that lacks a bisector (Figure 8-4 B). Two genera occur in the United States, *Dídymops* and *Macròmia.* The belted skimmers (*Dídymops*) are light brown in color, with light markings on the thorax; they occur along boggy pond shores. The river skimmers (*Macròmia*) are large species that occur along lake shores and large streams; these dragonflies are dark brown with yellowish markings on the thorax and abdomen (Figure 8-11), and are extremely fast fliers. The eyes of the Macromìidae are greenish in life (in *Macròmia,* usually a brilliant green).

FAMILY **Corduliidae**—Green-Eyed Skimmers: These skimmers are mostly black or metallic in color, and seldom have conspicuous light markings; the eyes of most species are brilliant green in life. The flight is usually direct, in many species interrupted by periods of hovering. The members of this group are more common in the northern states and Canada than in the south.

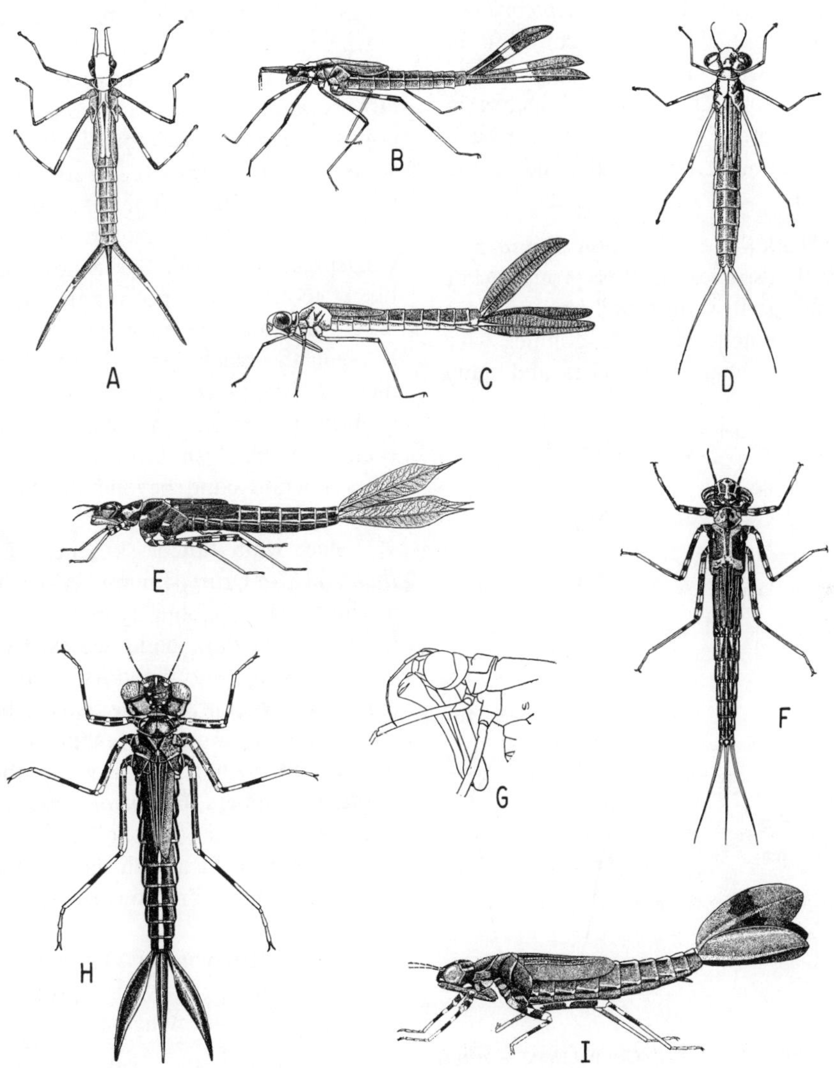

Fig. 8-7. Nymphs of damselflies (Zygóptera), dorsal and lateral views. A and B, *Ágrion aequábile* Say (Agriónidae); C and D, *Léstes drỳas* Kirby (Léstidae); E and F, *Ischnùra cervùla* Selys (Coenagriónidae); G, head of *Léstes drỳas* Kirby, lateral view; H and I, *Argia émma* Kennedy (Coenagriónidae). (Courtesy of Kennedy and the U.S. National Museum.)

The genus *Tetragoneùria* contains dark-colored dragonflies about 1½ to 1¾ inches in length, often with brownish color at the base of the hind wing; they occur chiefly around ponds and swamps. The largest genus in this group is *Somatochlòra,* which includes the bog skimmers; most of the bog skimmers are metallic in color and over 2 inches in length, and they usually occur along small wooded streams or in bogs. The royal skimmer, *Epicordùlia prínceps* (Hagen), is the only corduliid in the northeast with black spots beyond the base of the wing; it is about 3 inches in length, with three blackish spots in each wing—basal, nodal, and apical—and occurs about ponds.

FAMILY **Libellùlidae**—Common Skimmers: Most of the species in this group occur about ponds and swamps, and many species are quite common. These dragonflies vary in length from about ¾ to 3 inches, and many species have the wings marked with spots or bands. The flight is usually rather erratic. This is a large group, and only a few of the commoner genera and species can be mentioned here.

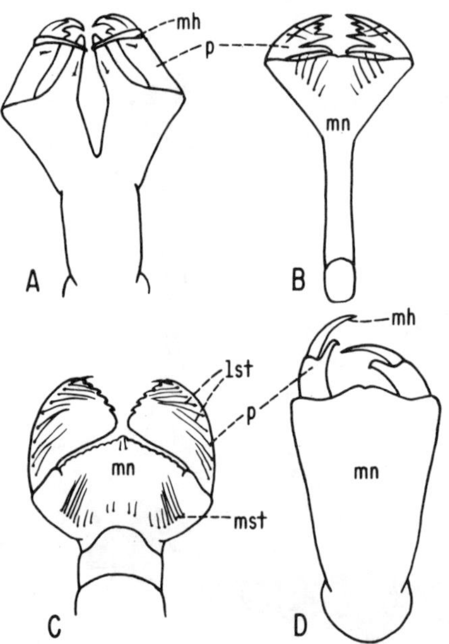

Fig. 8-8. Labia of nymphal Odonata. A, *Ágrion* (Agriónidae); B, *Léstes* (Léstidae); C, *Libéllula* (*Plathèmis*) *lýdia* Drury (Libellùlidae); D. *Ànax* (Aéshnidae). *lst,* lateral setae; *mh,* movable hook of palpus; *mn,* mentum; *mst,* mental setae; *p,* palpus or lateral lobe. (Redrawn from Garman.)

The smallest libellulid in the United States is the dwarf skimmer, *Nannothèmis bélla* (Uhler),[2] which is about ¾ inch in length and occurs in bogs in the eastern states. The males are bluish with clear wings, and the females are patterned with black and yellow and have the basal third or more of the wings yellowish brown. The large dragonflies that are common about ponds and have black or black and white spots on the wings are mostly species in the genus *Libéllula.* The tenspot skimmer, *L. pulchélla* Drury (Figure 8-12), with a wingspread of about 3½ inches, has three black spots (basal, nodal, and apical) on each wing, and the males have white spots between the black spots. The widow skimmer, *L. luctuòsa* Burmeister, which is slightly smaller, has the basal third or so of each wing blackish brown, and the males have a white band beyond the basal dark coloring of the wing.

The white-tailed skimmer, *L.* (*Plathèmis*) *lýdia* Drury (Figure 8-12), which has a wingspread of about 2½ inches, has in the male a broad dark band across the middle of each wing and the dorsal side of the abdomen nearly white; the females have the wings spotted as in the females of *L. pulchélla,* and do not have a white abdomen. Spotted skimmers (*Celithèmis*) are medium-sized (wingspread of about 2 inches), mostly reddish or brownish with darker markings, and with reddish or brownish spots on the wings.

The amber-winged skimmer, *Perithèmis ténera* (Say), with a wingspread of about 1½ inches, has the wings amber-colored in

[2] The pronunciation indicated for generic names ending in *-themis* is that used by the majority of workers on the Odonata; according to the rules of pronunciation, the accent should be on the syllable preceding the *-themis: Nannóthemis, Pláthemis, Celíthemis, Períthemis, Erýthemis.*

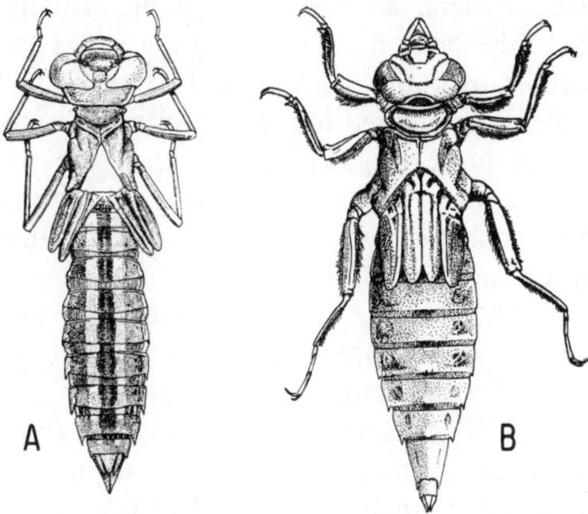

Fig. 8-9. Nymphs of Aeshnòidea. A, *Aéshna verticàlis* Hagen (Aéshnidae); B, *Gómphus quadricòlor* Walsh (Gómphidae). (Courtesy of Walker and *The Canadian Entomologist*.)

the male, and clear with brownish spots in the female. The dragonflies of the genus *Sympètrum* are medium-sized, late-summer, marsh-inhabiting insects; their color varies from yellowish brown to a bright brownish red, and the wings are usually clear except for a small basal spot of yellowish brown. The white-faced skimmers (*Leucorrhínia*), which have a wingspread of about 1½ inches, are dark-colored with a conspicuous white face; the most common species in the East is *L. intácta* Hagen, which has a yellow spot on the dorsal side of the seventh abdominal segment.

The blue pirate, *Pachydíplax longipénnis* (Burmeister), is a common pond species, particularly in the central and southern states; it varies in color from a patterned brown and yellow to a uniform bluish, and the wings are often tinged with brownish; it has a long cell just behind the stigma and has a wingspread of 2 to 2½ inches. The green-jacket skimmer, *Erythèmis simplicicóllis* (Say), is a little larger than *P. longipénnis*; it has clear wings, and the body color varies from light green patterned with black to a uniform light blue. The skimmers in the genera *Pantàla* and *Tràmea* are medium-sized to large (wingspread 3 to 4 inches), wide-ranging insects and have the base of the hind wings very broad; those in *Pantàla* are yellowish brown with a light yellowish or brownish spot at the base of the hind wing; those of *Tràmea* are largely black, with a large black or dark brown spot at the base of the hind wing.

FAMILY **Agriónidae**—Broad-Winged Damselflies: The members of this group are relatively large damselflies that have the base of the wings gradually narrowed, not stalked as in the Léstidae and Coenagriónidae; these insects occur along streams. Two genera occur in the United States, *Ágrion* (= *Calópteryx*) and *Hetaerìna.* The common eastern species of *Ágrion* is the black-winged damselfly, *A. maculàtum* Beauvais; the wings of the male are black, and those of the female are dark gray with a white stigma; the body is metallic greenish black. The most common species of *Hetaerìna* is the American ruby-spot, *H. americàna* (Fabricius), which is reddish in color, with a red or reddish spot in the basal third or fourth of the wings.

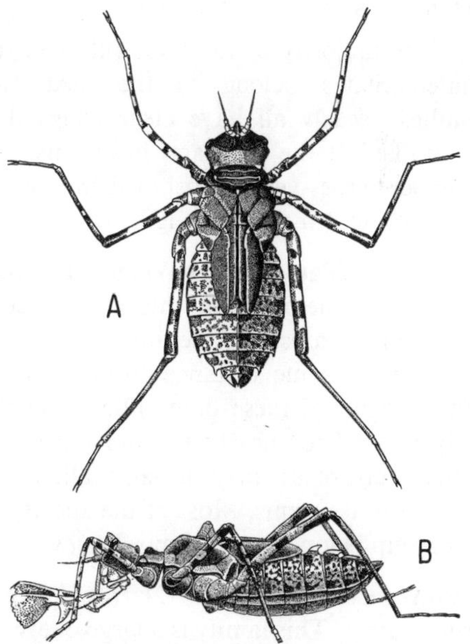

Fig. 8-10. Nymph of *Macròmia magnífica* MacLachlan (Macromìidae). A, dorsal view; B, lateral view, with labium extended. (Courtesy of Kennedy and the U.S. National Museum.)

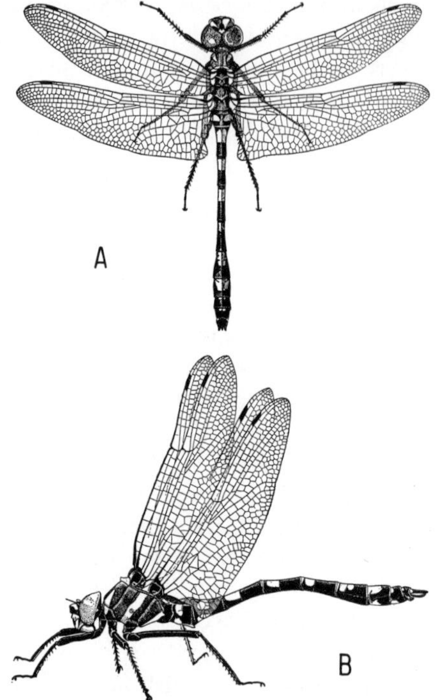

Fig. 8-11. *Macròmia magnífica* MacLachlan. A, dorsal view; B, lateral view. (Courtesy of Kennedy and the U.S. National Museum.)

The majority of the damselflies in the United States belong to the next two families. Nearly all have clear wings that are stalked at the base and have only two antenodal cross-veins. Most of them are between 1 and 2 inches in length.

FAMILY **Léstidae**—Spread-Winged Damselflies: The members of this group occur chiefly in swamps, but the adults occasionally wander some distance from swamps. When alighting, these damselflies hold the body vertical, or nearly so, and the wings partly outspread; they usually alight on plant or grass stems. Most of the species in this group belong to the genus *Léstes.*

FAMILY **Coenagriónidae**—Narrow-Winged Damselflies: This family is a large one, with many genera and species. These damselflies occur in a variety of habitats; some occur chiefly along streams, and others about ponds or swamps. Most of them are rather feeble fliers, and when alighting, usually hold the body horizontal and the wings together over the body. The two sexes are differently colored in most species, with the males more brightly colored than the females. Many of these damselflies are beautifully colored, but the color usually fades after the insect dies.

The dancers (*Árgia,* Figure 8-13) are chiefly stream species, and can be recognized by the long, close-set spines on the tibiae. The males of the violet dancer, *Árgia violàcea* (Hagen), a common species occurring along streams and pond shores, are a beautiful violet color. The green damsels (*Nehalénnia*) are small, slender, bronzy-green insects usually found in bogs and swamps. The bicolored bog damsel, *Amphiágrion sàucium* (Burmeister), is a small, stout-bodied, red and black damselfly usually found in bogs. The largest genus in this family is *Enallágma,* which includes the bluets; most species are light blue with black markings. Several species of *Enallágma* may be found about the same pond or lake. The common fork-tail, *Ischnùra verticàlis* (Say), is a very common species that occurs nearly everywhere that any

Fig. 8-12. Common pond dragonflies (Libellùlidae). Top, *Libéllula pulchélla* Drury, male; bottom, *Libéllula* (*Plathèmis*) *lýdia* Drury, male.

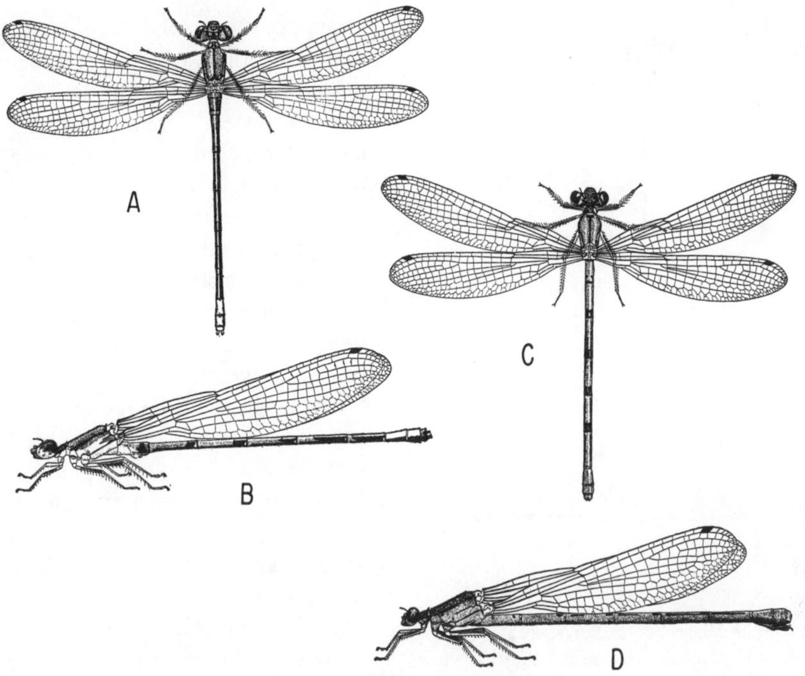

Fig. 8-13. *Árgia émma* Kennedy (Coenagriónidae). A and B, male; C and D, female. (Courtesy of Kennedy and the U.S. National Museum.)

damselfly is to be found; the males are dark-colored, with green stripes on the thorax and blue on the tip of the abdomen; most of the females are bluish green with faint dark markings (older individuals), or brownish orange with black markings (recently emerged individuals); a very few of the females are colored like the males.

COLLECTING AND PRESERVING ODONATA

Many of the Odonata are powerful fliers, and their capture often presents a challenge to the collector. Many are so adept on the wing that they can easily dodge a net, even when the net is swung as one would swing a baseball bat. If one wishes to catch these fast-flying insects, he must study their flight habits; many species have particular beats along which they fly at rather regular intervals, or have perches on which they frequently alight; if one is familiar with the insect's flight habits, he can often anticipate where it will fly and can be prepared for it. One should swing at a flying dragonfly from behind; if swung at from in front, the insect can see the net coming and can usually dodge it. In stalking a specimen one should use only the slowest motions until the final swing; movements of the legs and feet should be covered by vegetation as much as possible, for dragonflies often see motion below them better than that on a level with them.

The net used to capture Odonata should be an open-mesh net with little air resistance so that it can be swung rapidly. The rim size and handle length may depend on the collector, but for many species it is desirable to have a relatively large rim (12 to 15 inches in diameter) and a net handle at least 3 feet long.

Dragonflies beyond the reach of a net (many specimens will fall in this category) may often be collected with a sling shot loaded with sand, or with a gun loaded with

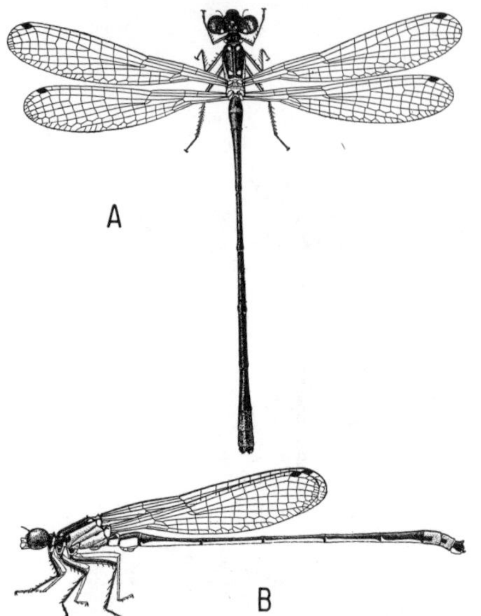

Fig. 8-14. *Ischnùra cervùla* Selys, male (Coenagriónidae). A, dorsal view; B, lateral view. (Courtesy of Kennedy and the U.S. National Museum.)

dust shot. Many specimens so collected may be slightly damaged, but a slightly damaged specimen is usually better than none at all.

Odonata occur in a great variety of habitats, and to obtain a large number of species, one should visit as many different habitats as possible. Two habitats that appear similar often contain different species, or the same habitat may harbor different species in different seasons. Many species have a short seasonal flight range, and one must be in the field at just the right season to collect them. Most species will be found near aquatic habitats—ponds, streams, marshes, and the like—but many are wide-ranging and may be found in meadows, woodlands, and the hillsides above aquatic habitats.

It is practically impossible to collect many Odonata without wading, for they often fly at some distance (beyond net reach) out from the shores of a pond or stream. Many species, particularly damselflies, can be obtained by sweeping in the vegetation along and near the shores of ponds and marshes; others patrol along the edge of the emergent vegetation, where the water is a few feet deep. Stream species, which are usually rare in collections and are often locally distributed, are best collected by wading streams (if the streams are small enough to wade); this often means wading for considerable distances.

Killing jars for Odonata should be relatively large and wide-mouthed, and should contain several pieces of cleansing tissue. Specimens should be removed from the killing jars as soon as they are killed, since they may become discolored if left in too long. Mating pairs or pairs in tandem should be pinned together before they are put into the killing jar, so they can be associated later. Specimens collected in the field should be placed in envelopes, with the wings folded above the body; ordinary letter envelopes will do for this, and the collecting data can be written on the outside. After returning from the field, the contents of the envelopes can be sorted and mounted.

Most of the bright colors of the Odonata fade after the insect dies; these colors are most likely to be retained if the specimens are dried rapidly—in the sun, under a lamp, or in an oven. If one collects Odonata in any numbers, they are best kept in triangular paper envelopes (Figure 32-5), one or two specimens to an envelope (never two species in the same envelope). If specimens are pinned, they may be pinned with the wings outspread, with the help of a spreading board, or they may be pinned sideways; it is usually preferable to pin the specimen sideways, with the pin passing through the thorax at the base of the wings and the left side of the insect uppermost. Some specimens, particularly dragonflies, will usually have to be placed in an envelope for a few days before they are pinned, so that the wings will stay together above the body. It is often necessary to support the abdomen of a pinned specimen, either with crossed insect pins under the abdomen, a strip of narrow cardboard on the pin under the insect, or by bristling (a heavy bristle or a very slender insect pin shoved through the fresh specimen from frons to anus).

The nymphs of Odonata may be collected by the various types of aquatic collecting equipment and methods described in Chapter 32. Nymphs should be preserved in 70 to 75 percent alcohol. Newly emerged adults and their exuviae should be preserved together in a pillbox, an envelope, or (preferably) in alcohol. If full-grown nymphs are collected in the field, they may be brought back to the laboratory (preferably wrapped in wet cloth or grass) and reared out in a fish-free balanced aquarium; a stick must be provided for the nymphs to crawl out of the water, and the aquarium should be covered with a screen or cloth.

REFERENCES ON THE ODONATA

Borror, Donald J. 1945. A key to the New World genera of Libellulidae (Odonata). Ann. Entomol. Soc. Am., 38(2):168-194; 72 f.

Corbet, Philip S. 1963. A biology of dragonflies. Chicago: Quadrangle Books, Inc. xvi+247 pp. Frontis. (color), 115 f., 6 pl.

Garman, Philip. 1917. The Zygoptera, or damselflies, of Illinois. Illinois State Lab. Nat. Hist. Bull., 12(4):411-587; pl. 58-73.

Garman, Philip. 1927. The Odonata or dragonflies of Connecticut. Conn. State Geol. and Nat. Hist. Survey, Bull., 39; 331 pp., 67 f., 22 pl.

Gloyd, Leonora K., and Mike Wright. 1959. Odonata. In: Fresh-water biology, ed. by W. T. Edmondson. New York: John Wiley & Sons, Inc. Pp. 917-940; 86 f.

Muttkowski, R. A. 1910. Catalogue of the Odonata of North America. Milwaukee Pub. Mus. Bull., 1(1):1-207.

Needham, James G., and Minter J. Westfall, Jr. 1955. A manual of the dragonflies of North America (Anisoptera). Los Angeles: University of California Press. xii+615 pp., frontis. +341 f.

Needham, James G., and Hortense B. Heywood. 1929. A handbook of the dragonflies of North America. Springfield, Ill.: Charles C. Thomas, Publisher. viii+378 pp.; illus.

Pennak, Robert W. 1953. Fresh-water invertebrates of the United States. New York: The Ronald Press Company. ix+769 pp., 470 f.

Ris, F. 1909-1919. Collections zoologiques du Baron Edm. de Selys Longchamps. Bruxelles: Hayez, Impr. des Academies. Fasc. IX-XVI, Libellulinen 4-8. 1278 pp., 692 f., 8 col. pl.

Smith, Ray F., and A. Earl Pritchard. 1956. Odonata. In: Aquatic insects of California, ed. by Robert L. Usinger. Berkeley, Calif.: University of California Press. Pp. 106-153; 92 f.

Tillyard, R. J. 1917. The biology of dragonflies. Cambridge: The University Press. xii+396 pp., 188 f., 4 pl.

Walker, Edmund M. 1953. The Odonata of Canada and Alaska; Vol. 1; general, the Zygoptera—damselflies. Toronto: University of Toronto Press. xi+292 pp., 42 pl.

Walker, Edmund M. 1958. The Odonata of Canada and Alaska; Vol. 2. The Anisoptera—four families. Toronto: University of Toronto Press. xi+318 pp., 64 pl.

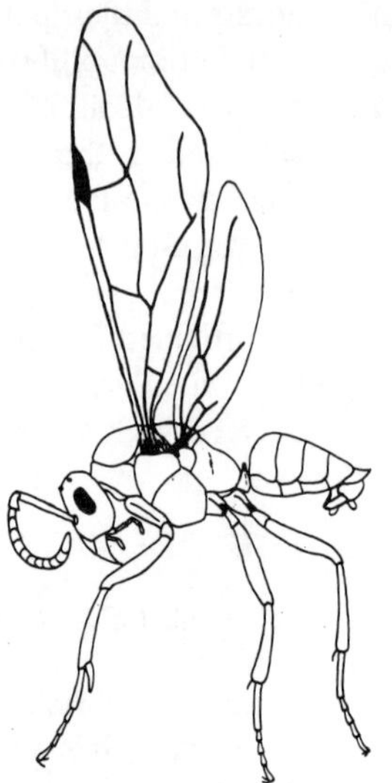

9

Order Orthoptera[1]: Grasshoppers, Katydids, Crickets, Cockroaches, Mantids, and Walking Sticks

The order Orthoptera contains a great many large and well-known insects. Most of the Orthoptera are plant feeders, and some are very destructive to vegetation; a few are predaceous, and a few are somewhat omnivorous in food habits.

The Orthoptera may be winged or wingless, and the winged forms usually have four wings. The front wings are generally long and narrow, many-veined, and somewhat thickened, and are usually referred to as tegmina (singular, tegmen); in the family Tetrígidae the front wings are reduced to small scalelike structures. The hind wings are membranous, broad, many-veined, and when at rest, are usually folded fanwise beneath the front wings. The body is elongate, and the cerci are usually well developed. Many species have a long ovipositor, often as long as the body. The mouth parts are of the chewing type, and the metamorphosis is simple.

SOUND PRODUCTION IN THE ORTHOPTERA

A great many types of insects "sing," but some of the best known insect songsters (grasshoppers and crickets) are in the order Orthoptera. The songs of these insects are produced chiefly by stridulation; that is, by rubbing one body part against another. The singing Orthoptera usually possess auditory organs—oval eardrums or tympana, located on the sides of the first abdominal segment (short-horned grasshoppers) or at the base of the front tibiae (long-horned grasshoppers and crickets; Figure 9-4 C, *tym*). These tympana are relatively insensitive to changes in pitch, but are capable of responding to rapid and abrupt changes in intensity. The songs of grasshoppers and crickets play an important role in their be-

[1] Orthoptera: *ortho,* straight; *ptera,* wings.

havior, and the songs of different species are usually different; the significant differences are in rhythm.

The crickets (Grýllidae) and long-horned grasshoppers (Tettigonìidae) produce their songs by rubbing a sharp edge (the scraper) at the base of one front wing along a filelike ridge (the file) on the ventral side of the other front wing (Figure 9-2 B-D). The bases of the front wings at rest lie one above the other; the left one is usually uppermost in the long-horned grasshoppers, and the right is usually uppermost in the crickets. Both front wings possess a file and scraper, but the file is usually longer in the upper wing and the scraper is better developed in the lower wing. In the long-horned grasshoppers the lower (right) front wing usually contains more membranous area than the upper one. The file on the lower front wing and the scraper on the upper one are usually nonfunctional.

When the song is produced, the front wings are elevated (Figure 9-1) and moved back and forth; generally, only the closing stroke of the wings produces a sound. The sound produced by a single stroke of the front wings is called a pulse; each pulse is composed of a number of individual tooth strikes of the scraper on the file. The pulse rate in a given insect varies with temperature, being faster at higher temperatures; in different species it varies from 4 or 5 per second to over 200 per second.

The songs of different species differ in the character of the pulses, the pulse rate, and in the way the pulses are grouped. The pulses of crickets are relatively musical; that is, they can usually be assigned a definite pitch (the pitch in cycles per second, which varies in different crickets from 1500 to 10,000, corresponds to the tooth strike rate); those of the long-horned grasshoppers (Figure 9-2 A) are more noiselike (that is, they contain a wide band of frequencies), clicking, or lisping, and cannot be assigned a definite pitch. The principal frequencies in the songs of some Orthoptera are quite high, between 10,000 and 20,000 cycles per second, and may be nearly or quite inaudible to some people. The pulses may be delivered at a regular rate for a considerable period, producing a more or less prolonged trill or buzz (some tree crickets and cone-headed grasshoppers); the pulses may be delivered in short bursts, a second or less in length, separated by silent intervals of a second or more (some tree crickets); the pulses may be delivered in short series of a few pulses each, producing chirps (most field crickets; see Figure 9-3, the calling songs); the pulses may be delivered in regularly alternating series of fast and slow pulses (meadow grasshoppers), or the pulse rhythm may be more complex.

The band-winged grasshoppers (Oedipodìnae) usually make their noises by snapping their hind wings in flight; the noises so produced are crackling or buzzing. The slant-faced grasshoppers (Acridìnae), and occasionally also the band-winged grasshoppers, "sing" by rubbing the hind legs

Fig. 9-1. A field cricket singing (note the elevated position of the front wings). (Courtesy of R. D. Alexander.)

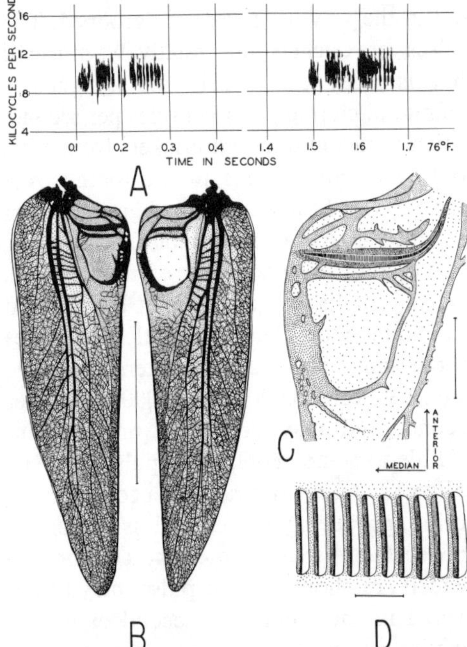

Fig. 9-2. Song and song-producing structures of the big green pine-tree katydid, *Hubbéllia margínifera* (Walker) (Tettigonìidae, Tettigoniìnae). A, an audiospectrograph of two pulses of the song (4 kilocycles per second is approximately the pitch of the top note of a piano); B, front wings, dorsal view (line = 10 mm); C, ventral surface of basal portion of the left front wing showing the file (line = 1 mm); D, several teeth of the file (line = 0.1 mm). (Courtesy of R. D. Alexander.)

against the front wings, producing a soft rasping sound; the hind femora of these insects are usually provided with a series of short peglike structures that function something like a file.

The females of a few Orthoptera may make a few soft noises, but most of the singing is done by the males. The short-horned grasshoppers usually move about while singing; the crickets and long-horned grasshoppers are usually stationary. Many Orthoptera, particularly some of the crickets and long-horned grasshoppers, are capable of producing two or more different types of songs (Figure 9-3); each type is produced under certain circumstances, and each produces a characteristic reaction by other individuals. Song (the "calling" song, Figure 9-3) in insects appears to function primarily in getting the two sexes together, but some sounds are characteristically produced in response to disturbance ("alarm" or "distress" sounds), and some are produced in the presence of another male ("warning", "intimidation", or "fighting" sounds; see Figure 9-3).

Some of the Orthoptera (for example, most katydids) sing only at night; many (for example, most crickets) sing both day and night; a few (for example, band-winged grasshoppers) sing only in the daytime. Many species (for example, some of the cone-headed grasshoppers and tree crickets) often "chorus"; that is, two or more individuals sing simultaneously, their pulses synchronized, or their chirps or phrases alternating and producing a pulsating sound.

CLASSIFICATION OF THE ORTHOPTERA

The insects here included in the order Orthoptera are by some authorities divided into five orders, with the name Orthoptera being retained for the groups in the suborders Caelífera and Ensífera, and each of the four remaining families being placed in an order by itself.

In the following outline of the Orthoptera an attempt has been made to show the various taxonomic arrangements that have been used in this order, and alternate names or spellings are given in parentheses.

Suborder Caelífera
- Tridactýlidae (Grýllidae in part, Gryllotálpidae in part)—pygmy mole crickets
- Tetrígidae (Acrydìidae; Acrídidae in part)—pygmy grasshoppers or grouse locusts
- Acrídidae (Locústidae)—short-horned grasshoppers
  - Cyrtacánthacridìnae (Cyrtacánthacrìnae, Romaleìnae, Locustìnae)—spur-throated grasshoppers

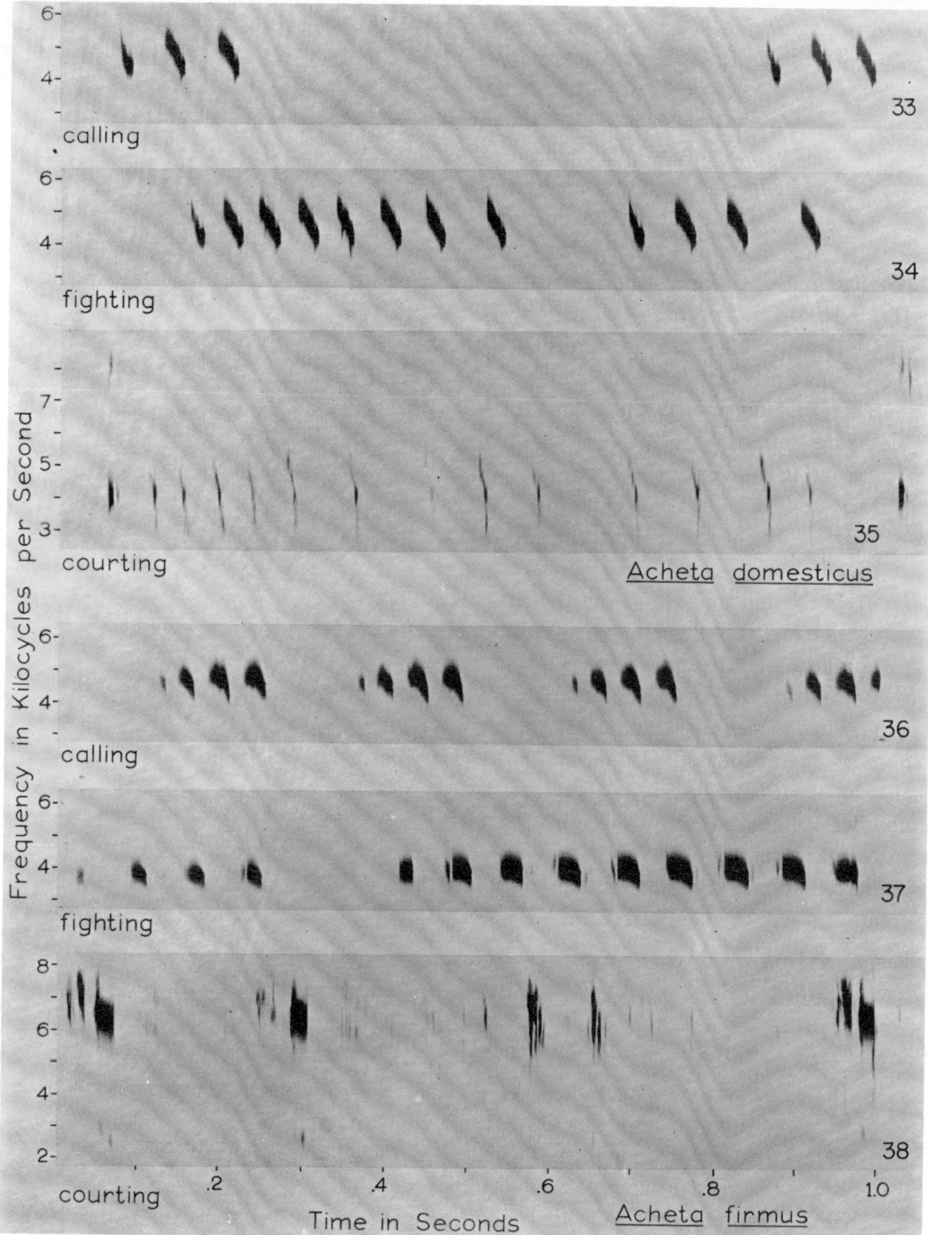

Fig. 9-3. Audiospectrographs of the calling, fighting, and courting songs of the house cricket (the three upper graphs) and the beach cricket (now *Grýllus fírmus* Scudder) (the three lower graphs). (Courtesy of R. D. Alexander.)

Acridìnae (Truxalìnae, Tryxalìnae)—slant-faced grasshoppers

Oedipodìnae—band-winged grasshoppers

Eumastácidae (Acrídidae in part)—wingless short-horned grasshoppers

Tanaocéridae (Eumastácidae in part)—wingless short-horned grasshoppers

Suborder Ensífera

Tettigonìidae—long-horned grasshoppers

Phaneropterìnae—bush and round-headed katydids
Copiphorìnae—cone-headed grasshoppers
Pseudophyllìnae—true katydids
Listroscelìnae (Decticìnae in part)—listrosceline grasshoppers
Prophalangopsìnae—prophalangopsine grasshoppers
Conocephalìnae—meadow grasshoppers
Decticìnae—shield-backed grasshoppers
Tettigoniìnae—pine tree katydids
Gryllacrídidae (Gryllácridae; Stenopelmátidae in part, Tettigonìidae in part)—wingless long-horned grasshoppers
Gryllacridìnae (Gryllacrìnae)—leaf-rolling grasshoppers
Rhaphidophorìnae (Ceuthophilìnae)—cave or camel crickets
Stenopelmatìnae—Jerusalem, sand, or stone crickets
Grýllidae—crickets
Oecanthìnae—tree crickets
Eneopterìnae—bush crickets
Trigonidiìnae—sword-bearing or sword-tailed crickets
Mogoplistìnae—short-winged crickets
Myrmecophilìnae—ant-loving crickets
Nemobiìnae (Gryllìnae in part)—ground crickets
Gryllìnae—house and field crickets
Brachytrupìnae (Gryllìnae in part)—short-tailed crickets
Gryllotalpìnae (Gryllotálpidae)—mole crickets
Suborder Phasmatòdea (Phasmòidea, Phasmòdea, Phásmida)—stick and leaf insects
Phásmidae (Phasmátidae)—walking sticks
Suborder Mantòdea (Mantòidea)—mantids
Mántidae—mantids
Suborder Blattòdea (Blattòidea, Blattària, Blattàriae)—cockroaches or roaches
Bláttidae—cockroaches or roaches
Suborder Grylloblattòdea (Notóptera)
Gryllobláttidae—grylloblattids

KEY TO THE FAMILIES OF ORTHOPTERA

1. Hind femora more or less enlarged (Figures 9-1, 9-6 to 9-9, 9-11 to 9-17); tarsi with 4 or fewer segments; usually jumping insects 2

1′. Hind femora not enlarged (Figures 9-18 to 9-20); tarsi nearly always 5-segmented; running or walking insects 10

2(1). Front legs enlarged and fitted for digging (Figure 9-17); tarsi with 3 or fewer segments 3

2′. Front legs not enlarged and fitted for digging (Figures 9-1, 9-6 to 9-9, 9-11 to 9-16), or if somewhat enlarged (Stenopelmatìnae), then tarsi are 4-segmented; tarsi 2- to 4-segmented 4

3(2). Front and middle tarsi 2-segmented, hind tarsi 1-segmented or absent; antennae 11-segmented; 3 small ocelli; hind femora greatly enlarged; body not pubescent; small insects, less than 10 mm in length........ .... **Tridactýlidae** p. 103

3′. Tarsi 3-segmented; antennae with more than 11 segments; 2 large ocelli;

hind femora not greatly enlarged; body pubescent or hairy; larger insects, 18 mm or more in length (Figure 9-17, Gryllotalpìnae)... **Grýllidae** p. 110

4(2′). Antennae usually short, seldom more than half as long as body (Figures 9-6 to 9-9); auditory organs (tympana), if present, on sides of first abdominal segment; hind tarsi 3-segmented, front and middle tarsi 2- or

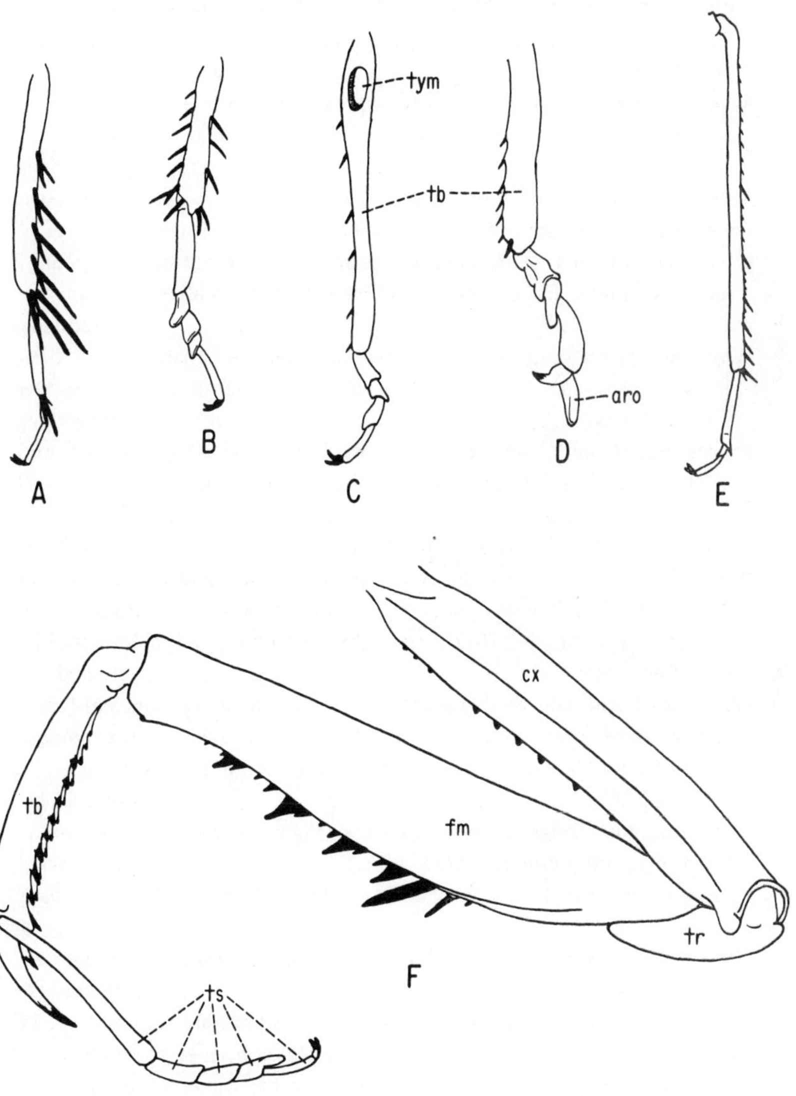

Fig. 9-4. Leg structure in Orthoptera; A-E, tibiae and tarsi; F, front leg. A, *Nemòbius* (Nemobiìnae, Grýllidae), hind leg; B, *Periplanèta* (Bláttidae), front leg; C, *Scuddèria* (Phaneropterìnae, Tettigonìidae), front leg; D, *Schistocérca* (Cyrtacánthacridìnae, Acrídidae), front leg; E, *Oecánthus* (Oecanthìnae, Grýllidae), hind leg; F, *Tenódera* (Mántidae), front leg; *aro*, arolium; *cx*, coxa; *fm*, femur; *tb*, tibia; *tr*, trochanter; *ts*, tarsus; *tym*, tympanum.

3-segmented; ovipositor short 5

4′. Antennae long, usually as long as body or longer (Figures 9-1, 9-11 to 9-16); auditory organs, if present, at base of front tibiae (Figure 9-4 C, *tym*); tarsi 3- or 4-segmented; ovipositor usually elongate 8

5(4). Pronotum prolonged backward over abdomen, and tapering posteriorly (Figure 9-6); front wings vestigial; no arolia; front and middle tarsi 2-segmented, hind tarsi 3-segmented . . . . **Tetrígidae** p. 103

5′. Pronotum not prolonged backward over abdomen (Figures 9-7 to 9-9); front wings usually well developed; arolia present (Figure 9-4 D); all tarsi 3-segmented 6

6(5′). Antennae shorter than front femora; wings absent; 8 to 19 mm in length; occurring in the chaparral country of southwestern United States. . . . . **Eumastácidae** p. 106

6′. Antennae longer than front femora; wings nearly always present; size variable, but usually over 15 mm in length; widely distributed 7

7(6′). Wings and tympana nearly always present; antennae not unusually long; males without a file on third abdominal tergum; widely distributed. . . . . **Acrídidae** p. 103

7′. Wings and tympana absent; antennae very long—in males longer than body; males with a file on third abdominal tergum; southwestern United States. . . . . **Tanaocéridae** p. 106

8(4′). At least middle tarsi, and usually all tarsi, 4-segmented (Figures 9-4 C and 9-10 E); ocelli usually present; ovipositor sword-shaped 9

8′. All tarsi 3-segmented (Figures 9-4 A, E); ocelli present or absent; ovipositor usually cylindrical or needle-shaped. . . . . **Grýllidae** p. 110

9(8). Wings always present (though sometimes very small), and with fewer than 8 principal longitudinal veins; males with stridulatory structures on front wings (Figure 9-2 B-D); front tibiae with tympana; color variable, but often green . . . . **Tettigoniidae** p. 106

9′. Wings usually absent, or if present, they have 8 or more principal longitudinal veins, and males lack stridulatory structures on front wings; front tibiae with or without tympana; color usually gray or brown. . . . . **Gryllacrídidae** p. 110

10(1′). Prothorax much longer than mesothorax (Figure 9-18); front legs modified for grasping prey (Figure 9-4 F). . . . . **Mántidae** p. 113

10′. Prothorax not greatly lengthened; front legs not modified for grasping prey 11

11(10′). Cerci 1-segmented; body very long and slender; wings usually lacking (Figure 9-19) . . . . **Phásmidae** p. 114

11′. Cerci with 8 or more segments; body and wings variable 12

12(11′). Body flattened and oval, the head more or less concealed from above by pronotum (Figure 9-20); ocelli usually present; wings usually present, though sometimes short; a common and widely distributed group. . . . . **Bláttidae** p. 114

12′. Body elongate and cylindrical, the head not concealed from above by pronotum; ocelli and wings absent; California and western Canada. . . . . **Grylloblàttidae** p. 116

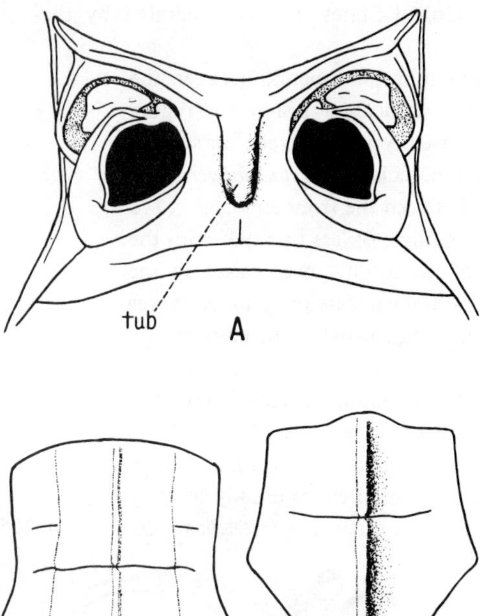

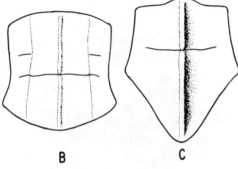

Fig. 9-5. Characters of Acrídidae. A, prothorax of *Melánoplus* (Cyrtacánthacridìnae), ventral view; B, pronotum of *Sýrbula* (Acridìnae); C, pronotum of *Chortóphaga* (Oedipodìnae). *tub*, prosternal tubercle.

FAMILY **Tridactýlidae**—Pygmy Mole Crickets: These insects are less than 10 millimeters in length, and can jump actively. They are burrowing, but are often found jumping about on the surface of the ground; they occur principally in moist sandy situations along the shores of streams and lakes. The males do not sing.

FAMILY **Tetrígidae**—Pygmy Grasshoppers or Grouse Locusts: The pygmy grasshoppers may be recognized by the characteristic pronotum, which extends backward over the abdomen and is narrowed posteriorly (Figure 9-6). Most species are between ½ and ¾ inch in length; the females are usually larger and heavier-bodied than the males. These are among the few grasshoppers that winter as adults, and the adults are most often encountered in the spring and early summer. The pygmy grasshoppers are not of very much economic importance.

FAMILY **Acrídidae**—Short-Horned Grasshoppers: To this family belong most of the grasshoppers that are so common in meadows and along roadsides from midsummer until fall. The antennae are usually much shorter than the body, the auditory organs are located on the sides of the first abdominal segment, the tarsi are 3-segmented, and the ovipositor is short. The males sing (during the day), either by rubbing the inner surface of the hind femur against the lower edge of the front wing (spur-throated and slant-faced grasshoppers) or by snapping the hind wings in flight (band-winged grasshoppers). In the two former groups, there is usually a row of small peglike spines on the inner surface of the hind femora, and the song produced is a low buzzing sound; in the latter group, the song is a sort of crackling sound.

The short-horned grasshoppers are plant feeders and are often very destructive to vegetation. Most species pass the winter in the egg stage, the eggs being laid in the ground; a few overwinter as nymphs, and a very few overwinter as adults.

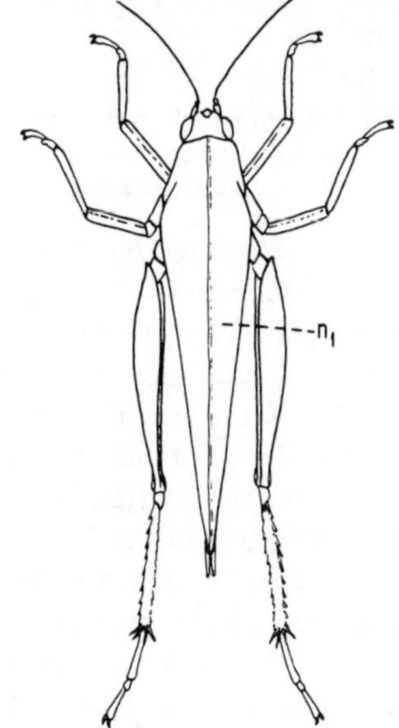

Fig. 9-6. A pygmy grasshopper, *Tettigídea lateràlis* (Say); $3\frac{1}{2}\times$. n_1, pronotum.

The three subfamilies of Acrídidae in the United States may be separated by the following key:

1. Prosternum with a conical or cylindrical spine or tubercle between the front legs (Figure 9-5 A); face usually vertical or nearly so (Figure 9-7 B, C); hind wings, when present, usually not colored; dorsum of pronotum flat, not strongly keeled or tuberculate. . *Cyrtacánthacridìnae* p. 104
1′. Prosternum without a spine or tubercle between the front legs 2
2(1′). Face in profile usually oblique, making an angle of less than 90° with the vertex (Figure 9-8); median carina of pronotum never raised in the form of a crest; caudal margin of pronotum truncate or rounded, never angulate mesally (Figure 9-5 B); hind wings usually not colored. . . . . *Acridìnae* p. 105
2′. Face in profile vertical or nearly so, making a rounded angle of about 90° with the vertex; median carina of pronotum often elevated in the form of a crest; caudal margin of pronotum produced backward and usually with an acute angle mesally (Figure 9-5 C); hind wings usually brightly colored (Figure 9-9) . . . . *Oedipodìnae* p. 105

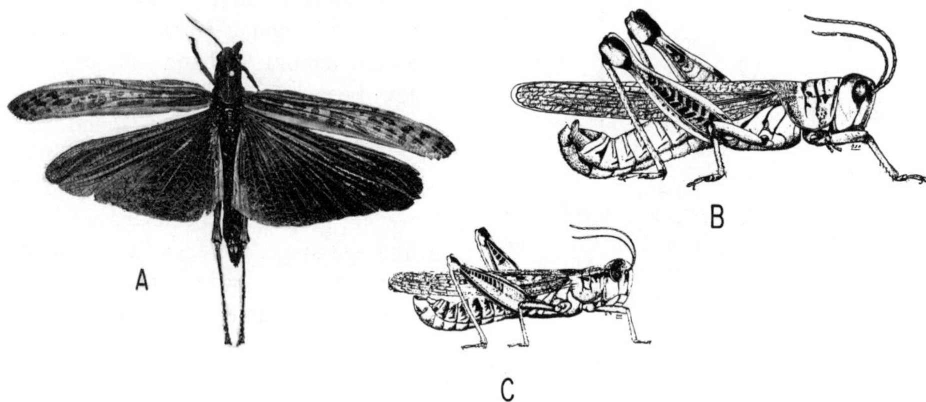

Fig. 9-7. Spur-throated grasshoppers. A, *Schistocérca americàna* (Drury), with wings outspread; B, *Melánoplus differentiàlis* (Thomas); C, *Melánoplus mexicànus* (Saussure). (A, courtesy of the Ohio Agricultural Experiment Station; B and C, courtesy of USDA.)

—Subfamily *Cyrtacanthacridìnae*—Spur-Throated Grasshoppers— The most injurious grasshoppers belong to this group; some of them have caused enormous damage in various parts of the world. The lubberly grasshoppers, *Romàlea micróptera* (Beauvais) in the southern states, and *Brachýstola mágna* (Girard) in the West, are very large insects, 2 to 2½ inches in length; the hind wings are bright red with a black border in *R. micróptera,* and pinkish and much reduced in size in *B. mágna.* The other species in this subfamily have the hind wings clear. The slender grasshopper, *Leptýsma marginicóllis* (Serville), which is more common in the southern states, has the face very oblique, much as in some of the slant-faced grasshoppers. The species in the genus *Schistocérca* are large and often brightly patterned (Figure 9-7 A). The largest genus in this group is *Melánoplus*; here belong our most common grasshoppers and the ones that are the most destructive.

Some species of spur-throated grasshoppers occasionally increase to tremendous numbers and migrate considerable distances, causing damage of catastrophic proportions. The migrating hordes of these in-

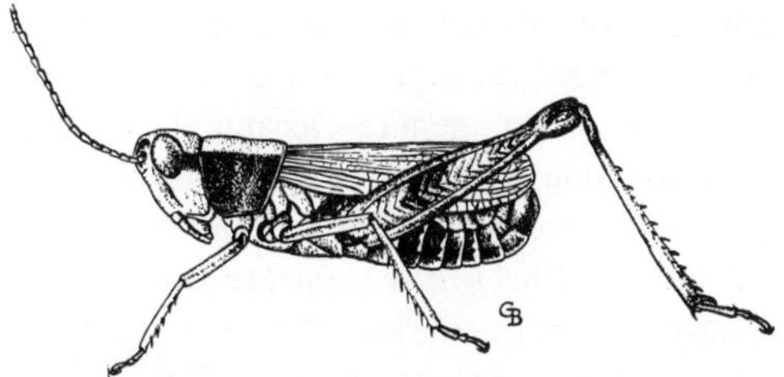

Fig. 9-8. A slant-faced grasshopper, *Chloeálthis conspérsa* Harris. (Courtesy of Institut de Biologie générale, Université de Montréal.)

sects may contain millions upon millions of individuals, and literally darken the sky. From 1874 to 1877 great swarms of migratory grasshoppers appeared in the plains east of the Rocky Mountains and migrated to the Mississippi valley and to Texas, destroying crops wherever they stopped in their flight. One migrating swarm during this period was estimated to contain 124 billion insects. This migratory behavior follows a tremendous build-up in numbers, resulting from a combination of favorable environmental conditions; when the numbers decrease, the insects remain sedentary.

Most of the damage to crops in this country by spur-throated grasshoppers is caused by four species of *Melánoplus,* the lesser migratory grasshopper, *M. mexicànus* (Saussure) (Figure 9-7 C), the differential grasshopper, *M. differentiàlis* (Thomas) (Figure 9-7 B), the two-striped grasshopper, *M. bivittàtus* (Say), and the red-legged grasshopper, *M. fèmur-rùbrum* (DeGeer).

—Subfamily *Acridìnae*—Slant-Faced Grasshoppers— These grasshoppers can be most readily distinguished from the band-wings (Oedipodìnae) by the form of the pronotum (Figure 9-5); in the Acridìnae the median carina is low, and the posterior margin is broadly rounded or truncate; in the Oedipodìnae the median carina is usually in the form of a crest, and the posterior margin is produced backward and more or less pointed. The Acridìnae usually have the face slanting and the hind wings clear. The Acridìnae are not so abundant as the other groups in this family and are most likely to be found along the borders of marshes, in wet meadows, and in similar environment. They are rarely numerous enough to do much damage to vegetation.

—Subfamily *Oedipodìnae*—Band-Winged Grasshoppers— These insects have the hind wings brightly colored, and they generally frequent areas of sparse vegetation. They often alight on bare ground with the hind

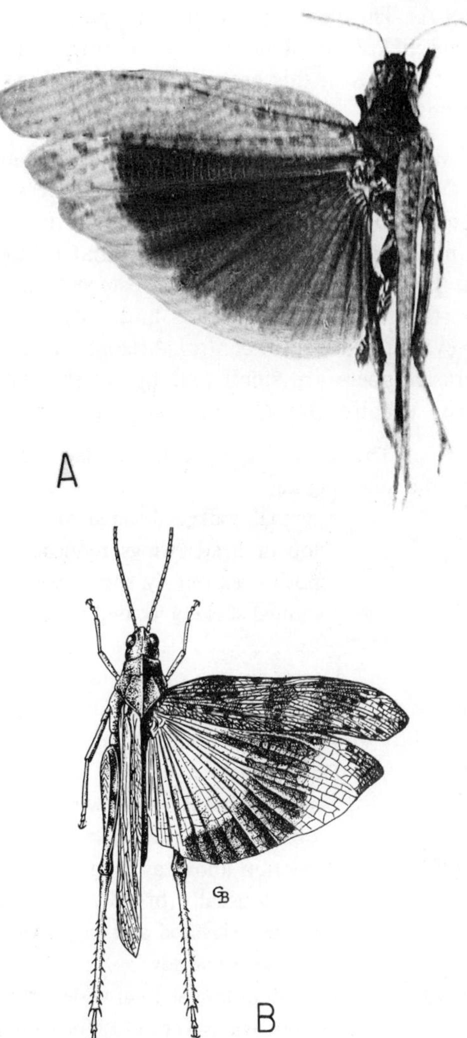

Fig. 9-9. Band-winged grasshoppers. A, *Dissosteìra carolìna* (Linn.); B, *Spharágenon bólli* Scudder. (B, courtesy of Institut de Biologie générale, Université de Montréal.)

wings concealed and the front wings blending with the background. These insects are quite conspicuous in flight, owing to the bright colors of the hind wings and the crackling sound made by the wings. The Oedipodìnae are the only short-horned grasshoppers that stridulate while flying. One of the more common species in this group is the Carolina grasshopper, *Dissosteìra carolìna* (Linn.), in which the hind wings are black with a pale border (Figure 9-9 A). The clear-winged grasshopper, *Cámnula pellùcida* (Scudder), is an important pest species in this group; it has clear hind wings.

FAMILIES **Eumastácidae** AND **Tanaocéridae**—Wingless Short-Horned Grasshoppers: These tropical groups are represented in the United States by several species that occur in the mountains of the southwestern states, north to San Francisco and southern Nevada, and east to central Arizona. These grasshoppers are small and brownish, and are usually found on the uppermost branches of bushes in chaparral country; they are excellent jumpers, and are difficult to catch. Two genera assigned to the Eumastácidae by some authorities, *Tanaócerus* and *Mohavácris,* are placed by Rehn and Grant (1961) in a separate family, the Tanaocéridae; the males of these two genera have very long antennae and a filelike stridulatory area on the third abdominal tergum.

FAMILY **Tettigonìidae**—Long-Horned Grasshoppers and Katydids: The members of this family can usually be recognized by the long hairlike antennae, the 4-segmented tarsi, the auditory organs (when present) located at the base of the front tibiae, and the laterally flattened bladelike ovipositor. Most species have well-developed stridulating organs and are noted songsters; each species has a characteristic song. The winter is usually passed in the egg stage, and in many species the eggs are inserted into plant tissues. Most species are plant feeders, but a few prey on other insects.

The subfamilies of Tettigonìidae occurring in the United States may be separated by the following key:

1. Antennal sockets located about halfway between epistomal suture and top of head; wings reduced, broad in male, minute in female; ovipositor extremely short; western United States. . . . *Prophalangopsìnae* p. 109

1′. Antennal sockets located near top of head; wings and ovipositor variable 2

2(1′). Dorsal surface of first tarsal segment laterally grooved (Figure 9-10 E); prosternal spines usually present (Figure 9-10 D); front wings about as long as or longer than hind wings 3

2′. Dorsal surface of first tarsal segment smoothly rounded; prosternal spines absent; hind wings longer than front wings, or front wings obliquely truncate at apex. . . . . *Phaneropterìnae* p. 108

3(2). Pronotum about as long as wide, and with 2 transverse grooves; front wings usually broadly oval and convex; mesal margins of antennal sockets elevated and ridgelike, and extending nearly or quite to dorsal surface of vertex. . . . . *Pseudophyllìnae* p. 108

3′. Pronotum longer than wide, and with only 1 transverse groove or none; front wings variable, but usually not broadly oval and convex; mesal margins of antennal sockets not particularly ridgelike, and rarely approaching dorsal part of vertex 4

4(3′). Anterior portion of vertex conical, sometimes acuminate, and extending well beyond basal antennal segment (Figure 9-10 C, *ver*). . *Copiphorìnae* p. 108

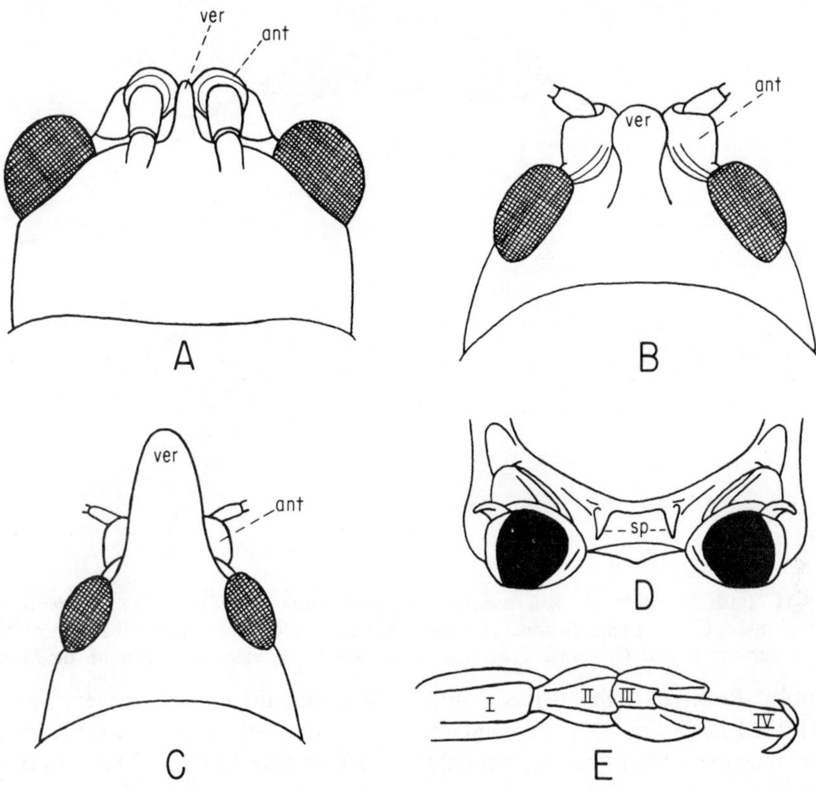

Fig. 9-10. Characters of Tettigonìidae. A, head of *Réhnia* (Listroscelìnae), dorsal view; B, head of *Orchélium* (Conocephalìnae), dorsal view; C, head of *Neoconocéphalus* (Copiphorìnae), dorsal view; D, prothorax of *Orchélimum* (Conocephalìnae), ventral view; E, hind tarsus of *Neoconocéphalus* (Copiphorìnae), dorsal view. *ant,* base of antenna; *sp,* prosternal spine; *ver,* vertex; I-IV, tarsal segments.

4′. Anterior portion of vertex usually not conical or acuminate and does not extend beyond basal antennal segment (Figure 9-10 A, B, *ver*)......5

5(4′). Anterior portion of vertex laterally compressed, much less than half as wide as basal antennal segment (Figure 9-10 A, *ver*); southwestern United States ....*Listroscelinae* p. 108

5′. Anterior portion of vertex variable, but always more than half as wide as basal antennal segment; widely distributed 6

6(5′). One or more spines on dorsal surface of front tibiae 7

6′. No spines on dorsal surface of front tibiae..............*Conocephalìnae* p. 109

7(6). Pronotum extending back to abdomen (except in a few long-winged forms); wings usually greatly reduced; front wings usually gray, brown, or spotted; prosternal spines present or absent; widely distributed.... .... *Decticìnae* p. 109

7′. Pronotum never extending back to abdomen; wings always well developed; front wings green, rarely spotted with brown; prosternal spines present; southeastern United States .... *Tettigoniìnae* p. 109

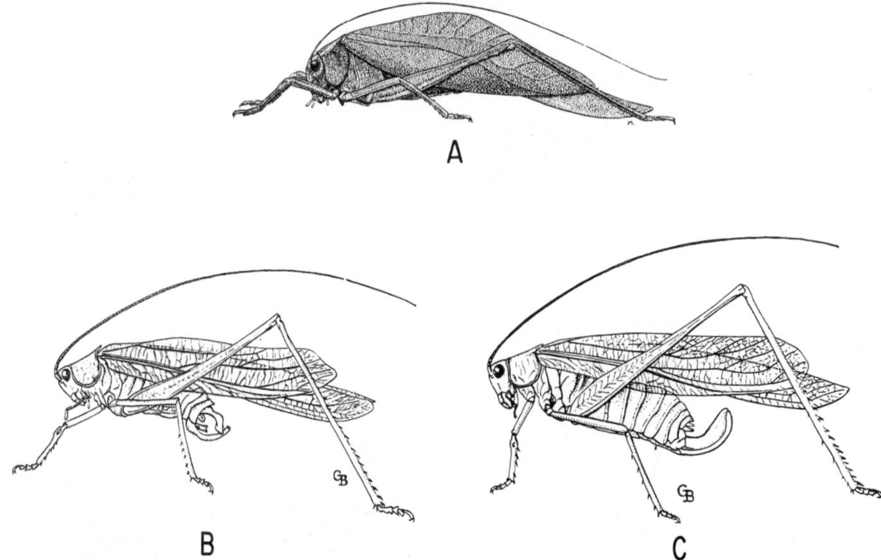

Fig. 9-11. Bush katydids. A, *Microcéntrum rhombifòlium* (Saussure); B, *Scuddèria furcàta* Brunner, male; C, *S, furcàta* Brunner, female. (A, courtesy of Hebard and the Illinois Natural History Survey; B and C, courtesy of Institut de Biologie générale, Université de Montréal.)

—Subfamily *Phaneropterìnae*—Bush and Round-Headed Katydids— The members of this and the next subfamily are commonly called katydids and are well known for their songs, which are usually heard in the evening and at night. The katydids belonging to this subfamily can be recognized by the absence of spines on the prosternum. The bush katydids (*Scuddèria* and *Microcéntrum,* Figure 9-11 A) have the wings rather long and narrow, and the vertex is narrowed anteriorly; the round-headed katydids (*Amblycòrypha*) have the wings elongate-oval in shape and have the vertex broad and rounded anteriorly. The katydids are normally green, but pink forms occasionally occur, especially in *Amblycòrypha*; these color forms are not distinct species.

—Subfamily *Copiphorìnae*—Cone-Headed Grasshoppers— The cone-heads are long-bodied grasshoppers which have the head conical (Figure 9-12) and the ovipositor long and swordlike. They occur in two color phases, green and brown. They are generally found in high grass or weeds and are rather sluggish; their jaws are very strong, and a person handling these insects carelessly may receive a healthy nip. The eastern species in this group belong to the genus *Neoconocéphalus.*

—Subfamily *Pseudophyllinae*—True Katydids— These katydids are principally arboreal in habit, living in the foliage of trees and shrubs. The northern true katydid, *Pterophýlla caméllifòlia* (Fabricius), is the insect whose "katy did, katy didn't" song is so commonly heard on summer evenings in the Northeast; its song contains from two to five pulses. The southern representatives of this katydid sing a somewhat longer and faster song, containing up to about a dozen pulses.

—Subfamily *Listroscelìnae*— These grasshoppers are very similar to the *Decticìnae,* and the United States genera (*Neobarréttia* and *Réhnia*) were formerly placed in the Decticìnae. This subfamily is principally tropical in distribution, and is represented in this country by a few species in the South Central States, from Texas north to Kansas.

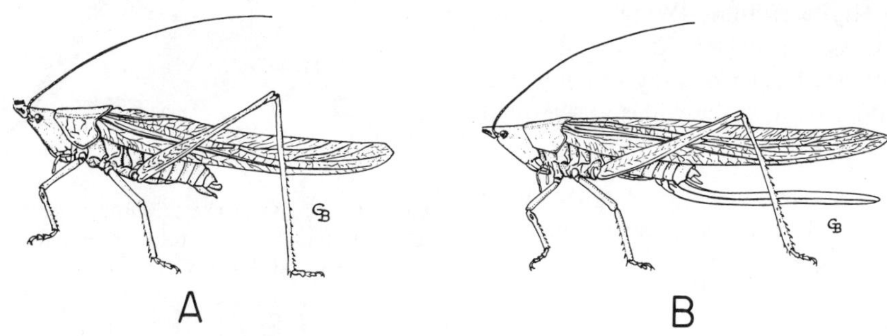

Fig. 9-12. A cone-headed grasshopper, *Neoconocéphalus énsiger* (Harris); A, male; B, female. (Courtesy of Institut de Biologie générale, Université de Montréal.)

—Subfamily *Prophalangopsìnae*— This subfamily is represented in the United States by a single genus, *Cyphodérris,* which occurs in the West.

—Subfamily *Conocephalìnae* — Meadow Grasshoppers— These are small to medium-sized, slender bodied, usually greenish grasshoppers (Figure 9-13) that are found principally in wet grassy meadows and along the margins of ponds and streams. Two genera are common in the eastern United States, *Orchélimum* (usually over 18 millimeters in length) and *Conocéphalus* (usually less than 17 millimeters in length).

—Subfamily *Decticìnae* — Shield-Backed Grasshoppers— These insects are brownish to black, short-winged, usually an inch or more in length, and have the pronotum extending back to the abdomen; most species are cricketlike in appearance. The eastern species, most of which belong to the genus *Atlánticus,* occur in dry upland woods. The majority of the Decticìnae occur in the West, where they may occur in fields or woods. Some of the western species often do serious damage to field crops; the Mormon cricket, *Ánabrus símplex* Haldeman, is a serious pest in the Great Plains states, and the coulee cricket, *Peránabrus scabricóllis* (Thomas), often does considerable damage in the arid regions of the Pacific Northwest. The work of gulls in checking an outbreak of the Mormon crickets in Utah is now commemorated by a monument to the gull in Salt Lake City.

—Subfamily *Tettigoniìnae*— This group includes a single United States species, *Hubbéllia marginífera* (Walker), the big green pine-tree katydid, which occurs in the southeastern states. The song and song-producing structures of this katydid are illustrated in Figure 9-2.

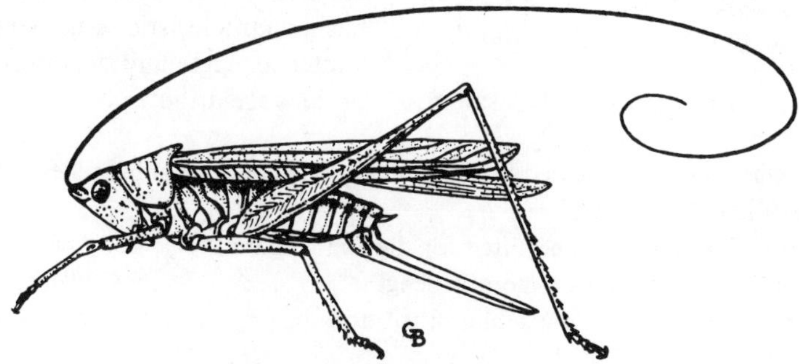

Fig. 9-13. A meadow grasshopper, *Conocéphalus fasciàtus* (DeGeer), female. (Courtesy of Institut de Biologie générale, Université de Montréal).

FAMILY **Gryllacrídidae**—Wingless Long-Horned Grasshoppers: The members of this family are brown or gray in color and lack auditory organs; the wings are vestigal or completely lacking.

The three subfamilies of Gryllacrídidae occurring in the United States may be separated by the following key:

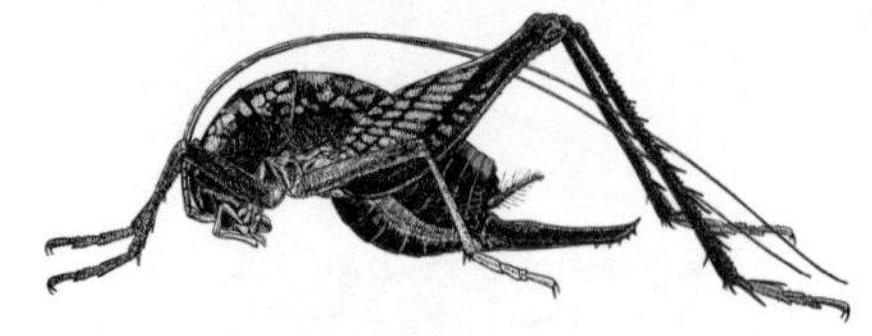

Fig. 9-14. A cave cricket, *Ceuthóphilus maculàtus* (Harris), female. (Courtesy of Hebard and the Illinois Natural History Survey.)

1.	Antennae at base contiguous or nearly so............ *Rhaphidophorìnae*	p. 110
1′.	Antennae at base separated by a distance equal to or greater than the length of the first antennal segment................................ 2	
2(1′).	Tarsi lobed and more or less flattened dorsoventrally; hind femora extending beyond apex of abdomen; eastern United States. . *Gryllacridìnae*	p. 110
2′.	Tarsi not lobed, and more or less flattened laterally; hind femora not extending beyond apex of abdomen; western United States.......... .... *Stenopelmatìnae*	p. 110

—Subfamily *Gryllacridìnae*—Leaf-Rolling Grasshoppers— This group is represented in the East by a single species, *Camptonòtus carolinénsis* (Gertstaecker), which seldom occurs north of New Jersey and Indiana. This insect is about 15 millimeters in length and nests in a leaf that it rolls up and ties with silk; it is nocturnal in habit, and feeds chiefly on aphids.

—Subfamily *Rhaphidophorìnae*—Cave or Camel Crickets— These insects are brownish and rather humpbacked in appearance (Figure 9-14), and are found in caves, hollow trees, under logs and stones, and in other dark moist places. The antennae are often extremely long. Most of the species in this group belong to the genus *Ceuthóphilus*.

—Subfamily *Stenopelmatìnae*—Jerusalem, Sand, or Stone Crickets—This group occurs in the West, principally along the Pacific Coast. The sand crickets are large brown insects with big heads, and they usually occur under stones in loose soil.

FAMILY **Grýllidae**—Crickets: The crickets resemble the long-horned grasshoppers in having long tapering antennae, stridulating organs on the front wings of the male, and the auditory organs on the front tibiae, but differ from them in having not more than three tarsal segments, the ovipositor needle-like or cylindrical rather than flattened, and the front wings bent down rather sharply at the sides of the body. Many of these insects are well-known songsters, and each species has a characteristic song. Most species over-winter as eggs, laid generally in the ground or in vegetation.

The Gryllidae are represented in the United States by nine subfamilies, which may be separated by the following key:

1.	Front legs enlarged and fitted for digging (Figure 9-17); body pubescent or hairy; 18 mm or more in length.................. *Gryllotalpìnae*	p. 113
1′.	Front legs not enlarged and fitted for digging; pubescence and size variable 2	
2(1′).	Second tarsal segment heart-shaped and flattened dorsoventrally......3	
2′.	Second tarsal segment small and flattened laterally (Figure 9-4 A, E)....4	

3(2). Hind tibiae with teeth between the spines; ovipositor cylindrical and nearly straight .... *Eneopterinae* p. 112

3′. Hind tibiae without teeth between the spines; ovipositor compressed and distinctly upcurved .... *Trigonidiinae* p. 112

4(2′). Hind femora very broad and oval; small, rounded, wingless insects living in ant nests .... *Myrmecophilinae* p. 112

4′. Hind femora more slender; usually large, elongate, free-living insects . . 5

5(4′). Wings vestigial or lacking; hind tibiae without spines but with 3 pairs of apical spurs; body covered with scales; southern United States...... .... *Mogoplistinae* p. 112

5′. Wings usually well developed; hind tibiae usually with 2 series of spines (Figure 9-4 A, E); body not covered with scales; widely distributed . . 6

6(5′). Ocelli present; head short, vertical (Figures 9-1, 9-16); hind tibiae without teeth between the spines (Figure 9-4 A); black or brown insects...... 7

6′. Ocelli absent; head elongate, horizontal (Figure 9-15); hind tibiae usually with minute teeth between the spines (Figure 9-4 E); usually pale-green insects .... *Oecanthinae* p. 111

7(6). Spines of hind tibiae long and movable (Figure 9-4 A); last segment of maxillary palpi at least twice as long as preceding segment; body usually less than 12 mm in length.............................. *Nemobiinae* p. 112

7′. Spines of hind tibiae stout and immovable; last segment of maxillary palpi only slightly longer than preceding segment; body usually over 14 mm in length 8

8(7′). Ocelli arranged in a nearly transverse row; ovipositor very short, often not visible; southeastern United States .... *Brachytrupinae* p. 113

8′. Ocelli arranged in an obtuse triangle; ovipositor at least half as long as hind femora; widely distributed......................... *Gryllinae* p. 112

—Subfamily *Oecanthìnae*—Tree Crickets—Most tree crickets are slender, whitish, or pale-green insects (Figure 9-15); all are excellent singers. Some species occur in trees and shrubs; others occur in weedy fields. The snowy tree cricket, *Oecánthus fúltoni* Walker, a shrub inhabitant, chirps; its chirping is at a very regular rate, which varies with temperature; 40 added to the number of its chirps in 15 seconds gives a good approximation of the temperature in degrees Fahrenheit. Most species of tree crickets deliver loud trills; some of the tree-inhabiting species have songs consisting of short bursts of pulses. Most of our tree crickets belong to the genus *Oecánthus*; the two-spotted tree cricket, *Neoxàbea bipunctàta* (DeGeer), differs from *Oecánthus* in lacking teeth on the hind tibiae, in having the hind wings much longer than the front wings, and in its buffy coloration. Tree crickets lay their eggs in bark or on stems (Figure 3-1 E), and often seriously damage twigs by their egg laying.

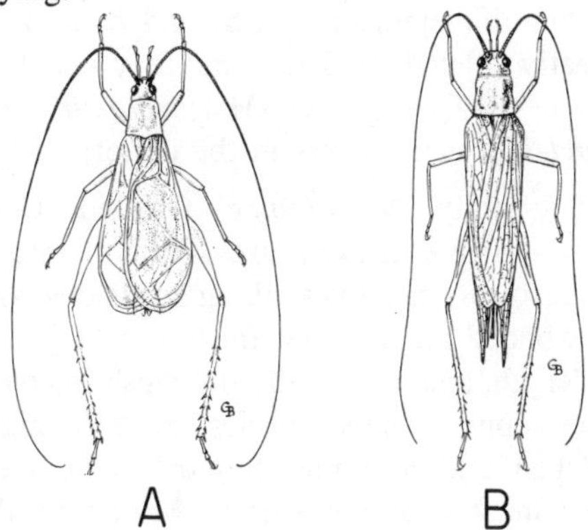

Fig. 9-15. A tree cricket, *Oecánthus quadrimaculàtus* Beutenmüller. A, male; B, female. (Courtesy of Institut de Biologie générale, Université de Montréal.)

—Subfamily *Eneopterìnae*—Bush Crickets — The crickets in this group are medium-sized, slender, and usually brownish in color; they are generally found in bushes or trees. The jumping bush cricket, *Orócharis saltàtor* Uhler, is a common eastern species.

—Subfamily *Trigonidiìnae*—Sword-Bearing Crickets— These small (4.0 to 8.5 millimeters in length) crickets are usually found on bushes or weeds near ponds or streams; they are fairly common, but are secretive and not often seen. Say's bush cricket, *Anáxipha exígua* (Say), is a common, brownish eastern species; the handsome bush cricket, *Phyllopálpus pulchéllus* (Uhler), another eastern species, is a pretty black and red insect.

—Subfamily *Mogoplistìnae*—Short-Winged Crickets— The members of this group are small, wingless or with very short wings, slender-bodied, flattened insects that are chiefly tropical in distribution; they occur on bushes or beneath debris in sandy localities near water. The body is covered with translucent scales that are easily rubbed off. The members of this group occurring in the southern states are 5 to 13 millimeters in length.

—Subfamily *Myrmecophilìnae*—Ant-Loving Crickets— These crickets are small (3 to 5 millimeters in length) and oval, with greatly dilated hind femora; they occur in ant nests. One species, *Myrmecóphila pergándei* Bruner, occurs in the eastern states.

—Subfamily *Nemobiìnae*—Ground Crickets— These crickets are common insects in pastures, meadows, along roadsides, and in wooded areas. They are less than ½ inch in length, and are usually brownish in color. The songs of most species are soft, high-pitched, and often pulsating trills or buzzes. Our most common species belong to the genus *Nemòbius* (Figure 9-16 A).

—Subfamily *Gryllìnae*—House and Field Crickets— These crickets are very similar to the ground crickets, but are generally larger (over ½ inch in length), and they vary in color from brownish to black. The field crickets (Figure 9-1) are very common insects in pastures, meadows, and along roadsides, and some enter houses. The several native species of *Grýllus* are very similar morphologically, and were formerly considered to represent a single species; now several species are recognized, which differ chiefly in habits, life history, and song. The most common of these species in the East is probably the northern field cricket, *Grýllus pennsylvánicus* Burmeister (Figure 9-16 C). The house cricket, *Achèta doméstica* (Linn.), a species introduced into this country from Europe and which often enters houses, differs from the native species of *Grýllus* in having the head light-colored, with dark cross-bars (Figure 9-16 B). Most of the field crickets chirp, and they sing both day and night.

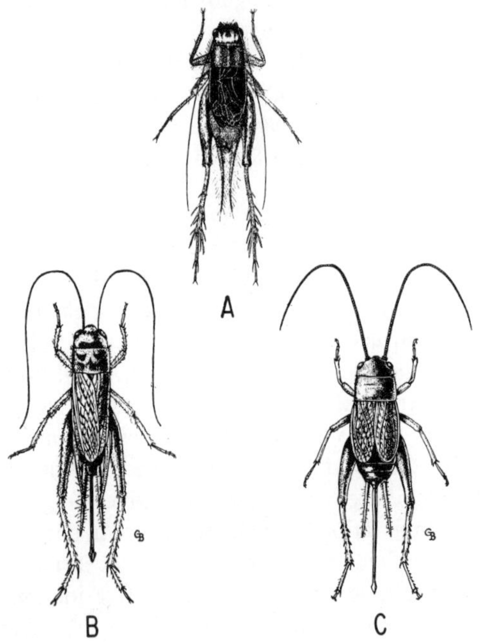

Fig. 9-16. A, a ground cricket, *Nemóbius fasciàtus* (DeGeer), male; B, the house cricket, *Achèta doméstica* (Linn.); C, a field cricket, *Grýllus pennsylvánicus* Burmeister. (A, courtesy of Hebard and the Illinois Natural History Survey; B and C, courtesy of Institut de Biologie générale, Université de Montréal.)

—Subfamily *Brachytrupìnae*—Short-Tailed Crickets— These crickets get their common name from the fact that their ovipositor is very short and often not visible, not long and slender as in most other crickets. The short-tailed crickets are burrowing in habit and usually occur in colonies, their burrows going a foot or more into the ground. They spend most of the time during the day in their burrows, and generally come out only at night. A single species of short-tailed cricket occurs in the southeastern states, *Anurogrýllus mùticus* (DeGeer); this insect is 12 to 17 millimeters in length, and yellowish brown in color.

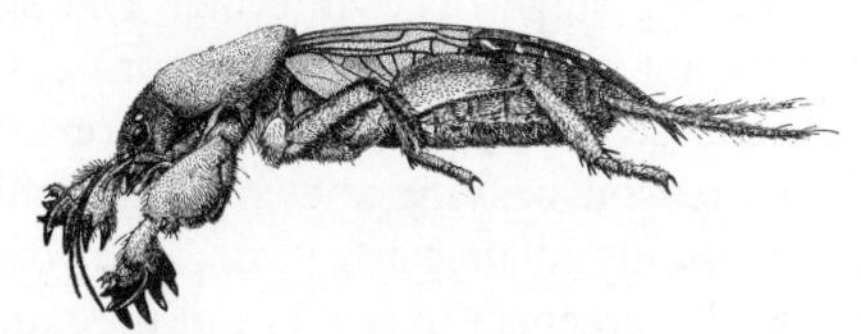

Fig. 9-17. A mole cricket, *Gryllotálpa hexadáctyla* Perty. (Courtesy of Hebard and the Illinois Natural History Survey.)

—Subfamily *Gryllotalpìnae*—Mole Crickets — Mole crickets are brownish insects, very pubescent, and an inch or more in length; they have short antennae, and the front legs are very broad and spadelike (Figure 9-17). They burrow in moist places, usually 6 to 8 inches below the surface. The most common eastern species is *Gryllotálpa hexadáctyla* Perty, and the only species in the West is *G. cúltriger* Uhler. This group is considered a family by some authorities.

FAMILY **Mántidae**—Mantids: Mantids are large, elongate, rather slow-moving insects that are striking in appearance due to their peculiarly modified front legs (Figures 9-4 F, 9-18). The prothorax is greatly lengthened, the front coxae are very long, and the front femora and tibiae are armed with strong spines and fitted for grasping prey. The head is highly movable; mantids are the only insects that can "look over their shoulders." These insects are highly predaceous and feed on a variety of insects (including other mantids). They usually lie in wait for their prey with the front legs in an upraised position; this position has given rise to the common names "praying mantid" and "soothsayer" that are often applied to these insects.

Mantids overwinter in the egg stage, and the eggs are deposited on twigs or grass stems in a paper-machelike egg case or ootheca; each egg case may contain 200 or more eggs.

The mantids are chiefly tropical in distribution. The Carolina mantid, *Stagmomántis carolìna* (Johannsen), which is about 2 inches in length (Figure 9-18), is the most common of the several species of mantids occurring in the southern states. The large

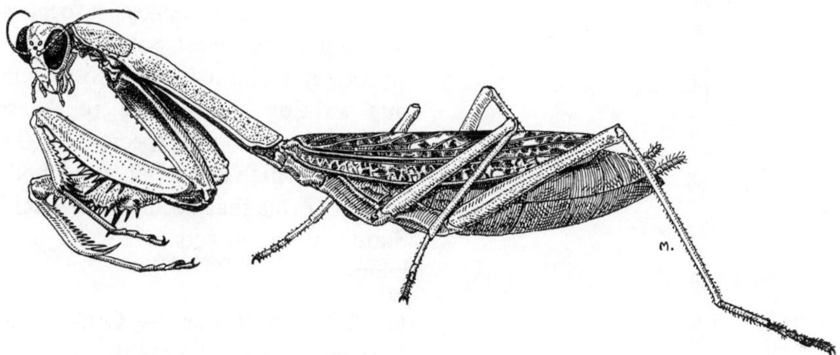

Fig. 9-18. The Carolina mantid *Stagmomántis carolìna* (Johannsen). (Courtesy of Hebard and the Illinois Natural History Survey.)

mantid (3 to 4 inches in length) which is locally common in the northern states is an introduced species, the Chinese mantid, *Tenódera aridifòlia sinénsis* Saussure; this species was introduced in the vicinity of Philadelphia about 50 years ago and has since become rather widely distributed through the transportation of egg masses. The European mantid, *Mántis religiòsa* Linn., a pale-green insect about 2 inches in length, was introduced in the vicinity of Rochester, New York, about 50 years ago, and now occurs throughout most of the eastern states. No males are known for *Brunnéria boreàlis* Scudder, a fairly common species in the South and Southwest.

FAMILY **Phásmidae**—Walking Sticks: The insects in this family are particularly striking in their resemblance to twigs and leaves. Some of the tropical species look very much like leaves, and are often called leaf-insects; the species in the United States are very elongate and twiglike, and are called walking sticks (Figure 9-19).

The walking sticks are slow-moving herbivorous insects that are usually found on trees or shrubs. They are very similar to twigs in appearance; this mimicry probably has protective value. Walking sticks are able to emit a foul-smelling substance from glands in the thorax; this behavior serves as a means of defense. Unlike most insects, the walking sticks are able to regenerate lost legs, at least in part. These insects are usually not sufficiently numerous to do much damage to cultivated plants, but when numerous they may do serious damage to trees.

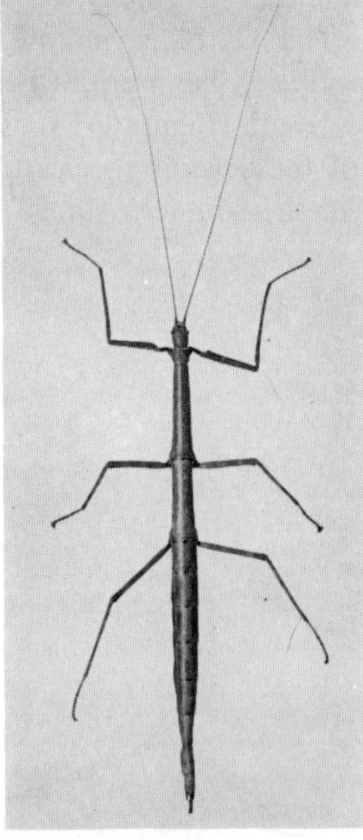

Fig. 9-19. A walking stick. (Courtesy of the Ohio Agricultural Experiment Station.)

The eggs are not laid in any particular situation, but are simply scattered on the ground. There is a single generation a year, with the egg stage overwintering. The eggs often do not hatch the following spring, but hatch the second year after they are laid; for this reason walking sticks are generally abundant only in alternate years. The young are usually greenish in color, and the adults are brownish.

The walking sticks are widely distributed, but the group is principally tropical, and is better represented in the southern states. The common walking stick in the northern states is *Diápheromèra femoràta* (Say). All walking sticks in this country are wingless except *Áplopus màyeri* Caudell, which occurs in southern Florida; this species has short oval front wings, and the hind wings project 2 or 3 millimeters beyond the front wings. This group contains the longest insect in the United States, *Megaphásma déntricrus* (Stål), which reaches a length of 6 or 7 inches; it occurs in the South and Southwest. Some tropical walking sticks get to be a foot or so in length. All our walking sticks have the tarsi 5-segmented except the species in the genus *Tímema,* which are small, stout-bodied, earwiglike forms that occur in the Pacific Coast States; these insects have the tarsi 3-segmented.

FAMILY **Bláttidae** — Cockroaches or Roaches: The cockroaches can usually be recognized by their oval, flattened shape, the head concealed under the pronotum, and

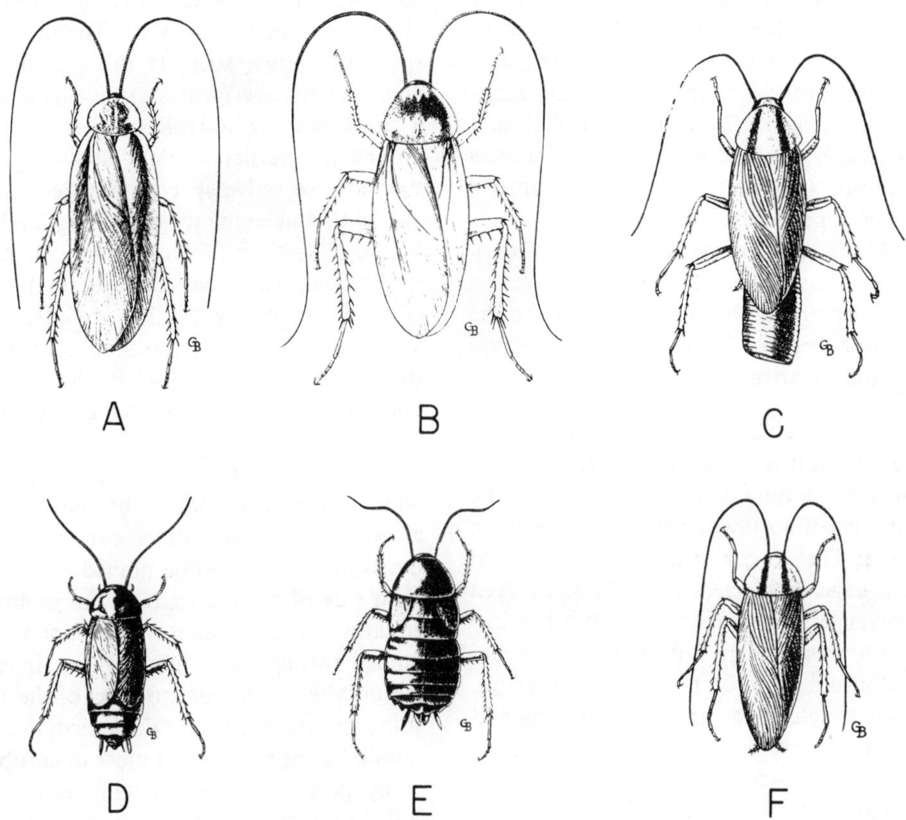

Fig. 9-20. Some common cockroaches, A, a wood cockroach, *Parcoblátta pennsylvánica* (DeGeer); B, the American cockroach, *Periplanèta americàna* (Linn.); C, the German cockroach, *Blatélla germánica* (Linn.), female; D, the oriental cockroach, *Blátta orientàlis* Linn., male; E, the oriental cockroach, female; F, the German cockroach, male. (Courtesy of Institut de Biologie générale, Université de Montréal.)

the long bristlelike antennae (Figure 9-20). The species that invade houses are well known, though they are more often known as "waterbugs" than as cockroaches. These insects are rather general feeders. The eggs are enclosed in capsules, which may be laid immediately after they are formed or may be carried about on the end of the abdomen of the female until they hatch. The females of many species have shorter wings than the males.

The importance of this group is due chiefly to the house-invading habits of a few species. None is known to be a specific vector of disease, but they feed on all sorts of things in a house; they contaminate food, they have an unpleasant odor, and they are often serious pests. The control of house-infesting cockroaches usually involves the use of various dusts, sprays, aerosols, or fumigation.

Three species of cockroaches commonly invade houses in the eastern United States: the German cockroach or crotonbug, *Blatélla germánica* (Linn.), a light-brown insect about $\frac{1}{2}$ inch in length with two longitudinal black stripes on the pronotum (Figure 9-20 C, F); the oriental cockroach, *Blátta orientàlis* Linn., which is about an inch long, dark brown, and broadly oval in shape, with short wings (Figure 9-20 D, E); and the American cockroach, *Periplanèta americàna* (Linn.), a reddish-brown insect with well-developed wings, and $1\frac{1}{4}$ to $1\frac{1}{2}$ inches in length (Figure 9-20 B). In some areas the brown-banded or tropical cockroach, *Supélla supellectílium* (Serville), and the smoky-brown cockroach, *Periplanèta fuliginòsa* (Serville), are also common household pests.

A common wood cockroach, *Parcoblátta pennsylvánica* (DeGeer), is about an inch in length and has a light border on the pronotum (Figure 9-20 A); the males are occasionally attracted to lights.

FAMILY **Gryllobláttidae:** The Grylloblattidae are rather unusual insects that are known from only a few localities in the mountains of northwestern U.S. and western Canada. They occur at high elevations and at the edge of glaciers, and probably feed as scavengers; they are active at rather low temperatures. The grylloblattids are slender and elongate, 15 to 30 millimeters in length, and are wingless; the antennae are long and filiform with 30 to 40 segments; the cerci are long and 8-segmented; the ovipositor is sword-shaped.

COLLECTING AND PRESERVING ORTHOPTERA

Many of the Orthoptera, because they are relatively large and numerous, are fairly easy to collect. The best time for collecting most species is from midsummer to late fall, though a few species should be looked for in early summer, and others (such as the house-infesting roaches) may be collected at almost any time of the year. The more conspicuous forms, such as the grasshoppers and crickets, are most easily collected with a net, either by sweeping vegetation or by aiming for particular individuals. Some of the more secretive species may be collected at night by listening for their songs and then locating them with a flashlight, or by means of various sorts of baited traps. Some forms can be caught by putting molasses or a similar material in the bottom of a trap like that shown in Figure 32-8 B; the insects so collected can simply be picked out of the trap.

Most nymphs and some soft-bodied adult specimens should be preserved in alcohol, but most adults can be pinned. Grasshoppers should be pinned through the right side of the rear part of the pronotum; crickets, roaches, and mantids should be pinned through the right tegmen, in about the middle (from front to rear) of the body. If the specimen is very soft-bodied, the body should be supported by a piece of cardboard or by pins; otherwise, it will sag at either end. In the case of grasshoppers, it is desirable to spread the wings, at least on one side (as in Figure 9-9 A), in order that the color and venation of the hind wing can be seen. It is sometimes desirable to eviscerate some of the larger grasshoppers before they are pinned, to facilitate drying and preservation. This may be done by making a short incision on the ventral side of the body near the base of the abdomen and removing as much as possible of the viscera.

REFERENCES ON THE ORTHOPTERA

Alexander, Richard D. 1957. Sound production and associated behavior in insects. Ohio J. Sci., 57(2):101-113; 1 text f., 4 pl.

Alexander, Richard D. 1957. The taxonomy of the field crickets of the eastern United States (Orthoptera: Gryllidae: *Acheta*). Ann. Entomol. Soc. Am., 50(6):584-602; 19 f.

Alexander, Richard D., and Donald J. Borror. 1956. The songs of insects. A 12-inch long-play phonograph record, published by the Cornell University Press, Ithaca, N.Y.

Alexander, Richard D., and Thomas J. Walker. 1962. Two introduced field crickets new to eastern United States (Orthoptera: Gryllidae). Ann. Entomol. Soc. Am., 55(1):90-94. (Includes a discussion of the status of the names *Grýllus* and *Achèta*.)

Blatchley, W. S. 1920. Orthoptera of northeastern America. Indianapolis, Ind.: The Nature Pub. Co. 784 pp., 246 f.

Chopard, Lucien. 1938. La biologie des Orthopteres. Paris: Lachevalier. 541 pp., 4 pl.

Froeschner, Richard C. 1954. The grasshoppers and other Orthoptera of Iowa. Iowa State Coll. J. Sci., 29(2):163-354; 123 f.

Gurney, A. B. 1951. Praying mantids of the United States. Smithsonian Inst. Rept., 1950: 339-362.

Hebard, M. 1934. The Dermaptera and Orthoptera of Illinois. Illinois Nat. Hist. Survey, Bull., 20(3):iv+125-179 pp.; 167 f.

Hebard, M. 1936. Orthoptera of North Dakota. N. Dakota Agr. Expt. Sta. Tech. Bull. No. 284. 66 pp., 1 map.

Lugger, Otto. 1897. The Orthoptera of Minnesota. Minn. Agr. Expt. Sta. Bull., 55, pp. 91-385; 187 f.

Morse, A. P. 1920. Manual of the Orthoptera of New England. Proc. Boston Soc. Nat. Hist., 35(6):197-556; 99 f., pl. 10-29.

Rehn, James A. G., and Harold J. Grant, Jr. 1961. A monograph of the Orthoptera of North America (north of Mexico). Vol. 1. Acad. Nat. Sci. Phila., Monog. No. 12; 257 pp., 401 f., 8 pl., 36 maps.

Uvarov, B. P. 1928. Locusts and grasshoppers. London: Imperial Bureau of Entomology. xiii+352 pp., 118 f., 9 pl.

Waldon, B. H. 1911. The Euplexoptera and Orthoptera of Connecticut. Conn. State Geol. and Nat. Hist. Survey, Bull. 16, pp. 39-169; 66 text f., 11 pl.

Walker, Thomas J. 1962. The taxonomy and calling songs of the United States tree crickets (Orthoptera: Gryllidae: Oecanthinae). I. The genus *Neoxabea* and the *niveus* and *varicornis* groups of the genus *Oecanthus*. Ann. Entomol. Soc. Am., 55(3):303-322; 17 f.

10

Order Isoptera[1]: Termites

Termites are small to medium-sized insects that live in social groups and have a highly developed caste system. Both winged and wingless individuals occur in a colony, and some individuals may be short-winged. The wings, when present, are four in number, membranous, with a somewhat reduced venation but often with numerous veinlike wrinkles. The front and hind wings are the same size and shape in American species (hence the order name), and when at rest are held flat over the body and extend beyond the tip of the abdomen (Figure 10-1). The mouth parts are of the chewing type, and the metamorphosis is simple.

Termites are sometimes called white ants, but they differ from the ants in several ways. Termites are very soft-bodied and usually light-colored, while ants are hard-bodied and usually dark-colored; the front and hind wings of a termite are similar in size and venation and are held flat over the abdomen at rest, but in ants the hind wings are smaller than the front wings and have fewer veins, and the wings at rest are usually held above the body. The abdomen in termites is broadly joined to the thorax, whereas in ants it is constricted at the base and connected to the thorax by a narrow petiole. The antennae of a termite are

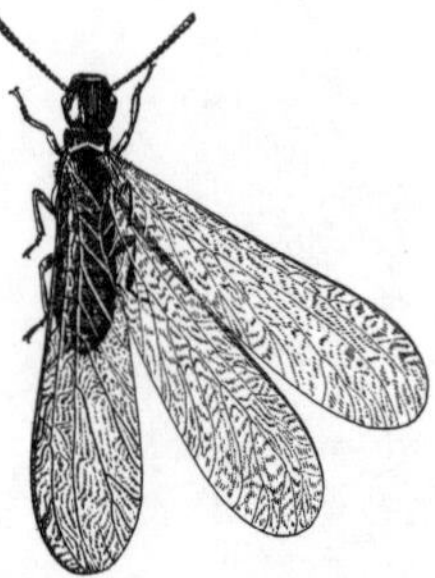

Fig. 10-1. A winged termite. (Courtesy of USDA.)

[1] Isoptera: *iso*, equal; *ptera*, wings.

moniliform or filiform, while those of ants are elbowed. The caste system differs somewhat in the two types of insects; termite workers and soldiers consist of individuals of both sexes, with all nymphs acting as workers; in ants the individuals of these castes are all females.

TERMITE CASTES

The reproductives (kings and queens) are the most highly developed individuals sexually. They have fully developed wings, compound eyes, and are usually heavily pigmented. The males are often small, and in some species the queens may become very large (3 inches or more in length in some tropical species); the queens sometimes live for several years, laying thousands of eggs. The kings and queens are usually produced in large numbers at certain seasons; they leave the colony in a swarm, mate, and individual pairs establish new colonies. This swarming occurs at different times of the year in different species; in the most common eastern species, *Reticulitérmes flávipes* (Kollar), it occurs in the spring; in many western species, it occurs in late summer. The reproductives shed their wings after mating; the wings break off along a weakened line at the base, leaving only a stub (the *scale*) attached to the thorax.

The supplementary reproductives have short wings and are less heavily pigmented

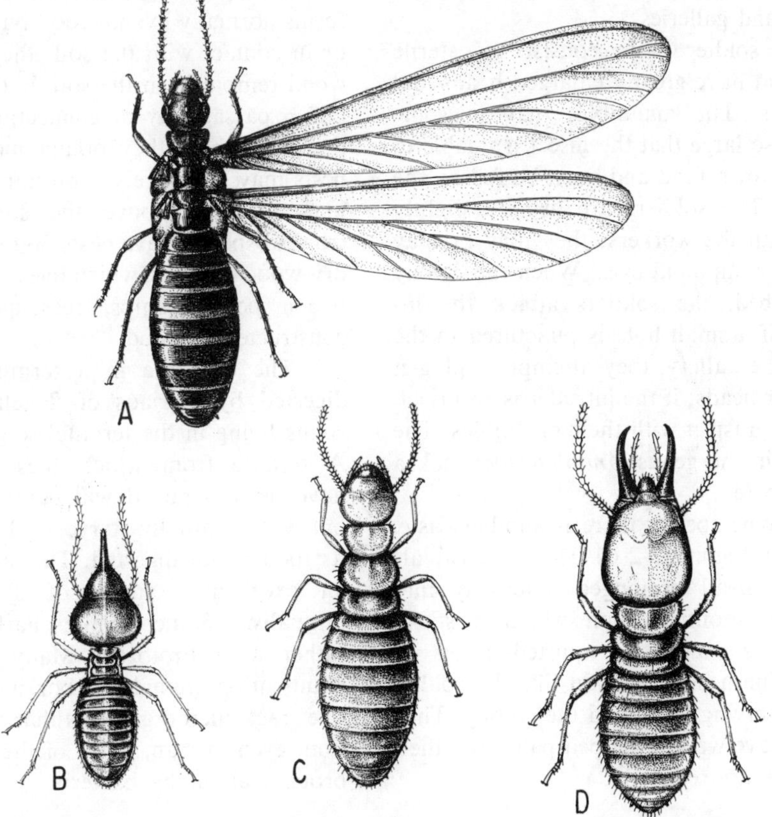

Fig. 10-2. Castes of termites. A, sexual winged adult, *Amitérmes tubifórmans* (Buckley), 10 ×; B, nasutus of *Constrictotérmes tenuiróstris* (Desneux), 15 ×; C, worker, and D, soldier, of *Prorhinotérmes símplex* (Hagen), 10 ×. (Courtesy of Banks and Snyder and the U.S. National Museum).

than the reproductives, and usually have smaller eyes. They sometimes carry on extensive reproduction in the nest and may supplement the queen in building the colony. In some species there may be a second group of supplementary reproductives, sometimes referred to as the third form adults; these are similar to the workers in appearance, but are able to reproduce.

The worker caste consists of nymphs and sterile adults; they are pale in color, wingless, and usually lack compound eyes; the mandibles are relatively small. These individuals perform most of the work of the colony; they collect food and feed the queens, soldiers, and newly hatched young; they construct and care for the fungus gardens; and they build nests, passageways, tunnels, and galleries.

The soldier caste consists of sterile adults that have greatly enlarged heads and mandibles. The mandibles may in some cases be so large that the insect is unable to secure its own food and must be fed by the workers. The soldiers are usually slightly larger than the workers; they may or may not have compound eyes. When the colony is disturbed, the soldiers attack the intruders; if a small hole is punctured in the wall of the gallery, they attempt to plug it with their heads; if the intruder is an insect, they will grasp it with their mandibles. The termites in the genus *Anoplotérmes* lack a soldier caste.

In some species there is another caste, the nasuti (Figure 10-2 B). These individuals have the head prolonged anteriorly into a narrow snout through which a sticky secretion is exuded or squirted at an intruder. The nasuti function like the soldier caste in serving to defend the colony. They usually have well-developed palpi, but their mandibles are reduced.

In some of the primitive species of termites, only two castes are developed, the reproductives and soldiers; the work of the colony is done by the immature individuals of these two castes.

HABITS OF TERMITES

Termites frequently groom each other with their mouth parts, probably as a result of the attraction of secretions that are usually available on the body. The food of termites is composed of the cast skins and feces of other individuals, dead individuals, and plant materials such as wood and wood products.

Some termites live in moist subterranean situations and others live in dry situations above ground. The subterranean forms normally live in wood buried beneath or in contact with the soil; they may enter wood remote from the soil, but must maintain a passageway or connecting gallery to the soil, where they obtain moisture. The nests may be entirely subterranean, or they may protrude above the surface; some tropical species have nests 30 feet high. The dry-wood termites, which live above ground, live in posts, stumps, trees, and buildings constructed of wood.

The cellulose in a termite's food is digested by myriads of flagellated protozoans living in the termite's digestive tract. A termite from which these protozoans have been removed will continue to feed, but will eventually starve to death because its food is not digested. This association is an excellent example of symbiosis, or mutualism. Some termites harbor bacteria rather than Protozoa. Many wood- and plant-eating animals harbor in their digestive tract microorganisms that aid in digestion; even in man, much of the digestion is brought about by bacteria.

CLASSIFICATION OF THE ISOPTERA

The order Isoptera is represented in the United States by four families; the winged forms and soldiers of these families may be separated by the following keys.

KEY TO THE FAMILIES OF ISOPTERA (WINGED ADULTS)

1. Fontanelle usually present (Figures 10-2 A and 10-3, *fon*); clypeus with a median sutural line; R (the longitudinal vein behind the costal margin) usually without anterior branches 2

1′. Fontanelle absent; clypeus usually without a median sutural line; R with one or more anterior branches 3

2(1). Scale of front wing longer than pronotum; pronotum flat; cerci 2-segmented; Rs present; widely distributed .... **Rhinotermítidae** p. 122

2′. Scale of front wing shorter than pronotum; pronotum saddle-shaped; cerci with 1 or 2 segments; Rs reduced or absent; southwestern United States .... **Termítidae** p. 122

3(1′). Ocelli present; Florida and western United States........ **Kalotermítidae** p. 122

3′. Ocelli absent; western United States.................. **Hodotermítidae** p. 122

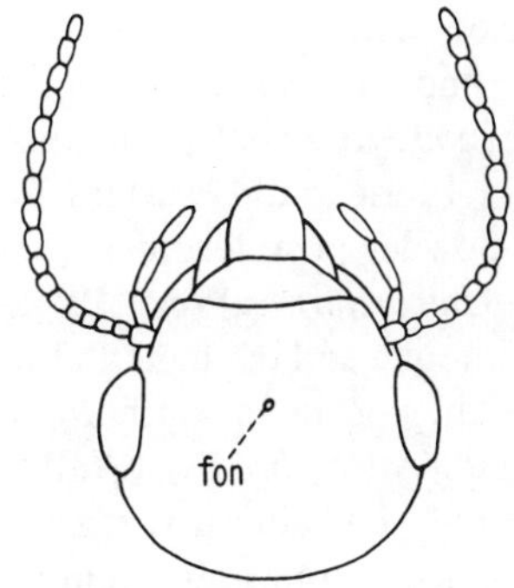

Fig. 10-3. Head of *Prorhinotérmes*, dorsal view, showing fontanelle (*fon*). (Modified from Banks and Snyder.)

KEY TO THE FAMILIES OF ISOPTERA (SOLDIERS)

1. Mandibles vestigial, the head produced anteriorly into a long noselike projection (nasuti, Figure 10-2 B) .... **Termítidae** p. 122

1′. Mandibles normal, head not as above 2

2(1′). Head longer than broad (Figure 10-2 D); mandibles with or without prominent marginal teeth 3

2′. Head short, hollowed out; mandibles without marginal teeth; southern United States (powder-post termites) .... **Kalotermítidae** p. 122

3(2). Mandibles with one or more prominent marginal teeth; southern and western United States.. 4

3′. Mandibles without marginal teeth (Figure 10-2 D); widely distributed.. .... **Rhinotermítidae** p. 122

4(3). Mandibles with only 1 prominent marginal tooth; head narrowed anteriorly .... **Termítidae** p. 122

4′. Mandibles with more than 1 prominent marginal tooth; head not narrowed anteriorly 5

5(4′). Third antennal segment modified; hind femora swollen.... **Kalotermítidae** p. 122

5′. Third antennal segment not modified; hind femora variable 6

6(5′). Hind femora swollen; antennae with at least 23 segments; cerci very long .... **Hodotermítidae** p. 122

6′. Hind femora not, or only slightly, swollen; antennae with fewer than 23 segments; cerci shorter .... **Kalotermítidae** p. 122

FAMILY **Kalotermítidae:** This family is represented in the United States by 16 species and includes the dry-wood, damp-wood, and powder-post termites. These termites have no worker caste, and the young of the other castes perform the work of the colony. The dry-wood termites (*Kalotérmes* and *Procryptotérmes*) attack dry sound wood and do not have a ground contact. Most infestations are in buildings, but furniture, utility poles, and piled lumber may also be attacked. *Kalotérmes snỳderi* Light, which occurs in the southeastern states from South Carolina to Texas, is the most important eastern species. The damp-wood termites (*Neotérmes* and *Paraneotérmes*) attack moist dead wood, tree roots, and the like; they occur in Florida and western United States. The powder-post termites (*Cryptotérmes* and *Calcaritérmes*) usually attack dry wood (without a soil contact) and reduce it to powder; they occur in southern United States. *Cryptotérmes brévis* (Walker) is probably the only introduced species of termite in the United States. It occurs along the Gulf Coast near Tampa and New Orleans, and has been found as far north as Tennessee; it was probably introduced in furniture. It attacks furniture, books, stationery, dry goods, and building timbers; it frequently does a great deal of damage. It is found only in buildings, never out of doors; where it is found, its colonies are numerous but small.

FAMILY **Hodotermítidae:** This family includes three species of *Zootermópsis*, the rotten-wood termites, which occur along the Pacific Coast. They attack dead wood, and although they do not require a ground contact, some moisture in the wood is required; they frequently damage buildings, utility poles, and lumber; the most important species is *Z. angusticóllis* (Hagen). These termites do not have a worker caste.

FAMILY **Rhinotermítidae:** This group is represented in the United States by eight species, and includes the subterranean termites (*Reticulitérmes* and *Heterotérmes*) and the damp-wood termites in the genus *Prorhinotérmes* (Figure 10-2 C, D); the subterranean termites are widely distributed over the country, but the damp-wood termites occur only in Florida. The common eastern subterranean termite, *Reticulitérmes flávipes* (Kollar) (Figure 10-4), is probably the most destructive species in the order, and it is the only termite occurring in the Northeast.

Fig. 10-4. A group of workers of the common eastern termite, *Reticulitérmes flávipes* (Kollar); note the soldier in the lower center portion of the picture. (Courtesy of Davidson.)

FAMILY **Termítidae:** This group is represented in the United States by 14 species, which occur in the Southwest; it includes the soldierless termites (*Anoplotérmes*), desert termites (*Amitermes* and *Gnáthamitérmes*), and the nasutiform termites (*Nasutitérmes* and *Tenuiróstritérmes*). The soldierless termites burrow under logs or cow chips, and are not of economic importance. The desert termites are subterranean, and occasionally damage the wood of buildings, poles, and fence posts. The nasutiform termites have a nasutus caste (Figure 10-2 B); they attack trees or other objects on the ground, and maintain a ground contact.

THE ECONOMIC IMPORTANCE OF TERMITES

Termites hold two positions from the economic point of view. They may be very destructive, since they feed upon and often destroy various structures or materials which man utilizes (wooden portions of buildings, furniture, books, telephone poles, fence posts; many fabrics, and the like), but on the other hand, they are beneficial in that they assist in the conversion of dead trees and plant products to substances that can be utilized by plants.

Reticulitérmes flávipes (Kollar) is the common termite throughout eastern United States. This species occurs in buried wood, fallen trees, and logs; it must maintain a ground connection to obtain moisture. It cannot initiate a new colony in the wood in a house; the nest in the soil must be established first. Once the soil nest is established, these termites may enter buildings from the soil in one of five ways: (1) through timbers that are in direct contact with the soil, (2) through openings in rough stone foundations, (3) through openings or cracks in concrete-block foundations, (4) through expansion joints or cracks in concrete floors, or (5) by means of earthen tubes constructed over foundations or in hidden cracks and crevices in masonry.

Fig. 10-5. Termite damage. (Courtesy of Davidson.)

Infestations of the subterranean termite in a building may be recognized by the swarming of the reproductives in the spring in or about the building, by mud protruding from cracks between boards or beams or along basement joists, by the earthen tubes extending from the soil to the wood, or by the hollowness of the wood in which the insects have been tunneling. A knife blade can easily be pushed into a timber hollowed out by termites, and such wood readily breaks apart.

Subterranean termites in buildings are controlled by two general methods: by proper construction of the buildings to render them termite proof, or by the use of chemicals to destroy the ground nests. The former involves construction in which no wood is in contact with the ground and in which the termites cannot reach the wooden part of the building through outside steps, sills, or through the foundation; the latter involves the use of such chemicals as sodium arsenite, benzine hexachloride, pentachlorophenol, chlordane, lindane, or trichlorobenzine. Telephone poles and fence posts, which must be in contact with the ground, may be rendered termite-proof by chemical treatment.

The dry-wood termites may be controlled by drilling small holes in infested timbers, forcing a small amount of arsenic or fluorine powder into the holes, and then plugging up the holes. Termites constantly groom one another, and once a few individuals get this powder on them, the other individuals of the colony will eventually obtain it and be killed.

COLLECTING AND PRESERVING ISOPTERA

Termites can be found by turning over dead logs or by digging into dead stumps; they may be collected with forceps or a moistened brush, or they may be shaken out of infested timbers onto a paper. Termites should be preserved in 70 to 80 percent alcohol; most individuals are very soft-bodied and shrivel or become distorted if mounted on pins or points. It is often necessary to mount these insects on microscope slides for detailed study.

REFERENCES ON THE ISOPTERA

Berger, B. G. 1947. How to recognize and control termites in Illinois. Illinois Nat. Hist. Survey, Circ. 41; 44 pp., 32 f.

Kofoid, A. C., *et al.* 1934. Termites and their control. Berkeley, Calif.: University of California Press. xxv+734 pp., 182 f.

Skaife, S. H. 1961. Dwellers in darkness. New York: Doubleday & Company, Inc. xi+180 pp., 26 f., 16 pl.

Snyder, T. E. 1935. Our enemy the termite. Ithaca, N.Y.: Comstock Publishing Associates. 196 pp., 56 f.

Snyder, Thomas E. 1949. Catalogue of the termites (Isoptera) of the world. Smiths. Misc. Coll., 112(3953):1-490.

Snyder, T. E. 1954. Order Isoptera—the termites of the United States and Canada. New York: Nat. Pest Control Assn. 64 pp., 27 f.

Snyder, Thomas E. 1956. Annotated, subject-heading bibliography of termites, 1350 B.C. to A.D. 1954. Smithsonian Inst. Misc. Coll, 130 (4258):iii+305 pp.

Weesner, F. M. 1960. Evolution and biology of the termites. Ann. Rev. Entomol., 5:153-170.

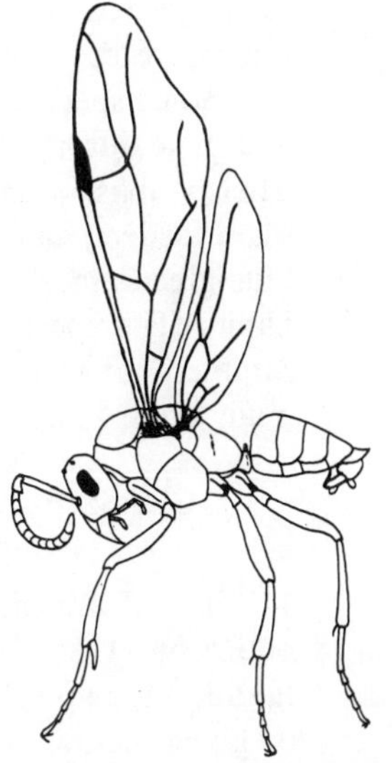

11

Order Plecoptera[1]: Stoneflies

Stoneflies are mostly medium-sized or small, somewhat flattened, soft-bodied, rather drab-colored insects found near streams or rocky lake shores. They are poor fliers, and are seldom found far from water. Most species have four membranous wings (Figure 11-4); the front wings are elongate and rather narrow and usually have a series of cross-veins between M and Cu_1, and between Cu_1 and Cu_2; the hind wings are slightly shorter than the front wings, and usually have a well-developed anal lobe that is folded fanwise when the wings are at rest. A few species of stoneflies have the wings reduced or absent in the male. Stoneflies at rest hold the wings flat over the abdomen (Figure 11-1). The antennae are long, slender, and many-segmented. The tarsi are 3-segmented. Cerci are present and are usually long. The mouth parts are of the chewing type, though in many adults (which do not feed) they are somewhat reduced. The stoneflies undergo simple metamorphosis, and the nymphal stages of development are aquatic.

Stonefly nymphs (Figures 11-2, 11-3) are somewhat elongate flattened insects with long antennae, long cerci, and with branched gills on the thorax and about the bases of the legs. They are very similar to mayfly nymphs, but lack a median caudal filament (that is, they have only two tails, while mayfly nymphs have three), and the gills are different; mayfly nymphs have leaflike gills along the sides of the abdomen (Figure 7-2). Stonefly nymphs are often found under stones in streams or along lake shores (hence the common name of these insects), but may

[1] Plecoptera: *pleco*, folded or plaited; *ptera*, wings (referring to the fact that the anal region of the hind wings is folded when the wings are at rest).

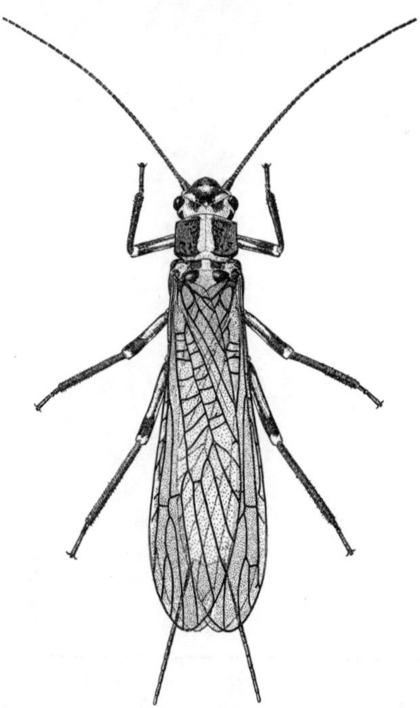

Fig. 11-1. A stonefly, *Isopérla confùsa* Frison (Isopérlidae). (Courtesy of Frison and the Illinois Natural History Survey.)

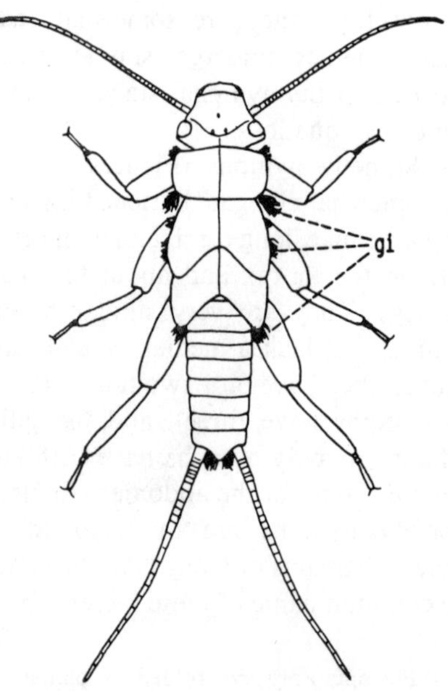

Fig. 11-2. A stonefly nymph. *gi,* gills. (Redrawn from Frison.)

occasionally be found anywhere in a stream where food is available. Some species are plant feeders in the nymphal stage, and others are predaceous or omnivorous.

Some species of stoneflies emerge, feed, and mate during the fall and winter months. The nymphs of these species are generally plant feeders, and the adults feed chiefly on blue-green algae and are diurnal in feeding habits. The species that emerge during the summer vary in nymphal feeding habits; many do not feed as adults.

CLASSIFICATION OF THE PLECOPTERA

The classification followed here is that of Frison (1935, 1942), who recognizes ten families, in two suborders; this arrangement is given below, with alternate names or arrangements in parentheses.

Suborder Hológnatha (Filipálpia)
- Pteronárcidae—giant stoneflies
- Peltopérlidae—roachlike stoneflies
- Taeniopterýgidae (Nemoùridae in part)—winter stoneflies
- Nemoùridae—spring stoneflies
- Leùctridae (Nemoùridae in part)—rolled-winged stoneflies
- Capnìidae (Nemoùridae in part)—small winter stoneflies

Suborder Systellógnatha (Setipálpia, Subulipálpia)
- Pérlidae—common stoneflies
- Perlódidae—perlodid stoneflies
- Isopérlidae—green-winged stoneflies
- Chloropérlidae—green stoneflies

The two suborders differ principally in the form of the nymphal labium; the Hológnatha have the glossae and paraglossae about the same size, whereas the glossae in the Systellógnatha are quite small, appearing almost as a basal segment of the paraglossae. The Hológnatha are principally plant feeders, both as nymphs and adults, while the Systellógnatha are mostly carnivorous as nymphs and are usually nonfeeding as adults.

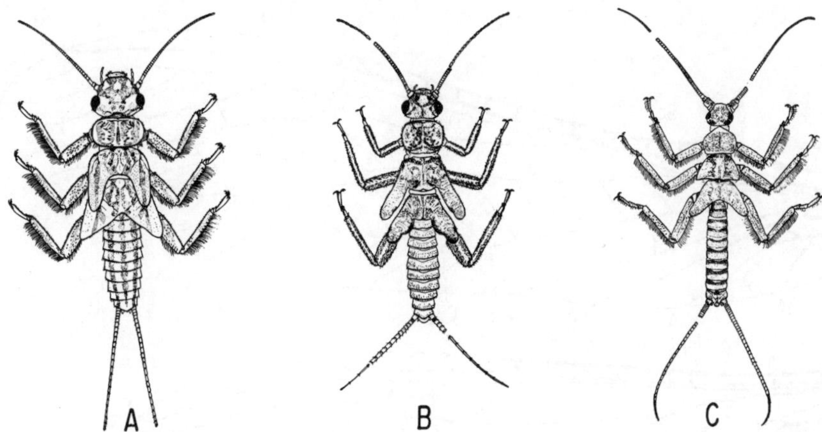

Fig. 11-3. Stonefly nymphs. A, *Isopérla transmárina* (Newman) (Isopérlidae); B, *Nemoùra trispinòsa* Claassen (Nemoùridae); C, *Taeniópteryx glaciàlis* (Newport) (Taeniopterýgidae). (Courtesy of Harden and the Entomological Society of America.)

The principal characters used to separate families are wing venation, the characters of the tarsi, the length of the cerci, the gill remnants, and genitalia. The gill remnants are usually shriveled and difficult to make out in pinned and dried specimens; their location on the thorax is shown in Figure 11-8. The characters of the gill remnants and genitalia are much easier to study in specimens that are preserved in alcohol.

KEY TO THE FAMILIES OF PLECOPTERA

1. Anal area of front wings with 2 or more rows of cross-veins (Figure 11-5) .... **Pteronárcidae** p. 129

1′. Anal area of front wings without cross-veins, or with only 1 row (Figures 11-6, 11-7) 2

2(1′). Cerci short, no longer than greatest width of pronotum 3

2′. Cerci long, much longer than greatest width of pronotum 6

3(2). Front wings with 10 or more costal cross-veins; 2 ocelli; no forked vein arising from basal anal cell in front wing; form somewhat roachlike.. .... **Peltopérlidae** p. 129

3′. Front wings with less than 10 costal cross-veins; 3 ocelli; a forked vein arising from basal anal cell in front wing (Figure 11-6); form not roachlike 4

4(3′). Second tarsal segment about as long as the other tarsal segments; cerci 1- to 6-segmented; winter and early-spring forms.... **Taeniopterýgidae** p. 129

4′. Second tarsal segment much shorter than the other tarsal segments; cerci 1-segmented; spring and early-summer forms 5

5(4′). Apical marginal space beyond tip of subcosta in front wings with an apical cross-vein (Figure 11-6 B, *apc*); front wings flat at rest.... **Nemoùridae** p. 130

5′. Apical marginal space beyond tip of subcosta in front wings without an apical cross-vein (Figure 11-7 A); front wings at rest bent down around sides of abdomen .... **Leuctridae** p. 130

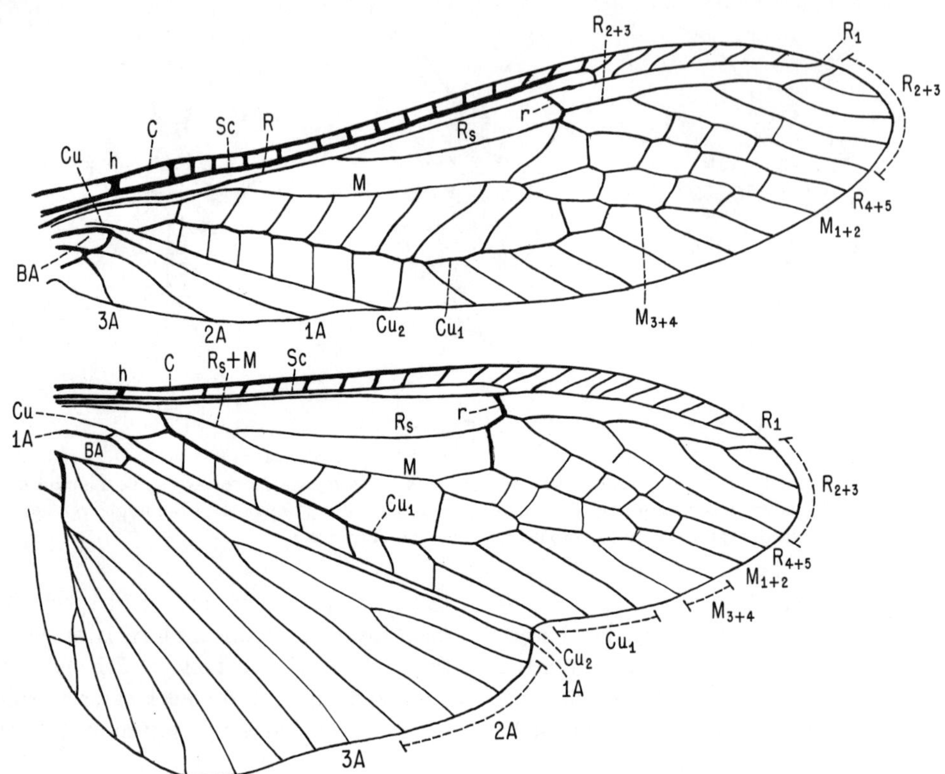

Fig. 11-4. Wings of a perlid. *BA*, basal anal cell.

6(2′). First tarsal segment about as long as third; front wings with few or no medial and cubital cross-veins (Figure 11-7 B); winter and early-spring forms .... **Capnìidae** p. 130

6′. First tarsal segment much shorter than third; front wings with several to many medial and cubital cross-veins (Figures 11-4, 11-6 A); late-spring and summer forms 7

7(6′). Remnants of branched filamentous gills on sides or venter of thorax (Figure 11-8); cu-a in front wing usually opposite basal anal cell or distad of it by no more than its own length .... **Pérlidae** p. 130

7′. No remnants of gills on thorax, or if gill remnants are present, they are unbranched and fingerlike processes; cu-a in front wing, if present, usually distad of basal anal cell by more than its own length........ 8

8(7′). Front corners of pronotum acute or narrowly rounded; no forked vein arising from basal anal cell in front wing; anal lobe of hind wing well developed, with 4 or more veins reaching wing margin; 6 to 25 mm in length 9

8′. Front corners of pronotum broadly rounded; sometimes a forked vein arising from basal anal cell in front wing; anal lobe of hind wing reduced (absent in *Hastapérla*), with not more than 3 veins reaching wing margin; 15 mm in length or less.................... **Chloropérlidae** p. 131

9(8). Males usually with a lobe on posterior margin of seventh abdominal sternum, and with tenth abdominal tergum usually distinctly cleft; subgenital plate of female usually well developed and often covering most of eighth abdominal sternum; Rs in front wings usually with 2 or more branches; wings not greenish; 10 to 25 mm in length......**Perlódidae** p. 131

9′. Males without a lobe on posterior margin of seventh abdominal sternum but with a lobe on eighth sternum, and with tenth abdominal tergum never distinctly cleft; subgenital plate of female, if developed, usually not covering most of eighth sternum; Rs in front wing usually with 2 branches; wings generally greenish; 6 to 15 mm in length....**Isopérlidae** p. 131

FAMILY **Pteronárcidae**—Giant Stoneflies: This group includes the largest insects in the order, and the females of a common eastern species, *Pteronárcys dorsàta* (Say), may sometimes reach a length (measured to the wing tips) of 2½ inches. The nymphs are plant feeders and occur in medium-sized to large rivers. The adults are nocturnal in habits and often come to lights; they do not feed. They appear in late spring and early summer.

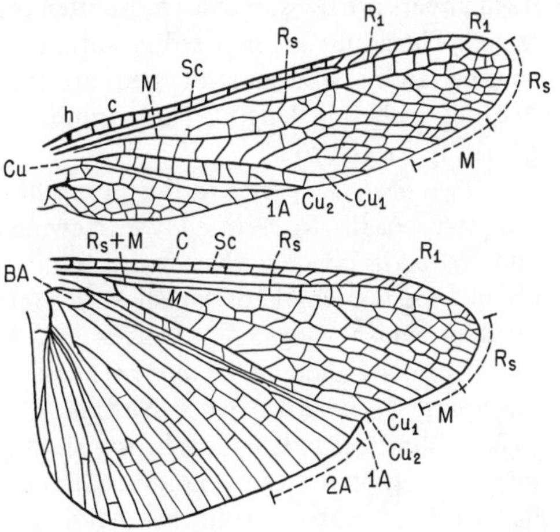

Fig. 11-5. Wings of *Pteronárcys* (Pteronárcidae). *BA*, basal anal cell.

FAMILY **Peltopérlidae**—Roachlike Stoneflies: Most of these stoneflies are western and northern in distribution. The nymphs are somewhat roachlike in appearance; hence the common name of the family. This group contains only one North American genus, *Peltopérla*; two brownish species occur in eastern United States: *P. arcuàta* Needham (14 to 18 millimeters in length) and *P. zìpha* Frison (12 millimeters in length).

FAMILY **Taeniopterýgidae**—Winter Stoneflies: The members of this group are dark-brown to blackish insects, generally ½ inch or less in length, which emerge from January to April. The nymphs (Figure 11-3 C) are phytophagous and occur in large streams

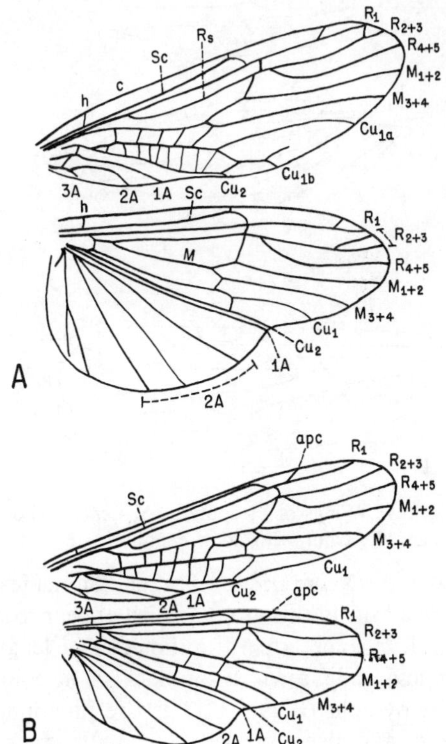

Fig. 11-6. Wings of Plecoptera. A, *Brachýptera* (Taeniopterýgidae); B, *Nemoùra* (Nemoùridae). *apc*, apical cross-vein.

and rivers; some adults are flower feeders. Two common eastern species in this group are *Taeniópteryx maùra* (Pictet), 8 to 12 millimeters in length, which emerges from January to March, and *Brachýptera fasciàta* (Burmeister) 10 to 15 millimeters in length, which emerges during March and April.

FAMILY **Leùctridae**—Rolled-Winged Stoneflies: These stoneflies are for the most part 10 millimeters in length or less and brownish or blackish in color; the wings at rest are bent down over the sides of the abdomen. These insects are most common in hilly or mountainous regions, and the nymphs usually occur in small streams. The adults appear from February to June. The eastern species belong to the genus *Leùctra.*

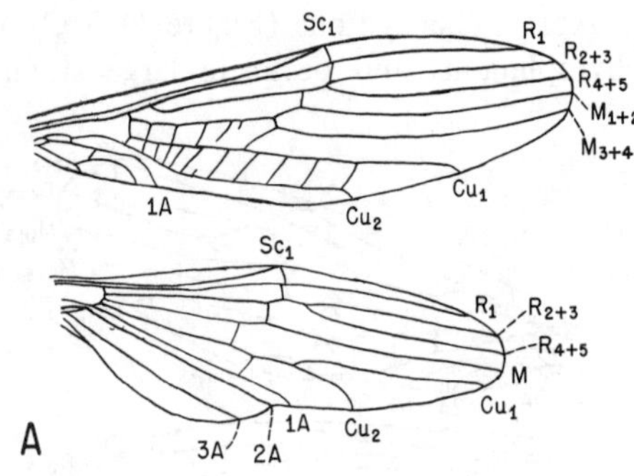

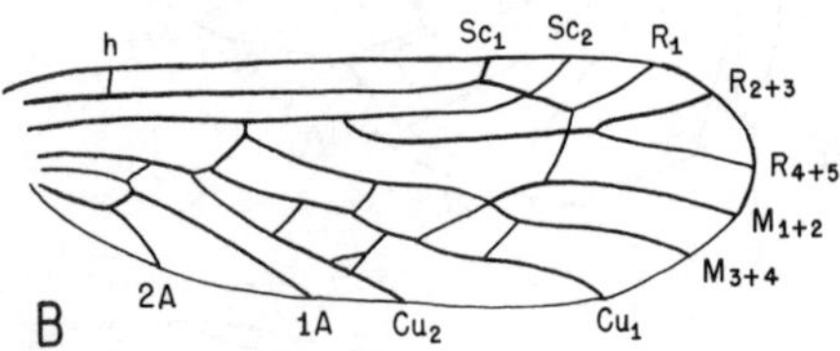

Fig. 11-7. Wings of Plecoptera. A, *Leùctra* (Leùctridae); B, front wing of a capniid.

FAMILY **Nemoùridae**—Spring Stoneflies: The adults of this group, which appear from April to June, are 15 millimeters in length or less and brownish or blackish in color. The nymphs (Figure 11-3 B) are phytophagous and usually occur in small streams with sandy bottoms. The single North American genus, *Nemoùra,* contains a number of species.

FAMILY **Capnìidae**—Small Winter Stoneflies: These stoneflies are blackish in color, mostly 10 millimeters in length or less, and emerge during the winter months. The wings are short or rudimentary in some males. Most of the small winter stoneflies occurring in the East belong to the genus *Allocápnia.*

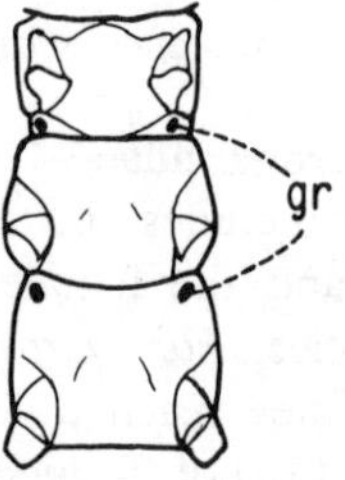

Fig. 11-8. Thorax of *Acroneùria* (Pérlidae), ventral view. *gr,* gill remnants. (Redrawn from Frison, courtesy of the Illinois Natural History Survey.)

FAMILY **Pérlidae**—Common Stoneflies: This family is the largest in the order, and its members are the stoneflies most often collected. The adults are nonfeeding spring and summer forms, and most of them are from $\frac{3}{4}$ to $1\frac{1}{2}$ inches in length. The nymphs are generally carnivorous.

Two eastern species in this group have only two ocelli, *Atopérla ephỳre* (Newman) and *Neopérla clýmene* (Newman); both are about $\frac{1}{2}$ inch in length, brownish, with somewhat brownish wings; *N. clýmene* has the ocelli close together, and *A. ephỳre* has them far apart. *Perlinélla drỳmo* (Newman), 10 to 20 millimeters in length, is brownish, with two black spots on the yellow head, and it has a row of cross-veins in the anal area of the front wing. *Perlésta plácida* (Hagen), 9 to 14 millimeters in length and nocturnal in habit, and *Neophasganóphora capitàta* (Pictet), 16 to 24 millimeters in length and diurnal in habit, have the costal edge of the front wing yellowish. One of the largest and most common genera is *Acroneùria*; the adults are relatively large (20 to 40 millimeters in length), and the males have a disclike structure in the middle of the posterior portion of the ninth abdominal sternum.

FAMILY **Perlódidae:** These stoneflies are relatively rare insects; they are brownish or blackish in color, and 10 to 25 millimeters in length. The nymphs occur in medium-sized to large streams, and the adults appear in the spring and early summer.

FAMILY **Isopérlidae**—Green-Winged Stoneflies: These stoneflies (Figure 11-1) usually have the wings greenish and the body yellowish or greenish, and are 6 to 15 millimeters in length. The adults are chiefly pollen feeders and diurnal in habit; the habits of the nymphs vary. This family contains the single genus *Isopérla.*

FAMILY **Chloropérlidae**—Green Stoneflies: The adults of this family are 6 to 15 millimeters in length and yellowish or greenish in color; they appear in the spring. *Hastapérla brévis* (Banks), a common eastern species, is 6 to 9 millimeters in length and bright green in color, and has no anal lobe in the hind wing. The stoneflies belonging to the genus *Allopérla,* of which there are several eastern species, are 8 to 15 millimeters in length, and have a small anal lobe in the hind wing.

COLLECTING AND PRESERVING PLECOPTERA

During the warmer days in the fall, winter, and spring, adults of the winter species may be found resting on bridges, fence posts, and other objects near the streams in which the nymphs develop. Many species may be collected by sweeping the foliage along the banks of streams. Bridges are a favorite resting place for many species throughout the year. Many of the summer forms are attracted to lights. The nymphs are to be found in streams, usually under stones or in the bottom debris.

Both adult and nymphal stoneflies should be preserved in alcohol; pinned adults often shrink so that some characters, particularly those of the genitalia and the gill remnants, are difficult to make out.

REFERENCES ON THE PLECOPTERA

Claasen, Peter W. 1931. Plecoptera nymphs of America (north of Mexico). Thomas Say Foundation, Pub. 3; 199 pp., 35 pl.

Frison, T. H. 1929. Fall and winter stoneflies, or Plecoptera, of Illinois. Illinois Nat. Hist. Survey, Bull. 18(2):340-409; 77 f.

Frison, T. H. 1935. The stoneflies, or Plecoptera, of Illinois. Illinois Nat. Hist. Survey, Bull. 20(4):281-471; 344 f.

Frison, T. H. 1942. Studies of North American Plecoptera, with special reference to the fauna of Illinois. Illinois Nat. Hist. Survey, Bull. 22(2):231-355; 126 f.

Jewett, Stanley G., Jr. 1956. Plecoptera. In: Aquatic insects of California, ed. by Robert L. Usinger. Berkeley: University of California Press. Pp. 155-181, 52 f.

Needham, J. G., and P. W. Claasen. 1925. A monograph of the Plecoptera or stoneflies of America north of Mexico. Thomas Say Foundation, Pub. 2; 397 pp., 29 f., 50 pl.

Pennak, Robert W. 1953. Fresh-water invertebrates of the United States. New York: The Ronald Press Company. ix+769 pp., 470 f.

Ricker, William E. 1943. Stoneflies of southwestern British Columbia. Indiana Univ. Pub., Sci. Ser. No. 12; 145 pp., 129 f.

Ricker, William E. 1950. Some evolutionary trends in Plecoptera. Proc. Indiana Acad. Sci., 59:197-209.

Ricker, William E. 1952. Systematic studies in Plecoptera. Indiana Univ. Stud., Sci. Ser., 18:1-200; 154 f.

Ricker, William E. 1959. Plecoptera. In: Fresh-water biology, ed. by W. T. Edmondson. New York: John Wiley & Sons, Inc. Pp. 941-957; 10 f.

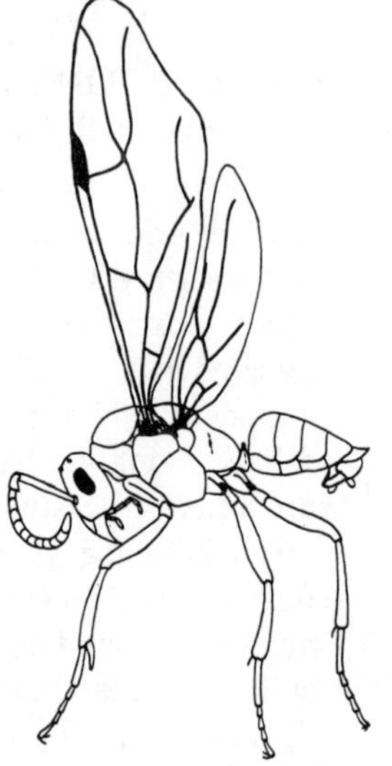

12

Order Dermaptera[1]: Earwigs

Earwigs are slender insects that resemble rove beetles but have large forcepslike cerci (Figure 12-1). The adults usually have four wings; the front wings are short, leathery, and veinless, and the hind wings (when present) are membranous and rounded with radiating veins, and when at rest are folded up under the front wings. The tarsi are 3-segmented. The mouth parts are of the chewing type, and the metamorphosis is simple.

Earwigs are largely nocturnal in habit and hide during the day in cracks, crevices, under bark, and in similar places. They are mainly scavengers, but are occasionally herbivorous. The eggs are laid in burrows in the ground and are carefully guarded by the female until they hatch. Earwigs overwinter in the adult stage.

Some species of earwigs have scent glands opening on the dorsal side of the second and third abdominal segments, and from these glands they can squirt a foul-smelling, yellowish-brown fluid some 3 or 4 inches; this probably serves as a means of protection.

The name "earwig" is derived from an old superstition that these insects enter people's ears. This belief is entirely without foundation, as earwigs are quite harmless to man.

The order Dermaptera is divided into three suborders, the Arixenìna, Diploglossàta, and Forficulìna. The Arixenìna and Diploglossàta have the cerci small and not forcepslike; the Arixenìna are Malayan ectoparasites of bats, and the Diploglossàta are South African ectoparasites of rodents. The Forficulìna is the only suborder occurring in this country.

[1] Dermaptera: *derma,* skin; *ptera,* wings (referring to the texture of the front wings).

Our four families of earwigs may be separated by the following key.

KEY TO THE FAMILIES OF DERMAPTERA

1. Second tarsal segment lobed beneath and prolonged distally beneath the third segment (Figure 12-3 D); antennae with 12 to 15 segments 2

1′. Second tarsal segment cylindrical, not lobed beneath and prolonged beneath the third segment (Figure 12-3 C); antennae with 11 to 30 segments..3

2(1). Second tarsal segment expanded laterally; widely distributed ....**Forficùlidae** p. 133

2′. Second tarsal segment not expanded laterally; California..**Chelisóchidae** p. 135

3(1′). Antennae with 15 to 30 segments, segments 4-6 together rarely longer than the first segment (Figure 12-3 B) ....**Labidùridae** p. 133

3′. Antennae with 11 to 15 segments, segments 4-6 together longer than the first segment (Figure 12-3 A) ....**Labìidae** p. 133

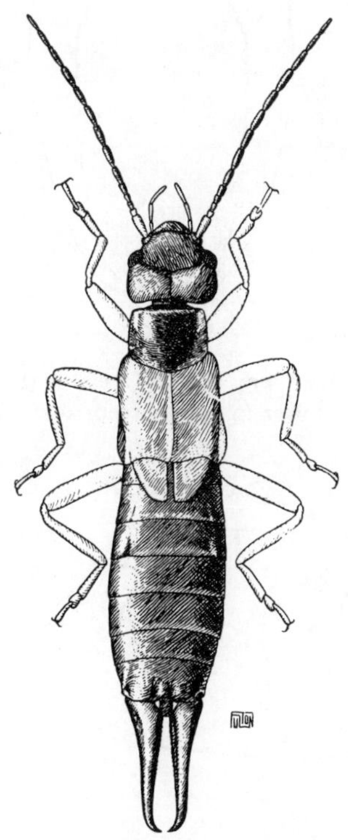

Fig. 12-1. The European earwig, *Forfícula auriculària* Linn., female. About 4 times natural size. (Courtesy of Fulton and the Oregon Agricultural Experiment Station.)

FAMILY **Labidùridae:** The family Labidùridae includes three common genera, *Anisólabis* and *Euboréllia* (adults wingless), and *Labidùra* (adults winged). The seaside earwig, *A. maritìma* (Géné), which occurs on both the Atlantic and Pacific coasts, is 18 to 20 millimeters in length and has 24-segmented antennae. The ring-legged earwig, *E. annùlipes* (Lucas), which occurs in the southern states, is 9 to 11 millimeters in length and has 15 to 16 antennal segments. The striped earwig, *L. bìdens* (Olivier), which occurs in the eastern states, is 13 to 20 millimeters in length.

FAMILY **Labìidae:** The family Labìidae contains several species, the most common of which is the little earwig. *Làbia mìnor* (Linn.), 4 to 5 millimeters in length and originally introduced from Europe (Figure 12-2 B). The handsome earwig, *Prolàbia pulchélla* (Serville), which is fairly common in the southern states, is 6.0 to 6.5 millimeters in length and dark brown in color. The toothed earwig, *Spongovóstox apicedentàtus* (Caudell), is fairly common among dead leaves and cacti in the desert regions of the Southwest.

FAMILY **Forficùlidae:** The most common species of Forficùlidae is the European earwig, *Forfícula auriculària* Linn., a brown insect 10 to 15 millimeters in length with 14 to 15 antennal segments (Figure 12-1). This species is widely distributed, and some-

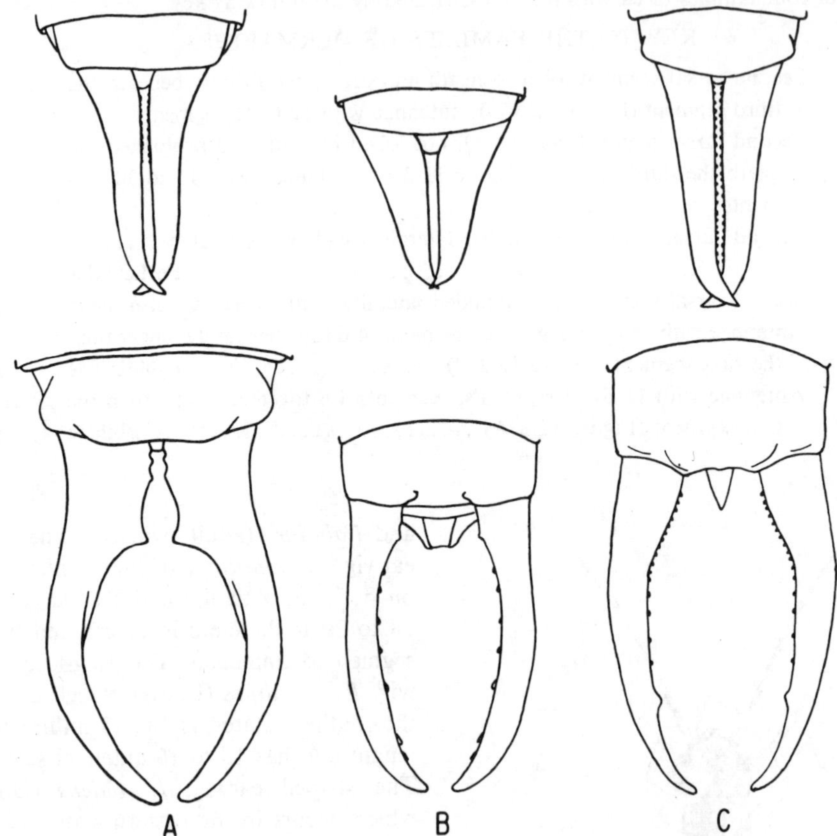

Fig. 12-2. Anal forceps of Dermaptera. A, *Forfícula auriculària* Linn.; B, *Làbia mìnor* (Linn.), C, *Dòru lıneàre* (Escholtz). Upper figures, forceps of female; lower figures, forceps of male.

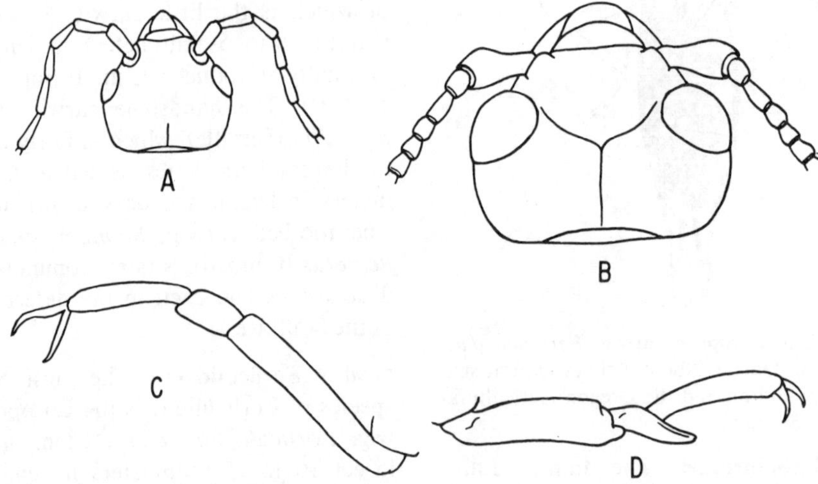

Fig. 12-3. Characters of Dermaptera. A, head of *Làbia mìnor* (Linn.), dorsal view; B, head of *Labidùra ripària* Pallas, dorsal view; C, tarsus of *Labidùra*; D, tarsus of *Forfícula*.

times attacks vegetable crops, fruit trees, and ornamental plants. The spine-tailed earwig, *Dòru aculeàtum* (Scudder), is 7.5 to 11.0 millimeters in length, with 12-segmented antennae.

FAMILY **Chelisóchidae:** The family Chelisóchidae is represented in the United States by a single species, *Chelísoches mòrio* (Fabricius), a large black earwig occurring in California.

REFERENCES ON THE DERMAPTERA

Blatchley, W. S. 1920. Orthoptera of northeastern America. Indianapolis, Ind.: The Nature Pub. Co. 784 pp., 246 f.

Hebard, Morgan. 1934. The Dermaptera and Orthoptera of Illinois. Illinois Nat. Hist. Survey, Bull. 20(3):iv+pp. 125-279; 167 f.

(See also the references on the Orthoptera, page 116).

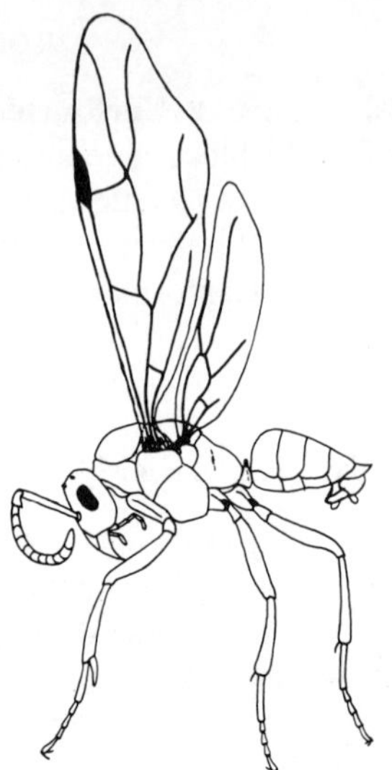

13

Order Embioptera[1]: Webspinners

The webspinners are small, slender insects that are chiefly tropical in distribution; a few species occur in southern United States. The body is somewhat flattened in the males and more or less cylindrical in the females and young; most species are between 4 and 7 millimeters in length. The antennae are filiform, ocelli are lacking, and the mouth parts are of the chewing type; the head is prognathous. The legs are short and stout, and the hind femora are thickened; the tarsi are 3-segmented, with the basal segment of the front tarsi enlarged and containing silk glands and hollow spinning hairs. The males of most species are winged, though some are wingless or have vestigial wings; the front and hind wings are similar in size and venation, and the venation is somewhat reduced (Figure 13-1 A). Both winged and wingless males may occur in the same species. The females are always wingless. The abdomen is 10-segmented and bears a pair of cerci that are generally 2-segmented; in certain genera the adult male has the left cercus 1-segmented. The terminal abdominal appendages are generally asymmetrical in the male and always so in the female. The webspinners undergo simple metamorphosis. At least one species is parthenogenetic.

These insects live in silken galleries spun in debris, in cracks in the soil, under stones, on or under bark, or among epiphytic plants, mosses, or lichens. In most silk-producing insects the silk is spun from modified salivary glands that open in the mouth, but in the webspinners, the silk glands and spinnerets are located in the basal segment of the front tarsi. All stages of these insects, even the first instar young, are able to spin silk. Most species live in colonies. The webspinners often feign death when disturbed, but on occasion can move very rapidly, usually running backward. The eggs are large and cylindrical, and are laid in the galleries and are often covered with chewed food particles; the eggs are attended by the females. Webspinners feed on various plant materials, principally dead grass and leaves, moss, lichens, and bark.

[1] Embioptera: *embio,* lively; *ptera,* wings.

CLASSIFICATION OF THE EMBIOPTERA

The three families of Embioptera represented in the United States may be separated by the following key.

KEY TO THE FAMILIES OF EMBIOPTERA

1. R_{4+5} in wings of male forked; left cercus 2-segmented.... **Teratembìidae** p. 137

1′. R_{4+5} in wings of male not forked (Figure 13-1 A); if wings are absent, then left cercus is 1-segmented 2

2(1′). Mandibles without apical teeth; tenth tergite of male completely divided by a median membranous area that reaches ninth tergite; left cercus of male usually with peglike spines on mesal side of basal segment...... .... **Anisembìidae** p. 137

2′. Mandibles with distinct apical teeth; tenth tergite of male incompletely divided by a median membranous area that does not extend to ninth tergite; left cercus of male smooth on mesal side ...... **Oligotómidae** p. 137

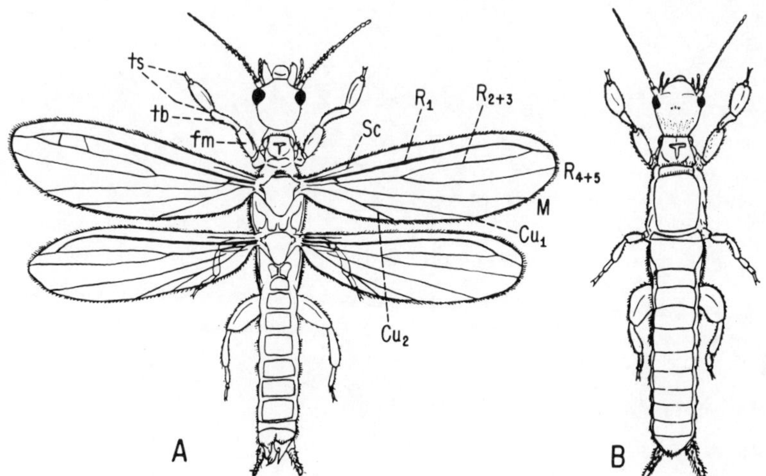

Fig. 13-1. *Oligótoma saundérsii* (Westwood). A, winged male; B, wingless female. *fm*, femur; *tb*, tibia; *ts*, tarsus. (Redrawn from E. O. Essig, *College Entomology*, copyright, 1942, by permission of The Macmillan Company.)

FAMILY **Anisembìidae:** The Anisembìidae are represented in the United States by two species, *Anisémbia texàna* (Melander) of eastern Texas, Louisiana, Mississippi, and Arkansas, and *Chelicérca rùbra* (Ross) of the Southwest. Both winged and wingless males occur in colonies of *A. texàna.*

FAMILY **Teratembìidae:** The Teratembìidae (= **Oligembiidae**) are represented in the United States by four species: *Oligémbia húbbardi* (Hagen) of southern Florida, *O. vandýkei* Ross (an arboreal species) of the southeastern states, *O. melanùra* Ross (another arboreal species) of southern Louisiana and the Gulf Coast of Texas, and *O. lobàta* Ross of the Brownsville region of Texas.

FAMILY **Oligotómidae:** The Oligotómidae are represented in the United States by three species, two of which have been introduced from the Old World. The introduced species are *Oligótoma saundérsii* (Westwood) of the Southeast, and *O. nìgra* Hagen of the Southwest.

REFERENCES ON THE EMBIOPTERA

Davis, Consett. 1940. Family classification of the order Embioptera. Ann. Entomol. Soc. Am., 33(4):677-682.

Hagen, H. A. 1885. Monograph of the Embiidina. Can. Entomologist, 17(8-11):141-155, 171-178, 190-199, 206-229.

Ross, Edward S. 1940. A revision of the Embioptera of North America. Ann. Entomol. Soc. Am., 33(4):629-676; 50 f.

Ross, Edward S. 1944. A revision of the Embioptera, or web-spinners, of the New World. Proc. U.S. Natl. Museum, 94(3175):401-504; f. 6-156, pl. 18-19.

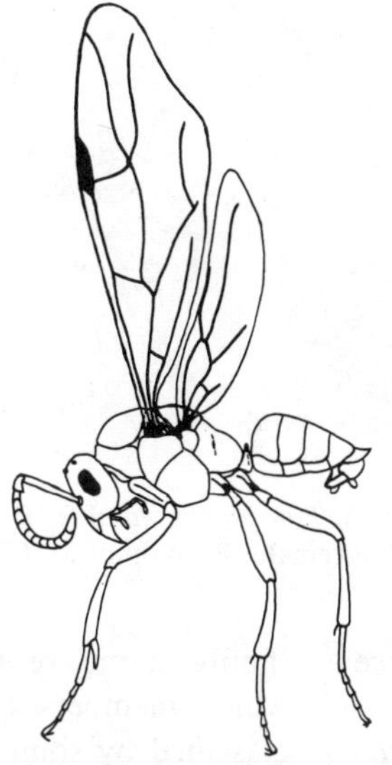

14

Order Psocoptera[1]: Psocids

The psocids are small, soft-bodied insects, most of which are less than $\frac{1}{4}$ inch in length. Wings may be present or absent, and both long-winged and short-winged individuals occur in some species. The winged forms have four membranous wings (rarely two, with the hind wings vestigial); the front wings are a little larger than the hind wings, and the wings at rest are usually held rooflike over the abdomen. The antennae are generally fairly long, the tarsi are 2- or 3-segmented, and cerci are lacking. Psocids have chewing mouth parts, and the clypeus is large and somewhat swollen. The metamorphosis is simple (Figure 14-1).

Some 40 genera and about 150 species of psocids are known from the United States, but most people see only a few species that occur in houses or other buildings. Most of the species found in buildings are wingless, and because they often live among books or papers, are usually called booklice. The majority of the psocids are outdoor species, with well-developed wings, and occur on the bark or foliage of trees and shrubs or under bark or stones; these psocids are sometimes called barklice.

The psocids feed on molds, fungi, cereals, pollen, fragments of dead insects, and similar materials. The term "lice" in the names "booklice" and "barklice" is somewhat misleading, for none of these insects is parasitic, and relatively few are louselike in appearance. The species occurring in buildings rarely cause much damage, but are frequently a nuisance.

The eggs of psocids are laid singly or in clusters and are sometimes covered by silk or debris. Most species pass through six nymphal instars. Some species are gregarious, living under thin silken webs; one southern species, *Archipsòcus nòmas*

[1] Psocoptera: *psoco,* rub small; *ptera,* wings (referring to the gnawing habits of these insects).

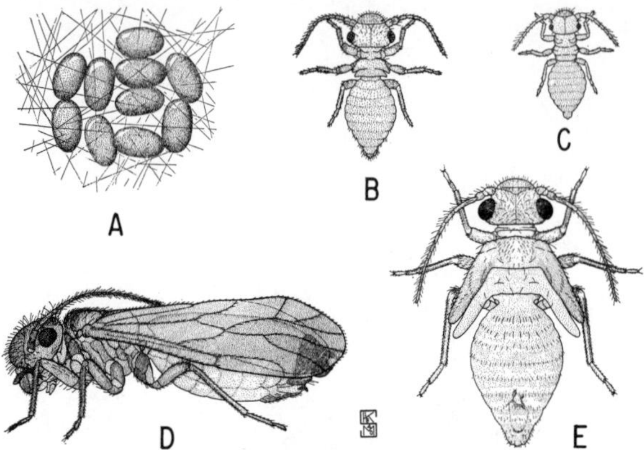

Fig. 14-1. Developmental stages of the psocid, *Ectopsòcus pùmilis* (Banks) (Pseudocaecilìidae). A, eggs; B, third instar; C, first instar; D, adult female; E, sixth instar. (Courtesy of Sommerman.)

Gurney, often makes unsightly webs on tree trunks and branches.

Certain psocids (species of *Liposcèlis* and *Rhyopsòcus*) have recently been found capable of acting as the intermediate hosts of the fringed tapeworm of sheep, *Thysanosòma ostiniòides* Diesing.

CLASSIFICATION OF THE PSOCOPTERA

The classification of this order is in a somewhat confused state; different authorities have different ideas of the groupings within the order, and there have been many shiftings of species and genera from one genus or family to another. Three fairly recent classifications of the Psocoptera are those of Banks (1929), Pearman (1936), and Roesler (1944); we follow here the arrangement of Roesler.

A synopsis of the Psocoptera occurring in the United States is given below. The names in parentheses following a particular family name represent other families in which members of this family have been classified by some authorities.

- Suborder Trogiomórpha
  - Trogìidae (Atrópidae, Psoquíllidae)
  - Lepidopsócidae (Lepidíllidae)
  - Psyllipsócidae (Psocathrópidae, Empherìidae)
- Suborder Troctomórpha
  - Pachytróctidae
  - Liposcélidae (Tróctidae, Embidopsócidae, Atrópidae)
- Suborder Eupsòcida
  - Epipsócidae
  - Myopsócidae (Psócidae)
  - Psócidae
  - Mesopsócidae (Philotársidae, Elipsócidae)
  - Pseudocaecilìidae (Archipsócidae, Pterodélidae, Peripsócidae, Trichopsócidae, Embidopsócidae, Caecilìidae, Psócidae, Empherìidae)
  - Polypsócidae (Caecilìidae, Psócidae)

The families of psocids occurring in the United States may be separated by the following key, which is modified from Roesler. The families marked with an asterisk are small and are not likely to be encountered by the general collector.

KEY TO THE FAMILIES OF PSOCOPTERA

1. Tarsi 2-segmented; labial palpi 1-segmented (Eupsòcida in part) 2

1′. Tarsi 3-segmented; labial palpi 1- or 2-segmented 5

2(1). Labial palpi broadly triangular (Figure 14-5 C); lacinia uniformly conical toward tip, acuminate, usually without definite teeth (Figure 14-5 G); lateral gonapophyses absent (Figure 14-7 B); Cu_{1b} in front wing very short or absent, Cu_{1a} ending in distal margin of wing. . . . **Polypsócidae*** p. 145

2′. Labial palpi short and appressed, sometimes semicircular (Figure 14-5 B); lacinia broad and oblique at end or distinctly toothed (Figure 14-5 H, I); lateral gonapophyses of female clothed with hairs, or if lateral gona-

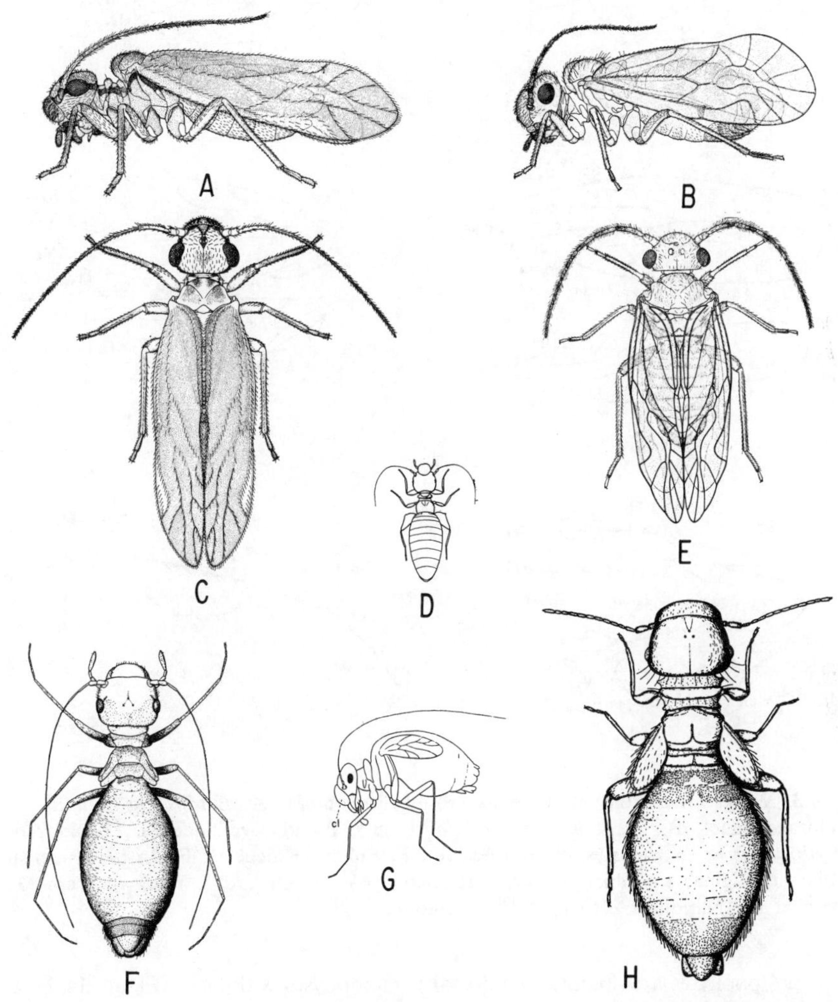

Fig. 14-2. Psocids. A, *Caecilius mánteri* Sommerman, female, lateral view (Polypsócidae); B, *Anomopsòcus amábilis* (Walsh), female, lateral view (Pseudocaecilìidae); C, *Caecílius mánteri* Sommerman, female, dorsal view (Polypsócidae); D, *Liposcèlis divinatòrius* (Müller), dorsal view (Liposcélidae); E, *Anomopsòcus amábilis* (Walsh), male dorsal view (Pseudocaecilìidae); F, *Psyllipsòcus rambùrii* Selys, short-winged female, dorsal view (Psyllipsócidae); G, *Psocathròpus* sp., lateral view (Psyllipsócidae); H, *Archipsòcus nòmas* Gurney, short-winged female, dorsal view (Pseudocaecilìidae). (A-C and E, courtesy of Sommerman; D and F-H, courtesy of Gurney; D and G reprinted by permission of Pest Control Technology, National Pest Control Association; A, courtesy of Psyche; B-C and E-F, courtesy of the Entomological Society of America; H, courtesy of the Washington Academy of Science.)

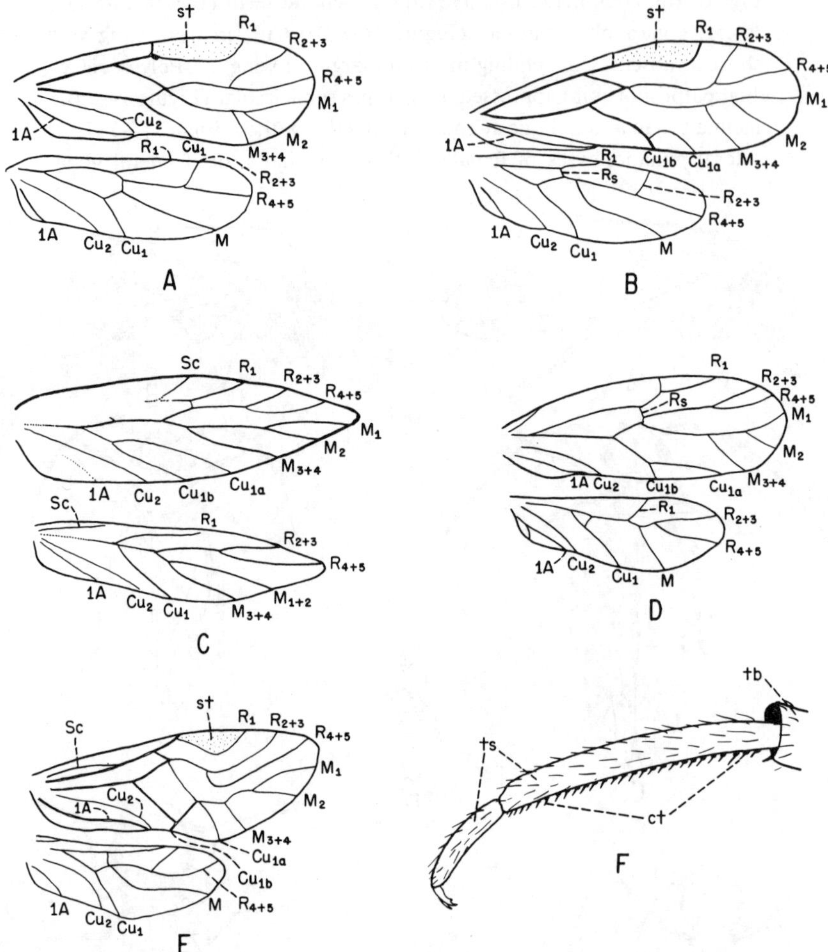

Fig. 14-3. Wings (A-E) and hind tarsus (F) of Psocoptera. A, *Ectopsòcus pùmilis* (Banks) (Pseudocaecilìidae); B, *Lachesílla pediculària* (Linn.) (Pseudocaecilìidae); C, Lepidopsócidae; D, *Psyllipsòcus rambùrii* Selys (Psyllipsócidae); E, *Psòcus* (Psócidae); F, *Psòcus* (Psócidae). *ct,* ctenidia; *st,* stigma; *tb,* tibia; *ts,* tarsal segments. (A, B, D, and E redrawn from Gurney, courtesy of the National Pest Control Association.)

pophyses are absent, then dorsal gonapophyses with hairs (Figure 14-7 A, C); Cu_1 variable 3

3(2′). Labrum with 2 internal sclerotized ridges that are often united anteriorly (Figure 14-5 D); lacinia somewhat bent, oblique, and broad at end with many small teeth (Figure 14-5 H); head long (Figure 14-4 C); tarsal claws straight, with preapical teeth (Figure 14-6 D) ...... **Epipsócidae*** p. 145

3′. Labrum with only 2 little tubercles internally, between which the anterior margin is semicircular (Figure 14-5 E); lacinia straight, usually with a few large teeth (Figure 14-5 I); head short and oblique (Figure 14-4 D) 4

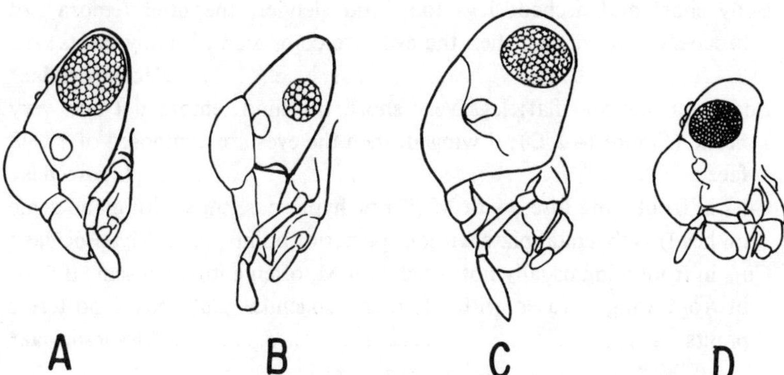

Fig. 14-4. Heads of Psocoptera, lateral view. A, Lepidopsócidae; B, Psyllipsócidae (*Psocathròpus*); C, Epipsócidae (*Epipsòcus*); D, Psócidae (*Psòcus*). (Drawn by Kathryn M. Sommerman.)

4(3′). Cu_{1a} in front wing fused with M (Figure 14-3 E) (if brachypterous, then with gland setae on head); female with lateral and dorsal gonapophyses (Figure 14-7 A) and male with prongs on paraprocts........**Psócidae** p. 145

4′. Cu_{1a} in front wing usually not fused with M (Figure 14-3 A, B), often entirely absent; if Cu_{1a} in front wing is fused with M, then male is without prongs on paraprocts and female has only lateral gonapophyses .... **Pseudocaeciliidae** p. 145

5(1′). Antennae long, with more than 20 segments, which are generally not secondarily ringed (Figure 14-2 F, G); labial palpi 2-segmented (Figure 14-5 A) (suborder Trogiomórpha) 6

5′. Antennae shorter, usually 13-segmented, sometimes with 15 to 17 segments, in which case the segments from 7 distad are secondarily ringed; labial palpi 1- or 2-segmented 8

6(5). Head short and oblique (Figure 14-4 A); winged forms with Cu_2 and 1A in front wing ending separately at wing margin (Figure 14-3 C); a sense peg on inner side of second segment of maxillary palpi (Figure 14-5 F) 7

6′. Head long and perpendicular (Figure 14-4 B); Cu_2 and 1A in front wing usually meeting at wing margin (Figure 14-3 D); no sense peg on inner side of second segment of maxillary palpi (except in the genus *Speléketor*, cave-inhabiting forms occurring in Arizona). . **Psyllipsócidae*** p.145

7(6). Tarsal claws with a preapical tooth (Figure 14-6 B); body and wings densely covered with scales ....**Lepidopsócidae*** p. 145

7′. Tarsal claws simple (Figure 14-6 A); body and wings not covered with scales; front wings either broadly rounded apically, knobby, or lacking ....**Trogìidae** p. 145

8(5′). Labial palpi 2-segmented (as in Figure 14-5 A); if antennae contain more than 13 segments, then the segments from 7 distad are secondarily ringed; hind tarsi of winged forms lacking ctenidia (suborder Troctomórpha) 9

8′. Labial palpi 1-segmented (Figure 14-5 B, C); antennal segments not secondarily ringed; hind tarsi of winged forms usually with ctenidia (Figure 14-3 F) (suborder Eupsòcida, in part) 10

9(8). Body short and arched; legs long and slender, the hind femora not broadened; if winged, then the eyes are composed of many facets.... .... **Pachytróctidae*** p. 145

9′. Body elongate and flat; legs very short, the hind femora flat and very broad (Figure 14-2 D); if winged, then the eyes are composed of 2 to 8 facets .... **Liposcélidae** p. 145

10(8′). Cu_{1a} in front wing fused with M (if brachypterous, then with gland setae on head); subgenital plate without posterior points...... **Myopsócidae*** p. 145

10′. Cu_{1a} in front wing usually not fused with M, often entirely absent; if Cu_{1a} in front wing is fused with M, then subgenital plate has 2 posterior points... **Mesopsócidae*** p. 145

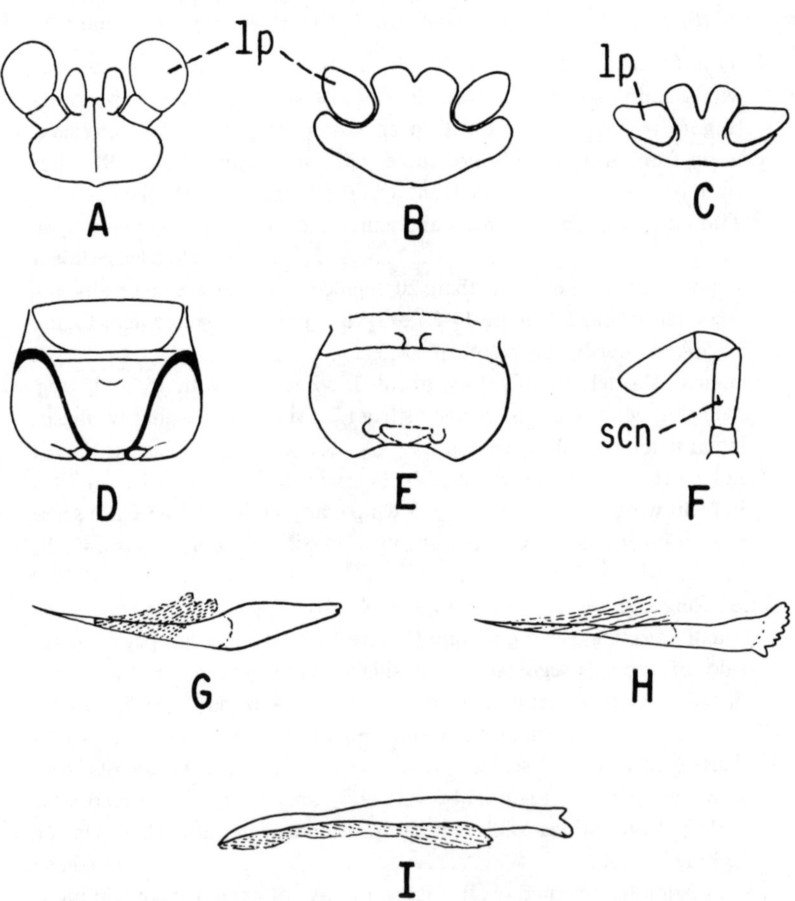

Fig. 14-5. Mouth parts of Psocoptera. A, labium of *Trògium* (Trogìidae); B, labium of *Epipsòcus* (Epipsócidae); C, labium of *Polypsòcus* (Polypsócidae); D, labrum of *Epipsòcus* (Epipsócidae); E, labrum of *Psòcus* (Psócidae); F, maxillary palpus of *Lepidopsòcus* (Lepidopsócidae); G, lacinia (tip at right) of *Polypsòcus* (Polypsócidae); H, lacinia of *Epipsòcus* (Epipsócidae); I, lacinia of *Psòcus* (Psócidae). *lp,* labial palpus; *scn,* sense peg. (Drawn by Kathryn M. Sommerman.)

Fig. 14-6. Tarsal claws of Psocoptera. A, *Trògium* (Trogìidae); B, Lepidopsócidae; C, *Psòcus* (Psócidae); D, *Epipsòcus* (Epipsócidae). (Drawn by Kathryn M. Sommerman).

SUBORDER **Trogiomórpha:** The members of the family **Trogìidae** are either wingless or have the wings reduced. A few species in this group occur in buildings. *Lepinòtus inquilìnus* Heyden is often found in granaries; *Trògium pulsàtor* (Linn.) occurs in houses, barns, and granaries, and is one of the commoner species of booklice. The **Lepidopsócidae** are rather small psocids that occur out of doors and have the wings and body covered with scales; this is a small group, with only three species occurring in the United States. The **Psyllipsócidae** are pale-colored psocids that occur principally in damp, dark places such as cellars and caves; a few species occasionally invade buildings. One species, *Psyllipsòcus rambùrii* Selys, commonly occurs in cellars about the openings of wine and vinegar barrels. Both long- and short-winged individuals occur in some species; in others, one or both pairs of wings may be reduced.

SUBORDER **Troctomórpha:** The family **Pachytróctidae** is a small group, with only two species occurring in the United States. The family **Liposcélidae** includes the booklouse *Liposcèlis divinatòrius* (Müller), which is perhaps the most common psocid occurring in buildings. It occurs in dusty places where the temperature and humidity are fairly high, on shelves, in the cracks of window sills, behind loose wallpaper, and in similar situations; it feeds principally on molds. It is a minute psocid that can be recognized by the enlarged hind femora (Figure 14-2 D).

SUBORDER **Eupsocida:** The majority of the winged psocids belong to this suborder. A few of these psocids may occur in buldings, but most of them occur out of doors. The **Epipsócidae** and **Myopsócidae** are small groups, with two and four species, respectively, occurring in the United States. The family **Psócidae** is the largest in the order, with over 40 species occurring in this country; most of the common barklice belong to this group. None of them is of economic importance. The **Mesopsócidae** and **Polypsócidae** are smaller groups, with 6 and 13 species, respectively, occurring in the United States; they contain barklice, which occur principally out of doors. The family **Pseudocaecilìidae** is a large group, with nearly 40 species occurring in this country; a few of these occasionally occur indoors, particularly in granaries. *Lachesílla pediculària* (Linn.) is often common in buildings where there are cereals, straw products, or fresh plant materials; *Archipsòcus nòmas* Gurney sometimes makes unsightly silken webs on tree trunks and branches in the southern states from Texas to Florida.

COLLECTING AND PRESERVING PSOCOPTERA

The psocids living out of doors can often be collected by sweeping or by beating the branches of trees and shrubs; some species are to be found under bark or stones. Indoor species can be trapped or collected with an aspirator or moistened brush. The best method of preserving psocids is in alcohol (about 80 or 90 percent); when specimens are mounted on pins or points, they shrivel and are usually unsatisfactory for study. The smallest specimens are generally mounted on microscope slides for detailed study.

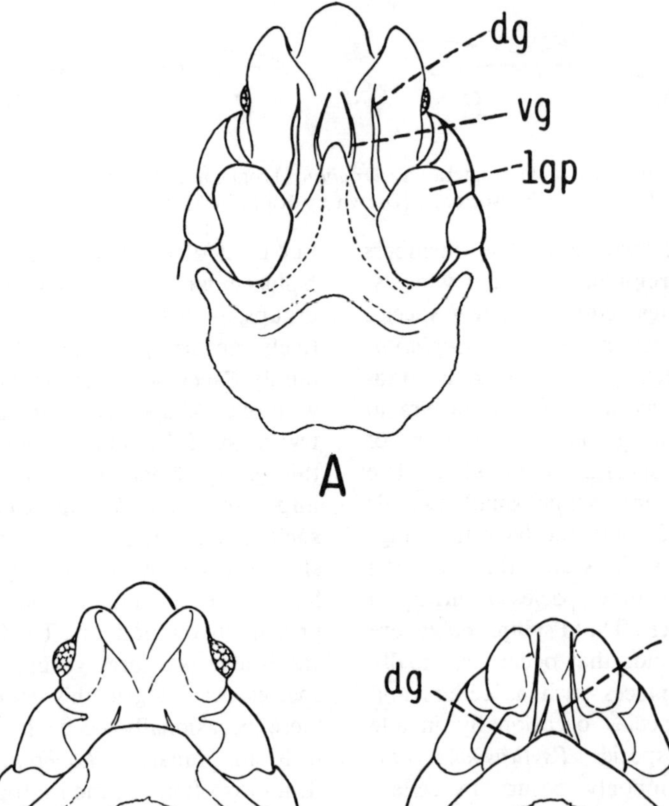

Fig. 14-7. Female genitalia of Psocoptera. A, *Psòcus* (Psócidae); B, *Polypsòcus* (Polypsócidae). with lateral gonapophyses absent; C, *Epipsòcus* (Epipsócidae). *dg,* dorsal gonapophysis; *lgp,* lateral gonapophysis; *vg,* ventral gonapophysis. (Drawn by Kathryn M. Sommerman.)

REFERENCES ON THE PSOCOPTERA

Banks, N. 1929. A classification of the Psocidae. Psyche, 36(4):321-325.

Chapman, P. J. 1930. Corrodentia of the United States of America. I. Suborder Isotecnomera. J. N.Y. Entomol. Soc., 38(3-4):219-290, 319-403; pl. 12-21.

Gurney, A. B. 1950. Corrodentia. In Pest Control Technology, Entomological Section, pp. 129-163, f. 61-63. New York: National Pest Control Association, Inc.

Pearman, J. V. 1936. The taxonomy of the Psocoptera; preliminary sketch. Proc. Roy. Entomol. Soc., London, Ser. B, 5(3):58-62.

Roesler, Rudolf. 1944. Die Gattungen der Copeognathen. Stettin Entomol. Ztg., 105:117-166.

Sommerman, Kathryn M. 1943. Bionomics of *Ectopsocus pumilis* (Banks) (Corrodentia, Caeciliidae). Psyche, 50(3-4):53-63; 7 f.

Sommerman, Kathryn M. 1944. Bionomics of *Amapsocus amabilis* (Walsh) (Corrodentia, Psocidae). Ann. Entomol. Soc. Am., 37(3):359-364; 5 f.

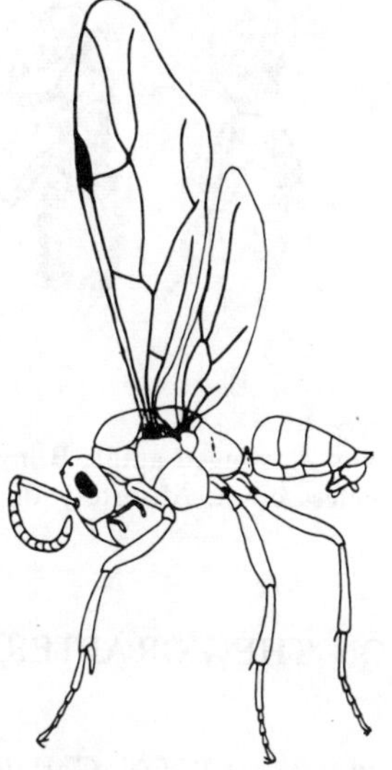

15

Order Zoraptera[1]: Zorapterans

The zorapterans are minute insects, 3 millimeters in length or less, and may be winged or wingless. The winged forms are generally dark-colored, and the wingless forms are pale. The zorapterans are a little like termites in general appearance, and they occur in colonies.

Both winged and wingless forms occur in both sexes. The wings are four in number, membranous, with a reduced venation and with the hind wings smaller than the front wings (Figure 15-1 A). The wings of the adult are eventually shed, as in ants and termites, leaving stubs attached to the thorax. The antennae are moniliform and 9-segmented. The wingless forms (Figure 15-1 D) lack both compound eyes and ocelli, but the winged forms have compound eyes and three ocelli. The tarsi are 2-segmented, and each tarsus bears two claws. The cerci are short and unsegmented and terminate in a long bristle. The abdomen is short, oval, and 10-segmented. The mouth parts are of the chewing type, and the metamorphosis is simple.

The order Zoraptera contains a single family, the **Zorotýpidae,** and a single genus, *Zorotỳpus.* There are 22 known species of zorapterans, of which two occur in the United States. *Z. húbbardi* Caudell has been taken in a number of localities in southeastern United States, from Maryland, Illinois, Missouri, and Oklahoma south to Florida and Texas; it is commonly found under slabs of wood buried in piles of old sawdust. Colonies are also found under bark and in rotting logs, often near termite galleries. *Z. snỳderi* Caudell occurs in Florida and Jamaica. The zorapterans appear to feed on other arthropods (probably as scavengers) and on fungus spores.

[1] Zoraptera: *zor,* pure; *aptera,* wingless. Only wingless individuals were known when this order was described, and the wingless condition was thought to be a distinctive feature of the order.

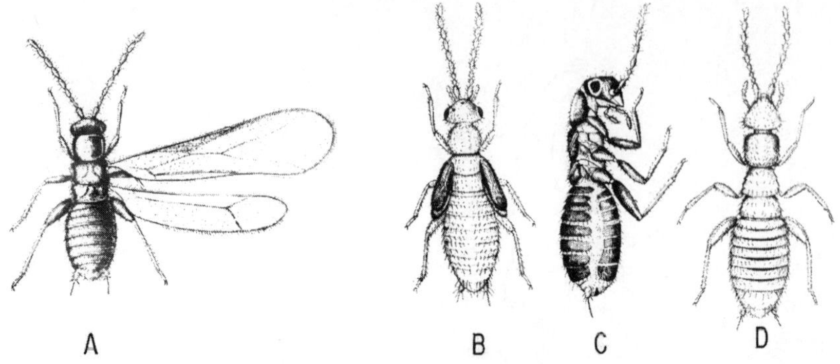

Fig. 15-1. *Zorotỳpus húbbardi* Caudell, female. A, winged adult; B, nymph of winged form; C, dealated winged adult, lateral view; D, wingless adult. (Courtesy of Caudell.)

REFERENCES ON THE ZORAPTERA

Caudell, A. N. 1918. *Zorotypus hubbardi*, a new species of the order Zoraptera from the United States. Can. Entomologist, 50(11):375-381.

Caudell, A. N. 1920. Zoraptera not an apterous order. Proc. Entomol. Soc. Wash., 22(5):84-97; pl. 6.

Caudell, A. N. 1927. *Zorotypus longiceratus*, a new species of Zoraptera from Jamaica. Proc. Entomol. Soc., Wash. 29(6):144-145; 2 f.

Gurney, Ashley B. 1938. A synopsis of the order Zoraptera, with notes on the biology of *Zorotypus hubbardi* Caudell. Proc. Entomol. Soc. Wash., 40(3):57-87; 56 f.

Riegel, Garland T. 1963. The distribution of *Zorotypus hubbardi* (Zoraptera). Ann. Antomol. Soc. Am., 56(6):744-747; 3 f.

Riegel, Garland T. and Max B. Ferguson. 1960. New state records of Zoraptera. Entomol. News, 71(8):213-216.

St. Amand, W. 1954. Records of the order Zoraptera from South Carolina. Entomol. News, 65(5):131.

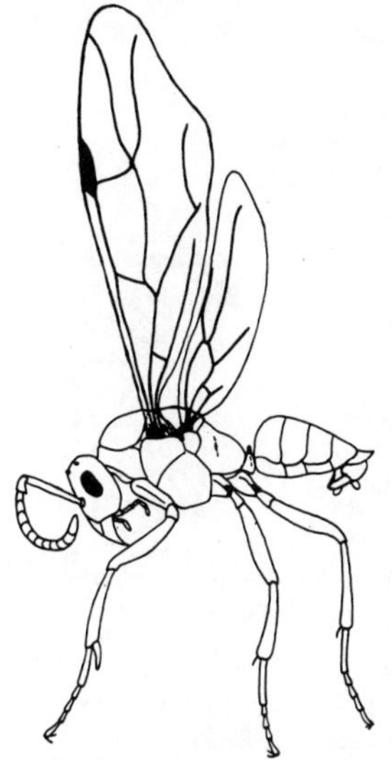

16

Order Mallophaga[1]: Chewing Lice

The chewing lice are small, usually flattened, wingless external parasites of birds and mammals; most of them are parasitic on birds, and the lice of this order are often referred to as the bird lice. They have chewing mouth parts and feed on bits of hair, feathers, or skin of the host. The young resemble the adults, and all stages are passed on the host. Transmission from one host to another is usually accomplished when two hosts come in contact, as in the nest; these lice are unable to survive long away from the host. Most species occur on only one or a few species of hosts. None of the Mallophaga is known to attack man; persons handling birds or other animals infested with these lice may occasionally get the lice on themselves, but the lice do not stay long on man.

Many chewing lice are important pests of domestic animals, particularly poultry. The lice cause considerable irritation, and heavily infested animals appear run-down and emaciated, and if not actually killed by the lice, are rendered easy prey for various diseases. Different species of lice attack different types of poultry and domestic mammals, and each species usually infests a particular part of the host's body. The control of chewing lice usually involves treatment of the infested animal with a suitable dust or dip.

[1] Mallophaga: *mallo,* wool; *phaga,* eat.

The Mallophaga are divided into several families, primarily on the basis of the structure of the antennae, mouth parts, and tarsi. The following key will serve to separate the families likely to be encountered on hosts in the United States.

KEY TO THE FAMILIES OF MALLOPHAGA

1. Antennae more or less clubbed, and usually concealed in grooves; maxillary palpi present (Figures 16-1 A and 16-2) (suborder Amblýcera) 2

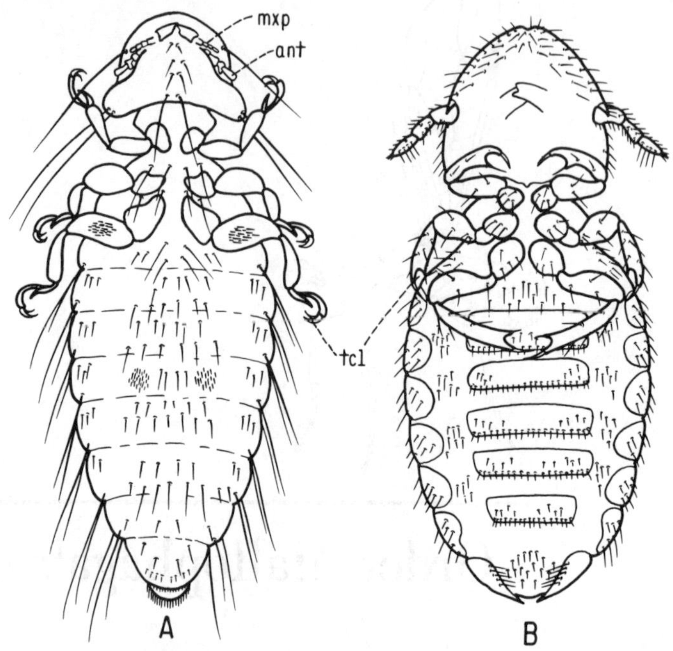

Fig. 16-1. A, the shaft louse of chickens, *Ménopon gállinae* (Linn.) (Menopónidae), ventral view of female; B, the cattle biting louse, *Bovícola bòvis* (Linn.). (Trichodéctidae), ventral view of female. *ant*, antenna; *mxp*, maxillary palpus; *tcl*, tarsal claws.

1′.	Antennae filiform and exposed; maxillary palpi absent (Figures 16-1 B and 16-3) (suborder Ischnócera) 5	
2(1).	Tarsi with 1 claw or none; parasitic on guinea pigs .... **Gyrópidae**	p. 150
2′.	Tarsi with 2 claws; parasitic on birds 3	
3(2′).	Antennae lying in grooves on sides of head; head broadly triangular, and expanded behind the eyes (Figure 16-1 A) .... **Menopónidae**	p. 150
3′.	Antennae lying in cavities, which open ventrally; head not broadly triangular and expanded behind the eyes (Figure 16-2) 4	
4(3′).	Sides of head with a conspicuous swelling in front of eye, at base of antennae (Figure 16-2 A) .... **Laemobothrìidae**	p. 150
4′.	Sides of head without such swellings (Figure 16-2 B).......... **Ricínidae**	p. 150
5(1′).	Tarsi with 2 claws; antennae 5-segmented (Figure 16-3); parasitic on birds .... **Philoptéridae**	p. 151
5′.	Tarsi with 1 claw; antennae usually 3-segmented (Figure 16-1 B); parasitic on mammals .... **Trichodéctidae**	p. 151

The family **Menopónidae** is a large one whose members attack birds; two important pests of poultry in this group are the chicken body louse, *Menacánthus stramíneus* (Nitzsch), and the shaft louse, *Ménopon gállinae* (Linn.) (Figure 16-1 A). The lice in the family **Gyrópidae** are chiefly confined to Central and South America; two species occur in the United States on guinea pigs. The **Laemobothrìidae** are a small group whose members are parasitic on water birds and on birds of prey. The **Ricínidae** are another small group, parasitic chiefly on sparrows and other passerine birds, and on

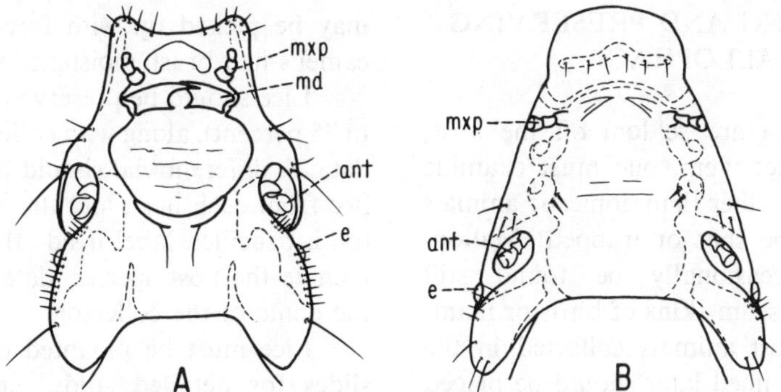

Fig. 16-2. A, head of *Laemobóthrion* (Laemobothrìidae), ventral view; B, head of a ricinid (Ricínidae), ventral view. *ant*, antenna; *e*, eye; *md*, mandible; *mxp*, maxillary palpus.

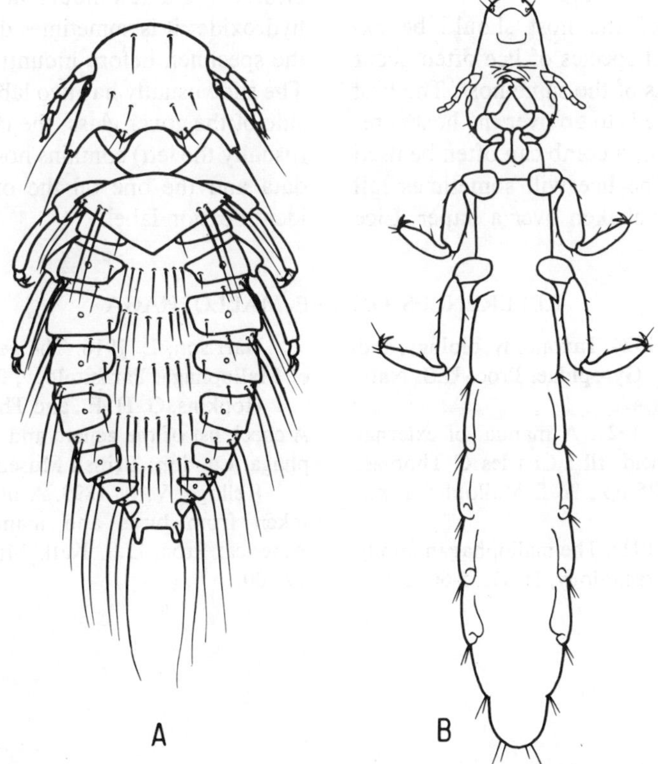

Fig. 16-3. Philoptéridae, ventral views. A, the large turkey louse, *Chelopístes meleágridis* (Linn.); B, *Esthiópterum crassicórne* (Scopoli), a louse of the blue-winged teal.

hummingbirds. The family **Philoptéridae** is the largest in the order and contains species parasitizing a wide variety of birds; two important pests of poultry in this group are the chicken head louse, *Cuclotogáster heterógraphus* (Nitzsch), and the large turkey louse, *Chelopístes meleágridis* (Linn.). The lice in the family **Trichodéctidae** are parasitic on mammals; some important pest species in this group are the cattle biting louse, *Bovícola bòvis* (Linn.) (Figure 16-1 B), the horse biting louse, *B. équi* (Linn.), and the dog biting louse, *Trichodéctes cànis* (DeGeer).

COLLECTING AND PRESERVING MALLOPHAGA

Mallophaga are seldom off the host; hence, to collect them, one must examine the host. Hosts other than domestic animals usually must be shot or trapped; Mallophaga may occasionally be found still attached to museum skins of birds or mammals. Small host animals collected in the field to be examined later should be placed in a paper bag and the bag tightly closed; any lice that fall or crawl off the host can then be found in the bag.

All parts of the host should be examined; different species of lice often occur on different parts of the same host. The best way to locate lice is to go over the host carefully with forceps; a comb can often be used to advantage. The lice will sometimes fall off if the host is shaken over a paper. Lice may be picked up with forceps or with a camel's-hair brush moistened with alcohol.

Lice should be preserved in alcohol (70 to 75 percent), along with collection and host data. A different vial should be used for the lice from each host, and the collection data (on a pencilled label inside the vial) should include the host species, date, locality, and the name of the collector.

Lice must be mounted on microscope slides for detailed study; specimens preserved on pins or points are usually unsatisfactory. Specimens to be mounted are first cleared for a few hours in cold potassium hydroxide; it is sometimes desirable to stain the specimen before mounting it on a slide. The slide usually has two labels, one on each side of the cover glass; the label on one side (usually the left) contains host and collection data and the one on the other side is the identification label.

REFERENCES ON THE MALLOPHAGA

Ewing, H. E. 1924. Taxonomy, biology, and distribution of the Gyropidae. Proc. U.S. Natl. Museum, 63(20):1-42.

Ewing, H. E. 1929. A manual of external parasites. Springfield, Ill.: Charles C Thomas, Publisher. xiv+225 pp., 96 f. Mallophaga, pp. 90-126.

Ferris, G. F. 1924. The mallophagan family Menoponidae. Parasitology, 16(1):55-66; 5 f.

Harrison, L. 1916. The genera and species of Mallophaga. Parasitology, 9(1):1-156.

Hopkins, G. H. E., and Theresa Clay. 1952. A check list of the genera and species of Mallophaga. London: British Museum. 362 pp.

Kellogg, V. L. 1899. A list of Mallophaga taken from birds and mammals of North America. Proc. U.S. Natl. Museum, 22(1183): 39-100.

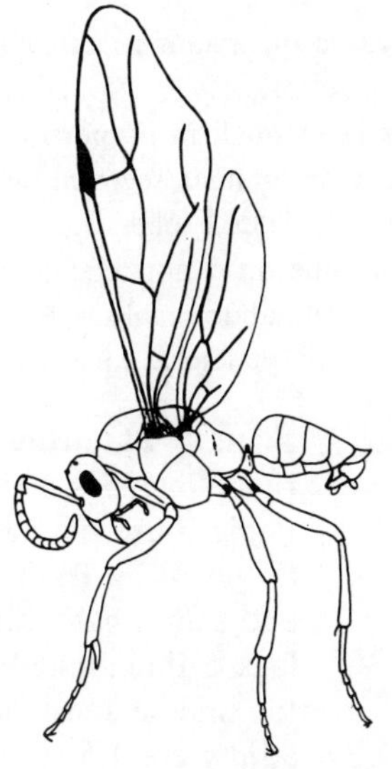

17

Order Anoplura[1]: Sucking Lice

The sucking lice are small wingless external parasites that feed by sucking blood. They differ from the chewing lice (Mallophaga) in that they have sucking rather than chewing mouth parts, and the head is narrower than the thorax. The Anoplura are parasites of mammals, while the Mallophaga are parasites of birds and mammals. The order Anoplura contains several species parasitic on domestic animals, and two species that attack man; these insects are irritating pests, and some of them are important vectors of disease. Most species are restricted to one or a few types of hosts. The metamorphosis is simple.

The mouth parts of a sucking louse consist of three piercing stylets that are normally carried withdrawn into a stylet sac in the head. When a louse feeds, the stylets are everted through a rostrum at the front of the head; the rostrum is provided with tiny hooks with which the louse attaches to its host while feeding.

The tarsi of the sucking lice are 1-segmented and provided with a single large claw that usually fits against a thumblike process at the end of the tibia; this forms an efficient mechanism for hanging to the hairs of the host.

[1] Anoplura: *anopl,* unarmed; *ura,* tail.

The four families of sucking lice that occur in the United States may be separated by the following key.

KEY TO THE FAMILIES OF ANOPLURA

1. Body thickly beset with short stout spines, or with spines and scales; parasitic on marine mammals .... **Echinophthiriidae** p. 154

1′. Body with spines or hairs, but never with scales; parasitic on land mammals 2

2(1′). Eyes or eye tubercles present (Figure 17-2); parasitic on man and other primates 3

2′. Eyes lacking (Figure 17-1); parasitic on mammals other than man and other primates .... **Haematopínidae** p. 154

3(2). Body broadly oval, crablike, the head small in proportion to the thorax (Figure 17-2 B); first apparent abdominal segment with 3 pairs of spiracles; abdominal segments with lateral lobes .... **Phthirìidae** p. 154

3′. Body more elongate, not crablike, the head not much smaller than the thorax (Figure 17-2 A); first apparent abdominal segment with 1 pair of spiracles; abdominal segments without lateral lobes ...... **Pedicùlidae** p. 154

FAMILY **Echinophthirìidae :** The lice in this group are spiny or scaly, and attack marine mammals such as seals, sea lions, and walruses. At least some species burrow into the skin of their host.

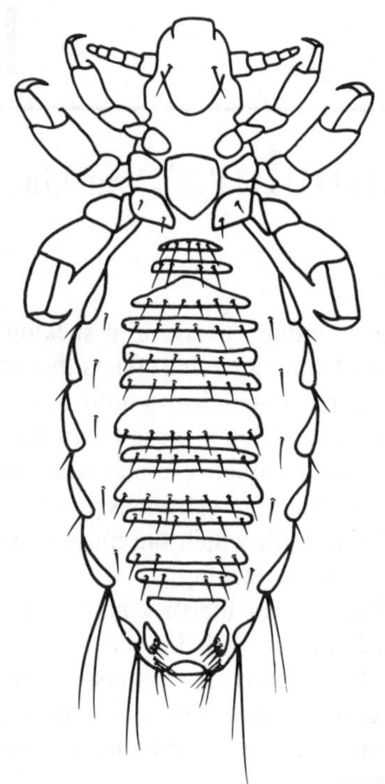

Fig. 17-1. The spined rat louse, *Pólyplax spinulòsa* (Burmeister), female, ventral view (Haematopínidae).

FAMILY **Haematopínidae:** The family Haematopínidae is a fairly large group and contains the sucking lice of horses, cattle, hogs, sheep, and other animals. The control of these lice usually involves treating the host with dusts, sprays, or dips.

FAMILY **Phthirìidae:** The family Phthirìidae includes a single species, the crab or pubic louse of man, *Phthírius pùbis* Linn. (Figure 17-2 B). This insect is broadly oval and somewhat crab-shaped, the front tibiae lack a thumblike process, and the claws of the middle and hind legs are very large; the adults are 1.5 to 2.0 millimeters in length. This louse occurs chiefly in the pubic region, but in hairy individuals may occur almost anywhere on the body. The eggs are attached to the body hairs.

FAMILY **Pedicùlidae :** The family Pedicùlidae includes the head and body lice of man; these lice are usually considered as two varieties of a single species, *Pedículus humànus* Linn. The head and body lice are narrower and more elongate than crab lice, each tibia bears a thumblike projection, and the abdomen lacks lateral projections (Figure 17-2 A); the adults vary in length from about 2.5 to 3.5 millimeters.

The head and body lice have a similar life history, but differ somewhat in habits. The head louse occurs chiefly on the head, and its eggs are attached to the hair; the body louse occurs chiefly on the body, and its eggs are laid on the clothing, chiefly along the seams. The eggs hatch in about a week, and the entire life cycle from egg to adult requires about a month. Lice feed at frequent intervals, and individual feedings last a few minutes. Body lice usually hang onto clothing while feeding and often remain on the clothing when it is removed. The head louse is transmitted from person to person largely through the promiscuous use of

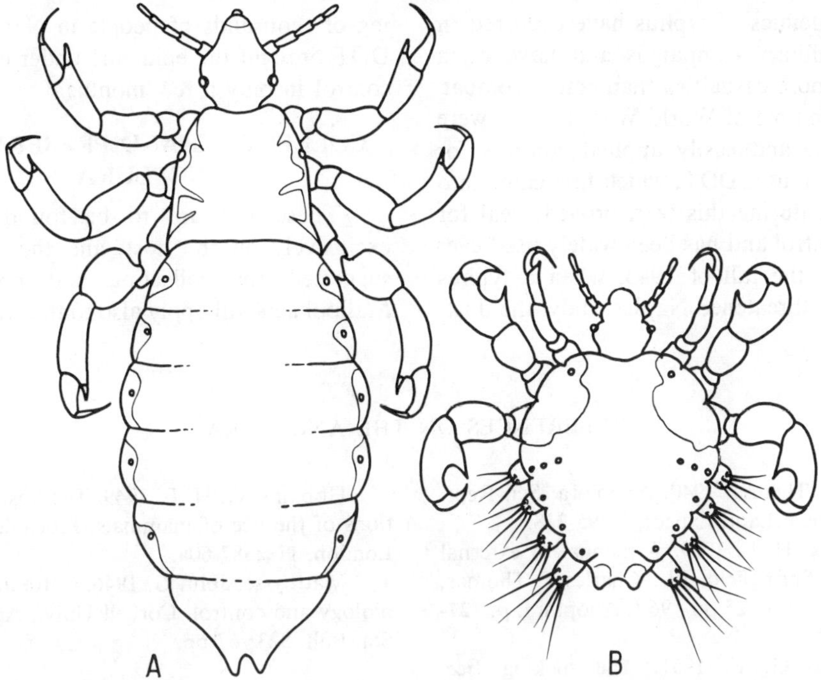

Fig. 17-2. Human lice. A, body louse, female (Pediculidae); B, crab louse, female (Phthiriidae). 20 ×. The abdominal projections in B are a feature that distinguishes the crab louse from the body louse.

combs, hair brushes, and caps; the body louse is transmitted by clothing and bedding, and at night may migrate from one pile of clothes to another.

The body louse (also called "cootie" or "seam squirrel") is an important vector of human disease. The most important disease it transmits is epidemic typhus, which frequently occurs in epidemic proportions and may have a mortality rate as high as 70 percent. Body lice become infected by feeding on a typhus patient and are able to infect another person a week or so later. Infection results from scratching the feces of the louse, or the crushed louse itself, into the skin; this disease is not transmitted by the bite of the louse. Another important louse-borne disease is a type of relapsing fever; this disease is transmitted by the infected louse being crushed and rubbed into the skin; neither the feces nor the bite of the louse is infective. A third louse-borne disease is trench fever; this disease occurred in epidemic proportions during World War I, but since then has not been very important.

People who bathe and change clothes regularly seldom become infested with lice, but when they go for long periods without bathing or changing clothes and live in crowded conditions, lousiness is likely to be prevalent. The latter conditions are often common during wartime, when living quarters are crowded, sanitation facilities are at a minimum, and people go for long periods without a change of clothes. If a louse-borne disease such as typhus ever gets started in a population that is heavily infested with body lice, it can quickly spread to epidemic proportions.

The control of body lice usually involves dusting individuals with DDT or some other insecticide; clothing must also be treated, for the eggs are laid on it, and adult lice often cling to clothing when it is removed. The treatment of clothing usually involves fumigation or sterilization by heat.

Epidemics of typhus have occurred in many military campaigns and have often caused more casualties than actual combat. Up to the time of World War II, there were no simple and easily applied controls for the body louse; DDT, which first came into wide use during this war, proved ideal for louse control and has been widely used ever since. In the fall of 1943, when a typhus epidemic threatened Naples, Italy, the dusting of thousands of people in Naples with DDT brought the epidemic under complete control in only a few months.

COLLECTING AND PRESERVING ANOPLURA

These lice are to be found almost exclusively on the host, and the methods suggested for collecting and preserving Mallophaga will apply also to the Anoplura.

REFERENCES ON THE ANOPLURA

Clay, Theresa. 1940. Anoplura. Sci. Rept. Brit. Graham Land Exped., 1:295-318.

Ewing, H. E. 1929. A manual of external parasites. Springfield, Ill.: Charles C Thomas, Publisher. xiv+225 pp., 96 f. Anoplura, p. 127-152.

Ferris, G. F. 1951. The sucking lice. Pacific Coast Entomol. Soc. Mem., 1:x+320 pp.; 124 f.

Hopkins, G. H. E. 1949. The host associations of the lice of mammals. Proc. Zool. Soc. London, 119:387-604.

Matthysse, John G. 1946. Cattle lice, their biology and control. Cornell Univ., Agr. Expt. Sta. Bull. 823; 67 pp.

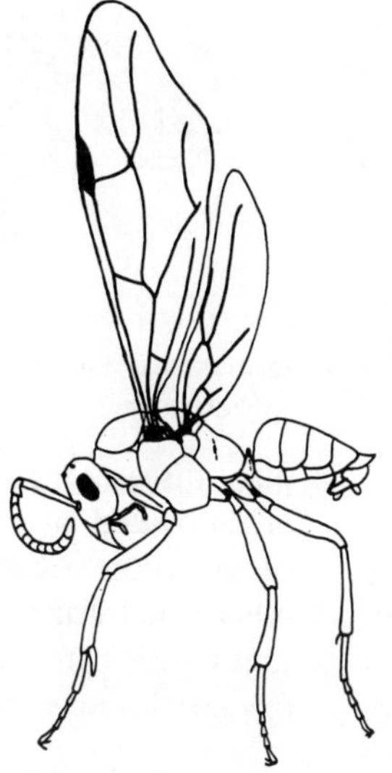

18

Order Thysanoptera:[1] Thrips

The thrips are minute slender-bodied insects 0.5 to 5.0 millimeters in length (some tropical species are nearly ½ inch in length). Wings may be present or absent; the wings when fully developed are four in number, very long and narrow with few or no veins, and fringed with long hairs. The fringe of hairs on the wings gives the order its name. The mouth parts are of the sucking type, and the proboscis is a stout, conical, asymmetrical structure located posteriorly on the ventral surface of the head; there are three stylets: one mandible (the left one; the right mandible is vestigial) and the laciniae of the two maxillae. The antennae are usually short, and 6- to 10-segmented. The tarsi are 1- or 2-segmented, with one or two claws, and are bladderlike at the tip. An ovipositor is present in some thrips; in others, the tip of the abdomen is tubular and an ovipositor is lacking.

The metamorphosis of thrips is somewhat intermediate between simple and complete (Figure 18-1). The first two instars have no wings externally and are usually called larvae; in at least some cases, the wings are developing internally during these two instars. In the suborder Terebrántia, the third and fourth instars (only the third instar in *Franklínothrips*) are inactive, do not feed, and have external wings; the third instar is called the prepupa, and the fourth the pupa. The pupa is sometimes enclosed in a cocoon. In the suborder Tubulífera, the third and fourth instars are prepupae (the third does not have external wings), and the fifth instar is the pupa. The stage following the pupa is the adult. This type of metamorphosis resembles simple metamorphosis in that more than one preadult instar (except in *Franklínothrips*) has external wings; it resembles complete metamorphosis in that at least some of the wing development is internal, and there is a quiescent (pupal) instar preceding the adult.

[1] Thysanoptera: *thysano,* fringe; *ptera,* wings.

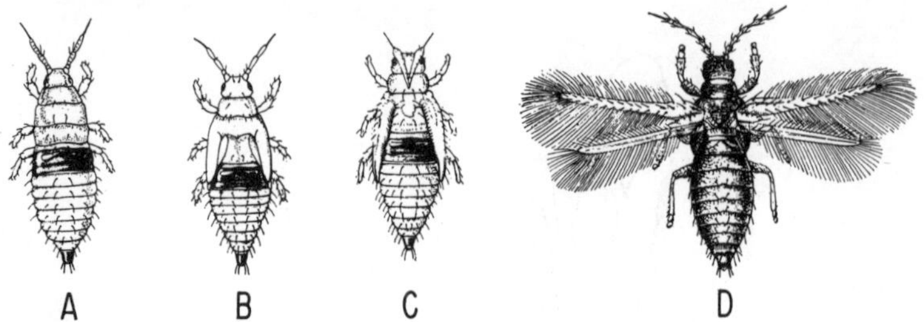

Fig. 18-1. The red-banded thrips, *Sélenothrips rubrocínctus* (Giard). A, full-grown larva; B, prepupa; C, pupa; D, adult female. (Courtesy of USDA.)

The two sexes of thrips are similar in appearance, but the males are usually smaller. Parthenogenesis occurs in many species, and males are either rare or unknown in some species. Those thrips that have an ovipositor usually insert their eggs in plant tissues; the thrips that lack an ovipositor usually lay their eggs in crevices or under bark. Young thrips are relatively inactive. Generally there are several generations a year.

A great many of the thrips are plant feeders, attacking flowers, leaves, fruit, twigs, or buds; they feed on a great many types of plants. They are particularly abundant in the flower heads of daisies and dandelions. They destroy plant cells by their feeding, and some species act as vectors of plant disease; many species are serious pests of cultivated plants. A few thrips feed on fungus spores, and a few are predaceous on other small arthropods. These insects sometimes occur in enormous numbers, and a few species may bite man.

CLASSIFICATION OF THE THYSANOPTERA

This order is divided into two suborders, the Terebrántia and the Tubulífera; the females of the Terebrántia have a sawlike ovipositor, and the abdomen in both sexes of the Tubulífera is tubular at the tip and there is no ovipositor. The thrips that are destructive to crop plants belong principally to the suborder Terebrántia. Each suborder is divided into a number of families.

The families occurring in the United States may be separated by the following key. The groups here treated as families are by some authorities considered superfamilies.

KEY TO THE FAMILIES OF THYSANOPTERA

1. Female usually with a sawlike ovipositor, the last abdominal segment conical (Figures 18-2 A, B and 18-4 A, B, D); apex of abdomen of male broadly rounded; front wings, if present, with 1 or 2 longitudinal veins, and the membrane with microscopic hairs; antennae with 6 to 10 segments (suborder Terebrántia) 2

1′. Female without an ovipositor, the last abdominal segment tubular in both sexes (Figures 18-2 C and 18-4 C); front wings, if present, either veinless or with a short median vein that does not extend to the wing tip, and the membrane without microscopic hairs; antennae with 7 to 8 segments (suborder Tubulífera)............................. **Phloeothrípidae** p. 160

2(1). Ovipositor curved upward (Figure 18-2 B); front wings relatively broad, with tips rounded; antennae 9-segmented (Figure 18-3 B); body not flattened; usually predaceous .... **Aeolothrípidae** p. 159

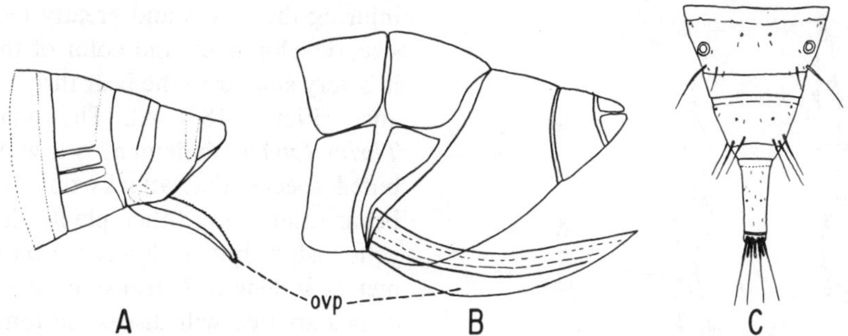

Fig. 18-2. Abdominal structures of Thysanoptera. A, apex of abdomen of *Taèniothrips incónsequens* (Uzel) (Thrípidae), lateral view, showing decurved ovipositor; B, apex of abdomen of *Mélanothríps* (Aeolothrípidae), lateral view, showing up-curved ovipositor; C, apex of abdomen of *Háplothríps hispánicus* Priesner (Phloeothrípidae), dorsal view. *ovp,* ovipositor. (Modified from Pesson.)

2′. Ovipositor, if developed, curved downward (Figure 18-2 A); front wings narrower, usually pointed at tip; antennae 6- to 10-segmented; body more or less flattened 3

3(2′). Pronotum with a longitudinal suture on each side; antennae moniliform, segments 3 and 4 without sense cones, but with a tympanumlike sensory area at apex; front and hind femora thickened; ovipositor much reduced . . . . **Merothrípidae** p. 159

3′. Pronotum without longitudinal sutures; antennae not moniliform, often with sense cones; femora slender; ovipositor well developed 4

4(3′). Antennae 9- or 10-segmented, either without sense cones or with short triangular ones; front tarsi usually with a clawlike appendage at base of second segment . . . . **Heterothrípidae** p. 159

4′. Antennae 6- to 9-segmented, and with slender sense cones (Figure 18-3 C); tarsi sometimes with clawlike appendages at apex of either first or second segment . . . . **Thrípidae** p. 159

FAMILY **Aeolothrípidae**—Broad-Winged or Banded Thrips: The front wings in this group are relatively broad, with two longitudinal veins extending from the base of the wing nearly to the tip, and usually with several cross veins. The adults are dark-colored and often have the wings banded or mottled. The most common species in this group is the banded thrips, *Aeólothrips fasciàtus* (Linn.). The adult is yellowish to dark brown, with three white bands on the wings; the larvae are yellowish, shading into orange posteriorly. The adults are about 1.6 millimeters in length. This species occurs on various plants and is often common in the flower heads of clover; it feeds on other thrips, aphids, mites, and various other small insects. It is widely distributed, and occurs in Europe, Asia, Africa, and Hawaii, as well as in North America.

FAMILY **Merothrípidae** — Large - legged Thrips: The members of this group may be recognized by the enlarged front and hind femora and by the two longitudinal sutures on the pronotum. The only common species in this family is *Mèrothrips mòrgani* Hood, which occurs in eastern United States under bark, in debris, and in fungi.

FAMILY **Heterothrípidae:** This family contains a fairly common species. *Héterothrips arisaèmae* Hood, which feeds in the flowers of jack-in-the-pulpit.

FAMILY **Thrípidae**—Common Thrips: This

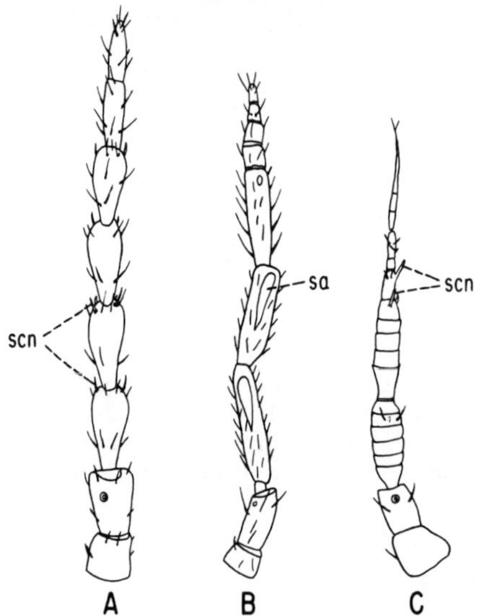

Fig. 18-3. Antennae of Thysanoptera. A, *Háplothrips* (Phloeothrípidae); B, *Aeólothrips* (Aeolothrípidae); C, *Hèliothrips* (Thrípidae). *sa,* sensory area; *scn,* sense cone. (Redrawn from Pesson.)

family is the largest in the order and contains most of the species that are of economic importance. The wings are narrower than in the Aeolothrípidae and are more pointed at the tip; the antennae are 6- to 9-segmented. These thrips are mostly plant feeders, and a number of species are serious pests of cultivated plants.

The pear thrips, *Taèniothríps incónsequens* (Uzel) (Figure 18-4 B), attacks the buds, blossoms, young leaves, and fruit of pears, plums, cherries, and other plants. The adults are brown with pale wings, and 1.2 to 1.3 millimeters in length. This species has a single generation a year and overwinters as a pupa in the soil. The adults emerge in early spring and attack the fruit trees, and oviposit on the petioles of the leaves and fruits. The young feed until about June, when they drop to the ground and remain dormant until about October, at which time they pupate and go into hibernation. This species occurs on the East and West coasts of the United States.

The gladiolus thrips, *Taèniothríps símplex* (Morison), is a serious pest of gladiolus, injuring the leaves and greatly reducing the size, development, and color of the flowers; it is very similar to the pear thrips in appearance (Figure 18-4 A). The onion thrips, *Thríps tabàci* Lindeman, is a widely distributed species that attacks onions, tobacco, beans, and many other plants; it is a pale yellowish or brownish insect 1.0 to 1.2 millimeters in length. It transmits the virus that causes spotted wilt disease in tomatoes and other plants. The greenhouse thrips, *Hèliothríps haémorrhoidàlis* (Bouché) (Figure 18-4 D), is a tropical species that occurs out of doors in the warmer parts of the world and is a serious pest in greenhouses in the North; the male of this species is very rare. The flower thrips, *Frankliniélla trítici* (Fitch), is a common and widely distributed pest of grasses, grains, truck crops, weeds, trees, and shrubs; it is a slender yellow and orange insect 1.2 to 1.3 millimeters in length. The six-spotted thrips, *Scòlothrips sexmaculàtus* (Pergande), is a little less than a millimeter in length and is yellow with three black spots on each front wing; it is predaceous on plant-feeding mites. The grain thrips, *Lìmothrips cereàlium* Haliday, is a dark-brown to black thrips, 1.2 to 1.4 millimeters in length, that feeds on various cereals and grasses; it is sometimes quite abundant, and may bite man.

FAMILY **Phloeothrípidae:** The family Phloeothrípidae is a rather large group, most species of which are larger and stouter-bodied than the thrips in the suborder Terebrántia. One Australian species, *Idólothrips marginàtus* Haliday, is 10 to 14 millimeters in length. These thrips are mostly dark brown or black, often with light-colored or mottled wings. Most of them are spore feeders; some are predaceous, feeding on small insects and mites; a few are plant feeders, and some of these may be of economic importance. The lily-bulb thrips, *Lìothrips vanèeckei* Priesner, is a dark-colored species about 2 millimeters in length (Figure 18-4 C) which feeds on lilies and injures the bulbs. The black hunter, *Lépto-*

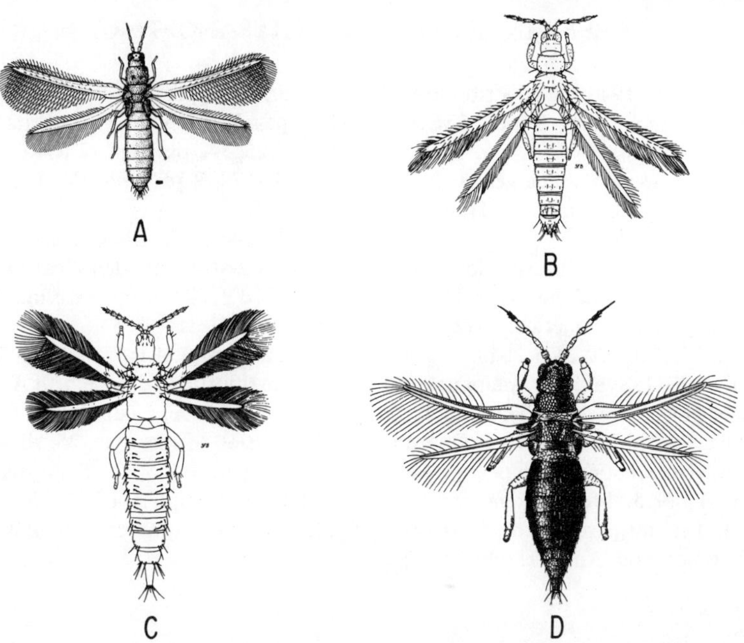

Fig. 18-4. Thrips. A, the gladiolus thrips, *Taèniothríps símplex* (Morison) (Thrípidae); B, the pear thrips, *Taèniothríps incónsequens* (Uzel) (Thrípidae); C, the lily bulb thrips. *Lìothrips vaneèckei* Preisner (Phloeothrípidae); D, the greenhouse thrips, *Hèliothríps haemorrhoidàlis* (Bouché) (Thrípidae). (A, courtesy of the Utah Agricultural Experiment Station; B, courtesy of Bailey and the University of California Experiment Station; C, courtesy of Bailey and the California Department of Agriculture; D, courtesy of USDA.)

thrips máli (Fitch), is a fairly common predaceous species. *Aleuródothrips fasciapénnis* (Franklin), which is common in Florida, is predaceous on whiteflies. *Háplothrips leucánthemi* (Schrank) is a black thrips that is common in daisy flowers.

COLLECTING AND PRESERVING THYSANOPTERA

Thrips may be found on flowers, foliage, fruits, bark, fungi, and in debris. The species occurring on vegetation are most easily collected by sweeping; they may be removed from the net by stunning the entire net contents and sorting out the thrips later, or the net contents may be shaken out onto a paper and the thrips picked up with an aspirator or with a moistened camel's-hair brush; dark species are best seen on a light paper, and the light species on a dark paper. If host data are desired, the specimens should be collected directly from the host plant; the best way to collect flower-frequenting species is to collect the flowers in a paper bag and examine them later in the laboratory. The species that occur in debris and in similar situations are usually collected by means of a Berlese funnel or by sifting the material in which they occur. Bark- and branch-inhabiting species can be collected with a beating umbrella.

Thrips should be preserved in liquid and mounted on microscope slides for detailed study; they may be mounted on points, but specimens so mounted are usually not very satisfactory. The best killing solution is AGA, which contains 8 parts of 95 percent alcohol, 5 parts of distilled water, 1 part of glycerine, and 1 part of glacial acetic acid; after a few weeks, specimens should be transferred from this solution to alcohol (about 80 percent) for permanent preservation.

REFERENCES ON THE THYSANOPTERA

Bailey, Stanley F. 1940. The distribution of injurious thrips in the United States. J. Econ. Entomol., 33(1):133-136.

Bailey, Stanley F. 1951. The genus *Aeolothrips* Haliday in North America. Hilgardia, 21(2):43-80; 73 f.

Hinds, W. E. 1902. Contribution to a monograph of the insects of the order Thysanoptera inhabiting North America. Proc. U.S. Natl. Muscum, 26(1310):79-242; 11 pl.

Moulton, D. 1911. Synopsis, catalogue, and bibliography of North American Thysanoptera. U.S. Dep. Agr. Bur. Entomol. Plant Quarantine, Tech. Ser., No. 21; 56 pp., 6 pl.

Peterson, A. 1915. Morphological studies on the head and mouthparts of the Thysanoptera. Ann. Entomol. Soc. Am., 8(1):20-67; 7 pl.

Priesner, H. 1926-1928. Die Thysanopteren Europas. Wien: Verlag Von Fritz Wagner. Abh. I-II, 1926, 342 pp., 4 pl., 2 text f. Abh. III, 1927, pp. 343-570, 2 pl. Abh. IV, 1928, pp. 571-755, 10 text f.

Priesner, H. 1949. Genera Thysanopterorum. Keys for the identification of the genera of the order Thysanoptera. Bull. Soc. Fouad I[er] Entomol., 33:31-157.

Stannard, Lewis J., Jr. 1957. The phylogeny and classification of the North American genera of the suborder Tubulifera (Thysanoptera). Illinois Biol. Monog. No. 25. vii+200 pp., 144 f.

Watson, J. R. 1923. Synopsis and catalogue of the Thysanoptera of North America. Univ. Florida Agr. Exp. Sta. Bull. 168; 100 pp.

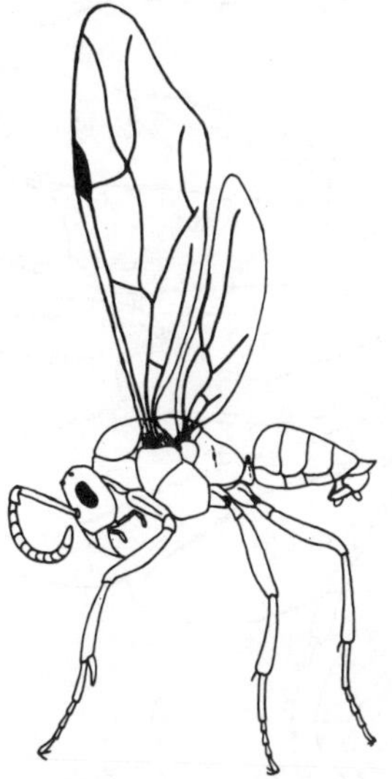

19

Order Hemiptera[1]: Bugs

The term "bug" is used by the general public for a great many different animals, and by entomologists for occasional insects in other orders (for example, mealybugs, lightningbugs); when used for an insect in this order, the "bug" of the name is written as a separate word. The Hemiptera are sometimes called the "true" bugs, to distinguish them from the occasional insects in other orders to which the term "bug" is applied.

One of the most distinctive features of the Hemiptera, and one from which the order gets its name, is the structure of the front wings. In most of the Hemiptera the basal portion of the front wing is thickened and leathery, and the apical portion is membranous; this type of wing is called a hemelytron (plural, hemelytra). The hind wings are entirely membranous and are slightly shorter than the front wings. The wings at rest are held flat over the abdomen, with the membranous tips of the front wings overlapping.

The mouth parts of the Hemiptera are of the piercing-sucking type and are in the form of a slender segmented beak that arises from the front part of the head and usually extends back along the ventral side of the body, sometimes as far as the base of the hind legs (Figure 19-1 B, *bk*). The segmented portion of the beak is the labium, which serves as a sheath for the four piercing stylets (two mandibles and two maxillae); the maxillae fit together in the beak to form two channels, a food channel and a salivary channel (Figure 2-11). There are no palpi, though certain tiny lobelike structures on the beak of some aquatic bugs are thought by some authorities to represent palpi.

The Hemiptera and the Homoptera are very similar in many respects and are

[1] Hemiptera: *hemi*, half; *ptera*, wings.

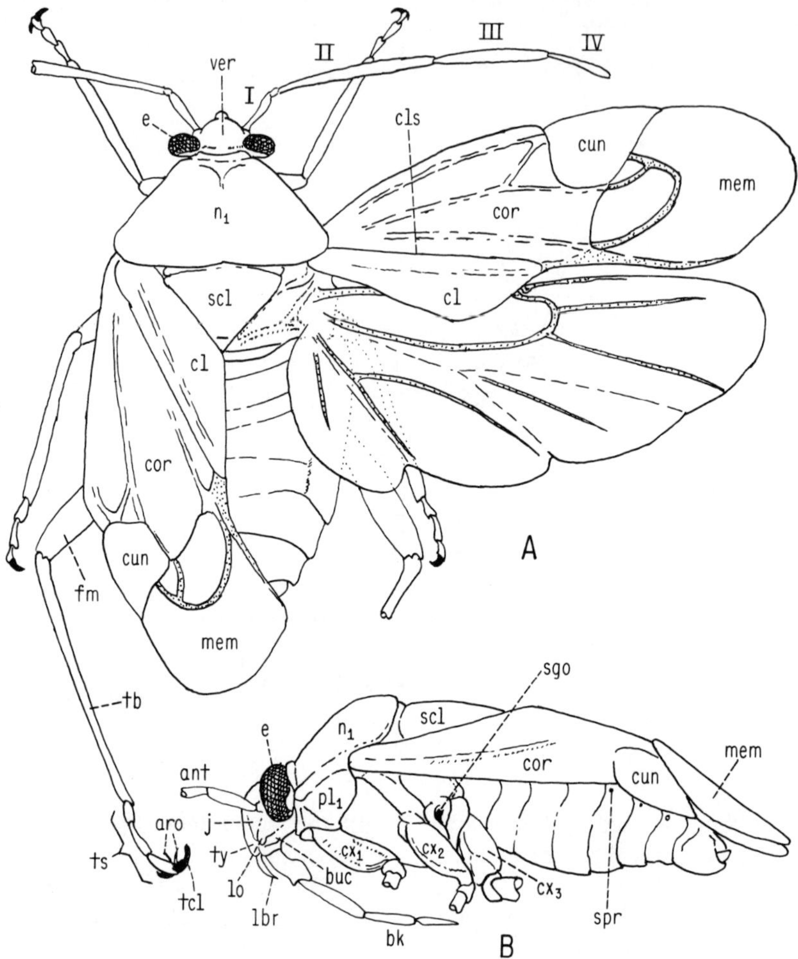

Fig. 19-1. Structure of a bug, *Lỳgus oblineàtus* (Say). A, dorsal view; B, lateral view. *ant,* antenna; *aro,* arolia; *bk,* beak; *buc,* buccula; *cl,* clavus; *cls,* claval suture; *cor,* corium; *cun,* cuneus; *cx,* coxa; *e,* compound eye; *fm,* femur; *j,* jugum; *lbr,* labrum; *lo,* lorum; *mem,* membrane; n_1, pronotum; pl_1, propleuron; *scl,* scutellum; *sgo,* scent gland opening; *spr,* spiracle; *tb,* tibia; *tcl,* tarsal claw; *ts,* tarsus; *ty,* tylus; *ver,* vertex; I-IV, antennal segments.

grouped by some authorities in a single order, the Hemiptera, with the two groups as the suborders Homoptera and Heteroptera (the latter including the true bugs). The two groups differ principally in the structure of the wings and in the location of the beak. The front wings in the Homoptera have a uniform texture throughout, either leathery or membranous (hence the name: *homo,* uniform; *ptera,* wings); in the Hemiptera the basal portion of the front wings is usually thickened. The beak in the Hemiptera arises from the front part of the head, whereas in the Homoptera it arises from the posterior part of the head (Figure 5-1).

The antennae are fairly long in most of the Hemiptera and consist of four or five segments. The compound eyes are nearly always well developed, but the ocelli (two in number) may be present or absent. Many Hemiptera have scent glands, usually opening on the side of the thorax (Figure 19-8 A, *sgo*), and give off a characteristic odor, particularly when they are disturbed; this odor is often unpleasant to man. Most of the Hemiptera have well-developed wings, but some species are wingless, some have very short wings, and in some species both long-winged and short-winged forms occur. The members of this order undergo simple metamorphosis.

The Hemiptera are a large and widely distributed group of insects. Most species are terrestrial, but many are aquatic; many feed on plant juices, and some of these are serious pests of cultivated plants; others are predaceous, and some of these are very beneficial to man; still others attack man and other animals and suck blood, and a few of these act as disease vectors.

CLASSIFICATION OF THE HEMIPTERA

The order Hemiptera is divided into two suborders, the Cryptocérata and the Gymnocérata, principally on the basis of antennal structure; the antennae of the Cryptocérata are very short and are usually concealed in grooves on the ventral side of the head; those of the Gymnocérata are long and not concealed in such grooves. The families of the Gymnocérata are usually grouped in a number of superfamilies.

A synopsis of the Hemiptera occurring in the United States is given below; synonyms are given in parentheses. In this list, the groups marked with an asterisk are rare and unlikely to be taken by the general collector.

Suborder Cryptocérata (Hydrocorìzae)—short-horned bugs, water bugs
- Coríxidae—water boatmen
- Notonéctidae (incl. Plèidae)—backswimmers
- Népidae—waterscorpions
- Belostomátidae (Belostómidae)—giant water bugs
- Naucóridae (incl. Aphelochíridae)—creeping water bugs
- Gelastocóridae (Galgùlidae, Nérthridae, Mononýchidae)—toad bugs
- *Ochtéridae (Pelogónidae)—velvety shore bugs

Suborder Gymnocérata (Geocorìzae)—long-horned bugs
- Superfamily Gerròidea—water striders
  - Gérridae (Hydrobátidae)—water striders
  - Veliidae—broad-shouldered water striders, ripple bugs
- Superfamily Dipsocoròidea—jumping ground bugs
  - *Schizoptéridae (Cryptostemmátidae in part)
  - *Dipsocóridae (Cryptostemmátidae, Ceratocómbidae)
- Superfamily Cimicòidea
  - Cimícidae (Acanthìidae, Clinocóridae)—bed bugs
  - Anthocóridae—flower bugs, minute pirate bugs
  - Míridae (Cápsidae)—leaf bugs, plant bugs
  - *Isometópidae—jumping tree bugs
  - *Microphýsidae—microphysid bugs
- Superfamily Reduviòidea
  - *Enicocephálidae (Henicocephálidae)—unique-headed bugs, gnat bugs
  - Phymátidae (Macrocephálidae)—ambush bugs
  - Reduvìidae—assassin bugs
  - Ploiarìidae (Emésidae; Reduvìidae in part)—thread-legged bugs
  - Nábidae—damsel bugs
- Superfamily Polyctenòidea
  - *Polycténidae—bat bugs

Superfamily Tingòidea (Tingidòidea)
  Tíngidae (Tingídidae, Tingítidae)—lace bugs
  *Piésmidae—ash-gray leaf bugs
Superfamily Lygaeòidea
  Neídidae (Berýtidae)—stilt bugs
  Lygaèidae (Geocóridae, Myodóchidae)—chinch bug, milkweed bugs, and others
  Pyrrhocóridae (incl. Lárgidae)—red bugs, stainers
Superfamily Coreòidea
  Corèidae—leaf-footed bugs
  Corízidae (Corèidae in part)—grass bugs, scentless plant bugs
  Coríscidae (Alýdidae; Corèidae in part)—broad-headed bugs
Superfamily Aradòidea
  Arádidae—flat bugs, fungus bugs
  *Termatophýlidae—termatophylid bugs
  Sáldidae—shore bugs
  Mesovelìidae—water treaders
  *Thaumastocóridae (Thaumastotherìidae)—royal palm bugs
  *Hébridae (Naeogaèidae)—velvet water bugs
  Hydrométridae (Limnobátidae)—water measurers, marsh treaders
Superfamily Scutelleròidea
  Cýdnidae—burrower bugs
  Corimelaènidae (Thyreocóridae; Cýdnidae in part)—negro bugs
  Scutelléridae—shield-backed bugs, shield bugs
  *Podópidae (Graphosomátidae)—terrestrial turtle bugs
  Pentatómidae—stink bugs

CHARACTERS USED IN IDENTIFYING HEMIPTERA

The principal characters used in separating the families of the Hemiptera are those of the antennae, beak, legs, and wings. The antennae may be either 4- or 5-segmented; they are very short and concealed in grooves under the head in the Cryptocérata and are fairly long and conspicuous in the Gymnocérata. The beak is usually 3- or 4-segmented and in some groups fits into a groove in the prosternum when not in use.

The front legs in most of the predaceous Hemiptera are more or less modified into grasping structures and are spoken of as being raptorial. A raptorial leg (Figure 19-2) usually has the femur enlarged and armed with large spines on the ventroposterior margin; the tibia fits tightly against this armed surface, and often it, too, bears conspicuous spines.

The Hemiptera generally have two or three tarsal segments, the last of which bears a pair of claws. The claws are apical in most of the Hemiptera, but in the water striders (Gerròidea) they are anteapical; that is, they arise slightly proximad of the tip of the last tarsal segment (Figure 19-3 B). Many Hemiptera have arolia, or lobelike pads, one at the base of each tarsal claw (Figure 19-3 A, *aro*).

The hemelytra are subject to considerable modification in different groups of bugs, and special names are given to the different parts of a hemelytron (Figure 19-4). The thickened basal part of the hemelytron consists of two sections, the corium (*cor*) and clavus (*cl*), which are separated by the claval suture (*cls*); the thin apical part of the hemelytron is the membrane (*mem*). In

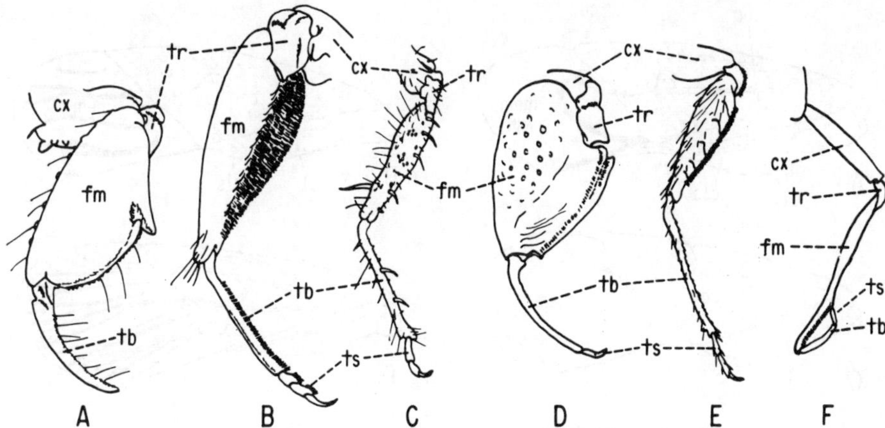

Fig. 19-2. Raptorial front legs of Hemiptera. A, *Phýmata* (Phymátidae); B, *Lethócerus* (Belostomátidae); C, *Sìnea* (Reduvìidae); D, *Pelócoris* (Naucóridae); E, *Nàbis* (Nábidae); F, *Ránatra* (Népidae). *cx,* coxa; *fm,* femur; *tb,* tibia; *tr,* trochanter; *ts,* tarsus.

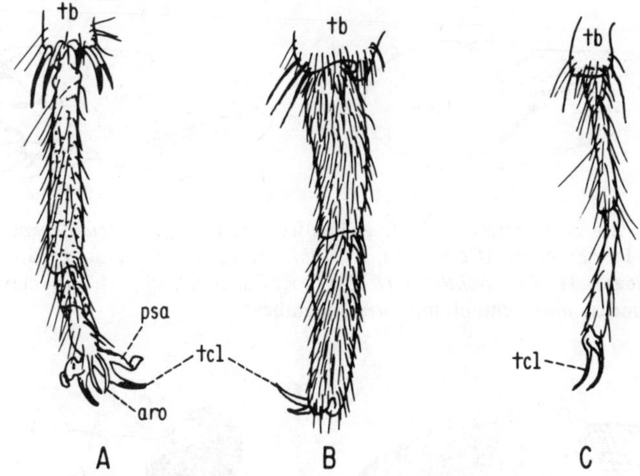

Fig. 19-3. Tarsi of Hemiptera. A, *Ligyrócoris* (Lygaèidae); B, *Gérris* (Gérridae); C, *Nàbis* (Nàbidae). *aro,* arolia; *psa,* pseudarolium; *tb,* tibia; *tcl,* tarsal claws.

some Hemiptera a narrow strip of the corium along the costal margin is set off from the remainder of the corium by a suture; this is the embolium (Figure 19-4 C, *emb*). In a few Hemiptera a cuneus (Figure 19-4 A, *cun*) is set off by a suture from the apical part of the corium. The membrane usually contains veins, the number and arrangement of which often serves to separate different families.

The principal difficulties likely to be encountered in using this key are those involving the interpretation of certain characters and those due to the small size of some specimens. If the front femora are thicker than the other femora, the legs are usually considered to be raptorial. In counting the antennal segments, the minute segments between the larger segments are not counted. It is often necessary to use considerable magnification to determine the number of beak segments, particularly in small specimens. Some short-winged forms may not run out correctly in this key.

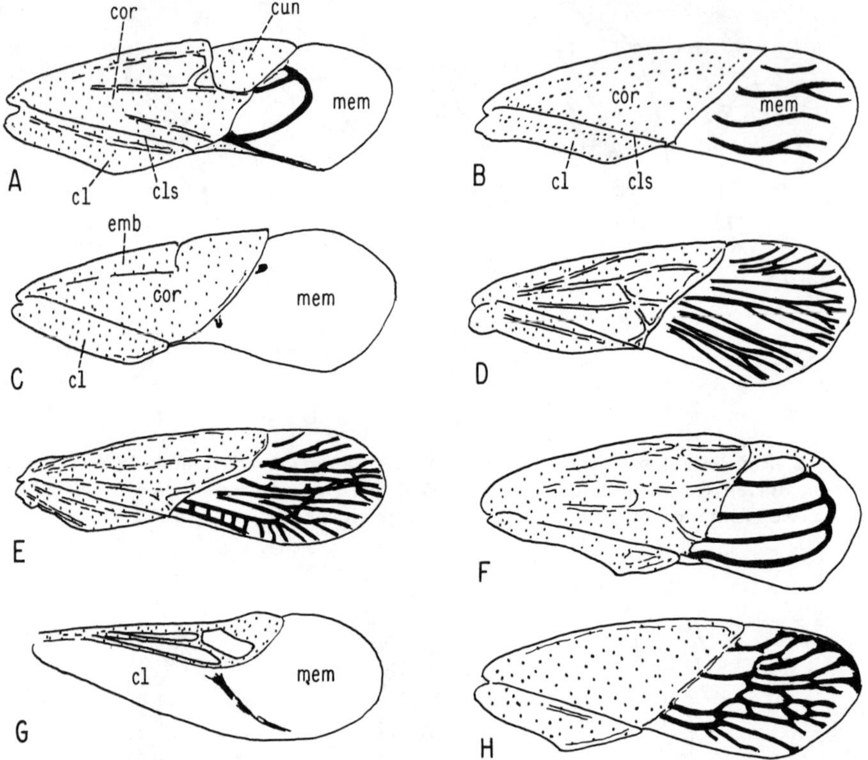

Fig. 19-4. Hemelytra of Hemiptera. A, *Lỳgus* (Míridae); B, *Ligyrócorus* (Lygaèidae); C, *Òrius* (Anthocóridae); D, *Leptócoris* (Corízidae); E, *Nàbis* (Nábidae); F, *Sáldula* (Sáldidae); G, *Mesovèlia* (Mesovelìidae); H, *Euryophthálmus* (Pyrrhocóridae). *cl*, clavus; *cls*, claval suture; *cor*, corium; *cun*, cuneus; *emb*, embolium; *mem*, membrane.

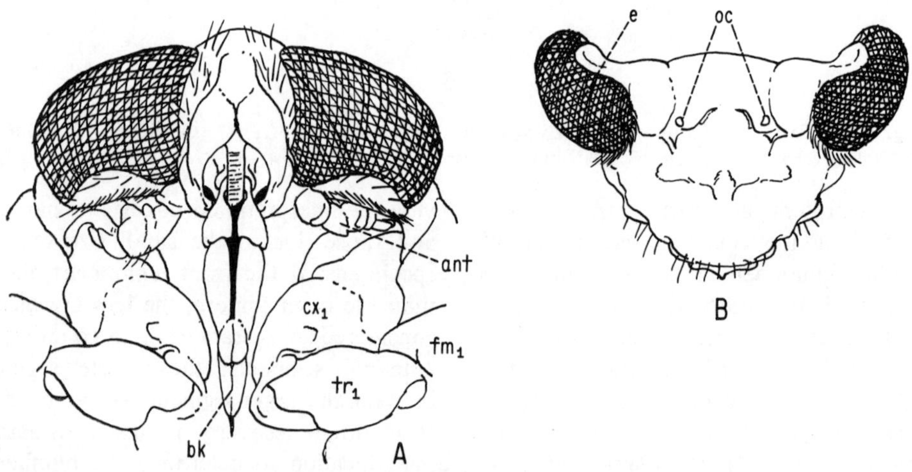

Fig. 19-5. Head structure in Cryptocerata. A, *Lethócerus* (Belostomátidae), ventro-anterior view; B, *Gelastócoris* (Gelastocóridae), dorso-anterior view. *ant*, antenna; *bk*, beak; *cx*, coxa; *e*, compound eye; *fm*, femur; *oc*, ocelli; *tr*, trochanter.

The following key includes the families of Hemiptera occurring in the United States. The families that are rare or unlikely to be taken by a general collector are indicated by an asterisk; couplets containing these groups may often be skipped over when running a specimen through the key.

KEY TO THE FAMILIES OF HEMIPTERA

1. Antennae shorter than head, usually (except Ochtéridae*) hidden in cavities beneath eyes (Figure 19-5 A); no arolia; aquatic or semiaquatic (suborder Cryptocérata) 2

1′. Antennae as long as or longer than head, usually free and visible from above; with or without arolia; habits variable (suborder Gymnocérata) 8

2(1). Ocelli present (Figure 19-5 B); 10 mm in length or less; shore species .. 3

2′. Ocelli absent; size variable; aquatic species 4

3(2). Antennae hidden; front legs raptorial, shorter than middle legs; eyes strongly protuberant (Figure 19-14); beak short, concealed by front femora .... **Gelastocóridae** p. 178

3′. Antennae exposed; front legs cursorial, as long as middle legs; eyes not strongly protuberant; beak long, extending at least to hind coxae .... **Ochtéridae*** p. 178

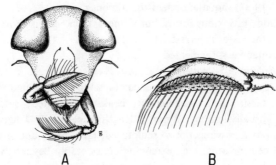

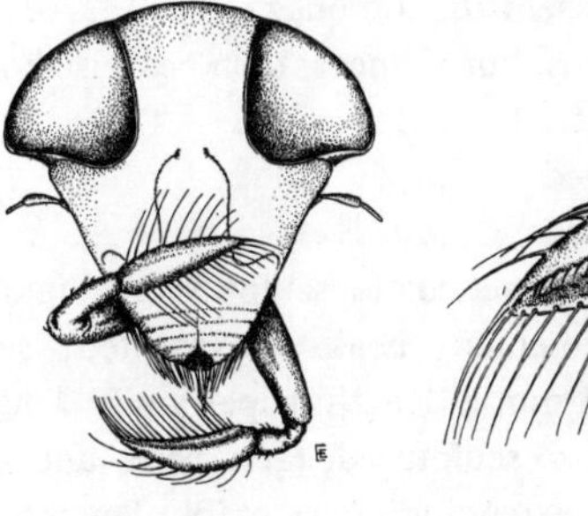

Fig. 19-6. *Corixa (*Coríxidae). A, head, anterior view; B, front leg. (Courtesy of Hungerford.)

4(2′). Front tarsi spatulate, 1-segmented (Figure 19-6 B); head overlapping pronotum; beak very short, 1- or 2-segmented .... **Coríxidae** p. 175

4′. Front tarsi not as above; head not overlapping pronotum; beak with 3 or more segments 5

5(4′). Front legs not raptorial, but fitted for swimming; hind tarsi usually without claws; body strongly convex above; aquatic bugs swimming upside down, with dorsal side of body usually light-colored ...... **Notonéctidae** p. 175

5′. Front legs raptorial, with femora thickened (Figure 19-2 B, D, F); hind tarsi with claws; body flattened or only slightly convex above; aquatic bugs usually swimming right side up, with dorsal side of body as dark as or darker than ventral side 6

6(5′). Membrane of hemelytra with veins; 20 mm in length or more 7

6′. Membrane of hemelytra without veins (Figure 19-13 B); 5 to 16 mm in length .... **Naucóridae** p. 178

7(6). Tarsi 1-segmented; apical abdominal appendages forming a long, slender, nonretractile breathing tube; hind legs cylindrical, fitted for walking (Figure 19-12) .... **Népidae** p. 176

7′. Tarsi 2-segmented (front tarsi 3-segmented in *Lethócerus*); apical abdominal appendages short, flat, and retractile; hind legs flattened and fringed, fitted for swimming (Figure 19-13 A)........ **Belostomátidae** p. 176

8(1′). Compound eyes present... 9

8′. Compound eyes absent; ectoparasites of bats, 3.5 to 5.0 mm in length; western United States .... **Polycténidae*** p. 184

9(8). Tarsal claws anteapical, tip of last tarsal segment more or less cleft (Figure 19-3 B); aquatic, surface-inhabiting (superfamily Gerròidea)..10

9′. Tarsal claws apical, tip of last tarsal segment entire 11

10(9). Middle legs arising closer to hind legs than to front legs; hind femora extending well beyond apex of abdomen (Figure 19-15 A); all tarsi 2-segmented; ocelli present but small; usually over 5 mm in length.... .... **Gérridae** p. 178

10′. Middle legs usually arising about midway between front and hind legs; if middle legs arise closer to hind legs than to front legs (*Rhagovèlia*), then front tarsi are 1-segmented (Figure 19-15 B); hind femora extending little if any beyond apex of abdomen; tarsi 1-, 2-, or 3-segmented; ocelli absent; 1.6 to 5.5 mm in length...................... **Veliidae** p. 179

11(9′). Body linear, head as long as entire thorax, and legs very slender (Figure 19-32); aquatic or semiaquatic bugs.................. **Hydrométridae** p. 190

11′. Body of various forms, but if linear, then head is shorter than thorax and the insect is terrestrial 12

12(11′). Antennae 4-segmented 13

12′. Antennae 5-segmented 40

13(12). Body and wings with reticulate sculpturing (Figures 19-22 B, 19-23); tarsi 1- or 2-segmented; beak 4-segmented; small flattened bugs, usually less than 5 mm in length (superfamily Tingòidea)..........14

13′. Body and wings not so sculptured; tarsi, beak, and size variable......15

14(13). Ocelli present; juga extending considerably beyond tylus; membrane of hemelytra not reticulate; pronotum not extending backward over scutellum (Figure 19-22 B) .... **Piésmidae*** p. 185

14′. Ocelli absent; juga not, or but slightly, longer than tylus; hemelytra entirely reticulate; pronotum with a triangular process that extends backward over scutellum (Figure 19-23)................... **Tíngidae** p. 184

15(13′). Antennae whiplike, the two basal segments short, the two apical segments very long and slender and hairy, the third segment thickened at base (Figure 19-7 A); ocelli present; tarsi 3-segmented; beak 3-segmented; small or minute bugs, 1 to 2 mm in length (superfamily Dipsocoròidea) 16*

15′. Antennae not as above, the third segment not thickened at base, and the second segment usually as long as, or longer than, third; ocelli, size, beak, and tarsi variable 17

16(15). Eyes projecting outward, not overlapping front angles of pronotum; head and tibiae with strong bristles .... **Dipsocóridae*** p. 179

16′. Eyes projecting outward and backward, overlapping front angles of pronotum; head and tibiae without strong bristles ...... **Schizoptéridae*** p. 179

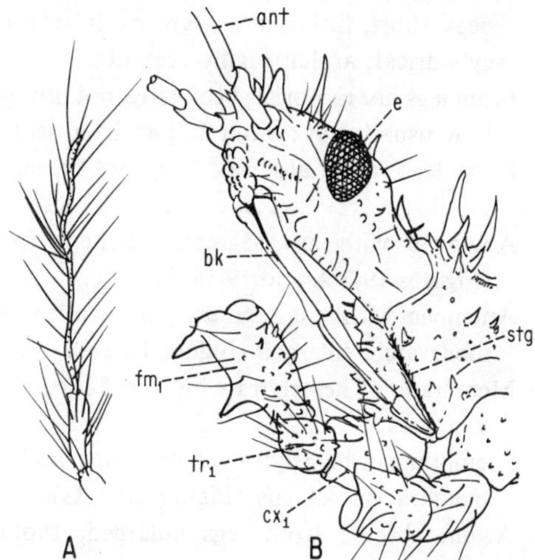

Fig. 19-7. A, antenna of *Cryptostemmátida* (Dipsocóridae); B, head of *Sìnea* (Reduvìidae). *ant*, antenna; *bk*, beak; *cx*, coxa; *e*, compound eye; *fm*, femur; *stg*, prosternal groove; *tr*, trochanter.

17(15′). Ocelli present 18

17′. Ocelli absent 33

18(17). Middle and hind tarsi with 2 or fewer segments; small or minute, usually rare bugs 19*

18′. Middle and hind tarsi 3-segmented; size variable 22

19(18). Clavus and membrane of hemelytra similar in texture (as in Figure 19-4 G); body densely clothed with short velvety hairs; small, stout-bodied, semiaquatic bugs (*Merragàta*) .... **Hébridae*** p. 190

19′. Clavus and membrane of hemelytra different in texture; body not as above 20*

20(19′). Hemelytra with a cuneus; shining black, 1.2 mm in length; recorded from Maryland and the District of Columbia.............. **Microphýsidae*** p. 181

20′. Hemelytra without a cuneus 21*

21(20′). Front legs enlarged, raptorial; beak 4-segmented; pronotum divided into 3 lobes; hemelytra entirely membranous; color variable, but usually not yellowish with red eyes; 3 to 4 mm in length (Figure 19-19 A); widely distributed.. **Enicocephálidae*** p. 181

21′. Front legs not enlarged, not raptorial; beak 3-segmented; pronotum not divided into 3 lobes; hemelytra thickened at base, with only the inner apical portion membranous, the corium extending to the wing tip; pale yellowish with red eyes; 2.0 to 2.5 mm in length; Florida .... **Thaumastocóridae*** p. 190

22(18′). Hemelytra with a cuneus or embolium, or both; small bugs, 1.2 to 5.0 mm in length, usually 2 to 3 mm 23

22′. Hemelytra with neither a cuneus nor an embolium; size variable...... 24

23(22). Beak 3-segmented; hemelytra with an embolium, the cuneus not very well defined (Figures 19-4 C and 19-16 B)................. **Anthocóridae** p. 180

23′. Beak 4-segmented; hemelytra with a well-defined cuneus, and with the embolium more or less well defined (Figure 19-18)...... **Isometópidae*** p. 180

24(22′). Beak 3-segmented 25

24′. Beak 4-segmented 28

25(24). Front legs usually more or less enlarged, raptorial (Figures 19-2 A, C); beak short, fitting into a groove in prosternum (Figure 19-7 B); head cylindrical; arolia usually present 26

25′. Front legs not raptorial; beak long, not fitting into a groove in prosternum; head usually not cylindrical; arolia absent (see also 25″)............27

25″. Front legs raptorial; beak long, not fitting into a groove in prosternum .... **Nábidae** p. 182

26(25). Antennae with last segment swollen; front femora greatly enlarged (Figures 19-2 A and 19-19 B) ....**Phymátidae** p. 181

26′. Antennae with last segment not swollen; front femora not more than moderately enlarged (Figure 19-2 C) ....**Reduvìidae** p. 182

27(25′). Membrane of hemelytra with 4 or 5 long closed cells (Figure 19-4 F).. **Sáldidae** p. 189

27′. Membrane of hemelytra without veins, and more or less confluent with the membranous clavus (Figure 19-4 G) ....**Mesovelìidae*** p. 190

28(24′). Arolia absent; front legs enlarged, raptorial; hemelytra (when well developed) with numerous marginal veins (Figure 19-4 E)....**Nábidae** p. 182

28′. Arolia present (Figure 19-3 A); front legs usually not enlarged; hemelytra variable 29

29(28′). Body and appendages long and slender; first segment of antenna long and clubbed, the last segment spindle-shaped; femora clubbed (Figure 19-24) .... **Neídidae** p. 185

29′. Body shape variable; antennae and femora not as above 30

30(29′). Membrane of hemelytra with only 4 or 5 veins (Figure 19-4 B)..**Lygaèidae** p. 185

30′. Membrane of hemelytra with many veins (Figure 19-4 D) (superfamily Coreòidea) 31

31(30′). Usually dark-colored and over 10 mm in length; scent glands present, their openings between middle and hind coxae (Figure 19-8 A); fourth and fifth abdominal terga concavely sinuate at base 32

31′. Usually pale-colored and less than 10 mm in length; scent glands absent; only the fourth abdominal tergum concave at base (Figure 19-8 B)..**Corízidae** p. 187

32(31). Head narrower and shorter than pronotum (Figure 19-28); exterior margin of hind coxal cavities nearly parallel to long axis of body (Figure 19-8 C) ....**Corèidae** p. 187

32′. Head nearly as broad and as long as pronotum (Figure 19-29 A); exterior margin of hind coxal cavities more or less transverse (Figure 19-8 D).. **Coríscidae** p. 188

33(17′). Front legs usually more or less enlarged, raptorial; beak short, fitting into a groove in prosternum (Figure 19-7 B); head cylindrical; beak 3-segmented 34

33′. Front legs not enlarged, not raptorial; beak usually longer and not fitting into a groove in prosternum, 3- to 4-segmented; head variable......35

34(33). Front coxae short; body robust, legs and body not linear (Figure 19-20) .... **Reduvìidae** p. 182

34′. Front coxae very long; body linear, the middle and hind legs long and slender (Figure 19-21) ....**Ploiarìidae** p. 182

35(33′). Beak 3-segmented; wings vestigial (Figure 19-16 A); ectoparasites of birds

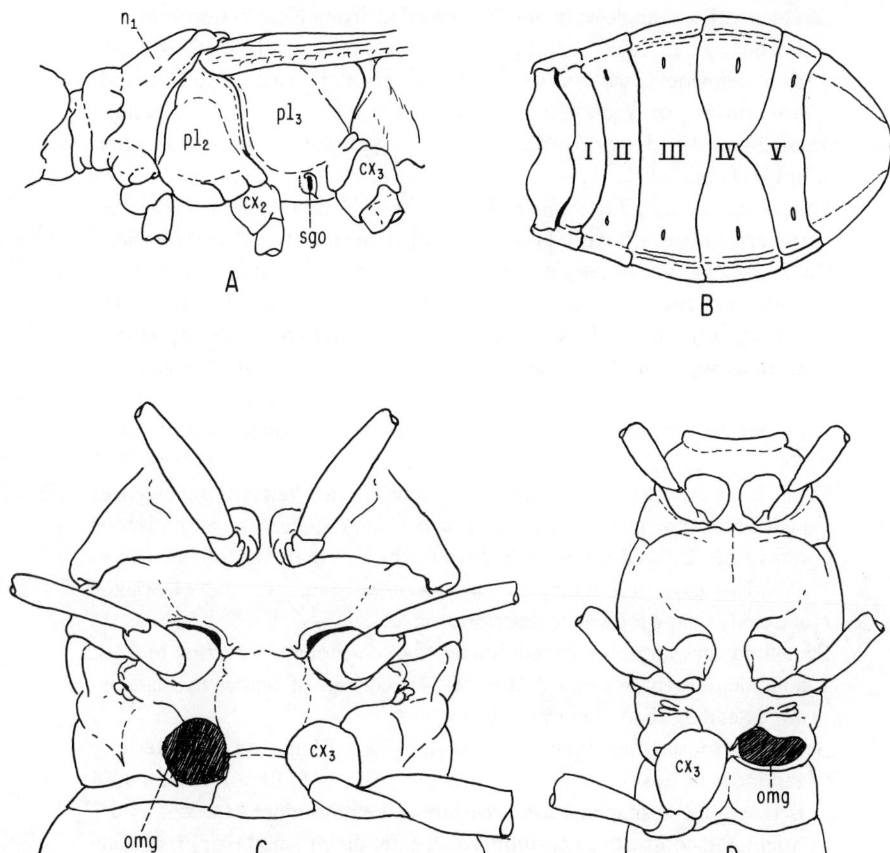

Fig. 19-8. Thoracic and abdominal structures of Hemiptera. A, thorax of *Coríscus* (Coríscidae), lateral view; B, abdomen of *Leptócoris* (Corízidae), dorsal view; C, thorax of *Ánasa* (Corèidae), ventral view; D, thorax of *Coríscus* (Coríscidae), ventral view. *cx,* coxa; n_1, pronotum; *omg,* outer margin of coxal cavity; pl_2, mesopleuron; pl_3, metapleuron; *sgo,* scent gland opening; I-V, abdominal tergites.

and mammals .... **Cimícidae** p. 179

35′. Beak 4-segmented; wings usually well developed.................... 36

36(35′). Hemelytra with a cuneus, the membrane with 1 or 2 closed cells and rarely with other veins (Figure 19-4 A); rarely (for example, *Hálticus*, Figure 19-17 A) membrane absent, in which case the cuneus is lacking and the hind femora are enlarged; meso- and metasternum formed of more than 1 sclerite 37

36′. Hemelytra without a cuneus, the membrane not as above; meso- and metasternum formed of a single sclerite.......................... 38

37(36). Basal segment of beak longer than wide, usually extending backward beyond hind margin of head; membrane of hemelytra with 2 closed cells (Figure 19-4 A), except in species such as *Hálticus* (Figure 19-17 A); a large and widespread group .... **Míridae** p. 180

37′. Basal segment of beak scarcely longer than wide and not extending backward beyond middle of eyes; membrane of hemelytra with a single large closed cell; a single rare species recorded from New Hampshire and Arizona .... **Termatophýlidae*** p. 189

38(36′). Tarsi 2-segmented, without arolia; body very flat; usually dull-colored, gray, brown, or black (Figure 19-30)...................... **Arádidae** p. 189

38′. Tarsi 3-segmented, with arolia; body not particularly flattened; often brightly colored 39

39(38′). Shining black bugs, 7 to 9 mm in length; front femora moderately swollen and armed beneath with 2 rows of teeth (*Cnèmodus*)........ **Lygaèidae** p. 185

39′. Color variable, but usually not shining black; 8 to 18 mm in length; front femora not swollen; usually not armed with teeth .... **Pyrrhocóridae** p. 187

40(12′). Front legs raptorial; black, shining bugs, 5 to 7 mm in length; second antennal segment about one-fifth as long as third (Protostemmìnae).... .... **Nábidae** p. 182

40′. Front legs not raptorial; size and color variable; antennae usually not as above 41

41(40′). Tarsi 2-segmented; body densely covered with velvety pubescence; hemelytra with clavus and membrane similar in texture and without veins; the 2 basal antennal segments thicker than the others; semi-aquatic bugs, 3 mm in length or less (*Hèbrus*)............. **Hébridae*** p. 190

41′. Not exactly fitting the above description 42

42(41′). Scutellum very large, **U**-shaped, longer than corium and covering most of abdomen (Figures 19-33 A and 19-34); corium of hemelytra narrow, not extending to anal margin of wing........................... 43

42′. Scutellum shorter, not longer than corium, usually narrowed posteriorly and more or less triangular (Figures 19-33 B, 19-35, 19-36); if scutellum is large and **U**-shaped (*Stíretrus*, family Pentatómidae) the colors are bright and contrasting; corium broad, extending to anal margin of wing 45

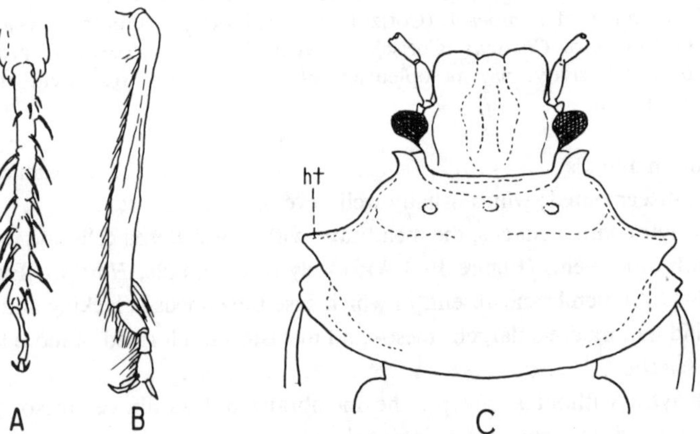

Fig. 19-9. A, tibia of *Pangaèus* (Cýdnidae); B, tibia of *Murgántia* (Pentatómidae); C, head and pronotum of a podopid. *ht,* humeral tooth.

43(42). Tibiae armed with strong spines; small, rounded, usually shining black bugs (Figure 19-33 A)............................ **Corimelaènidae** p. 190

43′. Tibiae not armed with strong spines; color rarely shining black........ 44

44(43′). Sides of pronotum with a prominent tooth or lobe in front of humeral angle (Figure 19-9 C and 19-34 B)........................ **Podópidae*** p. 191

44′. Sides of pronotum without such teeth or lobes (Figure 19-34 A)........ .... **Scutelléridae** p. 191

45(42′). Tibiae armed with strong spines (Figure 19-9 A); front legs fossorial; usually less than 7 mm in length (Figure 19-33 B).......... **Cýdnidae** p. 190

45′. Tibiae without strong spines, at most with weak spines (Figure 19-9 B); front legs not fossorial; usually over 7 mm in length (Figures 19-35 and 19-36) .... **Pentatómidae** p. 191

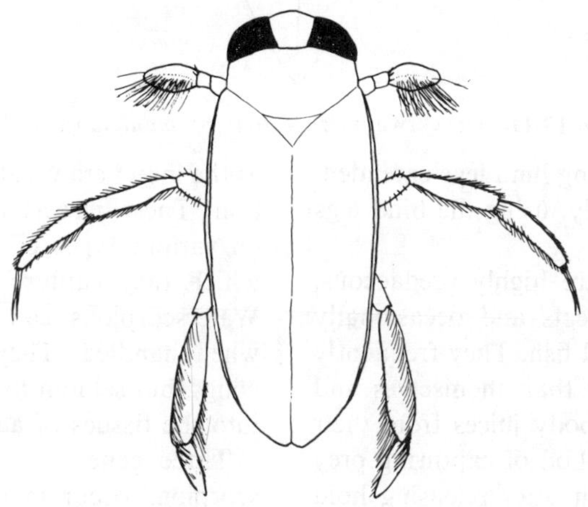

Fig. 19-10. A water boatman, *Sígara atropodónta* Hungerford; 7 ×.

FAMILY **Coríxidae**—Water Boatmen: These insects are aquatic and have the hind legs elongate and oarlike (Figure 19-10). The body is oval, somewhat flattened, and usually dark gray in color; the dorsal surface of the body is often finely cross-lined. The water boatmen are common insects in freshwater ponds and lakes; they occasionally occur in streams, and a few species occur in the brackish pools just above the high-tide mark along the seashore. As do all other aquatic bugs, they lack gills and get air at the surface of the water; they frequently carry a bubble of air under water, either on the surface of the body or under the wings. They can swim rapidly, but often cling to vegetation for long periods.

Most of the water boatmen feed on algae and other minute aquatic organisms, which they scoop up with their spatulate front tarsi (Figure 19-6 B). A few species are predaceous, feeding on midge larvae and other small aquatic animals. Unlike most of the other aquatic bugs, water boatmen will not bite man.

The eggs of water boatmen are usually attached to aquatic plants. In some parts of the world (for example, certain parts of Mexico) water boatmen eggs are used as food; they are collected from aquatic plants, dried, and later ground into flour. Water boatmen are an important item of food for many aquatic animals.

FAMILY **Notonéctidae** — Backswimmers: The backswimmers are so named because they swim upside down. They are very similar to the water boatmen in shape (Figure 19-11), but have the dorsal side of the body more convex and usually light-colored. They frequently rest at the surface of the water, with the body at an angle and the head

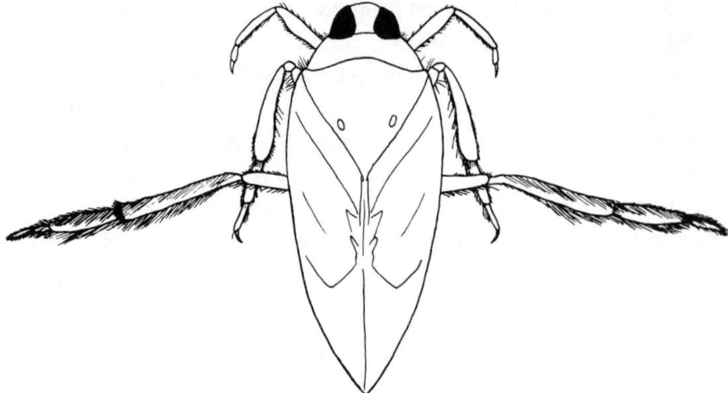

Fig. 19-11. A backswimmer, *Notonécta undulàta* (Say); 7 ×.

down, and with the long hind legs extended. They can swim rapidly, using the hind legs like oars.

Backswimmers are highly predaceous, feeding on other insects and occasionally on tadpoles and small fish. They frequently attack animals larger than themselves and feed by sucking the body juices from their prey. A common method of capturing prey is to drift up under it after releasing hold of submerged plants to which they have been clinging. These insects will bite man when handled, and the effect is much like a bee sting. Backswimmer eggs are deposited in the tissues or glued to the surface of aquatic plants.

Three genera of backswimmers occur in the United States: *Notonécta, Buénoa,* and *Plèa. Notonécta* includes the largest and most common species (Figure 19-11), which are 8 to 17 millimeters in length; the species of *Buénoa* are smaller, 5 to 9 millimeters in length, and more slender. The single species of *Plèa, P. striòla* Fieber, is very small, 1.6 to 2.3 millimeters in length, and has the dorsal surface of the body strongly arched.

FAMILY **Népidae**—Waterscorpions: The waterscorpions are predaceous aquatic bugs with raptorial front legs and with a long caudal breathing tube formed by the cerci. The breathing tube is often almost as long as the body, and is thrust up to the surface as the insect crawls about on aquatic vegetation. These insects move slowly and prey on various types of small aquatic animals, which they capture with their front legs. Waterscorpions can inflict a painful bite when handled. They have well-developed wings, but seldom fly. The eggs are inserted into the tissues of aquatic plants.

Three genera and 12 species of waterscorpions occur in the United States: the 9 species of *Ránatra* are slender and elongate with very long legs, and are somewhat similar to walking sticks in appearance (Figure 19-12 B); our only species of *Nèpa, N. apiculàta* Uhler, has the body oval and somewhat flattened (Figure 19-12 A); the body shape in *Curícta* is somewhat intermediate between those of *Ránatra* and *Nèpa.* Our most common waterscorpions belong to the genus *Ránatra*; *N. apiculàta* is less common, and occurs in the eastern states; the two species of *Curícta* are relatively rare, and occur in the Southwest.

FAMILY **Belostomátidae**—Giant Water Bugs: This family contains the largest bugs in the order, some of which (in the United States) may reach a length of over 2 inches; one species occurring in South America is over 4 inches in length. The giant water bugs are brownish in color, oval, and somewhat flattened, with the front legs raptorial (Figure 19-13 A). These insects are fairly common in ponds and lakes, where they

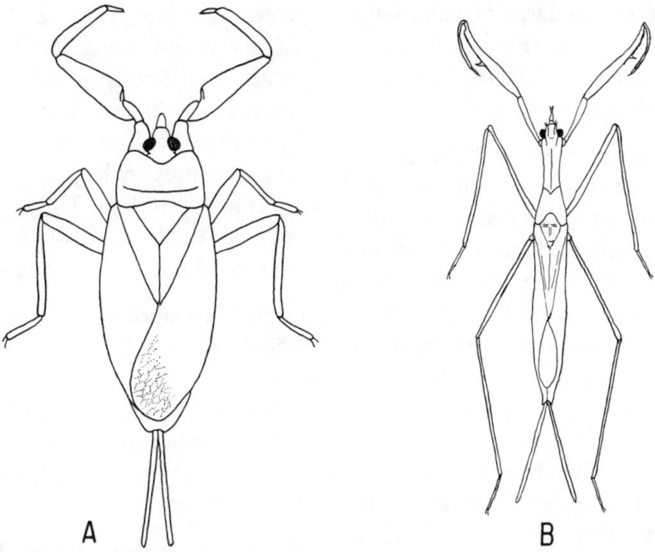

Fig. 19-12. Waterscorpions. A, *Nèpa apiculàta* Uhler, $2\frac{1}{2}\times$; B, *Ránatra fúsca* Beauvois, about natural size.

feed on other insects, snails, tadpoles, and even small fish. They frequently leave the water and fly about, and because they are often attracted to lights, they are sometimes called electric-light bugs. Giant water bugs can inflict a painful bite if handled carelessly. In some species (*Belóstoma* and *Ábedus*), the eggs are laid on the back of the male, which carries them about until they hatch; other species lay their eggs at the bottom of ponds or attached to aquatic vegetation. Three genera of giant water bugs occur in the United States: *Lethócerus* (including *Bénacus*), *Belóstoma,* and *Ábedus.* The first two are widely distributed, while *Ábedus* occurs in the South and West. The

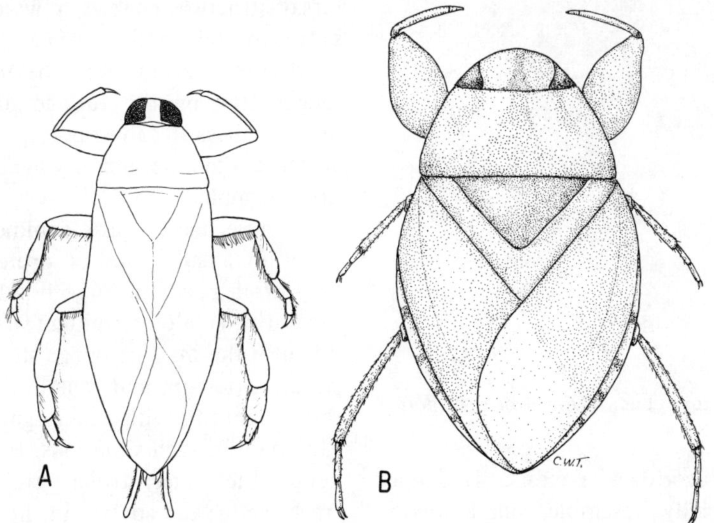

Fig. 19-13. A, a giant water bug, *Lethócerus gríseus* (Say), slightly reduced; B, a creeping water bug, *Pelócoris femoràtus* (Beauvois), $5\times$.

species of *Lethócerus* are large bugs, usually $1\frac{1}{2}$ inches or more in length (Figure 19-13 A), whereas the species of *Belóstoma* and *Ábedus* are smaller.

FAMILY **Naucóridae**—Creeping Water Bugs: These bugs are brownish in color, broadly oval, and somewhat flattened, generally about $\frac{1}{2}$ inch in length, and the front femora are greatly thickened (Figure 19-13 B). They live in quiet water and swim or creep about slowly through submerged vegetation in search of food; they feed on various small aquatic animals. They bite quite readily—and painfully—when handled. This family is a small one, with only a little over a dozen species occurring in North America; the two species occurring in the East belong to the genus *Pelócoris.*

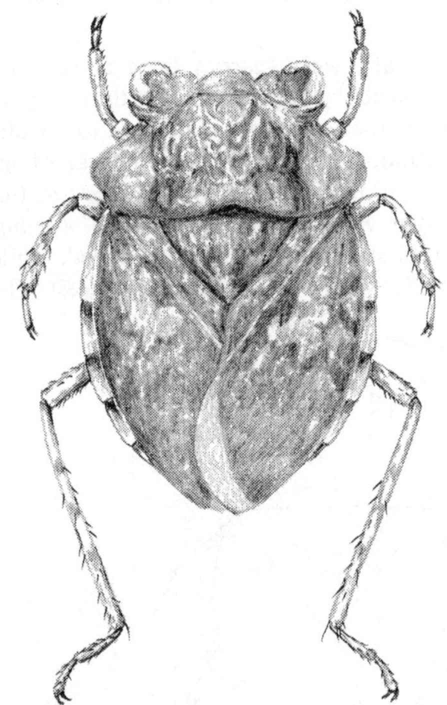

Fig. 19-14. A toad bug, *Gelastócoris oculàtus* (Fabricius); $7\frac{1}{2}\times$.

FAMILY **Gelastocóridae**—Toad Bugs: These bugs superficially resemble small toads, both in appearance and hopping habits. They are short and broad and have large projecting eyes (Figure 19-14), and are usually found along the moist margins of ponds and streams; one has to examine them closely to be certain they are not toads. Toad bugs feed on other insects; they capture their prey by leaping on it and grasping it in their front legs. The eggs are laid in the sand, and the adults often spend a portion of their life down in the sand.

FAMILY **Ochtéridae**—Velvety Shore Bugs: These are oval-bodied insects 4 to 5 millimeters in length which occur along the shores of quiet streams and ponds. They are velvety bluish or black in color, and are predaceous. Seven species occur in the United States.

FAMILY **Gérridae**—Water Striders: The water striders are long-legged insects (Figure 19-15 A) that live on the surface of the water, running or skating over the surface and feeding on insects that fall onto the surface. The front legs are short and are used in capturing food, and the middle and hind legs are long and are used in locomotion. Most species are black or dark-colored, and the body is long and narrow.

The tarsi of water striders are clothed with fine hairs and are difficult to wet; this tarsal structure enables a water strider to skate around on the surface of the water. If the tarsi become wet, the insect can no longer stay on the surface film and will drown unless it can crawl up on some dry surface; when the tarsi dry again, they function normally.

These insects are common on quiet water in small coves or protected places; they often occur in large numbers. Species inhabiting small intermittent streams burrow down in the mud or under stones when the stream dries up, and remain dormant until the stream fills with water again; the adults hibernate in such situations. Except for one genus, the water striders are restricted to fresh water; the species in the genus *Haló-bates* live on the surface of the ocean, often many miles from land. Winged and wingless

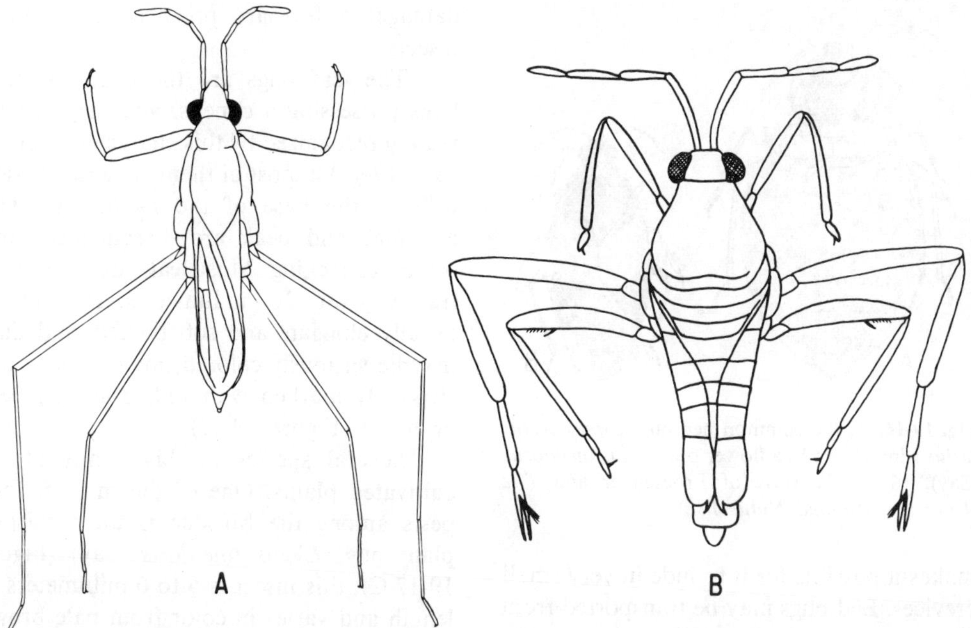

Fig. 19-15. Water striders. A, *Gérris maginàtus* (Say) (Gerridae), 5 ×; B, *Rhagovèlia* sp. (Veliidae), 10 ×.

individuals occur in many species, and the insect moves from one aquatic situation to another when in the winged stage. The eggs are laid at the surface of the water on floating objects.

FAMILY **Veliidae**—Broad-Shouldered Water Striders or Ripple Bugs: These water striders are small (1.6 to 5.5 millimeters in length), brown or black in color and often with silvery markings, and they usually occur in or near the ripples (or riffles) of small streams. They are gregarious, and a single sweep of a dip net sometimes yields up to 50 or more specimens. The body is usually widest near the bases of the middle and hind legs, with the abdomen narrower (Figure 19-15 B). They feed on small insects and other aquatic animals. Three widely distributed genera occur in the United States: *Vèlia, Microvèlia,* and *Rhagovèlia.*

FAMILIES **Schizoptéridae** AND **Dipsocóridae**: The Schizoptéridae and Dipsocóridae, or jumping ground bugs, are minute oval bugs 1.0 to 1.5 millimeters in length, which live in moist places on the ground, beneath dead leaves, or in moist soil. They jump actively when disturbed. Only seven species in these two families occur in the United States, and they are principally southern in distribution.

FAMILY **Cimícidae**—Bed Bugs: The bed bugs are flat, broadly oval, wingless bugs about $\frac{1}{4}$ inch in length (Figure 19-16 A), which feed by sucking blood from birds and mammals. The group is a small one, but some of the species are widely distributed and well known. The common bed bug that attacks man is *Cìmex lectulàrius* Linn.; this species is frequently a serious pest in houses, hotels, barracks, and other living quarters; it also attacks animals other than man. A tropical species, *Cìmex hemípterus* (Fabricius), also bites man. Other species in this family attack bats and various birds.

The common bed bug is largely nocturnal, and during the day hides in cracks in a wall, under the baseboard, in the springs of a bed, under the edge of a mattress, under wallpaper, and in similar places. Its flatness

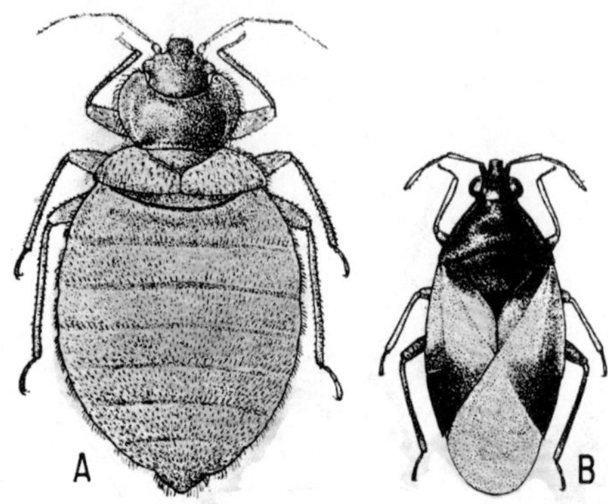

Fig. 19-16. A, the common bed bug, *Cìmex lectulàrius* Linn., 7 ×; B, a flower bug, *Òrius insidiòsus* (Say), 16 ×. (Courtesy of Froeschner and *The American Midland Naturalist.*)

makes it possible for it to hide in very small crevices. Bed bugs may be transported from place to place on clothing, in luggage or furniture, or they may migrate from house to house. They lay their eggs, 100 to 250 per female, in cracks; development to the adult stage requires about two months in warm weather. The adults may live for several months and can survive long periods without food. Bed bugs are important primarily because of their irritating bites; they are apparently unimportant as disease vectors.

FAMILY **Anthocóridae**—Flower Bugs or Minute Pirate Bugs: These small predaceous bugs differ from most of the other Hemiptera in having a well-defined embolium (Figure 19-4 C). The commoner species are usually found on flowers, but some species occur under loose bark, in leaf litter, and in decaying fungi. Most species are black with white markings (Figure 19-16 B), and 3 to 5 millimeters in length. The anthocorids feed on small insects and insect eggs.

FAMILY **Míridae**—Leaf Bugs or Plant Bugs: This family is the largest in the order, and members of it are to be found on vegetation almost everywhere; some are very abundant. Practically all the leaf bugs feed on the juices of plants, often causing serious damage; a few are predaceous on other insects.

The leaf bugs are the only common bugs possessing a cuneus, and they can be readily recognized by this character (Figures 19-1, 19-4 A); most of them have two closed cells at the base of the membrane. The antennae and beak are 4-segmented, and ocelli are lacking. Most leaf bugs are small (rarely over 10 millimeters in length), usually elongate and soft-bodied, and they may be variously colored; many species are strikingly marked with red, orange, green, or white (Figure 19-17).

Several species in this family attack cultivated plants. One of the most serious pests among the Míridae is the tarnished plant bug, *Lỳgus lineolàris* (Say) (Figure 19-17 C); this insect is 5 to 6 millimeters in length and varies in color from pale brown to almost black. It feeds on a great variety of wild and cultivated plants. Another fairly common species is the four-lined plant bug, *Poecilocápsus lineàtus* (Fabricius), a yellowish or yellowish-green bug with four longitudinal black lines on the body (Figure 19-17 E); this species feeds particularly on currants and gooseberries, and inserts its eggs into the stems of these plants. In some fruit-growing areas the apple red bug, *Lygídea méndax* Reuter, a red-and-black bug about 6 millimeters in length (Figure 19-17 B), is a serious pest in apple orchards.

The garden fleahopper, *Hálticus bracteàtus* (Say), is a common leaf bug that is usually short-winged (Figure 19-17 A); it is a shining black, jumping bug about 1.5 to 2.0 millimeters in length, which feeds on many cultivated plants. The front wings usually lack a membrane and are much like the elytra of a beetle.

FAMILY **Isometópidae**—Jumping Tree Bugs: The members of this group are flattened oval bugs 2.0 to 2.6 millimeters in length; they are similar to the leaf bugs in having a cuneus, but differ in having ocelli (Figure 19-18). They are found on bark and dead twigs, and jump quickly when disturbed.

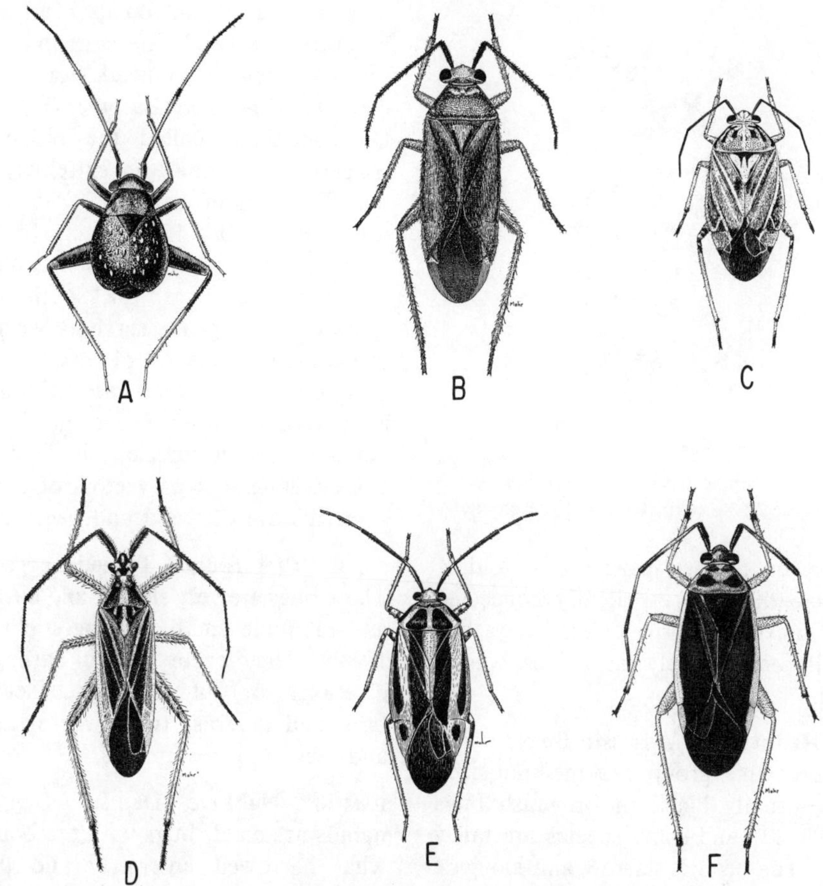

Fig. 19-17. Leaf bugs. A, the garden fleahopper, *Hálticus bracteàtus* (Say), female, 10 ×; B, the apple red bug, *Lygídea méndax* Reuter, female, 5 ×; C, the tarnished plant bug, *Lỳgus lineolàris* (Beauvois), 4 ×; D, the meadow plant bug, *Leptoptérna dolobràta* (Linn.), male, 4 ×; E, the four-lined plant bug, *Poecilocápsus lineàtus* (Fabricius), 4 ×; F, the rapid plant bug, *Adelphócoris rápidus* (Say), 4 ×. (Courtesy of the Illinois Natural History Survey.)

This group is a small one, with only five rare species occurring in eastern United States.

FAMILY **Microphýsidae:** The family Microphýsidae includes a single eastern species, *Mallochìola gagàtes* (McAtee and Malloch), which has been recorded from Maryland and the District of Columbia. This bug is broadly oval, somewhat flattened, shining black, and 1.2 millimeters in length.

FAMILY **Enicocephálidae**—Unique-Headed or Gnat Bugs: These are small, slender, predaceous bugs which have the head elongate and the front wings entirely membranous. A single rare species, *Systellóderes bìceps* (Say) (Figure 19-19 A), occurs in the United States.

FAMILY **Phymátidae**—Ambush Bugs: The phymatids are small stout-bodied bugs with raptorial front legs (Figure 19-19 B); the front femora are short and at least half as broad as long, and the tibiae are small and curved (Figure 19-2 A). Most of the ambush bugs are about ½ inch in length or less, yet they are able to capture insects as large as fair-sized bumble bees. They lie in wait for

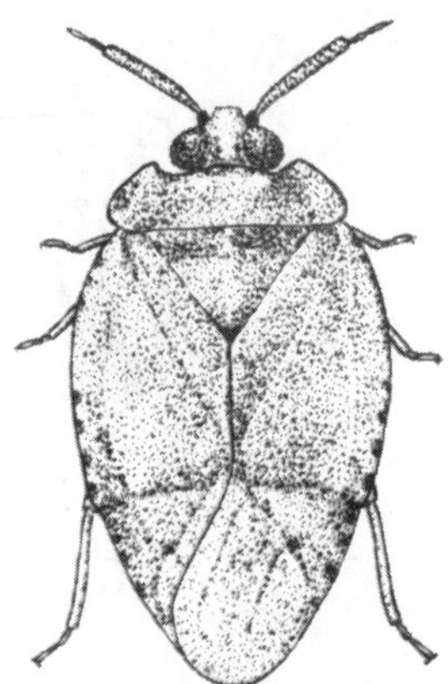

Fig. 19-18. A jumping tree bug, *Teratòdia emoritùra* Bergroth; 22 ×. (Courtesy of Froeschner.)

their prey on flowers, particularly goldenrod, where they are excellently concealed by their greenish yellow color. They feed principally on relatively large bees, wasps, and flies.

FAMILY **Reduvìidae**—Assassin Bugs: The members of this group are medium-sized to large, usually black or brownish bugs (Figure 19-20), and some species are fairly common. The head is narrow and elongate with the part behind the eyes necklike; the beak is 3-segmented, usually curved, and its tip fits into a groove in the prosternum (Figure 19-7 B). The abdomen is often widened at the middle, exposing the margins of the segments beyond the wings. Most of the assassin bugs are predaceous on other insects, but a few are blood-sucking and frequently bite man. Many species will inflict a painful bite if carelessly handled.

One of the most curious species in this group is the wheel bug, *Árilus cristàtus* (Linn.), a black bug about an inch long, with a semicircular crest on the pronotum that terminates in spurs and resembles a cogwheel (Figure 19-20 B); this species is fairly common. The masked hunter, *Redùvius personàtus* (Linn.), is a brownish-black bug that is often found in houses; it feeds on bed bugs but will also bite man. It has a habit of accumulating lint on its head and thus becomes "masked". The assassin bugs in the genus *Triátoma* also invade houses and bite man; *T. sanguisùga* (Leconte) (Figure 19-20 D), sometimes called the blood-sucking conenose, can inflict an extremely painful bite. The bugs in the genus *Triátoma* are in some areas called kissing bugs (because of their tendency to bite about the mouth) or Mexican bed bugs. In South America species of this genus serve as vectors of a trypanosome disease of man known as Chagas disease (several cases of this disease have recently been found in the United States); certain species in southwestern United States act as vectors of a trypanosome disease of wood and pack rats.

FAMILY **Ploiarìidae**—Thread-Legged Bugs: These bugs are very slender and long-legged, and resemble small walking sticks (Figure 19-21). They occur in old barns, cellars, dwellings, or out of doors beneath loose bark and in grass tufts, where they catch and feed on other insects.

FAMILY **Nábidae**—Damsel Bugs: The nabids are small bugs with the body somewhat narrowed anteriorly and the front

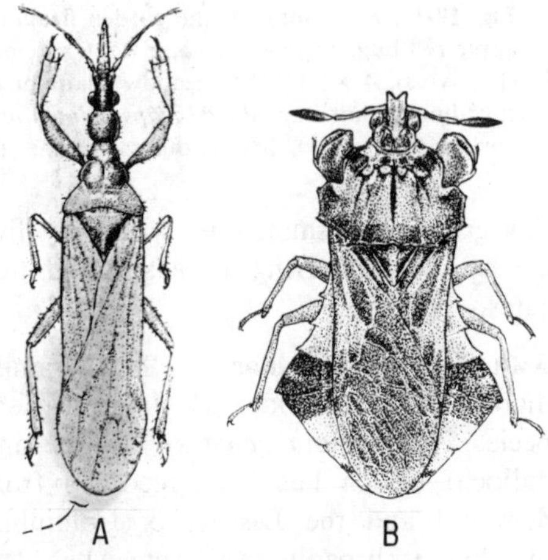

Fig. 19-19. A, a unique-headed bug, *Systellóderes bìceps* (Say), 15 ×; B, an ambush bug, *Phýmata fasciàta georgiénsis* Melin, 4½ ×. (Courtesy of Froeschner and *The American Midland Naturalist*.)

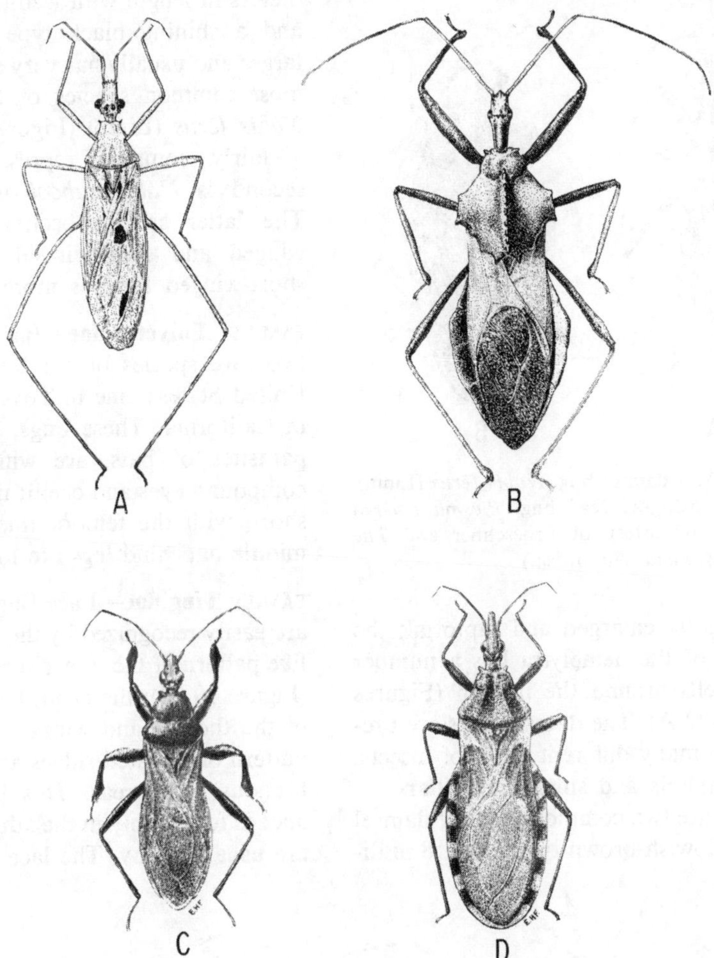

Fig. 19-20. Assassin bugs. A, *Narvèsus carolinénsis* Stål 2½ ×; B, the wheel bug, *Árilus cristàtus* (Linn.), 1½ ×; C, *Melanoléstes pìcipes* (Herrich-Schaeffer), 2 ×; D, a blood-sucking conenose, *Triátoma sanguisùga* (LeConte), 2 ×. (Courtesy of Froeschner and *The American Midland Naturalist.*)

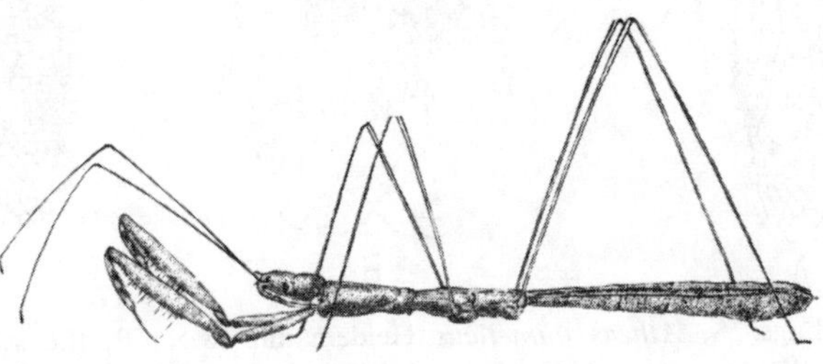

Fig. 19-21. A thread-legged bug, *Metápterus ùhleri* (Banks), 5½ ×. (Courtesy of Froeschner.)

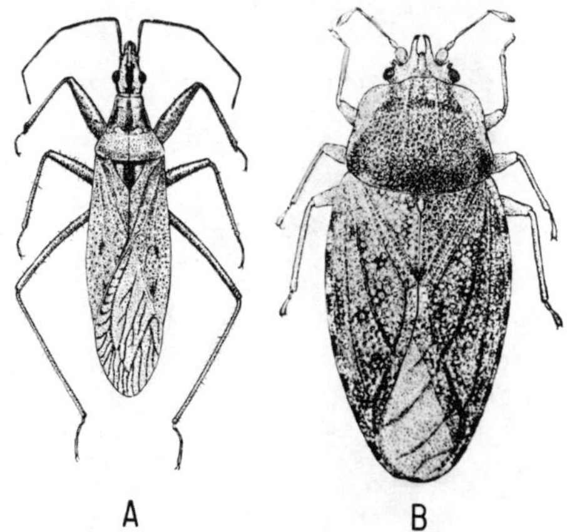

Fig. 19-22. A, a damsel bug, *Nàbis fèrus* (Linn.), 5 ×; B, an ash-gray leaf bug, *Piésma cinèrea* (Say), 15 ×. (Courtesy of Froeschner and *The American Midland Naturalist.*)

femora slightly enlarged and raptorial; the membrane of the hemelytra has a number of small cells around the margin (Figures 19-4 E, 19-22 A). The damsel bugs are predaceous on many different types of insects, including aphids and small caterpillars.

There are two common types of damsel bugs, a yellowish-brown type about 8 millimeters in length with well-developed wings, and a shining black type that is a little larger and usually has very short wings. The most common species of the first type is *Nàbis fèrus* (Linn.) (Figure 19-22 A), and a fairly common representative of the second is *Nàbis subcoleoptràtus* (Kirby). The latter species occurs in both long-winged and short-winged forms, but the short-winged form is more common.

FAMILY **Polycténidae**—Bat Bugs: Only two rare species of bat bugs occur in the United States: one in Texas and the other in California. These bugs, which are ectoparasites of bats, are wingless and lack compound eyes and ocelli; the front legs are short, with the femora thickened, and the middle and hind legs are long and slender.

FAMILY **Tíngidae**—Lace Bugs: These bugs are easily recognized by the sculptured lacelike pattern of the upper surface of the body (Figure 19-23); the head, lateral expansions of the thorax, and wings usually present a pattern of elevated ridges and sunken membranous oval areas. This lacelike appearance is found only in the adults; the nymphs are usually spiny. The lace bugs are small,

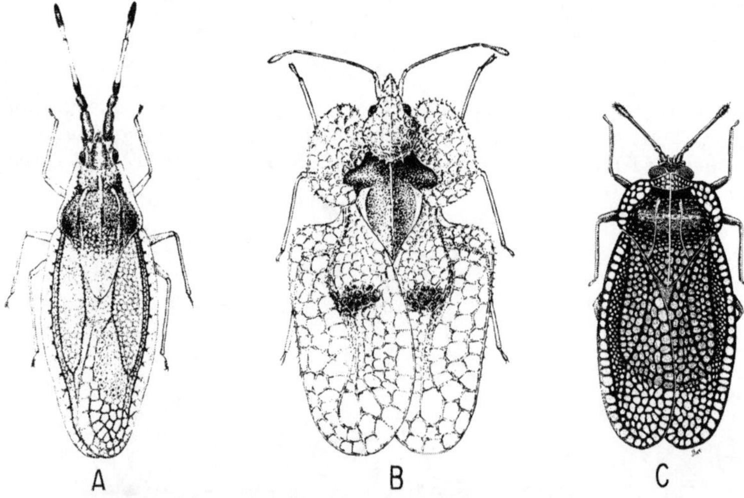

Fig. 19-23. Lace bugs. A, *Àtheas miméticus* Heidemann, 18 ×; B, the sycamore lace bug; *Corythùca ciliàta* (Say), 13 ×; C, *Acalýpta lilliànis* Bueno, 14 ×. (A and B, courtesy of Froeschner and *The American Midland Naturalist;* C, courtesy of Osborn and Drake and the Ohio Biological Survey.)

usually whitish insects (the nymphs are black) about 5 or 6 millimeters in length. They feed chiefly on the leaves of trees and shrubs; their feeding first causes a yellow spotting of the leaf, but with continued feeding the leaf becomes entirely brown and falls off. The eggs are usually laid on the under sides of leaves. *Corythùca ciliàta* (Say) (Figure 19-23 B) is a common species that feeds on sycamore.

FAMILY **Piésmidae**—Ash-Gray Leaf Bugs: These bugs are similar to the lace bugs, but are more slender and do not have as much lacelike sculpturing on the dorsal side of the body (Figure 19-22 B). They feed on the foliage of various weeds and trees.

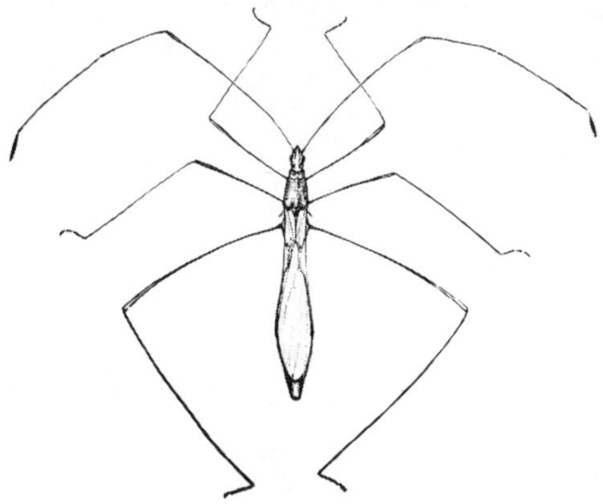

Fig. 19-24. A stilt bug, *Jálysus wíckhami* Van Duzee, 3½ ×. (Courtesy of Froeschner and *The American Midland Naturalist.*)

FAMILY **Neídidae**—Stilt Bugs: The stilt bugs are slender, long-legged bugs (Figure 19-24) that feed on plants. They are 5 to 9 millimeters in length and are usually brownish in color; they are rather sluggish insects, and are generally found in dense herbaceous vegetation.

FAMILY **Lygaèidae:** This family is a relatively large one, and most of its members are phytophagous. Many species are very common, and one species, the chinch bug, *Blíssus leucópterus* (Say), is a serious pest of wheat, corn, rye, and barley; this family is sometimes called the chinch bug family, but the majority of the lygaeids do not look a great deal like the chinch bug (Figures 19-25, 19-26).

The lygaeids have the beak and the antennae 4-segmented, ocelli are present, and there are four or five simple veins in the membrane of the hemelytra (Figure 19-4 B). They differ from the leaf bugs (Míridae) in lacking a cuneus and in possessing ocelli, and they are harder-bodied; they differ from the bugs in the superfamily Coreòidea in that they have only a few veins in the membrane of the wing. The lygaeids are small bugs, the largest being only about ½ inch or so in length. Many species are conspicuously marked with spots or bands of red, white, or black.

The chinch bug (Figure 19-25) is probably the most injurious bug in this family, attacking wheat, corn, and other cereals. It is about 3.5 millimeters in length and is black with white front wings; each front wing has a black spot near the middle of the costal margin. Both long-winged and short-winged forms occur in this species (Figure 19-25 C, D). Chinch bugs overwinter as adults in grass clumps, fallen leaves, fence rows, and other protected places, and emerge about the middle of April and begin feeding on small grains. The eggs are laid during May, either in the ground or in grass stems near the ground, and hatch about a week or ten days later; each female may lay several hundred eggs. The nymphs feed on the juices of grasses and grains and reach maturity in four to six weeks. By the time these nymphs become adult, the small grains (wheat, rye, oats, and barley) are nearly mature and no longer succulent, and the adults (along with nymphs nearly adult) migrate to other fields of more succulent grain, usually corn. They migrate on foot, often in great numbers. The females lay eggs for a second generation on the corn, and this generation reaches maturity in late fall and then seeks out places for hibernation.

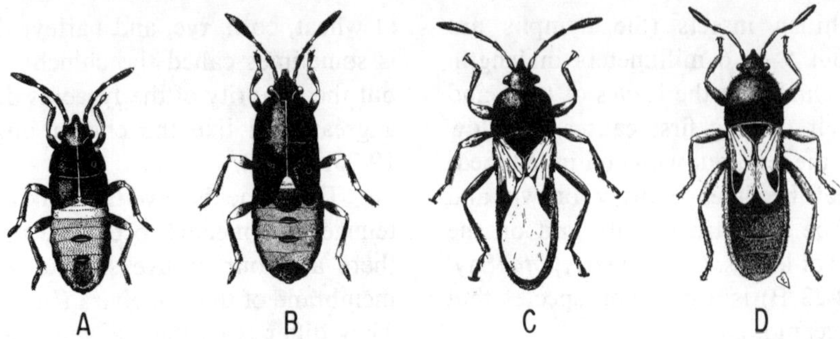

Fig. 19-25. The chinch bug, *Blissus leucópterus* (Say). A, fourth-instar nymph; B, fifth-instar nymph; C, adult; D, short-winged adult. (Courtesy of USDA.)

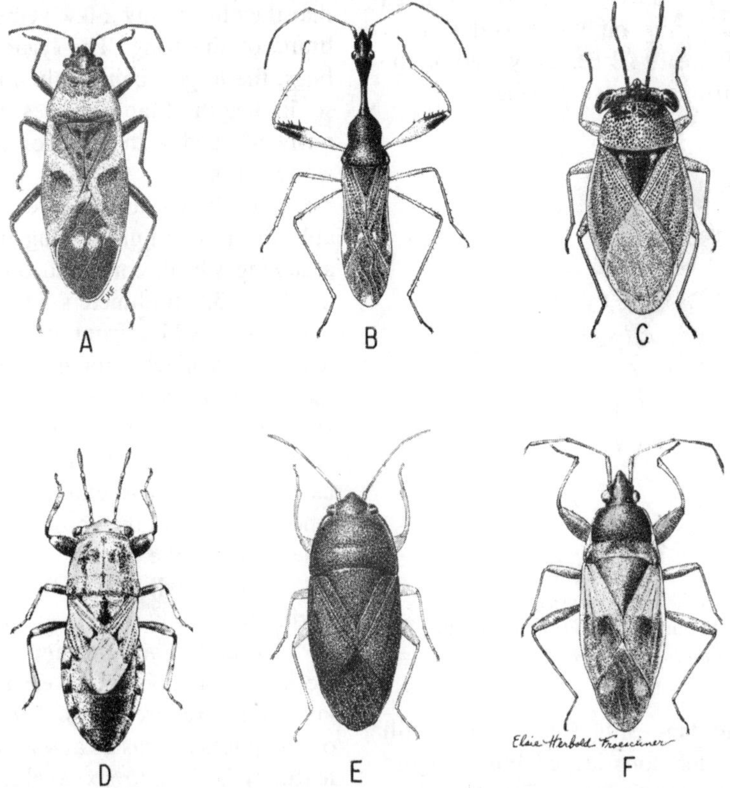

Fig. 19-26. Lygaeid bugs. A, the small milkweed bug, *Lygaèus kálmii* Stål, 3 ×; B, *Myódocha sérripes* Olivier, 4 ×, C, *Geócoris púnctipes* (Say), 8 ×; D, *Phlégyas abbreviàtus* (Uhler), 8 ×; E, *Aphànus illuminàtus* (Distant), 6 ×; F, *Eremócoris fèrus* (Say), (Courtesy of Froeschner and *The American Midland Naturalist.*)

When chinch bugs are abundant, whole fields of grain may be destroyed.

Several species in this group are brightly marked with red and black. The small milkweed bug, *Lygaèus kálmii* Stål (Figure 19-26 A), has a red **X**-shaped area on the hemelytra and a broad red band across the base of the pronotum; the large milkweed bug, *Oncopéltus fasciàtus* (Dallas), is broadly banded with red and black.

A few of the lygaeids are predaceous, and have the front legs raptorial. The big-eyed bugs (*Geócoris,* Figure 19-26 C) are predaceous on various small insects; these bugs are commonly found beneath grass or weeds on sandy beaches. *Myódocha sérripes* Olivier, a blackish bug 8 to 10 millimeters in length, has a very long slender neck (Figure 19-26 B).

FAMILY **Pyrrhocóridae**—Red Bugs and Stainers: The members of this group are elongate-oval bugs that are usually brightly marked with red and black. They resemble the lygaeids, but lack ocelli and have more branched veins and cells in the membrane of the hemelytra (Figure 19-4 H). They are phytophagous and gregarious. The most important pest species in this family is the cotton stainer, *Dysdércus suturéllus* (Herrich-Schaeffer), which is a serious pest of cotton in the southern states; it stains the cotton fibers by its feeding and greatly reduces their value. Some of the red bugs, such as *Árhaphe carolìna* (Herrich-Schaeffer), which is common in the southern states, are very antlike in appearance and have short hemelytra (Figure 19-27 A).

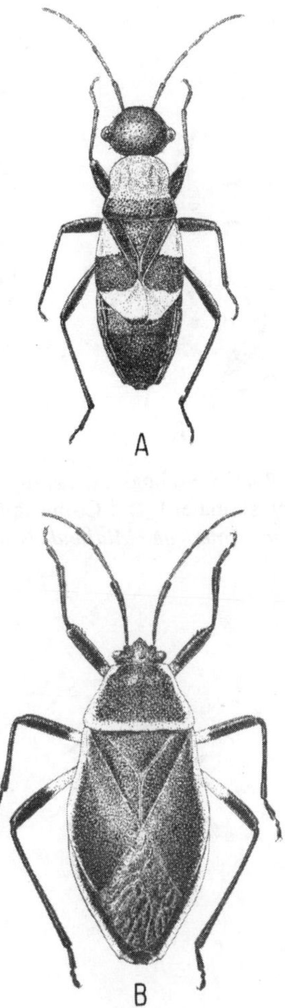

Fig. 19-27. Red bugs (Pyrrhocóridae). A, *Árhaphe carolìna* (Herrich-Schaeffer), 4 ×; B, *Euryophthálmus succínctus* (Linn.), 3 ×. (Courtesy of Froeschner and *The American Midland Naturalist.*)

FAMILY **Corèidae** — Leaf-Footed Bugs: Many species in this group have the legs flattened and leaflike (Figure 19-28 A), and are appropriately called leaf-footed bugs, but this character is not found in all members of the family. The coreid group is a large one, and most of its members are relatively large bugs; they are somewhat similar to the lygaeids, but have numerous veins in the membrane of the hemelytra (Figure 19-4 D). Some species are phytophagous and others are predaceous. The squash bug, *Ánasa trístis* (DeGeer) (Figure 19-28 C), a serious pest of cucurbits, is dark brown in color and about $\frac{3}{4}$ inch in length; it has one generation a year and passes the winter in the adult stage in debris and other sheltered places.

FAMILY **Corízidae**—Grass Bugs: The grass bugs differ from the coreids in being smaller, usually light-colored, and they lack scent glands; they are sometimes called the scentless plant bugs. They occur principally on weeds and similar vegetation and are phytophagous; they are more common in late summer and early fall. The boxelder bug,

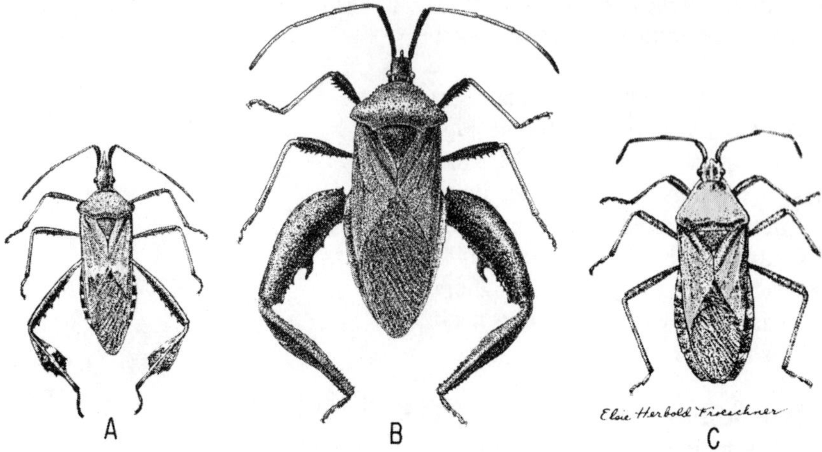

Fig. 19-28. Coreid bugs. A, *Leptoglóssus clypeàlis* Heidemann, $1\frac{1}{2}$ ×; B, *Acanthocéphala femoràta* (Fabricius), male, $1\frac{1}{2}$ ×; C, the squash bug, *Ánasa trístis* (DeGeer), 2 ×. (Courtesy of Froeschner and *The American Midland Naturalist.*)

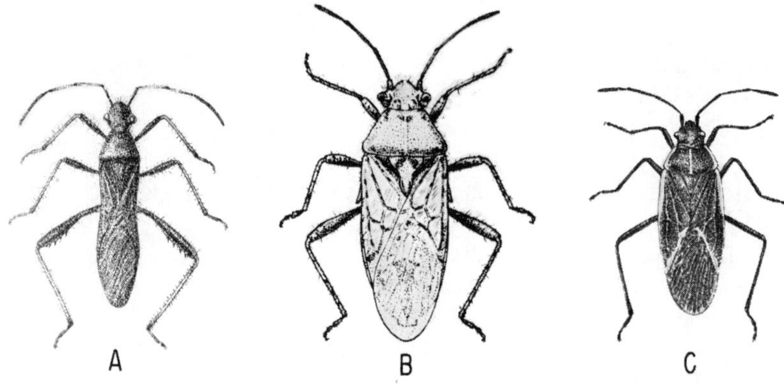

Fig. 19-29. A, a broad-headed bug, *Coríscus eurìnus* (Say), 2 ×; B, a grass bug, *Corìzus lateràlis* (Say), 5 ×; C, the boxelder bug, *Leptócoris trivittàtus* (Say), 2 ×. (Courtesy of Froeschner and *The American Midland Naturalist.*)

Leptócoris trivittàtus (Say), a common species in this group, is blackish with red markings, and 11 to 14 millimeters in length (Figure 19-29 C). It often enters houses and other sheltered places in the fall, sometimes in considerable numbers, in search of hibernating quarters. It feeds on box elder and occasionally on other trees.

FAMILY **Coríscidae**—Broad-Headed Bugs: These bugs are very similar to the coreids, but the head is much larger and broader, and the body is usually long and narrow (Figure 19-29 A). The broad-headed bugs might well be called stink bugs, as they often "stink" much worse than the bugs in the family Pentatómidae, to which the name "stink bug" is usually applied; they give off an odor reminiscent of someone with a bad case of halitosis. The openings of the scent glands are conspicuous oval openings between the middle and hind coxae (Figure 19-8 A). These bugs are fairly common on the foliage of weeds and shrubs along roadsides and in woodland areas.

Most of the bugs in this group are either yellowish brown or black in color; some of the black species have a red band across the middle of the dorsal side of the abdomen. A common brown coriscid occurring in the Northeast is *Pròtenor belfrágei* Haglund; it is 12 to 15 millimeters in length. Some of the black coriscids (for example, *Coríscus,* Figure 19-29 A) look very much like ants in their nymphal stage, and the adults in the field look much like some of the spider wasps.

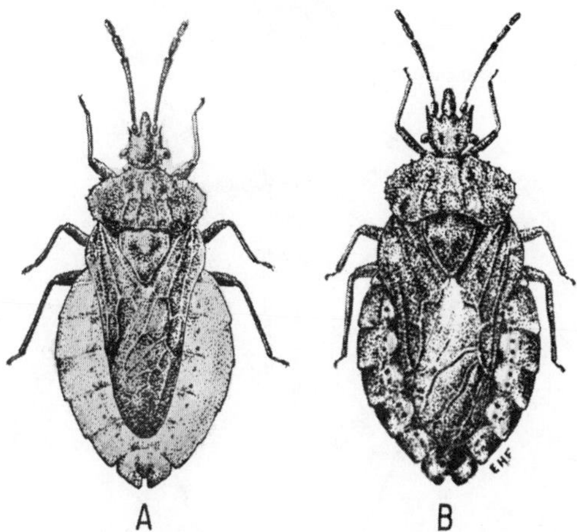

Fig. 19-30. Flat bugs (Arádidae). A, *Áradus inornàtus* Uhler, 4½ ×; B, *Áradus acùtus* (Say), 5½ ×. (Courtesy of Froeschner and *The American Midland Naturalist.*)

FAMILY **Arádidae**—Flat Bugs or Fungus Bugs: These small, usually dark-brownish, very flat bugs (Figure 19-30) are found under loose bark or in crevices of dead or decaying trees. They feed on the sap of fungi or the moisture in bark or decaying wood. The wings are well developed but small and do not cover the entire abdomen; the antennae and beak are 4-segmented, the tarsi are 2-segmented, and there are no ocelli.

FAMILY **Termatophýlidae:** This family is represented in the United States by a single very rare species, *Hesperóphylum heìdemanni* Reuter and Poppius, which has been recorded from New Hampshire and Arizona. It is dark brown with the scutellum yellowish white, and is about 4 millimeters in length. Some authorities place this species in the subfamily Doraecorìnae of the Míridae.

FAMILY **Sáldidae**—Shore Bugs: The shore bugs are small, oval, flattened, usually brownish bugs that are often common along the shores of streams, ponds, or the ocean; some are burrowing in habit. When disturbed, they fly quickly for short distances and then scurry under vegetation or into a crevice. They are predaceous on other insects. The shore bugs can usually be recognized by the four or five long closed cells in the membrane of the hemelytra (Figure 19-4 F).

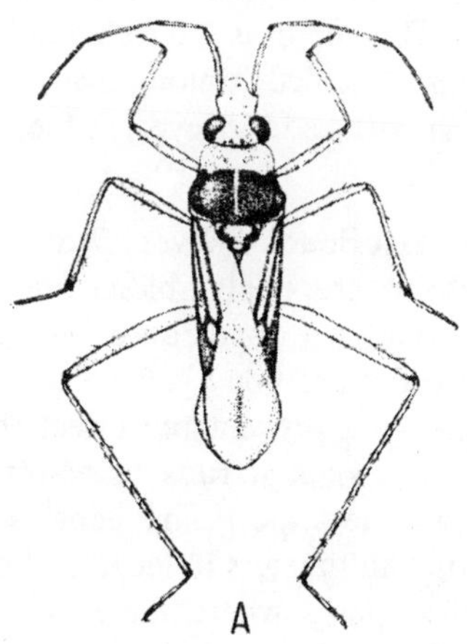

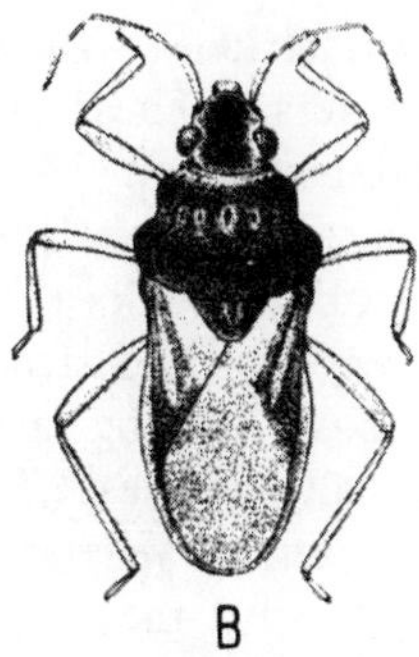

Fig. 19-31. A, a water treader, *Mesovèlia mulsánti* White, 9 ×; B, a velvet water bug, *Hèbrus sobrìnus* Uhler, 16 ×. (Courtesy of Froeschner and *The American Midland Naturalist.*)

FAMILY **Mesoveliidae**—Water Treaders: These bugs are usually found crawling over floating vegetation at the margins of ponds or pools, or on logs projecting from the water; when disturbed, they run rapidly over the surface of the water. They are small (5 millimeters in length or less), slender, and usually greenish or yellowish green in color (Figure 19-31 A); some are winged, and some are wingless. These insects feed on small aquatic organisms on and just beneath the surface of the water.

FAMILY **Thaumastocóridae**—Royal Palm Bugs: This group is represented in the United States by a single species, *Xylastódoris lutèolus* Barber, which occurs in Florida. This insect is 2.0 to 2.5 millimeters in length, flattened, oblong-oval, and pale yellowish with reddish eyes; it feeds on the royal palm.

FAMILY **Hébridae**—Velvet Water Bugs: The hebrids are small oblong bugs with a broad-shouldered appearance (Figure 19-31 B), and the entire body is covered with velvety hairs that prevent the insect from becoming wet when it runs or walks on the surface of the water. The hebrids are all less than 3 millimeters in length. They occur in shallow pools where there is an abundance of aquatic vegetation. The group is a small one, and only seven species are known in the United States.

FAMILY **Hydrométridae**—Water Measurers or Marsh Treaders: These bugs are small (about 8 millimeters in length), usually grayish in color, and very slender; they resemble tiny walking sticks (Figure 19-32). The head is very long and slender, with the eyes conspicuously bulging laterally. These insects are usually wingless. They occur in shallow water among vegetation and feed on minute organisms; they frequently walk very slowly over surface vegetation or over the surface of the water. The eggs, which are elongate and about one-fourth as long as the adult, are laid singly and glued to objects near the water.

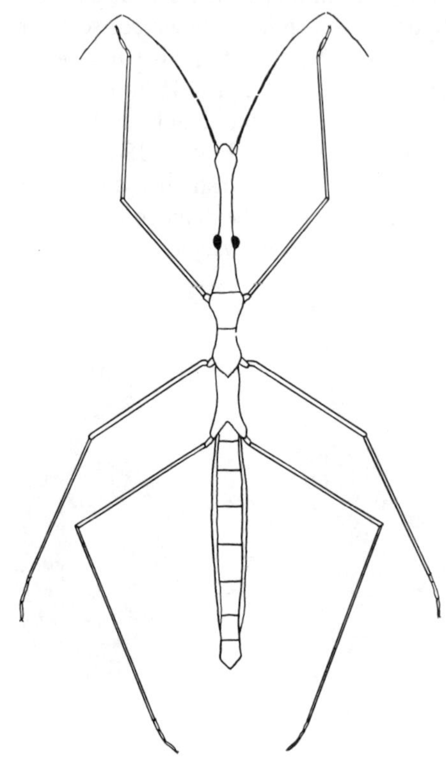

Fig. 19-32. A water measurer, *Hydrómetra mártini* Kirkaldy; $7\frac{1}{2}\times$.

FAMILY **Cýdnidae**—Burrower Bugs: The burrower bugs are generally 7 millimeters in length or less, oval, and usually black in color; they are similar in general appearance to the stink bugs, but have the tibiae expanded and spiny (Figures 19-9 A and 19-33 B). They are usually found burrowing beneath stones or boards, in sand, or in the mold about the roots of grass tufts; sometimes they are found in ant nests.

FAMILY **Corimelaènidae**—Negro Bugs: The negro bugs are small (3 to 6 millimeters in length), broadly oval, strongly convex, shining black bugs that are very beetlelike in appearance (Figure 19-33 A). The scutellum is very large and covers most of the abdomen and wings. These insects are phytophagous and are fairly common on grasses, weeds, berries, and flowers.

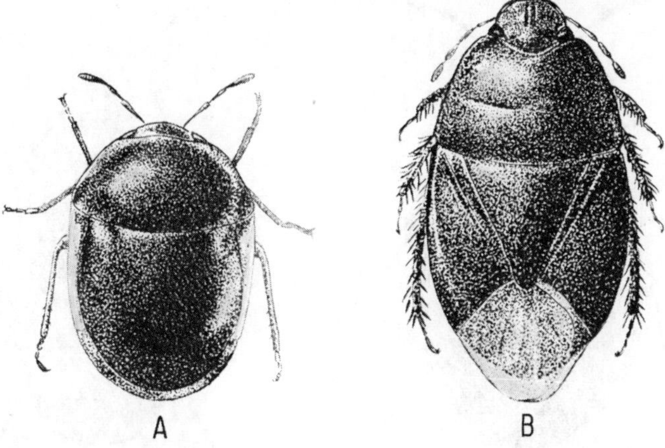

Fig. 19-33. A, a negro bug, *Allócoris pulicària* (Germar), $6\frac{1}{2}\times$; B, a burrower bug, *Pangaèus bilineàtus* (Say), $7\frac{1}{2}\times$. (Courtesy of Froeschner and *The American Midland Naturalist*.)

FAMILY **Scutelléridae**—Shield-Backed Bugs: These bugs look very much like stink bugs, but have the scutellum very large and extending to the apex of the abdomen; the wings are visible only at the edge of the scutellum (Figure 19-34 A). Most of these bugs are brownish and 8 to 10 millimeters in length. They are seldom abundant, but may be found on woodland vegetation; they are phytophagous.

FAMILY **Podópidae** — Terrestrial Turtle Bugs: The podopids are small brownish bugs, similar to the shield-backed bugs in appearance but smaller (3.5 to 6.5 millimeters in length). The scutellum is long, as in the shield-backed bugs, but the pronotum has a prominent tooth or lobe in front of the humeral angle (Figures 19-9 C, 19-34 B). These insects are not common.

FAMILY **Pentatómidae**—Stink Bugs: This group is large and well known, and its members are easily recognized by the broad shieldlike shape, the 5-segmented antennae, and the large triangular scutellum (Figures 19-35 and 19-36). Many species are brightly colored or conspicuously marked. The pentatomids are the most common and abundant of the bugs that produce a disagreeable odor, but some other bugs (particularly the Coríscidae) produce an odor that is stronger and more disagreeable than that produced by the pentatomids.

Some of the stink bugs are phytophagous, some feed on other insects, and some feed on both plant and insect food. Some of the predaceous species will feed on plants if insect prey is not easily found. The family Pentatómidae is divided into three subfamilies: the Acanthosomìnae, Pentatomìnae, and Asopìnae. The Acanthosomìnae and Asopìnae are mostly predaceous, and the Pentatomìnae are mostly phytophagous. The Acanthosomìnae (a small group) have only two tarsal segments; the other two subfamilies have three. In the Pentatomìnae the bucculae are parallel, and the first segment of the beak is slender and is normally embedded between them; in the Asopìnae the bucculae converge posteriorly, and the first segment of the beak, which is short and stout, has only its base between the bucculae.

The eggs of stink bugs, which are usually barrel-shaped and have the upper end ornamented with spines, are usually laid in groups—like so many little brightly colored barrels lined up side by side (Figure 3-2).

One rather important pest species in this group is the harlequin bug, *Murgántia his-*

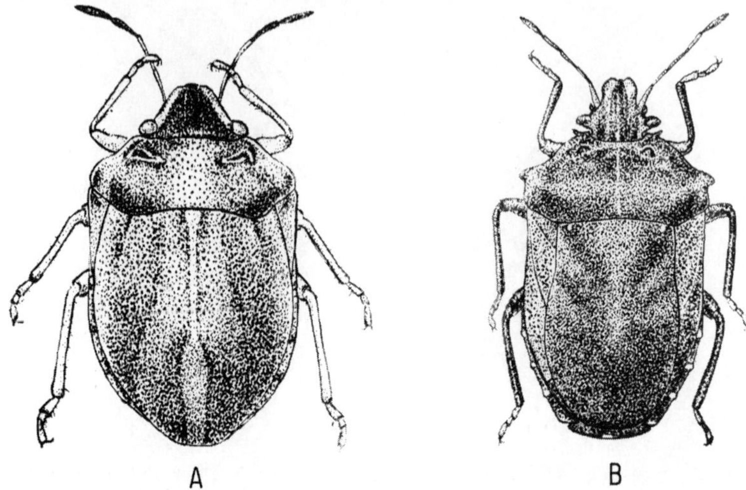

Fig. 19-34. A, a shield-backed bug, *Homaèmus párvulus* (Germar); 8 ×; B, a terrestrial turtle bug, *Pòdops cínctipes* (Say), 8 ×. (Courtesy of Froeschner and *The American Midland Naturalist.*)

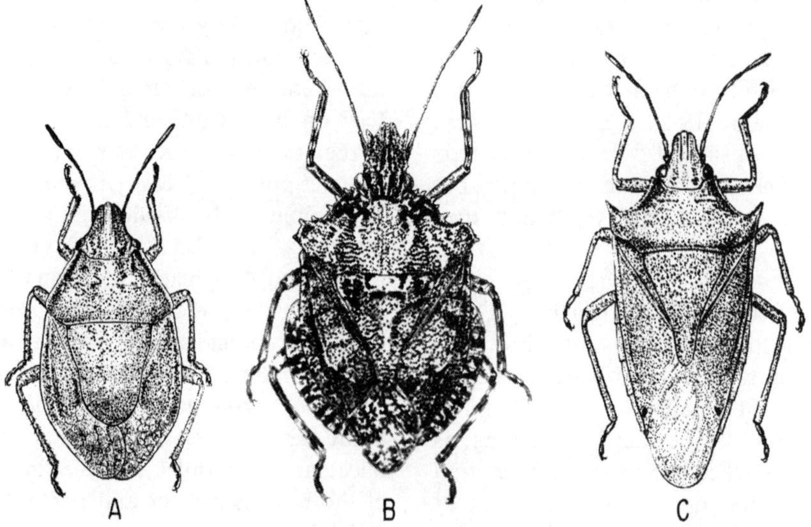

Fig. 19-35. Stink bugs. A, *Coènus dèlius* (Say), $3\frac{1}{2}$ ×; B, *Brochýmena arbòrea* (Say), 3 ×; C, *Solùbea púgnax* (Fabricius), $4\frac{1}{2}$ ×. (Courtesy of Froeschner and *The American Midland Naturalist.*)

triónica (Hahn) (Figure 19-36 B); this brightly colored insect is often very destructive to cabbage and other cruciferous plants, particularly in the southern part of the country. The other stink bugs, which are plant feeders (Figures 19-35 and 19-36 A, C), usually attack grasses or other plants and are not of very great economic importance. The spined soldier bug, *Pódisus maculivéntris* (Say) (Figure 19-36 D), is predaceous on lepidopterous larvae.

COLLECTING AND PRESERVING HEMIPTERA

The aquatic bugs can be collected by means of the aquatic collecting equipment

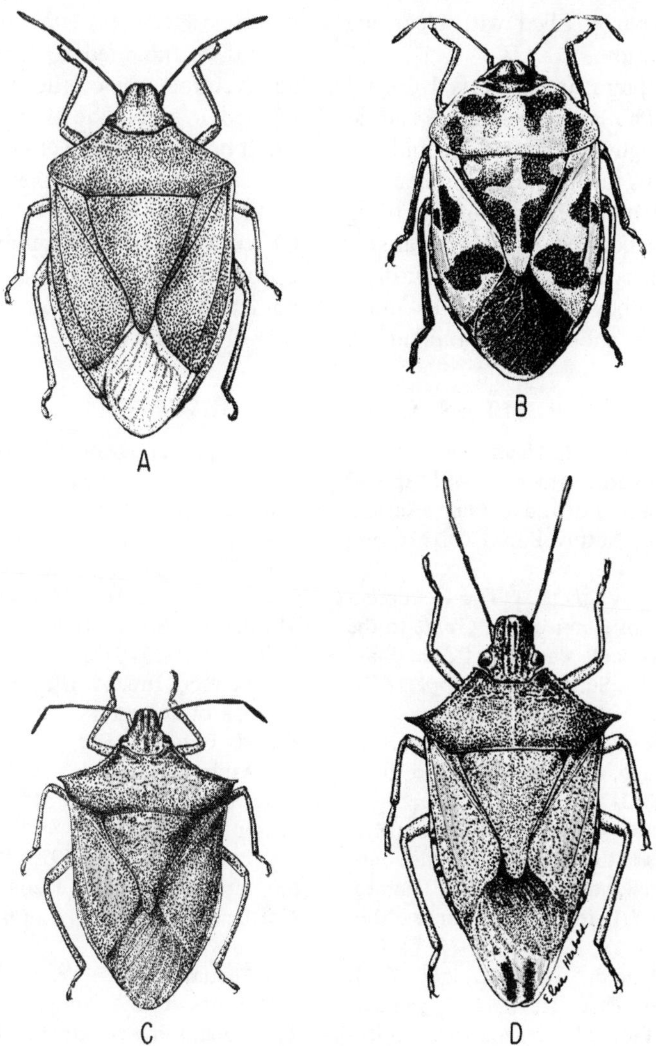

Fig. 19-36. Stink bugs. A, *Thyánta custàtor* (Fabricius), $4\frac{1}{2}\times$; B, the harlequin bug, *Murgántia histriónica* (Hahn), $4\times$; C, *Euschístus variolàrius* (Beauvois), $3\times$; D, the spined soldier bug, *Pódisus maculivéntris* (Say), $4\frac{1}{2}\times$. (Courtesy of Froeschner and *The American Midland Naturalist.*)

and methods described in Chapter 32; a few aquatic species, particularly water boatmen and giant water bugs, may often be collected at lights. One should examine a variety of aquatic habitats, as different species occur in different types of situations. Terrestrial forms may be collected with a net (particularly by sweeping vegetation), at lights, or by examining such specialized habitats as leaf litter, under bark, and in fungi.

The best type of killing bottle for most Hemiptera is a small vial such as that shown in Figure 32-4 A, which should be partly filled with small pieces of cleansing tissue or lens paper. One should have several such vials, since large and heavy-bodied specimens should not be put into the same killing vial with small and delicate specimens. After the specimens have been killed, they should be taken from the vial and placed in pillboxes that are partly filled with cleansing tissue or cellucotton.

Most Hemiptera are preserved dry on pins or points. The larger specimens should be pinned through the scutellum, and the smaller specimens through the right hemelytron; care must be taken in pinning a bug not to destroy structures on the ventral side of the thorax that will be used in identification. Most Hemiptera less than 10 millimeters in length should be mounted on points. Specimens mounted on points should be mounted so that the beak, legs, and ventral side of the body are not embedded in glue; the best way to mount a small bug on a point is to bend the tip of the point down and glue the bug to the point by the right side of the thorax (Figure 32-11 C). If a specimen is mounted dorsal side up on the tip of a point, the point should not extend beyond the middle of the ventral side of the insect.

REFERENCES ON THE HEMIPTERA

Blatchley, W. S. 1926. Heteroptera or true bugs of eastern North America, with special reference to the faunas of Indiana and Florida. Indianapolis, Ind.: Nature Pub. Co. 1116 pp., 215 f., 12 pl.

Britton, W. E., *et al.* 1923. The Hemiptera or sucking insects of Connecticut. Guide to the Insects of Connecticut. Part IV. Conn. State Geol. and Nat. Hist. Survey; 807 pp., pl. I-XX, 168 f.

Fracker, S. B. 1912. A systematic outline of the Reduviidae of North America. Proc. Iowa Acad. Sci., 19:217-247.

Froeschner, R. C. 1941-1949. Contributions to a synopsis of the Hemiptera of Missouri. Part I, 1941, Scutelleridae, Podopidae, Pentatomidae, Cydnidae, Thyreocoridae, Amer. Midland Naturalist, 26(1):122-146, f. 1-36. Part II, 1942, Coreidae, Aradidae, Neididae, *ibid.*, 27(3): 591-609, f. 37-55. Part III, 1944, Lygaeidae, Pyrrhocoridae, Piesmidae, Tingidae, Enicocephalidae, Phymatidae, Ploiariidae, Reduviidae, Nabidae, *ibid.*, 31(3):638-683, f. 56-88. Part IV, 1949, Hebridae, Mesoveliidae, Cimicidae, Anthocoridae, Cryptostemmatidae, Isometopidae, Miridae, *ibid.*, 42(1):123-188, f. 89-123.

Hart, C. A. and J. R. Malloch. 1919. Pentatomoidea of Illinois with keys to nearctic genera. Illinois Nat. Hist. Survey, Bull. 13(7): 157-223; pl. XVI-XXI.

Hungerford, H. B. 1948. The Corixidae of the Western Hemisphere (Hemiptera). Univ. Kansas Sci. Bull. 32:1-827; 19 f., 112 pl.

Hungerford, H. B. 1959. Hemiptera. In: Fresh-water biology, ed. by W. T. Edmondson. New York: John Wiley & Sons, Inc. Pp. 958-972; 5 f.

Knight, H. H. 1917. A revision of the genus *Lygus* as it occurs in America north of Mexico, with biological data on the species from New York. N.Y. (Cornell) Agr. Expt. Sta. Bull. No. 391:555-645; pl. 23, f. 158-208.

Knight, H. H. 1941. The plant bugs or Miridae of Illinois. Illinois Nat. Hist. Survey, Bull. 22(1):1-234; 181 f.

Lawson, Fred A. 1959. Identification of the nymphs of common families of Hemiptera. J. Kansas Entomol. Soc., 32(2):88-92; 15 f.

Miller, N. C. E. 1956. Biology of the Heteroptera. London: Methuen & Co., Ltd. 172 pp.

Parshley, H. M. 1925. A bibliography of the North American Hemiptera-Heteroptera. Northampton, Mass.: Smith College. ix+252 pp.

Pennak, Robert W. 1953. Fresh-water invertebrates of the United States. New York: The Ronald Press Company. ix+769 pp., 470 f.

Readio, P. A. 1927. Studies on the biology of the Reduviidae of America north of Mexico. Univ. Kansas Sci. Bull. 17:1-248; 21 pl.

Stoner, D. 1920. The Scutelleroidea of Iowa. Iowa Univ. Stud. Nat. Hist., 8(4):1-140; 7 pl.

Usinger, Robert L. 1956. Aquatic Hemiptera. In: Aquatic insects of California, ed. by Robert L. Usinger. Berkeley, Calif.: University California Press. Pp. 182-228; 43 f.

Van Duzee, E. P. 1917. Catalogue of the Hemiptera of America north of Mexico, excepting the Aphididae, Coccidae, and Aleyrodidae. Calif. Univ. Pubs., Tech. Bull. Entomol. II. xiv+902 pp.

Order Homoptera[1]: Cicadas, Hoppers, Whiteflies, Aphids, and Scale Insects

This order contains a large and diverse group of insects closely related to the Hemiptera. They exhibit considerable variation in body form, and many species are rather degenerate structurally. The life history of some Homoptera is very complex, involving bisexual and parthenogenetic generations, winged and wingless individuals and generations, and sometimes regular alternations of food plants. All the Homoptera are plant feeders, and many species are serious pests of cultivated plants; some species transmit plant diseases. A few Homoptera are beneficial and serve as a source of shellac, dyes, or other materials.

The mouth parts are similar to those of the Hemiptera; they are sucking, with four piercing stylets (the mandibles and maxillae). The beak arises from the back of the head, in some cases appearing to arise between the front coxae; in the Hemiptera the beak arises from the front of the head. In some adults the mouth parts are vestigial or lacking.

Winged Homoptera usually have four wings; the front wings have a uniform structure throughout, either membranous or slightly thickened, and the hind wings are membranous. The wings at rest are usually held rooflike over the body, with the inner margins overlapping slightly at the apex. In some groups one or both sexes may be wingless, or both winged and wingless individuals may occur in the same sex. Male scale insects have only one pair of wings.

[1] Homoptera: *homo,* alike, uniform; *ptera,* wings (referring to the fact that the front wings are uniform in texture throughout).

The members of this group usually undergo simple metamorphosis; the development in whiteflies and male scale insects resembles complete metamorphosis in that the last nymphal instar is quiescent and pupalike.

The antennae are very short and bristlelike in some Homoptera and longer and usually filiform in others. Ocelli may be present or absent; if present, there are either two or three. The compound eyes are usually well developed.

CLASSIFICATION OF THE HOMOPTERA

The order Homoptera is divided into two suborders—the Auchenorrhýncha and the Sternorrhýncha—each of which is further divided into superfamilies and families. There are differences of opinion regarding the taxonomic status that should be given the various groups in this order; the arrangement followed in this book is outlined below, with alternate names or arrangements indicated in parentheses.

- Suborder Auchenorrhýncha
  - Superfamily Cicadòidea
    - Cicàdidae—cicadas
    - Membrácidae—treehoppers
    - Cicadéllidae (Jássidae)—leafhoppers
    - Cercópidae—froghoppers, spittlebugs
  - Superfamily Fulgoròidea (Family Fulgóridae)—planthoppers
    - Fulgóridae—fulgorid planthoppers
    - Dérbidae—derbid planthoppers
    - Achílidae—achilid planthoppers
    - Delphácidae (Areopódidae)—delphacid planthoppers
    - Dictyophàridae—dictyopharid planthoppers
    - Cixìidae—cixiid planthoppers
    - Flátidae—flatid planthoppers
    - Acanalonìidae (Amphiscépidae)—acanaloniid planthoppers
    - Íssidae—issid planthoppers
    - Ricanìidae—ricaniid planthoppers
    - Lophópidae—lophopid planthoppers
- Suborder Sternorrhýncha (Gularóstria)
  - Superfamily Psyllòidea
    - Psýllidae (Psyllìidae, Chérmidae)—jumping plant lice
  - Superfamily Aleyrodòidea
    - Aleyródidae (Aleuródidae)—whiteflies
  - Superfamily Aphidòidea
    - Aphídidae (Áphidae)—aphids, plant lice
    - Eriosomátidae (Aphídidae in part)—woolly and gall-making aphids
    - Adélgidae (Chérmidae; Phylloxéridae in part)—pine and spruce aphids
    - Phylloxéridae—phylloxerans
  - Superfamily Coccòidea (Family Cóccidae)—scale insects
    - Margaródidae (Monophlébidae)—giant coccids, ground pearls, cottony cushion scales
    - Ortheziidae—ensign coccids
    - Diaspídidae—armored scales
    - Cóccidae (Lecanìidae)—soft scales, wax scales, tortoise scales
    - Aclérdidae—aclerdid scales
    - Lacciféridae (Tachardìidae)—lac insects
    - Asterolecanìidae—pit scales

Pseudocóccidae—mealybugs
Eriocóccidae (Conchaspídidae; Pseudocóccidae in part)—eriococcid scales
Dactylopìidae (Cóccidae)—cochineal insects
Kérmidae (Kermésidae, Hemicóccidae)—gall-like coccids

In the Auchenorrhýncha the antennae are short and bristlelike, there are three tarsal segments, and the beak plainly arises from the back of the head; the members of this suborder are active and free-living, and all but the cicadas are jumping insects. In the Sternorrhýncha the antennae are usually long and filiform, the tarsi are either 1- or 2-segmented, and the beak appears to arise between the front coxae; many members of this suborder are relatively inactive or sedentary.

The superfamilies and families of the Auchenorrhýncha are separated principally on the basis of the character of the ocelli, the position of the antennae, the form of the pronotum, and the spination of the legs. The superfamilies of the Sternorrhýncha are separated on the basis of the number of antennal and tarsal segments, the structure and venation of the wings, and other characters. The families of scale insects are separated on the basis of characters of the female.

The student should have no great difficulty in running winged specimens of Homoptera through the following key, but he is likely to have trouble with some of the wingless forms. Many female scale insects (Coccòidea) lack legs and antennae and do not look very insectlike, and some of the wingless Aphidòidea can be separated only if one is familiar with their life history. The separation of the families of scale insects is based on females (unless otherwise indicated), and it will usually be necessary to have female specimens mounted on microscope slides in order to run them through the key.

KEY TO THE FAMILIES OF HOMOPTERA

1. Tarsi 3-segmented; antennae very short and bristlelike; beak arising from back of head; active insects (suborder Auchenorrhýncha) 2

1′. Tarsi 1- or 2-segmented (when legs are present); antennae usually long and filiform; beak, when present, arising between front coxae; usually not active insects (suborder Sternorrhýncha) 16

2(1). Antennae arising on front of head between eyes (Figures 20-1 B and 20-4 B), or at least anterior to eyes (Figure 20-4 A); middle coxae short and close together; tegulae usually absent; no **Y**-vein in anal area of front wing (Figures 20-1 A and 20-2 A) (superfamily Cicadòidea) 3

2′. Antennae arising on side of head beneath eyes (Figure 20-4 C); middle coxae elongated and separated; tegulae usually present; 2 anal veins in front wing usually meeting apically to form a **Y**-vein (Figure 20-6 A, B) (superfamily Fulgoròidea) 6

3(2). Three ocelli (Figure 20-4 B); large insects with front wings membranous (Figure 20-9); males usually with sound-producing organs ventrally at base of abdomen (Figure 20-10); not jumping insects...... **Cicàdidae** p. 204

3′. Two (rarely 3) ocelli (Figure 20-1 B) or none; smaller insects, sometimes with the front wings thickened; sound-producing organs absent; usually jumping insects 4

4(3′). Pronotum extending backward over abdomen (Figure 20-11) .... **Membrácidae** p. 207

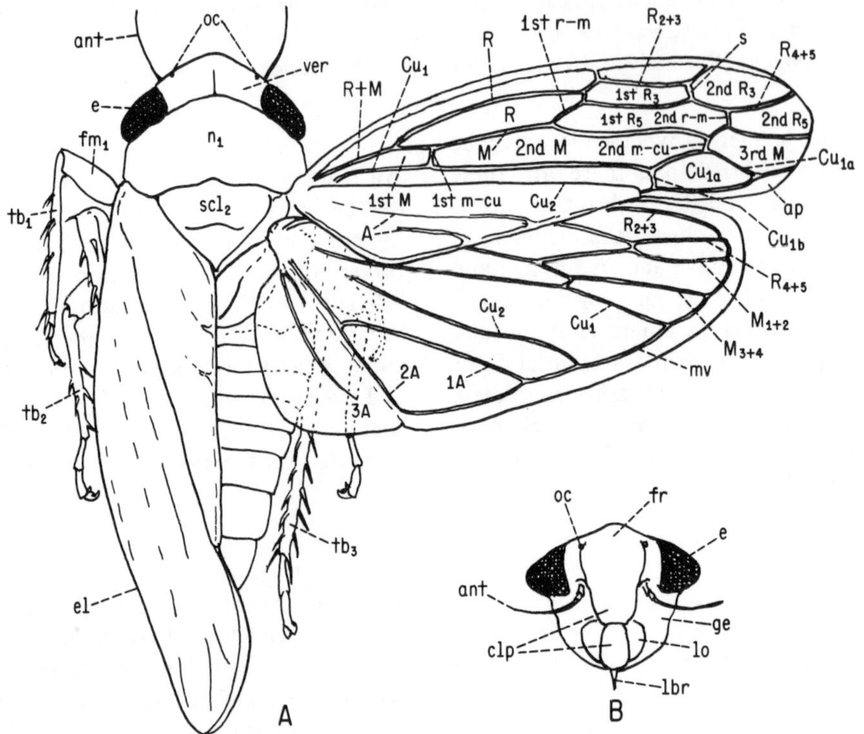

Fig. 20-1. Structure of a leafhopper, *Paraphlépsius irroràtus* (Say). A, dorsal view; B, anterior view of head. *ant*, antenna; *ap*, appendix; *clp*, clypeus; *e*, compound eye; *el*, elytron or front wing; *fm*, femur; *fr*, frons; *ge*, gena; *lbr*, labrum; *lo*, lorum; *mv*, marginal vein; n_1, pronotum; *oc*, ocelli; scl_2, mesoscutellum; *tb*, tibia; *ver*, vertex. The venational terminology follows the Comstock-Needham system, except for the veins posterior to the media. Students of the leafhoppers usually use a different terminology for the venational characters of the front wing; a comparison of their terminology with that used here is given in the following table.

VEINS		CELLS	
TERMS IN THIS FIGURE	OTHER TERMS	TERMS IN THIS FIGURE	OTHER TERMS
R + M	first sector	R	discal cell
R	outer branch of first sector	1st R_3	outer anteapical cell
M	inner branch of first sector	2nd R_3	first apical cell
Cu_1	second sector	1st R_5	anteapical cell
Cu_2	claval suture	2nd R_5	second apical cell
A	claval veins	2nd M	inner anteapical cell
1st m-cu	first cross-vein	3rd M	third apical cell
2nd m-cu	apical cross-vein	Cu_{1a}	fourth apical cell
s	apical cross-vein		
1st r-m	cross-vein between sectors		
2nd r-m	apical cross-vein		

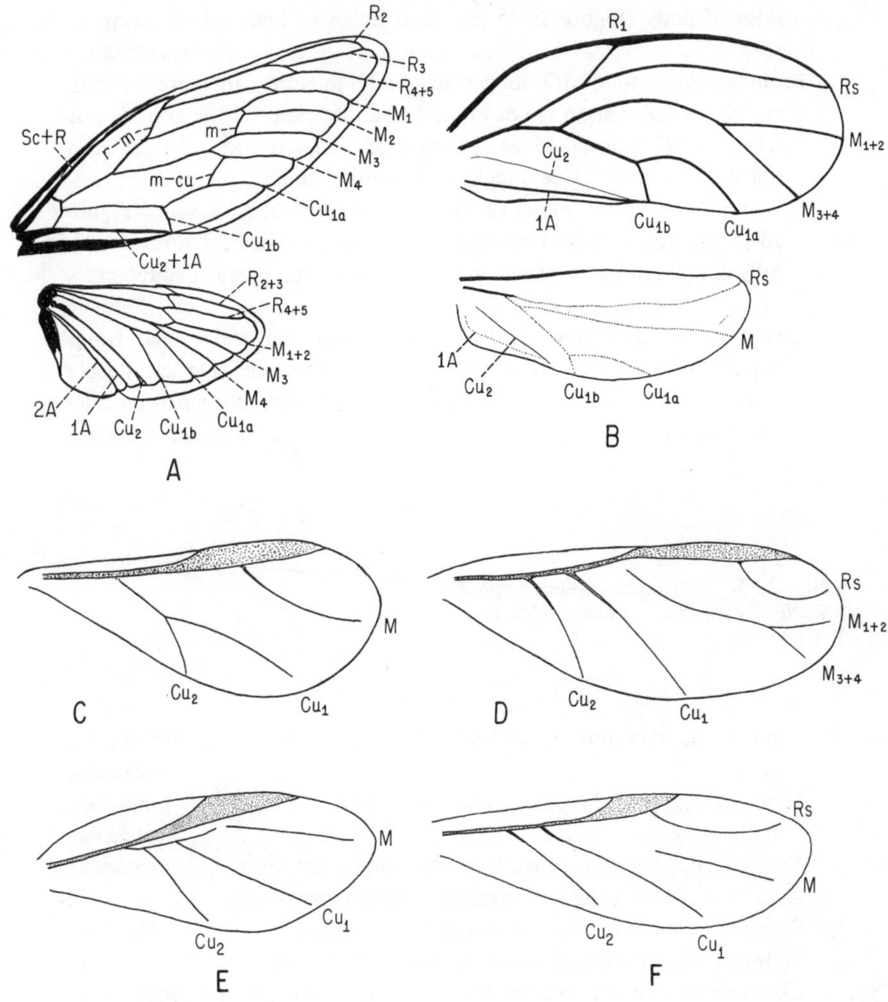

Fig. 20-2. Wings of Homoptera. A, Cicàdidae (*Magicicàda*); B, Psýllidae (*Psýlla*); C, Phylloxéridae (*Phylloxèra*); D, Aphídidae (*Macrosìphum*); E, Adélgidae (*Adélges*); F, Eriosomátidae (*Cólopha*).

4′. Pronotum not extending backward over abdomen (Figures 20-12 and 20-14) 5

5(4′). Hind tibiae with 1 or 2 stout spines and usually a series or circlet of spines at apex (Figure 20-5 B); hind coxae short and conical . . . . . **Cercópidae** p. 207

5′. Hind tibiae with 1 or more rows of small spines (Figure 20-5 A); hind coxae transverse . . . . **Cicadéllidae** p. 209

6(2′). Second segment of hind tarsi small, often very small, its apex with 2 spines or none 7

6′. Second segment of hind tarsi larger, its apex with a row of small spines . . 11

7(6). Second segment of hind tarsi with a spine on each side (Figure 20-6 D) . . 8

7′. Second segment of hind tarsi without spines 10

8(7). Front wings very broad, with costal margin broadly rounded and venation reticulate, longer than body, and when at rest, held almost vertically at sides of body (Figure 20-15 E); hind tibiae without spines except at apex . . . . **Acanalonìidae** p. 212

8′. Front wings variable, but if longer than body, then they are more elongate and the costal margin is not broadly rounded, and the venation is not reticulate (Figure 20-15 F); position of wings at rest variable; hind tibiae with spurs on side, in addition to apical spurs 9

9(8′). Costal and (or) apical border of wings with numerous cross-veins (Figure 20-15 F); wings longer than body, and when at rest, held almost vertically at sides of body; clavus with numerous small pustulelike tubercles . . . . **Flátidae** p. 212

9′. Costal border of wings usually without numerous cross-veins; wings variable in size, often shorter than body, and usually held less steeply when at rest (Figure 20-15 L); clavus without numerous small pustulelike tubercles . . . . **Íssidae** p. 212

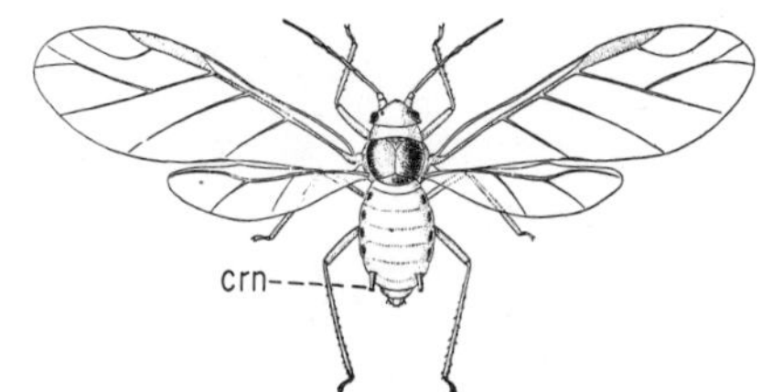

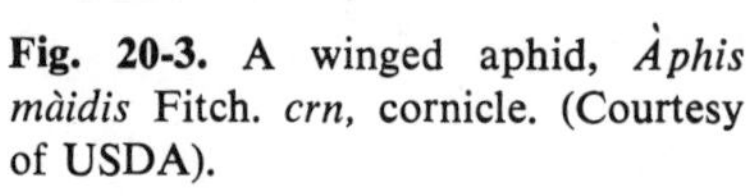
Fig. 20-3. A winged aphid, *Àphis màidis* Fitch. *crn,* cornicle. (Courtesy of USDA).

10(7′). Hind trochanters directed ventrally; basal segment of hind tarsi short . . . . **Ricanìidae** p. 212

10′. Hind trochanters directed backwards; basal segment of hind tarsi moderately long . . . . **Lophópidae** p. 212

11(6′). Anal area of hind wing reticulate, with many cross-veins . . . . . . **Fulgóridae** p. 211

11′. Anal area of hind wing not reticulate, without cross-veins 12

12(11′). Terminal segment of beak about as long as wide . . . . **Dérbidae** p. 211

12′. Terminal segment of beak distinctly longer than wide 13

13(12′). Claval vein extending to apex of clavus (Figure 20-6 A, *clv*); body somewhat flattened, the front wings overlapping at apex (Figure 20-15 C) . . . . **Achílidae** p. 212

13′. Claval vein not reaching apex of clavus (Figure 20-6 B, *clv*); body not particularly flattened, the front wings usually not overlapping at apex 14

14(13′). Hind tibiae with a broad movable apical spur (Figure 20 6 C, *sp*); a large group of minute forms, many dimorphic (with the wings well developed or short), the sexes often very different . . . . **Delphácidae** p. 211

14′. Hind tibiae without a broad movable apical spur 15

15(14′). Head prolonged in front (Figure 20-15 G-I), or if not, then the frons bears 2 or 3 carinae, or the tegulae are absent and the claval suture is obscure . . . . **Dictyopháridae** p. 211

15′. Head not prolonged in front (Figure 20-15 A, D), or only moderately so; frons either without carinae or with a median carina only; tegulae present; claval suture distinct . . . . **Cixìidae** p. 211

16(1′). Tarsi 2-segmented, with 2 claws; winged forms with 4 wings; mouth parts usually well developed in both sexes, with the beak long 17

16′. Tarsi 1-segmented, with a single claw (when legs are present); female wingless and often legless, scalelike, or grublike and wax-covered; male with only 1 pair of wings, and without a beak (superfamily Coccòidea) 22

17(16). Antennae with 5 to 10 (usually 10) segments; front wings often thicker than hind wings; jumping insects .... **Psýllidae** p. 213

17′. Antennae with 3 to 7 segments; wings membranous or opaque whitish; not jumping insects 18

18(17′). Wings usually opaque, whitish, and covered with a whitish powder; hind wings nearly as large as front wings .... **Aleyródidae** p. 213

18′. Wings membranous and not covered with a whitish powder; hind wings much smaller than front wings (Figure 20-3) (superfamily Aphidòidea) 19

19(18′). Rs in front wing present (Figure 20-2 D, F); cornicles usually present (Figure 20-3); sexual females oviparous, parthenogenetic females viviparous 20

19′. Rs in front wing absent (Figure 20-2 C, E); cornicles absent; all females oviparous 21

20(19). Cornicles nearly always present and conspicuous; M in front wing branched (Figure 20-2 D); females, and usually also males, with functional mouth parts; without abundant wax glands ...... **Aphídidae** p. 214

20′. Cornicles indistinct or lacking; M in front wing not branched (Figure 20-2 F); sexual forms with mouth parts atrophied and not functional; wax glands usually abundant .... **Eriosomátidae** p. 217

21(19′). Wings at rest held rooflike over body; Cu_1 and Cu_2 in front wing separated at base (Figure 20-2 E); apterous parthenogenetic females covered with waxy flocculence; on conifers .... **Adélgidae** p. 217

21′. Wings at rest held horizontal; Cu_1 and Cu_2 in front wing stalked at base (Figure 20-2 C); apterous parthenogenetic females not covered with waxy flocculence (at most, covered with a powdery material) .... **Phylloxéridae** p. 218

22(16′). Abdominal spiracles present (Figure 20-8 A, *spr*); male usually with compound eyes and ocelli 23

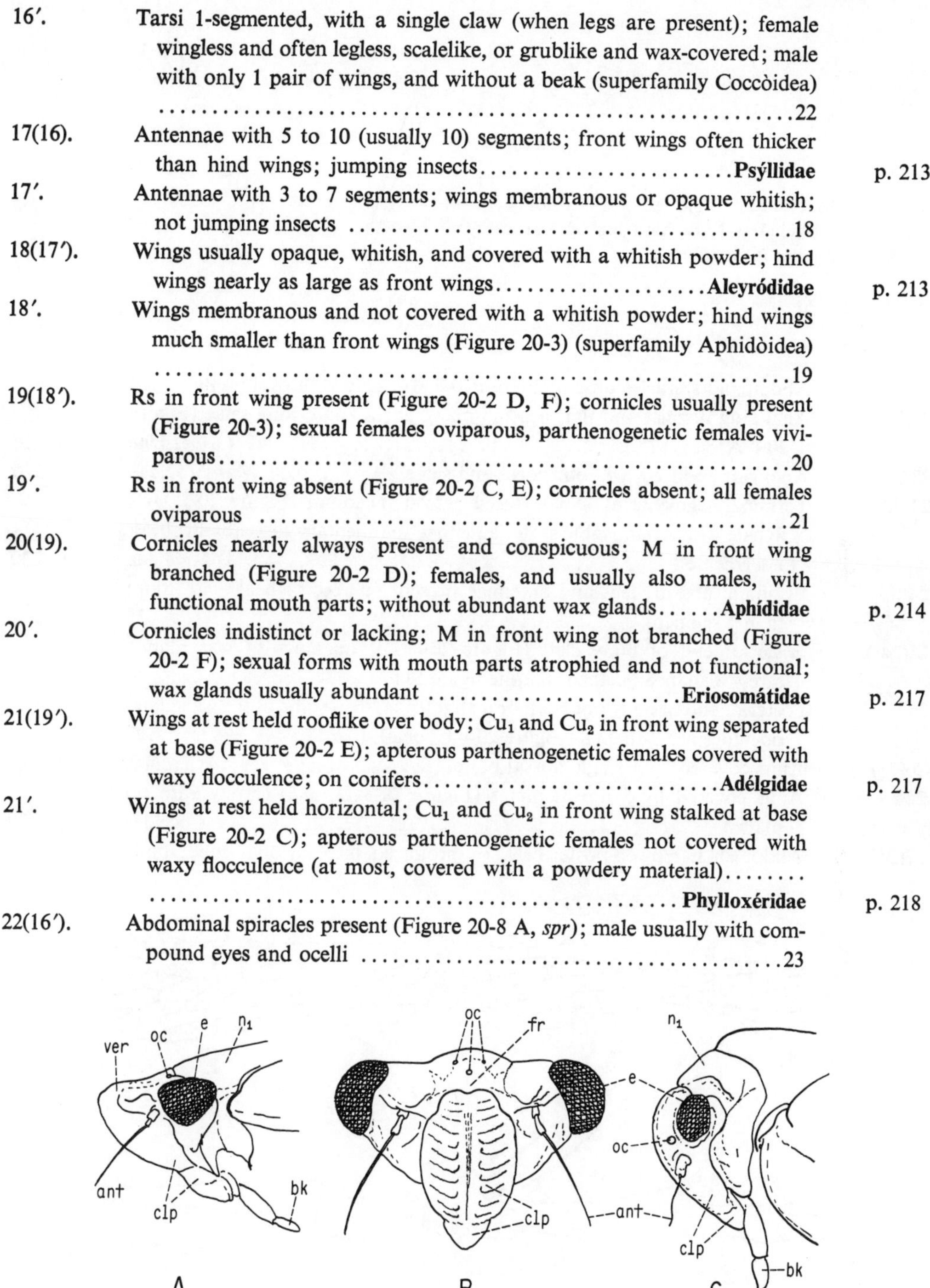

Fig. 20-4. Head structure in Homoptera. A, froghopper (*Philaènus*), lateral view; B, cicada (*Magicicàda*), anterior view; C, planthopper (*Órmenis*) lateral view. *ant*, antenna; *bk*, beak; *clp*, clypeus; *e*, compound eye; *fr*, frons; n_1, pronotum; *oc*, ocelli; *ver*, vertex.

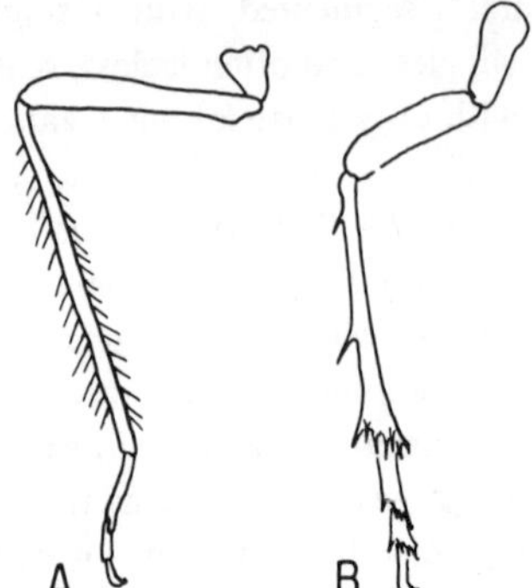

Fig. 20-5. A, hind leg of a leafhopper (Cicadéllidae); B, hind leg of a froghopper (Cercópidae).

22′. Abdominal spiracles absent (Figure 20-7 B); male with ocelli only....24

23(22). Anal ring distinct and flat, bearing many pores and 6 long setae (Figure 20-8 A) ....**Ortheziidae** p. 220

23′. Anal ring reduced, without pores and setae.............**Margaródidae** p. 220

24(22′). Terminal segments of female fused into a pygidium (Figure 20-7, *py*); female with a removable scale; antennae rudimentary; legs absent; beak 1-segmented ....**Diaspídidae** p. 220

24′. Pygidium absent; legs and antennae present or absent; beak with more than 1 segment 25

25(24′). Posterior end of body cleft (Figure 20-8 D); openings of wax glands rarely 8-shaped (shaped like the figure 8) 26

25′. Posterior end of body not cleft, or if slightly so, then some of the wax gland openings are 8-shaped (Figure 20-8 C, *mpo*).....................27

26(25). Anus covered by a single dorsal plate.....................**Aclérdidae** p. 222

26′. Anus covered by 2 dorsal plates (Figure 20-8 D, *anp*) (rarely with no plates) ....**Cóccidae** p. 223

27(25′). Abdomen narrower posteriorly, or produced into an anal tube; body

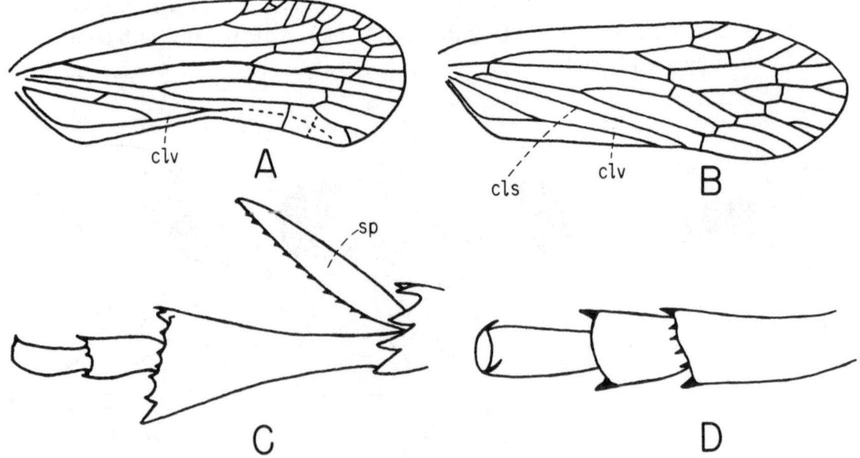

Fig. 20-6. Characters of Fulgoròidea. A, front wing of *Epiptera* (Achílidae); B, front wing of *Cíxius* (Cixìidae); C, hind tarsus of a delphacid; D, hind tarsus of *Órmenis* (Flátidae). *cls*, claval suture; *clv*, claval vein; *sp*, apical spur of hind tibia.

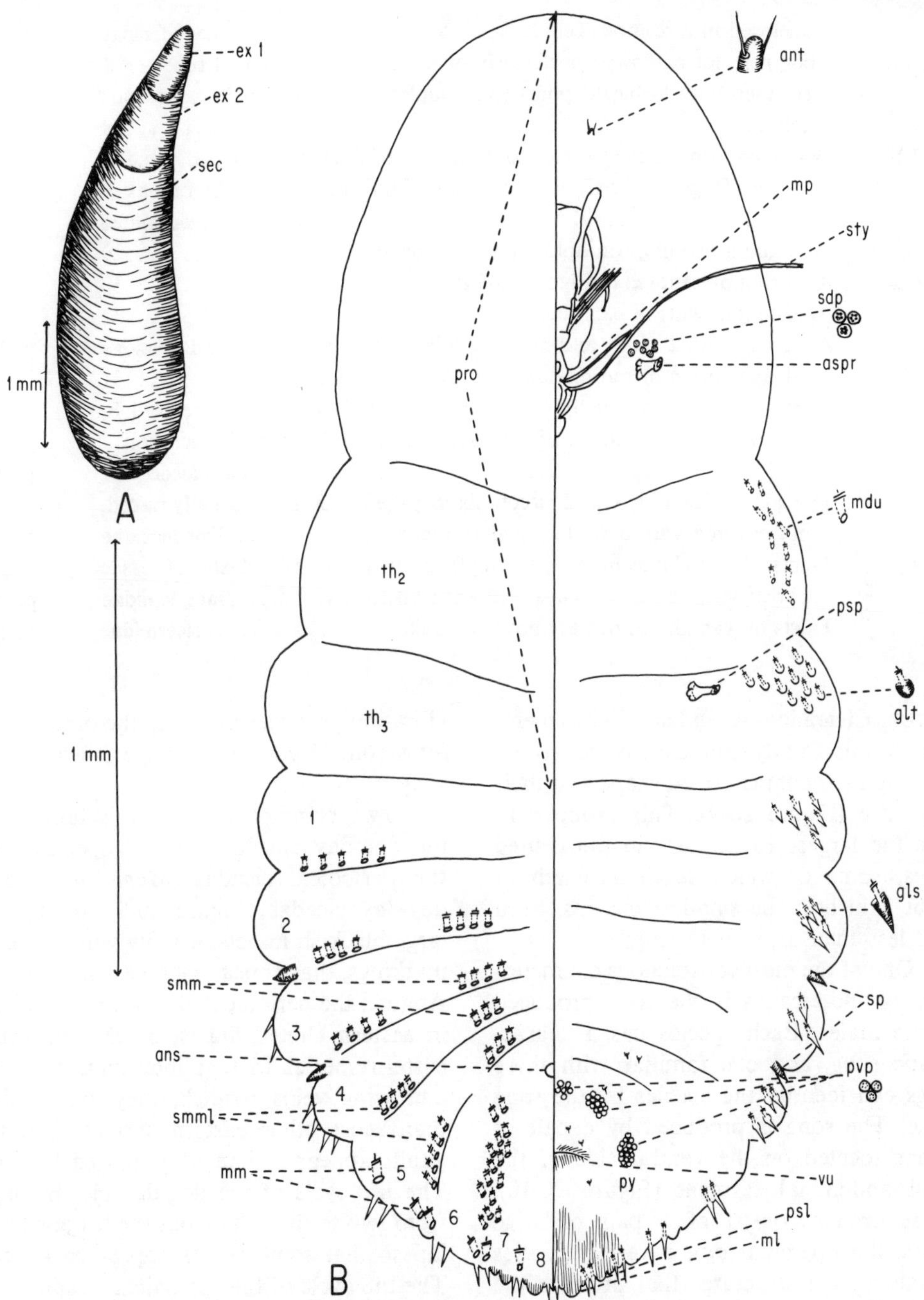

Fig. 20-7. Characters of scale insects. A, scale of female; B, diagrammatic drawing of a female armored scale. The left side of B represents a dorsal view, and the right side a ventral view. *ans,* anus; *ant,* antenna; *aspr,* anterior spiracle; *ex* 1, first exuvia; *ex* 2, second exuvia; *gls,* gland spines; *glt,* gland tubercle; *mdu,* microduct; *ml,* median lobe; *mm,* marginal macroduct; *mp,* mouth parts; *pro,* prosoma; *psl,* paired second lobe; *psp,* posterior spiracle; *pvp,* perivulvar pores; *py,* pygidium; *sdp,* spiracular disc pore; *sec,* secretion of adult; *sum,* submedian macroduct; *smml,* submarginal macroducts; *sp,* spur; *sty,* stylets; th_2, mesothorax; th_3, metathorax; *vu,* vulva. (Figure prepared by Dr. Michael Kosztarab.)

enclosed in a resinous cell .... **Lacciféridae** p. 223

27′. Abdomen not narrowed posteriorly or produced into an anal tube, or if so, then with 8-shaped pores (see couplet 25); body not in a resinous cell 28

28(27′). Wax gland openings (mostly along margin of dorsum) 8-shaped, usually in rows (Figure 20-8 C, *mpo*); legs vestigial or absent; usually on oak.. .... **Asterolecaniidae** p. 223

28′. Wax gland openings on dorsum not 8-shaped...................... 29

29(28′). Anal ring present (as in Figure 20-8 A)........................... 30

29′. Anal ring absent 32

30(29). Anal ring with 2 setae, and never cellular; on palms........ **Diaspídidae** p. 220

30′. Anal ring with 4 or more setae, and often cellular 31

31(30′). Dorsal ostioles and usually 1 to 4 central circuli present (Figure 20-8 B, *do* and *vc*); the insect in life covered with a white powdery secretion.. .... **Pseudocóccidae** p. 224

31′. Dorsal ostioles and ventral circuli absent; the insect in life usually naked, not covered with a white powdery secretion............ **Eriocóccidae** p. 224

32(29′). Ducts of wax glands minute, arising from the center of a cluster of sessile pores; setae stout and cut off at end; on cactus........ **Dactylopiidae** p. 224

32′. Ducts of wax glands not as above; on oaks.................. **Kérmidae** p. 224

FAMILY **Cicàdidae**—Cicadas: The members of this family can usually be recognized by their characteristic shape and their large size (Figure 20-9). This group contains the largest Homoptera in the United States, some of which reach a length of about 2 inches; the smallest cicadas are a little less than an inch in length.

One of the most conspicuous characteristics of the cicadas is the song produced by the males. Each species has a characteristic song, and one familiar with these songs can identify the species by the song alone. The song is produced by a pair of organs located on the ventral side of the basal abdominal segment (Figure 20-10). These organs consist of a pair of large plates, the opercula (*op*), covering cavities containing the structures that produce the sound. In the anterior portion of the cavity beneath each operculum is a yellowish membrane (*mem*), and a shining mirror (*mr*) is located in the posterior part of the cavity; in the lateral wall of the cavity is an oval, ribbed structure, the tymbal (*tmb*). The tymbals are vibrated by strong muscles, and this vibration produces the song; the other structures control various characteristics of the song.

Two common types in this family are the dog-day cicadas (various species) and the periodical cicadas (*Magicicàda*). The dog-day cicadas (Figure 20-9) are mostly large blackish insects, usually with greenish markings, that appear each year in July and August; the periodical cicadas, which occur in eastern United States, differ from other eastern species in that they have the eyes and wing veins reddish, they are smaller than most other eastern species, and the adults appear in late May and early June. The life cycle of the dog-day cicadas lasts from two to five years, but the broods overlap so that some adults appear each year. The life cycle of the periodical cicadas lasts 13 or 17 years, and in any given area, adults are not present each year.

There are at least 13 broods of 17-year cicadas and 5 of 13-year cicadas; these broods emerge in different years, and have different geographic ranges. The 17-year cicadas are generally northern and the 13-

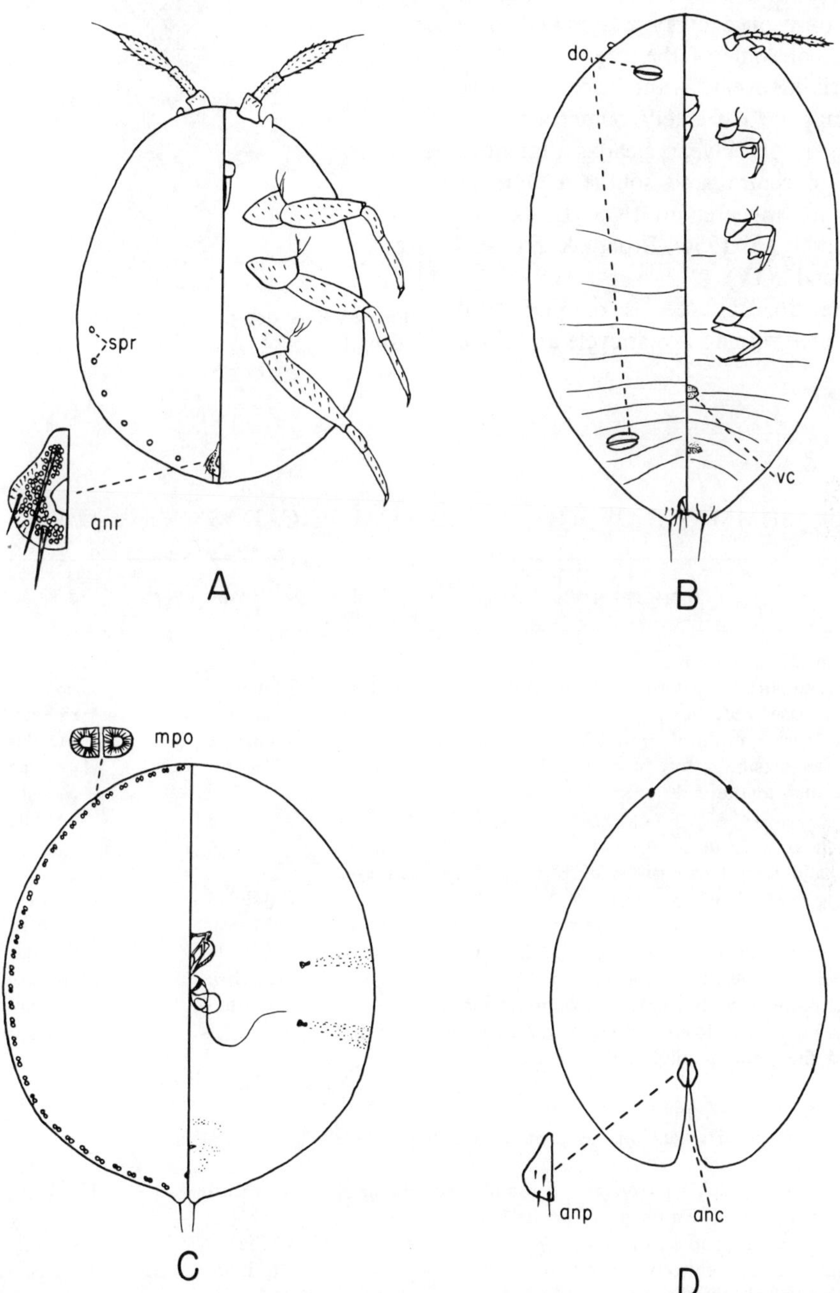

Fig. 20-8. Characters of female scale insects (diagrammatic). A, Ortheziidae; B, Pseudocóccidae; C, Asterolecaniidae; D, Cóccidae. *anc*, anal cleft; *anp*, anal plate; *anr*, anal ring; *do*, dorsal ostioles; *mpo*, marginal 8-shaped pores; *spr*, abdominal spiracles; *vc*, ventral circulus. (Figure prepared by Dr. Michael Kosztarab.)

year cicadas southern, but there is considerable overlap, and both life-cycle types may occur in the same woods (but would emerge together only once every 221 years). The emergence of some of the larger broods is a very striking event, as the insects in these broods may be extremely numerous. The large broods of 17-year cicadas that have occurred in central and southern Ohio in recent years appeared in 1948 (Brood V), 1953 (Brood X), 1956 (Brood XIII), and 1957 (Brood XIV).

There are six species of periodical cicadas, three with a 17-year cycle and three

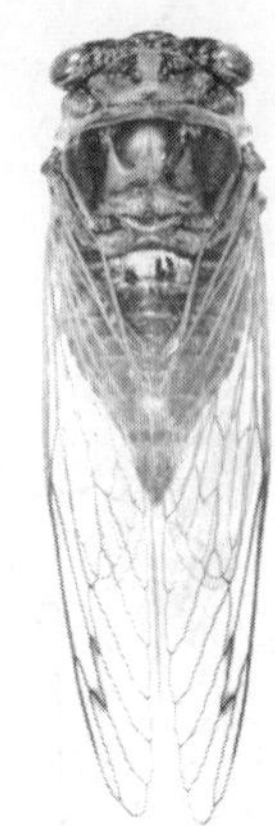

Fig. 20-9. A dog-day cicada, *Tibìcen* sp.; about natural size.

Table 20-1 SUMMARY OF THE PERIODICAL CICADAS (*Magicicàda*)[a]

CHARACTERISTICS	17-YEAR CYCLE	13-YEAR CYCLE
Body length, 27 to 33 mm Propleura and lateral extensions of pronotum between eyes and wing bases reddish Abdominal sterna primarily reddish brown or yellow Song: "Phaaaaaroah," a low buzz, 1 to 3 sec in length, with a drop in pitch at the end	Linnaeus' 17-year Cicada, *M. septéndecim* (Linn.)	Riley's 13-year Cicada, *M. trédecim* Walsh and Riley
Body length, 20 to 28 mm Propleura and lateral extensions of pronotum between eyes and wing bases black Abdominal sterna all black, or a few with a narrow band of reddish brown or yellow on apical third, this band often constricted or interrupted medially Last tarsal segment with apical half or more black Song: 2 to 3 secs of ticks alternating with 1 to 3 sec buzzes that rise and then fall in pitch and intensity	Cassin's 17-year Cicada, *M. cássini* (Fisher)	Cassin's 13-year Cicada, *M. tredecássini* Alexander and Moore
Body length, 19 to 27 mm Propleura and lateral extensions of pronotum between eyes and wing bases black Abdominal sterna black basally, with a broad apical band of reddish yellow or brown on posterior half of each sternum, this band not interrupted medially Last tarsal segment entirely brownish or yellowish, or at most, the apical third black Song: 20 to 40 short high-pitched phrases, each like a short buzz and tick delivered together, at the rate of 3 to 5 per sec, the final phrases shorter and lacking the short buzz	The Little 17-year Cicada, *M. septendécula* Alexander and Moore	The Little 13-year Cicada, *M. tredécula* Alexander and Moore

[a] Data from Alexander and Moore (1962).

with a 13-year cycle. The three species in each life-cycle group differ in size, color, and song (see Table 20-1); each 17-year species has a similar or sibling species with a 13-year cycle, from which it can be separated only by differences in life cycle and distribution. Most broods of each life-cycle type contain more than one species, and many contain all three.

Cicadas deposit their eggs in the twigs of various trees and shrubs. The twigs are usually so severely injured by this egg-laying that the terminal part of the twig dies. The eggs generally hatch in a month or so and the nymphs drop to the ground, enter the soil, and feed on roots. The nymphs remain in the ground until they are ready to molt the last time; in the case of the periodical cicadas, this period is 13 to 17 years. When the last nymphal instar digs its way out of the ground, it climbs up on some object, usually a tree, fastens its claws in the bark, and the final molt then takes place. The adult stage lasts a month or more.

The principal damage done by cicadas is caused by the egg-laying of the adults. When the adults are numerous, as in years when the periodical cicadas emerge, they may do considerable damage to young trees and nursery stock.

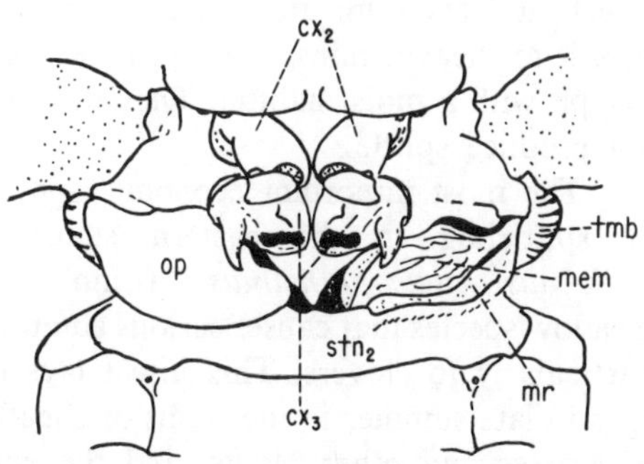

Fig. 20-10. Thorax of a cicada (*Magicicàda*), ventral view, showing the sound-producing organs; the operculum at the right has been removed. *cx*, coxa; *mem*, membrane; *mr*, mirror; *op*, operculum; *stn*, abdominal sternum; *tmb*, tymbal.

FAMILY **Membrácidae**—Treehoppers: The members of this group can be recognized by the large pronotum that covers the head, extends back over the abdomen, and often assumes various peculiar shapes (Figure 20-11). Many species appear more or less humpbacked; others have various spines, horns, or keels on the pronotum, and some species are shaped like thorns. The wings are largely concealed by the pronotum. These insects are rarely over 10 to 12 millimeters in length.

Treehoppers feed chiefly on trees and shrubs, and most species feed only on specific types of host plants. Some species feed on grass and weeds in the nymphal stage. The treehoppers have one or two generations a year and usually pass the winter in the egg stage.

Only a few species in this group are considered of economic importance, and most of their damage is caused by egg-laying. The buffalo treehopper, *Sticto-céphala bubàlus* (Fabricius), is a common pest species that lays its eggs in the twigs of apple and several other trees. The eggs are placed in slits cut in the bark, and the terminal portion of the twig beyond the eggs often dies. The eggs overwinter and hatch in the spring, and the nymphs drop to herbaceous vegetation where they complete their development, returning to the trees to lay their eggs.

FAMILY **Cercópidae**—Froghoppers or Spittlebugs: Froghoppers are small hopping insects, rarely over $\frac{1}{2}$ inch in length, some species of which vaguely resemble tiny frogs in shape (Figure 20-12). They are very similar to the leafhoppers, but can be distinguished by the spination of the hind tibiae (Figure 20-5). They are usually brown or gray in color; some species have a characteristic color pattern.

These insects feed on shrubs and herbaceous plants, the different species feeding on different food plants. The nymphs surround themselves with a frothy spittlelike mass (Figure 20-13), and are usually called

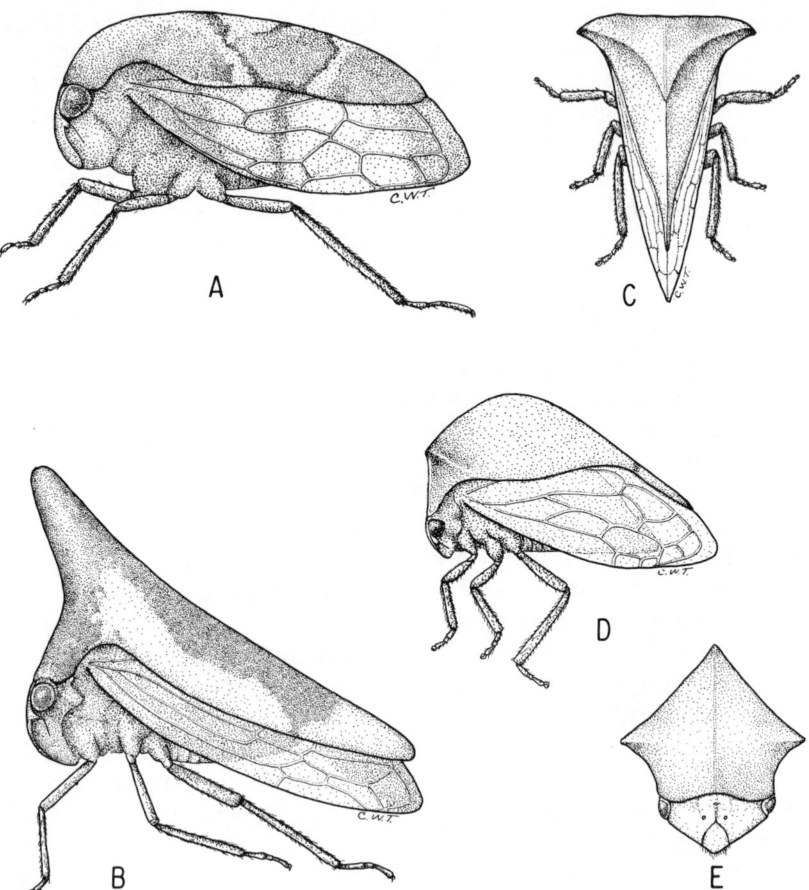

Fig. 20-11. Treehoppers. A, *Cyrtólobus pallidifróntis* (Emmons); B, *Thèlia bimaculàta* (Fabricius), male; C, *Stictocéphala bubàlus* (Fabricius), dorsal view; D, same, lateral view; E, same, anterior view.

spittlebugs. Thesc masses of spittle are sometimes quite abundant in meadows; each mass contains one or more greenish or brownish spittlebugs. After the last molt the insect leaves the spittle and moves about actively.

The spittle is derived from fluid voided from the anus and from a mucilaginous substance excreted by the epidermal glands on the seventh and eight abdominal segments. Air bubbles are introduced into the spittle by means of the caudal appendages of the insect. A spittlebug usually rests head downward on the plant, and as the spittle forms, it flows down over and covers the insect; it lasts some time, even when exposed to heavy rains, and provides the nymph with a moist habitat. The adults do not produce spittle.

The most important economic species of spittlebug in the eastern states is *Philaènus leucophthálmus* (Linn)., a meadow species that causes serious stunting, particularly to clovers. This insect lays its eggs in late summer in the stems or sheaths of grasses and other plants, and the eggs hatch the following spring; there is one generation a year. Most of the spittlebugs attack grasses and herbaceous plants, but a few attack trees; *Aphróphora parállela* (Say) and *A. saratogénsis* (Fitch) are important pests of pine.

FAMILY **Cicadéllidae**—Leafhoppers: Leafhoppers are similar to froghoppers but have one or more rows of small spines extending the length of the hind tibiae. The leafhoppers constitute a very large group, and they are of various forms, colors, and sizes (Figure 20-14); many are marked with a beautiful color pattern. They rarely exceed ½ inch in length, and many are only a few millimeters long.

Leafhoppers occur on almost all types of plants, including forest, shade, and orchard trees, shrubs, grasses, flowers, and many field and garden crops; they feed principally on the leaves of their food plant. The food of most species is quite specific, and the habitat is therefore well defined. In many cases a specialist in this group can examine a series of specimens taken in a given habitat and can describe the habitat and often determine the general region of the country from which the specimens came.

Most leafhoppers have a single generation a year, but a few have two or three. The winter is usually passed in either the adult or the egg stage, depending on the species.

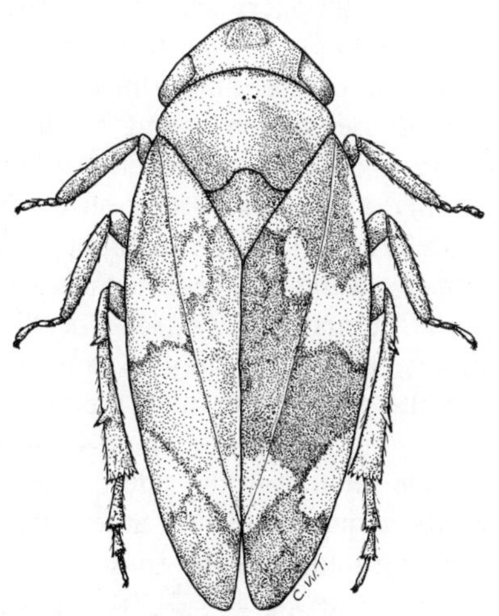

Fig. 20-12. A froghopper, *Philaènus leucophthálmus* (Linn.).

There are many economically important pest species in this group, and they cause five major types of injury to plants: (1) Some species remove excessive amounts of sap, and reduce or destroy the chlorophyll in the leaves; this causes the leaves to become covered with minute white or yellowish spots, and with continued feeding, the leaves turn yellowish or brownish. This type of injury is produced on apple leaves by various species of *Erythroneùra, Typhlocỳba,* and *Empoásca.* (2) Some species interfere with the normal physiology of the plant; the potato leafhopper, *Empoásca fàbae* (Harris) (Figure 20-14 A), mechanically plugs the phloem and xylem vessels in the leaves, so that transport of food materials is impaired. A browning of the outer portion of the leaf, and eventually of the entire leaf, results from this type of feeding. (3) A few species injure plants by ovipositing in green twigs; the egg punctures of various species of *Gyponàna* are similar to those of the buffalo treehopper, but are smaller. (4) Many species of leafhoppers are vectors of organisms that cause plant diseases. Some of the more important plant diseases transmitted by leafhoppers are potato yellow dwarf, transmitted by *Aceratagállia sanguinolénta* (Provancher); phony peach, transmitted by species of *Cuérna, Oncometòpia,* and *Homalodísca*; Pierce's disease of grape, transmitted by many species in the subfamily Tettigoniellìnae; corn stunt, transmitted by *Baldùlus màidis* (DeLong and Wolcott); aster yellows, transmitted by *Macrostèles dívisus* (Uhler); California aster yellows, transmitted by many species, mostly in the subfamily Athysanìnae; phloem necrosis in elm, transmitted by *Scaphòideus luteòlus* Van Duzee; and curly top in sugar beets, transmitted by *Circùlifer tenéllus* (Baker). (5) Some species, such as *Empoásca fàbae* (Harris), cause stunting and leaf curling in such plants as bush beans, due to the inhibition of growth on

Fig. 20-13. Spittle mass of a spittlebug. (Courtesy of the Illinois Natural History Survey.)

the under surface of the leaves where the leafhoppers feed.

Some species of leafhoppers are very strikingly colored. One of our largest and most common species is *Graphocéphala coccínea* (Förster), which is similar in size and shape to *Draeculacéphala mollipes* (Say) (Figure 20-14 C), but has the wings reddish striped with bright green; it is often found on forsythia and other ornamental shrubs. The nymphs of this species are bright yellow.

Many species of leafhoppers emit from the anus a liquid called honeydew; this is composed of unused portions of plant sap to which are added certain waste products of the insect. This honeydew may be produced in sufficient quantities to cause the surface of objects beneath to become sticky.

SUPERFAMILY **Fulgoròidea**—Planthoppers: This is a large group, but its members are seldom as abundant as the leafhoppers or froghoppers. The species in the United States are seldom over 10 or 12 millimeters in length, but some tropical species reach a length of 2 inches or more. Many of the planthoppers have the head peculiarly modified, with that part in front of the eyes greatly enlarged and more or less snout-like (Figure 20-15, especially G-I).

The planthoppers can be separated from the leafhoppers and froghoppers by the spination of the hind tibiae and the location of the antennae and ocelli. The planthoppers differ from the leafhoppers in having only a few large spines on the hind tibiae, and from both the leafhoppers and froghoppers in having the antennae arising below the compound eyes; the ocelli are usually located immediately in front of the eyes, on the side (rather than the front) of the head (Figure 20-4 C). There is often a sharp angle separating the side of the head (where the compound eyes, antennae, and ocelli are located) and the front.

The food plants of these insects range from trees and shrubs to herbaceous plants and grasses. The planthoppers feed on the

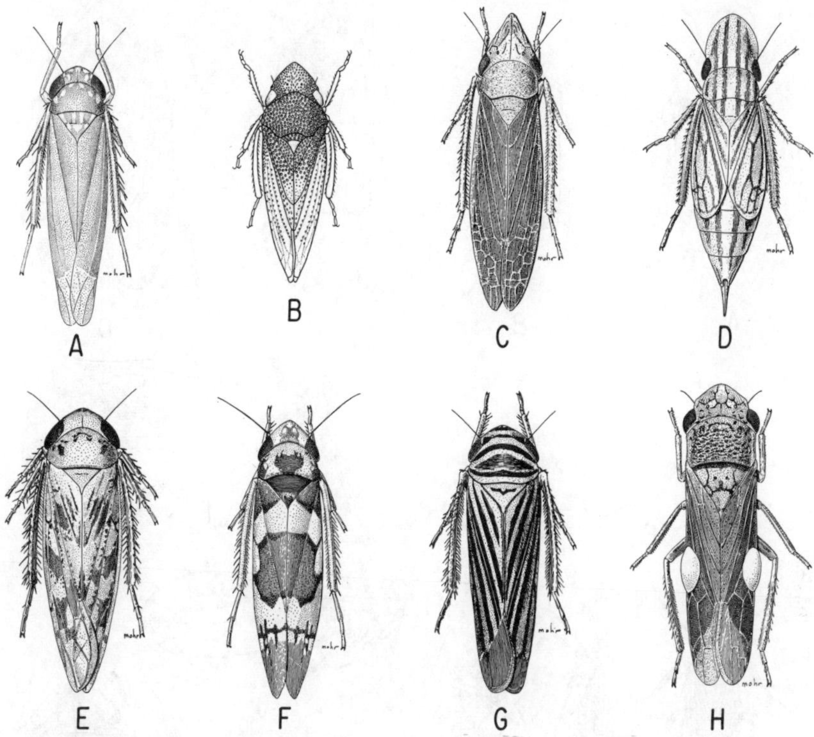

Fig. 20-14. Leafhoppers. A, the potato leafhopper, *Empoásca fàbae* (Harris); B, *Xerophloèa major* Baker; C, *Draeculacéphala móllipes* (Say); D, *Hécalus lineàtus* (Uhler), female; E, *Circùlifer tenéllus* (Baker); F, *Erythroneùra vítis* (Harris); G, *Tylozỳgus bìfidus* (Say); H, *Oncometòpia undàta* (Fabricius). (Courtesy of the Illinois Natural History Survey.)

plant juices and, like many other Homoptera, produce honeydew. Many of the nymphal forms are ornamented with wax filaments. Very few planthoppers cause economic damage to cultivated plants.

The **Cixìidae** is one of the larger families of planthoppers; its members are widely distributed, but most species are tropical. Some species are subterranean feeders on the roots of grasses during their nymphal stage. The wings are transparent, and frequently ornamented with spots along the veins (Figure 20-15 A, D). The **Delphácidae** is the largest family of planthoppers, and its members can be recognized by the large flattened spur at the apex of the hind tibiae (Figure 20-6 C, *sp*); most species are small, and many have reduced wings. The sugarcane leafhopper, *Perkinsiélla sacchárida* Kirkaldy, which at one time was a very destructive pest in Hawaii, is a member of this family. The **Dérbidae** are principally tropical, and feed on woody fungi; most species have long wings and are rather delicate in build (Figure 20-15 K). The **Dictyopháridae** are widely distributed, and usually have the head distinctly prolonged anteriorly (Figure 20-15 G.-I).

The **Fulgóridae** (Figure 20-15 M) contains some of the largest planthoppers, some tropical species of which have a wing spread of about 6 inches. This group can usually be recognized by the reticulated anal area of the hind wings. Some of these planthoppers have the head greatly inflated anteriorly, producing a peanutlike process; this was at one time believed to be luminous, thereby giving rise to the name "lanternflies" for these insects; this name is inappropriate, as none of the planthoppers is

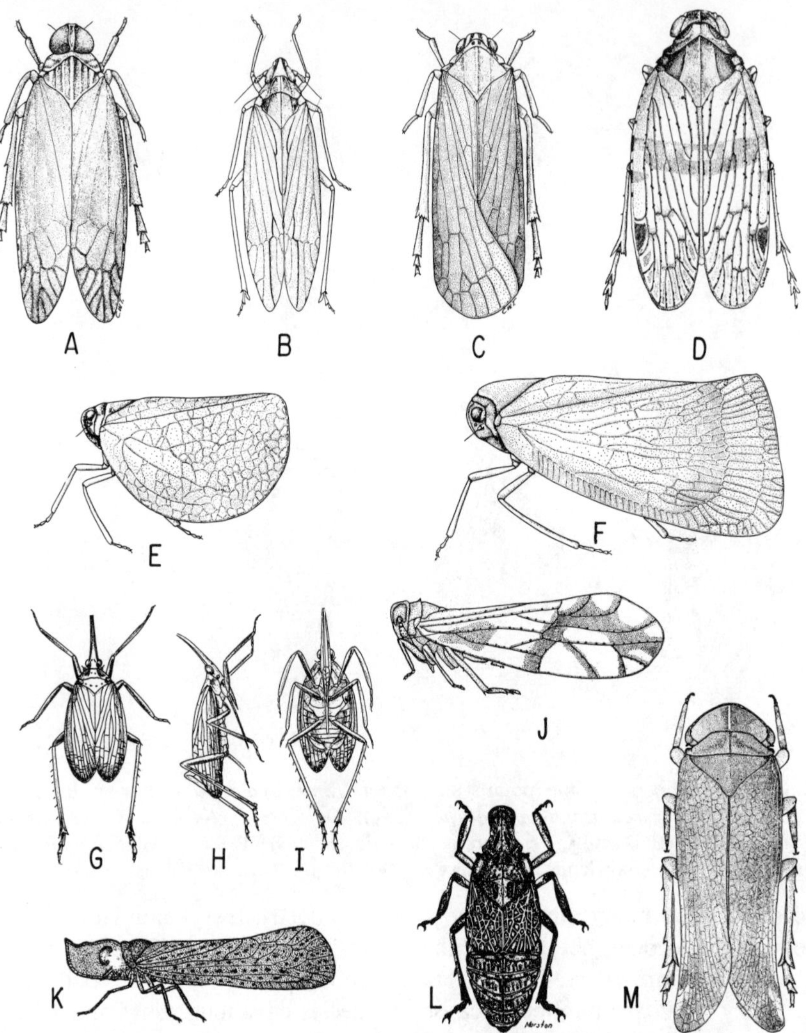

Fig. 20-15. Planthoppers. A, *Oècleus boreàlis* Van Duzee (Cixìidae); B, *Stenocrànus dorsàlis* Fitch (Delphácidae); C, *Catònia impunctàta* (Fitch) (Achílidae); D, *Cíxius angustàtus* Caldwell (Cixìidae); E, *Acanalònia bivattàta* (Say) (Acanalonìidae); F, *Órmenis septentrionàlis* (Spinola) (Flátidae); G, H, and I, *Scòlops pérdix* Uhler (Dictyopháridae), dorsal, lateral and ventral views; J, *Liburnílla ornàta* (Stål) (Delphácidae); K, *Apáche degeèrii* (Kirby) (Dérbidae); L, *Fitchiélla róbertsoni* (Fitch) (Íssidae); M, *Cyrpóptus belfrágei* Stål (Fulgóridae). (Courtesy of Osborn and the Ohio Biological Survey.)

known to be luminescent. The **Flátidae** have a wedge-shaped appearance when at rest (Figure 20-15 F), and there are usually numerous cross veins in the costal area of the front wings. This is a large and widely distributed group. The **Acanalonìidae** is a small group, the members of which can usually be recognized by the characteristic shape (Figure 20-15 E).

The planthoppers in the families **Ricanìidae** and **Lophópidae** are somewhat mothlike in appearance, and are mainly tropical in distribution. The **Achílidae** can usually be recognized by the overlapping front wings (Figure 20-15 C); the nymphs of these planthoppers usually live under loose bark or in depressions in dead wood. The **Íssidae** is a large and widely distributed

Fig. 20-16. The alder psyllid, *Psýlla floccòsa* (Patch). A, groups of nymphs on alder (these groups form white cottony masses on the twigs, particularly at the base of leaf petioles); B, a newly emerged adult; below the adult is the cast skin of the nymph, still covered with the cottony secretions characteristic of the nymphs of this species.

group; some species have short wings and a beetlelike snout (Figure 20-15 L).

FAMILY **Psýllidae**—Jumping Plant Lice: These insects are small, 2 to 5 millimeters in length, and usually resemble miniature cicadas in form (Figures 20-16 B and 20-17). They are somewhat similar to the aphids, but have strong jumping legs and relatively long antennae. The adults of both sexes are winged, and the beak is short and 3-segmented. The nymphs of many species produce large amounts of a white waxy secretion, causing them to superficially resemble the woolly aphids. The jumping plant lice feed on plant juices, and as in the case of most of the Homoptera, the food-plant relationships are quite specific.

Two important pest species in this group, the pear psylla, *Psýlla pyrícola* Förster, and the apple sucker, *Psýlla máli* Schmidberger, have been imported from Europe. A western species, the potato or tomato psyllid, *Paratriòza cockerélli* (Sulc) (Figure 20-17), transmits a virus that causes psyllid yellows in potatoes, tomatoes, peppers, and eggplants; this disease causes a reduction in yield due to the dwarfing and discoloration of the plant.

The cottony alder psyllid, *Psýlla floccòsa* (Patch), is a common member of this group occurring in the Northeast. The nymphs feed on alder and produce large amounts of wax, and groups of the nymphs on alder twigs resemble masses of cotton (Figure 20-16 A). These insects may sometimes be confused with the woolly alder aphid, *Procíphilus tessellàtus* (Fitch); the psyllid is to be found on the alder only during the early part of the summer, while the aphid occurs up until fall. The adults of the cottony alder psyllid (Figure 20-16 B) are pale green in color.

A few of the psyllids are gall-making forms; species of *Pachypsýlla* produce small galls on the leaves of hackberry (Figure 20-18).

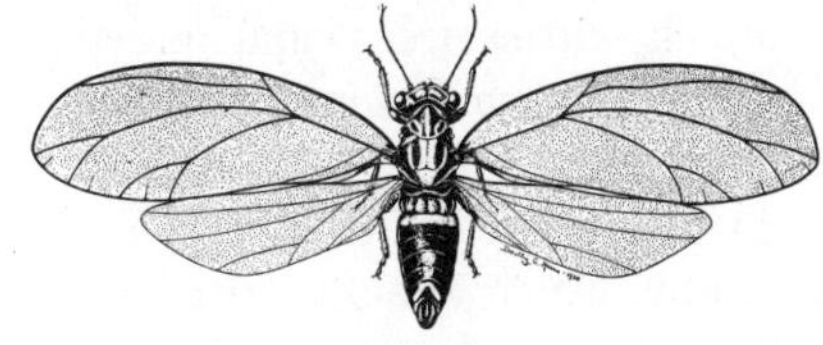

Fig. 20-17. The potato psyllid *Paratriòza cockerélli* (Sulc). (Courtesy of Knowlton and Janes and the Entomological Society of America.)

FAMILY **Aleyródidae** — Whiteflies: The whiteflies are minute insects, rarely over 2 or 3 millimeters in length, which resemble

Fig. 20-18. Galls of *Pachypsýlla céltidis-mámma* Riley on hackberry. (Courtesy of Moser.)

tiny moths. The adults of both sexes are winged, and the wings are covered with a white dust or waxy powder. The adults are usually active whitish insects that feed on leaves.

The metamorphosis of whiteflies is somewhat different from that of most other Homoptera. The first-instar young are active, but subsequent immature instars are sessile and look like scales; the scalelike covering is a waxy secretion of the insect and has a rather characteristic appearance (Figure 20-19). The wings develop internally during metamorphosis, and the early instars are usually called larvae; the next to the last instar is quiescent and is usually called a pupa. The wings are everted at the molt of the last larval instar.

The whiteflies are most abundant in the tropics and subtropics, and the most important pest species in this country are those that attack citrus trees and greenhouse plants. The damage is done by sucking sap from the leaves. One of the most serious pests in this group is *Aleurocánthus wóglumi* Ashby, which attacks citrus trees and is well established in the West Indies and Mexico. An objectionable sooty fungus often grows on the honeydew excreted by whiteflies and interferes with photosynthesis; this fungus is more prevalent in the South and in the tropics than in the North.

FAMILY **Aphídidae**—Aphids or Plant Lice: The aphids constitute a large group of small, soft-bodied insects that are frequently found in large numbers sucking the sap from the stems or leaves of plants. Such aphid groups often include individuals in all stages of development. The members of this family can usually be recognized by their characteristic pearlike shape, a pair of cornicles at the posterior end of the abdomen, and the fairly long antennae; winged forms can usually be recognized by the venation and the relative size of the front and hind wings

Fig. 20-19. "Pupae" of mulberry whiteflies, *Tetraleuròdes mòri* (Quaintance). (Courtesy of the Ohio Agricultural Experiment Station.)

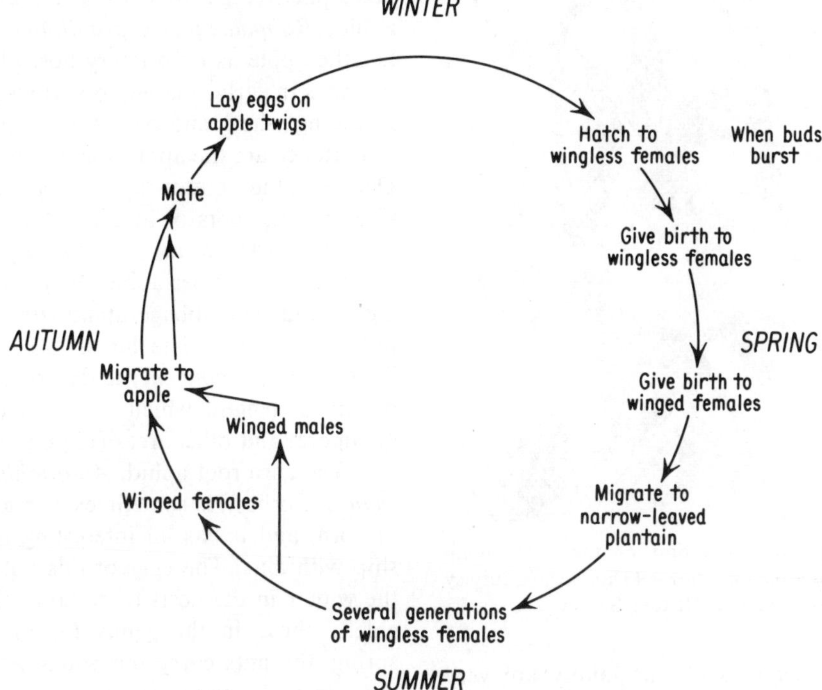

Fig. 20-20. Diagram of the life history of the rosy apple aphid, *Anuràphis ròsea* Baker.

(Figure 20-3). The wings at rest are generally held vertically above the body.

The cornicles of aphids are tubelike structures arising from the dorsal side of the fifth or sixth abdominal segment. They act as wax-secreting tubes, and in some species the body is more or less covered with white waxy fibers. Aphids also excrete honeydew, which is emitted from the anus; the honeydew consists mainly of excess sap ingested by the insect, to which are added excess sugars and waste material. Honeydew is a favorite food of many ants, and some species [for example, the corn root aphid, *Anuràphis màidirádicis* (Forbes)] are tended like cows by certain species of ants.

The life cycle of many aphids is rather unusual and complex (Figure 20-20). Most species overwinter in the egg stage, and these eggs hatch in the spring into females that reproduce parthenogenetically and give birth to living young. Several generations may be produced during the season in this way, with only females being produced and the young being born alive. The first generation or two usually consist of wingless individuals, but eventually winged individuals appear; in many species these winged forms migrate to a different host plant, and the reproductive process continues. In the latter part of the season the aphids migrate back to the original host plant, and a generation consisting of both males and females appears. The individuals of this bisexual generation mate, and the females lay the eggs which overwinter.

Enormous populations of aphids can be built up in a relatively short time by this method of reproduction. The aphids would be a great deal more destructive to vegetation were it not for their numerous parasites and predators. The principal parasites of aphids are braconids and chalcids, and the most important predators are ladybird beetles, lacewings, and the larvae of certain syrphid flies.

Fig. 20-21. An infestation of the rusty plum aphid, *Hysteroneùra setàriae* (Thomas). (Courtesy of the Illinois Natural History Survey.)

The members of this family are very similar to the Eriosomátidae, but differ in having the cornicles nearly always well developed, the wax glands much less abundant, the sexual female (and usually also the male) with functional mouth parts, and the ovipositing female producing more than one egg.

This family contains a number of serious pests of cultivated plants. The aphids cause a curling or wilting of the food plant by their feeding (Figure 20-22), and they serve as vectors of a number of important plant diseases. Several virus diseases are transmitted by aphids, including the mosaics of beans, sugar cane, and cucumbers by species of *Àphis, Macrosìphum,* and *Mỳzus,* beet mosaic by *Àphis rùmicis* Linn., cabbage ring spot and crucifer mosaic by *Mỳzus pérsicae* (Sulzer) and potato yellow dwarf by *Mỳzus pérsicae* (Sulzer).

The rosy apple aphid, *Anuràphis ròsea* Baker, overwinters on apple and related trees and passes the early summer generations there, then migrates to the narrow-leaved plantain as the secondary host; later in the season, migration back to the apple takes place (Figure 20-20). The apple grain aphid, *Rhopalosìphum prunifòliae* (Fitch), has the apple as its primary host plant and migrates in early summer to various grasses, including wheat and oats. Other species of importance are the apple aphid, *Àphis pòmi* DeGeer, the cotton aphid, *A. gossýpii* Glover, the potato aphid, *Macrosìphum solanifòlii* (Ashmead), the rose aphid, *M. ròsae* (Linn.), the pea aphid, *M. pìsi* (Kaltenbach), and the cabbage aphid, *Brevicóryne brássicae* (Linn.). The largest aphid in the East is *Longistígma cáryae* (Harris), 6 millimeters in length, which feeds on hickory, sycamore, and other trees (Figure 20-23).

The corn root aphid, *Anuràphis màidirádicis* (Forbes), is sometimes a serious pest of corn, and it has an interesting relationship with ants. The eggs of this aphid pass the winter in the nests of certain field ants, chiefly those in the genus *Làsius.* In the spring, the ants carry the young aphids to the roots of smartweed and other weeds, where the aphids feed; later in the season, the ants transfer the aphids to the roots of corn. When the aphid eggs are laid in the fall, they are gathered by the ants and stored in their nest for the winter. All during the

Fig. 20-22. Curling of the leaves of wild sunflower caused by *Àphis debilicòrnis* (Gillette and Palmer). (Courtesy of the Illinois Natural History Survey.)

Fig. 20-23. A colony of apterous viviparous females and nymphs of the sycamore aphid. *Longistígma càryae* (Harris). (Courtesy of the Illinois Natural History Survey.)

season the aphids are tended by the ants, which transfer them from one food plant to another; the ants feed on the honeydew produced by the aphids.

FAMILY **Eriosomátidae**—Woolly and Gall-Making Aphids: The cornicles are reduced or absent in this group, and wax glands are abundant; the sexual forms lack mouth parts, and the ovipositing female produces only one egg. Nearly all the members of this family alternate between host plants, with the primary host (on which the overwintering eggs are laid) usually a tree or shrub, and the secondary host a herbaceous plant. These aphids may feed either on the roots of the host plant or on the part of the plant above the ground. Many species produce galls or malformations of the tissues of the primary host, but usually do not produce galls on the secondary host.

The woolly apple aphid, *Eriosòma lanígerum* (Hausmann) (Figure 20-24), is a common and important example of this group. This species feeds principally on the roots and bark and can be recognized by the characteristic woolly masses of wax on its body. These aphids usually overwinter on the elm, and the first generations of the season are spent on that host; in early summer, winged forms appear and migrate to apple, hawthorn, and related trees. Later in the season some of these migrate back to the elm, where the bisexual generation is produced, and the overwintering eggs are laid; other individuals migrate from the branches of the apple tree to the roots, where they produce gall-like growths. The root-inhabiting forms may remain there a year or more, passing through several generations. This aphid transmits perennial canker.

The woolly alder aphid, *Procíphilus tessellàtus* (Fitch) is often found in dense masses on the branches of alder and maple. All the generations may be passed on the alder, or the species may overwinter on maple and migrate to the alder in the summer and then back to maple in the fall, where the sexual forms are produced. The species may overwinter in either the egg or nymphal stages.

Some of the more common gall-making species in this group are *Cólopha ulmícola* (Fitch), which causes the cockscomb gall on elm leaves (Figure 20-25 A), *Hormàphis hamamélidis* (Fitch), which causes the cone gall on the leaves of witch hazel, *Hamamelístes spinòsus* Shimer, which forms a spiny gall on the flower buds of witch hazel (Figure 20-25 B), and *Pémphigus pópulitransvérsus* Riley, which forms a marble-shaped gall on the stems of poplar leaves (Figure 20-25 C).

FAMILY **Adélgidae**—Pine and Spruce Aphids: The members of this group feed only on conifers; they live on the needles, twigs, or in galls. Most species alternate in their life history between two different conifers, forming galls only on the primary host tree. All the females are oviparous. The antennae are 5-segmented in the winged forms, 4-segmented in the sexual forms, and 3-segmented in the wingless parthenogenetic-

Fig. 20-24. A colony of woolly apple aphids, *Eriosòma lanígerum* (Hausman). (Courtesy of the Ohio Agricultural Experiment Station.)

ally reproducing females. The body is often covered with waxy threads, and the wings at rest are held rooflike over the body. Cu_1 and Cu_2 in the front wing are separated at the base (Figure 20-2 E).

The eastern spruce gall aphid, *Adélges abiètis* (Linn.), is a fairly common species attacking spruce in the northeastern part of the country and forming pineapple-shaped galls on the twigs (Figure 20-26). It has two generations a year, and both generations consist entirely of females; there is no bisexual generation. Both generations occur on spruce. The winter is passed as partly grown nymphs attached to the base of the spruce buds. The nymphs mature into females the following April or May and lay their eggs at the base of the buds. The feeding of these females on the needles of the new shoots causes the needles to swell. The eggs hatch in about a week, and the nymphs settle on the needles that have become swollen by the feeding of the mother; the twig-swelling continues and a gall is formed, and the nymphs complete their development in cavities in the gall. Later in the summer, winged females emerge from the galls and lay their eggs on the needles of nearby branches; these eggs hatch and the nymphs overwinter.

FAMILY **Phylloxéridae**—Phylloxerans: The antennae in this group are 3-segmented in all forms, and the wings at rest are held flat over the body. Cu_1 and Cu_2 in the front wing are stalked at the base (Figure 20-2 C). These insects do not produce waxy threads, but some species are covered with a waxy powder. The phylloxerans feed on plants other than conifers, and the life history is often very complex.

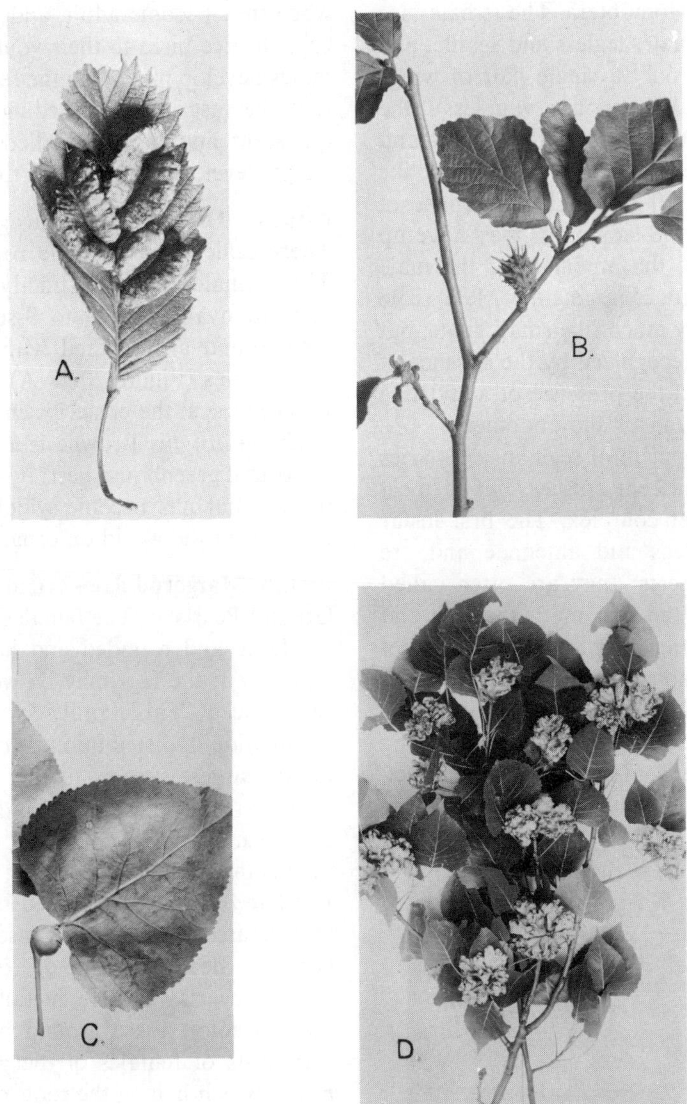

Fig. 20-25. Aphid galls. A, the elm cockscomb gall, caused by *Cólopha ulmícola* (Fitch); B, the spiny bud gall of witch hazel, caused by *Hamamelístes spinòsus* Shimer; C, the leaf petiole gall of poplar, caused by *Pémphigus populítransvérsus* Riley; D, the vagabond gall of poplar, caused by *Pémphigus vagabúndus* Walsh. (A-C courtesy of the Illinois Natural History Survey; D, courtesy of the Ohio Agricultural Experiment Station.)

The grape phylloxera, *Phylloxèra vitifòliae* (Fitch), is a common and economically important species in this group. This minute form attacks both the leaves and the roots of the grape, forming small galls on the leaves (Figure 20-27) and gall-like swellings on the roots. The European grapes are much more susceptible to the attacks of this insect than are the native American grapes.

SUPERFAMILY **Coccòidea**—Scale Insects: This group is a large one and contains forms that are minute and highly specialized; many are so modified that they look very little like other Homoptera. The females are wingless and usually legless and sessile, and the males have only a single pair of wings (rarely, the males too are wingless); the males lack mouth parts and do not feed, and the abdomen terminates in a long stylelike process (Figure 20-28 A). The antennae of the female may be lacking or may have up to 11 segments; the antennae of the male have from 10 to 25 segments. Male scale insects look very much like small gnats, but can usually be recognized by the absence of mouth parts and the presence of a stylelike process at the end of the abdomen.

The development of scale insects varies somewhat in different species, but in most cases it is rather complex. The first instar nymphs have legs and antennae and are fairly active insects; they are often called crawlers. After the first molt, the legs and antennae are often lost and the insect becomes sessile, and a waxy or scalelike covering is secreted and covers the body. In the armored scales (Diaspídidae), this covering is often separate from the body of the insect. The females remain under the scale covering when they become adult, and produce their eggs or give birth to their young there. The males develop much like the females, except that the last instar preceding the adult is quiescent and is often called a pupa; the wings develop externally in the pupa.

Fig. 20-26. The pineapple spruce gall, caused by *Adélges abìetis* (Linn.). (Courtesy of the Ohio Agricultural Experiment Station.)

FAMILY **Ortheziidae** — Ensign Coccids: These scales occur on the roots of plants. The females are distinctly segmented, elongate-oval, with 4- to 9-segmented antennae, and are covered with hard, white, waxy plates (Figure 20-29 A); some have a wax egg sac at the posterior end of the body. *Orthèzia insígnis* Browne is a common and important greenhouse pest; it is native to the tropics, but has become widely distributed throughout the world on ornamental plants.

FAMILY **Margaródidae**—Giant Coccids and Ground Pearls: The females in this group are large and rounded and have the body segmented; the legs may be well developed or reduced. This family is small but is world-wide in distribution. It contains some of the largest species in the superfamily; some in the genera *Llavèia* and *Callipáppus* may reach a length of about an inch. An interesting species occurring in Mexico, *Llavèia áxin* (Llave), is used by the natives as a source of substances used in making varnish. Beads are made from tropical ground pearls that are metallic bronze or gold in color; these ground pearls are the wax cysts of females of the genus *Margaròdes,* which live on the roots of plants. The cottony cushion scale, *Icérya púrchasi* Maskell, is an important pest of citrus in the West. A few other species in this group occur in southern United States.

FAMILY **Diaspídidae**—Armored Scales: This is the largest family of scale insects and contains a number of very important pest species. The females are very small and soft-bodied and are concealed under a scale covering that is usually free from the body of the insect beneath. The scale covering is formed of wax secreted by the insect, together with the cast skins of the early in-

Fig. 20-27. Galls on grape leaves caused by the grape phylloxera, *Phylloxèra vitifòliae* (Fitch). (Courtesy of the Ohio Agricultural Experiment Station.)

stars. The scales vary in different species; they may be circular or elongate, smooth or rough, and variously colored; the scales of the male are usually smaller and more elongate than those of the female. The adult females have the body small, flattened, and disclike, and the segmentation is frequently obscure; they have neither eyes nor legs, and the antennae are absent or vestigial; the males are winged and have well-developed legs and antennae.

Reproduction may be bisexual or parthenogenetic; some species are oviparous, and others give birth to living young. The eggs are laid under the scale. The first instar young, or crawlers, are active insects and may travel some distance; they are able to live several days without food. A species is spread in this crawler stage, either by the locomotion of the crawler itself, or by the crawlers' being transported on the feet of birds or by other means. Eventually the crawlers settle down, insert their mouth parts into the host plant, and remain sessile the remainder of their lives.

These insects injure plants by sucking sap, and when numerous may kill the plant. The armored scales feed principally on trees and shrubs and may sometimes heavily encrust the twigs or branches. Several species are important pests of orchard and shade trees.

The San Jose scale, *Aspidiòtus perniciòsus* Comstock (Figure 20-30), is a very serious pest. It first appeared in California about 1880, probably from the Orient, and has since spread throughout the country. It attacks a number of different trees and shrubs, including orchard trees, shade trees, and ornamental shrubs, and when numerous may kill the host plant. The scale is somewhat circular in shape. This species gives birth to living young.

The oystershell scale, *Lepidósaphes úlmi* (Linn.), is another important species; it is so named because of the shape of its scale (Figure 20-31). This widely distributed species attacks a number of plants, including most fruit trees and many ornamental trees and shrubs. Plants heavily infested are often killed. The oystershell scale lays eggs, which overwinter under the scale of the female.

A number of other armored scales are somewhat less important than the two just mentioned. The scurfy scale, *Chionáspis*

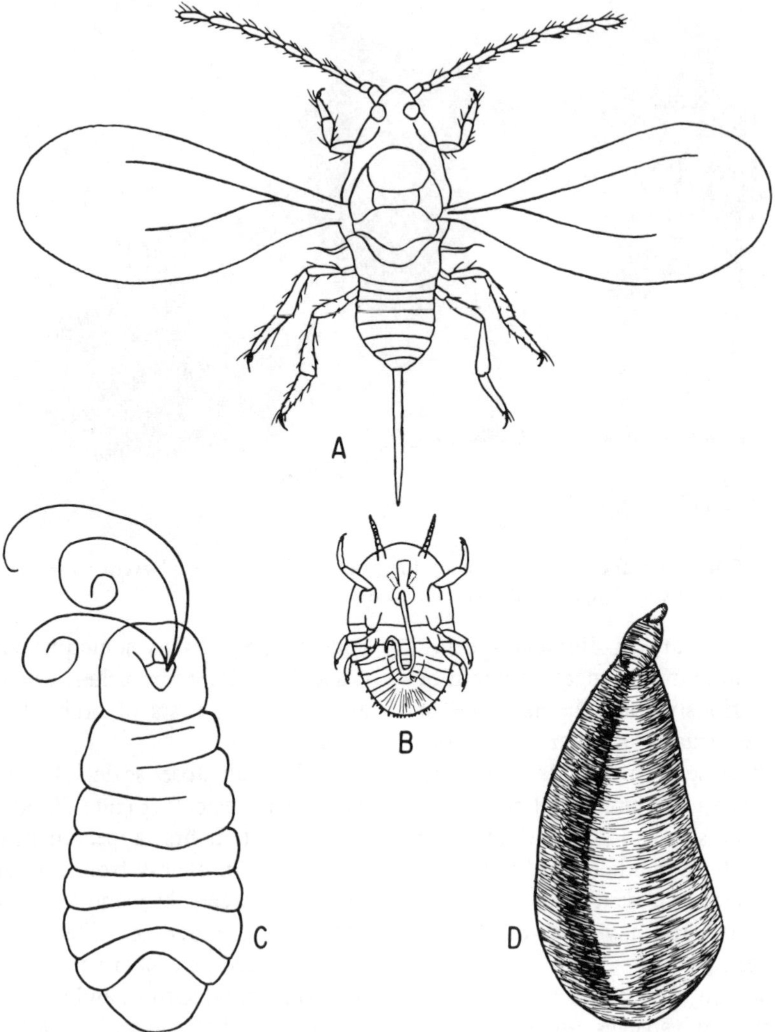

Fig. 20-28. The oystershell scale, *Lepidósaphes úlmi* (Linn.). A, adult male; B, newly hatched young, or crawler; C, adult female; D, scale of female. (Redrawn from various sources.)

fúrfura (Fitch), is a common whitish scale that attacks a number of trees and shrubs. The rose scale, *Aulacáspis ròsae* (Bouché), is a reddish insect with a white scale and attacks various types of berries and roses; heavily infested plants look as though they have been whitewashed. The pine needle scale, *Phenacáspis pinifòliae* (Fitch), is common throughout the country on pine and sometimes attacks other evergreens.

Several tropical or subtropical species in this group attack citrus or greenhouse plants. The California red scale, *Aonidiélla aurántii* (Maskell), is an important pest of citrus in Florida and California; the female has a circular scale slightly larger than that of the San Jose scale.

FAMILY **Aclérdidae**: This is a small family, most of the members of which attack grasses; these scales usually occur beneath the leaf sheaths or are crowded among the crowns of the roots. A few species occur on orchids and species of Cyperàceae and Combretàceae.

FAMILY **Cóccidae**—Soft Scales, Wax Scales, and Tortoise Scales: The females in this group are flattened elongate-oval insects with a hard smooth exoskeleton, or are covered with wax; legs are present or absent, and the antennae are either absent or much reduced. The males may be winged or wingless. The female of many species is somewhat tortoise-shaped.

This family contains a number of injurious species. The black scale, *Saissètia òleae* (Bernard), is a tropical species that is widely distributed; it is an important pest of citrus and other plants in the South. The hemispherical scale, *S hemisphaèrica* (Targioni), is a common pest of ferns and other plants in homes and greenhouses. Several species attack various shade and fruit trees; the tuliptree scale, *Toumeyélla liriodéndri* (Gmelin), is one of the largest scale insects in this country, the adult female being about 8 millimeters in length; the cottony maple scale, *Pulvinària innumerábilis* (Rathvon), is a relatively large species (about 6 millimeters in length) in which the eggs are laid in a large cottony mass that protrudes from the end of the scale (Figure 20-32). Soft scales belonging to the genus *Lecànium* attack a variety of plants and often become pests in greenhouses.

The Chinese wax scale, *Ericèrus pè-la* Chavannes, is an interesting and important oriental species. The males secrete large amounts of a pure white wax that is used in making candles. Wax is also produced by the wax scales of the genus *Ceroplástes*; the Indian wax scale, *C. ceríferus* Anderson, produces a wax that is used for medicinal purposes.

FAMILY **Lacciféridae**—Lac Insects: The females in this group are globular in form, legless, and have minute 3- or 4-segmented antennae. These insects live in cells of resin, and most of them are tropical or subtropical. The Indian lac insect, *Láccifer lácca* (Kern), is the most important species in this group, and one of great commercial value. It occurs on fig, banyan, and other plants in India, Indo-China, Formosa, Ceylon, and the Philippine Islands. The bodies of the females become covered with heavy exudations of wax or lac, and are sometimes so numerous that the twigs are coated with lac to a thickness of $\frac{1}{4}$ to $\frac{1}{2}$ inch. The twigs are cut and the lac is melted off, refined, and used in the preparation of shellac and varnishes. About 4 million pounds of this material are produced yearly. A few species in the genus *Tachardiélla* occur in southwestern United States, where they feed on cactus and other desert plants. They all produce lac, some of which is highly pigmented.

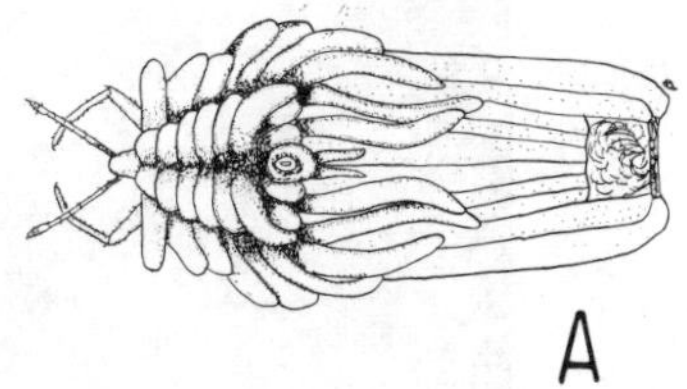

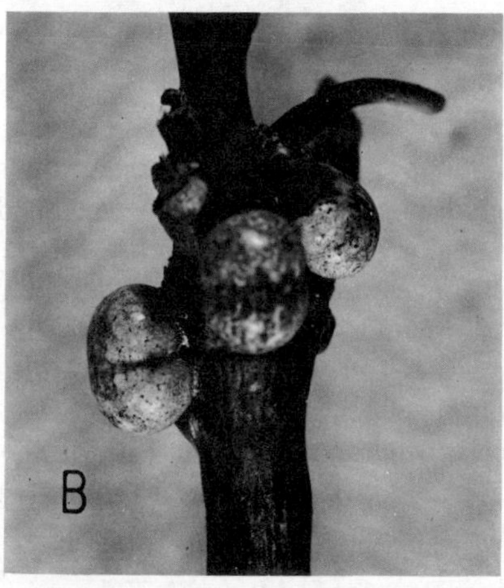

Fig. 20-29. A, an ensign coccid, *Orthèzia solidáginis* (Sanders), female; B, the bur oak gall-like coccid, *Kérmes pubéscens* (Bogue). (A, redrawn from Sanders; B, courtesy of the Ohio Agricultural Experiment Station.)

FAMILY **Asterolecanìidae**—Pit Scales: The pit scales are small, elongate-oval coccids in

Fig. 20-30. The San Jose scale, *Aspidiòtus perniciòsus* Comstock. (Courtesy of the Ohio Agricultural Experiment Station.)

which the body of the female may be covered by a tough waxy film or embedded in a waxy mass; the legs are vestigial or absent, eyes are lacking, and the antennae are short and 4- to 6-segmented. The oak wax scale, *Cerocóccus quércus* Comstock, is completely encased in a mass of wax; this species occurs on oak in California and Arizona, and was once used as chewing gum by the Indians.

FAMILY **Pseudocóccidae**—Mealybugs: The name mealybug is derived from the mealy or waxy secretions that cover the bodies of these insects. The body of the female is elongate-oval, segmented, and has well-developed legs (Figure 20-33). Some species lay eggs, and others give birth to living young; when eggs are laid, they are placed in loose cottony wax. Mealybugs may be found on almost any part of the host plant. Most of the important pest species in this group are in the genus *Pseudocóccus*; *P. cítri* (Risso) and *P. frágilis* Brain are serious pests of citrus and also attack greenhouse plants, and *P. longispìnus* (Targioni) is often found in greenhouses, where it attacks a variety of plants.

FAMILY **Eriocóccidae**—Mealybugs: These insects are similar to the pseudococcids, but the body of the immature stages is bare or only slightly covered with wax. This is a widely distributed group.

FAMILY **Dactylopìidae**—Cochineal Insects: These insects resemble the mealybugs in appearance and habits. The females are red in color, elongate-oval in shape and distinctly segmented, and the body is covered with white waxy plates; the legs and antennae are short. This family contains only two genera, *Epicóccus* and *Dactylòpius*. The cochineal insect, *D. cóccus* Costa, feeds on opuntia (prickly pear) cacti and is important as the source of a crimson dye produced by the natives of Mexico. The females, when mature, are brushed from the cacti, dried, and the pigments are extracted from the dried bodies. These insects were commercially important until about 1875, when aniline dyes were introduced.

FAMILY **Kérmidae**—Gall-like Coccids: The females in this group are spherical, hemispherical, or oval; legs are absent in the adult, and the antennae are 6-segmented. The elm scale, *Eriocóccus spùrius* Modeer, is a common pest of elms in North America and Europe. Members of the genus *Kérmes* live on the twigs of oak; they are spherical in shape and resemble tiny galls (Figure 20-29 B). This family contains the tamarisk manna scale, *Trabutìna mannípara* (Ehrenberg), which produced the manna for the Children of Israel. This species feeds on plants in the genus *Támarix*, and the females excrete large quantities of honeydew; in arid regions the honeydew solidifies on the leaves and accumulates in thick layers to form a sweet sugarlike material called manna.

COLLECTING AND PRESERVING HOMOPTERA

The methods of collecting and preserving Homoptera vary with the group concerned; the active species are collected and preserved much like other insects, but special techniques are used for such forms as the aphids and scale insects.

Most of the active species of Homoptera are best collected by sweeping. Different species occur on different types of plants, and one should collect from as many different types of plants as possible to secure a large number of species. The smaller hopping species may be removed from the net with an aspirator, or the entire net contents can be stunned and sorted later. Forms that are not too active can be collected from foliage or twigs directly into a killing jar, without using a net. Some of the cicadas, which spend most of their time high in trees, may be collected with a long-handled net; they may be dislodged with a long stick in the hope that they will land within net range, or they may be shot. A slingshot loaded with sand or fine shot, or a rifle or shotgun loaded with dust shot, may be used to collect cicadas that are out of reach of a net.

Fig. 20-31. The oystershell scale, *Lepidósaphes últmi* (Linn). (Courtesy of the Ohio Agricultural Experiment Station.)

Cicadas, the various hoppers, whiteflies, and psyllids are usually mounted dry, either on pins or points; whiteflies and psyllids are sometimes preserved in fluids and mounted on microscope slides for study.

Fig. 20-32. The cottony maple scale. *Pulvinària innumeràbilis* (Rathvon). (Courtesy of the Ohio Agricultural Experiment Station.)

Fig. 20-33. The citrus mealybug, *Pseudocóccus citri* (Risso). (Courtesy of the Ohio Agricultural Experiment Station.)

Aphids that are pinned or mounted on points usually shrivel; these insects should be preserved in fluids and mounted on microscope slides for detailed study.

Scale insects may be preserved in two general ways: The part of the plant containing the scales may be collected, dried, and mounted (pinned or in a Riker mount), or the insect may be specially treated and mounted on a microscope slide. No special techniques are involved in the first method; this is satisfactory if one is interested only in the form of the scale; the insects themselves must be mounted on microscope slides for detailed study. The best way to secure male scale insects is to rear them; very few are ever collected with a net.

In mounting a scale insect on a microscope slide, the scale is removed and the insect is cleared, stained, and mounted. Some general suggestions for mounting insects on microscope slides are given on pp. 687-692; the following procedures are specifically recommended for mounting scale insects.

1. Place the dry scale insect, or fresh specimens that have been in 70 percent alcohol for at least 2 hours, in 10 percent potassium hydroxide until the body contents are soft.
2. While the specimen is still in the potassium hydroxide, remove the body contents by making a small hole in the body (at the anterior end or at the side where no taxonomically important characters will be damaged) and pressing the insect.
3. Transfer the specimen to acetic acid alcohol for 20 min or more. Acetic acid alcohol is made by mixing 1 part of acetic acid, 1 part of distilled water, and 4 parts of 95 percent alcohol.
4. Stain in acid fuchsin for 10 min or more; then transfer to 70 percent alcohol for 5 to 15 min, to wash out excess stain.
5. Transfer the specimen to 95 percent alcohol for 5 to 10 min.
6. Transfer the specimen to 100 percent alcohol for 5 to 10 min.
7. Transfer the specimen to clove oil for 10 min or more.
8. Mount in balsam.

Aphids should be preserved in 80 or 85 percent alcohol and can often be collected from the plant directly into a vial of alcohol. Winged forms are usually necessary for specific identification and should be mounted on microscope slides.

REFERENCES ON THE HOMOPTERA

Alexander, Richard D., and Thomas E. Moore. 1962. The evolutionary relationships of 17-year and 13-year cicadas, and three new species (Homoptera, Cicadidae, *Magicicada*). Misc. Pub., Museum Zool., Univ. Mich., No. 121; 59 pp., frontis. (color)+10 text f.

Britton, W. E., *et al.* 1923. The Hemiptera or sucking insects of Connecticut. Conn. State Geol. and Nat. Hist. Survey, Bull. 34; 807 pp., 169 f., 20 pl.

Caldwell, John S. 1938. The jumping plant-lice of Ohio (Homoptera: Chermidae). Ohio Biol. Survey, Bull. 6(5):229-281; 11 pl.

Crawford, D. L. 1914. Monograph of the jumping plant lice or Psyllidae of the New World. U.S. Natl. Museum, Bull. No. 85; 186 pp., 30 pl.

DeLong, D. M. 1948. The leafhoppers, or Cicadellidae, of Illinois (Eurymelinae-Balcluthinae). Illinois Nat. Hist. Survey, Bull. 24(2): 91-376; 514 f.

Doering, K. 1930. Synopsis of North American Cercopidae. J. Kansas Entomol. Soc., 3(3-4):53-64, 81-108; 6 pl.

Evans, J. W. 1946a. A natural classification of leafhoppers (Jassoidea, Homoptera). Part 1. External morphology and systematic position. Trans. Royal Entomol. Soc. London, 96(3): 47-60; 25 f.

Evans, J. W. 1946b. A natural classification of leafhoppers (Jassoidea, Homoptera). Part 2. Aetalionidae, Hyticidae, Eurymelidae. Trans. Royal Entomol. Soc. London, 97(2):39-54; 3 f.

Evans, J. W. 1947. A natural classification of leafhoppers (Jassoidea, Homoptera). Part 3. Jassidae. Trans. Royal Entomol. Soc. London, 98(6):105-271; 36 f.

Evans, J. W. 1963. The phylogeny of the Homoptera. Ann. Rev. Entomol., 8:77-94; 1 f.

Ferris, G. F. 1937-1953. Atlas of the scale insects of North America. Stanford University, Calif.: Stanford University Press. 6 vols., illus.

Funkhouser, W. D. 1917. Biology of the Membracidae of the Cayuga Lake basin. N.Y. (Cornell) Agr. Expt. Sta. Mem., 11:177-445; f. 34-43, pl. 23-44.

Horvath, G., and H. M. Parshley (ed.). 1927-1948. General catalogue of the Hemiptera. Northampton, Mass: Smith College. Fasc. I, 1927, Membracidae, 581 pp. Fasc. IV, Fulgoroidea; Part 1, 1932, 74 pp.; Part 2, 1936, 274 pp.; Part 3, 1943, 552 pp.; Parts 4-7, 1945, 256 pp.; Part 8, 1946, 250 pp.; Part 9, 1947, 280 pp.; Part 10, 1948, 85 pp.

Hottes, F. C., and T. H. Frison. 1931. The plant lice, or Aphididae, of Illinois. Illinois Nat. Hist. Survey, Bull. 19(3):121-447; 47 f., 10 pl.

Kennedy, J. S., and H. L. G. Stroyan. 1959. Biology of aphids. Ann. Rev. Entomol., 4:139-160.

MacGillivray, A. D. 1921. The Coccidae. Urbana, Ill.: Scarab Co. vi+502 pp.

Metcalf, Z. P. 1923. Fulgoridae of eastern North America. J. Elisha Mitchell Sci. Soc., 38:139-230; pl. 39-69 (Res. Bull. No. 1).

Metcalf, Z. P. 1942. A bibliography of the Homoptera (Auchenorrhyncha). Vol. 1, Authors' list, A-Z; 886 p. Vol. 2, List of journals and topical index; 186 pp.

Metcalf, Z. P. 1954-1960. General catalogue of the Homoptera. Raleigh, N.C.: North Carolina State College. Fasc. IV, Fulgoroidea. Part 11, Tropiduchidae, 1954, 176 pp.; Part 12, Nogodinidae, 1954, 84 pp.; Part 13, Flatidae and Hypochthonellidae, 1957, 574 pp.; Part 14, Acanaloniidae, 1954, 64 pp.; Part 15, Issidae, 1958, 570 pp.; Part 16, Ricaniidae, 1955, 208 pp.; Part 17, Lophopidae, 1955, 84 pp.; Part 18, Eurybrachidae and Gengidae, 1956, 90 pp.

Metcalf, Z. P. 1960-1962. General catalogue of the Homoptera. Raleigh, N.C.: North Carolina State College. Fasc. VII, Cercopoidea. A bibliography of the Cercopoidea, 1960, 266 pp.; Part 1, Macherotidae, 1960, 56 pp.; Part 2, Cercopidae, 1961, 616 pp.; Part 3, Aphrophoridae, 1962, 608 pp.; Part 4, Clastopteridae, 1962, 66 pp.

Metcalf, Z. P. 1962+. General catalogue of the Homoptera. Raleigh, N.C.: North Carolina State College. Fasc. VIII, Cicadoidea. A bibliography of the Cicadoidea, 1962, 234 pp.; Part 1, Cicadidae (in press); Part 2, Tibicinidae (in press).

Metcalf, Z. P. 1962+. General catalogue of the Homoptera. U.S. Dep. Agr., ARS Fasc. VI, Cicadelloidea. Part 2, Hylicidae, 1962, 18 pp.; Part 3, Gyponidae, 1962, 229 pp.; Part 4, Ledridae, 1962, 147 pp.; Part 5, Ulopidae, 1962, 101 pp.; Part 6, Evacanthidae, 1963, 63 pp.; Parts 1 and 8-17 are in press or in preparation

Oman, Paul W. 1949. The nearctic leafhoppers (Homoptera: Cicadellidae), a generic classification and check list. Entomol. Soc. Wash. Mem. No. 3, 253 pp., 44 pl.

Osborn, Herbert. 1938. The Fulgoridae of Ohio. Ohio Biol. Survey, Bull. 6(6):283-349; 42 f.

Osborn, Herbert. 1940. The Membracidae of Ohio. Ohio Biol. Survey, Bull. 7(2):51-101; 31 f.

Ribaut, Henri. 1936. Homopteres—Auchenorhynques, I. Typhlocybidae. Faune de France, 31:1-230; 629 f.

Ribaut, Henri. 1952. Homopteres — Auchenorhynques, II. Jassidae. Faune de France, 57:1-474; 1212 f.

Way, M. J. 1963. Mutualism between ants and honeydew-producing Homoptera. Ann. Rev. Entomol., 8:307-344.

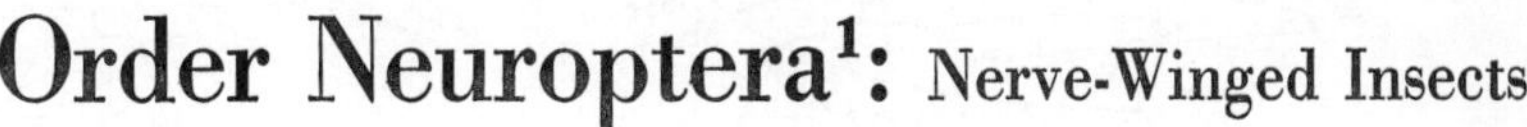

Order Neuroptera[1]: Nerve-Winged Insects

The Neuroptera have four membranous wings that usually have a great many cross-veins and extra branches of the longitudinal veins. There are generally a number of cross-veins along the costal border of the wing between the costa and the subcosta. The radial sector often bears a number of parallel branches. The front and hind wings of most Neuroptera are similar in shape and venation and are held rooflike over the abdomen when at rest. The mouth parts are of the chewing type, the antennae are generally long and many-segmented, the tarsi are 5-segmented, and cerci are absent.

These insects undergo complete metamorphosis. The larvae are generally campodeiform and often have long, sicklelike jaws. Pupation usually occurs in a silken cocoon; this silk is not derived from modified salivary glands as in most insects, but is produced by the Malpighian tubules and is spun from the anus.

Most Neuroptera are predaceous, both as larvae and as adults. Adults of Siálidae and Corydálidae probably feed little or not at all, and the larvae of the Sisýridae feed on freshwater sponges. The larvae of the Mantíspidae are parasitic in the egg sacs of spiders. In those larvae that have long sicklelike jaws (lacewings, antlions) the feeding is done by sucking the body fluids of the victim through a narrow channel formed between the mandibles and the maxillae.

The insects here included in the order Neuroptera are by some authorities divided into three orders: the Megalóptera, Raphidiòdea, and the Neuróptera. We are treating these three groups as suborders. An out-

[1] Neuroptera: *neuro,* nerve (referring to the wing veins); *ptera,* wings.

line of the groups in this order is given below; alternate names or spellings are given in parentheses, and groups that are rare or unlikely to be taken by the general collector are marked with an asterisk.

- Suborder Megalóptera (Sialòdea)
  - Corydálidae—fishflies, dobsonflies, hellgrammites
  - Siálidae—alderflies
- Suborder Raphidiòdea (Raphidiòidea)—snakeflies
  - Raphidiìdae—raphidiid snakeflies
  - Inocellìidae—inocellid snakeflies
- Suborder Planipénnia (Neuróptera in the narrow sense)
  - Superfamily Coniopterygòidea
    - *Coniopterýgidae—dusty-wings
  - Superfamily Hemerobiòidea—lacewings
    - Mantíspidae—mantidflies
    - *Diláridae—pleasing lacewings
    - Hemerobìidae (incl. Sympherobìidae)—brown lacewings
    - *Polystoechótidae—large lacewings
    - Sisýridae—spongillaflies
    - Chrysópidae—green lacewings, common lacewings
    - *Beróthidae—beaded lacewings
  - Superfamily Myrmeleontòidea
    - Ascaláphidae—owlflies
    - Myrmeleóntidae—antlions

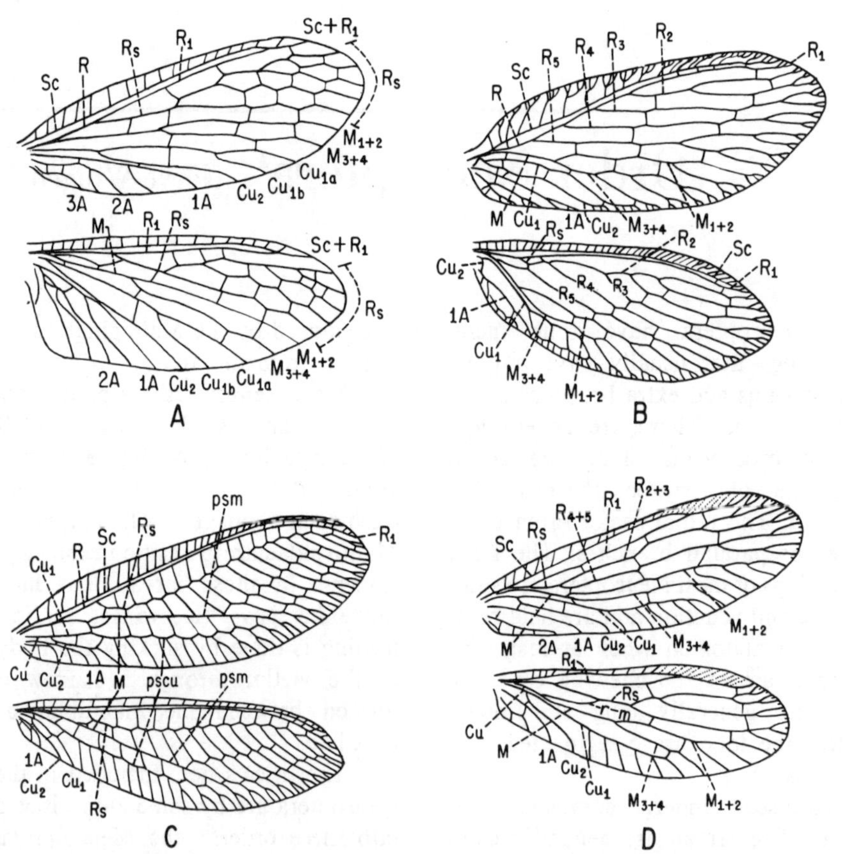

Fig. 21-1. Wings of Neuroptera. A, *Chauliòdes* (Corydálidae); B, *Micròmus* (Hemerobìidae); C, *Chrysòpa* (Chrysópidae); D, *Climàcia* (Sisýridae). In the Chrysópidae it has been shown by Comstock that what appears to be the media is in reality the fused branches of Rs, and this vein may be termed the pseudomedia (*psm*); similarly, what appears to be the cubitus is in reality the branches of M and Cu_1 fused, and this vein may be termed the pseudocubitus (*pscu*).

The key to the families of Neuroptera includes all the families of Neuroptera occurring in the United States; the groups marked with an asterisk are relatively rare and are unlikely to be taken by the general collector.

KEY TO THE FAMILIES OF NEUROPTERA

1. Hind wings broader at base than front wings, and with an enlarged anal area that is folded fanwise when at rest (Figure 21-1 A); larvae aquatic (suborder Megalóptera) 2

1′. Front and hind wings usually similar in shape, the hind wings without an enlarged anal area that is folded fanwise at rest (Figures 21-1 B-D and 21-2 to 21-4); larvae usually terrestrial 3

2(1). Ocelli present; fourth tarsal segment cylindrical; body usually an inch or more in length .... **Corydálidae** p. 233

2′. Ocelli absent; fourth tarsal segment dilated and deeply bilobed; body usually less than an inch in length (Figure 21-5).............. **Siálidae** p. 233

3(1′). Wings with relatively few veins, the radial sector with only 2 branches (Figure 21-2); wings covered with a whitish powder; minute insects.. .... **Coniopterýgidae*** p. 235

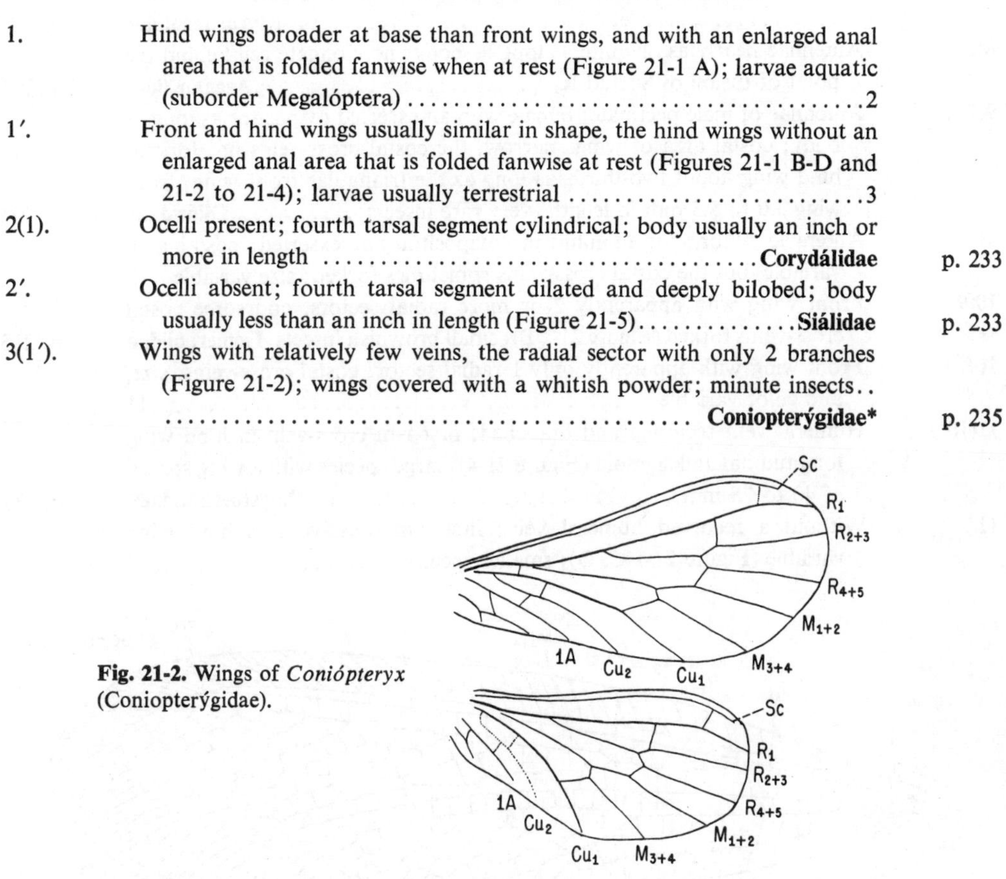

Fig. 21-2. Wings of *Conióptery* (Coniopterýgidae).

3′. Wings with many veins, the radial sector usually with more than 2 branches (Figures 21-1 B-D, 21-3, and 21-4); wings not covered with a whitish powder; size variable, but usually not minute...................... 4

4(3′). Prothorax elongate (Figures 21-8 and 21-9).......................... 5

4′. Prothorax of normal size, not elongate 7

5(4). Front legs raptorial, and arising from anterior end of prothorax (Figure 21-9); mantidlike insects, widely distributed ....**Mantíspidae** p. 235

5′. Front legs not raptorial, and arising from posterior end of prothorax (Figure 21-8); western United States (suborder Raphidiòdea)........ 6

6(5′). Ocelli present; pterostigma bordered proximally by a veinlet from R_1.... ....**Raphidìidae** p. 234

6′. Ocelli absent; pterostigma not bordered proximally by a veinlet from R_1 ....**Inocellìidae** p. 234

7(4′). Antennae clubbed or knobbed; insects with the abdomen long and slender, and resembling damselflies or dragonflies in appearance (Figure 21-11) 8

7′. Antennae filiform, moniliform, or pectinate, not clubbed or knobbed; usually not particularly resembling damselflies or dragonflies in appearance 9

8(7). Antennae about as long as head and thorax together (Figure 21-11); an elongate cell behind the point of fusion of Sc and R_1 (Figure 21-3, *trc*) .... **Myrmeleóntidae** p. 237

8′. Antennae nearly as or quite as long as body; no elongate cell behind the point of fusion of Sc and R_1.......... **Ascaláphidae** p. 238

9(7′). Antennae of male pectinate; female with an exserted ovipositor as long as body; costal area of wings narrow, the costal cross-veins not forked; hind wing about two-thirds as long as the triangular front wing; front wing 3.0 to 5.5 mm in length; very rare insects.......... **Diláridae*** p. 235

9′. Antennae filiform or moniliform; ovipositor not exserted; costal area variable, but the costal cross-veins sometimes forked; size variable.. 10

10(9′). Front wing with apparently 2 or more radial sectors, and some costal cross-veins forked (Figure 21-1 B); small brownish insects **Hemerobìidae** p. 235

10′. Front wing with apparently only 1 radial sector; costal cross-veins, size, and color variable.......... 11

11(10′). Humeral vein recurved and branched; first r-m cross-vein in hind wing longitudinal and sigmoid (Figure 21-4); large species with a wing spread of 40 to 75 mm .... **Polystoechótidae*** p. 237

11′. Without a recurved humeral vein; first r-m cross-vein in hind wing variable (Figure 21-1 C, D); smaller species.......... 12

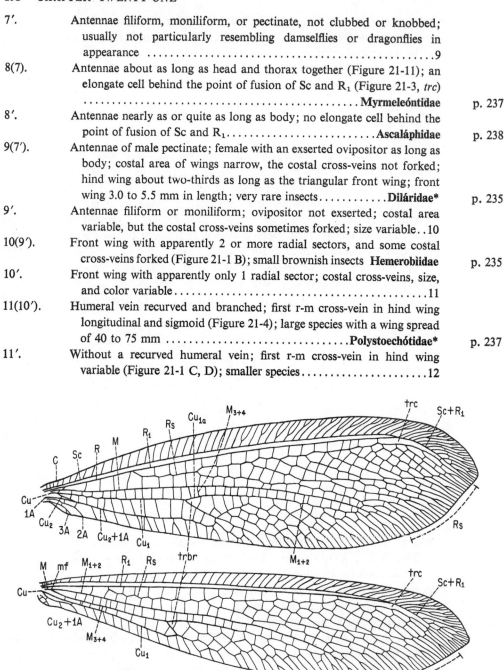

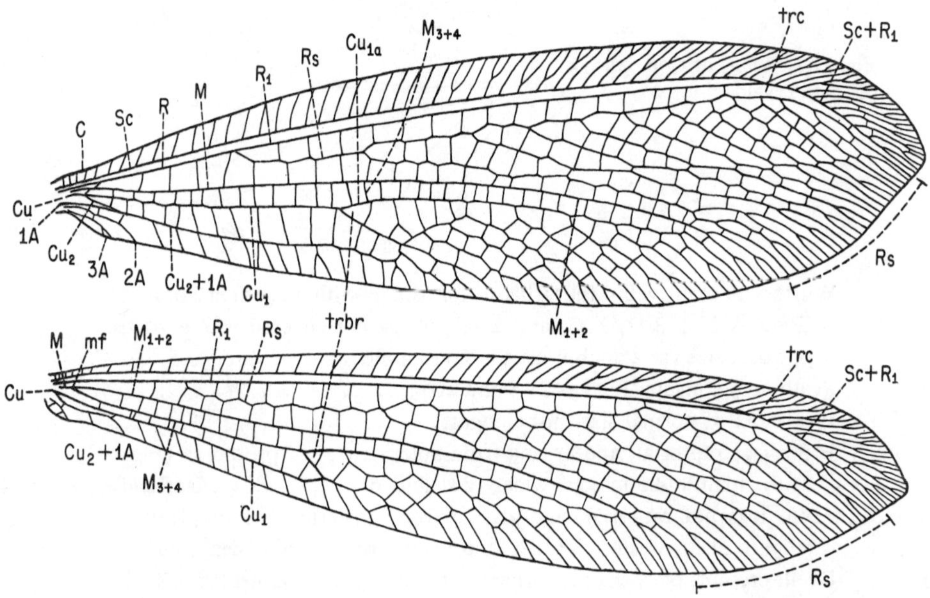

Fig. 21-3. Wings of *Dendròleon* (Myrmeleóntidae). *mf*, fork of M; *trc*, truss cell (a long cell behind the point of fusion of Sc and R_1); *trbr*, trigonal brace (formed by the fork of Cu_1 in the front wing and by the fork of M_{3+4} in the hind wing). M_{3+4} in the front wing usually appears as an oblique cross-vein. The vein on the anterior side of the trigonal brace (Cu_{1a} in the front wing and M_{3+4} in the hind wing) is often called the trigonal vein.

12(11′). Front wing with Sc and R_1 not fused near wing tip, and costal cross-veins not forked (Figure 21-1 C); wings usually greenish (at least in life); common insects .... **Chrysópidae** p. 237

12′. Front wing with Sc and R_1 fused or separated near wing tip, and costal cross-veins variable; wings not greenish.......................... 13

13(12′). Some costal cross-veins forked; Sc and R_1 fused or separated near wing tip; Rs in front wing with definitive accessory veins; vertex flattened; very rare insects; over 8 mm in length .... **Beróthidae*** p. 237

13′. No costal cross-veins forked; Sc and R_1 fused near wing tip; Rs without definitive accessory veins (Figure 21-1 D); vertex convex; 6 to 8 mm in length; uncommon, but not particularly rare .... **Sisýridae** p. 235

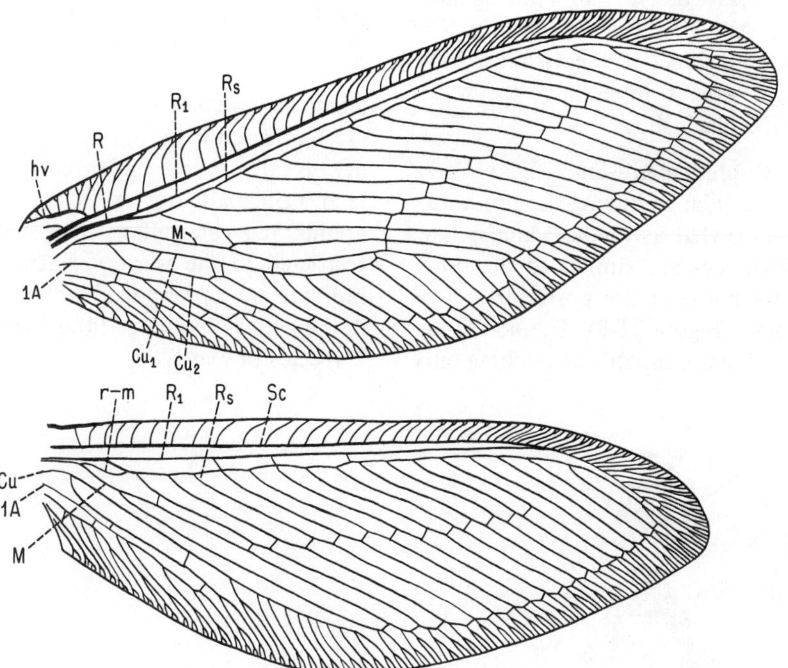

Fig. 21-4. Wings of *Polystoechòtes* (Polystoechótidae). *hv*, humeral vein.

FAMILY **Siálidae**—Alderflies: The alderflies (Figure 21-5) are dark-colored insects, about an inch in length or less, and are usually found near water. The larvae are aquatic and are usually found under stones in streams; they are predaceous on small aquatic insects. The larvae of alderflies (Figure 21-7 C) differ from those of the Corydálidae in that they have a terminal filament, seven pairs of lateral filaments, and no hooked anal prolegs. *Sìalis infumàta* Newman is a common eastern species; it is about $\frac{3}{4}$ inch in length and has smoky wings.

FAMILY **Corydálidae**—Dobsonflies and Fishflies: These insects are similar to the alderflies, but are in general larger (usually over an inch in length) and have ocelli; they are soft-bodied and have a rather fluttery flight, and are usually found near water. Some species are attracted to lights, and may be found some distance from water. The larvae (Figure 21-7 A, B) are aquatic and usually occur under stones in streams; they differ from alderfly larvae in that they have a pair of hooked anal prolegs, no terminal filament, and eight pairs of lateral filaments. These larvae are sometimes called hellgrammites and are frequently used as bait by fishermen; the jaws can inflict a painful nip.

The largest species in this group is the dobsonfly, *Corýdalus cornùtus* (Linn.) (Figure 21-6), which has a wing spread of 4 or 5 inches; the males have extremely long mandibles (Figure 21-6 B). The remaining species in the group, which range in length from 1 to 2 inches, arc commonly called fishflies; these belong to the genera *Chauliòdes, Neohérmes,* and *Nigrònia.* The dobsonfly and some of the fishflies have clear wings; other fishflies have the wings spotted with blackish.

SUBORDER **Raphidiòdea**—Snakeflies: These insects are peculiar in having the prothorax elongate, somewhat as in the Mantíspidae, but the front legs are similar to the other legs and are borne at the posterior end of the prothorax (Figure 21-8). The adults are predaceous, but are capable of catching only small and weak prey. The eggs are laid in clusters in crevices in bark, and the larvae are usually found under bark; the larvae feed principally on small insects such as aphids and caterpillars. The snakeflies are restricted to the western states. The **Raphidìidae** are represented by about 17 species in the genus *Agúlla,* and the **Inocellìidae** by 2 species of *Inocéllia.*

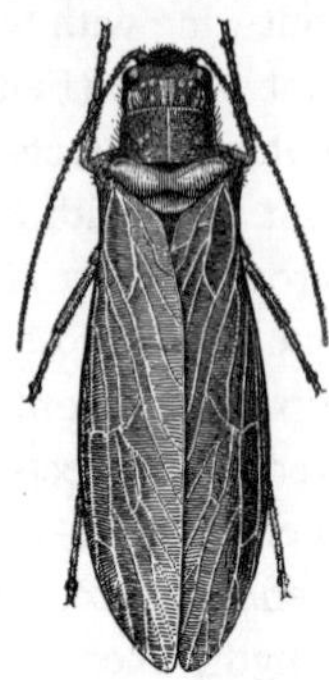

Fig. 21-5. An alderfly, *Sìalis mòhri* Ross. (Courtesy of the Illinois Natural History Survey.)

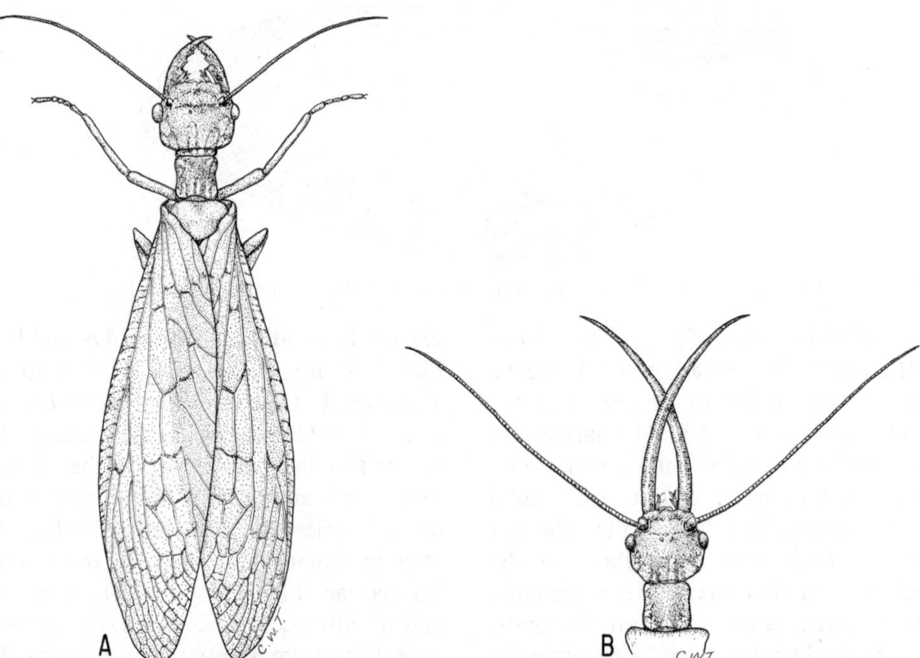

Fig. 21-6. The dobsonfly, *Corýdalus cornùtus* (Linn.). A, female; B, head of male showing the greatly enlarged mandibles; about natural size.

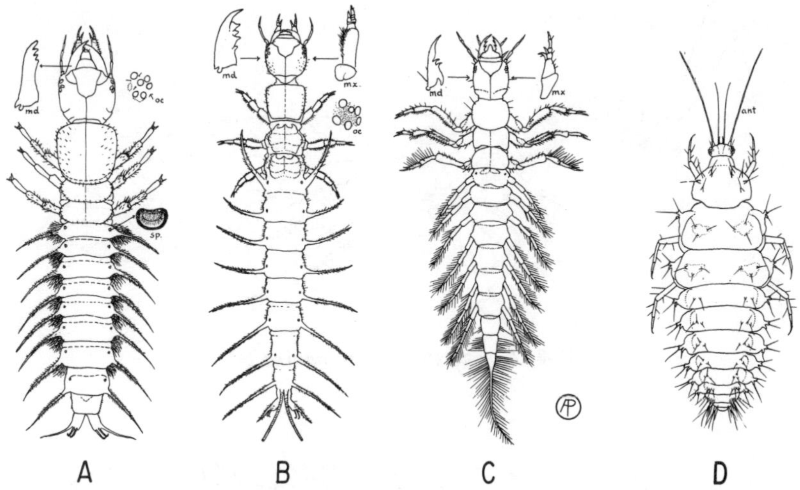

Fig. 21-7. Larvae of aquatic Neuroptera. A, *Corýdalus* (Corydálidae); B, *Chauliòdes* (Corydálidae); C, *Sìalis* (Siálidae); D, *Climàcia* (Sisýridae). *ant*, antenna; *md*, mandible; *mx*, maxilla; *oc*, ocelli; *sp*, spiracle. (Courtesy of Peterson. Reprinted by permission.)

FAMILY **Coniopterýgidae** — Dusty-Wings: These are minute insects, 3 millimeters in length or less, and are covered with a whitish powder. The group is a small one and its members are relatively rare. The larvae feed on small insects and insect eggs.

FAMILY **Mantíspidae**—Mantidflies: These insects resemble mantids in having the prothorax lengthened and the front legs enlarged and fitted for grasping prey (Figure 21-9); they have a wing spread of an inch or so. The adults are predaceous, and the larvae are parasitic in the egg sacs of ground spiders. Mantidflies undergo hypermetamorphosis; the first instar larvae are active and campodeiform, and the subsequent larval instars are scarabaeiform. These insects are more common in the South.

FAMILY **Sisýridae** — Spongillaflies: The spongillaflies look very much like tiny, brownish lacewings. They are usually found near ponds or streams, for the larvae (Figure 21-7 D) are aquatic and feed on freshwater sponges. When full grown, the larvae emerge from the water and pupate in silken cocoons attached to objects near the water; these cocoons are constructed inside hemispherical lacelike cocoon covers. Two genera of spongillaflies occur in the United States, *Climàcia* and *Sísyra.*

FAMILY **Hemerobiidae**—Brown Lacewings: These insects are very much like the common lacewings (Chrysópidae) in appearance, but are brownish instead of green, are generally much smaller, and have a different wing venation (compare Figure 21-1 B and C). Most of the brown lacewings appear to have three or more radial sectors (Figure 21-1 B); two genera that appear to have only two radial sectors (*Periéctra* and *Sympheròbius*) are placed by some authorities in a separate family, the Sympherobìidae. The brown lacewings are found in much the same situations as the common lacewings, but are usually less abundant. Both adults and larvae are predaceous.

FAMILY **Diláridae**—Pleasing Lacewings: This group contains two very rare North American species: *Nallàchius americànus* (MacLachlan) (front wing 4.5 millimeters in length) has been recorded from several eastern states, from Michigan to Georgia; *N. pulchéllus* (Banks) (front wing 3.0 to 5.5 millimeters in length) has been recorded

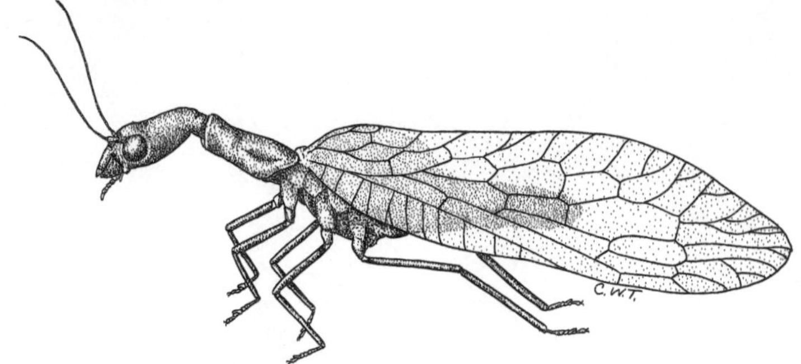

Fig. 21-8. A snakefly, *Agúlla adnixa* (Hagen).

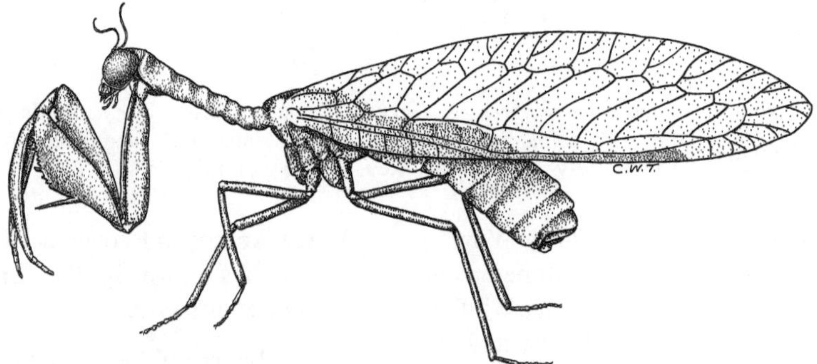

Fig. 21-9. A mantispid, *Mantispa cincticórnis* Banks.

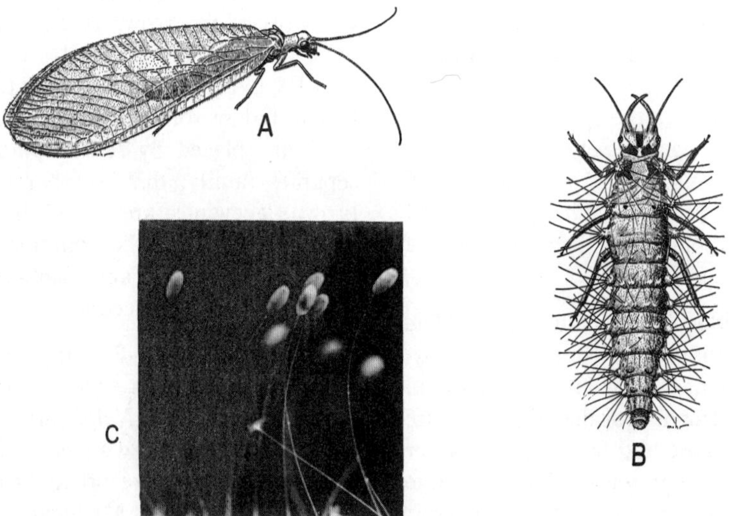

Fig. 21-10. Adult (A), larva (B), and eggs (C) of a common lacewing *(Chrysòpa* sp.). (A and B, courtesy of the Illinois Natural History Survey.)

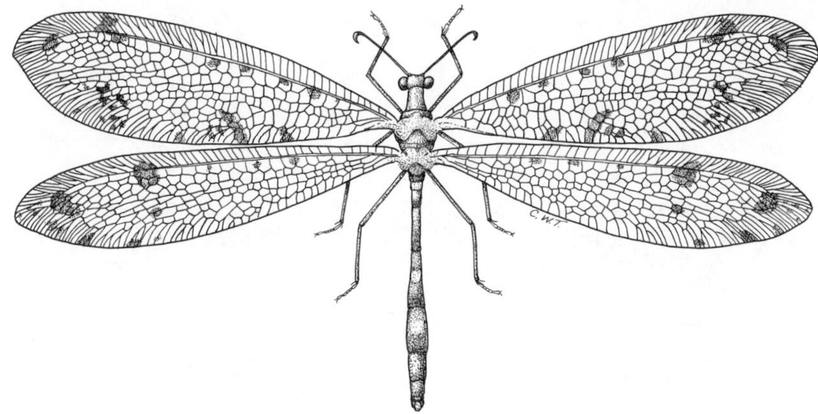

Fig. 21-11. An adult antlion, *Dendròleon obsolètum* (Say).

from Cuba and Arizona. These insects have an ovipositor that is a little longer than the body. The eggs are laid in crevices or under bark, and the larvae are predaceous.

FAMILY **Beróthidae**—Beaded Lacewings: This group is represented in North America by about a dozen rather rare species in the genus *Lomamỳia.* The eggs are stalked, and the larvae are predaceous. In some species the outer margin of the front wing is somewhat indented just behind the apex. The females of some species have scales on the wings and thorax.

FAMILY **Polystoechótidae** — Large Lacewings: These lacewings have a wing spread of 40 to 75 millimeters. They are quite rare, and only two species are known in North America: the larvae are terrestrial and predaceous.

FAMILY **Chrysópidae**—Common Lacewings: These insects are quite common in grass, weeds, and on the foliage of trees and shrubs. Most of them are greenish in color with golden- or copper-colored eyes (Figure 21-10 A). The lacewings give off a very disagreeable odor when handled, and are sometimes called stinkflies. Both adults and larvae are predaceous, chiefly on aphids, and the larvae are often called aphidlions. The eggs are usually laid on foliage, and each egg is laid at the end of a tiny stalk (Figure 21-10 C). The larvae pupate in silken cocoons that are usually attached to the under side of leaves. Most of our species belong to the genus *Chrysòpa.*

FAMILY **Myrmeleóntidae**—Antlions: The adults of this group are very similar in general appearance to damselflies, with long, narrow, many-veined wings and a long slender abdomen (Figure 21-11); they differ from damselflies in being very soft-bodied, in having long clubbed antennae, and in having a quite different wing venation (compare Figures 21-3 and 8-3). They are rather feeble fliers and are often attracted to lights. The wings are clear in some species and irregularly spotted in others.

Antlion larvae, or doodlebugs, are queer-looking creatures with long, sicklelike jaws (Figure 21-12 A). They have an interesting method of capturing their prey; they conceal themselves at the bottom of a small conical pit, made in dry sand or dust, and feed on ants and other insects that fall down into this pit. The pits are generally 1½ to 2 inches across, and an inch or two deep. It is not always easy to dig one of these larvae from its pit because, when disturbed, the larva usually remains motionless. If it is dug out, it is covered with a layer of dust or sand and is easily overlooked. Pupation occurs in the soil in a cocoon of sand and silk.

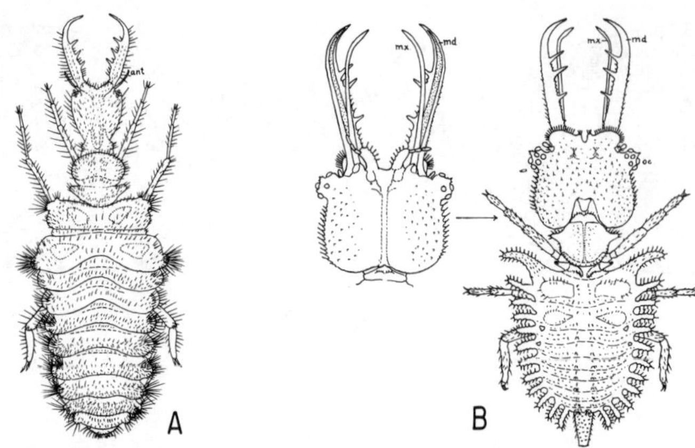

Fig. 21-12. A, larva of *Myrméleon immaculàtus* DeGeer (Myrmeleóntidae); B, larva of *Ascalóptynx appendiculátus* (Fab.) (Ascaláphidae). *ant*, antenna; *md*, mandible; *mx*, maxilla; *oc*, ocelli. (Courtesy of Peterson. Reprinted by permission.)

Antlions are much more common in the South and Southwest than in the northeastern part of the country. The pits of the larvae are usually found in dry situations such as under overhanging cliffs or under buildings.

FAMILY **Ascaláphidae**—Owlflies: The owlflies are large, dragonflylike insects with long antennae; they are fairly common in the South and Southwest, but are quite rare in the northern states. The larvae (Figure 21-12 B) are similar to the larvae of the antlions, but do not dig pits; they lie in ambush for their prey on the surface of the ground, often more or less covered with debris, and attack small insects that pass by.

REFERENCES ON THE NEUROPTERA

Banks, N. 1903. A revision of nearctic Chrysopidae. Trans. Entomol. Soc. Am. 29:137-162; 1 pl.

Banks, N. 1906. A revision of nearctic Hemerobiidae. Trans. Entomol. Soc. Am., 32: 21-51; pl. III-V.

Banks, N. 1906. A revision of the nearctic Coniopterygidae. Proc. Entomol. Soc. Wash., 8(3-4):77-86; pl. vi-vii.

Banks, N. 1927. Revision of nearctic Myrmeleontidae. Harvard Univ., Museum Compar. Zool., Bull. 68:1-84; 4 pl.

Carpenter, F. M. 1936. Revision of the nearctic Raphidiodea (recent and fossil). Proc. Am. Acad. Arts Sci., 71(2):89-157; 25 f., 13 text f.

Carpenter, F. M. 1940. A revision of the nearctic Hemerobiidae, Berothidae, Sisyridae, Polystoechotidae, and Dilaridae (Neuroptera). Proc. Am. Acad. Arts Sci., 74(7):193-280; 103 f.

Chandler, H. P. 1956. Megaloptera. In: Aquatic insects of California, ed. by Robert L. Usinger. Berkeley, Calif.: University of California Press. Pp. 229-233; 7 f.

Davis, K. C. 1903. Sialididae of North and South America, N.Y. State Museum, Bull. 68: 442-486; pl. li-lii.

Froeschner, Richard C. 1947. Notes and keys to the Neuroptera of Missouri. Ann. Entomol. Soc. Am., 40(1):123-136; 20 f.

Gurney, Ashley B. 1947. Notes on Dilaridae and Berothidae, with special reference to the immature stages of the nearctic genera (Nueroptera). Psyche, 54(3):145-169; 22 f.

Gurney, Ashley B., and Sophy Parfin. 1959. Neuroptera. In: Fresh-water biology, ed. by W. T. Edmondson. New York: John Wiley & Sons, Inc. Pp. 973-980; 4 f.

Parfin, Sophy I., and A. B. Gurney. 1956. The spongillaflies, with special reference to those of the western hemisphere (Sisyridae, Neuroptera). Proc. U.S. Natl. Museum, 105:421-529; 24 f., 3 pl.

Rehn, John W. H. 1939. Studies in North American Mantispidae (Neuroptera). Trans. Entomol. Soc. Am., 65:237-263; 22 f.

Smith, Roger C. 1922. The biology of the Chrysopidae. N.Y. (Cornell) Agr. Expt. Sta. Mem. 58, pp. 1285-1377, f. 154-163, pl. 85-88.

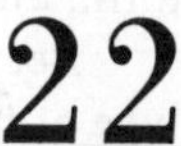

22

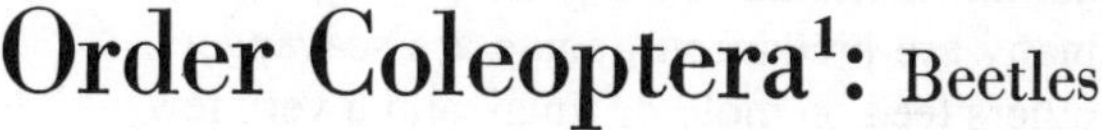

Order Coleoptera[1]: Beetles

The order Coleoptera is the largest order of insects and contains about 40 percent of the known species in the class Insecta. Over a quarter of a million species of beetles have been described, and over 26,000 of this number occur in the United States. These insects vary in length in this country from less than a millimeter up to about 2 inches, and some tropical species reach a length of 4 or 5 inches. The beetles vary considerably in habits, and are to be found almost everywhere; many species are of great economic importance.

One of the most distinctive features of the Coleoptera is the structure of the wings. Most beetles have four wings, with the front pair thickened, leathery, or hard and brittle, and usually meeting in a straight line down the middle of the back and covering the hind wings (hence the order name). The hind wings are membranous, usually longer than the front wings, and when at rest, are folded up under the front wings. The front wings of a beetle are called elytra (singular, elytron). The elytra normally serve only as protective sheaths; the hind wings are the only ones ordinarily used for flight. The front or hind wings are greatly reduced in a few beetles.

The mouth parts in this order are of the chewing type, and the mandibles are well developed. The mandibles of many beetles are stout and are used in crushing seeds or gnawing wood; in others they are slender and sharp, with a groove or channel through which the insect sucks the blood of its prey. In the snout beetles the front of the head is drawn out into a more or less elongated snout, with the mouth parts at the end.

The beetles undergo complete metamorphosis. The larvae vary considerably in form in different families; most beetle larvae are campodeiform or scarabaeiform,

[1] Coleoptera: *coleo*, sheath; *ptera*, wings (referring to the elytra).

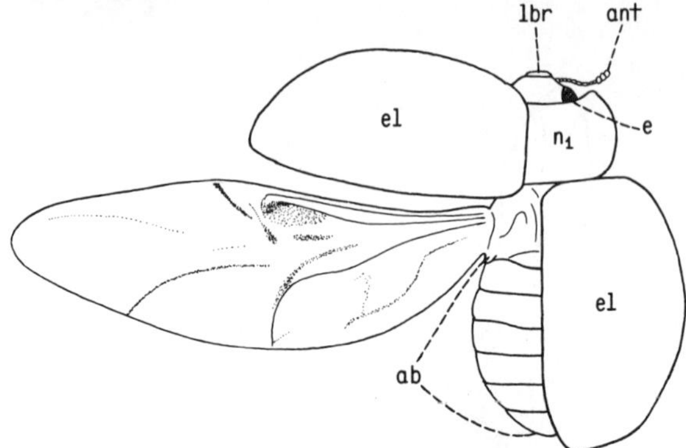

Fig. 22-1. Dorsal view of a ladybird beetle (*Adàlia* sp.), with left wings extended. *ab*, abdomen; *ant*, antenna; *e*, compound eye; *el*, elytron; *lbr*, labrum; n_1, pronotum.

but some are platyform, some are elateriform, and a few are vermiform.

Beetles may be found in almost every type of habitat in which any insect is found, and they feed on all sorts of plant and animal materials. Many are phytophagous, many are predaceous, some are scavengers, others feed on mold or fungi, and a very few are parasitic. Some are subterranean in habit, many are aquatic or semiaquatic, and a few live as commensals in the nests of social insects. Some of the phytophagous species are free feeders on foliage, some bore into the wood or fruit, some are leaf miners, some attack the roots, and some feed on parts of the blossoms; any part of a plant may be fed upon by some type of beetle. Many beetles feed on stored plant or animal products, including many types of foods, clothing, and other organic materials. One species is remarkable for its ability to bore through the lead sheathing of telephone cables in California. Many beetles are of value to man because they destroy injurious insects or act as scavengers.

The life cycle in this order varies in length from four generations a year to one generation in several years; most species have one generation a year. The winter may be passed in any of the life stages, depending on the species. Many overwinter as partly grown larvae, many overwinter as pupae in chambers in the soil or in wood or in other protected situations, and many overwinter as adults; relatively few species overwinter as eggs.

CLASSIFICATION OF THE COLEOPTERA

There are differences of opinion among coleopterists regarding the relationships of the various groups of beetles, the groups that should be given family status, and their arrangement into superfamilies. The arrangement of suborders and superfamilies followed in this book is taken from various sources, principally the Leng Catalogue and Böving and Craighead's larval synoposis (1930). Some recent workers on this order (for example, Arnett, 1960-1962; Crowson, 1955) follow a slightly different arrangement. Many authorities give family status to more groups than we do.

An outline of the groups in the order Coleoptera, as they are treated in this book, is given below. Names in parentheses represent different spellings, synonyms, or another treatment of the group. Families marked with an asterisk are relatively rare, or are not very likely to be taken by the general collector.

Suborder Archostémata
  Superfamily Cupesòidea
    *Cupésidae (Cupédidae, Cùpidae)—reticulated beetles
    *Micromálthidae—micromalthid beetles
Suborder Adéphaga
  Superfamily Rhysodòidea
    Rhysódidae (Rhyssódidae)—wrinkled bark beetles
  Superfamily Carabaeòidea
    Cicindélidae—tiger beetles
    Carábidae—ground beetles
    Omophrónidae (Carábidae in part)—round sand beetles
    Halíplidae—crawling water beetles
    *Amphizòidae—trout-stream beetles
    Dytíscidae—predaceous diving beetles
    *Notéridae (Dytíscidae in part)—burrowing water beetles
  Superfamily Gyrinòidea
    Gyrínidae—whirligig beetles
Suborder Polýphaga
  Superfamily Lymexylonòidea
    *Lymexlyónidae (Lymexýlidae)—ship-timber beetles
    *Telegeùsidae—telegeusid beetles
  Superfamily Hydrophilòidea
    Histéridae—hister beetles
    Hydrophílidae (incl. Hydróchidae and Sperchaèidae)—water scavenger beetles
    *Limnebìidae (Hydraènidae; Hydrophílidae in part)—minute moss beetles
    *Hydroscáphidae (Hydrophílidae in part)—skiff beetles
  Superfamily Staphylinòidea (Brachyélytra)
    *Platypsýllidae (Leptinidae in part)—beaver parasites
    *Ptilìidae (Ptílidae, Trichopterýgidae)—feather-winged beetles
    *Limulódidae (Limulodìnae of Ptilìidae and Cephaloplectìnae of Staphylínidae)—horseshoe crab beetles
    *Leptínidae—mammal-nest beetles
    *Leiódidae (Anisotómidae; Sílphidae in part)—round fungus beetles
    *Leptodíridae (Catópidae; Sílphidae in part)—small carrion beetles
    Sílphidae—carrion beetles
    Scaphidìidae—shining fungus beetles
    *Brathínidae—grass-root beetles
    Staphylínidae—rove beetles
    Pseláphidae—short-winged mold beetles
    *Clavigéridae (Pseláphidae in part)—ant-loving beetles
    *Clámbidae—fringe-winged beetles
    *Scydmaènidae—antlike stone beetles
    *Sphaerítidae—false clown beetles
    *Orthopéridae (Corylóphidae)—minute fungus beetles
    *Sphaerìidae (Orthopéridae in part)—minute bog beetles
  Superfamily Canthardìidea
    Canthándae (Lampýridae in part)—soldier beetles
    Lampýridae—lightningbugs, fireflies

*Phengódidae (Lampýridae in part)—glow-worms
Lýcidae (Lampýridae in part)—net-winged beetles
Superfamily Cleròidea
Derméstidae—skin beetles, carpet beetles, larder beetles, and others
Malachìidae (Melýridae in part)—soft-winged flower beetles
*Dasýtidae (Melýridae in part)—soft-winged flower beetles
Císidae (Cìidae, Ciòidae)—minute tree-fungus beetles
Ostómidae (Ostomátidae, Temnochílidae, Trogosítidae)—bark-gnawing beetles
Cléridae (incl. Corynétidae or Korynétidae)—checkered beetles, bone beetles, ham beetles
Superfamily Elateròidea (Sternóxia)
Sandálidae (Rhipicéridae in part)—sandalid beetles
*Rhipicéridae—cedar beetles
*Cerophtýidae—cerophytid beetles
*Cebriónidae—cebrionid beetles
Elatéridae (incl. Plastocéridae)—click beetles
Eucnémidae (Melásidae)—false click beetles
*Perothópidae (Eucnémidae in part)—perothopid beetles
Thróscidae (Trixágidae)—throscid beetles
Bupréstidae (incl. Schizophágidae)—metallic wood-boring beetles
Superfamily Dascillòidea
Dascíllidae (Dascýllidae; incl. Eucinétidae, Brachypséctridae, and Eurypogónidae)—soft-bodied plant beetles
*Ptilodactýlidae (Dascíllidae in part)—ptilodactylid beetles
Helódidae (Cyphónidae; Dascíllidae in part)—marsh beetles
Superfamily Byrrhòidea
Býrrhidae—pill beetles
*Nosodéndridae (Býrrhidae in part)—wounded-tree beetles
*Chelonarìidae—chelonariid beetles
Superfamily Dryopòidea
*Dryópidae (Párnidae)—long-toed water beetles
*Limníchidae (Dryópidae in part)—minute marsh-loving beetles
Psephénidae (Párnidae in part)—water-penny beetles
Élmidae (Hélmidae; Párnidae in part)—riffle beetles
*Heterocéridae—variegated mud-loving beetles
*Georýssidae—minute mud-loving beetles
Superfamily Cucujòidea
Derodóntidae—tooth-necked fungus beetles
*Monotómidae (Rhizophágidae in part, Nitidùlidae in part)—small flattened bark beetles
*Rhizophágidae (Nitidùlidae in part)—root-eating beetles
*Monómmidae (Monommátidae)—monommid beetles
*Sphíndidae—dry-fungus beetles
*Cryptophágidae (incl. Biphýllidae or Diphýllidae)—silken fungus beetles
Erotýlidae (incl. Dácnidae)—pleasing fungus beetles
Languriidae (Erotýlidae in part)—lizard beetles
Cucùjidae—flat bark beetles
Silvánidae (Cucùjidae in part)—flat grain beetles
Phalácridae—shining flower beetles

Nitidùlidae—sap beetles
*Murmidiidae—murmidiid beetles
*Monoèdidae (Adiméridae; Colydìidae in part)—monoedid beetles
Lathridìidae—minute brown scavenger beetles
*Mycetaèidae (Endomýchidae in part)—mycetaeid fungus beetles
Endomýchidae—handsome fungus beetles
Coccinéllidae—ladybird beetles, ladybugs
*Bytùridae (Derméstidae in part)—fruitworm beetles
*Colydìidae (incl. Bothridéridae)—cylindrical bark beetles
Anthícidae—antlike flower beetles
*Euglénidae (Hylophílidae, Adéridae, Xylophílidae; Anthícidae in part)—antlike leaf beetles
*Mycetophágidae (Tritómidae)—hairy fungus beetles
*Cephalòidae—false longhorn beetles
Oedeméridae—false blister beetles
*Othnìidae (Elacátidae)—false tiger beetles
*Eurystéthidae (Aegialítidae; Salpíngidae in part)—eurystethid beetles
Salpíngidae (Myctéridae; incl. Pýthidae and Cononótidae)—narrow-waisted bark beetles
Pyrochròidae—fire-colored beetles
*Pedílidae (Anthícidae in part)—pedilid beetles
*Hemipéplidae (Cucùjidae in part)—hemipeplid beetles

Superfamily Meloòidea (Melòidea; Heterómera in part)
Melòidae (Lýttidae; incl. Tetraonýchidae)—blister beetles, oil beetles
*Rhipiphóridae—wedge-shaped beetles

Superfamily Mordellòidea (Heterómera in part)
Mordéllidae—tumbling flower beetles

Superfamily Tenebrionòidea (Heterómera in part)
Allecùlidae (Cistélidae)—comb-clawed beetles
Tenebriónidae—darkling beetles
Lagrìidae—long-jointed bark beetles
Melandrỳidae (Serropálpidae; incl. Synchròidae, Anáspidae, and Scraptìidae)—false darkling beetles

Superfamily Bostrichòidea (Ptinòidea)
Ptínidae—spider beetles
Anobìidae—drugstore and death-watch beetles
Bostríchidae (Bostrýchidae, Apátidae)—branch and twig borers
Psòidae (Bostríchidae in part)—psoid branch and twig beetles
Lýctidae (Bostríchidae in part)—powder-post beetles

Superfamily Scarabaeòidea (Lamellicórnia)
Lucánidae—stag beetles, pinchingbugs
Passálidae—bessbugs
Scarabaèidae (incl. Acanthocéridae, Geotrùpidae, and Trógidae)—scarab beetles: June beetles, tumblebugs, dung beetles, skin beetles, leaf chafers, and others

Superfamily Cerambycòidea (Phytóphaga in part)
Cerambýcidae (incl. Spondýlidae)—long-horned wood-boring beetles

Superfamily Chrysomelòidea (Phytóphaga in part)
Chrysomélidae—leaf beetles, including flea beetles, tortoise beetles, asparagus beetles, cucumber beetles, potato beetles, and others

Brùchidae (Mylábridae, Acanthoscélidae, Larìidae)—seed beetles, pea and bean weevils

Superfamily Curculionòidea (Rhynchóphora)

*Bréntidae (Brénthidae)—primitive weevils

Anthríbidae (Platystómidae, Bruchélidae, Chorágidae, Platyrrhínidae)—fungus weevils

*Nemonýchidae (Rhinomacéridae, Diodyrhýnchidae, Dorydirhýnchidae; Curculiónidae in part)—pine-flower snout beetles

Curculiónidae (incl. Cyládidae, Bélidae or Ithycéridae, and Oxycorýnidae)—snout beetles

*Platypódidae—pin-hole borers, flat-footed ambrosia beetles

Scolýtidae (incl. Ípidae)—bark or engraver beetles, ambrosia or timber beetles

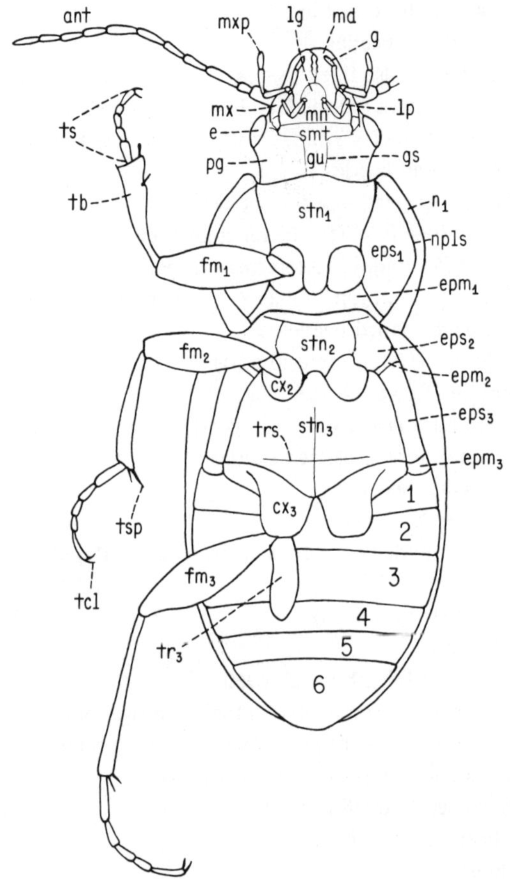

Fig. 22-2. Ventral view of a ground beetle (*Omàseus* sp.). *ant*, antenna; *cx*, coxa; *e*, compound eye; epm_1, proepimeron; epm_2, mesepimeron; epm_3, metepimeron; eps_1, proepisternum; eps_2, mesepisternum; eps_3, metepisternum; *fm*, femur; *g*, galea; *gs*, gular suture; *gu*, gula; *lg*, ligula; *lp*, labial palpus; *md*, mandible; *mn*, mentum; *mx*, maxilla; *mxp*, maxillary palpus; n_1, pronotum; *npls*, notopleural suture; *pg*, postgena; *smt*, submentum; stn_1, prosternum; stn_2, mesosternum; stn_3, metasternum; *tb*, tibia; *tcl*, tarsal claws; *tr*, trochanter; *trs*, tranverse suture on metasternum; *ts*, tarsus; *tsp*, tibial spurs; 1-6, abdominal sternites.

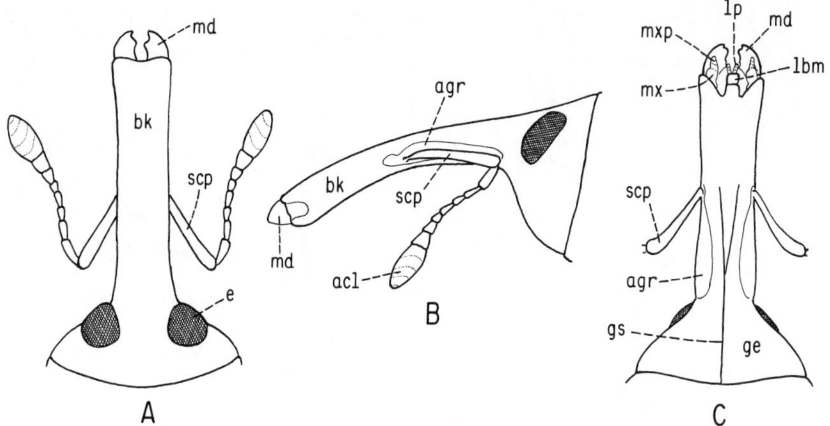

Fig. 22-3. Head of a snout beetle (*Pissòdes,* Curculiónidae). A, dorsal view; B, lateral view; C, ventral view. *acl,* antennal club; *agr,* groove in beak for reception of antennal scape; *bk,* beak or snout; *e,* compound eye; *ge,* gena; *gs,* gular suture; *lbm,* labium; *lp,* labial palpus; *md,* mandible; *mx,* maxilla; *mxp,* maxillary palpus; *scp,* scape of antenna.

CHARACTERS USED IN THE IDENTIFICATION OF BEETLES

The principal characters of beetles used in identification are those of the head, antennae, thoracic sclerites, legs, elytra, and abdomen; occasionally characters such as size, shape, and color are used. In most cases the ease of recognizing these characters depends on the size of the beetle; some characters require careful observation, often at high magnification, for accurate interpretation.

HEAD CHARACTERS: The principal head character used involves the development of a snout. In the Curculionòidea the head is more or less prolonged forward into a snout; the mouth parts are reduced in size and are located at the tip of the snout, and the antennae usually arise on the sides of it. In many cases (Figure 22-3) the snout is quite distinct and occasionally may be as long as the body or longer; in other cases (for example, the Scolýtidae and Platypódidae) the snout is poorly developed and not very evident as such. The families in the Curculionòidea are sometimes placed in a separate suborder, the Rhynchóphora. These beetles differ from most of the other members of the order in having the gular sutures fused (Figure 22-3 C). There is some development of a snout in a few beetles outside this superfamily, but such beetles have the gular sutures separated (Figure 22-2).

ANTENNAE: The antennae of beetles are subject to considerable variation in different groups, and these differences are used in identification. The various types of antennae have been described in Chapter 2 (see Figure 2-9). The term "clubbed," as used in the key, refers to any condition in which the terminal segments of the antennae are thicker than the segments just preceding them, and includes the conditions termed clavate, capitate, lamellate, and flabellate.

THORACIC CHARACTERS: The thoracic characters of importance are chiefly the shape or form of the pronotum and the size and shape of the various sclerites on the ventral side of the thorax. The ventral thoracic sclerites are shown in Figure 22-2. When the sclerites of the prothorax extend around the front coxae, these coxal cavities are said to be *closed* (Figure 22-4 B); when the sclerite immediately behind the front coxae is a sclerite of the mesothorax, these

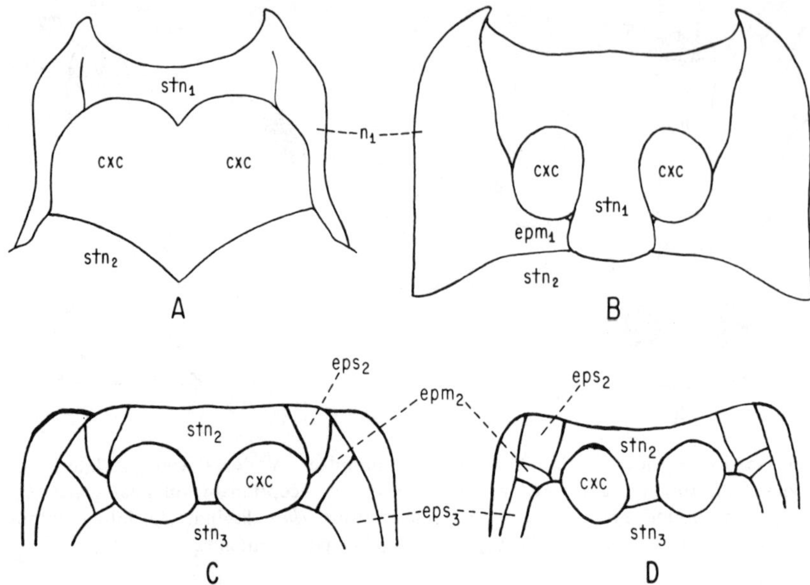

Fig. 22-4. Prosterna (A, B) and mesosterna (C, D), showing open and closed coxal cavities. A, meloid beetle, front coxal cavities open; B, tenebrionid beetle, front coxal cavities closed; C, *Sapérda* (Cerambýcidae), middle coxal cavities open; D, *Leiòpus* (Cerambýcidae), middle coxal cavities closed. *cxc*, coxal cavity; epm_1, proepimeron; epm_2, mesepimeron; eps_2, mesepisternum; eps_3, metepisternum; stn_1, prosternum; stn_2, mesosternum; stn_3, metasternum.

coxal cavities are said to be *open* (Figure 22-4 A). When the middle coxae are surrounded by sterna and are not touched by any pleural sclerites (Figure 22-4 D), they are said to be *closed*; when at least some of the pleural sclerites reach the middle coxae (Figure 22-4 C), these coxae are said to be *open*. The presence or absence of a prosternal spine, illustrated in Figure 22-13 A, is also of taxonomic importance; it fits into a cavity in the mesosternum and is freely movable in and out of that cavity in the Elatéridae, less movable in the Thróscidae and Eucnémidae, and it is completely immobile in the Bupréstidae.

LEG CHARACTERS: The coxae of beetles vary greatly in size and shape. In some cases they are globose and project only slightly; when they are more or less elongate laterally without projecting very much (Figure 22-5 C), they are said to be *transverse*; sometimes they are more or less conical, and project ventrad noticeably. A few beetles have a small sclerite, the trochantin, located in the anterolateral portion of the coxal cavity (Figure 22-5 B). The coxae of some beetles, particularly the middle and (or) hind coxae, are more or less grooved, and when the legs are folded up, the femora fit into these grooves.

The trochanters of most beetles do not lie directly between the coxae and the femora, but are situated more or less to one side, with the suture between the trochanter and the femur slanting and not at a right angle to the long axis of the leg. In a few cases (Figure 22-2, tr_3) the trochanters are off to one side, with the femur appearing to articulate with the coxa. Occasionally (Figure 22-5 D) the trochanter-femur union is almost at right angles to the long axis of the leg; such a trochanter is said to be interstitial.

The number and relative size and shape of the tarsal segments are very important characters for the identification of beetles; it is necessary to examine the tarsi of almost

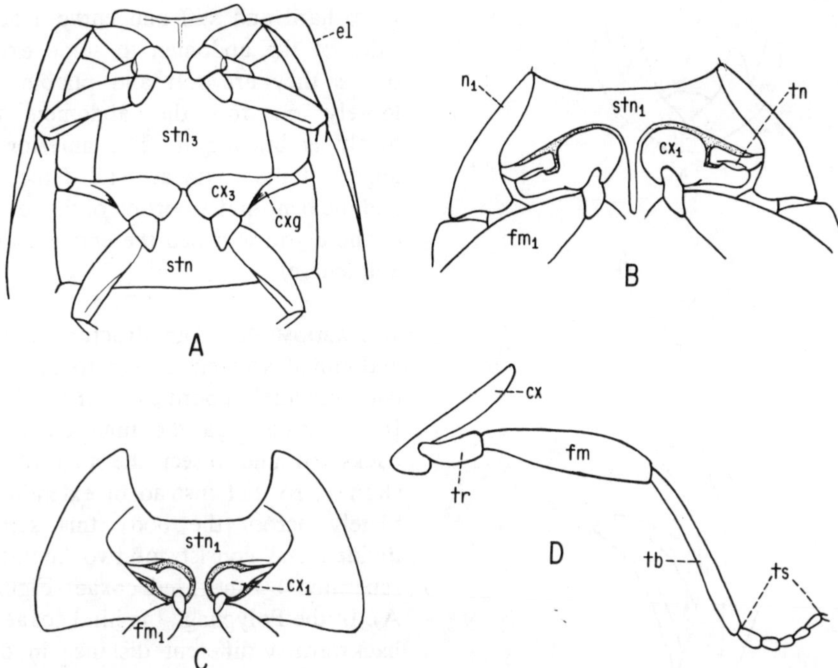

Fig. 22-5. Leg and coxal structure of Coleoptera. A, thorax of *Derméstes* (Derméstidae), ventral view, showing grooved hind coxae; B, prothorax of *Psephènus* (Psephénidae), ventral view, showing trochantin; C, prothorax of *Lobìopa* (Nitidùlidae), ventral view, showing transverse front coxae; D, hind leg of *Trichodésma* (Anobìidae), showing interstitial trochanter. *cx*, coxa; *cxg*, groove in coxa; *el*, elytron; *fm*, femur; n_1, pronotum; *stn*, sternum of first abdominal segment; stn_1, prosternum; stn_3, metasternum; *tb*, tibia; *tn*, trochantin; *tr*, trochanter; *ts*, tarsus.

any beetle one wishes to run through the key. The number of tarsal segments in most beetles varies from three to five; it is usually the same on all tarsi, but some groups have one less segment in the hind tarsi than in the middle and front tarsi, and others have fewer segments in the front tarsi. The tarsal formula is an important part of any group description, and is given as 5-5-5, 5-5-4, 4-4-4, 3-3-3, and so on, indicating the number of tarsal segments on the front, middle, and hind tarsi, respectively. Most of the Coleoptera have a 5-5-5 tarsal formula.

In a few groups, including some very common beetles, the next to the last tarsal segment is very small and inconspicuous. In such cases, this segment may be very difficult to see, except by very careful examination under high magnification. These tarsi thus appear to have one segment less than they actually have, and are so described in the key; for example, a 5-segmented tarsus such as that shown in Figure 22-10 A is described in the key as "apparently 4-segmented."

A few groups have the basal tarsal segment very small (Figure 22-10 D), and visible only if the tarsus is properly oriented.

If the tarsi of a beetle appear to be 4-segmented and the third segment is relatively large and more or less **U**-shaped (Figure 22-10 A), the tarsus is generally 5-segmented, with the fourth segment very small. If the tarsi appear to be 4-segmented and the third segment is slender and not greatly different from the terminal segment, then they are either actually 4-segmented or are 5-segmented with the basal segment very small.

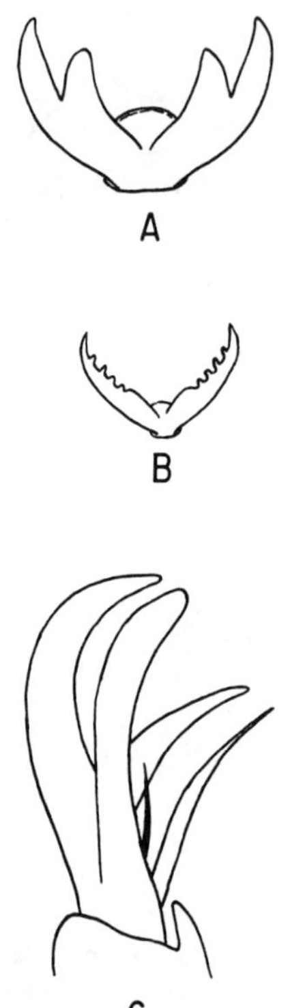

Fig. 22-6. Tarsal claws of Coleoptera. A, toothed (coccinellid); B, pectinate (alleculid); C, cleft (meloid).

The tarsal claws of beetles are subject to some variation; in most cases they are simple, that is, without branches or teeth, but in some cases they are toothed, cleft, or pectinate (Figure 22-6).

THE ELYTRA: The elytra vary principally in length and texture. In most beetles they cover all the abdominal segments, but in some cases one or more abdominal segments may be exposed beyond the tips of the elytra. When the elytra are short, the number of exposed segments serves to separate different groups. The elytra in some groups are variously sculptured, with ridges, grooves or striae, punctures, tubercles, and the like; in other cases they are quite smooth. If the elytra appear hairy under low or medium magnification, they are said to be pubescent. The elytra of some beetles are quite hard and stiff and curve around the sides of the abdomen to some extent; in others they are soft and pliable and lie loosely on top the abdomen without firmly embracing it. The anterior lateral angles of the elytra are called the humeri, and the bent-under portion of the lower edge of the elytra is called the epipleura (plural, epipleurae).

THE ABDOMEN: The structure of the first abdominal segment serves to separate the two principal suborders of the Coleoptera. In the Adéphaga the hind coxae extend backward and bisect the first abdominal sternite, so that instead of extending completely across the body this sternite is divided and consists of two lateral pieces separated by the hind coxae (Figure 22-7 A). In the Polýphaga the hind coxae extend backward a different distance in different groups, but the first abdominal sternite is never completely divided, and its posterior edge extends completely across the body.

The number of visible abdominal sterna varies in different groups and is repeatedly used in the key. In a few cases (for example, the Bupréstidae) the first two visible sterna are more or less fused together, and the suture between them is much less distinct than the other abdominal sutures. If the sutures between the abdominal sterna are all equally distinct, then none of the segments is said to be fused.

The last abdominal tergite is often called the pygidium, and is sometimes exposed beyond the tips of the elytra.

OTHER CHARACTERS: Characters such as the size, shape, or color should not prove particularly difficult. The term "base" is used to distinguish the two ends of various body parts; when speaking of an appendage, the base is that end nearest the body; the base of the head or pronotum is the posterior end, and the base of the elytra or abdomen is the anterior end. The segments of the tarsi or antennae are numbered from the base distad.

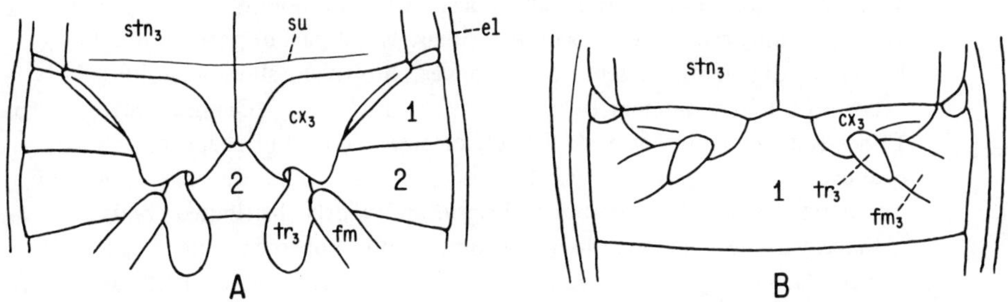

Fig. 22-7. Base of abdomen, ventral view, showing difference between Adéphaga and Polýphaga. A, tiger beetle (Adéphaga); B, pleasing fungus beetle (Polýphaga). cx_3, hind coxa; *el*, elytron; *fm*, hind femur; stn_3, metasternum; *su*, transverse metasternal suture; tr_3, hind trochanter; 1 and 2, abdominal sternites.

The following key is rather long, not only because this is the largest order of insects, but also because there is quite a bit of variation in many families and the key is constructed to take this variation into account. The families in the key that are marked with an asterisk are relatively rare, or are not very likely to be taken by the general collector.

If at any point in the key one is in doubt which way to go, he should try both alternatives and then check the descriptions of the groups reached. In many cases the key is so arranged that the specimen will key out correctly from either alternative. The student should have relatively little difficulty with the larger beetles, but a microscope with magnifications up to 60 × or more will be necessary to see all the characters of the smaller beetles.

KEY TO THE FAMILIES OF COLEOPTERA

1. Form beetlelike, the elytra and (or) hind wings present 2

1′. Larviform, the elytra and hind wings lacking; females 248*

2(1). Hind coxae expanded into large plates that conceal most of abdomen (Figure 22-17 B); antennae 10-segmented; small aquatic beetles, 4.5 mm in length or less . . . . **Halíplidae** p. 277

2′. Hind coxae not so expanded; antennae, size, and shape variable 3

3(2′). First abdominal sternum divided by hind coxae, the posterior margin of the sternum not extending completely across abdomen (Figure 22-7 A); prothorax usually with notopleural sutures (Figure 22-2, *npls*); tarsi usually 5-segmented; antennae usually filiform (suborder Adéphaga). . 4

3′. First abdominal sternum not divided by hind coxae, the posterior margin of the sternum extending completely across abdomen (Figure 22-7 B); prothorax usually without notopleural sutures; tarsi and antennae variable 12

4(3). Antennae moniliform (Figure 22-8 B); body slender and elongate; hind coxae widely separated; pronotum with at least 3 longitudinal grooves; terrestrial beetles, 5.5 to 7.5 mm in length. . . . . **Rhysódidae** p. 275

4′. Antennae seldom moniliform, usually filiform; beetles not agreeing with the above description 5

5(4′). Metasternum usually with a transverse suture just in front of hind coxae (Figure 22-2, *trs*); usually terrestrial beetles. 6

5′. Metasternum without a transverse suture just in front of hind coxae; hind legs fringed with hairs and modified for swimming; aquatic beetles . . 10

6(5). Head including eyes narrower than widest part of pronotum 7

6′. Head including eyes as wide as or wider than widest part of pronotum . . 9

7(6). Scutellum apparently absent; oval, convex, brownish, shore-inhabiting beetles, 5 to 8 mm in length . . . . **Omophrónidae** p. 277

7′. Either scutellum present and distinct, or size, color, and shape not as above 8

8(7′). Terrestrial beetles, 4 to 35 mm in length, and widely distributed; body shape variable; antennae long, slender, usually pubescent; tarsal segments slender; legs usually long . . . . **Carábidae** p. 276

8′. Aquatic beetles, 11.0 to 15.5 mm in length, occurring in streams in western United States; body oval but bluntly pointed at each end; antennae thick, glabrous, coarsely punctate in basal half, and not reaching base of pronotum; first 4 tarsal segments thick and with dense tufts of bristles beneath . . . . **Amphizòidae*** p. 278

9(6′). Antennae inserted between eyes and base of mandibles; clypeus not produced laterally beyond bases of antennae; small beetles, 6.0 to 8.5 mm in length . . . . **Carábidae** p. 276

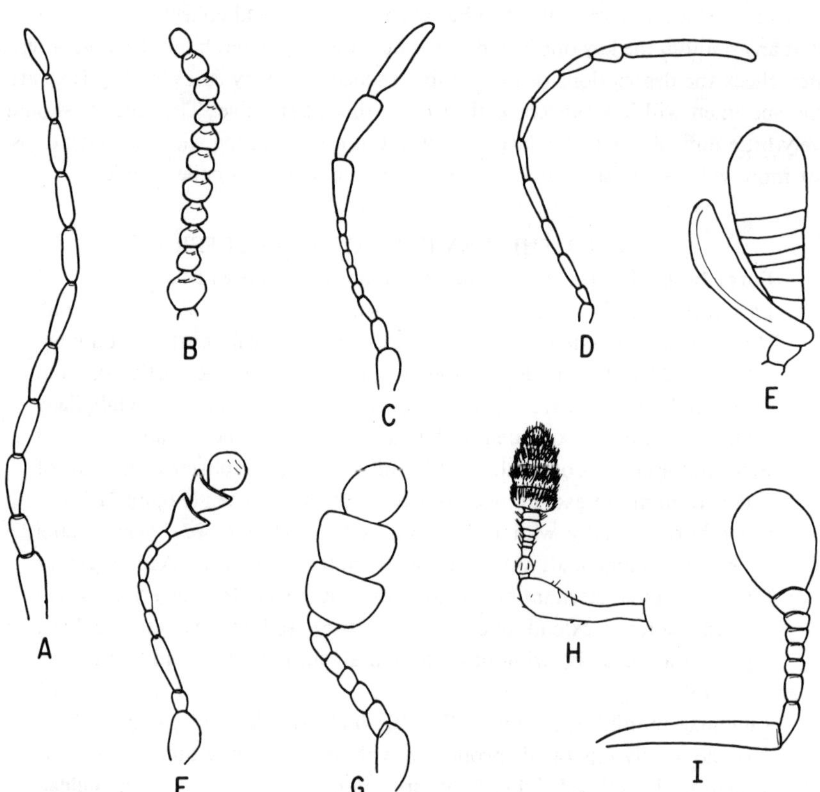

Fig. 22-8. Antennae of Coleoptera. A, *Hárpalus* (Carábidae); B, *Rhysòdes* (Rhysódidae); C, *Trichodésma* (Anobìidae); D, *Arthromácra* (Lagrìidae); E, *Dineùtes* (Gyrínidae); F, *Lobìopa* (Nitidùlidae); G, *Derméstes* (Derméstidae); H, *Hylurgópinus* (Scolýtidae); I, *Hololépta* (Histéridae). (H, redrawn from Kaston.)

9′. Antennae inserted on front above base of mandibles; clypeus produced laterally beyond bases of antennae; larger beetles, usually 10 to 24 mm in length; mandibles long and sickle-shaped; color usually greenish or brown, with light markings on elytra .... **Cicindélidae** p. 276

10(5′). Two pairs of compound eyes, one dorsal and one ventral (Figure 22-11 C); antennae very short and stout (Figure 22-8 E); beetles often swimming rapidly in circles on surface of water....................... **Gyrínidae** p. 279

10′. One pair of compound eyes; antennae long and slender..............11

11(10′). Scutellum concealed; hind tarsi with 2 curved claws of equal length; abdomen with 5 sterna; front coxal cavities closed behind; hind coxae small, with longitudinal plates overlapping articulations of trochanters; 1.2 to 5.5 mm in length.............................. **Notéridae*** p. 279

11′. Scutellum variable but, if concealed, then hind tarsi usually with a single straight claw; abdomen with 6 sterna; front coxal cavities open behind; hind coxae large, without longitudinal plates overlapping articulations of trochanters; 1 to 40 mm in length.................... **Dytíscidae** p. 278

12(3′). Prothorax with notopleural sutures (as in Figure 22-2)..............13*

12′. Prothorax without notopleural sutures............................15

13(12). Antennae filiform; tarsi 5-segmented; pronotum much narrower than base of elytra; elytra with several longitudinal ridges between which are rows of large square punctures; body scaly, head warty or tuberculate; 7 to 11 mm in length................................. **Cupésidae*** p. 275

13′. Antennae clubbed; tarsi 2- or 3-segmented; elytra and body not as above; less than 2 mm in length; western United States 14*

14(13′). Abdomen with 3 visible sterna; hind coxae large and contiguous; elytra completely covering abdomen; antennae 11-segmented, with a 3-segmented club; length 0.5 to 0.75 mm................ **Sphaerìidae*** p. 285

14′. Abdomen with 6 to 7 visible sterna; hind coxae small and well separated; elytra short, leaving at least 2 abdominal terga exposed; antennae 9-segmented, with a 1-segmented club; length about 1.5 mm.......... .... **Hydroscáphidae*** p. 282

15(12′). Head prolonged into a beak or snout (Figures 22-3, 22-81 to 22-85), with mandibles usually visible at its tip; antennae usually arising far in front of eyes, on snout 16

15′. Head not prolonged into a beak or snout; antennae arising on front or sides of head, nearer eyes..32

16(15). Antennae 10-segmented, the last segment elongate and as long as the 4 or 5 preceding segments combined (Figure 22-78 E, F); body antlike, 5 to 6 mm in length, with the pronotum reddish and the elytra blue-black (Figure 22-81); occurring principally in the southern states (*Cyladinae*) .... **Curculiónidae** p. 334

16′. Not exactly fitting the above description 17

17(16′). Antennae clubbed (Figures 22-8 H and 22-78 C-J)..................18

17′. Antennae not clubbed (Figure 22-78 A, B) 25

18(17). Tarsal formula 5-5-4; beak very broad and flat; front coxal cavities distinctly open behind..19*

18′. Tarsal formula 5-5-5 or 4-4-4 20

19(18). Middle coxal cavities open, the coxae prominent and contiguous (*Rhino-*

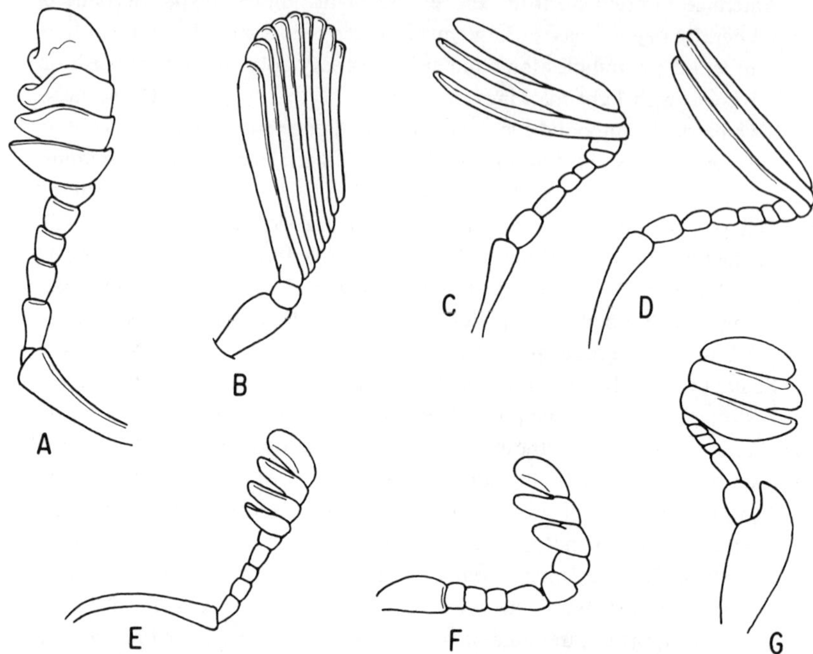

Fig. 22-9. Antennae of Coleoptera. A, *Nicróphorus* (Silphidae); B, *Sándalus*, male (Sandálidae); C, *Phyllóphaga* (Scarabaèidae), terminal segments expanded; D, same, terminal segments together forming a club; E, *Lucànus* (Lucánidae); F, *Popílius* (Passálidae); G, *Tróx* (Scarabaèidae).

plàtia) .... **Oedeméridae*** p. 301

19′. Middle coxal cavities closed, the coxae variable .... **Salpíngidae*** p. 302

20(18′). Tarsal formula 5-5-5 21

20′. Tarsal formula 4-4-4 23

21(20). The outer 5 to 7 antennal segments gradually enlarged to form a feeble club .... **Brùchidae** p. 328

21′. The outer 1 to 4 antennal segments abruptly and greatly enlarged to form a compact and distinct club 22

22(21′). Tarsi very slender and threadlike, the basal segment as long as the next 3 combined (Figure 22-10 K); head broader than pronotum; body slender and narrow .... **Platypódidae*** p. 337

22′. Tarsi shorter and broader, the basal segment never longer than the next 3 combined (Figure 22-10 G); head no broader than pronotum; body usually cylindrical or somewhat oval (Figure 22-86) .... **Scolýtidae** p. 337

23(20′). Labrum present; palpi distinctly segmented and flexible (Figure 22-79 B) 24

23′. Labrum absent; palpi rigid, the segments usually not apparent and the palpi often concealed within the mouth (Figure 22-3) .... **Curculiónidae** p. 330

24(23). Pronotum posteriorly with sharp keel-like lateral margins and usually a transverse ridge; beak usually very short and broad (Figure 22-77); tibiae without articulated spurs; gular sutures more or less obsolete; middle coxal cavities broadly open .... **Anthríbidae** p. 329

24′. Pronotum without sharp lateral margins or a transverse ridge; beak usually slender and as long as pronotum; tibiae with articulated spurs; gular sutures distinct and separate; middle coxal cavities closed or very slightly open .... **Nemonýchidae*** p. 330

25(17′). Tarsal formula 5-5-4; elytra completely covering abdomen; front coxal cavities open behind .... **Cephalòidae*** p. 301

25′. All tarsi with the same number of segments........................26

26(25′). First tarsal segment very long, the second and third segments bearing hairy pads beneath, and the third bilobed; tips of elytra rounded and not covering pygidium; hind femora usually dilated and with a large tooth; 7.5 mm in length or less (Figure 22-76)................... **Brùchidae** p. 328

26′. Not exactly fitting the above description 27

27(26′). A pair of ocelli present (*Omaliinae*) .... **Staphylínidae*** p. 284

27′. Ocelli absent, or with a single ocellus only..........................28

28(27′). Abdomen with 7 sterna; elytra with a network of ridges; western United States (*Lycóstomus*) .... **Lýcidae** p. 287

28′. Abdomen with 6 or fewer sterna; elytra variable, usually without such ridges; widespread 29

29(28′). Tarsal formula 5-5-5..30

29′. All tarsi with fewer than 5 segments 31

30(29). Gular sutures confluent; 5 visible abdominal sterna; female with a very long and slender beak that is directed straight forward, male with a short broad beak bearing large mandibles at the tip (Figure 22-79 D, F); usually brownish in color (*Arhenòdes minùtus*)........... **Bréntidae*** p. 329

30′. Gular sutures separated; 6 visible abdominal sterna; beak and color not as above 241

31(29′). Pygidium covered by elytra; femora clubbed; body elongate, the female with a long slender beak that is directed straight forward, the male with a broad horizontal beak bearing large mandibles at the tip (Figure 22-79 D, F) .... **Bréntidae*** p. 329

31′. Pygidium not covered by elytra; femora slender, not clubbed; body stout and oval (Figure 22-77); beak short, broad, flat, vertical, and sometimes indistinct.. **Anthríbidae** p. 329

32(15′). Antennae 2-segmented; each tarsus with only 1 claw; head and pronotum much narrower than elytra; brownish-yellow beetles, 2.5 mm in length or less, living in ant nests .... **Clavigèridae*** p. 285

32′. Not exactly fitting the above description 33

33(32′). Minute (mostly less than 1 mm in length) convex beetles, shaped a little like a horseshoe crab, with the abdomen tapering posteriorly; compound eyes and hind wings absent; tarsi 2-segmented, or 3-segmented with the first segment minute and concealed in apex of tibia; antennae short and retractile into grooves on under side of head, with a 2-segmented club, or (*Cephaloplèctus*) nearly filiform; prosternal process broad and long, extending backward over mesosternum; abdomen with 5 to 7 visible sterna; living in ant nests..................... **Limulódidae*** p. 282

33′. Not exactly fitting the above description 34

34(33′). Terminal segments of antennae enlarged, forming a club of various sorts (Figures 22-8 C, F-I and 22-9)..................................35

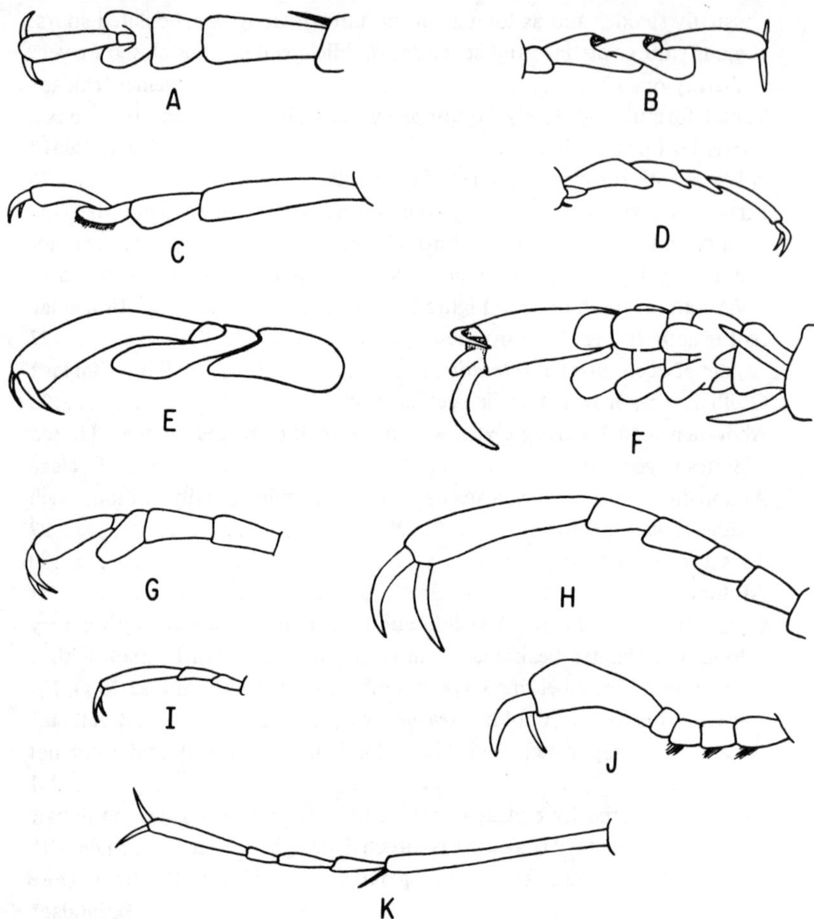

Fig. 22-10. Tarsi of Coleoptera. A, *Megacyllène* (Cerambýcidae); B, *Necròbia* (Cléridae); C, *Nacérda* (Oedeméridae), hind leg; D, *Trichòdes* (Cléridae); E. *Chilócorus* (Coccinéllidae); F, *Sándalus* (Sandálidae); G, *Scólytus* (Scolýtidae); H, *Psephènus* (Psephénidae); I, a lathridiid; J, *Parándra* (Cerambýcidae); K, *Plátypus* (Platypódidae).

34′. Antennae not clubbed, but filiform, moniliform, serrate, pectinate, or gradually and only slightly enlarged distally 136

35(34). Elytra short, leaving 1 or more complete abdominal terga exposed.... 36

35′. Elytra covering tip of abdomen, or leaving only a part of the last abdominal tergum exposed 52

36(35). More than 3 abdominal terga exposed dorsally 37

36′. Not more than 3 (usually only 1 or 2) abdominal terga exposed dorsally 39

37(36). Tarsal formula usually 5-5-5, rarely 4-4-4 or 3-3-3; antennae gradually enlarged apically, the club not abrupt; usually at least 7 abdominal sterna visible; 1 to 25 mm in length.................... **Staphylínidae** p. 284

37′. Tarsal formula 5-5-5 or 4-4-4; antennae with an abrupt club; abdomen with 5 or 6 visible sterna; size variable (see also 37″)............. 38

37″. Tarsal formula 3-3-3 (rarely 2-2-2); abdomen with 5 or 6 visible sterna; antennae usually abruptly clubbed; 0.5 to 5.5 mm in length.. **Pseláphidae** p. 284

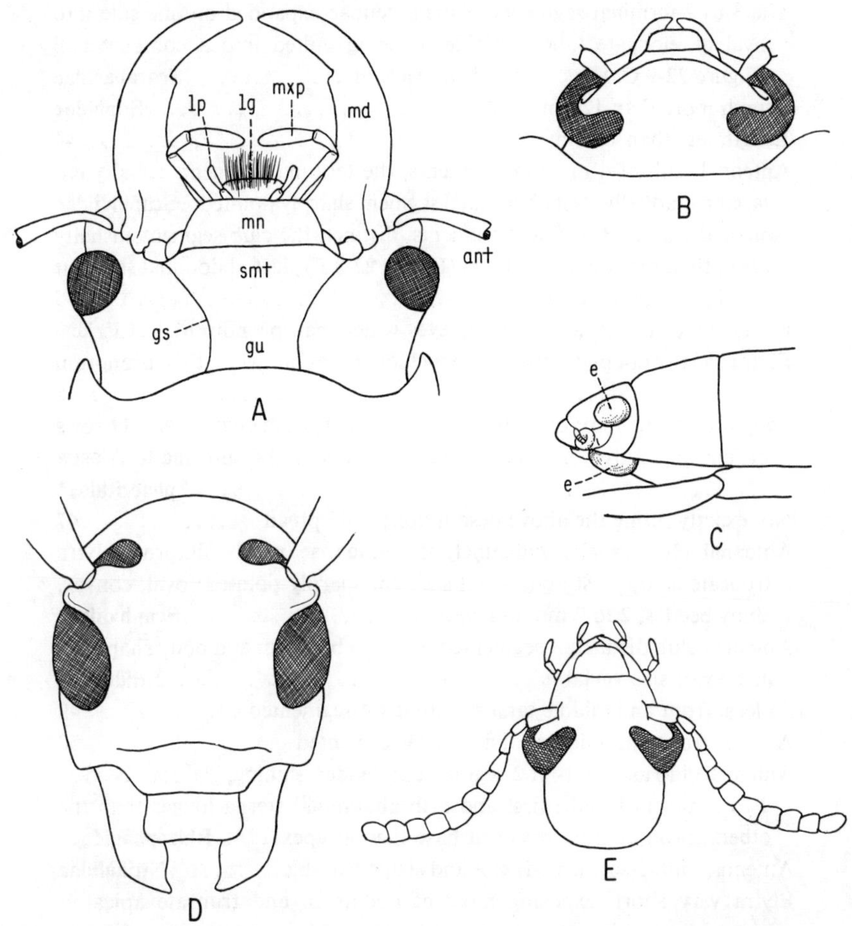

Fig. 22-11. Heads of Coleoptera. A, *Lucànus* (Lucánidae), ventral view; B, *Diapèris* (Tenebriónidae), dorsal view; C, *Dineùtes* (Gyrínidae), lateral view; D, *Sapérda* (Cerambýcidae), anterior view; E, *Brùchus* (Brùchidae), dorsal view. *ant*, base of antenna; *e*, compound eye; *gs*, gular suture; *gu*, gula; *lg*, ligula; *lp*, labial palpus; *md*, mandible; *mn*, mentum; *mxp*, maxillary palpus; *smt*, submentum.

38(37′).	Antennal club 3-segmented; length 8 mm or less............	**Nitidùlidae**	p. 298
38′.	Antennal club with more than 3 segments; length 12 mm or more	**Sílphidae**	p. 283
39(36′).	Tarsal formula 5-5-5..	40	
39′.	Tarsi with 4 or fewer segments	48	
40(39).	Antennae elbowed (Figure 22-8 I); shiny, hard-bodied beetles, 0.5 to 10.0 mm in length (Figure 22-22)............................	**Histéridae**	p. 281
40′.	Antennae not elbowed	41	
41(40′).	Antennae lamellate, the terminal segments expanded on one side to form a lopsided club (Figure 22-9 A, C, D)........................	42	
41′.	Antennae not lamellate, the club symmetrical.....................	43	
42(41).	The 4 terminal segments of the antennae expanded laterally into rounded lobes not capable of being united to form a compact ball (Figure 22-9 A); elytra usually red and black (Figure 22-24); 15 to 35 mm in length (*Nicróphorus*)	**Sílphidae**	p. 283

42′. The 3 to 7 terminal segments of the antennae expanded on one side into oval or elongate lobes capable of being united into a compact ball (Figure 22-9 C, D); color and size variable .... **Scarabaèidae** p. 310
43(41′). Length more than 12 mm .... **Sílphidae** p. 283
43′. Length less than 12 mm 44
44(43′). Antennal club of 4 or more segments, the terminal segments usually enlarging gradually; last abdominal segment sharply pointed . . **Scaphidìidae** p. 284
44′. Antennal club of 3 or fewer segments, distinct, the club segments usually abruptly larger than the others (Figure 22-8 F); last abdominal segment usually not pointed 45
45(44′). Elytra pubescent; head including eyes wider than pronotum .... **Cléridae** p. 288
45′. Elytra usually not pubescent; head including eyes not wider than pronotum 46
46(45′). Length 4.5 to 5.5 mm; black with a bluish luster; each elytron with 11 rows of faint punctures; hind coxae conical; Idaho and California to Alaska .... **Sphaerítidae*** p. 285
46′. Not exactly fitting the above description; widespread 47
47(46′). Antennal club usually indistinct, the antennae nearly filiform; elytra truncate at tip; last abdominal segment sharply pointed; oval, convex, shiny beetles, 2 to 7 mm in length .... **Scaphidìidae** p. 284
47′. Antennal club distinct, 3-segmented; elytra, abdomen, and body shape not as above; size variable .... **Nitidùlidae** p. 298
48(39′). At least front and middle tarsi apparently 4-segmented 49
48′. At least front and middle tarsi 2- or 3-segmented 50
49(48). Antennal club usually 1- or 2-segmented; slender, shining, glabrous beetles, 2 to 5 mm in length; first and fifth abdominal sterna longer than the others; pronotum narrower at base than at apex ...... **Rhizophágidae*** p. 296
49′. Antennal club 3-segmented; size and shape variable .... **Nitidùlidae** p. 298
50(48′). Elytra very short, exposing most of abdomen, and truncate apically; brownish or yellowish pubescent beetles, antlike in appearance, 5.5 mm in length or less .... **Pseláphidae** p. 284
50′. Elytra longer, usually not more than 2 or 3 abdominal terga exposed beyond elytra; not particularly antlike in appearance; less than 2 mm in length 51*
51(50′). Antennae with numerous long hairs .... **Ptilìidae*** p. 282
51′. Antennae without long hairs .... **Orthopéridae*** p. 285
52(35′). Maxillary palpi long and slender, as long as or longer than antennae (Figure 22-23) 53
52′. Maxillary palpi much shorter than antennae 54
53(52). Abdomen with 6 or 7 visible sterna; 1.2 to 1.7 mm in length . . **Limnebìidae*** p. 282
53′. Abdomen with 5 visible sterna; size variable, up to 40 mm in length .... **Hydrophílidae** p. 281
54(52′). All tarsi with apparently 4 or fewer segments 55
54′. Front and (or) middle tarsi 5-segmented 98
55(54). All tarsi apparently 3-segmented 56
55′. All tarsi apparently 4-segmented (see also 55″) 61
55″. Front tarsi 3-segmented and hairy beneath; middle and hind tarsi 4-segmented; 2.0 to 5.5 mm in length .... **Mycetophágidae*** p. 301

56(55). Second tarsal segment dilated; tarsi actually 4-segmented, the third segment minute and fused to base of fourth (Figure 22-10 E) 57

56′. Second tarsal segment slender, not dilated; tarsi actually 3-segmented (Figure 22-10 I) 58

57(56). Tarsal claws toothed at base (Figure 22-6 A); antennae short, the antennae and head usually hidden from above; terminal segment of maxillary palpi hatchet-shaped .... **Coccinéllidae** p. 299

57′. Tarsal claws not toothed at base; antennae and head easily visible from above; terminal segment of maxillary palpi oval or slightly triangular .... **Endomýchidae** p. 299

58(56′). Tip of abdomen exposed beyond elytra; first and fifth abdominal sterna longer than the others 59*

58′. Elytra completely covering abdomen; all abdominal sterna usually about equal in length 60

59(58). Front coxae transverse .... **Nitidùlidae*** p. 298

59′. Front coxae globose .... **Monotómidae*** p. 296

60(58′). Elytral punctures in 6 to 8 rows; head easily visible from above .... **Lathridìidae** p. 299

60′. Elytral punctures not in rows; head deflexed and usually not visible from above .... **Císidae** p. 288

61(55′). Tibiae dilated and very spiny; body broad and flat, the mandibles and labrum projecting forward prominently; first and fourth tarsal segments much longer than second and third; the last 7 antennal segments forming a long serrate club; semiaquatic, mud-inhabiting beetles, 4.0 to 6.5 mm in length .... **Heterocéridae*** p. 296

61′. Not exactly fitting the above description 62

62(61′). The first 3 or 4 abdominal sterna more or less fused together 63*

62′. All abdominal sterna freely movable 64

63(62). Length 1.5 mm or less; antennae inserted on front; front coxae enclosed behind by mesosternum .... **Murmidìidae*** p. 298

63′. Length 2.0 to 6.5 mm; antennae inserted under a distinct frontal ridge; front coxae usually distant from mesosternum .... **Colydìidae*** p. 300

64(62′). First tarsal segment broad, flat, and oval, with a dense pad of short hairs below, the second and third segments minute, the second arising from upper surface of first near its base, the fourth large, long; head and pronotum of about equal width, parallel-sided; elytra parallel-sided, about one-third wider than pronotum; reddish-yellow or tawny, with black antennae and scutellum, and with 5 elongate black marks on each elytron; 2 mm in length .... **Monoèdidae*** p. 299

64′. Not exactly fitting the above description 65

65(64′). Elytra pubescent 66

65′. Elytra not pubescent 82

66(65). Front coxae transverse, not prominent; pronotum rather widely separated from base of elytra except at attachment point in center (Figure 22-28); 5 to 20 mm in length .... **Ostómidae** p. 288

66′. Not exactly fitting the above description 67

67(66′). Base of pronotum distinctly narrower than base of elytra; tarsal segments often bearing broad lobes beneath 68

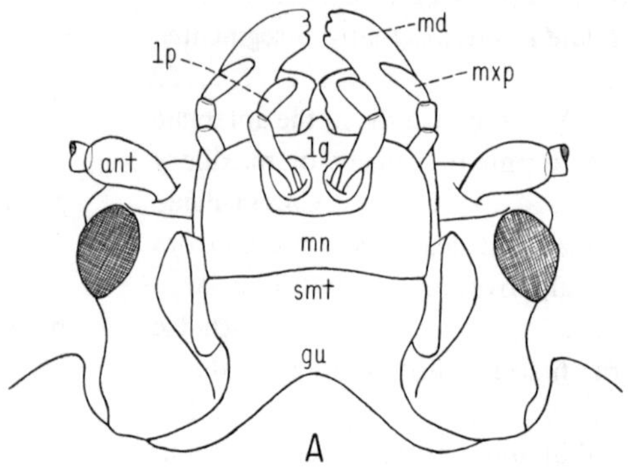

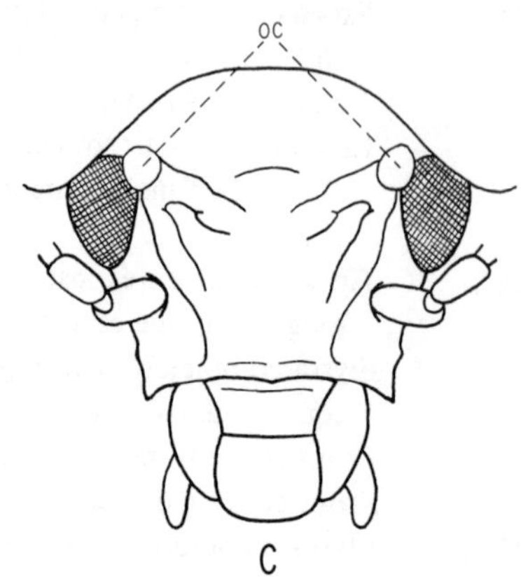

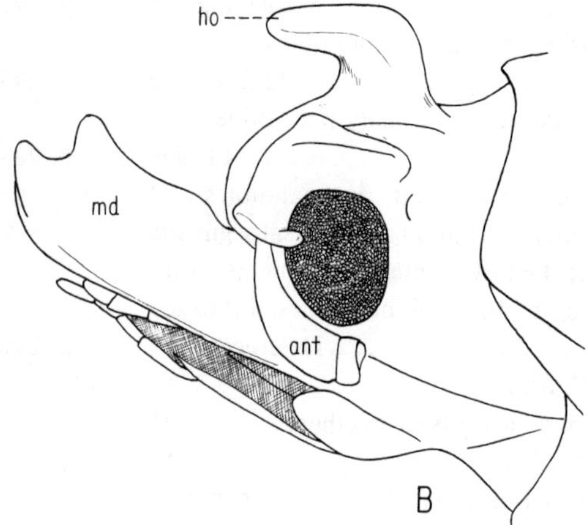

Fig. 22-12. Heads of Coleoptera. A, ventral view, and B, lateral view of *Popílius disjúnctus* (Illiger) (Passálidae) C, *Derodóntus* (Derodóntidae). *ant*, base of antenna; *gu*, gula; *ho*, horn; *lg*, ligula; *lp*, labial palp; *md*, mandible; *mn*, mentum; *mxp*, maxillary palp; *oc*, ocelli; *smt*, submentum.

67′. Base of pronotum about as wide as base of elytra 72

68(67). Tarsal segments slender, without lobes or hairy pads beneath, the first segment minute; antennal club of 3 segments 69

68′. The first 3 tarsal segments more or less expanded, with lobes or hairy pads beneath 71

69(68). Head deflexed and generally not visible from above (Figure 22-52); mandibles not particularly large; mostly 3.5 to 12.0 mm in length (one western species, *Dinápate wrìghti* Horn, is about 50 mm in length) .. .. **Bostríchidae** p. 307

69′. Head not deflexed, easily visible from above 70

70(69′). Mandibles large and strong; 6 to 28 mm in length; western United States .... **Psòidae** p. 307

70′. Mandibles not unusually large; 2.5 to 7.0 mm in length; widely distributed .... **Lýctidae** p. 308

71(68′). Pronotum distinctly margined; 3.5 mm in length or less (*Laricòbius*).... .... **Derodóntidae*** p. 296

71′. Pronotum rounded or finely margined laterally; length variable, up to 12 mm .... **Cléridae** p. 288

72(67′). Basal segment of antennae usually very large; antennal club very large and dilated, composed of 1 to 4 segments that are often solidly fused together (Figure 22-8 H); small, compact, cylindrical beetles (Figure 22-86).... .... **Scolýtidae** p. 337

72′. Antennae not as above, the club not particularly large, and the terminal segments usually enlarging gradually............................73

73(72′). Antennal club usually 6- or 7-segmented; third tarsal segment more or less bilobed..74

73′. Antennal club 2- or 3-segmented; third tarsal segment usually not bilobed 75

74(73). Length 4.5 to 6.5 mm; black, with dense gray pubescence; body and pronotum robust, almost cylindrical ....**Chrysomélidae** p. 322

74′. Length 1.5 to 5.5 mm; pronotum greatly narrowed anteriorly; tip of abdomen exposed (Figure 22-76) ....**Brùchidae** p. 328

75(73′). Antennal club 2-segmented...76

75′. Antennal club 3-segmented...78

76(75). Size variable, up to 6 mm in length; anterior part of pronotum wider than posterior part; hind coxae not particularly dilated 77

76′. Length 1 mm or less; pronotum not as above; hind coxae dilated into broad plates that conceal hind legs in repose..............**Clámbidae*** p. 285

77(76). Length 3.5 to 6.0 mm; body elongate and slender..............**Lýctidae** p. 308

77′. Length less than 3 mm; body flat ....**Monotómidae*** p. 296

78(75′). Head easily visible from above...................................79*

78′. Head scarcely or not at all visible from above.....................81

79(78). Front coxae globose ....**Mycetaèidae*** p. 299

79′. Front coxae oval or conical 80*

80(79′). Front coxae usually conical; usually uniformly colored beetles; 3.5 to 4.5 mm in length ....**Bytùridae*** p. 300

80′. Front coxae oval; often brightly colored beetles; mostly 3 mm in length or less ....**Mycetophágidae*** p. 301

81(78′). Front coxae separated; 3 mm in length or less..................**Císidae** p. 288

81′. Front coxae contiguous or nearly so; mostly 3.4 to 12.0 mm in length (one western species, *Dinápate wrìghti* Horn, is about 50 mm in length).... .... **Bostríchidae** p. 307

82(65′). Body extremely flattened; 4 mm in length or less............**Silvánidae** p. 298

82′. Body not unusually flattened; size variable 83

83(82′). Tarsi actually 5-segmented, either the fourth segment very small and the third more or less bilobed, or the first segment very small and difficult to see; antennal club variable 84

83′. Tarsi actually 4-segmented, the third segment not bilobed and the first segment not unusually short; antennal club 2- to 4-segmented.. 90

84(83). Lateral margins of pronotum with 3 or 4 broad teeth or scallops; a pair of ocelli present near compound eyes (Figure 22-12 C); 3.5 mm in length or less (*Derodóntus*) ....**Derodóntidae** p. 296

84′. Lateral margins of pronotum not toothed or scalloped; no ocelli; size variable 85

85(84′). Elongate, cylindrical beetles, 5.5 to 12.0 mm in length, usually with the

	pronotum yellow or red and the elytra black (Figure 22-39 B)........ ....**Languriidae**	p. 297
85′.	Body shape and color usually not as above 86	
86(85′).	Antennal club 1- or 2-segmented; anterior half of pronotum wider than posterior half; length 2 to 5 mm....................**Rhizophágidae***	p. 296
86′.	Antennal club of 3 or more segments; pronotum with anterior part as wide as or narrower than posterior part; size variable..............87	
87(86′).	Front coxae transverse, not prominent; pronotum rather widely separated from base of elytra except at attachment point in center (Figure 22-28); 5 to 20 mm in length................................ **Ostómidae**	p. 288
87′.	Not exactly fitting the above description 88	
88(87′).	Antennal club 3-segmented..............................**Erotýlidae**	p. 297
88′.	Antennal club of 5 or more segments..............................89	
89(88′).	Head more or less produced anteriorly into a broad muzzle; tip of abdomen exposed (Figure 22-76) ....**Brùchidae**	p. 328
89′.	Head not produced anteriorly into a broad muzzle; tip of abdomen usually covered by elytra............................**Chrysomélidae**	p. 322
90(83′).	Front coxae transverse...91	
90′.	Front coxae globose, oval, or conical.............................92	
91(90).	Oval, convex, usually brightly colored beetles; pronotum and elytra usually closely joined completely across body ....**Coccinéllidae**	p. 299
91′.	Usually elongate, more or less flattened beetles, usually not brightly colored; pronotum rather widely separated from elytra except at attachment point in center (Figure 22-28) ....**Ostómidae**	p. 288
92(90′).	Front coxae globose or oval.......................................93	
92′.	Front coxae conical and prominent...............................122	
93(92).	Front coxae oval; length 3 mm or less 94	
93′.	Front coxae globose; length usually 3 mm or more..................95	
94(93).	Front coxae separated; body cylindrical; head usually not visible from above ....**Císidae**	p. 288
94′.	Front coxae contiguous; body oval......................**Georýssidae***	p. 296
95(93′).	Body oval, not particularly flattened, usually more or less convex above; color variable...96	
95′.	Body elongate and flattened, usually brownish in color..............219	
96(95).	Body broadly oval, very convex, dark-colored, shiny........**Phalácridae**	p. 298
96′.	Body more elongate and less convex, usually yellow or red and black..97	
97(96′).	Front coxal cavities open behind; length 3 to 4 mm........**Mycetaèidae***	p. 299
97′.	Front coxal cavities closed behind; length 3 to 8 mm........**Erotýlidae**	p. 297
98(54′).	Hind tarsi 3- or 4-segmented 99	
98′.	All tarsi 5-segmented 100	
99(98).	Tarsal formula 5-4-4 or 5-3-3; antennal club 3- to 5-segmented; small, oval, convex beetles, 1.5 to 6.5 mm in length ....**Leiódidae**	p. 283
99′.	Tarsal formula 5-5-4; size variable 169	
100(98′).	Antennae lamellate (Figure 22-9 C-G) or flabellate (Figure 22-9 B), the terminal segments expanded on one side to form a lopsided club....101	
100′.	Antennae not lamellate or flabellate, the club usually symmetrical....106	
101(100).	First tarsal segment very small and difficult to see; pronotum rather widely separated from base of elytra except at attachment point in	

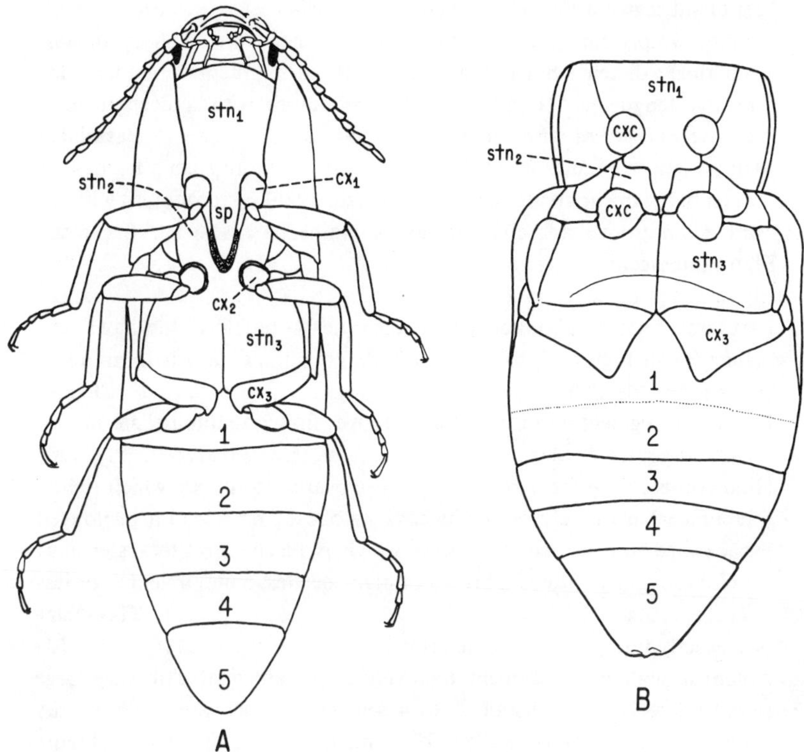

Fig. 22-13. A, ventral view of a click beetle (*Agriòtes*); B, ventral view of the thorax and abdomen of a metallic wood-boring beetle (*Chrysóbothris*). *cx*, coxa; *cxc*, coxal cavity; *sp*, prosternal spine; stn_1, prosternum; stn_2, mesosternum; stn_3, metasternum; 1-5, abdominal sternites.

center (Figure 22-28); 5 to 20 mm in length................**Ostómidae** p. 288

101′. First tarsal segment of normal size 102

102(101′). Antennae flabellate, the terminal 8 or 9 segments expanded laterally into long, thin, parallel-sided, leaflike lobes (Figure 22-9 B); 24 mm in length or less 103

102′. Antennae lamellate, the terminal 3 or 4 segments expanded laterally into oval or elongate lobes capable of being united into a compact ball (Figure 22-9 C, D, G); 4 to 50 mm in length (see also 102″) **Scarabaèidae** p. 310

102″. Terminal (or intermediate) segments of antennae expanded laterally into rounded lobes that are flattened and are not capable of being united into a compact ball (Figure 22-9 E, F); usually large beetles 104

103(102). Tarsi with a hairy projection between claws, the first 4 tarsal segments with lobes beneath (Figure 22-10 F); antennae not received in grooves on front; more or less flattened beetles, 16 to 24 mm in length..**Sandálidae** p. 289

103′. Tarsi not as above; antennae received in transverse grooves on front; more or less cylindrical beetles, usually less than 16 mm in length.... ....**Eucnémidae** p. 291

104(102″). Last tarsal segment elongate, about as long as the other 4 segments combined (as in Figure 22-10 H); length 6 mm or less (*Drỳops*)..**Dryópidae*** p. 294

104′. Last tarsal segment not so lengthened; size variable 105

105(104′). Mentum deeply emarginate (Figure 22-12 A); head with a short, dorsal, anteriorly directed horn (Figure 22-12 B); first antennal segment not greatly lengthened (Figure 22-9 F); pronotum with a deep median groove and elytra with longitudinal grooves . . . . **Passálidae** p. 309

105′. Mentum entire (Figure 22-11 A); head usually without such a horn; first antennal segment greatly lengthened (Figure 22-9 E); pronotum without a median groove, and elytra usually smooth . . . . **Lucánidae** p. 309

106(100′). Elytra pubescent 107

106′. Elytra not pubescent 120

107(106). Last tarsal segment about as long as the other 4 combined, the claws very long (as in Figure 22-10 H); first 3 abdominal sterna usually more or less fused together . . . . **Élmidae** p. 295

107′. Last tarsal segment and claws not as above; first 3 abdominal sterna not fused together 108

108(107′). Hind corners of pronotum prolonged backward into points which tightly embrace base of elytra; front coxae globose; prosternum prolonged backward into a median process which is received by mesosternum; oblong, slightly flattened, brown or black beetles, 5 mm in length or less . . . . **Thróscidae** p. 291

108′. Not exactly fitting the above description 109

109(108′). Antennae with basal segment relatively large; antennal club very large and dilated, composed of 1 to 4 segments, which are often solidly fused together (Figure 22-8 H); small, cylindrical beetles (Figure 22-86) 110

109′. Antennae not as above, the club not particularly large, and the terminal segments usually enlarging gradually 111

110(109). Tarsi very slender and threadlike, the basal segment as long as the next 3 combined (Figure 22-10 K); head broader than pronotum; body slender and narrow . . . . **Platypódidae*** p. 337

110′. Tarsi shorter and broader, the basal segment never longer than the next 3 combined (Figure 22-10 G); head not broader than pronotum; body usually cylindrical or somewhat oval (Figure 22-86) . . . . **Scolýtidae** p. 337

111(109′). Head narrowed behind eyes into a definite neck; body antlike, 1 to 5 mm in length . . . . **Scydmaènidae*** p. 285

111′. Head closely attached to thorax, without a prominent neck behind eyes; size variable 112

112(111′). Front coxae globose or oval; usually uniformly yellowish brown, with a silky luster causer by the fine pubescence; first abdominal segment longer than any of the others; length 4 mm or less . . . . **Cryptophágidae*** p. 297

112′. Front coxae more or less conical (see also 112″) 113

112″. Front coxae transverse; body broadly oval and flat, 5 to 8 mm in length (*Thýmalus*) . . . . **Ostómidae** p. 288

113(112′). Hind coxae dilated into plates that are grooved for the reception of the femora (Figure 22-5 A) 114

113′. Hind coxae not so dilated, not grooved 117

114(113). Head usually concealed from above; front coxal cavities open behind; tarsal segments without lobes beneath 115

114′. Head prominent from above; front coxal cavities closed behind; second and third tarsal segments with large lobes beneath........**Bytùridae*** p. 300

115(114). Antennal club abrupt (Figure 22-8 G); body often scaly....**Derméstidae** p. 287

115′. Antennal club less abrupt, the terminal segments only slightly enlarged (Figure 22-8 C) 116

116(115′). The terminal 2 or 3 antennal segments very long, as long as all the other segments combined (Figure 22-8 C)......................**Anobìidae** p. 307

116′. Antennae not as above; hind coxae very large, extending to lower edge of elytra ....**Býrrhidae** p. 294

117(113′). Pronotum more or less spherical or quadrate, the hind corners usually rounded and separated from base of elytra laterally; head often shielded by front edge of pronotum and scarcely visible from above; more or less cylindrical beetles 122

117′. Pronotum not as above; head quite prominent from above..........118

118(117′). Tarsi simple, without lobes on any segments; body more or less oval, 2 to 5 mm in length ....**Leptodíridae*** p. 283

118′. Some tarsal segments with lobes beneath; size variable.............119

119(118′). Uniformly colored, reddish-yellow, brown, or black; 3.5 to 4.5 mm in length ....**Bytùridae*** p. 300

119′. Usually marked with bands, stripes, or spots (Figure 22-29); usually over 5 mm in length ....**Cléridae** p. 288

120(106′). Head bent downward, and almost or entirely concealed in dorsal view..121

120′. Head not concealed in dorsal view 125

121(120). Elytra rough and striate; pronotum with hind angles rounded........122

121′. Elytra never rough and striate; pronotum with hind angles not rounded 123

122(92′, 117, 121). First abdominal segment much longer than the others; antennal club 2-segmented; length 3.5 to 6.0 mm.........................**Lýctidae** p. 308

122′. All abdominal sterna of about equal length; antennal club 3- or 4-segmented (see also couplets 69 and 81′)...............**Bostríchidae** p. 307

123(121′). Last tarsal segment about as long as the others combined; tibiae greatly dilated; hind coxae very large, extending to lower edges of elytra.... .... **Býrrhidae** p. 294

123′. Last tarsal segment of normal size; tibiae more slender; hind coxae not as above..124

124(123′). Shiny, oval, convex beetles, 3 mm in length or less..........**Phalácridae** p. 298

124′. Not exactly fitting the above description.................**Derméstidae** p. 287

125(120′). Pronotum widely separated from base of elytra except at attachment point in center (Figure 22-28); front coxae transverse; usually black or brown beetles, 5 to 20 mm in length...........................**Ostómidae** p. 288

125′. Pronotum and elytra usually closely joined completely across body; front coxae and color variable.....................................126

126(125′). Antennal club 4- to 6-segmented; elytra wrinkled or furrowed and rather soft; brown or black beetles, usually over 10 mm in length, the pronotum often yellowish or reddish with a dark spot in the center (Figure 22-24) ....**Sílphidae** p. 283

126′. Antennal club usually 1- to 3-segmented, if 4-segmented, then not fitting the above description..127

127(126′). Oval, convex, uniformly dark-colored beetles......................128

127′. Body either elongate or not particularly convex; color variable......129

128(127). Shiny beetles, 3 mm in length or less......................**Phalácridae** p. 298

128′. Not particularly shiny, 5 to 6 mm in length ....**Nosodéndridae*** p. 294

129(127′). Lateral margins of pronotum with 3 or 4 large teeth or scallops; a pair of ocelli present near compound eyes (Figure 22-12 C); 3.5 mm in length or less ....**Derodóntidae** p. 296

129′. Lateral margins of pronotum either without teeth or with more than 4; no ocelli; size variable 130

130(129′). First 3 abdominal sterna more or less fused together; last tarsal segment and tarsal claws very long (as in Figure 22-10 H); less than 7 mm in length (*Macrónychus*) ....**Elmidae** p. 295

130′. First 3 abdominal sterna not fused together; tarsi not as above......131

131(130′). Elytra with longitudinal rows of deep punctures, and usually with a ridge between each two rows; antennae apparently 8-segmented, with a 2-segmented club (*Hispìnae*) ....**Chrysomélidae** p. 325

131′. Elytra smooth or only feebly punctate, or if distinctly punctate, then the antennae have a 3- or 4-segmented club and the body is distinctly flattened 132

132(131′). Body extremely flat; 4 mm in length or less........................133

132′. Body not extremely flat; size variable............................134

133(132). Antennae with a distinct 3-segmented club; third antennal segment shorter than second; tarsi never lobed beneath....................**Silvánidae** p. 298

133′. Antennal club not very distinct; third antennal segment not shorter than second; tarsi often lobed beneath..............................219

134(132′). First segment of hind tarsi very short, one-fourth as long as second or less; front coxae globose; 6 to 28 mm in length; western United States.... .... **Psòidae** p. 307

134′. First segment of hind tarsi as long as second or longer; coxae and size variable..135

135(134′). Antennal club 3- or 4-segmented; front coxae globose or oval, and without a trochantin; 2.3 to 21.0 mm in length, shiny, usually black with reddish markings (Figure 22-39 A) and not particularly flattened (*Dacnìni*).... .... **Erotýlidae** p. 297

135′. Antennal club 3-segmented; front coxae transverse, with a trochantin; length 12 mm or less; color variable; body rather broad and flat.... .... **Nitidùlidae** p. 298

136(34′). Terminal segment of maxillary palpi greatly enlarged 137*

136′. Terminal segment of maxillary palpi not greatly enlarged............138

137(136). Antennae filiform or serrate; 5 to 6 mm in length; Arizona and California ....**Telegeùsidae*** p. 280

137′. Antennae not serrate; 0.5 to 5.5 mm in length; widely distributed...... ....**Pseláphidae** p. 284

138(136′). Elytra short, leaving one or more complete abdominal terga exposed..139

138′. Elytra longer, either completely covering abdomen or leaving only a part of the last tergum exposed..................................153

139(138). Hind wings, if present, folded under elytra at rest; elytra usually square-cut or broadly rounded at apex................................140

139′. Hind wings at rest not folded under elytra but extended back over abdomen; elytra often pointed at apex....152

140(139). At least 4 abdominal terga exposed beyond elytra....141

140′. Only 1 or 2 abdominal terga exposed beyond elytra....147

141(140). Tarsal formula 5-5-4; body rather soft, robust, and with a slender neck; 11 to 30 mm in length....**Melòidae** p. 302

141′. Tarsal formula 3-3-3, 4-4-4, 5-5-5, or 5-4-4 (usually 3-3-3 or 5-5-5)....142

142(141′). Eyes absent; front coxae flat; small, flattened, wingless, ectoparasites of beavers, 2.5 to 3.0 mm in length....**Platypsýllidae*** p. 282

142′. Eyes present; front coxae variable....143

143(142′). Abdomen parallel-sided or tapering posteriorly, with 6 to 8 visible sterna; tarsi usually 5-segmented; size variable....144

143′. Abdomen oval, usually with 5 to 6 visible sterna; tarsi 3-segmented; brownish or yellowish beetles, less than 5.5 mm in length..**Pseláphidae** p. 284

144(143). Prosternum prolonged posteriorly into a slender spine which fits loosely into a deep cavity in mesosternum (Figure 22-13 A); prothorax and elytra depressed near their junction; western United States; 9 mm in length or more....**Elatéridae*** p. 290

144′. Thorax not as above; widely distributed; size variable....145

145(144′). Tarsi distinctly 5-segmented, the third segment not bilobed....146

145′. Tarsi apparently 4-segmented, the third segment bilobed; abdomen with 5 or 6 visible sterna....159

146(145). Pronotum tapering posteriorly; 5 abdominal terga exposed beyond elytra; the first 2 antennal segments longer than any others, the remaining segments beadlike and scarcely extending beyond head; elongate, parallel-sided, shiny, dark, with legs and antennae yellowish or brownish; 1.8 to 2.5 mm in length....**Micromálthidae*** p. 275

146′. Not exactly fitting the above description....**Staphylínidae** p. 284

147(140′). All tarsi distinctly 5-segmented....148

147′. Tarsal formula 5-5-4 or 4-4-3 (see also 147″)....150

147″. All tarsi apparently 4-segmented....155

148(147). Abdomen with 6 or fewer visible sterna....149

148′. Abdomen with 7 or 8 visible sterna....244

149(148). Last abdominal segment pointed; shiny, oval, convex beetles, 2 to 7 mm in length....**Scaphidiidae** p. 284

149′. Not exactly fitting the above description....241

150(147′). Elytra and body soft; neck slender and distinct; body robust but never compressed; 4 to 30 mm in length....**Melòidae** p. 302

150′. Elytra firm; shape not as above; often somewhat humpbacked; 2 to 13 mm in length, usually 6 mm or less....151

151(150′). Pronotum with sharp lateral margins....164

151′. Pronotum rounded laterally....188

152(139′). All tarsi apparently 4-segmented, the third segment bilobed; antennae long and filiform; abdomen with 5 or 6 visible sterna....**Cerambýcidae** p. 317

152′. All tarsi distinctly 5-segmented, the third segment not bilobed; abdomen with 7 or 8 visible sterna; antennae variable (see also 152″)....246

152″. Tarsal formula 5-5-4, the third segment usually not bilobed; antennae serrate or pectinate; 4 to 10 mm in length....**Rhipiphóridae*** p. 304

153(138′). A pair of ocelli present (*Omaliinae*) .... **Staphylínidae*** p. 284
153′. Ocelli absent, or with a single ocellus only 154
154(153′). Tarsal formula apparently 4-4-4 or 3-4-4 155
154′. Tarsal formula 5-5-4 or 4-4-3 (see also 154″) 160
154″. Tarsal formula 5-5-5 (4-5-5 in some male Malachìidae) 189
155(147″, 154). Head somewhat prolonged anteriorly into a broad quadrate muzzle; antennae serrate or pectinate; elytra pubescent; body brownish or yellowish, more or less oval, the tip of the abdomen exposed (Figure 22-76); mostly 5 mm in length or less .... **Brùchidae** p. 328
155′. Head not prolonged anteriorly into a broad quadrate muzzle; antennae usually serrate or filiform 156
156(155′). Body elongate and extremely flat, the dorsal and ventral surfaces flat and parallel 219
156′. Body not so flattened 157
157(156′). Head scarcely or not at all visible from above; scutellum heart-shaped, notched anteriorly; male antennae pectinate, with long processes arising from segments 4-10; 4 to 6 mm in length .... **Ptilodactýlidae*** p. 294
157′. Head usually visible from above; scutellum not as above; antennae not pectinate; size variable 158
158(157′). Tarsal formula 3-4-4; tarsi hairy beneath; front coxae oval; very hairy, often brightly patterned beetles, 2.0 to 5.5 mm in length .... **Mycetophágidae*** p. 301
158′. Tarsal formula apparently 4-4-4; other characters variable 159
159(145′, 158′). Antennae usually more than half as long as body, inserted on frontal prominences, their insertion often partly surrounded by eyes (Figure 22-11 D); eyes often emarginate; first antennal segment at least 5 or 6 times as long as second; body usually elongate and parallel-sided; 3 to 50 mm in length, usually over 12 mm .... **Cerambýcidae** p. 317
159′. Antennae short, usually less than half as long as body, not inserted on frontal prominences; eyes usually entire; body usually oval; small beetles, mostly less than 12 mm in length .... **Chrysomélidae** p. 322
160(154′). Antennae serrate, pectinate, or flabellate 161
160′. Antennae filiform or moniliform, or very gradually enlarged apically .. 168
161(160). Front coxal cavities closed behind 162
161′. Front coxal cavities open behind 163
162(161). Tarsal claws pectinate (Figure 22-6 B); antennae serrate ...... **Allecùlidae** p. 304
162′. Tarsal claws not pectinate; antennae flabellate (*Cheróstus* and *Rhipidándrus*) .... **Tenebriónidae*** p. 305
163(161′). Body laterally compressed, higher than wide; base of pronotum as wide as elytra; pronotum often with sharp lateral margins; tarsal formula 5-5-4 164
163′. Body not laterally compressed, not higher than wide; pronotum with rounded lateral margins and usually narrower than elytra; tarsal formula 5-5-4 or apparently 4-4-3 165
164(151, 163). Tip of abdomen slender and pointed, and extending beyond elytra (Figure 22-46) .... **Mordéllidae** p. 304
164′. Tip of abdomen not slender and pointed; elytra variable .. **Rhipiphóridae*** p. 304
165(163′). Antennae serrate 166

165′. Antennae pectinate 167

166(165). Tarsal claws simple; body flattened; prothorax not rounded or spherical; usually black, with pronotum reddish or yellowish; 9 to 17 mm in length .... **Pyrochròidae** p. 302

166′. Tarsal claws with a large, sharp, basal tooth; body cylindrical, the prothorax rounded, almost spherical; usually less than 10 mm in length.... .... **Pedílidae*** p. 302

167(165′). Head and pronotum narrower than elytra; 5 visible abdominal sterna; usually black, with pronotum reddish or yellowish; 9 to 17 mm in length .... **Pyrochròidae** p. 302

167′. Head and pronotum about as wide as elytra; 4 visible abdominal sterna; color not as above; 3 mm in length or less................ **Euglénidae*** p. 301

168(160′). Body elongate and extremely flat, the dorsal and ventral surfaces flat and parallel; front coxae globular; metepimera covered; metasternum quadrate 219

168′. Body usually not particularly flattened, the dorsal and ventral surfaces not flat and parallel; if highly flattened (*Dolièma*, family Tenebriónidae), a frontal ridge is present, the eyes are emarginate, and the front coxal cavities are closed behind 169

169(99′, 168′). Front coxal cavities closed behind (Figure 22-4 B).................. 170

169′. Front coxal cavities open behind (Figure 22-4 A) 177

170(169). Tarsal claws pectinate (Figure 22-6 B); elongate-oval, usually black or brown beetles, 4 to 12 mm in length .... **Alleculidae** p. 304

170′. Tarsal claws not pectinate; size and color variable................. 171

171(170′). Last antennal segment lengthened, as long as the preceding 3 or more segments combined (Figure 22-8 D); head and pronotum narrower than elytra; eyes entirely or only slightly emarginate; elongate, usually shiny beetles, 6 to 14 mm in length (Figure 22-49 B)............. **Lagriidae** p. 305

171′. Last antennal segment not so lengthened; size and shape variable.... 172

172(171′). Six abdominal sterna, the first 2 fused together; head sunk in prothorax almost to eyes; black, subcylindrical, long-legged beetles, 2 to 4 mm in length, living in rock cracks below the high tide mark along the Pacific Coast .... **Eurystéthidae*** p. 301

172′. Not exactly fitting the above description.......................... 173

173(172′). Antennae with a distinct 3- to 5-segmented club (*Pentaphýllus*, family Tenebriónidae, will key out here; see couplet 176) 174*

173′. Antennae with a 1- or 2-segmented club, or somewhat clavate with the club indistinct and composed of more than 5 segments................ 175

174(173). Base of elytra distinctly wider than base of pronotum; body elongate, parallel-sided, somewhat flattened, cleridlike; mostly western United States .... **Othnìidae*** p. 301

174′. Base of elytra about as wide as base of pronotum; body oval, convex, coccinellidlike; 1.5 to 6.5 mm in length; widely distributed. . **Leiódidae*** p. 283

175(173′). Antennal club composed of 1 or 2 segments; tarsi 5-segmented, but fourth segment very small and closely united with fifth (except in males, which have only 4 segments in hind tarsi); slender, shining, glabrous beetles, 2 to 5 mm in length................................ **Rhizophágidae*** p. 296

175′. Antennae only slightly clavate, the club indistinct or with more than 5 segments 176

176(175′). Antennae almost always 11-segmented, and arising beneath a frontal ridge; eyes often emarginate; antennae filiform, moniliform, or slightly clavate (very rarely capitate or flabellate); last tarsal segment not unusually lengthened; 2 to 35 mm in length............. **Tenebriónidae** p. 305

176′. Antennae 10-segmented, not arising under a frontal ridge; eyes entire; antennae terminating in a distinct 2- or 3-segmented club; last tarsal segment longer than the others combined; 1.5 to 3.0 mm in length.... .... **Sphíndidae*** p. 297

177(169′). Eyes absent; dorsal surface glabrous (*Catopocerìnae*)........ **Leiódidae*** p. 283

177′. Eyes present; dorsal surface variable 178

178(177′). Antennae with a 2- or 3-segmented club, and received in grooves on under side of prothorax; legs retractile; oval, flattened beetles, with head partly concealed in prothorax; 2 to 6 mm in length; southeastern and western United States .... **Monómmidae*** p. 297

178′. Not exactly fitting the above description......................... 179

179(178′). Pronotum with sharp lateral margins 180

179′. Pronotum with rounded lateral margins......................... 182

180(179). Body somewhat wedge-shaped, as high as or higher than wide, hump-backed, with the head bent down and the abdomen pointed apically (Figure 22-46); generally black or mottled gray, 14 mm in length or less .... **Mordéllidae** p. 304

180′. Body more or less flattened, not as above; size and color variable.... 181

181(180′). Pronotum with 2 dents or depressions near posterior margin (Figure 22-49 A); antennae usually not clubbed; first segment of hind tarsi much longer than any other segment, usually as long as the other segments combined; 2 to 20 mm in length..................... **Melandrýidae** p. 307

181′. Pronotum without such dents or depressions; antennae with a 3-segmented club; first segment of hind tarsi not greatly lengthened; 4 mm in length or less... **Cryptophágidae*** p. 297

182(179′). Pronotum with 2 dents or depressions near posterior margin (Figure 22-49 A); first segment of hind tarsi much longer than any other segment, usually as long as the other segments combined (*Pénthe*)..**Melandrỳidae** p. 307

182′. Pronotum without such dents or depressions; first segment of hind tarsi usually not greatly lengthened 183

183(182′). Head prolonged in front of eyes and muzzlelike, and narrowing gradually behind eyes into a slender neck; tarsal claws pectinate, with a large pad under each claw; antennae with a 3-segmented club; yellowish to dark-brown beetles, 9 to 15 mm in length................... **Cephalòidae*** p. 301

183′. Head and tarsal claws not as above; size and color variable.......... 184

184(183′). Penultimate segment of hind tarsi dilated and with a dense brush of hairs beneath; middle coxae very prominent and contiguous; slender, soft-bodied beetles, 3.5 to 12.0 mm in length .... **Oedeméridae** p. 301

184′. Hind tarsi usually not as above; middle coxae, size, and shape variable.. 185

185(184′). Head not constricted behind eyes; rear edge of pronotum usually very narrow, the pronotum much more slender at base than at apex; 2.5 to 15.0 mm in length.................................. **Salpíngidae** p. 302

185′. Head usually constricted behind eyes to form a narrow neck........186

186(185′). Tarsal claws toothed or cleft (Figure 22-6 C); penultimate segment of hind tarsi cylindrical; 6 visible abdominal sterna; cylindrical beetles, 4 to 30 mm in length..**Melòidae** p. 302

186′. Tarsal claws simple; penultimate segment of hind tarsi short and densely hairy beneath; 4 or 5 (rarely 6 in some males) visible abdominal sterna 187

187(186′). Eyes emarginate; hind coxae contiguous or nearly so 188

187′. Eyes not emarginate, and coarsely granulated; hind coxae usually well separated; body more or less antlike, 2 to 6 mm in length..**Anthícidae** p. 300

188(151′, 187). Tarsal formula 5-5-4; eyes finely granulated; head constricted far behind eyes; first 2 abdominal sterna not fused, 5 sterna visible; 6 to 15 mm in length...**Pedílidae*** p. 302

188′. Tarsal formula apparently 4-4-3; eyes coarsely granulated; head constricted just behind eyes; first 2 abdominal sterna fused, apparently only 4 sterna visible; 3 mm in length or less..................**Euglénidae*** p. 301

189(154″). Antennae serrate, pectinate, or flabellate (some *Parándra* may key out here; see couplet 223′) 190

189′. Antennae filiform or moniliform...............................206

190(189). Abdomen with 5 visible sterna 191

190′. Abdomen with 6 visible sterna (see also 190″).....................199

190″. Abdomen with 7 or more visible sterna; elytra usually soft..........205

191(190). The first 3 abdominal sterna more or less fused together; front coxae transverse; last tarsal segment long, with long claws (as in Figure 22-10 H); aquatic, pubescent beetles, 2.5 to 6.5 mm in length....**Dryópidae*** p. 294

191′. The first 3 abdominal sterna not fused together (though the first and second may be); front coxae usually globose or conical 192

192(191′). The first 2 abdominal sterna more or less fused together, the suture between them very weak (Figure 22-13 B); hard-bodied, more or less metallic beetles ....**Bupréstidae** p. 291

192′. All abdominal sterna free and movable, separated by equally distinct sutures 193

193(192′). Prosternum prolonged backward as a process that fits into the mesosternum (Figure 22-13 A); posterior corners of pronotum usually pointed 224

193′. Prosternum either without such a process, or if one is present, it does not fit into the mesosternum...194

194(193′). Body elongate and very flat, the dorsal and ventral surfaces flat and parallel; front coxae globose...................................219

194′. Body not so flattened; front coxae not globose...................195

195(194′). Antennae serrate, rarely somewhat pectinate; tarsi usually without a hairy projection between claws; color variable, but if black or brown, then less than 7 mm in length..196

195′. Antennae pectinate or flabellate; tarsi sometimes with a hairy projection between claws; black or brown beetles, 3.5 to 20.0 mm in length ..201

196(195). Elytra pubescent or hairy 197

196′. Elytra not pubescent; hind coxae flat, close together, and almost reaching elytra on each side; 2 to 6 mm in length........................213

197(196). Head including eyes wider than pronotum; usually marked with bands, stripes, or spots, and over 5 mm in length .... **Cléridae** p. 288

197′. Head including eyes narrower than pronotum 198

198(197′). Tarsi considerably shorter than tibiae; head concealed in dorsal view.... .... **Anobìidae** p. 307

198′. Tarsi as long as tibiae, and usually bearing long slender lobes beneath; head clearly visible from above; mandibles prominent 213

199(190′). Last tarsal segment greatly lengthened, the tarsal claws very large (Figure 22-10 H); first 3 abdominal sterna more or less fused together; small aquatic beetles, 4 to 6 mm in length .... **Psephénidae** p. 295

199′. Tarsi and abdomen not as above 200

200(199′). Elytra not pubescent; usually black or brown beetles, up to 24 mm in length 201

200′. Elytra pubescent; size and color variable 203

201(195′, 200). Length 11 to 24 mm; head easily visible in dorsal view 202

201′. Length 6 mm or less; head concealed in dorsal view (males of *Ptílinus*).. .... **Anobìidae** p. 307

202(201). First 4 tarsal segments with 2 prominent lobes beneath (Figure 22-10 F); antennal processes long and slender; mandibles large, stout, and prominent; 16 to 24 mm in length .... **Sandálidae** p. 289

202′. Tarsal segments not lobed beneath; antennal processes short and thick, not much longer than the segments; mandibles small; 11 to 15 mm in length .... **Rhipicéridae*** p. 289

203(200′). Hard-bodied beetles, uniformly colored; prosternum prolonged backward into a slender spine which fits loosely into a cavity in mesosternum; 11 to 19 mm in length; southern and western United States 204*

203′. Soft-bodied beetles, often brightly colored; prosternum not as above; 1.7 to 13.0 mm in length; widely distributed 239

204(203). Tibial spurs well developed; labrum fused with clypeus; 15 to 25 mm in length .... **Cebriónidae*** p. 290

204′. Tibial spurs small and weak; labrum and clypeus separated; 11 to 17 mm in length .... **Elatéridae*** p. 290

205(190″). Middle coxae separated; elytra usually with reticulate sculpturing.. **Lýcidae** p. 287

205′. Middle coxae contiguous; elytra not reticulate 244

206(189′). Abdomen with 4 or 5 visible sterna 207

206′. Abdomen with 6 visible sterna (see also 206″) 233

206″. Abdomen with 7 or more visible sterna 244

207(206). Last tarsal segment and claws very long (Figure 22-10 H); less than 7 mm in length; first 3 abdominal sterna more or less fused together...... 208

207′. Tarsi and claws not as above; first 3 abdominal sterna not fused together (though first and second may be); size variable 210

208(207). Elytra distinctly pubescent; the 2 basal segments of the antennae enlarged; front coxae transverse 209*

208′. Elytra not, or but slightly, pubescent; the 2 basal segments of the antennae of normal size; front coxae globose .... **Élmidae** p. 295

209(208). Middle coxae widely separated, hind coxae contiguous or nearly so; 1 to 2 mm in length .... **Limníchidae*** p. 295

209′. Middle coxae variable, but if widely separated, then hind coxae are equally so; 1 to 8 mm in length .... **Dryópidae*** p. 294

210(207′). Tibiae dilated and grooved; hind coxae grooved; legs stout and retractile; tibial spurs distinct; third tarsal segment bilobed; pronotum with sharp lateral margins; oval, convex beetles 4 to 5 mm in length, with pronotum red, elytra black with patches of white pubescence; Florida .... **Chelonariìdae*** p. 294

210′. Not exactly fitting the above description 211

211(210′). Head scarcely or not at all visible in dorsal view; less than 7 mm in length 212

211′. Head easily visible in dorsal view; size variable 217

212(211). Elytra much wider than pronotum, and usually oval in shape (Figure 22-50) .... **Ptínidae** p. 307

212′. Elytra not at all, or only very slightly, wider than pronotum, and either oval or parallel-sided and elongate 213

213(196′, 198′, 212′). Last 3 antennal segments enlarged, usually as long as all the other segments combined (Figure 22-8 C); sides of elytra subparallel; not shiny...... .... **Anobìidae** p. 307

213′. Last 3 antennal segments not so enlarged, the antennae filiform or serrate; elytra variable 214

214(213′). Second segment of maxillary palpi long, about as long as third and fourth segments combined (*Eurypogonìnae*) .... **Dascíllidae*** p. 293

214′. Second segment of maxillary palpi not so long; much shorter than third and fourth segments combined 215

215(214′). Hind coxae large and oblique; tarsi without lobed segments (*Eucinetìnae*) .... **Dascíllidae*** p. 293

215′. Hind coxae of normal size, not as above; tarsi with at least the fourth segment lobed beneath 216

216(215′). Tarsi with only fourth segment lobed beneath; head with a longitudinal keel below compound eye; mandibles inconspicuous; usually oval, more or less shiny beetles, sometimes with hind femora thickened . . **Helódidae** p. 294

216′. Tarsi with segments 2 to 4 strongly lobed beneath; head without a longitudinal keel below compound eye; mandibles usually prominent; usually elongate and not shining; hind femora not thickened . . **Dascíllidae** p. 293

217(211′). Head including eyes wider than pronotum; elytra soft and distinctly pubescent, usually marked with bands, stripes, or spots; front coxae conical and prominent .... **Cléridae** p. 288

217′. Head including eyes not wider than pronotum; elytra relatively firm and hard, and usually not pubescent; color variable; front coxae usually globose 218

218(217′). Body elongate and very flat, the dorsal and ventral surfaces flat and parallel 219

218′. Body not so flattened 220

219(95′, 133′, 156, 168, 194, 218). Third tarsal segment lobed; front coxal cavities closed behind.......... .... **Hemipéplidae*** p. 302

219′. Third tarsal segment not lobed; front coxal cavities open behind. **Cucùjidae** p. 297

220(218′). First 2 abdominal sterna more or less fused together, the suture between them much less distinct that the sutures between the other sterna (Figure 22-13 B), or absent; body usually metallic .... **Bupréstidae** p. 291

220′. All abdominal sterna free and movable, separated by equally distinct sutures 221

221(220′). Body very convex and oval, nearly cylindrical; leg segments grooved and entire body capable of being contracted into a spherical mass; western United States (*Amphicyrtinae*) .... **Býrrhidae*** p. 294

221′. Body elongate and more or less flattened, and not capable of being contracted into a spherical mass; widely distributed 222

222(221′). Palpi large, flabellate in male; outer 7 to 9 antennal segments larger than basal segments, and equal in size; front coxae conical; pronotum with sharp lateral margins; head narrowed behind eyes into a slender neck; long, slender, soft-bodied beetles, 9.0 to 13.5 mm in length.......... .... **Lymexylónidae*** p. 280

222′. Not exactly fitting the above description.......................... 223

223(222′). Prosternum prolonged backward into a process that fits into mesosternum (Figure 22-13 A); posterior corners of pronotum usually pointed. . 224

223′. Prosternum not as above; segments 3-11 of antennae bearing 2 deep longitudinal grooves on anterior edge; fourth tarsal segment short; reddish-brown beetles, 9 to 18 mm in length (*Parándra*).......... **Cerambýcidae** p. 319

224(193, 223). Prothorax firmly attached to mesothorax and not movable.......... 225

224′. Prothorax loosely attached to mesothorax and freely movable........ 226

225(224). Tips of elytra contiguous; small, usually oval beetles, uniformly colored black or brown (not metallic), 5 mm in length or less...... **Thróscidae** p. 291

225′. Tips of elytra separated; larger, usually more elongate beetles, often patterned or metallic (Figure 22-34 C), 12 mm or more in length (*Dicérca*).................................... **Bupréstidae** p. 291

226(224′). Antennae pectinate or flabellate 227

226′ Antennae serrate to nearly filiform 231

227(226). Antennae flabellate, with the first segment extremely long and the others small and equal (*Hemírhipus*)........................ **Elatéridae*** p. 290

227′. Antennae pectinate, with the first segment not much longer than the third 228

228(227′). Middle and hind tarsi long, nearly as long as femora; pronotum much wider than long, but narrower than base of elytra; oblong black beetles, 7.5 to 8.5 mm in length .... **Cerophýtidae*** p. 290

228′. Middle and hind tarsi of normal size; size, shape, and color variable. . 229

229(228′). Antennae bipectinate (eastern United States) or tripectinate (western United States), with 2 or 3 long slender processes extending from bases of segments 4-11 (*Pityòbius*).......................... **Elatéridae*** p. 290

229′. Antennae only singly pectinate, with only 1 process extending from segments 3-10 or 4-10 230

230(229′). Tarsi with membranous lobes beneath third and fourth segments; antennal processes arising from base of segments 3-10; 5 visible abdominal sterna 231

230′. Tarsi slender and not bearing lobes beneath; antennal processes arising from apex of segments 4-11; 11 to 17 mm in length; 6 visible abdominal sterna; Utah and Arizona to California .... **Elatéridae*** p. 290

231(226′, 230). Prosternum usually lobed in front (Figure 22-13 A); antennae arising near eyes under a frontal margin; labrum visible; beetles able to click and jump 232

231′. Prosternum not lobed in front; antennae arising on front between eyes, and received in transverse grooves on front; labrum concealed; beetles may or may not be able to click and jump .... **Eucnémidae** p. 291

232(231). Labrum free; tarsal claws variable; size variable, up to 40 mm in length; a large group .... **Elatéridae** p. 290

232′. Labrum fused with front; tarsal claws serrate or pectinate; 10 to 18 mm in length (*Pérothops*) .... **Perothópidae*** p. 291

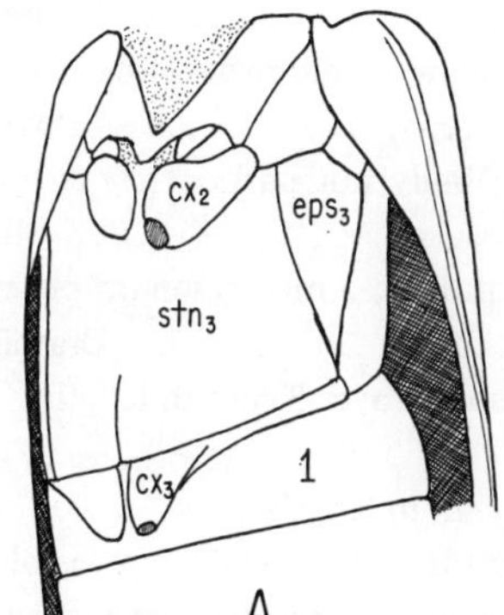

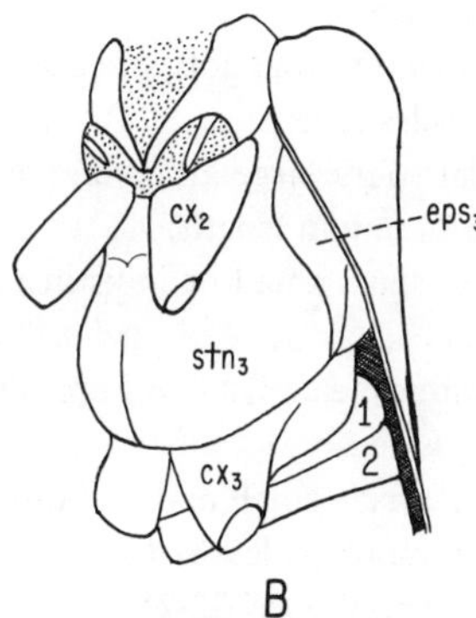

Fig. 22-14. Lateroventral view of thorax and base of abdomen. A, *Photùrus* (Lampýridae); B, *Chauliógnathus* (Cantháridae). *cx*, coxa; eps_3, metepisternum; stn_3, metasternum; 1-2, abdominal sternites.

233(206′). Front coxae globose or transverse 234

233′. Front coxae more or less conical and prominent 236

234(233). Last tarsal segment and claws very long (Figure 22-10 H); first 3 abdominal sterna more or less fused together; aquatic beetles, 4 to 6 mm in length .... **Psephénidae** p. 295

234′. Tarsi not as above; first 3 abdominal sterna freely movable; size variable 235*

235(234′). Length 15 to 19 mm; southern and southwestern United States .... **Cebriónidae*** p. 290

235′. Length 2.0 to 2.5 mm; widely distributed .... **Leptínidae*** p. 282

236(233′). Elytra pubescent 237

236′. Elytra not pubescent 243

237(236). Palpi large, in male flabellate; outer 7 to 9 antennal segments equal in size, larger than basal segments; pronotum with sharp lateral margins; head narrowed behind eyes into a slender neck; long, slender, soft-bodied beetles, 9.0 to 13.5 mm in length .... **Lymexylónidae*** p. 280

237′. Palpi normal, small; other characters variable 238

238(237′). Body antlike, brownish, 1 to 5 mm in length .... **Scydmaènidae*** p. 285

238′. Body not particularly antlike, 1.7 to 13.0 mm in length 239

239(203′, 238′). Pronotum rounded laterally; head not prolonged far beyond eyes; the 2 basal antennal segments normal, not particularly enlarged .... **Cléridae** p. 288

239′. Pronotum with sharp lateral margins; head prolonged anterior to eyes into a short broad muzzle; the 2 basal antennal segments sometimes greatly enlarged in male 240

240(239′). The last 4 antennal segments shorter than the preceding segments; elytra punctate; elongate oval, black beetles, 5 mm in length (*Prionochaèta*) .... **Leptodíridae*** p. 283

240′. Not exactly fitting the above description 241

241(30′, 149′, 240′). Head with a single median ocellus (*Thylódrias contráctus* Motschulsky, male) .... **Derméstidae** p. 287

241′. Ocelli absent 242

242(241′). A membranous lobe beneath each tarsal claw; extensile vesicles along sides of abdomen .... **Malachiidae** p. 288

242′. No membranous lobes beneath tarsal claws; abdomen without extensile vesicles .... **Dasýtidae*** p. 288

243(236′). Tibial spurs large and well developed; body not particularly antlike; up to 24 mm in length .... **Sílphidae** p. 283

243′. Tibial spurs small or indistinct; body antlike; 6 mm in length or less .... **Brathínidae*** p. 284

244(148′, 205′, 206″). Front coxae conical and prominent; usually over 3 mm in length 245

244′. Front coxae small and globose; 2 to 6 mm in length 247

245(244). Head more or less concealed by pronotum and usually not visible from above (Figure 22-26 A); mesal margins of metepisterna straight or nearly so (Figure 22-14 A) .... **Lampýridae** p. 285

245′. Head not concealed by pronotum and easily visible from above (Figure 22-26 B); mesal margins of metepisterna variable 246

246(152′, Antennae filiform or serrate; mesal margins of metepisterna more or less

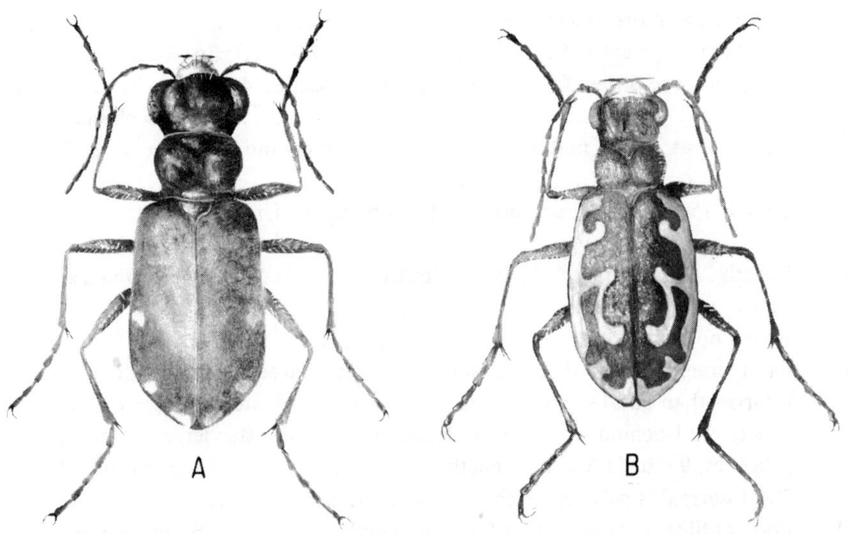

Fig. 22-15. Tiger beetles. A, *Cicindèla sexguttàta* (Fabricius); B, *C. repánda* (DeJean).

245′). curved (Figure 22-14 B); elytra usually broadly rounded apically...... .... **Cantháridae** p. 285

246′. Antennae serrate, pectinate, or flabellate; mesal margins of metepisterna straight; elytra narrowed and more or less pointed apically.......... .... **Phengódidae*** p. 287

247(244′). Length 2.0 to 2.5 mm; found in mammal nests.............. **Leptínidae*** p. 282

247′. Length 4 to 6 mm; found in or near streams.............. **Psephénidae** p. 295

248(1′). Length 2.5 to 3.3 mm; distinctly pubescent (females of *Thylódrias contráctus* Motschulsky) .... **Derméstidae*** p. 287

248′. Length 4.0 mm or more; pubescence usually absent or minute......249*

249(248′). Head more or less retracted into thorax; tarsi with a single claw........ .... **Phengódidae*** p. 287

249′. Head prominent, not retracted into thorax; tarsi with 2 claws.......... .... **Rhipiphóridae*** p. 304

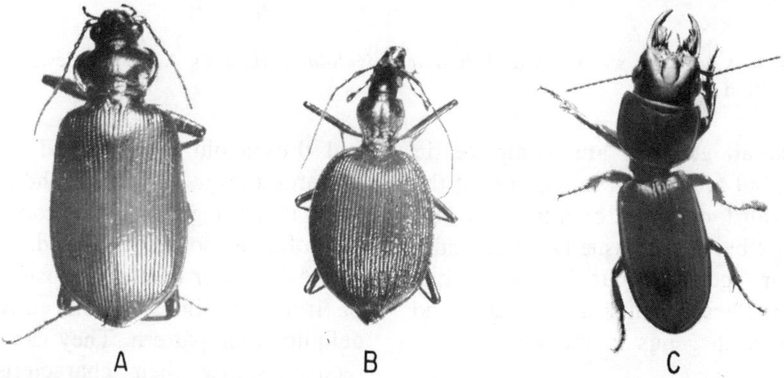

A B C

Fig. 22-16. Ground beetles. A, *Calosòma scrutàtor* (Fabricius); B, *Scaphinòtus guyòti* (LeConte); C, *Scarìtes subterràneus* (Fabricius). All figures slightly enlarged. (C, courtesy of the Illinois Natural History Survey.)

FAMILY **Cupésidae**—Reticulated Beetles: This is a small and little known group, with only four species occurring in the United States. All are densely scaly, with the elytra reticulate and the tarsi distinctly 5-segmented. The prosternum extends backward as a narrow process that fits into a groove in the mesosternum, much as in click beetles. The common species in eastern United States, *Cùpes cóncolor* Westwood, is 7 to 11 millimeters in length and brownish gray in color; in the Rocky Mountains and the Sierra Nevada the most common species is *Priácma serràta* LeConte, which is gray with faint black bands across the elytra. These beetles are usually found under bark.

FAMILY **Micromálthidae:** This family includes a single rare species, *Micromálthus débilis* LeConte, which has been taken in several localities in eastern United States. The adults are 1.8 to 2.5 millimeters in length, elongate and parallel-sided, dark, shiny, with yellowish legs and antennae; the tarsi are 5-segmented. This insect has a remarkable life cycle, with paedogenetic larvae; the larvae are able to reproduce (both oviparously and viviparously) parthenogenetically. These beetles have been found in decaying logs, principally oak and chestnut logs.

FAMILY **Rhysódidae** — Wrinkled Bark Beetles: The members of this group are slender, brownish beetles 5.5 to 7.5 millimeters in length with three fairly deep longitudinal grooves on the pronotum and with the antennae moniliform (Figure 22-8 B).

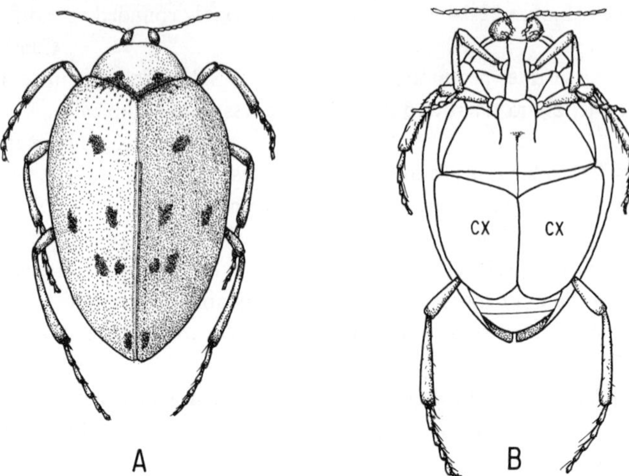

Fig. 22-17. A crawling water beetle, *Peltódytes edéntulus* (LeConte). A, dorsal view; B, ventral view. *cx*, hind coxa.

The pronotal grooves are complete in *Rhysòdes,* but are present in only about the posterior third of the pronotum in *Cliní-dium.* These beetles are usually found under bark. Four species occur in the United States, one of each genus in the East, and another of each genus in the West.

FAMILY **Cicindélidae**—Tiger Beetles: The tiger beetles are active, usually brightly colored insects found in open sunny situations; they are often common on sandy beaches. They can run or fly rapidly and are very wary and difficult to approach. When approached, they take flight quickly, sometimes after running a few feet, and usually alight some distance away facing the pursuer. They are predaceous and feed on a variety of small insects, which they capture with their long sicklelike mandibles; when handled, they can sometimes administer a painful bite.

The larvae are predaceous and live in vertical burrows in the soil in dry paths or fields or in sandy beaches. They prop themselves at the entrance of their burrow, with the traplike jaws wide apart, waiting to capture some passing insect. The larva has a hooklike spine on the fifth abdominal tergum with which it can anchor itself in its burrow and thus avoid being pulled out when it captures a large prey. After the prey is subdued, it is dragged to the bottom of the burrow, often a foot underground, and eaten.

Adult tiger beetles are usually metallic or iridescent in color and often have a definite color pattern. They can usually be recognized by their characteristic shape (Figure 22-15), and most of them are between 10 and 20 millimeters in length. Most of our tiger beetles belong to the genus *Cicindèla.*

FAMILY **Carábidae**—Ground Beetles: This family is a large one, containing hundreds of species. It exhibits considerable variation in size, shape, and color, but most species are dark, shiny, and somewhat flattened (Figure 22-16). Ground beetles are commonly found under stones, logs, leaves, bark, debris, or running about on the ground; when disturbed, they run rapidly, but seldom fly. Most species hide during the day and feed at night; a few are attracted to lights. Nearly all are predaceous on other insects, and many are very beneficial. The members of a few genera (for example, *Scaphinòtus*) feed on snails. The larvae are also predaceous and occur in burrows in the soil, under bark, or in debris.

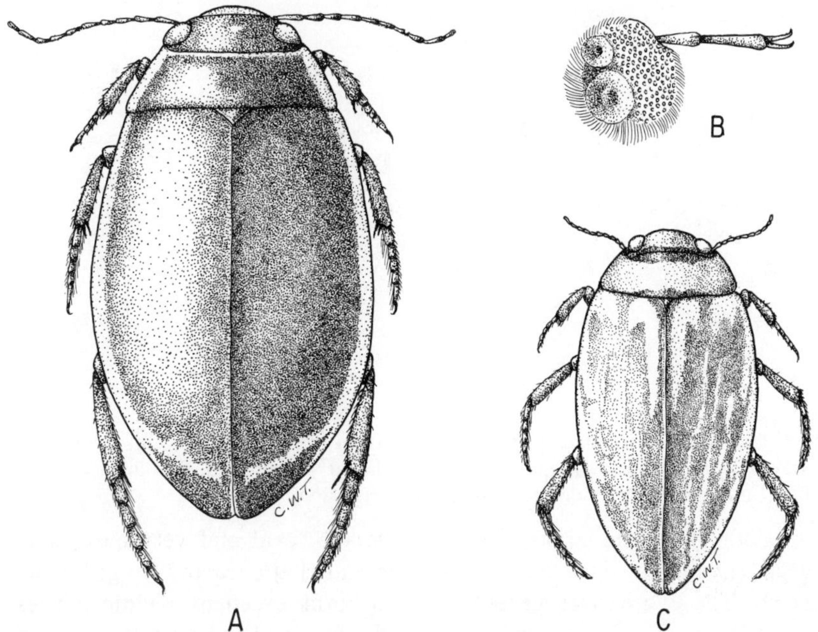

Fig. 22-18. Predaceous diving beetles. A, *Dytíscus verticàlis* (Say), female; B, same, front tarsus of male; C, *Coptótomus interrogàtus* (Fabricius).

The largest and most brilliantly colored ground beetles belong to the genus *Calosòma*; these are often called caterpillar-hunters, since they feed chiefly on caterpillars, particularly those that attack trees and shrubs. Most of these beetles are an inch or more in length. When handled, they give off a very disagreeable odor. *C. sycophánta* Linn., a brilliant greenish beetle with a dark-blue pronotum, was introduced from Europe to aid in the control of the gypsy moth. These beetles are attracted to lights.

The species in the genus *Bráchinus* are called bombardier beetles because of their habit of ejecting from the anus what looks like a puff of smoke. This is a glandular fluid that is ejected with a popping sound and which vaporizes into a cloud when it comes in contact with the air; the discharge of some species may irritate tender skin. This habit apparently serves both as a means of protection and of offense.

FAMILY **Omophrónidae** — Round Sand Beetles: The omophronids are small, oval, convex beetles that occur in wet sand along the shores of lakes and streams. They may be found running over the sand or burrowing in it (particularly under stones), and may occasionally be found running over the surface of the water. They run when disturbed, and apparently seldom fly. They may often be forced out of hiding in the sand or mud by splashing water up onto the shore. Both adults and larvae are predaceous, but the larvae occasionally feed on seedlings of crops planted in moist soil.

FAMILY **Halíplidae** — Crawling Water Beetles: The haliplids are small, oval, convex beetles 2.5 to 4.5 millimeters in length which live in or near water. They are usually yellowish or brownish with black spots (Figure 22-17 A) and may be distinguished from similar aquatic beetles by their very large and platelike hind coxae (Figure 22-17 B). They are fairly common in and about ponds; they swim or move about rather slowly. They frequently occur in masses of vegetation on or near the surface

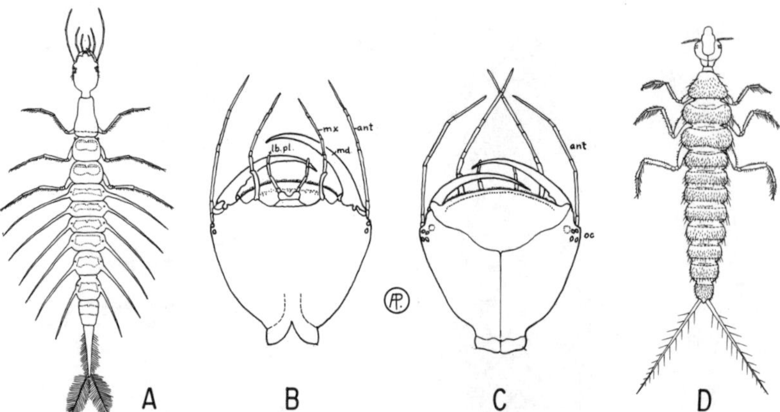

Fig. 22-19. Larvae of Dytíscidae. A, *Coptótomus;* B, head of *Dytíscus*, ventral view; C, same, dorsal view; D, *Hydróporus*. *ant*, antenna; *lbpl*, labial palpus; *md*, mandible; *mx*, maxilla; *oc*, ocelli. (Courtesy of Peterson. Reprinted by permission.)

of the water. Both adults and larvae (Figure 22-21 B) feed chiefly on algae and other plant materials. The two eastern genera in this family may be separated by the presence or absence of two round black spots at the base of the pronotum; these spots are present in *Peltódytes* and absent in *Háliplus*.

FAMILY **Amphizòidae** — Trout - Stream Beetles: This family contains five species in the genus *Amphizòa,* four occurring in western North America and one in eastern Tibet. These beetles are usually oval and dark-colored, and are 11.0 to 15.5 millimeters in length. Both adults and larvae occur in the water of cold swift mountain streams, where they crawl about on submerged stones, logs, or debris. If dislodged, they float helplessly in the water or sink to the bottom and crawl ashore, as they are unable to swim. They apparently feed on dead or sluggish insects. When agitated, the adults emit an odor somewhat like that of decaying wood or cantaloupes and exude a viscous yellowish fluid from the anus. The larvae do not have gills and must obtain oxygen at the surface of the water.

FAMILY **Dytíscidae**—Predaceous Diving Beetles: This is a large group of aquatic beetles that are usually very common in ponds and quiet streams. The body is smooth, oval and very hard, and the hind legs are flattened and fringed with long hairs to form excellent paddles. These beetles obtain air at the surface of the water, but can remain submerged for long periods because they carry air in a chamber under the elytra. They often hang head downward from the surface of the water. These insects may leave the water at night and fly to lights.

The dytiscids are very similar to another group of beetles common in fresh water, the Hydrophílidae. The adults of these two groups may be distinguished by the structure of the antennae and the maxillary palpi, and sometimes by the structure of the metasternum. The dytiscids have long filiform antennae and very short maxillary palpi (Figure 22-8), whereas the antennae of the hydrophilids are short and clubbed, and the maxillary palpi are longer than the antennae (Figure 22-23). The metasternum in many hydrophilids is prolonged posteriorly in a long spine (Figure 22-23 B). An excellent field character for separating these two groups is their method of swimming; the dytiscids move the hind legs simultaneously, like oars, whereas the hydrophilids move the hind legs alternately, as though they were running through the water.

Both adults and larvae of the dytiscids are highly predaceous and feed on a variety of small aquatic animals, including small fish. The larvae (Figure 22-19) are often called water tigers; they have long sickle-like jaws which are hollow, and when they attack a prey they suck out its body fluids through the channels in the jaws. These larvae are very active and will not hesitate to attack an animal much larger than themselves.

Adult dytiscids vary in length from 3 to 35 millimeters; most of them are brownish, blackish, or greenish. The males of some species (Figure 22-18 B) have peculiar front tarsi that bear large suction discs; these discs are used in holding the smooth slick elytra of the female at the time of mating. Some of the larger species have a pale yellow band along the lateral margins of the pronotum and elytra (Figure 22-18 A).

FAMILY **Notéridae** — Burrowing Water Beetles: These beetles are very similar to the dytiscids, but have the scutellum hidden and have two equal claws on the hind tarsi. They are broadly oval, smooth, brownish to black beetles, 1.2 to 5.5 millimeters in length, and are similar to the dytiscids in habits. The common name of this group refers to the larvae, which burrow into the mud around the roots of aquatic plants.

FAMILY **Gyrínidae**—Whirligig Beetles: The gyrinids are oval black beetles that are commonly seen swimming in endless gyrations on the surface of ponds and quiet streams. They are equally at home on the surface of the water or beneath the surface. They are extremely rapid swimmers, swimming principally by means of the highly flattened middle and hind legs; the front legs are elongate and slender (Figure 22-20). These insects are peculiar in having each compound eye divided; they have a pair of compound eyes on the upper surface of the head and another pair on the ventral surface

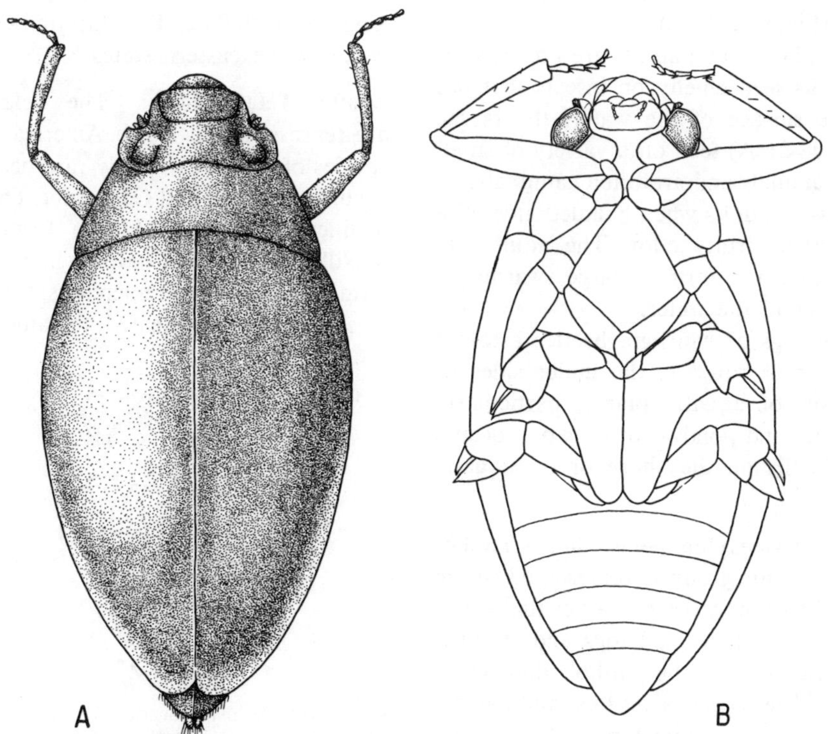

Fig. 22-20. A whirligig beetle, *Dineùtes americánus* (Say). A, dorsal view; B, ventral view.

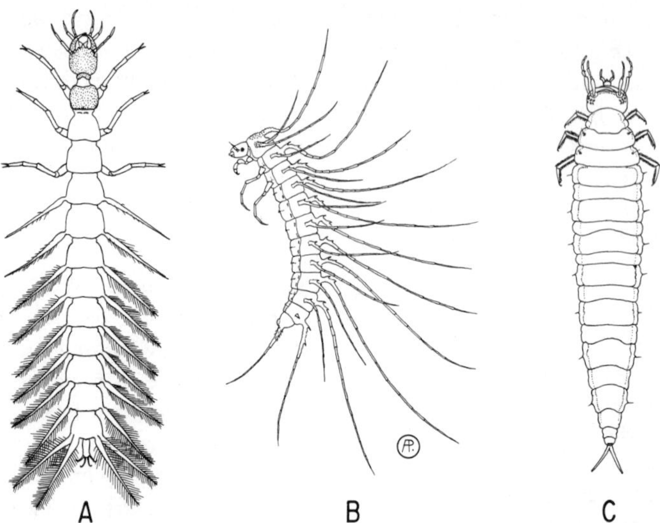

Fig. 22-21. Larvae of aquatic beetles. A, *Dineùtes* (Gyrínidae); B, *Peltódytes* (Halíplidae), lateral view; C, *Hydróphilus triangulàris* (Say) (Hydrophílidae). (Courtesy of Peterson. Reprinted by permission.)

(Figure 22-11 C). The antennae are very short, somewhat clubbed, and have the third segment greatly expanded and somewhat earlike (Figure 22-8 E).

Both larvae and adults are predaceous. The adults feed chiefly on insects that fall onto the surface of the water; the larvae (Figure 22-21 A) feed on a variety of small aquatic animals and are often cannibalistic. Many of the adults when handled give off a characteristic fruity odor. The adults are often gregarious, forming large swarms on the surface of the water.

The eggs of whirligig beetles are laid in clusters or rows on the under sides of the leaves of aquatic plants, particularly water lilies and pondweed; pupation occurs in mud cells on the shore or on aquatic plants.

FAMILY **Lymexylónidae** — Ship - Timber Beetles: This group is represented in the United States by two rare species that occur under bark and in dead logs and stumps; they cause much of the pin-hole damage in chestnut. These beetles are long and narrow and 9.0 to 13.5 millimeters in length; the head is bent down and narrowed behind the eyes to form a short neck; the antennae are filiform to serrate; the tarsi are 5-segmented; and the maxillary palpi in the males are long and flabellate. The ship-timber beetles occur in the eastern states.

FAMILY **Telegeùsidae:** The Telegeùsidae are represented in North America by three species of small, extremely rare beetles that occur in Arizona and California. Their most distinctive character is the form of the maxillary and labial palpi, which have the terminal segment tremendously enlarged. The tarsi are 5-segmented, the antennae are

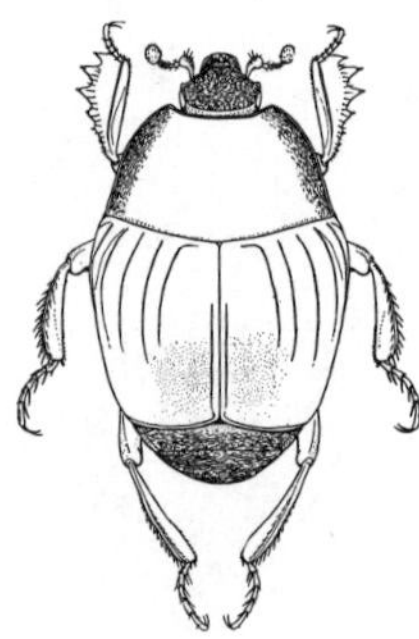

Fig. 22-22. A hister beetle, *Geomysáprinus góffi* (Ross). (Courtesy of Ross and the Entomological Society of America.)

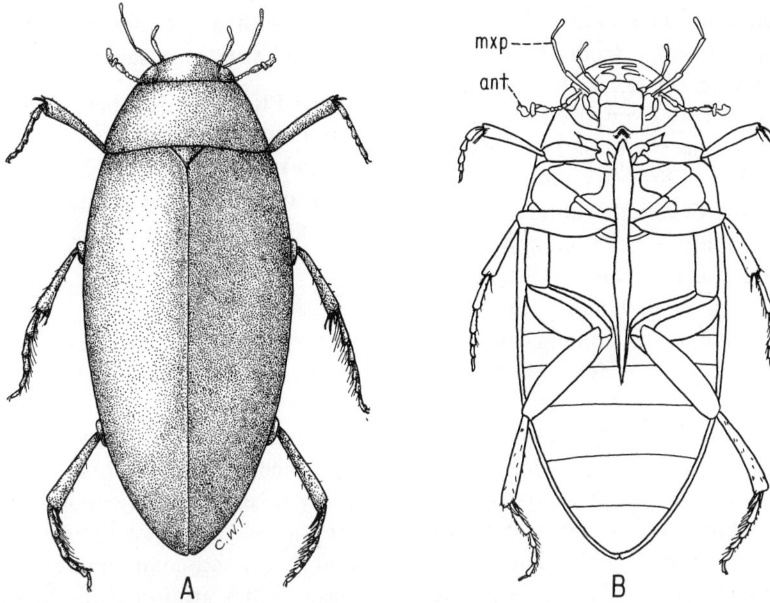

Fig. 22-23. A water scavenger beetle, *Hydróphilus trianguláris* (Say). A, dorsal view; B, ventral view. *ant*, antenna; *mxp*, maxillary palpus.

serrate, and the seven or eight abdominal segments are less than half covered by the short elytra. The telegeusids are slender, 5 to 6 millimeters in length, and resemble small rove beetles.

FAMILY **Histéridae**—Hister Beetles: Hister beetles are small (0.5 to 10.0 millimeters in length), broadly oval beetles that are usually shining black in color; the elytra are cut off square at the apex, exposing one or two apical abdominal segments (Figure 22-22). The antennae (Figure 22-8 I) are elbowed and clubbed. These beetles are usually found in or near decaying organic matter such as dung, fungi, and carrion, but are apparently predaceous on other small insects living in these materials. Some species, which are very flat, occur under the loose bark of stumps or logs; a few live in the nests of ants or termites. When disturbed, the hister beetles usually draw in their legs and antennae and become motionless. The appendages fit so snugly into shallow grooves on the ventral side of the body that it is often difficult to see them, even with considerable magnification.

FAMILY **Hydrophílidae**—Water Scavenger Beetles: The hydrophilids are oval, somewhat convex beetles that can be recognized by the short clubbed antennae and the long maxillary palpi (Figure 22-23 B). Most species are aquatic and are very similar in general appearance to the Dytíscidae. The aquatic species are generally black in color, and they vary in length from a few millimeters up to about 40 millimeters. The metasternum in many species is prolonged posteriorly as a sharp spine (Figure 22-23 B); this spine may be jabbed into the fingers of a person who is careless in handling one of these insects.

The water scavenger beetles differ somewhat from the dytiscids in habits. They rarely hang head downward from the surface of the water, as the dytiscids frequently do, and they carry air with them below the water in a silvery film over the ventral side of the body. In swimming, the hydrophilids move their legs alternately, whereas the dytiscids move the legs simultaneously, like a frog. The adults are principally scavengers, as the name implies, but the larvae are usually predaceous. The larvae of the water scavenger beetles differ from those of the predaceous diving beetles in that they have only a single tarsal claw (dytiscid larvae have two), and the mandibles are usually toothed. The larvae are very voracious and feed on all sorts of aquatic animals.

The hydrophilids are common insects in ponds and quiet streams. A large and common species, *Hydróphilus triangulàris* Say, is shining black and about 1½ inches in length (Figure 22-23). A few hydrophilids are terrestrial and occur in dung; the most common dung-inhabiting species is *Sphaerídium scarabaeòides* (Linn.), which has a faint red spot and a fainter yellow spot on each elytron. Some of the aquatic species are attracted to lights at night. The aquatic species lay their eggs in silken cases, which are usually attached to aquatic plants. The full-grown larvae leave the water to pupate in earthen cells underground.

FAMILY **Limnebìidae**—Minute Moss Beetles: These beetles are similar to the hydrophilids, but differ in having six or seven sterna (only five in the Hydrophílidae). They are elongate or oval, dark-colored beetles 1.2 to 1.7 millimeters in length, and occur in matted vegetation along stream margins, in wet moss, and along the seashore; they are probably scavengers.

FAMILY **Hydroscáphidae**—Skiff Beetles: The skiff beetles are about 1.5 millimeters or less in length, with 3-segmented tarsi and short elytra, and are somewhat similar in general appearance to the staphylinids. They occur in the filamentous algae growing on rocks in streams. The group is represented in this country by a single species, *Hydroscápha nàtans* LeConte, which occurs in southern California, southern Nevada, and Arizona.

FAMILY **Platypsýllidae**—Beaver Parasites: This family contains a single species, *Platypsýllus cástoris* Ritsema, which is an ectoparasite of beavers. This beetle is elongate, flattened, and 2.5 to 3.0 millimeters in length, with short elytra; compound eyes and hind wings are lacking.

FAMILY **Ptilìidae**—Feather-Winged Beetles: This family includes some of the smallest beetles known; few exceed 1 millimeter and many are less than 0.5 millimeter in length. The body is oval, and the hind wings are featherlike. These beetles occur in rotting wood, dung, and fungi.

FAMILY **Limulódidae** — Horseshoe Crab Beetles: The limulodids are usually a millimeter or less in length and are somewhat similar to horseshoe crabs in general appearance. They are oval in shape, with the elytra short and the abdomen somewhat tapering, and yellowish to brownish in color. Hind wings and compound eyes are absent. These beetles are found in ant nests, where they usually ride on the ants, feeding an exudations from the bodies of the ants. The group is a small one (four species in the United States), but is widely distributed.

FAMILY **Leptínidae**—Mammal-Nest Beetles: The leptinids are brownish, oblong-oval beetles, 2.0 to 2.5 millimeters in length, and occur in the nests of mice, moles, and other small mammals, and occasionally in bumble bee nests. Only three species occur in the United States, of which one, *Leptìnus testàceus* Müller, occurs in the eastern states. These beetles are thought to feed on the eggs and young of mites and other small arthropods found in mammal nests.

Fig. 22-24. Carrion beetles. Left, *Sílpha;* right, *Nicróphorus.*

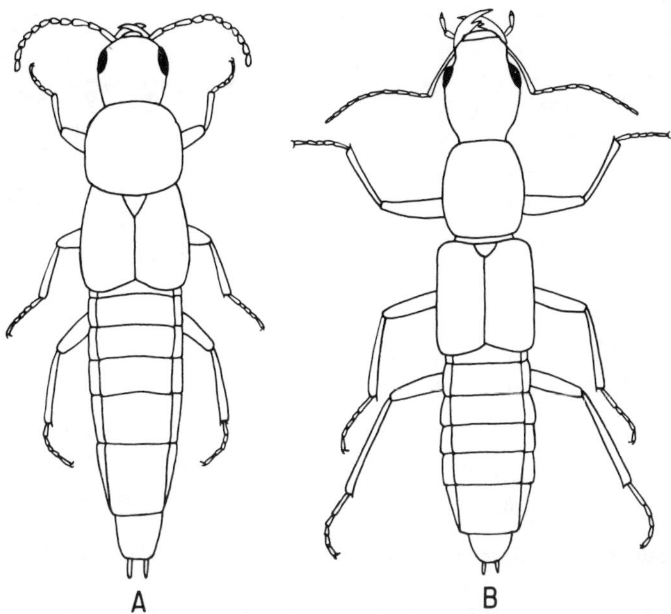

Fig. 22-25. Rove beetles. A, *Quèdius peregrìnus* (Gravenhorst); B, *Hesperòbium cribràtum* (LeConte). $7\frac{1}{2}\times$.

FAMILY **Leiódidae**—Round Fungus Beetles: These beetles occur in fungi, under bark, in decaying wood or other vegetation, and in similar places. They are convex, shiny, oval beetles 1.5 to 6.5 millimeters in length, and brown to black in color. When alarmed, they usually bend the head and thorax down under the body.

FAMILY **Leptodíridae** — Small Carrion Beetles: These beetles are elongate oval, somewhat flattened, brownish to black, pubescent, and 2 to 5 millimeters in length; they often have faint cross-striations on the elytra and pronotum. Most species occur in carrion, but some occur in fungi, and still others in ant nests.

FAMILY **Sílphidae**—Carrion Beetles and Burying Beetles: The common species in this group are relatively large and often brightly colored insects that occur about the bodies of dead animals. The body is soft and somewhat flattened, the antennae are clubbed, and the tarsi are 5-segmented.

Two common genera in this group are *Sílpha* and *Nicróphorus* (= *Necróphorus*). In *Sílpha* (Figure 22-24) the body is broadly oval and flattened, 10 to 24 millimeters in length, and the elytra are rounded or acute at the apex and almost cover the abdomen. In some species (for example, *S. americàna* Linn.) the pronotum is yellowish with a black spot in the center. In *Nicróphorus* (Figure 22-24) the body is more elongate, the elytra are short and truncate apically, and most species are red and black in color. The beetles of the genus *Nicróphorus* are often known as burying beetles; they excavate beneath the dead body of a mouse or other small animal, and the body sinks into the ground. These beetles are remarkably strong; a pair may move an animal as large as a rat several feet to get it to a suitable spot for burying. After the body is buried, the eggs are laid on it. Both adults and larvae feed on carrion and are usually found beneath the bodies of the dead animals.

Other species of silphids occur in various types of decaying animal matter; some occur in fungi, and a few occur in ant nests. A few are predaceous on maggots and other animals that occur in decaying organic

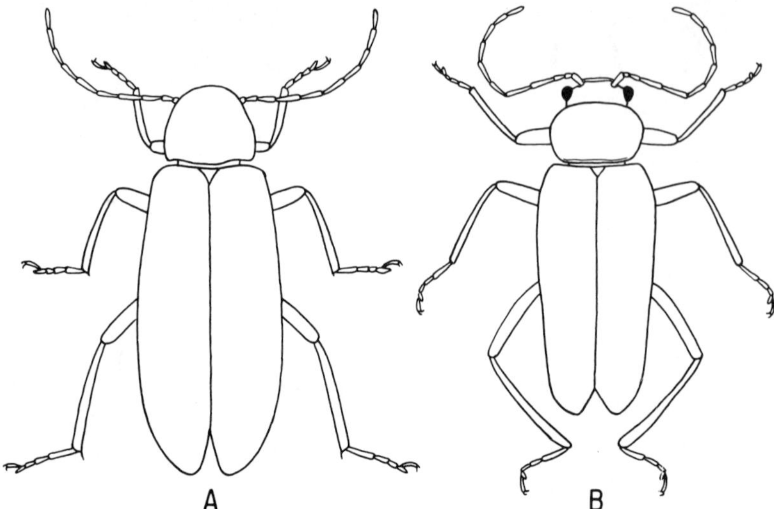

Fig. 22-26. A, a lightningbug (*Photùrus*); B, a soldier beetle (*Chauliógnathus*). $3\frac{3}{4}\times$.

matter. In some species (for example, *Nicró-phorus*) the newly hatched larvae are fed carrion that is regurgitated by the parent beetles.

FAMILY **Scaphidìidae** — Shining Fungus Beetles: The scaphidiids are 2 to 7 millimeters in length, shiny, convex, and appear pointed at each end. The elytra are short and truncate at the apex, and expose the last abdominal tergum. The members of this group occur in fungi, dead leaves, rotting wood, and under bark.

FAMILY **Brathínidae**—Grass-Root Beetles: The brathinids are small, slender, long-legged, shiny, antlike beetles 3.5 to 6.0 millimeters in length. The coxae are very large and contiguous, and hind wings are lacking. These beetles may be found about the roots of grass in moist places. They are rather rare, and only three species occur in the United States (two in the Northeast, and one in California).

FAMILY **Staphylínidae**—Rove Beetles: The rove beetles are slender and elongate, and can usually be recognized by the very short elytra; the elytra are usually not much longer than their combined width, and a considerable portion of the abdomen is exposed beyond their apices (Figure 22-25). The hind wings are well developed, and when at rest, are folded under the short elytra. Rove beetles are active insects, and run or fly rapidly. When running, they frequently raise the tip of the abdomen, much as do scorpions. The mandibles are very long, slender, and sharp, and usually cross in front of the head; some of the larger rove beetles can inflict a painful bite when handled. Most of these beetles are black or brown in color; they vary considerably in size, but the largest are about an inch in length.

Rove beetles occur principally in and about decaying animal or vegetable matter, particularly dung and carrion. Most species appear to be predaceous on other insects that occur in these materials. A few are found in ant nests.

FAMILY **Pseláphidae**—Short-Winged Mold Beetles: The pselaphids are small yellowish or brownish beetles, 0.5 to 5.5 (mostly about 1.5) millimeters in length, and are found under stones and logs, in rotting wood, or in moss; a few are found in ant or termite nests. The elytra are short and rather square at the tip, and cover only about half of the abdomen. This group is a large one, with about 500 species occurring in the United States.

FAMILY **Clavigéridae**—Ant-Loving Beetles: These beetles are similar to the pselaphids, but are usually smaller (less than 2.5 millimeters in length) and the antennae are 2-segmented. They occur in ant nests, where they are "milked" by the ants of a secretion on which the ants feed.

FAMILY **Clámbidiae** — Fringe - Winged Beetles: The clambids are broadly oval, convex, brownish to black, rather hairy beetles about 1 millimeter in length, and have a fringe of long hairs on the hind wings. The tarsi are 4-segmented, and the antennae terminate in a 2-segmented club. These beetles occur in decaying plant material. Only nine species of clambids occur in the United States.

FAMILY **Scydmaènidae** — Antlike Stone Beetles: The members of this group are small, brownish, hairy beetles 1 to 5 millimeters in length, and are somewhat antlike in shape. They occur under stones and logs and in ant nests. The elytra completely cover the abdomen, the tarsi are 5-segmented, and the hind coxae are distinctly separated. These beetles are usually somewhat secretive in habits, but they sometimes fly about in large numbers at twilight.

FAMILY **Sphaerítidae**—False Clown Beetles: This group is represented in North America by a single species that occurs in carrion, manure, and decaying fungus from Alaska to northern Idaho and California. This species, *Sphaerìtes polìtus* Mannerheim, is 4.5 to 5.5 millimeters in length and black with a metallic bluish luster. It is very similar to certain Histeridae, but differs in that it has the front coxae contiguous and only the terminal abdominal tergum not covered by the elytra. Each elytron bears 11 rows of rather faint punctures. The antennae terminate in an abrupt 3-segmented club.

FAMILY **Orthopéridae** — Minute Fungus Beetles: These beetles are rounded or oval and generally less than 1 millimeter in length; the tarsi are 4-segmented, but the third segment is small and concealed in a notch of the bilobed second segment, and the tarsi appear 3-segmented; the antennae are clubbed, and the club is usually 3-segmented. The hind wings are clothed with long hairs. These beetles occur in decaying vegetable matter and in debris.

FAMILY **Sphaerìidae**—Minute Bog Beetles: These beetles are broadly oval, blackish, and 0.5 to 0.75 millimeter in length; they are found in mud or under stones near water, among the roots of plants, or in wet moss. The group is represented in this country by two or three species that occur in Texas, southern California, and Washington.

FAMILY **Cantháridae**—Soldier Beetles: The cantharids are elongate, soft-bodied beetles that are very similar to the lightningbugs (Lampýridae) but they differ in that the head protrudes forward beyond the pronotum and is visible from above (not concealed by the pronotum as in the Lampýridae). These beetles do not have light-producing organs, and they have the fourth tarsal segment lobed beneath.

Adult soldier beetles are usually found on flowers; the larvae are predaceous on other insects. One common species, *Chauliógnathus pennsylvánicus* DeGeer (Figure 22-26 B), about ½ inch in length, has each elytron yellowish with a black spot or stripe; members of other genera are yellowish, black, or brown in color. Female soldier beetles are similar in appearance to the males; the females of some lampyrids are wingless and larviform in appearance.

FAMILY **Lampýridae**—Lightningbugs or Fireflies: Many members of this common and well-known group possess a "tail light" —segments near the end of the abdomen with which the insects are able to produce light. These luminous segments can be recognized, even when they are not glowing, by their yellowish-green color. During cer-

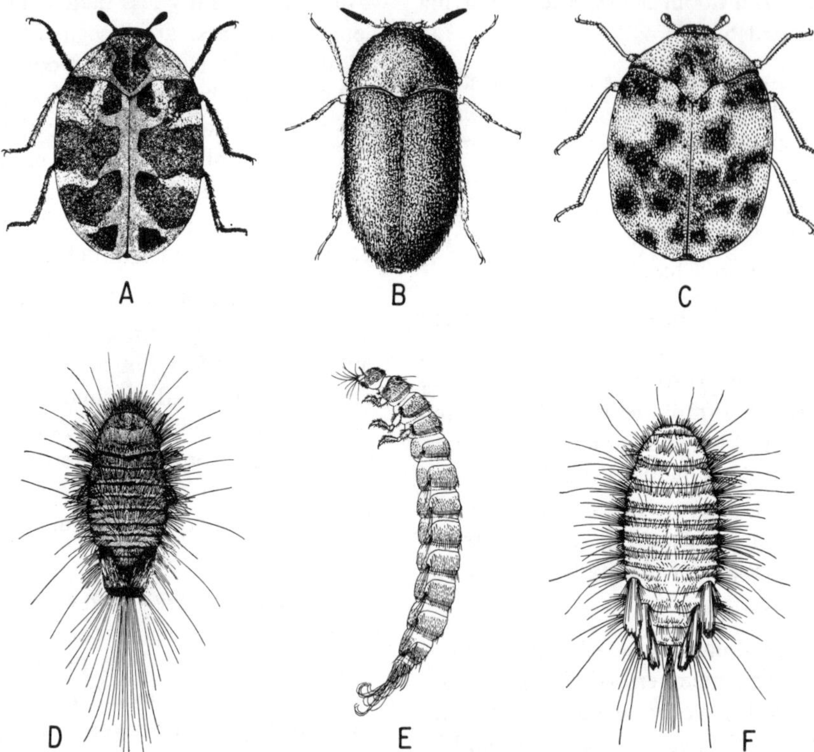

Fig. 22-27. Dermestid beetles. A, the carpet beetle, *Anthrènus scrophulàriae* (Linn.), adult; B, the black carpet beetle. *Attágenus pìceus* (Olivier), adult; C, the furniture carpet beetle. *Anthrènus flávipes* LeConte, adult; D, larva of *A, scrophulàriae* (Linn.), dorsal view; E, larva of *A. pìceus* (Olivier), lateral view; F, larva of *A. flávipes* LeConte, dorsal view. (E, courtesy of Peterson, reprinted by permission; other figures, courtesy of the Cornell University Agricultural Experiment Station.)

tain seasons, usually early summer, these insects fly about in the evenings and are conspicuous by their blinking yellow lights.

The lampyrids are elongate and very soft-bodied beetles in which the pronotum extends forward over the head so that the head is largely or entirely concealed from above (Figure 22-26 A). The elytra are soft, flexible, and rather flat except for the epipleurae. Most of the larger members of this group have luminescent organs, but many of the smaller ones do not.

The light emitted by these insects is unique in being cold; nearly 100 percent of the energy given off appears as light. In the electric arc light, only 10 percent of the energy is light, and the other 90 percent is given off as heat. The light given off by a firefly is produced by the oxidation of a substance called luciferin, which is produced in the cells of the light-producing organs. These organs have a rich tracheal supply, and the insect controls the emission of light by controlling the air supply to the organs. When air is admitted, the luciferin (in the presence of an enzyme called luciferinase) is almost instantly oxidized, releasing the energy as light. The flashing of fireflies is probably a mating response, and each species has a characteristic flashing rhythm; an expert can identify species by the length of the flashes and the interval between flashes. In some tropical species in this group, large numbers of individuals congregate and flash in unison.

During the day the lampyrids are

usually found on vegetation. The larvae are predaceous and feed on various smaller insects and on snails. The females of many species are wingless and look very much like larvae. These wingless females and most lampyrid larvae are luminescent and are often called "glow-worms."

FAMILY **Phengodidae**—Glow-Worms: This is a small group of relatively uncommon beetles closely related to the Lampýridae. Most of them are broad and flat, with the elytra short and pointed, and the posterior part of the abdomen covered only by the membranous hind wings. The antennae are usually serrate, but in some males they may be pectinate or almost plumose. These insects vary in length from 4 to 13 millimeters and are found on foliage or on the ground. The adult females of many species are wingless and luminescent, as in the Lampýridae, and look much like larvae. The larvae are predaceous.

FAMILY **Lýcidae**—Net-Winged Beetles: The lycids are elongate soft-winged beetles somewhat similar to the soldier beetles and fireflies, but may be readily recognized by the peculiar network of raised lines on the elytra. Some western species (*Lycóstomus*) have a distinct snout. The elytra in some species are slightly widened posteriorly. The adults occur on foliage and tree trunks, usually in wooded areas; they feed on the juices of decaying plant materials and occasionally on other insects. The larvae are predaceous.

One of the more common members of this group is *Calópteron reticulàtum* (Fabricius), 11 to 19 millimeters in length; the elytra are yellow, with the posterior half and a narrow cross-band in the anterior part black; the pronotum is black, margined with yellow. Most of the lycids are brightly colored, with red, black, or yellow.

FAMILY **Derméstidae**—Dermestid or Skin Beetles: This group contains a number of very destructive and economically important species. The dermestids are mostly scavengers and feed on a great variety of plant and animal products, including leather, furs, skins, museum specimens, woolen or silk materials, rugs, stored food materials, and carrion. Most of the damage is done by the larvae.

Adult dermestids are small, oval, convex beetles with short clubbed antennae, and they vary in length from 2 to 10 or 12 millimeters; they are usually hairy or covered with scales (Figure 22-27 A-C). They may be found in the materials mentioned above, and many feed on flowers. Some are black or dull-colored, but many have a characteristic color pattern. The larvae are usually brownish and are covered with long hairs (Figure 22-27 D-F).

The larger dermestids belong to the genus *Derméstes*. *D. lardàrius* Linn., often called the larder beetle, is a common species in this genus; it is a little over $\frac{1}{4}$ inch in length and is black with a light-brown band across the base of the elytra. It feeds on a variety of stored foods, including meats and cheese, and occasionally damages the specimens in insect collections.

Some of the smaller dermestids are often common in houses and may do serious damage to carpets, upholstery, and clothing. Two common species of this type are the black carpet beetle, *Attágenus pìceus* (Olivier), and the carpet beetle, *Anthrènus scrophulàriae* (Linn.); the former is a grayish black beetle 3.5 to 5.0 millimeters in length (Figure 22-27 B), and the latter is a pretty little black-and-white patterned species 3 to 5 millimeters in length (Figure 22-27 A). Most of the damage done by these species is done by the larvae; the adults are often found on flowers.

This is one group of insects that every entomology student will sooner or later encounter. All he has to do to get some dermestids is to make an insect collection and not protect it against these pests; the dermestids will eventually find the collection and ruin it. Many species in this group are serious pests in homes, markets, and food-storage places.

While many of the dermestids are serious pests, they are nevertheless of value as scavengers—aiding in the removal of dead organic matter. Some of the species that feed on carrion, notably *Derméstes canìnus* Germar, have been used by vertebrate zoologists to clean skeletons for study.

One species in this family, *Thylódrias contráctus* Motschulsky, is unusual in having the antennae filiform and the female wingless and larviform.

FAMILIES **Malachìidae** AND **Dasýtidae**—Soft-Winged Flower Beetles: The members of these two families are small, elongate-oval, soft-bodied beetles, 7 millimeters in length or less, and are commonly found on flowers. Most of them are rather brightly colored with brown or red and black. The Malachìidae differ from the Dasýtidae in having peculiar orange-colored structures along the sides of the abdomen, which may be everted and saclike or withdrawn into the body and inconspicuous. In some cases the two basal segments of the antennae are greatly enlarged. Most adults and larvae in these groups are predaceous. Our most common species belong to the genus *Cóllops* (family Malachìidae); *C. quadrimaculàtus* (Fabricius) is a reddish beetle with two bluish black spots on each elytron.

FAMILY **Císidae**—Minute Tree-Fungus Beetles: The cisids are brownish to black beetles, 2 to 3 millimeters in length, and are similar in appearance to the Scolýtidae and Bostríchidae. The body is cylindrical, the head is deflexed and not visible from above, the tarsi are 4-segmented (with the first three segments short and the fourth long), and the antennae terminate in a 3-segmented club. These beetles occur under bark, in rotting wood, or in dry woody fungi, often in considerable numbers. Some species occasionally invade buildings and attack furniture and woodwork, much like the powder-post beetles.

FAMILY **Ostómidae** — Bark - Gnawing Beetles: These beetles are 5 to 20 millimeters in length and have the head and pronotum large and the union between the pronotum and the elytra narrow (Figure 22-28). One species, *Tenebrioìdes mauritánicus* (Linn.), commonly occurs in granaries; the larvae, usually called "cadelles," are believed to feed both on other insects in the grain and on the grain itself. Other species in this group occur under bark and under logs. A common eastern species in this group is *Temnóchilus viréscens* (Fabricius), a bright blue-green beetle about 20 millimeters in length; it can administer a vicious bite with its powerful mandibles.

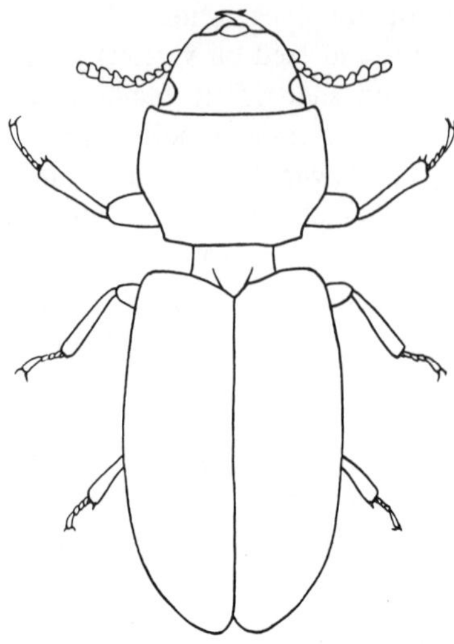

Fig. 22-28. An ostomid beetle. *Tenebriòides* sp.; 7½ ×.

FAMILY **Cléridae**—Checkered Beetles: Most of the clerids are brightly marked and covered with a dense pubescence, and have the pronotum narrower than either the head or the base of the elytra (Figure 22-29). The tarsi are 5-segmented, but in many species the first or the fourth segment is very short and difficult to see. Most clerids are between 5 and 12 millimeters in length.

The majority of the checkered beetles are predaceous both as adults and larvae. Many are common on or within tree trunks and logs, where they prey on the larvae of various wood-boring insects (chiefly bark beetles); others occur on flowers and foliage.

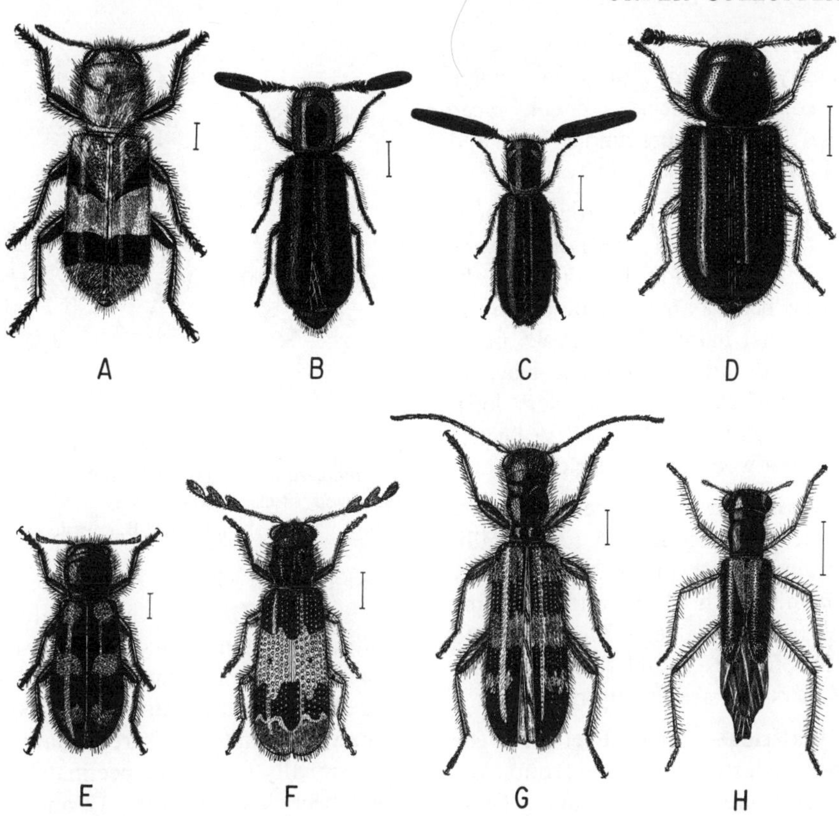

Fig. 22-29. Checkered beetles. A, *Enóclerus ichneumòneus* (Fabricius); B, *Monophýlla terminàta* (Say), female; C, *Monophýlla terminàta* (Say), male; D, *Necròbia rùfipes* (DeGeer); E, *Trichòdes nutálli* (Kirby); F, *Corinthíscus leucophaèus* (Klug); G, *Cymatódera undulàta* (Say); H, *Isohydnócera curtipénnis* (Newman). The lines represent 1 mm. (Courtesy of Knull and the Ohio Biological Survey.)

A few (for example, members of the genera *Trichòdes* and *Hydnócera*) are pollen feeders in the adult stage and sometimes also in the larval stage; *Trichòdes* larvae are predaceous in the nests of bees and wasps.

Some of the clerids, which have the fourth tarsal segment very small and difficult to see, have been placed by some authorities in a separate family, the Corynétidae. These beetles are similar in general appearance and habits to the other clerids. One species in this group, *Necròbia rùfipes* (DeGeer) (Figure 22-29 D), sometimes called the red-legged ham beetle, is occasionally destructive to stored meats.

FAMILY **Sandálidae:** The sandalids are elongate-oval, brownish beetles, 16 to 24 millimeters in length, with the short antennae flabellate in the males (Figure 22-9 B) and serrate in the females. The mandibles are large and prominent, and the first four tarsal segments each bear two small lobes beneath (Figure 22-10 F). These beetles usually occur on or near elm or ash trees; they are excellent fliers. The larvae are parasitic on the nymphs of cicadas. The only genus in the family is *Sándalus.*

FAMILY **Rhipicéridae**—Cedar Beetles: The cedar beetles are somewhat similar to the sandalids, but are smaller (11 to 15 millimeters in length), the mandibles are much smaller, the tarsi lack the lobes characteristic of the sandalids, and the processes on the antennal segments of the males are not much longer than the segments. This family contains only a single rare United States species, *Zénoa pìcea* (Beauvois), which occurs under logs and bark in Florida.

FAMILY **Cerophýtidae:** This group includes two very rare species of *Ceróphytum,* one occurring in the East and the other in California. These beetles are elongate-oblong in shape, somewhat flattened, 7.5 to 8.5 millimeters in length, and brownish to black in color. The hind trochanters are very long, nearly as long as the femora. These beetles occur in rotten wood and under dead bark.

FAMILY **Cebriónidae:** The cebrionids are elongate brownish beetles, 15 to 25 millimeters in length, with the body quite hairy and the mandibles hooklike and extending forward in front of the head. The larvae and females live in the ground; the males are excellent fliers and are largely nocturnal.

FAMILY **Elatéridae**—Click Beetles: The click beetles constitute a large group, and many species are quite common. These beetles are peculiar in being able to "click" and jump; in most of the related groups, the union of the prothorax and mesothorax is such that little or no movement at this point is possible. The clicking is made possible by the flexible union of the prothorax and mesothorax, and a prosternal spine that fits into a groove on the mesosternum (Figure 22-13 A).

If one of these beetles is placed on its back on a smooth surface, it is usually unable to right itself by means of its legs. It bends its head and prothorax backward, so that only the extremities of the body are touching the surface on which it rests; then, with a sudden jerk and clicking sound, the body is straightened out; this movement snaps the prosternal spine into the mesosternal groove and throws the insect into the air, spinning end over end. If the insect does not land right side up, it continues snapping until it does.

The click beetles can usually be recog-

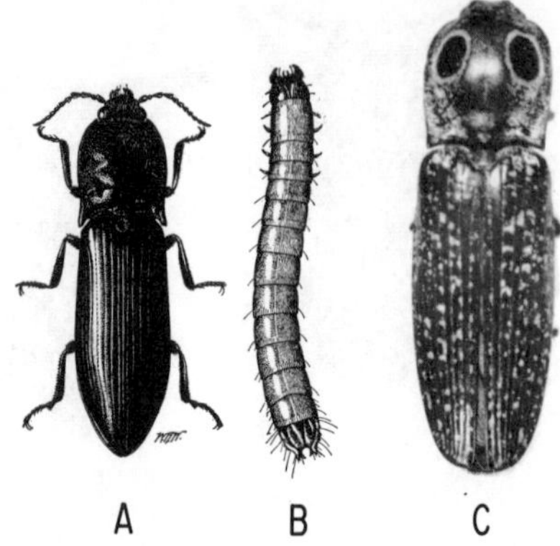

Fig. 22-30. Click beetles. A, adult, and B, larva, of *Ctenícera nóxia* (Hyslop) (slightly enlarged); C, the eyed click beetle, *Álaus oculàtus* (Linn.) (about natural size). (A and B, courtesy of USDA.)

nized by their characteristic shape (Figure 22-30 A, C). The body is elongate, usually parallel-sided, and rounded at each end. The posterior corners of the pronotum are prolonged backward into sharp points or spines. The antennae are usually serrate (occasionally filiform or pectinate). Most of these beetles are between 12 and 30 millimeters in length, but a few exceed these limits. The largest and most easily recognized species is the eyed click beetle, *Álaus oculàtus* (Linn)., a mottled-gray beetle with the pronotum bearing two large black eyelike spots (Figure 22-30 C); this species may reach $1\frac{1}{2}$ inches or more in length. Most elaterids are inconspicuously colored with black or brown.

Adult click beetles are phytophagous and occur on flowers, under bark, or on vegetation. The larvae are slender, hard-bodied, and shiny, and are commonly called wireworms (Figure 22-30 B). The larvae of many species are very destructive, feeding on newly planted seed and the roots of beans, cotton, potatoes, corn, and cereals. Many elaterid larvae occur in rotting logs; some of these feed on other insects. Pupation occurs in the ground, under bark, or in dead wood.

Species of *Pyróphorus* in the southern states and in the tropics have two light-producing spots on the posterior edge of the prothorax. The light is much stronger than that of the lampyrids, and a large number flying about at night is a striking sight.

FAMILY **Eucnémidae**—False Click Beetles: This family is very closely related to the Elatéridae. Its members are relatively rare beetles usually found in wood that has just begun to decay, chiefly in beech and maple. Most of them are brownish in color and about 10 millimeters in length or less. The pronotum is quite convex above, and the antennae are inserted rather close together on the front of the head, and there is no distinct labrum. These beetles quiver their antennae almost constantly, a habit not occurring in the Elatéridae.

FAMILY **Perothópidae:** These beetles are similar to the Eucnémidae, but have the prothorax free and the tarsal claws pectinate. They are 10 to 18 millimeters in length, brownish in color, and are found on the trunks and branches of old beech trees. Three species of *Pérothops* occur in the United States, from Pennsylvania to Florida, and in California.

FAMILY **Thróscidae:** The throscids are brown or black in color, oblong in shape, and 5 millimeters in length or less. They are similar to the elaterids, but have the prosternal spine firmly attached to the mesosternum and they do not "click." The prosternum anteriorly almost conceals the mouth parts; in closely related families the mouth parts are clearly visible in ventral view. These beetles occur chiefly on flowers, particularly those of milkweed, dogwood, and May apple.

FAMILY **Bupréstidae**—Metallic Wood-Boring Beetles: Most buprestid larvae bore under bark or in wood, attacking either living trees or newly cut or dying logs and branches; many do serious damage to trees and shrubs. The eggs are usually laid in crevices in the bark; the larvae, on hatching, tunnel under the bark, and some species eventually bore into the wood. The galleries

Fig. 22-31. Galleries of a buprestid larva. (Courtesy of Davidson.)

under the bark are often winding and filled with frass; the galleries in the wood are oval in cross-section and usually enter the wood at an angle (Figure 22-31). Pupation occurs in the galleries. Buprestid larvae usually have the anterior end expanded and flattened (Figure 22-33), and are often known as flat-headed borers. The larvae of some species make winding galleries under the bark of twigs (Figure 22-32 B), others make galls (Figure 22-32 A), and one species girdles twigs.

The adults of this group are often rather metallic—coppery, green, blue, or black—especially on the ventral side of the body and on the dorsal surface of the abdomen. They are hard-bodied and compactly built, and usually have a characteristic shape (Figures 22-34, 22-35). Many adult buprestids are attracted to dead or dying trees and logs and to slash; others occur on the foliage of trees and shrubs. These beetles run or fly rapidly and are often difficult to catch; some are colored like the bark and are very inconspicuous when they remain motionless. Many of the larger beetles in this group are common in sunny situations.

The larvae of *Chrysóbothris femoràta* (Olivier) attack a number of trees and shrubs and frequently do serious damage to fruit trees. The larvae of different species of *Ágrilus* attack raspberries, blackberries, and other shrubs; *Ágrilus champlàini* Frost

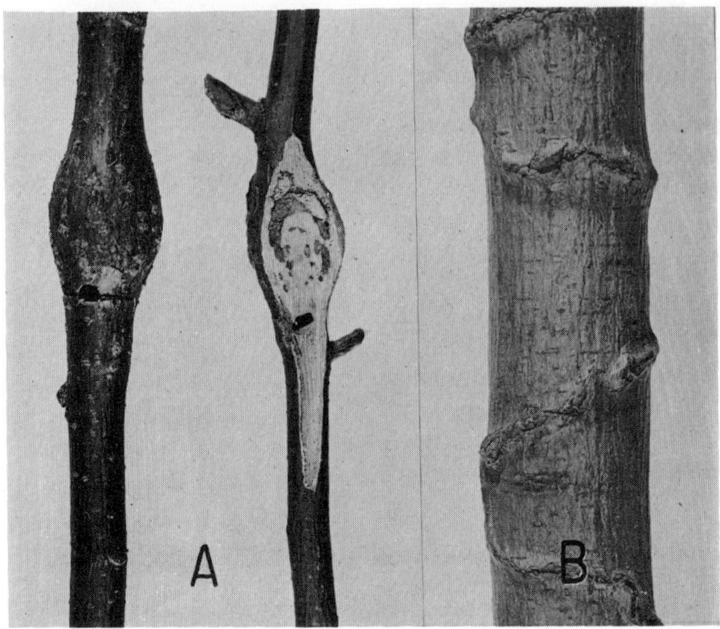

Fig. 22-32. A, galls of *Agrilus champlàini* Frost, in ironwood (*Ostrỳa*); B, the work of *Agrilus bilineàtus carpìni* Knull, on blue beech (*Carpìnus*). (Courtesy of Knull.)

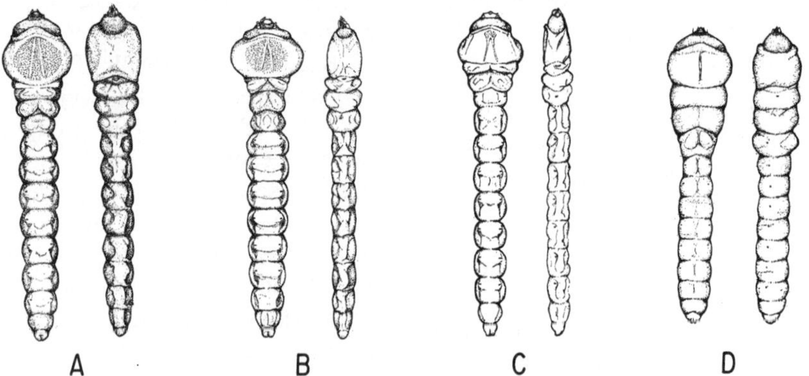

Fig. 22-33. Larvae of Bupréstidae. A, *Chrysóbothris trinérva* (Kirby); B, *Melanóphila drúmmondi* (Kirby); C, *Dicérca prolongàta* (LeConte); D, *Acmaeódera prórsa* (Fall). Dorsal view at left in each figure, lateral view at right. (Courtesy of USDA.)

makes galls in ironwood (Figure 22-32 A), and *A. ruficóllis* (Fabricius) makes galls in raspberry and blackberry; *A. arcuàtus* (Say) is a twig-girdler. The adults of the genus *Ágrilus* are rather long and narrow (Figure 22-35 C); most are dark-colored with metallic shades, and some have light markings. The larvae of the species of *Bráchys* (Figure 22-34 D) are leaf miners. Most buprestids fly when disturbed, but the beetles in the genus *Bráchys* draw up their legs, "play dead," and fall off the foliage onto the ground. These smaller buprestids are usually found on foliage.

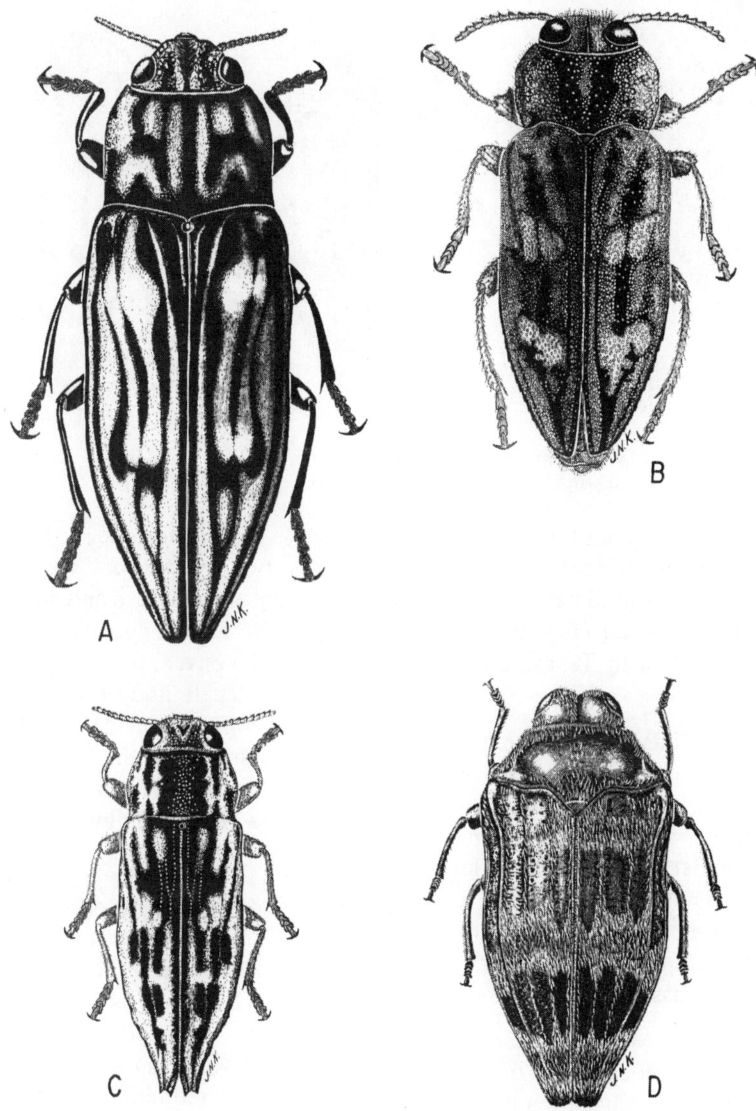

Fig. 22-34. Metallic wood-boring beetles. A, *Chalcóphora fórtis* LeConte, which breeds in dead white pine; B, *Chrysóbothris florícola* Gory, which breeds in pine; C, *Dicérca lépida* LeConte, which breeds in dead ironwood and hawthorn; D, *Bráchys ovàtus* Weber, which mines in oak leaves. (Courtesy of Knull.)

FAMILY **Dascíllidae**—Soft-Bodied Plant Beetles: This group consists of soft-bodied, pubescent beetles 3 to 9 millimeters in length, which occur principally on vegetation in moist places. *Ectópria nervòsa* (Melsheimer), an eastern species, is black, sparsely pubescent, and 3 to 5 millimeters in length (Figure 22-36). Another eastern species, *Odontónyx trivíttis* (Germar), is a dark, oblong, pubescent beetle 8 to 9 millimeters in length, with the pronotum reddish yellow and bearing two black spots. The species in the genus *Eucinètus* occur under bark and in fungi. *Brachypséctra fúlva*

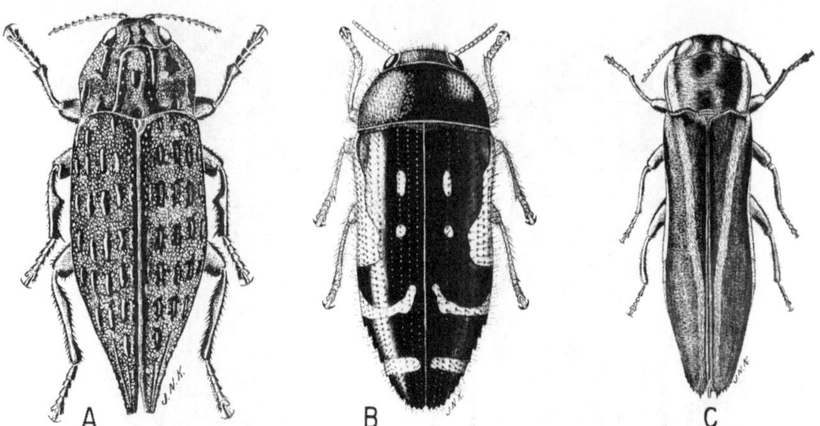

Fig. 22-35. Metallic wood-boring beetles. A, *Dicérca tenebròsa* (Kirby); B, *Acmaeódera pulchélla* (Herbst); C, *Ágrilus bilineàtus* (Weber). (Courtesy of Knull.)

LeConte, sometimes placed in a separate family (the Brachypséctridae) is a yellowish-brown beetle, 5 to 6 millimeters in length and shaped like a broad click beetle; this beetle has been taken in Texas, Utah, and California.

FAMILY **Ptilodactýlidae:** The members of this group are elongate-oval in shape, brownish in color, and 4 to 6 millimeters in length; segments 4 to 10 of the antennae bear a long slender basal process as long as the segments. The ptilodactylids occur on vegetation in swampy places. The larvae of some species are aquatic, while others occur in leaf mold or grass roots.

FAMILY **Helódidae**—Marsh Beetles: The helodids are oval beetles 2 to 4 millimeters in length and occur on vegetation in swampy places and in damp rotting debris; some species have enlarged hind femora and are active jumpers. The larvae are aquatic.

FAMILY **Býrrhidae**—Pill Beetles: The pill beetles are oval, convex, 5 to 10 millimeters in length, with the head bent downward and concealed from above, and with wide hind coxae that extend to the elytra. These insects usually occur in sandy situations, such as lake shores, where they may be found under debris. When disturbed, they draw up their legs and remain motionless.

FAMILY **Nosodéndridae:** This family includes two species of *Nosodéndron,* one occurring in the East and the other in the West. The eastern species, *N. unicólor* Say, is an oval, convex, black beetle 5 to 6 millimeters in length and occurs under the bark of dead logs and in debris. The nosodendrids are similar to the Býrrhidae, but have the head visible from above and the elytra bear rows of short yellow hairs.

FAMILY **Chelonarìidae:** Only one rare species of chelonariid occurs in the United States, *Chelonàrium lecóntei* Thomson, which occurs from North Carolina to Florida. This insect is oval, convex, 4 to 5 millimeters in length, and is black with patches of white pubescence on the elytra. The legs are retractile, and the third tarsal segment is bilobed. The larvae are aquatic, and the adults are found on vegetation.

FAMILY **Dryópidae** — Long-Toed Water Beetles: The members of this and the following three families are sometimes called the long-toed water beetles because the tarsi and claws of the adults are very long (Figure 22-10 H), and the larvae (and usually also the adults) are aquatic. The dryopids are 1 to 8 millimeters in length, dull gray or brown in color, with the head more or less withdrawn into the prothorax, and have the body covered with fine pubescence. The pubescence serves to hold a film of air around the body when the insect submerges. These beetles are usually found crawling about on the bottoms of streams; the adults may leave the streams and fly about, especially at night. The larvae are flat and oval, and also occur in streams.

FAMILY **Limníchidae**—Minute Marsh-Loving Beetles: The members of this group are very similar to the dryopids, but have the middle coxae widely separated and the hind coxae contiguous or nearly so. The limnichids are 1 to 2 millimeters in length, broadly oval, very convex, and have the body densely clothed with fine pubescence. They are found in the wet sand or soil along the margins of streams.

FAMILY **Psephénidae**—Water-Penny Beetles: These beetles derive their common name from the peculiar shape of the larvae (Figure 22-37). The larvae (called water pennies) are very flat and almost circular, and occur on the under sides of stones or other objects in streams and wave-swept shores. A single species, *Psephènus hérricki* DeKay, occurs in the East; the adult (Figure 22-38 A) is a somewhat flattened blackish beetle 4 to 6 millimeters in length, which may be found in the vegetation bordering streams, or in the water where the larvae occur. Some other species occur in the West.

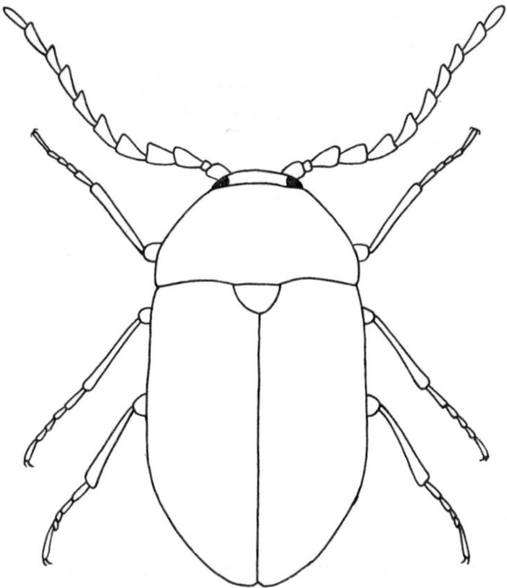

Fig. 22-36. A soft-bodied plant beetle, *Ectópria nervòsa* (Melsheimer) (Dascíllidae).

FAMILY **Élmidae**—Riffle Beetles: These beetles generally occur on the stones or debris in the riffles of streams; a few species occur in ponds and swamps, and a few are terrestrial. Riffle beetles are somewhat cylindrical in shape, with very smooth elytra (Figure 22-38 B), and most of them

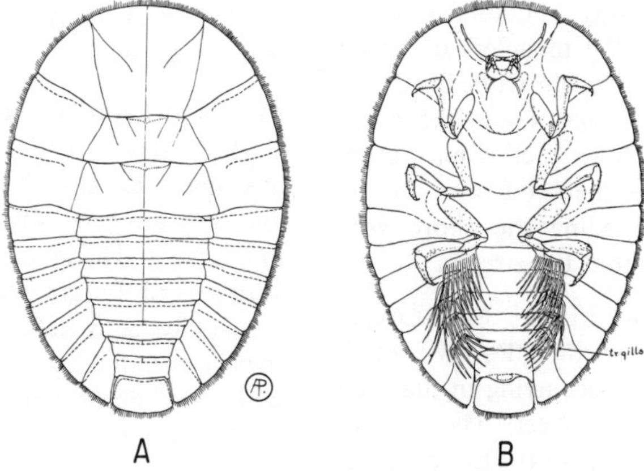

Fig. 22-37. A water penny, the larva of *Psephènus hérricki* DeKay. A, dorsal view; B, ventral view; *tr gills*, tracheal gills. (Courtesy of Peterson. Reprinted by permission.)

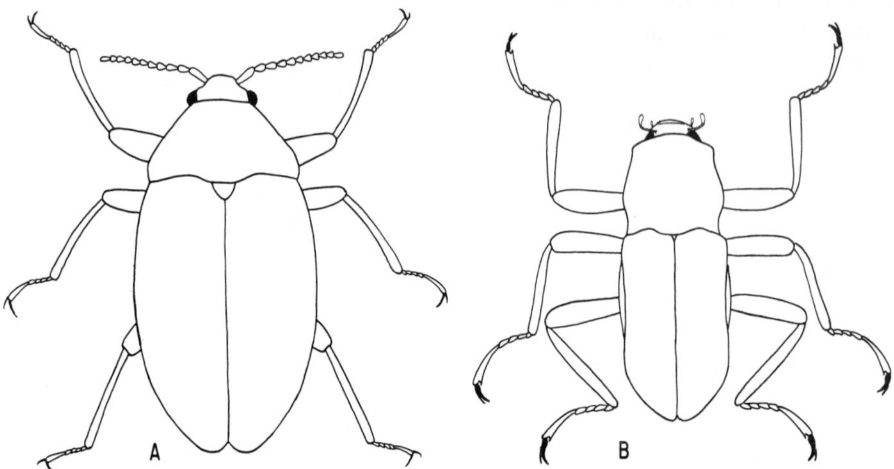

Fig. 22-38. Long-toed water beetles. A, a water-penny beetle, *Psephènus hérricki* DeKay; B, a riffle beetle, *Macrónychus glabràtus* (Say). 15 ×.

are 3.5 millimeters in length or less. The larvae of most species, which occur in the same situations as the adults, are long and slender; those of *Élmis* (=*Hélmis*) are flat and elliptical, resembling somewhat the larvae of the Psephénidae.

FAMILY **Heterocéridae**—Variegated Mud-Loving Beetles: The heterocerids are a small group of flattened, oblong, densely pubescent beetles that live in mud or sand along the banks of streams or lakes. The front and middle tibiae are greatly dilated and spiny and are used in burrowing. The larvae are found in the same situations as the adults. The family contains a single genus, *Heterócerus,* the members of which are blackish or brownish with bands or spots of dull yellow, and 4.0 to 6.5 millimeters in length. These beetles may often be forced to leave their burrows in the stream bank by flooding the shore with water splashed up from the stream.

FAMILY **Georýssidae**—Minute Mud-Loving Beetles: This group includes two small and rare species, one occurring in the East and the other in the West. The eastern species, *Georyssus pusíllus* LeConte, is about 1.7 millimeters in length, black, and broadly oval in shape. These beetles occur in the mud along the banks of lakes and streams.

FAMILY **Derodóntidae**—Tooth-Necked Fungus Beetles: The derodontids are small, usually brownish beetles less than 4 millimeters in length, and have a pair of ocelli on the head near the inner margins of the compound eyes (Figure 22-12 C). The members of the genus *Derodóntus* have three or four strong teeth or notches along the lateral margins of the pronotum; other genera lack these teeth. The elytra completely cover the abdomen, and each bears many rows of large square punctures. These beetles occur on fungi and under the bark of rotting logs.

FAMILY **Monotómidae** — Small Flattened Bark Beetles: The members of this group are small, less than 3 millimeters in length, and they are generally found under bark or in ant nests. The antennae are 10-segmented with a 1- or 2-segmented club, and the head is usually constricted behind the eyes to form a slender neck. The body is covered with short dense pubescence, to which dirt often adheres.

FAMILY **Rhizophágidae** — Root - Eating Beetles: These are small, slender, dark-colored beetles, 1.5 to 5.0 millimeters in length, and usually occur under bark; a few species live in ant nests. The antennae have a 1- or 2-segmented club, the posterior edge of the pronotum is a little narrower than the anterior edge, and the first and fifth abdominal sterna are longer than the others.

FAMILY **Monómmidae:** The monommids are black oval beetles, 5 to 12 millimeters in length, and are flattened ventrally and convex dorsally. They have a 5-5-4 tarsal formula with the first segment relatively long; the anterior coxal cavities are open behind; and the antennae terminate in a 2- or 3-segmented club and are received in grooves on the under side of the prothorax. The adults are found in leaf litter, and the larvae live in rotten wood. The group is a small one, with the five United States species occurring in the southern states, from Florida to southern California.

FAMILY **Sphíndidae**—Dry-Fungus Beetles: The sphindids are broadly oval to oblong, convex, dark brown to black beetles 1.5 to 3.0 millimeters in length. They have a 5-5-4 tarsal formula, and the 10-segmented antennae terminate in a 2- or 3-segmented club. The sphindids occur in dry fungi, such as the shelf fungi on tree trunks. Six relatively rare species occur in the United States.

FAMILY **Cryptophágidae**—Silken Fungus Beetles: These beetles are 1 to 5 millimeters in length, elongate-oval in shape, and yellowish brown and covered with a silky pubescence. They feed on fungi, decaying vegetation, and similar materials, and usually occur in decaying vegetable matter; some species occur in the nests of wasps or bumble bees.

FAMILY **Erotýlidae** — Pleasing Fungus Beetles: The erotylids are small to medium-sized, oval, and usually shiny beetles that are found on fungi or may be attracted to sap; they often occur beneath the bark of dead stumps, especially where rotting fungus abounds. Some of the erotylids are brightly patterned with orange or red and black. The species in this group that have the tarsi distinctly 5-segmented are by some authorities placed in a separate family, the Dácnidae; the largest species of dacnids (*Megalodácne*) are about 20 millimeters in length and are black with two orange-red bands across the elytra (Figure 22-39 A). In other erotylids the fourth tarsal segment is very small, so that the tarsi appear 4-segmented; these beetles are smaller, 8 millimeters in length or less. Some erotylids are fairly common insects.

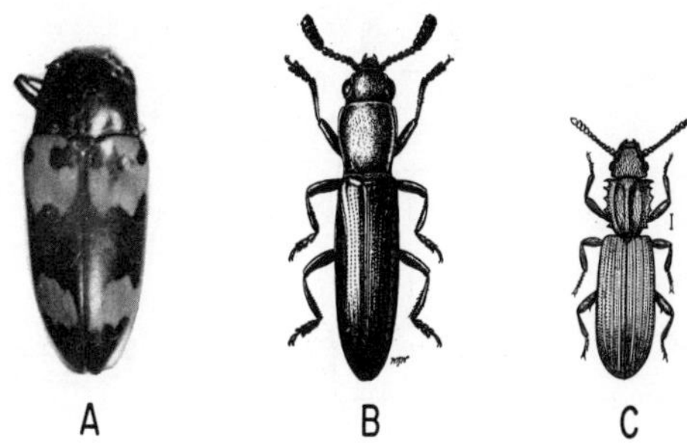

Fig. 22-39. A, a pleasing fungus beetle, *Megalodácne hèros* (Say), $1\frac{1}{2}\times$; B, a lizard beetle, *Langùria mozárdi* Latrielle, $3\times$; C, the saw-toothed grain beetle, *Oryzaéphilus surinaménsis* (Linn.) (the line indicates one half the actual length). (B and C, courtesy of USDA.)

FAMILY **Languriidae**—Lizard Beetles: The lizard beetles are narrow and elongate, 5 to 10 millimeters in length, and have the pronotum reddish and the elytra black (Figure 22-39 B). They feed on the leaves and stems of many common plants, including goldenrod, ragweed, fleabane, and clover. The larvae of many species are stem borers; the larvae of the clover stem borer (*Langùria mozárdi* Latrielle) attack clover and sometimes cause considerable damage.

FAMILY **Cucùjidae**—Flat Bark Beetles: The beetles in this group are extremely flat and are either reddish, brownish, or yellowish in color. They are usually found under the bark of freshly cut logs, chiefly maple, beech, elm, ash, and poplar. The largest cucujids, which belong to the genera

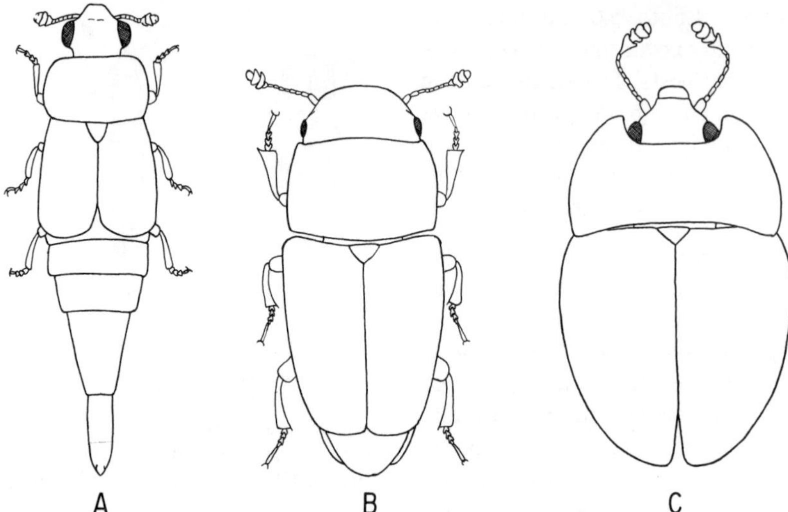

Fig. 22-40. Representative Nitidùlidae. A, *Conótelus obscùrus* Erichson, 15 ×; B, *Glischró-chilus quadrisignàtus* (Say), $7\frac{1}{2}$ ×; C, *Lobìopa* sp., $7\frac{1}{2}$ ×.

Cùcujus and *Catogènus,* reach a length of about $\frac{1}{2}$ inch. Our only species of *Cùcujus, C. clávipes* Fabricius, is uniform red in color; a common species of *Catogènus, C. rùfus* (Fabricius) is brown and has the elytra grooved.

Most of the cucujids are predaceous on mites and small insects, which they find under bark. The larvae are usually flattened. Some species, including those of *Catogènus,* are parasitic in the larval stage on species of Cerambýcidae and Bracónidae, and undergo a hypermetamorphosis.

FAMILY **Silvánidae**—Flat Grain Beetles: The silvanids are very closely related to the Cucùjidae, and are included in that family by some authorities. They are small, elongate, flattened beetles, usually less than 3 millimeters in length; they differ from most of the cucujids in that they have the antennae clubbed, the third antennal segment shorter than the second, and the tarsi never lobed beneath. Some species occur under bark, and others feed on stored grain or meal. One of the most important species of the latter type is the saw-toothed grain beetle, *Oryzaéphilus surinaménsis* Linn., so called because of the toothed lateral margins of the pronotum (Figure 22-39 C).

FAMILY **Phalácridae** — Shining Flower Beetles: The phalacrids are oval, shining, convex beetles, 1 to 3 millimeters in length, and are usually brownish in color. They are sometimes quite common on the flowers of goldenrod and other composites; the larvae develop in the heads of these flowers.

FAMILY **Nitidùlidae**—Sap Beetles: The members of this family vary considerably in size, shape, and habits. Most of them are small, 12 millimeters in length or less, elongate or oval, and in a few the elytra are short and expose the terminal abdominal segments (Figure 22-40). Most nitidulids are found where plant fluids are fermenting or souring; for example, around decaying fruits or melons, flowing sap, and some types of fungi. A few occur on or near the dried carcasses of dead animals, and several occur in flowers. Others are very common beneath the loose bark of dead stumps and logs, especially if these are damp enough to be moldy.

FAMILY **Murmidìidae:** This group includes a few species of minute beetles, 1.5 millimeters in length or less. They are oval in shape and somewhat flattened, the antennae are 10-segmented with a 2-segmented club that is received in a cavity of the prothorax, the coxae are widely separated, and the basal segment of the abdomen is longer than the others. The five United States species in this group are placed in the family Colydìidae by some authorities.

FAMILY **Monoèdidae:** The monoedids are represented in the United States by a single species, *Monoèdus guttàtus* Leconte, found in southern Florida. This beetle is 2 millimeters in length and is reddish yellow with the antennae and scutellum black and with five elongate black marks on each elytron; it is a tropical species and is quite rare in this country.

FAMILY **Lathridìidae**—Minute Brown Scavenger Beetles: The lathridiids are elongate-oval, reddish-brown beetles 1 to 3 millimeters in length; the pronotum is narrower than the elytra, and each elytron bears six or eight rows of punctures. The tarsi are 3-segmented (Figure 22-10 I), or (males) 2-3-3 or 2-2-3. These beetles are found in moldy material and debris, and sometimes on flowers.

FAMILY **Mycetaèidae**—Mycetaeid Fungus Beetles: These are small beetles, 4 millimeters in length or less, that are closely related to the Endomýchidae (and are placed in that family by some authorities). The tarsi are 4-segmented, with the third segment easily visible, and the antennal club is 3-segmented. Some mycetaeids are found on flowers, and others occur in debris and decaying materials. One species, *Mycetaèa hírta* (Marsham), is occasionally a pest in granaries and warehouses, due to its spreading mold infection. This group is a small one, with only 15 species in the United States.

FAMILY **Endomýchidae**—Handsome Fungus Beetles: These are small oval beetles, 3.5 to 8.0 millimeters in length, somewhat similar to the Coccinéllidae, but they have the head easily visible from above, and there are two longitudinal grooves in the posterior half of the pronotum. They are smooth and shiny, and usually brightly colored. Most of them occur under bark in rotting wood, in fungi, or in decaying fruits; they feed on fungi and mold.

FAMILY **Coccinéllidae**—Ladybird Beetles or Ladybugs: The ladybird beetles are a well-known group of small, oval, convex, and often brightly colored insects. They may be distinguished from the chrysomelids, which have a similar shape, by the three distinct tarsal segments (chrysomelids appear to have four tarsal segments). Most of the lady-

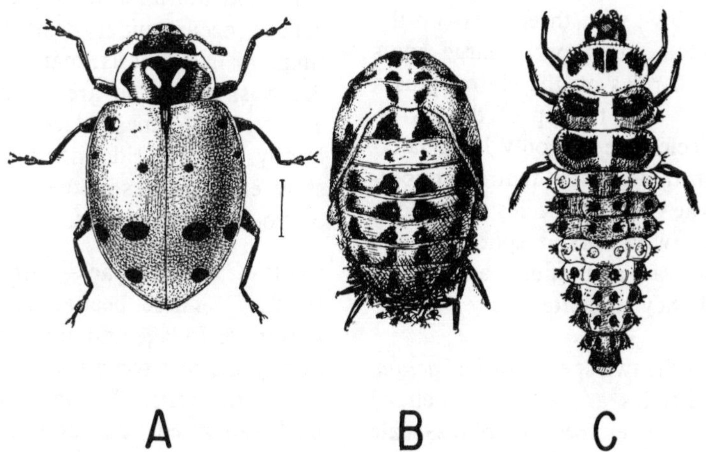

Fig. 22-41. A ladybird beetle, *Hippodàmia convérgens* Guerin. A, adult; B, pupa; C, larva. The line at right of adult indicates actual size. (Courtesy of USDA.)

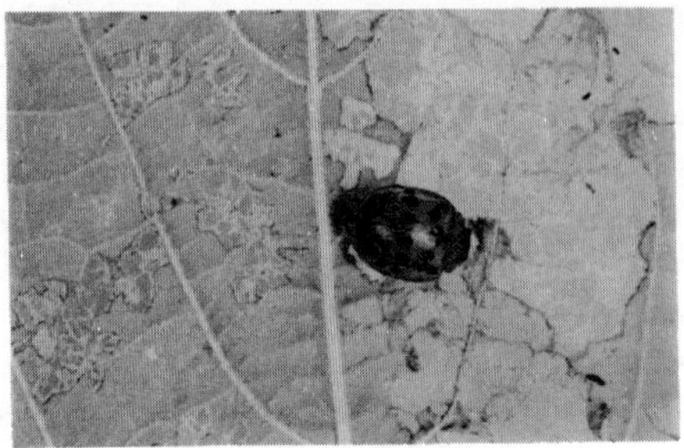

Fig. 22-42. The Mexican bean beetle, *Epiláchna varivéstis* Mulsant. (Courtesy of the Illinois Natural History Survey.)

bird beetles are predaceous, both as larvae and adults, and feed chiefly on aphids; they are frequently quite common, particularly on vegetation where aphids are numerous. Ladybirds hibernate as adults, frequently in large aggregations, under leaves or in debris.

The larvae of ladybird beetles (Figure 22-41 C) are elongate, somewhat flattened, and covered with minute tubercles or spines. They are usually spotted or banded with bright colors. These larvae are usually found in aphid colonies.

Two fairly common phytophagous species in this group are serious garden pests, the Mexican bean beetle, *Epiláchna varivéstis* Mulsant, and the squash beetle *E. boreàlis* (Fabricius). The Mexican bean beetle (Figure 22-42) is yellowish, with eight spots on each elytron; the squash beetle is pale orange-yellow, with three spots on the pronotum and a dozen or so large spots arranged in two rows on the elytra, plus a large black dot near the tip of the elytra. These two species are the only large ladybird beetles in this country that are pubescent. The larvae of these species are yellow, oval in shape, with forked spines on the body. Both larvae and adults are phytophagous, and they are often very destructive.

Except for the two species of *Epiláchna,* the ladybird beetles are a very beneficial group of insects. They feed on aphids, scale insects, and many other injurious species. During serious outbreaks of aphids or scale insects, large numbers of ladybird beetles are sometimes imported into the infested areas to serve as a means of control; the cottony cushion scale, *Icérya púrchasi* Maskell, a pest of citrus in California, has been kept under control for a number of years by means of a ladybird beetle, *Rodòlia cardinàlis* (Mulsant), imported from Australia.

FAMILY **Bytùridae**—Fruitworm Beetles: The byturids are small, oval, hairy beetles, pale brown to orange in color and mostly 3.5 to 4.5 millimeters in length, with clubbed antennae. The second and third tarsal segments are lobed beneath. The group is a small one, with only five species in the United States; the only common eastern species is *Bytùrus unicólor* Say, a reddish yellow to blackish beetle 3.5 to 4.5 millimeters in length, which feeds on the flowers of raspberry and blackberry; the larvae, which are often called raspberry fruitworms, sometimes do serious damage to berries.

FAMILY **Colydiidae** — Cylindrical Bark Beetles: The colydiids are hard-bodied, shiny beetles 1 to 18 millimeters in length; most species are elongate and cylindrical, but some are oval or oblong and somewhat flattened. The antennae are 10- or 11-segmented and terminate in a 2- or 3-segmented club, and the tarsi are 4-segmented. These beetles occur under dead bark, in shelf fungi, or in ant nests; many species are predaceous, but some are plant feeders, and a few (sometimes placed in a separate family, the Bothridéridae) are in the larval stage ectoparasites of the larvae and pupae of wood-boring beetles.

FAMILY **Anthícidae** — Antlike Flower Beetles: These beetles usually occur on flowers or foliage and are somewhat antlike in appearance; some occur under stones or logs or in debris. The hind coxae are usually well separated, the eyes are entire and coarsely faceted, and the head is deflexed and strongly constricted behind the eyes.

The anthicids are 2 to 12 millimeters in length. The species of *Notóxus* have the pronotum prolonged over the head in an anterior protuberance.

FAMILY **Euglénidae**—Antlike Leaf Beetles: These beetles are similar to those in the preceding family, but have only four abdominal sterna (the first two are fused together), and the eyes are emarginate. The euglenids are somewhat antlike in appearance, reddish yellow to dark in color, and 1.5 to 3.0 millimeters in length. They are found on foliage or flowers.

FAMILY **Mycetophágidae**—Hairy Fungus Beetles: The mycetophagids are broadly oval, very hairy beetles, 1.5 to 5.5 millimeters in length; they are brown to black in color, and are often brightly marked with reddish or orange. These beetles occur under bark and in fungi.

FAMILY **Cephalòidae**—False Longhorn Beetles: These beetles are elongate, convex, and somewhat similar to a cerambycid in shape (hence the common name). They are brownish to dark in color, 8 to 20 millimeters in length, and the head is somewhat diamond-shaped—narrowed behind the eyes to form a slender neck. They have a 5-5-4 tarsal formula, and the tarsal claws are provided with rows of long spines beneath, and there is a long pad under each claw. The group is a small one, with ten species known from the United States; little is known of their habits except that the adults are sometimes found on flowers.

FAMILY **Oedeméridae**—False Blister Beetles: The oedemerids are slender, soft-bodied beetles 5.0 to 20 millimeters in length. They are usually pale in color, but often have blue, yellow, red, or orange markings; the common eastern oedemerids are yellowish brown with the tip of the elytra black. They have a 5-5-4 tarsal formula, and the penultimate tarsal segment is dilated and densely hairy beneath (Figure 22-10 C); the segment preceding this dilated segment is sometimes so firmly united with it that the tarsal formula may appear to be 4-4-3. The pronotum is somewhat narrowed posteriorly and narrower than the elytra, and the eyes are often emarginate. The adults are usually found on flowers or foliage, and are attracted to lights at night; the larvae breed in moist decaying wood, especially driftwood.

FAMILY **Othnìidae**—False Tiger Beetles: These beetles are superficially similar to tiger beetles, but have a 5-5-4 tarsal formula and the antennae terminate in a 3-segmented club. They are brown to dark in color, often mottled, and 5 to 9 millimeters in length. The adults are found on the leaves of trees and on cacti, and the larvae live in rotting leaves or under bark. Five species of *Elacàtis* occur in the United States; one has been reported from Virginia, while the others occur in the western states.

FAMILY **Eurystéthidae:** The eurystethids are 3 to 4 millimeters in length, black, subcylindrical, long-legged beetles belonging to the extremely rare genus *Eurystèthes* (= *Eurystèthus*), and are found along the seashore from California to Alaska (and also in Iran). They have a 5-5-4 tarsal formula, and all the tarsal segments are pubescent beneath; the tarsal segments are equal in size except the last, which is long and strong and has large, simple claws. There are six visible abdominal sternites, but the first two are firmly fused together and the suture between them is almost entirely obliterated. The head is sunk in the thorax almost to the eyes. The elytra meet imperfectly, each being broadly rounded apically and almost covering the tip of the abdomen; there are no hind wings. These interesting little insects spend their entire life in thin, deep cracks in the rocks below the high-tide level along the seacoast, and are often submerged for hours at a time; they are so rare that few professional entomologists have ever seen a specimen, even in museums.

FAMILY **Salpíngidae**—Narrow-Waisted Bark Beetles: The common name of these beetles refers to the fact that many species have the pronotum narrowed basally, causing them to superficially resemble some of the ground beetles. They are dark in color and 2 to 15 millimeters in length; in some species the head is more or less prolonged into a snout. The adults and larvae are predaceous; the adults occur under rocks, under bark, in leaf litter, or on vegetation.

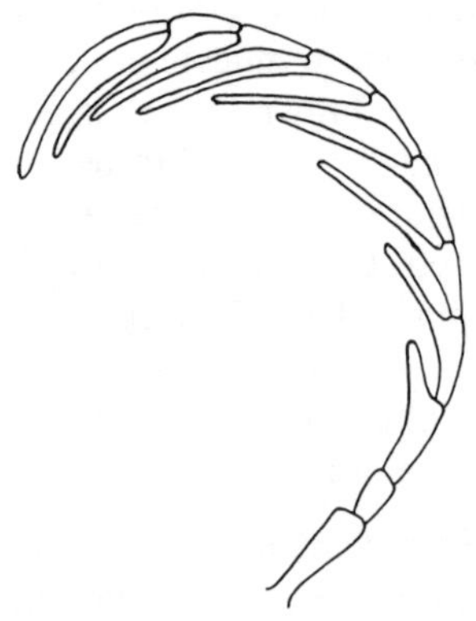

Fig. 22-43. Antenna of *Pyrochròa* (Pyrochròidae).

FAMILY **Pyrochròidae** — Fire - Colored Beetles: The pyrochroids are 9 to 17 millimeters in length, and are usually black, with the pronotum reddish or yellowish. The head and pronotum are narrower than the elytra, and the elytra are somewhat broader posteriorly. The antennae are serrate to pectinate, and in the males almost plumose (Figure 22-43), with long slender processes on segments 3 to 10. The eyes are often quite large. The adults are found on foliage and flowers, and sometimes under bark; the larvae occur under the bark of dead trees.

FAMILY **Pedílidae:** The pedilids are closely related to the anthicids, but differ in having the hind coxae usually contiguous and the eyes finely faceted and usually emarginate. They are elongate, cylindrical, or slightly flattened beetles 7 to 13 millimeters in length, and are brown to black in color with pale or red markings. The pronotum is narrowed posteriorly and more or less oval or rounded. Some pedilids (for example, *Pédilus*) are commonly found on vegetation in damp areas; others, particularly in the western states, occur in dry sandy areas.

FAMILY **Hemipéplidae:** The hemipeplids are elongate, slender, flattened, yellowish brown beetles that were formerly included in the Cucùjidae. They are 8 to 12 millimeters in length. Two species of *Hemipéplus* occur in Florida, Georgia, and California.

FAMILY **Melòidae**—Blister Beetles: The blister beetles are narrow and elongate, the elytra are soft and flexible, and the pronotum is narrower than either the head or the elytra (Figure 22-44). These beetles are called blister beetles because the body fluids of the commoner species contain cantharadin, a substance that often causes blisters when applied to the skin. This substance is extracted from the bodies of a common European species [*Lýtta vesicatòria* (Linn.), sometimes called the Spanish-fly] and used as a drug; in medical practice, this drug is used to stimulate certain internal organs.

Several species of blister beetles are important pests, feeding on potatoes, tomatoes, and other plants. Two of these are often called the "old-fashioned potato beetles," *Epicàuta vittàta* (Fabricius) (with orange and black longitudinal stripes) and *E. marginàta* (Fabricius) (black, with the margins of the elytra and the sutural stripe gray, Figure 22-44 C); these beetles are from 12 to 20 millimeters in length. *E. pennsylvánica* (DeGeer) is a common black meloid, 7 to 13 millimeters in length, that occurs on the flowers of goldenrod.

The larvae of most blister beetles are considered beneficial, for they feed on grasshopper eggs. A few live in bee nests in the larval stage, where they feed on bee eggs and on the food stored in the cells with the eggs.

The life history of blister beetles is rather complex; these insects undergo a

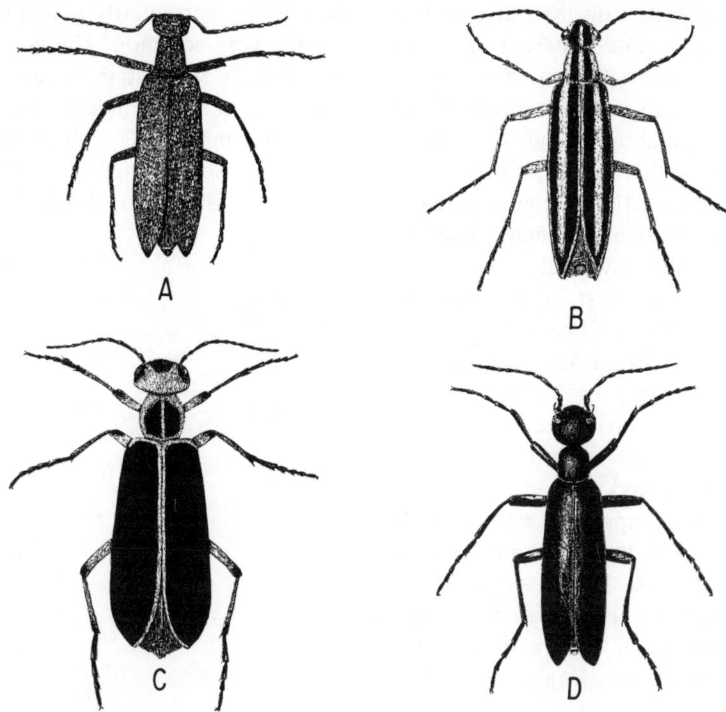

Fig. 22-44. Blister beetles. A, *Macrobàsis unicólor* (Kirby); B, the three-striped blister beetle, *Epicàuta lemniscàta* (Fabricius); C, *Epicàuta marginàta* (Fabricius); D, *Epicàuta fùnebris* Horn. (Courtesy of Baerg and the Arkansas Agricultural Experiment Station.)

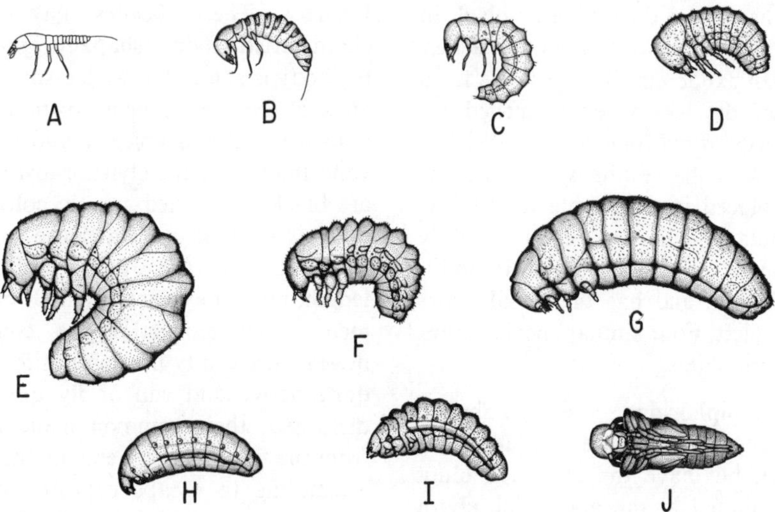

Fig. 22-45. Larval and pupal instars of the black blister beetle, *Epicàuta pennsylvánica* (DeGeer), showing hypermetamorphosis. A, newly hatched first instar, or triungulin; B, fully fed first instar; C, second instar; D, third instar; E, fourth instar; F, newly molted fifth instar; G, gorged fifth instar; H, sixth instar (coarctate larva or pseudopupa); I, seventh instar; J, pupa. (Courtesy of Horsfall and the Arkansas Agricultural Experiment Station.)

hypermetamorphosis, with the different larval instars being quite different in form (Figure 22-45). The first larval instar is an active, long-legged form called a triungulin; it seeks out a grasshopper egg or a bee's nest, and then molts. In the species that develop in bee nests, the triungulin usually climbs upon a flower and attaches itself to a bee that visits the flower; the bee carries the triungulin to the nest, whereupon the triungulin attacks the bee's eggs. The second instar is somewhat similar to the triungulin, but the legs are shorter. In the third, fourth, and fifth instars the larva becomes thicker and somewhat scarabaeiform. The sixth instar has a darker and thicker exoskeleton and lacks functional appendages; this instar is usually known as the coarctate larva or pseudopupa, and it is the instar that hibernates. The seventh instar is small, white, and active (though legless), but apparently does not feed and soon transforms to the true pupa.

The members of the genus *Méloe,* some of which are about an inch in length, have very short elytra that overlap just behind the scutellum, and the hind wings are lacking; these insects are dark blue or black in color. They are sometimes called oil beetles, for they often exude an oily substance from the joints of the legs when disturbed.

Tetraónyx quadrimaculàta Fabricius, which occurs in the southeastern states, is sometimes placed in a separate family, the Tetraonýchidae. This beetle is brightly colored orange and black, about 10 millimeters in length, and has the tarsal claws very deeply cleft. Four similar species occur in the western states.

FAMILY **Rhipiphóridae** — Wedge-Shaped Beetles: These beetles are similar to the Mordéllidae, but have the abdomen blunt instead of pointed at the apex. The elytra are more or less pointed apically and usually do not cover the tip of the abdomen; in some species the elytra are quite short. The antennae are pectinate in the males and serrate in the females. These beetles occur on flowers, particularly goldenrod, but they are not very common. The larval stages are parasitic on various wasps (Véspidae, Scolìidae, and Tiphìidae); they undergo a hypermetamorphosis similar to that in the Melòidae. Some females in this family are wingless and look much like larvae.

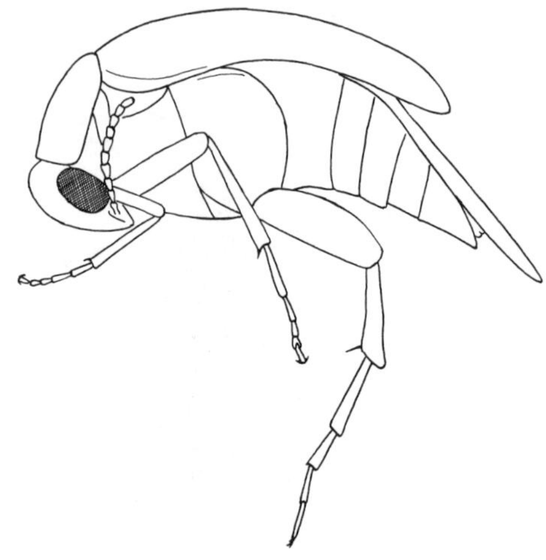

Fig. 22-46. A tumbling flower beetle, *Mordélla marginàta* Melsheimer; 15 ×.

FAMILY **Mordéllidae**—Tumbling Flower Beetles: These beetles have a rather characteristic body shape (Figure 22-46); the body is somewhat wedge-shaped, humpbacked, the head is bent down, and the abdomen is pointed apically and extends beyond the tips of the elytra. Most mordellids are black or mottled gray in color, and the body is covered with a dense pubescence. Most of them are 3 to 7 millimeters in length, but some reach a length of 14 millimeters. These beetles are common on flowers, especially the composites. They are quite active and run or fly quickly when disturbed; their common name is derived from the tumbling movements they make in attempting to escape capture. The larvae live in decaying wood and in plant pith; some are predaceous.

FAMILY **Allecùlidae** — Comb - Clawed Beetles: The members of this family are small beetles, 4 to 12 millimeters in length, elongate-oval, and usually brownish or black with a somewhat glossy or shiny appearance due to the pubescence on the body. They can be distinguished from related groups by the pectinate tarsal claws (Figure 22-6 B). The adults are found on flowers and foliage, fungi, and under dead bark; the larvae resemble wireworms and live in rotting wood, plant debris, or fungi.

FAMILY **Tenebriónidae**—Darkling Beetles: The tenebrionids are a large and varied group, but can be distinguished by the 5-5-4 tarsal formula, the front coxal cavities closed behind (Figure 22-4 B), the eyes usually notched (Figure 22-11 B), the antennae nearly always 11-segmented and either filiform or moniliform, and five visible abdominal sterna. Most tenebrionids are black or brownish (Figures 22-47, 22-48), but a few (for example, *Diapèris*) have red markings on the elytra. Many are black and smooth and resemble ground beetles. Some of the species that feed on the bracket fungi are brownish and rough-bodied and resemble bits of bark; one such species, *Bolitothèrus cornùtus* (Panzer), has two hornlike protuberances extending forward from the pronotum. The fungus-inhabiting members of the genus *Diapèris* are somewhat similar in general appearance to the ladybird beetles (Figure 22-48 B).

Throughout the arid regions of the United States these beetles take over the ecological niche that is occupied by the Carábidae in the more verdant areas, being very common under stones, rubbish, beneath loose bark, and even being attracted to lights at night.

The most distinctive habit of the members of the extremely large genus *Eleòdes* is the ridiculous position they assume when running from possible danger; the tip of the abdomen is elevated to an angle of about 45 degrees from the ground, and the beetles almost seem to be standing on their head as they run. When disturbed or picked up, they emit a black fluid with a very disagreeable odor.

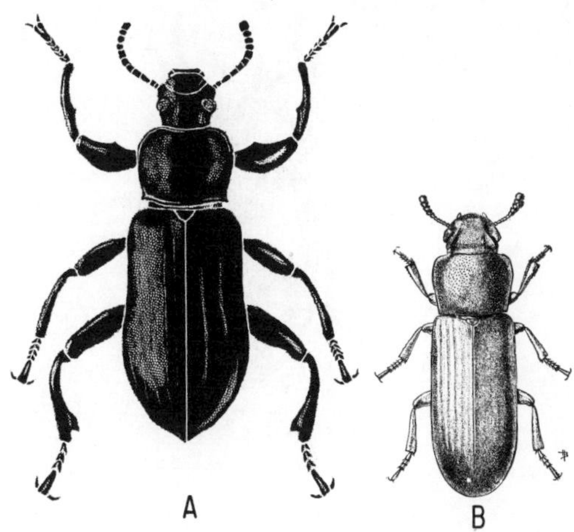

Fig. 22-47. Darkling beetles. A, *Mérinus laèvis* (Olivier), 2 ×; B, the confused flour beetle, *Tribòlium confùsum* Duval, 10 ×. (A, courtesy of Triplehorn; B, courtesy of USDA.)

Most tenebrionids feed on plant materials of some sort. A few are common pests of stored grain and flour and are often very destructive. The beetles in the genus *Tenèbrio* are black or dark brown, 13 to 17 millimeters in length, and feed on stored grain in both larval and adult stages; the larvae are commonly called mealworms and are quite similar to wireworms. The members of the genus *Tribòlium* are oblong brown beetles, 5 millimeters or less in length (Figure 22-47 B); both adults and larvae commonly occur in flour, corn meal, dog food, cereals, dried fruits, and similar materials.

About 1400 species of tenebrionids occur in the United States, of which only about 140 occur in the East.

FAMILY **Lagrìidae**—Long-Jointed Bark Beetles: The lagriids are slender beetles that can usually be recognized by their characteristic shape (Figure 22-49 B), their 5-5-4 tarsal formula, and the elongate apical antennal segment (Figure 22-8 D). They are 10 to 15 millimeters in length and dark metallic in color. The adults are found on foliage or occasionally under bark; the larvae breed in plant debris and under the bark of fallen trees.

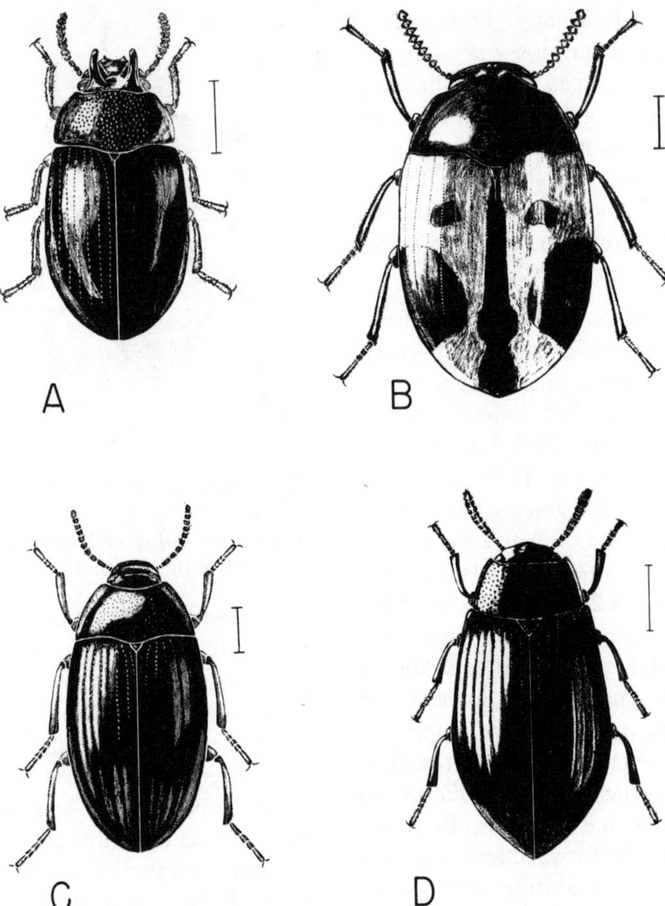

Fig. 22-48. Darkling beetles. A, *Neomìda bicórnis* (Fabricius); B, *Diapèris maculàta* (Olivier); C, *Platydèma subcostàtum* Laporte and Brulle; D, *Scaphidèma aenèolum* LeConte. The lines represent 1 mm. (Courtesy of Triplehorn.)

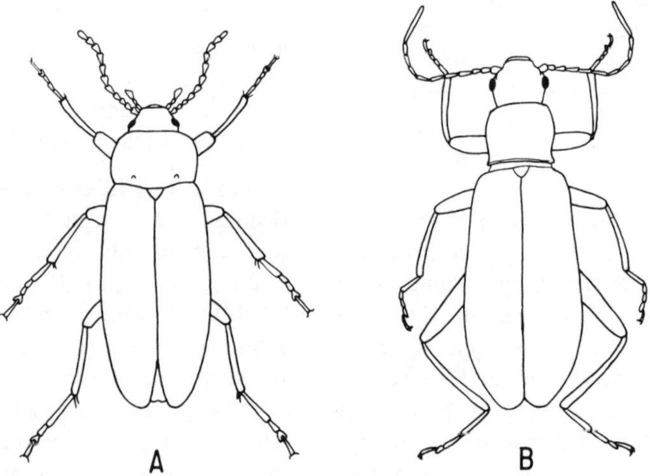

Fig. 22-49. A, a melandryid, *Émmesa labiàta* (Say); B, a lagriid, *Arthromácra* sp. 4 ×.

FAMILY **Melandrỳidae**—False Darkling Beetles: The members of this group are elongate-oval, somewhat flattened beetles that are usually found under bark or logs; some species occur on flowers and foliage. They are mostly dark-colored and vary in length from 3 to 20 millimeters; they can usually be recognized by the 5-5-4 tarsal formula and the two dents or impressions near the posterior border of the pronotum (Figure 22-49 A). The most common melandryids are the oval, black, eastern members of *Pénthe,* which are 5 to 8 millimeters long and are common under old dead bark; *P. pimèlia* (Fabricius) is entirely black, and *P. obliquàta* (Fabricius) has a bright orange scutellum.

FAMILY **Ptínidae**—Spider Beetles: The ptinids are long-legged beetles 1 to 5 millimeters in length that have the head and pronotum much narrower than the elytra, and are somewhat spiderlike in appearance (Figure 22-50). They are found in museums, where they attack collections, and often in old wooden buildings; some infest stored products; one species is known to pass its larval stages in rat droppings.

FAMILY **Anobiidae**—Drugstore and Death-Watch Beetles: These beetles are cylindrical to oval in shape, 1.2 to 9.0 millimeters in length, and have the head bent down under the prothorax and not visible from above (Figure 22-51). Most of them live in dry vegetable materials such as logs and twigs or under the bark of dead trees. Others pass the larval stage in fungi or in the seeds and stems of various plants. Some species, such as *Xestòbium rufovillòsum* (DeGeer) (Figure 22-51 F), are called death-watch beetles because they make a ticking sound as they bore through wood. Some of the anobiids are common and destructive pests. The drugstore beetle, *Stegòbium panícea* (Linn.) (Figure 22-51 E), infests various drugs and cereals; the cigarette beetle, *Losiodérma serricórne* (Fabricius) (Figure 22-51 C), is common in dried tobacco, museum specimens, and insect collections. Some wood-boring species, such as the furniture beetle, *Anòbium punctàtum* DeGeer (Figure 22-51 B), bore in timbers, woodwork, and furniture.

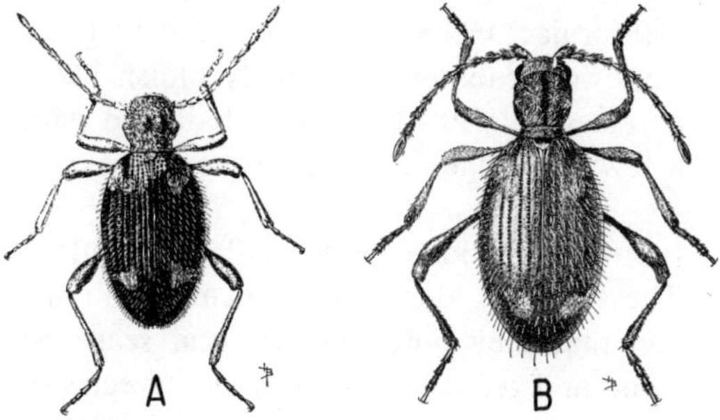

Fig. 22-50. Spider beetles, A, *Ptínus vílliger* (Reitter); B, *Ptínus fúr* (Linn.). (Courtesy of USDA.)

FAMILY **Bostríchidae**—Branch and Twig Borers: The beetles in this group are elongate, somewhat cylindrical, and the head is bent down and scarcely visible from above (Figure 22-52). Most species vary in length from 3.5 to 12.0 millimeters, but one western species, *Dinápate wrìghti* Horn, which breeds in palms, reaches a length of 52 millimeters. Most species in this group are wood-boring and attack living trees, dead twigs and branches, or seasoned lumber. The apple twig borer, *Amphícerus bicaudàtus* (Say), attacks the twigs of apple, pear, cherry, and other trees.

One species in this family that occurs in the West, *Scobícia déclivis* (LeConte), is rather unusual in that adults often bore into the lead sheathing of telephone cables. This insect normally bores in the wood of oak, maple, and other trees; it apparently does not feed as it bores into the cables. The beetle makes holes in the sheathing about 0.1 inch in diameter; these holes allow moisture to enter the cable, causing a short-circuiting of the wires and a consequent interruption of service. This insect is commonly known as the lead cable borer, or short-circuit beetle.

FAMILY **Psòidae**—Psoid Branch and Twig Beetles: These western beetles differ from

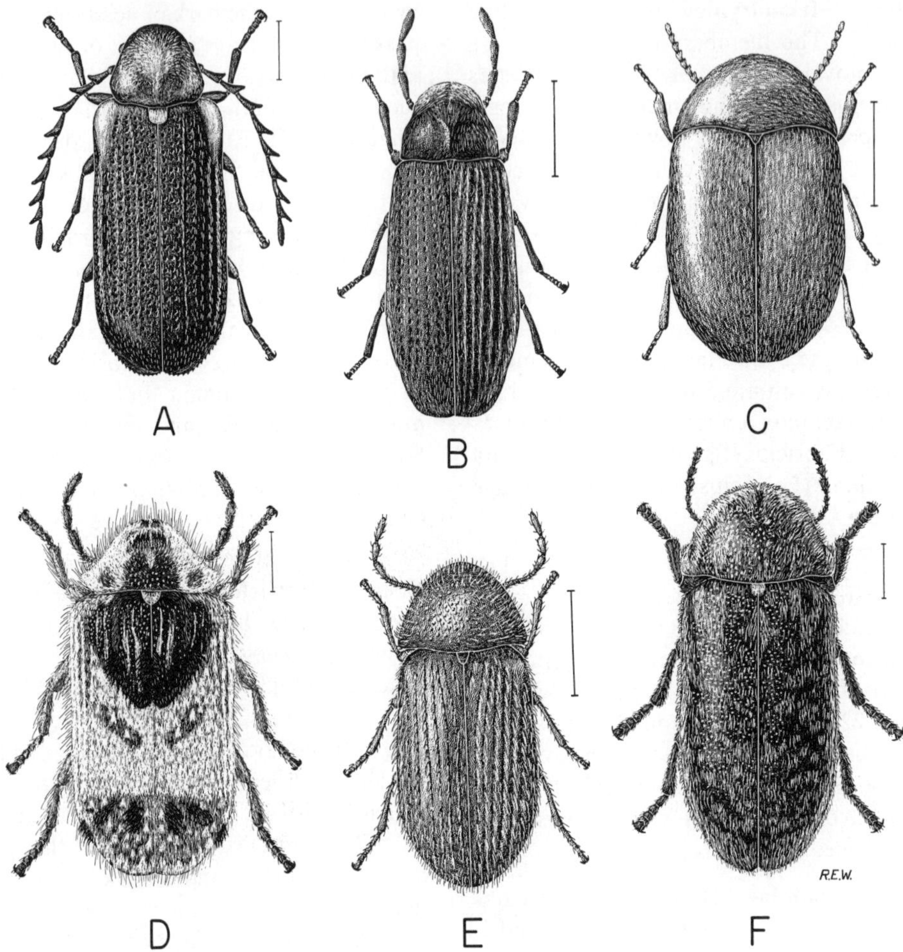

Fig. 22-51. Drugstore and death-watch beetles (Anobìidae). A, *Eucràda humeràlis* (Melsheimer); B, the furniture beetle, *Anòbium punctátum* DeGeer; C, the cigarette beetle, *Lasiodérma serricórne* (Fabricius); D, *Trichodésma gibbòsa* (Say); E, the drugstore beetle, *Stegòbium paníceum* (Linn.); F, death-watch beetle, *Xestòbium rufovillòsum* (DeGeer). The lines represent 1 mm. (Courtesy of R. E. White and the Ohio Biological Survey.)

the Bostríchidae chiefly in that they have the head large and easily visible from above and are equipped with large and strong mandibles. The members of the genus *Polý-caon* are 14 to 28 millimeters long, brown or black in color, and often cause great damage to orchards in California and Oregon by severely pruning the trees. The larvae tunnel through the heartwood of these trees, but the adults seldom enter the wood. *Psòa maculàta* (LeConte), 6 millimeters long, is the "spotted limb borer" of California; it breeds only in dead twigs of trees or shrubs and is usually bluish black or greenish with dense gray hair and with a few large lighter spots on the elytra.

FAMILY **Lýctidae**—Powder-Post Beetles: These beetles derive their name from the fact that they bore into dry and seasoned wood and reduce it to a powder. Species of *Lyctus* may completely destroy furniture, wooden beams (particularly in barns and cabins), tool handles, and hardwood floors.

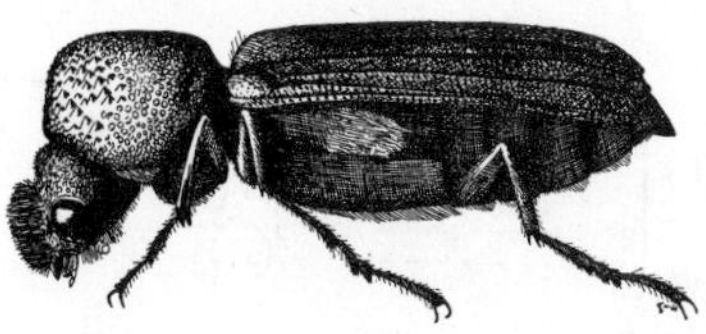

Fig. 22-52. A bostrichid beetle, *Ápate mónacha* Fabricius. (Courtesy of Wolcott and the *Journal of Agriculture* of the University of Puerto Rico.)

They live beneath the surface for months, and timbers from which the adults have emerged may be peppered with tiny holes, as though fine shot had been fired into them. These beetles do not enter wood that is painted or varnished. The powder-post beetles are 2.5 to 7.0 millimeters in length, elongate, slender; the head projects forward and is prominent from above.

FAMILY **Lucánidae**—Stag Beetles or Pinchingbugs: These large brownish or black beetles are sometimes called pinchingbugs because of the large mandibles of the males (Figure 22-54 A). In some males the mandibles are half as long as the body or longer and are branched like the antlers of a stag (hence the name "stag" beetle). These beetles are closely related to the Scarabaèidae, but differ in that the antennae are elbowed and the terminal segments cannot be held tightly together as in the scarabs (Figure 22-9 F). The larger lucanids are 1½ inches or more in length. These insects are usually found in woods, and the adults are often attracted to lights at night. The larvae are found in decaying wood and are similar to the white grubs that are found in grassy soil; they feed on the juices of decaying wood.

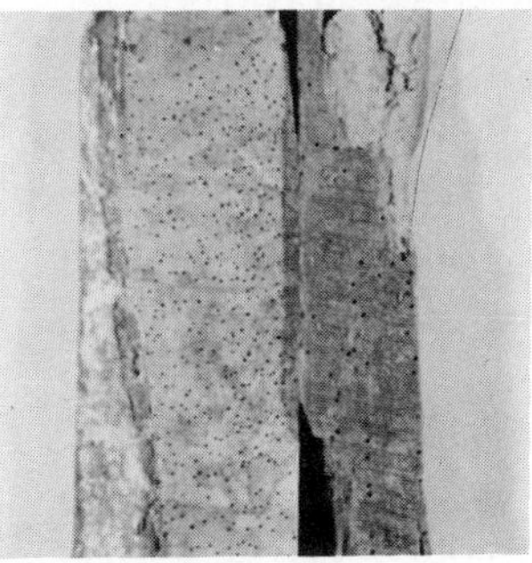

Fig. 22-53. Board damaged by powder-post beetles, and showing exit holes of the beetles.

FAMILY **Passálidae** — Bessbugs: These beetles are called by a variety of names—bessbugs, betsy-beetles, patent-leather beetles, and horned passalus beetles. Three species occur in the United States, only one of which occurs in the East. The eastern species, *Popílius disjúnctus* Illiger (Figure 22-54 C), is a shining black beetle, 32 to 36 millimeters in length, with longitudinal grooves in the elytra and a characteristic horn on the head (Figure 22-12 B). This family is closely related to the Lucánidae, but differs in that the mentum of the labium is deeply notched. The western species of the family occur in southern Texas.

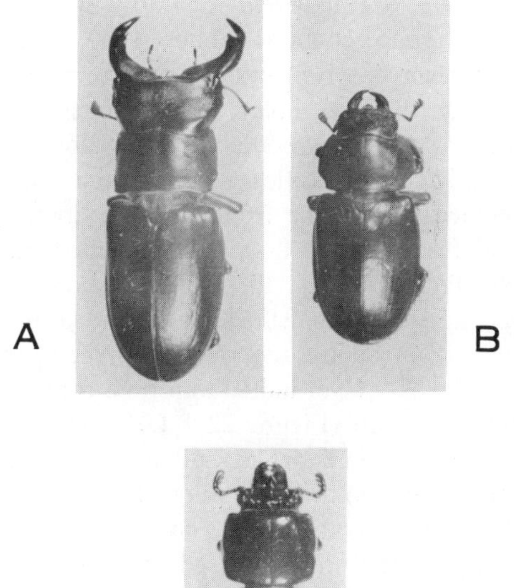

Fig. 22-54. A, male, and B, female, of a stag beetle, *Pseudolucànus caprèolus* (Linn.); C, a bessbug, *Popílius disjúnctus* (Illiger). About natural size.

The passalids are somewhat social, and

their colonies occur in galleries in decaying logs. The adults are able to produce a squeaking sound by rubbing roughened areas on the under side of the wings across similar areas on the dorsal side of the abdomen. This sound is produced when the insect is disturbed; normally it probably serves as a means of communication. The adults prepare food (decaying wood) with their salivary secretions and feed it to the young. The passalids are fairly common insects.

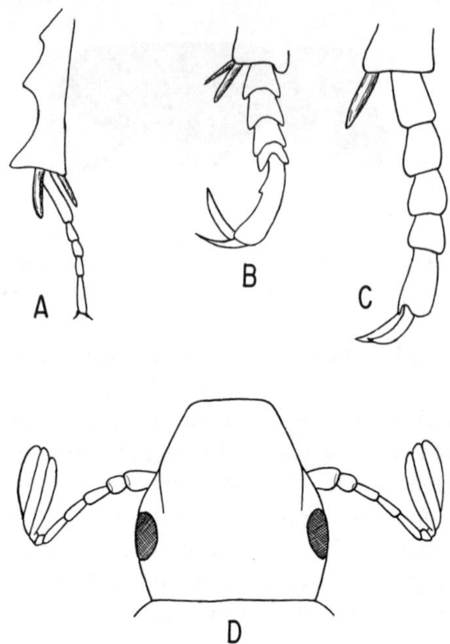

Fig. 22-55. Characters of Scarabaèidae. A, hind tibia and tarsus of *Aphòdius* (Aphodiìnae); B, hind tarsus of *Popíllia* (Rutelìnae); C, hind tarsus of *Cánthon* (Scarabaeìnae); D, head of *Macrodáctylus* (Melolonthìnae), dorsal view.

FAMILY **Scarabaèidae**—Scarab Beetles: This group contains about 1280 North American species, and its members vary greatly in size, color, and habits. The scarabs are heavy-bodied, oval or elongate, usually convex beetles, with the tarsi 5-segmented (rarely, the front tarsi are absent), and the antennae 8- to 11-segmented and lamellate. The last three (rarely more) of the antennal segments are expanded into platelike structures that may be spread apart (Figure 22-9 C) or united to form a compact terminal club (Figure 22-9 D). The front tibiae are more or less dilated, with the outer edge toothed or scalloped.

The scarabs vary considerably in habits. Many are dung feeders, or feed on decomposing plant materials, carrion, and the like; some live in the nests or burrows of vertebrates, or in the nests of ants or termites; a few feed on fungi; many feed on plant materials such as grasses, foliage, fruits, and flowers, and some of these are serious pests of lawns, golf greens, or various agricultural crops.

The family Scarabaèidae is divided into a number of subfamilies, which may be separated by the following key.

KEY TO THE SUBFAMILIES OF THE SCARABAÈIDAE

1.	Second antennal segment arising from apex of first (Figure 22-9 C, D); elytra smooth or with longitudinal ridges or small punctures; abdomen with 5 or 6 visible sterna 2	
1′.	Second antennal segment arising from a point proximad of apex of first (Figure 22-9 G); elytra rough, with irregular ridges and elevations; abdomen with 5 or fewer visible sterna . . . . *Trogìnae*	p. 314
2(1).	Antennae 11-segmented 3	
2′.	Antennae 8- to 10-segmented 4	
3(2).	Antennal club 3-segmented; elytra striate; widely distributed . . *Geotrupìnae*	p. 313
3′.	Antennal club 5- to 7-segmented; elytra not striate; rare western beetles (*Pleócoma, Benedíctia*) . . . . *Pleocomìnae*	p. 313

4(2′). Middle and hind tibiae thickened and greatly dilated, their front edges finely toothed or with numerous, minute, bristlelike spines; tarsi with long fine hairs on under side; body capable of being contrácted into a ball-like mass; 5 to 6 mm in length, blackish and shining.. *Acanthocerìnae* p. 314

4′. Middle and hind tibiae not as above; body not capable of being contracted into a ball-like mass; 5 to 60 mm in length..................5

5(4′). Elytra tapering posteriorly, their tips distinctly separated and short, exposing 2 or 3 abdominal terga; body very hairy; brownish in color and 13 to 18 mm in length; rare beetles ....*Glaphyrinae* p. 314

5′. Not exactly fitting the above description...........................6

6(5′). Hind legs situated far back on body, usually nearer tip of abdomen than middle legs (Figure 22-56 A); abdominal spiracles covered by elytra; segments of antennal club usually hairy; dung feeders..............7

6′. Hind legs situated at about middle of body, closer to middle legs than to tip of abdomen (Figure 22-56 B); at least 1 (often more) of the abdominal spiracles not covered by elytra; segments of antennal club smooth or only sparsely hairy; plant feeders 11

7(6). Hind tibiae with 1 apical spur (Figure 22-55 C); pygidium partly exposed; middle coxae widely separated; scutellum small and usually not visible .... *Scarabaeìnae* p. 312

7′. Hind tibiae usually with 2 apical spurs (Figure 22-55 A); pygidium usually covered by elytra; middle coxae approximate (Figure 22-56 A); scutellum well developed and visible...................................8

8(7′). Antennae 9-segmented 9

8′. Antennae 10-segmented 10

9(8). Clypeus expanded, the mandibles not visible from above, and usually notched at apex ....*Aphodiìnae* p. 313

9′. Mandibles not concealed by clypeus, and visible from above; clypeus not notched at apex......................................*Aegialiìnae* p. 313

10(8′). Metepimera visible; abdominal sterna more or less fused together; segments of antennal club cup-shaped, telescopic; blackish beetles, about 7 mm in length; southern and western United States......*Hybosorìnae* p. 313

10′. Metepimera concealed; abdominal sterna free; antennal club not as above; reddish-brown beetles, 5 to 6 mm in length; widely distributed... *Ochodaeìnae* p. 313

11(6′). Tarsal claws (at least on hind legs) of unequal size, the outer claw larger (Figure 22-55 B); hind tibiae with 2 apical spurs; pygidium exposed; often brightly colored beetles...........................*Rutelìnae* p. 315

11′. Tarsal claws, at least on hind legs, of equal size (except in some males of the Dynastìnae, which have horns on the head or pronotum, and in *Hóplia*, subfamily Melolonthìnae, 6 to 9 mm in length, which has only 1 simple claw on hind legs), or hind tibiae without apical spurs 12

12(11′). Tarsal claws usually toothed or bifid; usually only 1 pair of abdominal spiracles exposed below edges of elytra................*Melolonthìnae* p. 314

12′. Tarsal claws simple; usually at least 2 pairs of abdominal spiracles exposed below edges of elytra.......................................13

13(12′). Front coxae transverse; body usually convex above; males often with

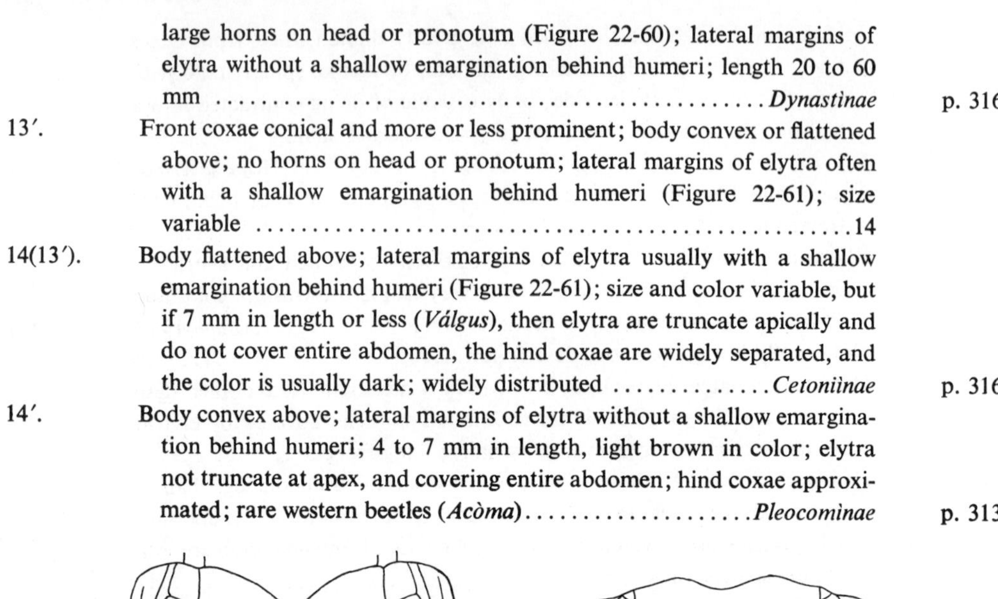

large horns on head or pronotum (Figure 22-60); lateral margins of elytra without a shallow emargination behind humeri; length 20 to 60 mm . . . . *Dynastinae* p. 316

13′. Front coxae conical and more or less prominent; body convex or flattened above; no horns on head or pronotum; lateral margins of elytra often with a shallow emargination behind humeri (Figure 22-61); size variable 14

14(13′). Body flattened above; lateral margins of elytra usually with a shallow emargination behind humeri (Figure 22-61); size and color variable, but if 7 mm in length or less (*Válgus*), then elytra are truncate apically and do not cover entire abdomen, the hind coxae are widely separated, and the color is usually dark; widely distributed . . . . *Cetoniìnae* p. 316

14′. Body convex above; lateral margins of elytra without a shallow emargination behind humeri; 4 to 7 mm in length, light brown in color; elytra not truncate at apex, and covering entire abdomen; hind coxae approximated; rare western beetles (*Acòma*). *Pleocomìnae* p. 313

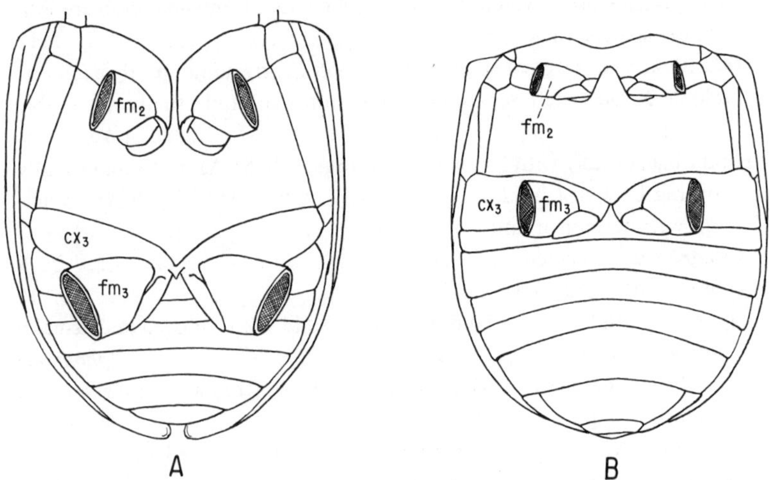

Fig. 22-56. Ventral views of thorax and abdomen of Scarabaèidae. A, a dung-feeding scarab (*Aphòdius*, Aphodiìnae); B, a plant-feeding scarab (*Pelidnòta*, Rutelìnae). cx_3, hind coxa; fm_2, middle femur; fm_3, hind femur.

—Subfamily *Scarabaeìnae* (=*Coprìnae*)— Dung Beetles and Tumblebugs— These beetles are rubust, 5 to 30 millimeters in length, and feed chiefly on dung. Most of them are a dull black, but some are metallic green in color. The tumblebugs (*Cánthon* and *Deltochìlum*) are black, about an inch in length or less, with the hind tibiae rather slender, and there are no horns on the head or pronotum. The members of other genera in this subfamily have the middle and hind tibiae swollen at the tip; in *Phánaeus* (Figure 22-57 C, D), which is usually a little less than an inch in length, the body is a brilliant green with the pronotum golden, and the males have a long horn on the top of the head. Other beetles in this subfamily range in length from 4 to 9 millimeters.

The tumblebugs are usually common in pastures and are interesting insects to watch. They chew off a piece of dung, work it into a ball, and roll this ball a considerable distance; they usually work in pairs, one pushing and the other pulling, rolling

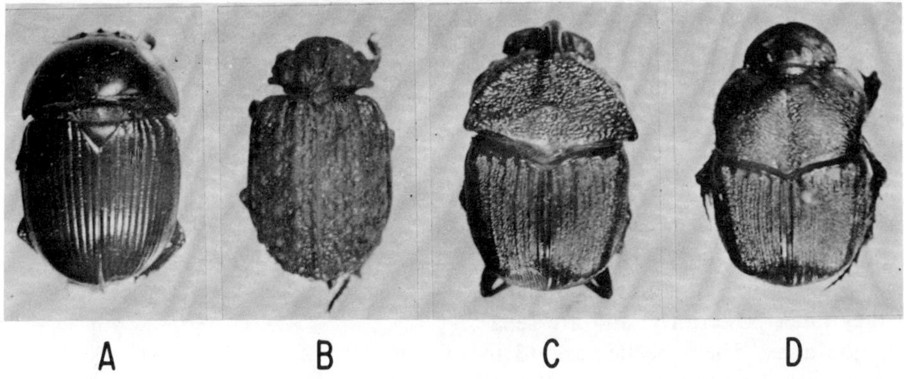

Fig. 22-57. Scarab beetles. A, an earth-boring dung beetle, *Geotrùpes spléndidus* (Fabricius); B, a skin beetle. *Tróx scabrósus* Beauvois; C, male, and D, female, of a dung beetle, *Phánaeus cárnifex* (Linn.). $1\frac{1}{2}\times$.

the ball with their hind legs. The ball is then buried in the soil, and the eggs are laid in the ball. The larvae are thus assured a food supply, and the location of the ball provides protection.

The sacred scarab of ancient Egypt, *Scarabaèus sàcer* Linn., is a member of this group, and has habits similar to those of the tumblebugs. In Egyptian mythology the ball of dung represented the earth and its rotation.

—Subfamily *Aphodiìnae*—Aphodian Dung Beetles— This is a fairly large group of small dung beetles, and some are quite common, particularly in cow dung. They are usually black, or red and black.

—Subfamily *Aegialiìnae*— The members of this group are similar to the Aphodiìnae, but have the mandibles visible from above. The group is a small one, and most of its members (including all the eastern species) belong to the genus *Aegiàlia.*

—Subfamily *Ochodaeìnae*— This is a small group, and most of its members occur in the western states; one species, *Ochodaèus músculus* (Say), a reddish-brown oval beetle 5 to 6 millimeters in length with striate elytra, occurs in northern states.

—Subfamily *Hybosorìnae*— These beetles are about 7 millimeters in length, brownish black to black in color, and are shaped a little like a miniature June beetle. Three rare species occur in the United States, one in the southeastern states and the other two in Arizona and California.

—Subfamily *Geotrupìnae* — Earth-Boring Dung Beetles— These beetles are very similar to some of the other dung-feeding scarabs, but have the antennae 11-segmented. They are stout-bodied, convex, oval beetles that are black or dark brown in color (Figure 22-57 A); the elytra are usually grooved or striate, the tarsi are long and slender, and the front tibiae are broadened and toothed or scalloped on the outer edges. The elytra completely cover the abdomen. These beetles vary in length from 5 to 25 millimeters, and are found beneath cow dung, horse manure, or carrion; some occur in logs or in decaying fungi. The larvae occur in or beneath dung or carrion; they feed on this material and hence are of value to man as scavengers.

—Subfamily *Pleocomìnae*— The members of this group are western in distribution and are relatively rare beetles. The larvae live in the soil and feed on the roots of plants, and the adults live in burrows in the ground, usually coming out only at dusk or after a rain. The members of the genus *Pleócoma* are stout-bodied, relatively large (about an inch in length), and rather pubescent; the burrows of *P. fimbriàta* LeConte are about an inch in diameter and up to 2 feet or more in depth. The members of the genus *Acòma* are much smaller, 4 to 7 millimeters in length, and light brown in color.

—Subfamily *Glaphyrìnae*— The members of this group are elongate, brownish, and have the body very hairy. The elytra are short, exposing two or three abdominal terga; they taper posteriorly, and are separated at the apex. These beetles are 13 to 18 millimeters in length. Our species belong to the genus *Lichnánthe*; some occur in the Northeast, and some in the West; all are quite rare.

—Subfamily *Acanthocerìnae*— These beetles are round, blackish, 5 to 6 millimeters in length, with the middle and hind tibiae greatly dilated and bearing rows of spines along their entire length. When disturbed, these beetles draw in their legs and antennae and form a hemispherical mass, and in this position they remain motionless. They occur under bark, in rotten logs and stumps, and occasionally on flowers. Three species occur in the United States; two species of *Cloeòtus*, which are widely distributed throughout the East, and *Acanthócerus aèneus* MacLeay, which occurs in Georgia and Florida.

—Subfamily *Trogìnae*—Skin Beetles— The members of this group have the dorsal surface of the body very rough, and the second antennal segment arises before the tip of the first instead of from its apex (Figure 22-9 G). These beetles are oblong, convex, dark brown in color (and often covered with dirt), and are shaped much like June beetles (Figure 22-57 B). They are usually found on old, dry animal carcasses, where they feed on the hide, feathers, hair, or the dried tissues on the bones. They represent one of the last stages in the successions of insects living in animal carcasses. Some species occur in owl pellets, beneath bark, or on roots. When disturbed, these beetles draw in their legs and lie motionless, resembling dirt or rubbish, and are often overlooked. They overwinter as adults beneath leaves and in debris. Two genera occur in the United States: *Tróx* (widely distributed) and *Glarèsis* (western United States).

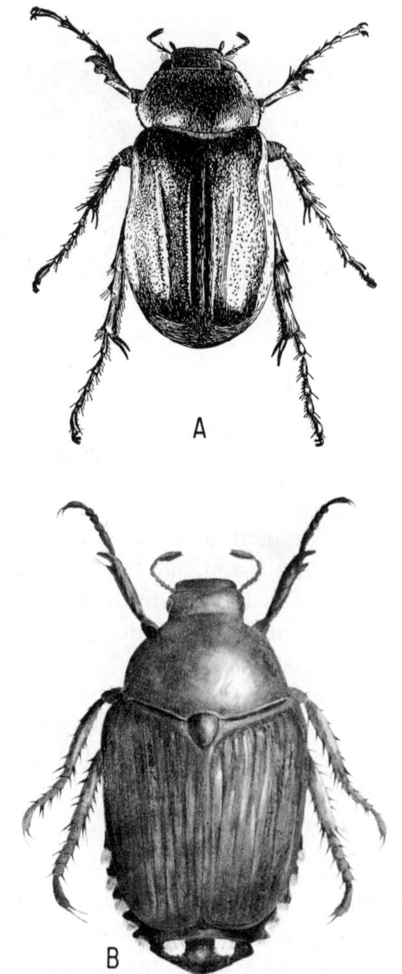

Fig. 22-58. Plant-feeding scarabs. A, a June beetle, *Phyllóphaga portoricénsis* Smythe, $1\frac{1}{2}\times$; B, the Japanese beetle, *Popíllia japónica* Newman, $4\frac{1}{2}\times$. (A, courtesy of Wolcott and the *Journal of Agriculture* of the University of Puerto Rico.)

—Subfamily *Melolonthìnae*—June Beetles, Chafers, and Others— This is a large and widely distributed group, and all its members are plant feeders; many species are of considerable economic importance. The

Fig. 22-59. White grubs (*Phyllóphaga* sp.). (Courtesy of the Ohio Agricultural Experiment Station.)

best-known beetles in this group are the June beetles or May beetles, sometimes called junebugs, which are usually brown in color and are common around lights in the spring and early summer (Figure 22-58 A). Most of them belong to the genus *Phyllóphaga* (= *Lachnostérna*), which contains nearly a hundred eastern species. The adults feed at night on foliage and flowers. The larvae (Figure 22-59) are the well-known white grubs that feed in the soil on the roots of grasses and other plants. White grubs are very destructive insects and do a great deal of damage to pastures, lawns, and such crops as corn, small grains, potatoes, and strawberries. The life cycle usually requires three years to complete. The greatest damage to field crops occurs when fields are rotated from grass or meadow to corn.

This subfamily also contains the chafers (*Macrodáctylus*). The rose chafer, *M. subspinòsus* (Fabricius), is a slender, tan, long-legged beetle that feeds on the flowers and foliage of roses, grapes, and various other plants; it often feeds on peaches and other fruits. The larvae are small white grubs that occur in light soil and often do serious damage to roots. Poultry that eat these beetles become extremely ill and quite often are killed.

—Subfamily *Rutelìnae*—The Shining Leaf Chafers— The larvae of these beetles feed on plant roots, and the adults feed on foliage and fruits. Many of the adults are very brightly colored. A number of important pest species are included in this subfamily.

One of the most serious pests in this group is the Japanese beetle, *Popíllia japónica* Newman (Figure 22-58 B). This species was introduced into eastern United States on nursery stock from Japan about 1916; since then, it has spread over a large part of eastern United States, where it is a serious pest on lawns, golf courses, fruits, and shrubbery. The adult is a very pretty insect; the head and thorax are bright green, the elytra are brownish tinged with green on the edges, and there are white spots along the sides of the abdomen. This species has one generation a year and overwinters in the larval stage in the soil.

Another rather common and destructive species is the grape pelidnota, *Pelidnòta punctàta* (Linn.). The adult is an inch or more in length and looks a little like a large June beetle, but is yellowish with three black spots on each elytron (Figure 22-62 B). Most of the damage done by this species is done by the adult; the larvae feed chiefly in rotting wood.

The members of the genus *Cotálpa* are usually large beetles, uniform green or yellowish above and dark beneath; the larvae do considerable damage to the roots of berries, corn, and grass. One distinctive species in this genus is *C. lanígera* (Linn.), 20 to 26 millimeters in length and entirely yellow with a metallic luster; it occurs on or near catalpa trees.

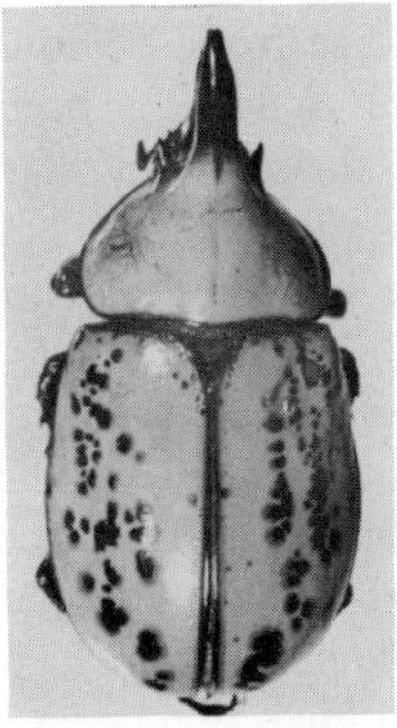

Fig. 22-60. A unicorn beetle, *Dynástes títyus* (Linn.); male at left, female at right.

From Baja California to Utah the common members of the Rutelìnae are the black and reddish brown members of the genus *Pocálta,* of which at least ten species are recognized. In Texas and Arizona are found the real jewels of this subfamily, species belonging to the genus *Plusiòtis*. These large scarabs are a brilliant green, sometimes with added longitudinal lines of metallic golden color; they are favored items among collectors.

—Subfamily *Dynastìnae* — Rhinoceros Beetles, Unicorn Beetles, and Elephant Beetles— This group contains some of the largest North American beetles, some of which may reach a length of 2½ inches. The dorsal surface of the body is rounded and convex, and the males usually have horns on the head and (or) pronotum (Figure 22-60); the females lack these horns.

The most common Dynastìnae in the East and Midwest belong to the genus *Dynástes.* The largest eastern species is the unicorn beetle, *D. títyus* (Linn.), a southern beetle 2.0 to 2.5 inches in length; it is greenish gray in color, mottled or blotched with large black areas, and the pronotal horn extends forward over the head. *D. gránti* Horn is very similar but slightly larger, with a longer pronotal horn; it occurs in Arizona. The big brown scarabs occurring in the southern states and Texas, the elephant beetles (species of *Stratègus*), have three horns on the pronotum, but none on the head; these beetles are from 1.5 to 2.0 inches in length. In the rhinoceros beetle, *Xyloryctes sátyrus* (Fabricius), a dark-brown species a little over an inch in length, the males have a single large upright horn on the head (the females have a small tubercle instead of a horn); the larva of this species feeds on the roots of ash trees. The rhinoceros beetle is an eastern species, occurring from Connecticut to Texas. The members of the genus *Phileùrus*, which are almost an inch long and have two horns on the head, occur in the southern and southwestern states.

The smaller members of this subfamily, particularly the species in the genera *Lígyrus* and *Euetheòla,* are often serious pests of corn, sugarcane, and cereal crops; both adult and larval stages cause damage.

—Subfamily *Cetoniìnae*—Flower Beetles and Others— The members of this group are principally pollen feeders and are common on flowers; many occur under loose bark or in debris, and a few occur in ant nests. The larvae feed on organic matter in the soil; some species damage the roots of plants. This subfamily includes the goliath beetles of Africa, which are among the largest insects known; some species reach a length of 4 inches or more.

In *Cótinus* and *Euphòria,* two common genera in this subfamily, the mesepimera are visible from above, between the hind angles of the pronotum and the humeri of the elytra (Figure 22-61). The members of the genus *Cótinus* are over 18 millimeters in length and have a very small scutellum; those of *Euphòria* are smaller and have a large scutellum. The green June beetle or fig-eater, *C. nítida* Linn., is a common dark-green beetle nearly an inch long; the adults feed on grapes, ripening fruits, and young corn, and the larvae often seriously damage lawns, golf courses, and various crops. The beetles in the genus *Euphòria* are somewhat bumblebeelike, and are often called bumble flower beetles; they are brownish yellow and black, very pubescent, and act much like bumble bees.

Perhaps the least known and most interesting members of this subfamily are those in the genus *Cremastochèilus*. These beetles, which are 9 to 15 millimeters in length, are kept captive in ant nests to provide the ants with a nutritive fluid. The ants cling to the beetle's thorax and gnaw at pubescent glandular areas on the exposed mesepimera. Nearly 30 species belonging to this genus are known in the United States.

In the other common genera of Cetoniìnae the mesepimera are not visible from above. The hermit flower beetle, *Osmo-*

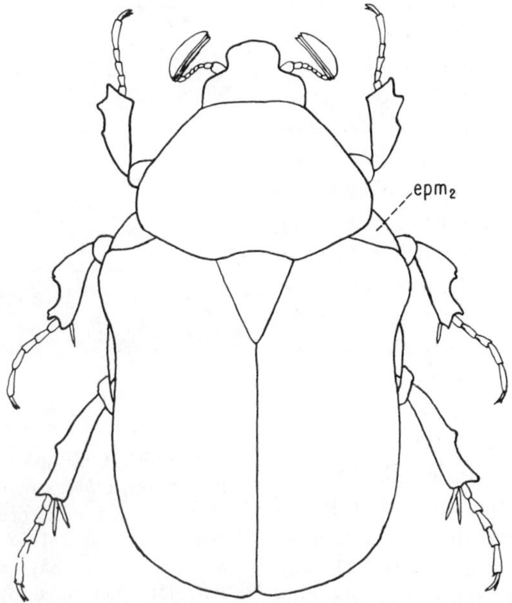

Fig. 22-61. A bumble flower beetle, *Euphòria índa* (Linn.). epm_2, mesepimeron.

Fig. 22-62. Plant-feeding scarabs. A, the hermit flower beetle, *Osmodérma eremícola* Knoch, slightly enlarged; B, the grape pelidnota, *Pelidnòta punctàta* (Linn.), $1\frac{1}{2}\times$; C, a flower beetle, *Trichiótinus texànus* (Horn), $4\times$.

dérma eremícola Knoch, is a brownish-black insect about an inch in length, with the elytra longer than wide (Figure 22-62 A); the larvae feed in decaying wood, and the adults are frequently found under dead bark or in tree cavities. The adults emit a very disagreeable odor when disturbed. In *Válgus* and *Trichiótinus* the elytra are about as long as wide; the members of *Válgus* are small, less than 7.5 millimeters in length, and are brown in color and covered with scales; those of *Trichiótinus* are brightly colored and pubescent (Figure 22-62 C). The adults of these two genera occur on various types of flowers, and the larvae live in decaying wood.

FAMILY **Cerambýcidae** — Long-Horned Wood-Boring Beetles: This family is a large one, with over 1200 species occurring in this country, and its members are all phytophagous. Most of the long-horns are elongate and cylindrical with long antennae, and many are brightly colored. The tarsi appear 4-segmented with the third segment bilobed, but are actually 5-segmented; the fourth segment is small and concealed in the notch of the third, and is often very difficult to see (Figure 22-10 A).

Both the Cerambýcidae and Chrysomélidae have this type of tarsal structure, and these two groups are sometimes difficult to separate. In the Cerambýcidae the antennae are usually at least half as long as the body and are often much longer; in the Chrysomélidae the antennae are nearly always less than half as long as the body. The Cerambýcidae are usually elongate and cylindrical, and most of them are over $\frac{1}{2}$ inch in length; the Chrysomélidae are generally more oval and flattened, and are usually less than $\frac{1}{2}$ inch in length. In most of the Cerambýcidae the inner margins of the eyes are notched and the antennae arise just opposite or within this notch (Figure 22-11 D), while in the Chrysomélidae the eyes are nearly always oval.

Most adult cerambycids, particularly the brightly colored ones, feed on flowers. Many, usually not brightly colored, are nocturnal in habit and during the day may be found under bark or resting on trees or logs; some of these make a squeaking sound when picked up.

Fig. 22-63. Galleries of the poplar borer, *Sapérda calcaràta* Say. (Courtesy of the Ohio Agricultural Experiment Station.)

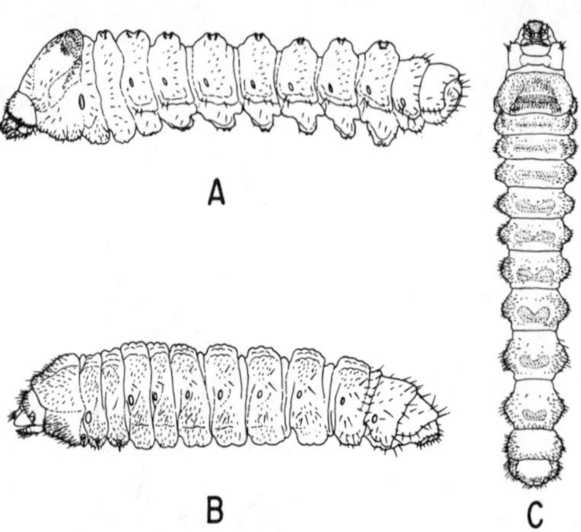

Fig. 22-64. Cerambycid larvae. A, the dogwood twig borer, *Obèrea tripunctàta* (Swederus), lateral view; B, the twig pruner, *Elaphídion villòsum* (Fabricius), lateral view; C, the linden borer, *Sapérda véstita* Say, dorsal view. (Courtesy of Peterson. Reprinted by permission.)

Most of the Cerambýcidae are woodboring in the larval stage, and many species are very destructive to shade, forest, and fruit trees, and to freshly cut logs. The adults lay their eggs in crevices in the bark, and the larvae bore into the wood. The larval tunnels in the wood (Figure 22-63) are circular in cross-section (thereby differing from most buprestid tunnels, which are oval in cross-section) and usually go straight in a short distance before turning. Different species attack different types of trees and shrubs. A few will attack living trees, but most species appear to prefer freshly cut logs, or weakened and dying trees or branches. A few girdle twigs and lay their eggs just above the girdled band. Some bore into the stems of herbaceous plants. The larvae (Figure 22-64) are elongate, cylindrical, whitish and legless, and differ from the larvae of the Buprestidae in that the anterior end of the body is not broadened and flattened; they are often called roundheaded borers, to distinguish them from the flat-headed borers (larvae of Bupréstidae).

The family Cerambýcidae is divided into several subfamilies; some of these are not very clear-cut, and different authorities do not agree on the limits of the different subfamilies. The four subfamilies usually recognized are the Prionìnae, Lamiìnae, Lepturìnae, and Cerambycìnae. The Prionìnae differ from the others in that they have the prothorax sharply margined laterally; the Lamiìnae have the last segment of the maxillary palpi cylindrical and pointed apically (Figure 22-65 A), whereas in the Lepturìnae and Cerambycìnae this segment is not cylindrical and is usually blunt apically (Figure 22-65 B); in most of the Lepturìnae the bases of the antennae are not surrounded by the eyes, whereas in most of the Cerambycìnae the inner margins of the eyes are notched and the bases of the antennae are more or less surrounded by the eyes.

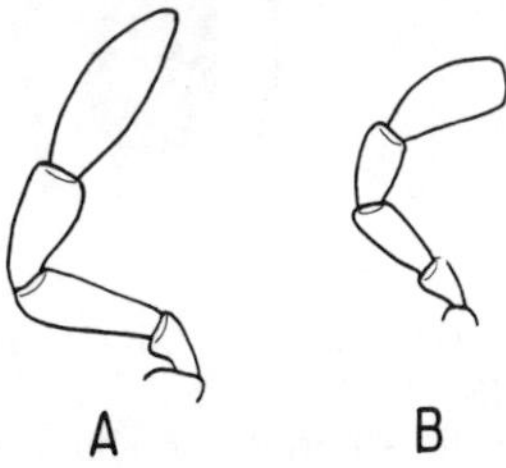

Fig. 22-65. Maxillary palpi of Cerambýcidae. A, *Monóchamus* (Lamiìnae); B, *Anoplódera* (Lepturìnae).

—Subfamily *Prionìnae*— The cerambycids in the genus *Parándra* are quite different in general appearance from the other beetles in this family, and are sometimes called the aberrant long-horned beetles; they are placed by some authorities in a separate family, the Spondýlidae. These beetles are elongate-oval, somewhat flattened, bright reddish brown, generally about $\frac{3}{4}$ inch in length, with the antennae short and not extending beyond the base of the prothorax (Figure 22-68 F); the fourth tarsal segment is quite distinct and about half as large as the third (Figure 22-10 J). These beetles look a little like small lucanids. They live under the bark of dead pine trees; the larvae burrow in dry dead wood of logs and stumps.

The genus *Priònus* includes some of the largest cerambycids in the United States. These beetles are broad, somewhat flattened, blackish brown in color, and some reach a length of 2 inches (Figure 22-66 E). The prothorax has sharp lateral margins that bear three broad teeth, and the front coxae are transverse; the antennae contain 12 or more segments, and in the females are serrate. Even larger are members of the species *Ergàtes spiculàtus* LeConte, which occur in the Douglas fir region of the Pacific Northwest, the Rocky Mountains, and in California; these beetles are also brown, but have eight or ten small spines along each side of the pronotum, and the two sexes look alike. Other large members of this subfamily include *Derobráchus* (similar to *Priònus* but more slender and with 11-segmented antennae) and *Tragosòma* (with the pronotum very hairy).

—Subfamily *Lamiìnae*— The beetles in the genus *Monóchamus* (Figure 22-67) are often called sawyer beetles. They are usually over an inch in length and are either black or a mottled gray in color; the first antennal segment has a scarlike area near the tip. The antennae of the males are sometimes twice as long as the body; they are about as long as the body in the females. The larvae feed on evergreens, usually on freshly cut logs, but they may sometimes attack living trees. The holes made by the larvae are at least as large in diameter as a lead pencil, and those of some species are nearly $\frac{1}{2}$ inch in diameter.

The genus *Sapérda* contains a number of important pest species. These beetles are an inch or so in length and are sometimes strikingly colored. *S. cándida* Fabricius is white, with three broad, brown longitudinal stripes on the back; the larva bores in apple and other trees, and is commonly called the roundheaded apple tree borer. Other important species in this genus are

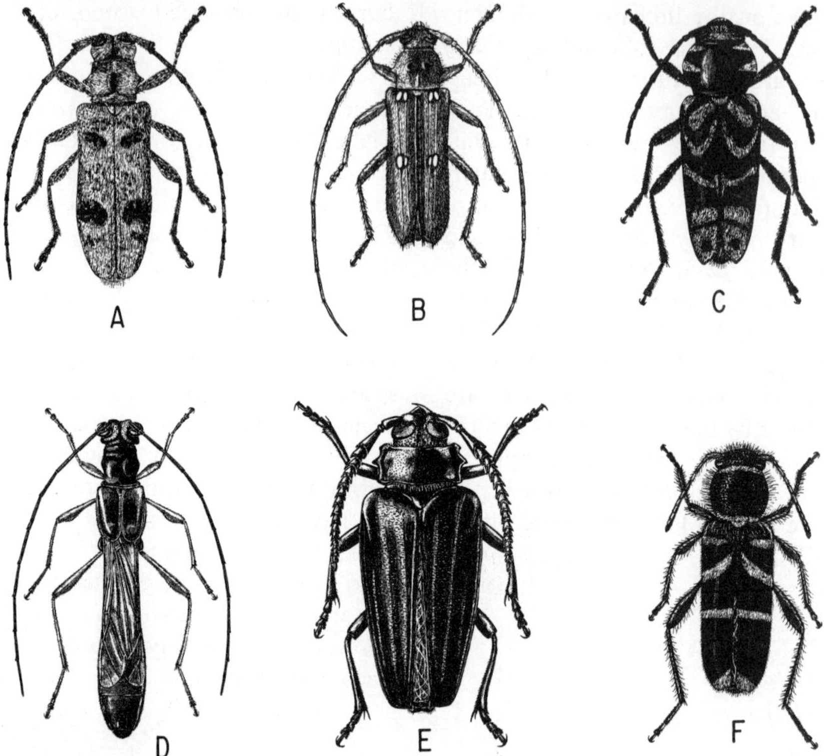

Fig. 22-66. Long-horned wood-boring beetles. A, *Gòes tigrìnus* (DeGeer); B, *Ebùria quadrigeminàta* (Say); C, the sugar-maple borer, *Glycòbius speciòsus* (Say); D, *Necýdalis méllita* Say; E, *Priònus imbricórnis* (Linn.); F, *Clŷtus marginicóllis* Castelnau. (Courtesy of Knull and the Ohio Biological Survey.)

the poplar borer, *S. calcaràta* Say, and the elm borer, *S. tridentàta* Olivier.

The species in the genus *Obèrea* are very slender and elongate. The raspberry cane borer, *O. bimaculàta* (Olivier), is black, with the pronotum yellow and bearing two or three black spots; the larvae are often serious pests in canes of raspberries and blackberries.

The species of *Tetraòpes* are about ½ inch in length and are red with black spots. The compound eyes are divided, so that there are apparently two compound eyes on each side of the head. *T. tetraophthálmus* Forster is a common species feeding on milkweed, and is often called the red milkweed beetle.

The twig girdler, *Oncíderes cingulàta* (Say), lays its eggs under the bark near the tips of living branches of hickory, elm, apple, and other deciduous trees. Before the egg is deposited, the beetle gnaws a deep groove around the twig, girdling it; the twig eventually dies and drops to the ground, and the larva completes its development in the twig.

—Subfamily *Lepturìnae*— A striking eastern species in this group is the elderberry long-horn, *Desmócerus palliàtus* (Forster) (Figure 22-68 C). This is a dark-blue beetle about an inch long, with the basal third of the elytra orange yellow, and with segments 3 to 5 of the antennae thickened at the tips. The adult occurs on the flowers and foliage of elderberry, and the larva bores in the pith of this plant. Several other species of *Desmócerus* occur on elderberry in the western states; they are similar in

Fig. 22-67. A sawyer beetle, *Monóchamus notàtus* (Drury); female at left, male at right. (Courtesy of Knull.)

general coloration, with the males having brilliant scarlet elytra and a black pronotum; the females have very dark-green elytra bordered narrowly with red along the outer margin.

This subfamily contains many species found on flowers; in most of them the elytra are broadest at the base and narrowed toward the apex, giving the insect a rather broad-shouldered appearance (Figure 22-68 A, B, D, H). Some common genera are *Anoplodèra, Typócerus, Toxòtus,* and *Stenócorus.* Most of these beetles are brightly colored, often with yellow and black bands or stripes; in many cases the elytra do not cover the tip of the abdomen. All are excellent fliers.

—Subfamily *Cerambycìnae*— This group is a large one, and its members vary considerably in size and general appearance. One of the most strikingly marked species in this subfamily is the locust borer, *Megacyllène*

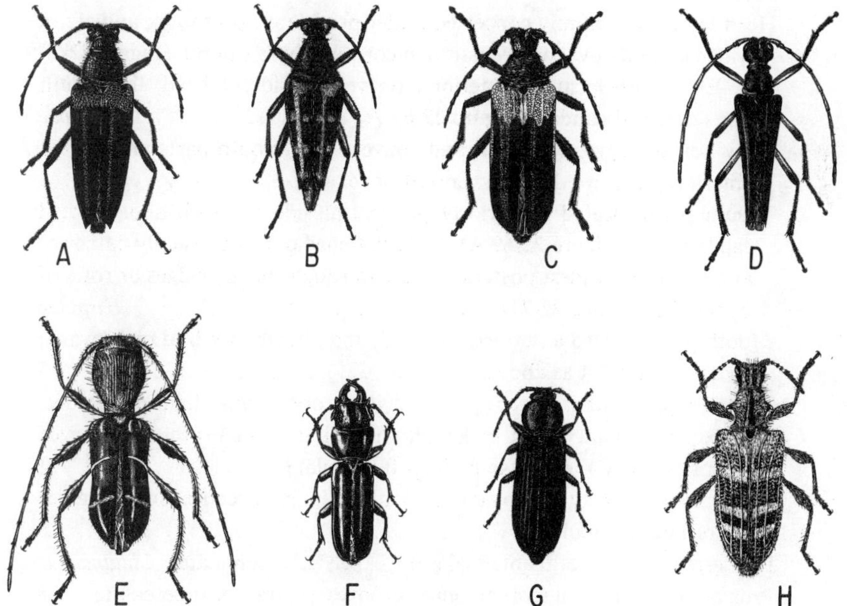

Fig. 22-68. Long-horned wood-boring beetles. A, *Anoplódera canadénsis* (Olivier); B, *Typócerus decéptus* Knull; C, *Desmócerus palliàtus* (Forster); D, *Toxòtus cylindricóllis* (Say); E, *Eudérces pìni* (Olivier); F, *Parándra pólita* Say; G, *Ásemum àtrum* Eschscholtz; H. *Stenócorus inquísitor* (Linn.) (Courtesy of Knull and the Ohio Biological Survey.)

robíniae (Forster), the larva of which bores into the trunks of black locust. The adult is black with bright-yellow markings, and is relatively common on goldenrod in late summer. Another easily recognized species in this group is *Ebùria quadrigeminàta* (Say), a brownish species 14 to 24 millimeters in length, which has two pairs of elevated ivory-colored swellings on each elytron (Figure 22-66 B). The members of some genera in this group (*Smòdicum, Ásemum,* and others) are somewhat flattened and have relatively short antennae (Figure 22-68 G); others (for example, *Eudérces,* Figure 22-68 E) are small, less than 9 millimeters in length, and somewhat antlike in appearance.

FAMILY **Chrysomélidae**—Leaf Beetles: The leaf beetles are closely related to the Cerambýcidae; both groups have a similar tarsal structure (Figure 22-10 A), and both are phytophagous. The leaf beetles usually have much shorter antennae and are smaller and more oval in shape than the cerambycids. The chrysomelids in the United States are all less than ½ inch in length; most of the cerambycids are larger. Many are brightly colored.

Adult leaf beetles feed principally on flowers and foliage; the larvae are phytophagous, but vary quite a bit in appearance and habits. Some of the larvae are free feeders on foliage, some are leaf miners, some feed on roots, and some bore in stems. Many members of this family are serious pests. Most species overwinter as adults.

This family has been divided into a number of subfamilies, primarily on the basis of differences in the larvae; many authorities give family rank to these subfamily groups. The subfamily of most species of leaf beetles may be determined by the following key.

KEY TO THE SUBFAMILIES OF THE CHRYSOMÉLIDAE

1. Head largely or entirely concealed under prothorax; prothorax and elytra widened; body oval or circular, and convex; elytra smooth (Figure 22-70 B, E); mouth located posteriorly on ventral side of head, the mouth parts directed caudad (Figure 22-69 A) .... *Cassidinae* p. 324

1′. Body not as above, or if oval and convex, then mouth parts are located anteriorly and are directed ventrad or forward 2

2(1′). Mouth parts located posteriorly on ventral side of head, and directed caudad (as in Figure 22-69 A); body flattened dorsally, usually narrower anteriorly and widest posteriorly; elytra roughened by ridges or rows of punctures (Figure 22-71) .... *Hispìnae* p. 325

2′. Mouth parts located anteriorly on head, and directed ventrad or forward; elytra usually not as above.................................3

3(2′). Pygidium prominent, not covered by elytra; robust, subcylindrical beetles, mostly less than 6 mm in length; head buried in prothorax to eyes (Figure 22-69 C); elytra sometimes tuberculate 4

3′. Pygidium usually covered by elytra; oval or elongate beetles; size variable; elytra not tuberculate...8

4(3). Prosternum with lateral antennal grooves; elytra tuberculate. . *Chlamisinae* p. 325

4′. Prosternum without lateral antennal grooves; elytra not tuberculate....5

5(4′). Antennae filiform or slightly clavate...............................6

5′. Antennae serrate or pectinate 7

6(5). Base of pronotum narrower than base of elytra; southern Texas........ .... *Megascelìnae* p. 326

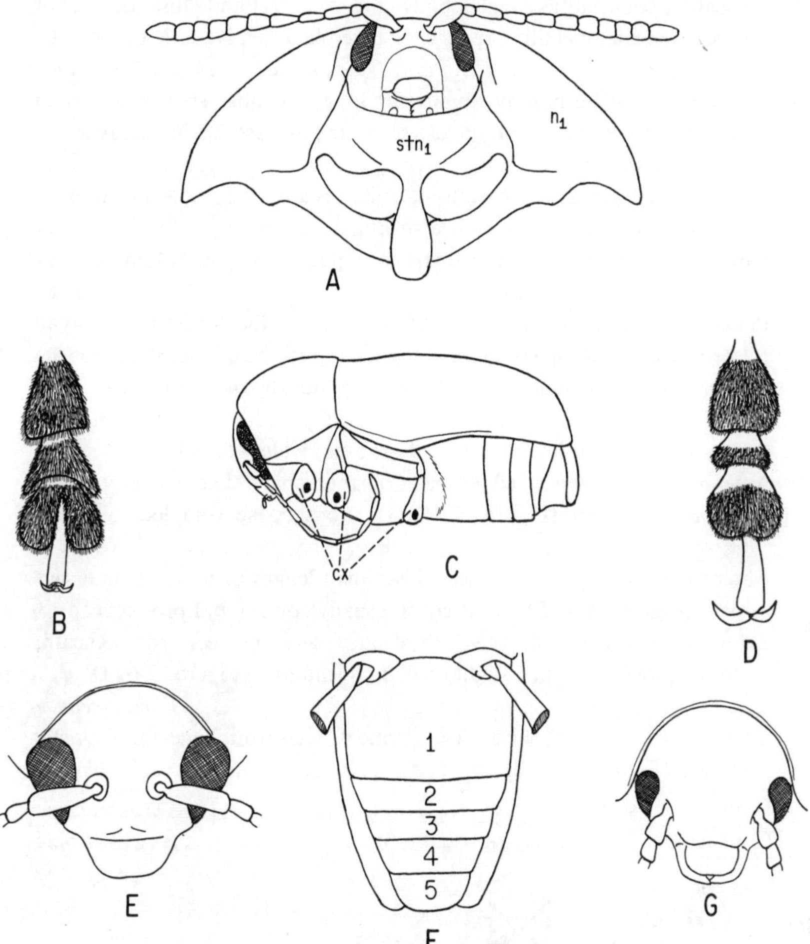

Fig. 22-69. Characters of the Chrysomélidae. A, head and prothorax of *Chelymórpha* (Cassidìnae), ventral view; B, tarsus of *Diabrótica* (Galerucìnae), ventral view; C, body of *Cryptocéphala* (Cryptocephalìnae), lateral view; D, tarsus of *Leptinotársa* (Chrysomelìnae), ventral view; E, head of *Diabrótica* (Galerucìnae), anterior view; F, abdomen of *Donàcia* (Donaciìnae), ventral view; G, head of *Chrýsochus* (Eumolpìnae), anterior view. *cx*, coxae; n_1, pronotum; stn_1, prosternum; 1-5, abdominal sternites.

6′. Base of pronotum as wide as base of elytra, or nearly so; widely distributed .... *Cryptocephalìnae* p. 325

7(5′). Head more or less constricted behind eyes; eyes usually large and deeply emarginate........ *Zeugophorìnae* p. 326

7′. Head usually not constricted behind eyes; eyes usually not large or deeply emarginate .... *Clytrìnae* p. 325

8(3′). Base of pronotum narrower than base of elytra, the pronotum with or without sharp lateral margins 9

8′. Base of pronotum usually as wide as base of elytra, or nearly so; the pronotum usually margined........ 12

9(8). First abdominal sternum very long (Figure 22-69 F); antennae long, usually about half as long as body (Figure 22-72) and close together at base; elongate, metallic coppery, or blue-black semiaquatic beetles.... .... *Donaciìnae* p. 326

9′. First abdominal sternum not unusually long; antennae shorter, less than half as long as body, and widely separated at base (as in Figure 22-69 G); color variable..10

10(9′). Pronotum margined; southwestern United States........*Aulacoscelìnae* p. 326

10′. Pronotum not margined; widely distributed........................11

11(10′). Punctures of elytra in rows; elytra not pubescent; pronotum without lateral teeth...*Criocerìnae* p. 327

11′. Punctures of elytra not in rows, or if in rows, then the pronotum has small lateral teeth and the elytra have scattered pubescence....*Orsodacnìnae* p. 327

12(8′). Prosternum with lateral antennal grooves; Florida and California...... .... *Lamprosomatìnae* p. 325

12′. Prosternum without lateral antennal grooves; widely distributed......13

13(12′). Antennae widely separated at base, farther apart than length of first antennal segment (Figure 22-69 G); front coxae rounded, oval, or transverse 14

13′. Antennae close together at base, closer than length of first antennal segment (Figure 22-69 E); front coxae usually conical and prominent..15

14(13). Front coxae oval or transverse; third tarsal segment, seen from beneath, entire apically or with a slight median indentation (Figure 22-69 D).... .... *Chrysomelìnae* p. 327

14′. Front coxae rounded; third tarsal segment, seen from beneath, distinctly bilobed (Figure 22-69 B) ....*Eumolpìnae* p. 328

15(13′). Hind femora slender; elytra soft..........................*Galerucìnae* p. 328

15′. Hind femora swollen; elytra usually firm....................*Alticìnae* p. 326

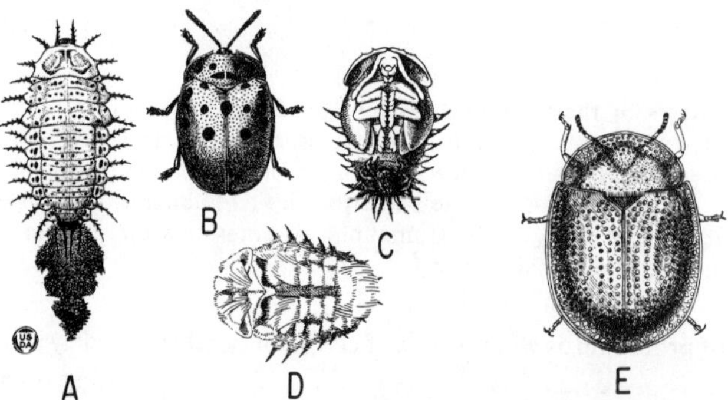

Fig. 22-70. Tortoise beetles. A-D, the Argus tortoise beetle, *Chelymórpha cassídea* (Fabricius), $1\frac{1}{2}\times$; E, the eggplant tortoise beetle, *Cássida pallídula* Boheman, $5\times$. A, larva, with anal fork (covered with fecal material) extended; B, adult; C, pupa, ventral view; D, pupa, dorsal view. (Courtesy of USDA.)

—Subfamily *Cassidìnae*—Tortoise Beetles — The tortoise beetles are broadly oval or circular, with the elytra wide and the head largely or entirely covered by the pronotum. Some of them are shaped very much like ladybird beetles. Many of the smaller tortoise beetles (5 to 6 millimeters in length) are very brilliantly colored, often with

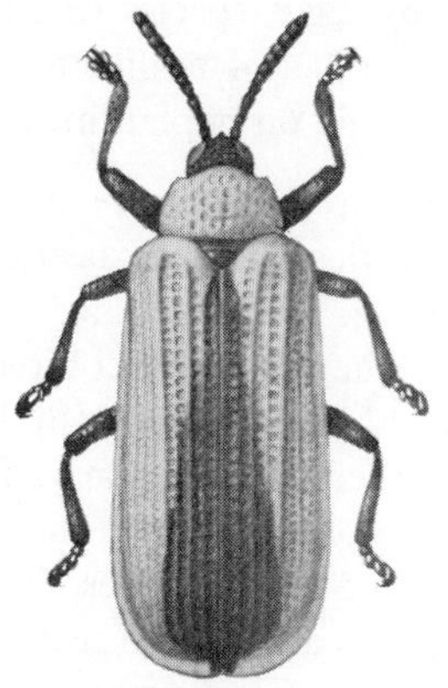

Fig. 22-71. The locust leaf miner, *Xenochálepus dorsàlis* (Thunberg); left, the adult beetle, 6 ×; right, mines of the larvae in black locust. (Courtesy of the Ohio Agricultural Experiment Station.)

golden coloring or markings; *Delòyola guttàta* (Olivier) has black markings on a reddish-gold background, and *Metriòna bicólor* (Fabricius) is brilliant golden or bronzy without the black markings. The largest beetle in this subfamily is *Chelymórpha cassídea* (Fabricius), which is 9.5 to 11.5 millimeters in length and is shaped very much like a box turtle; it is red with six black spots on each elytron and one black spot along the suture overlapping both elytra (Figure 22-70 B).

The larvae of tortoise beetles are elongate-oval, somewhat flattened, and very spiny. At the posterior end of the body is a forked process that is usually bent upward and forward over the body; to this process are attached cast skins and excrement, which form a parasol-like shield over the body (Figure 22-70 A). The larvae and adults feed principally on morning-glories and related plants.

—Subfamily *Hispìnae*—Wedge-Shaped or Leaf-Mining Leaf Beetles— These beetles are 4 to 7 millimeters in length, elongate, and peculiarly ridged (Figure 22-71). Most of the Hispìnae are leaf-mining in the larval stage, and some are rather serious pests. *Xenochálepus dorsàlis* (Thunberg), an orange-yellow beetle with a broad black stripe down the middle of the back (Figure 22-71), is a serious pest of black locust; its mines are oval or irregular areas in the leaves, and a tree may be defoliated when these insects are numerous.

—Subfamilies *Clytrìnae, Cryptocephalìnae, Chlamisìnae* (=*Chlamysìnae* or *Chlamydìnae*), and *Lamprosomatìnae*—Case-Bearing Leaf Beetles— The members of these groups are small, robust, somewhat cylindrical beetles that have the head buried in the prothorax almost to the eyes (Figure 22-69 C). When disturbed, they draw in

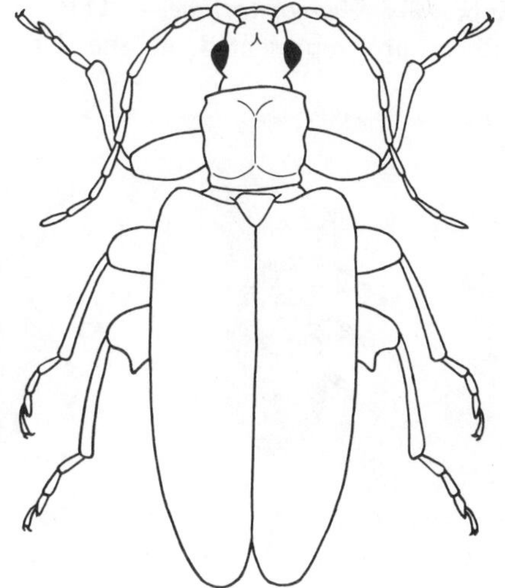

Fig. 22-72. A long-horned leaf beetle, *Donàcia* sp.; $7\frac{1}{2}$ ×.

their legs and fall to the ground and remain motionless. Most of these beetles are dark-colored, often with reddish or yellowish markings. The larvae are small fleshy grubs that crawl about dragging a small protective case, usually made of their own excrement; these cases are shorter than the body, and the posterior portion of the larva is bent downward and forward in the case. Pupation occurs within this case.

The members of these four subfamilies can be separated by the characters given in the key. The first three of these subfamilies are large and widely distributed groups; the Lamprosomatìnae are represented in the United States by only two species, one occurring in Florida and the other in California.

—Subfamily *Aulacoscelìnae* (*Sagrìnae* in part)— This group is represented in the United States by three rare species, which occur in New Mexico, Arizona, and California; the adults are leaf feeders, and the larvae are unknown.

—Subfamily *Megascelìnae*— This is a tropical group that is represented in the United States by a single species, *Megascèlis texàna* Linell, which has been recorded from the Brownsville area of Texas.

—Subfamily *Zeugophorìnae*— This is a small group, represented in the United States by eight species of *Zeugóphora*; the adults are 3 to 4 millimeters in length and occur chiefly on poplar, hickory, and oak.

—Subfamily *Donaciìnae* — Long-Horned Leaf Beetles— These beetles are elongate and slender and have long antennae (Figure 22-72). They are dark-colored and metallic, 5.5 to 12.0 millimeters in length, usually black, greenish, or coppery. They are active, fast-flying beetles, and in this respect resemble the tiger beetles. The long-horned leaf beetles are seldom seen far from water; the adults are generally found on the flowers or foliage of water lilies, pondweed, and other aquatic plants. The eggs are usually laid on the under sides of the leaves of water lily, in a whitish crescent-shaped mass near a small circular hole cut in the leaf by the adult. The larvae feed on the submerged parts of aquatic plants and obtain air through the plant stems; they pupate in cocoons that are fastened to vegetation below the water surface.

—Subfamily *Álticinae* (*Hálticinae*)—Flea Beetles— The flea beetles are small jumping leaf beetles that have the hind femora greatly enlarged. Most of them are blue or greenish, but many are black or black with light markings (Figure 22-73). A number of the flea beetles are very important pests of garden and field crops. *Épitrix párvula*

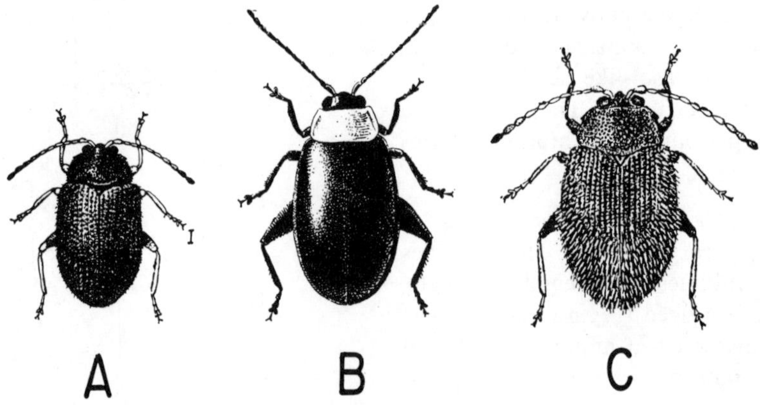

Fig. 22-73. Flea beetles. A, the potato flea beetle, *Épitrix cucùmeris* (Harris); B, the spinach flea beetle, *Disonýchia xanthómelas* (Dalman); C, the eggplant flea beetle, *Épitrix fúscula* Crotch. (Courtesy of USDA.)

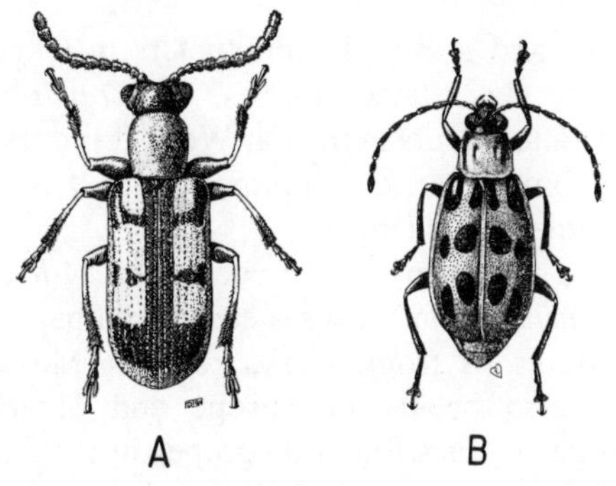

Fig. 22-74. A, asparagus beetle, *Crióceris aspáragi* (Linn.); B, the spotted cucumber beetle, *Diabrótica undécimpunctàta hówardi* Barber. (A, courtesy of the Utah State Agricultural College; B, courtesy of USDA.)

(Fabricius) attacks tobacco, *E. cucùmeris* (Harris) feeds on melons and cucumbers, and *E. fúscula* Crotch feeds on potatoes and tomatoes; these are small blackish beetles about 2 millimeters in length. *Áltica chalýbea* Illiger, a blue-black beetle 4 to 5 millimeters in length, feeds on the buds and leaves of grape. Adult flea beetles feed on the leaves of the food plant and eat tiny holes in them; the leaves of a heavily infested plant look as if small shot had been fired into them. The larvae usually feed on the roots of the same plant.

—Subfamily *Criocerìnae* — Asparagus Beetles— The members of this subfamily have the head narrowed behind the eyes to form a slender neck, and the punctures of the elytra are arranged in rows. Two genera are fairly common, *Lèma* and *Crióceris. L. trilineàta* (Olivier) is 6 to 7 millimeters in length, and reddish yellow in color, with three broad black stripes on the elytra; it frequently damages potatoes and related plants. The genus *Crióceris* includes two species, both imported from Europe, that attack asparagus; these beetles often do serious damage to asparagus. Both species of *Crióceris* are about 7 millimeters in length; *C. aspáragi* (Linn.) has a red prothorax and light-yellow markings on the bluish-green elytra (Figure 22-74 A); *C. 12-punctàta* (Linn.) is brownish, with six large black spots on each elytron. Both adults and larvae of the striped asparagus beetle (*C. aspáragi*) feed on the new shoots and cause damage to the growing plant; the larvae of the spotted asparagus beetle (*C. 12-punctàta*) feed inside the berries and do not injure the shoots.

—Subfamily *Orsodacnìnae* (including *Synetìnae*)— This group is a small one, and the only species in it of much economic importance is the western fruit beetle, *Synèta álbida* LeConte, which damages the buds of many kinds of fruit trees along the North Pacific Coast. The only eastern genera are *Orsodácne* (7 to 8 millimeters in length and found chiefly on willow and dogwood flowers) and *Synèta.*

—Subfamily *Chrysomelìnae*— Most of the members of this large subfamily are oval, convex, and brightly colored, 3.5 to 12.0 millimeters in length, and have the head sunk into the prothorax almost to the eyes. The potato beetle, *Leptinotársa decimlineàta* (Say), is the best known and most important species in this group. This is a large, yellow beetle striped with black (Figure 22-75), and is a very serious pest of potato plants over most of the country. Before the introduction of the potato into the United States, this species was confined to Colorado and neighboring states, where it fed on various wild species of nightshade (*Solànum*); since the introduction of the potato, this beetle has spread throughout the United States (except California and

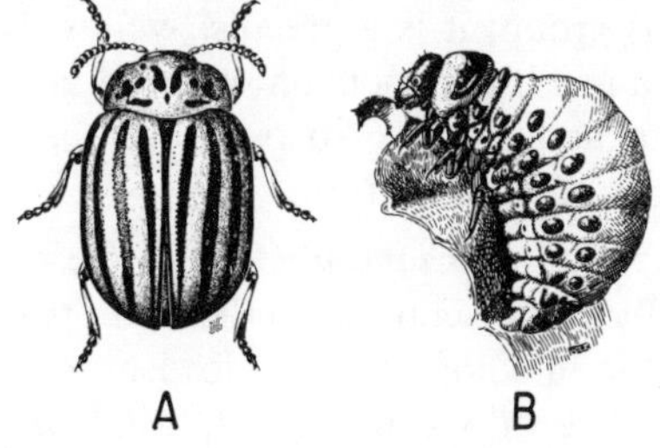

Fig. 22-75. The Colorado potato beetle, *Leptinotársa decimlineàta* (Say). A, adult; B, larva. (Courtesy of the Utah Agricultural Experiment Station.)

Nevada), and has been transported to Europe, where it is also a serious pest. It is frequently called the "Colorado" potato beetle.

Most of the other species in this subfamily feed on various wild plants and are of little economic importance. Species of *Labidómera* (relatively large red-and-black beetles) feed on milkweed; *Phyllodécta* (metallic blue or purple) feed on willow and poplar; and *Callígrapha* (whitish, with dark streaks and spots) feed on willow, alder, and other plants.

—Subfamily *Galerucìnae* — Cucumber Beetles and Others— The members of this group are small soft-bodied beetles, 2.5 to 11.0 millimeters in length, and most of them are yellowish, with dark spots or stripes. The spotted cucumber beetle, *Diabrótica undécimpunctàta howardi* Barber (Figure 22-74 B), and the striped cucumber beetle, *Acalýmma vittàta* (Fabricius), feed on cucumbers and related plants; these beetles do serious damage to cucurbits by their feeding and they act as vectors of cucurbit wilt. The wilt bacilli pass the winter in the alimentary tract of the beetles; new plants are inoculated when the beetles begin to feed on them in the spring. The larvae of these two species are small, white, and soft-bodied, and feed on the roots and underground stems of cucurbits; the larva of the spotted cucumber beetle also feeds on the roots of corn and other plants. The elm leaf beetle, *Galerucélla xanthomelaèna* (Schrank), is another important pest species in this group; it is a greenish yellow beetle with a few black spots on the head and pronotum and a black stripe down the outer margin of each elytron.

—Subfamily *Eumolpìnae*— These are usually oblong convex beetles that are either metallic in color or are yellowish and spotted. The dogbane beetle, *Chrýsochus auràtus* (Fabricius), which occurs on dogbane and milkweed, is one of the most brilliantly colored of the leaf beetles; it has an iridescent blue-green color with a coppery tinge, and is 8 to 11 millimeters in length. A closely related species, *C. cobaltìnus* LeConte, occurs in the Far West; it is darker and bluer than *C. auràtus,* and is 9 to 10 millimeters in length.

The western grape rootworm, *Adóxus obscùrus* (Linn.), causes serious damage to grape crops from Alaska to New Mexico and also occurs in Europe and Siberia. Similar species found on grapes in the East belong to the genus *Fídia,* and are small, oval, hairy, and dark brown to black in color.

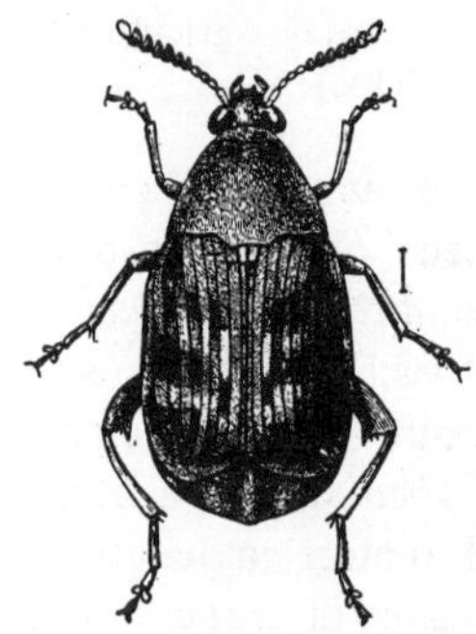

Fig. 22-76. The bean weevil, *Acanthoscélides obtéctus* (Say). The line at the right represents the actual length. (Courtesy of USDA.)

FAMILY **Brùchidae**—Seed Beetles: The members of this family are short, stout-bodied beetles, mostly less than 5 millimeters in length, with the elytra shortened and not covering the tip of the abdomen. The body is often somewhat narrowed anteriorly (Figure 22-76), and is usually dull grayish or brownish in color. The head is produced anteriorly into a short broad snout.

Two common species in this family are the bean weevil, *Acanthoscélides obtéctus* (Say), and the pea weevil, *Brùchus pisòrum* (Linn.). These beetles lay their eggs on the pods of beans or peas, and the larvae bore into the seeds; the adults emerge through little round holes cut in the seed. The bean weevil may breed indoors throughout the year in stored dried beans, but the pea weevil attacks the peas only in the field and does not oviposit on dried peas. These insects cause serious damage in stored seeds that are not protected. The housewife frequently sees bean weevils for the first time when they try to escape through the windows, and does not account for their appearance until she later empties a sack of dried beans and finds them full of holes.

SUPERFAMILY **Curculionòidea:** The members of this group are sometimes called snout beetles, as most of them have the head more or less prolonged into a beak or snout; they were formerly placed in a subdivision of the order called the Rhynchóphora. The Scolýtidae and Platypódidae have the snout scarcely developed, and therefore it seems inappropriate to call them snout beetles.

Certain other characters besides the development of a beak distinguish the Curculionòidea from the beetles already described. The gular sutures are nearly always confluent or lacking, and there is no gula developed (Figure 22-3 C); prosternal sutures are lacking (except in the Anthríbidae), and in all except the Anthríbidae and Nemonýchidae the palpi are rigid or invisible and the labrum is absent (Figure 22-3 A, B). The mouth parts are small and more or less hidden in most of these beetles; the mandibles are usually the only mouth-part structures easily seen without dissection. The mandibles are located at the tip of the snout, and if there are segmented palpi present, they are generally concealed within the mouth cavity. The tarsi are apparently 4-segmented (5-segmented in the Bréntidae, Scolýtidae and Platypódidae).

This is a large and important group of beetles, with about 3000 species occurring in the United States (over 2500 of which are in the family Curculiónidea). Practically all species feed on plant materials, and most of the larval stages are burrowing in habit, infesting nuts, twigs, and the like. The larvae are whitish, **C**-shaped, more or less cylindrical, and usually legless. A great many are of considerable economic importance as pests of field or garden crops, forests, shade and fruit trees, or of stored products.

FAMILY **Bréntidae**—Primitive Weevils: The Bréntidae are long (over 6.5 millimeters in length) narrow beetles with the two sides of the body almost parallel and with the prothorax almost as long as the elytra. The females are much smaller than the males, but have a much more elongate snout that projects straight forward (Figure 22-79 F). This group is principally tropical, and the only common eastern species is *Arrhenòdes* (=*Eùpsalus*) *minùtus* Drury, which usually occurs under the loose bark of dead oak, poplar, and beech trees; the larvae are wood-boring and often attack living trees.

FAMILY **Anthríbidae** — Fungus Weevils: This family includes a few small to minute beetles, 0.5 to 11.0 millimeters in length, that have the beak short and broad and the antennae not elbowed (Figure 22-77). The tarsi are 4-segmented, but sometimes appear 3-segmented because the second segment is triangular and partly covers the third. Some species have slender antennae that may be longer than the body (hence they look a little like some Cerambýcidae), and others have short antennae with a 3-segmented club. The adults of this group are usually

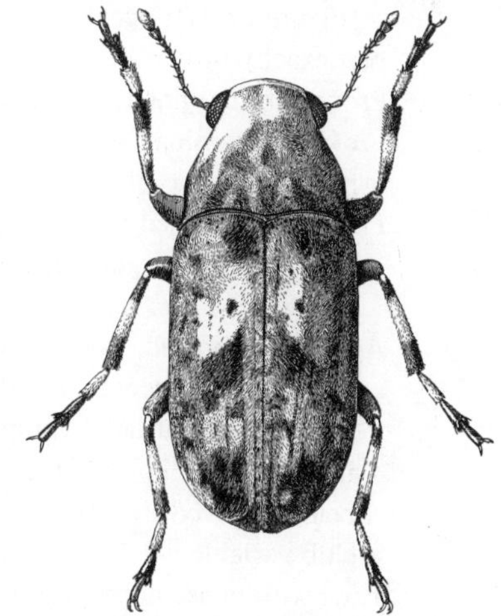

Fig. 22-77. A fungus weevil, *Eupàrius marmòreus* (Olivier) (Anthríbidae). (Courtesy of Pierce and the U.S. National Museum.)

found on dead twigs or beneath loose bark. The larvae vary in habits; some breed in woody fungi, some breed in the fungi of certain crops (for example, corn smut), some feed on seeds, and a few bore in dead wood. The introduced coffee bean weevil, *Araècerus fasciculàtus* (DeGeer), is an important pest of seeds, berries, and dried fruits.

FAMILY **Nemonýchidae**—Pine-Flower Snout Beetles: This is a small group, with only seven species occurring in the United States. These beetles are 3.0 to 4.5 millimeters in length, with the snout as long as the prothorax and somewhat flattened and narrowed at the base. The adult and larval beetles usually feed on the staminate flowers of various conifers, but may occasionally be found on plum or peach trees.

FAMILY **Curculiónidae**—Snout Beetles: The members of this family are by far the most abundant and most common snout beetles. There is considerable variation in size, shape, and the length of the snout in this group, and the family is divided into a number of subfamilies. In most species the snout is fairly well developed, with the elbowed and clavate antennae arising about the midlength of the snout; in some of the nut weevils (for example, *Curcùlio,* Figure 22-82) the snout is very long and slender, as long as the body or longer.

The snout beetles drill deep holes in fruits, nuts, and other plant tissues. The females usually make similar holes in which to oviposit, and the larvae generally feed inside fruits, buds, seeds, nuts, or stems. Most species overwinter as adults.

When disturbed, most snout beetles draw in their legs and antennae and fall to the ground and remain motionless. Many are colored and shaped like bits of bark or dirt, and when they remain motionless, they are very difficult to see.

The family Curculiónidae is divided into a number of subfamilies, which may be separated by the following key.

KEY TO THE SUBFAMILIES OF THE CURCULIÓNIDAE

1. Antennae 10-segmented, the last segment elongate and as long as the 4 or 5 preceding segments together (Figure 22-78 E, F); body antlike, 5 to 6 mm in length, with the pronotum reddish and the elytra blue-black (Figure 22-81); occurring principally in the southern states. . *Cyladìnae* p. 334

1′. Not exactly fitting the above description. 2

2(1′). Pronotum margined; antennae not elbowed; elytra short, exposing parts of 3 abdominal segments; small beetles, 2.8 to 3.2 mm in length, metallic indigo-blue in color. . . . . *Pterocolinae* p. 335

2′. Pronotum rounded laterally, or with only a faint indication of a keel on each lateral margin; antennae and size variable; color usually not as above. 3

3(2′). Antennae elbowed, the first segment very long (Figure 22-78 H-J); beak usually with grooves for the reception of the scape of the antennae; antennal club usually compact 4

3′. Antennae not elbowed, the scape of normal length and not capable of being received in grooves on the beak (Figure 22-78 D, G); antennal club variable 9

4(3). Tarsi with dense hairy pads covering entire bottom surface of each of the first 3 segments, and with third segment bilobed (Figure 22-80 C, E); if tarsi are without such hairy pads, then the third segment is not bilobed, and the first 3 tarsal segments are simply pilose at the sides, and the beak

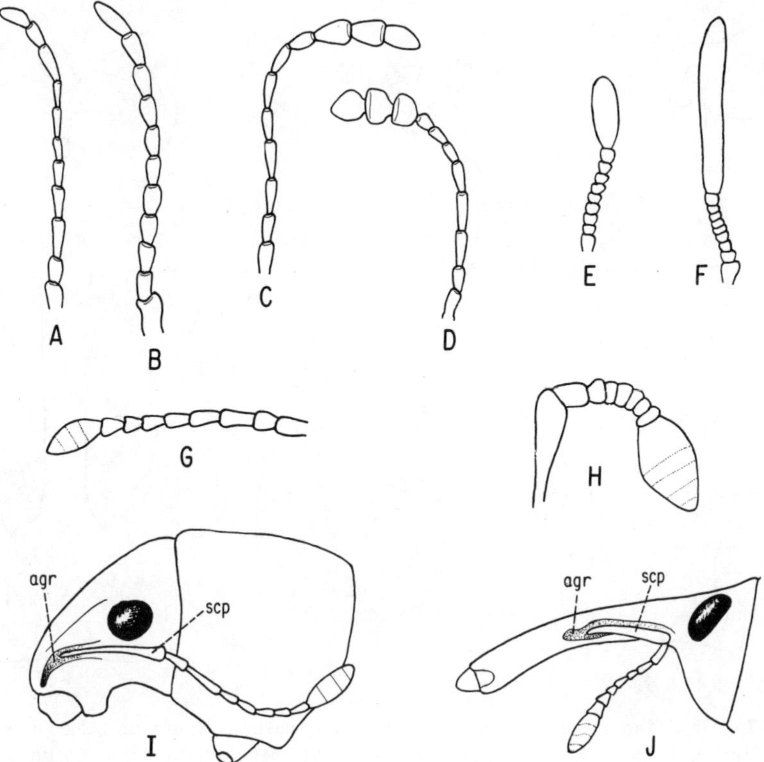

Fig. 22-78. Antennae of snout beetles. A, *Tropíderes* (Anthríbidae); B, *Arrhenòdes* (Bréntidae); C, *Címberis* (Nemonýchidae); D, *Rhýnchites* (Rhynchitìnae); E, *Cȳlas* (Cyladìnae), female; F, same, male; G, *Ithýcerus* (Belìnae); H, *Cossònus* (Cossonìnae); I, *Pantómorus* (Otiorhynchìnae); J, *Pissòdes* (Curculionìnae). *agr,* antennal groove; *scp,* scape.

is received in the prosternum in repose; antennal club usually annulated (Figure 22-78 I, J) 5

4′. Tarsi with hairy pads only along edges of first 3 segments, and with a smooth groove down the center (Figure 22-80 D), or with only the third segment bearing a densely hairy pad entirely covering bottom surface of segment; antennal club with basal segment enlarged (Figure 22-78 H) and (or) shining; front coxae more or less separated........8

5(4). Tarsi slender, not dilated beneath, the third segment not bilobed; first 3 tarsal segments each with 2 small spines beneath; prosternum forming a triangular plate in front of coxae; head and beak withdrawn into a cavity beneath prosternum in repose; 6.5 to 9.0 mm in length........ .... *Thecesternìnae* p. 336

5′. Tarsi somewhat dilated beneath; prosternum not forming a triangular plate in front of coxae; head never received in a cavity of prosternum; size variable 6

6(5′). Beak long and slender (Figures 22-82, 22-83, 22-84 A, B).... *Curculionìnae* p. 335

6′. Beak short and stout (Figure 22-84 C, D, F)........................7

7(6′). Mandibles with an apical projection or cusp that leaves an oval scar when

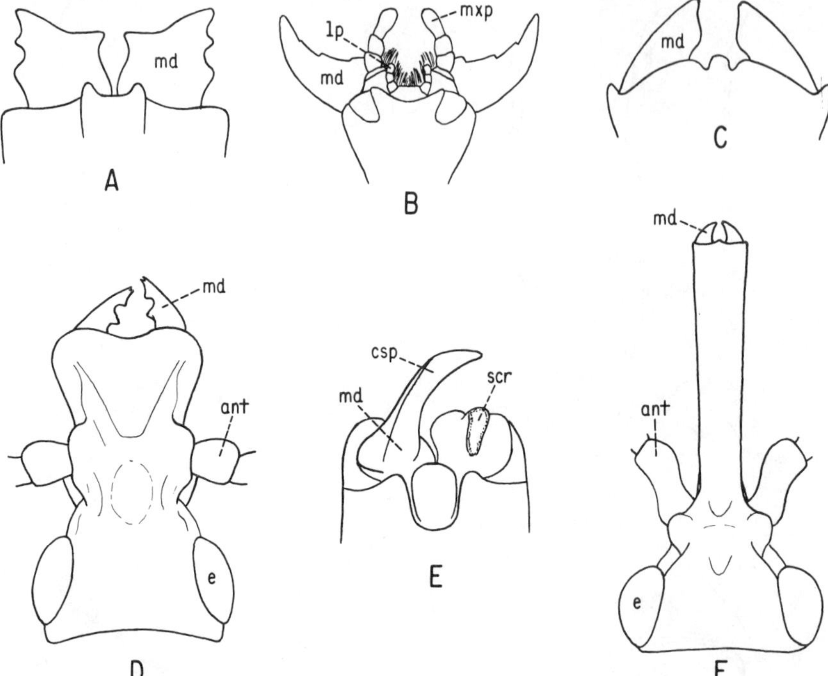

Fig. 22-79. Head and mouth-part structure in snout beetles. A, tip of beak of *Rhýnchites* (Rhynchitìnae); B, tip of beak of *Címberis* (Nemonýchidae), ventral view; C, tip of beak of *Attélabus* (Attelabìnae); D, head of *Arrhenòdes* (Bréntidae), male; E, tip of beak of *Pantómorus* (Otiorhynchìnae), ventral view, showing one mandibular cusp *(csp)* still present and the scar *(scr)* left after the other has broken off; F, head of *Arrhenòdes* (Bréntidae), female. *ant,* base of antenna; *csp,* cusp of mandible; *e,* compound eye; *lp,* labial palpus; *md,* mandible; *mxp,* maxillary palpus; *scr,* scar left on mandible where cusp has been broken off. (B, redrawn from Blatchley and Leng.)

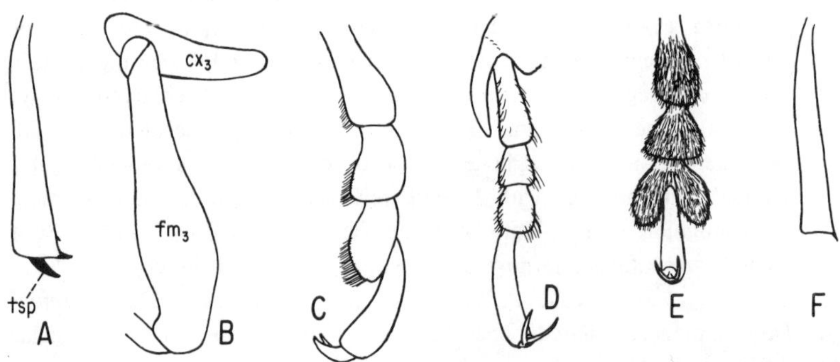

Fig. 22-80. Leg characters of snout beetles. A, tibia of *Attélabus* (Attelabìnae); B, hind femur of *Ithýcerus* (Belìnae); C-E, tarsi: C, *Pissòdes* (Curculionìnae); D, *Cossònus* (Cossonìnae); E, *Brachyrhìnus* (Otiorhynchìnae); F, tibia of *Rhýnchites* (Rhynchitìnae). *cx,* coxa; *fm,* femur; *tsp,* tibial spur.

it falls off (Figure 22-79 E); antennae arising from short wide openings, which are seldom crescent-shaped and which are too short for the scape to fit into; 2.5 to 12.0 mm in length.................. *Otiorhynchinae* p. 336

7′. Mandibles not as above; antennae arising from crescent-shaped or long curved grooves that are usually long enough for the scape to fit into; size variable .... *Curculioninae* p. 335

8(4′). Pygidium almost or completely covered by elytra; beak long, slender, and decurved; a long curved spine usually present at apex of front tibiae on inner side; if beak is short and broad (this group resembles the Scolýtidae, but lacks the series of external teeth on the tibiae), then there are curved spines at the apices of all tibiae................ *Cossoninae* p. 336

8′. Pygidium not largely covered by elytra.................... *Calendrinae* p. 337

9(3′). Segments of antennal club usually separated and forming a long loose club (Figure 22-78 D); length 7 mm or less; elytra parallel-sided in anterior two-thirds; base of pronotum often narrower than base of elytra; trochanters small and triangular, the femora contiguous with the coxae 10

9′. Segments of antennal club firmly united, forming a compact club (Figure 22-78 G); size variable, but if less than 7 mm in length, then elytra are either not parallel-sided in anterior two-thirds or base of pronotum is about as wide as base of elytra, or trochanters are elongate with the femora attached at their apices and thus removed from the coxae....12

10(9). Hind femora short and broad, their outer margins crenulate; beak long, slender, and curved; 3.5 to 4.2 mm in length; southern in distribution.. .... *Oxycoryninae* p. 334

10′. Hind femora somewhat clavate, their outer margins not crenulate; beak and size variable; widely distributed...........................11

11(10′). Tibiae with a short, straight, immovable terminal spur (Figure 22-80 F); mandibles flat and toothed on inner and outer edges (Figure 22-79 A); beak long, nearly parallel-sided .... *Rhynchitinae* p. 334

11′. Tibiae with 2 large, curved or hooked, basally articulated terminal spurs (Figure 22-80 A); mandibles stout, pincer-shaped (Figure 22-79 C); beak short, widened distally .... *Attelabinae* p. 334

12(9′). Trochanters elongate, the femora attached at their apices and thus removed from the coxae; pygidium covered by elytra; beak long; small, pear-shaped beetles, 4.5 mm in length or less, usually black in color *Apioninae* p. 335

12′. Trochanters triangular, the femora contiguous with the coxae; pygidium not covered by elytra 13

13(12′). The first 2 antennal segments about equal in size; hind legs very long, the femora spiny; hind coxae widely separated; small, very broad, toad-shaped beetles 3 mm in length or less, with dense tufts of hair on elytra .... *Tachygoninae* p. 335

13′. Not exactly fitting the above description 14

14(13′). Hind femora short and broad, their outer margins crenulate; small beetles, 3.5 to 4.2 mm in length, with a long, slender, curved beak; southern in distribution....................................... *Oxycoryninae* p. 334

14′. Hind femora clavate (Figure 22-80 B); beak short and broad; larger beetles, 12 to 18 mm in length .... *Belinae* p. 334

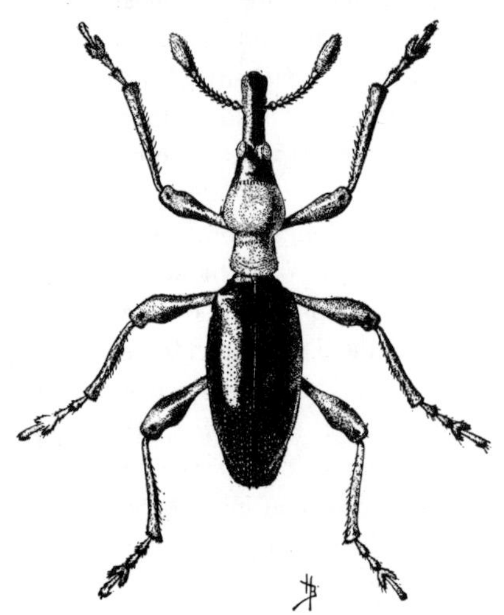

Fig. 22-81. The sweetpotato weevil, *Cỳlas formicàrius elegántulus* (Summers), female. (Courtesy of USDA.)

—Subfamily *Cyladìnae*— The only member of this group occurring in the United States is the sweetpotato weevil, *Cỳlas formicàrius elegántulus* (Summers); this is an introduced species and occurs principally in the southern states. These beetles are slender, elongate, antlike, 5 to 6 millimeters in length, with the pronotum reddish brown and the elytra blue-black (Figure 22-81). The larvae are often called sweetpotato root borers. This insect is a serious pest of sweet potatoes because the larvae bore in the vines and roots and the plants are often killed. The larvae may continue to burrow through the tubers after they are harvested, and adults may emerge after the sweet potatoes are on the market or in storage.

—Subfamily *Belìnae*— This subfamily includes a single species, the New York weevil, *Ithýcerus novaboracénsis* (Forster). This beetle is shiny black, clothed with patches of gray and brown pubescence, and has the scutellum yellowish; it is 12 to 18 millimeters in length. It occurs principally on the limbs or foliage of oak, hickory, and beech trees. The larvae bore in the twigs and branches of these trees.

—Subfamily *Rhynchitìnae* (*Cimberìnae*)— Tooth-Nosed Snout Beetles— These beetles are so named because of the teeth on the inner and outer edges of the mandibles (Figure 22-79 A). The members of this group are 1.5 to 6.5 millimeters in length and are usually found on low vegetation. *Rhýnchites bicólor* Fabricius is a common species occurring on roses; the adult is about 6 millimeters in length and is red, with the snout and the ventral side of the body black, and has a broad-shouldered appearance; the larvae feed on rose fruits. Other species breed in buds, fruits, and nuts.

—Subfamily *Attelabìnae* — Leaf-Rolling Weevils— These beetles are short and robust, 3 to 6 millimeters in length, and are somewhat similar to the Rhynchitìnae; most of them are black, red, or black with red markings. The most interesting characteristic of this group is their method of laying eggs, from which their common name is derived. When a female is ready to oviposit, she cuts a slit near the base of the leaf, from the midrib to each edge, and rolls the part of the leaf beyond the slit into a neat and solid roll in which she usually lays a single egg. She then gnaws the petiole of the leaf partly in two, and the leaf roll eventually drops to the ground. The larvae feed on the inner portion of this leaf roll and pupate either in the roll or in the ground.

The eight species of leaf-rolling weevils in the United States belong to the genus *Attélabus.* Most species occur on oak, hickory, or walnut, but one species (*A. nígripes* LeConte, a red species 3.5 to 4.5 millimeters in length) feeds on sumac, and another (*A. rhòis* Boheman, 4.5 to 5.5 millimeters in length, and varying in color from dark reddish to black) feeds on alder and hazelnut.

—Subfamily *Oxycorynìnae* (*Allocorhynìnae, Allocorynìnae*)— This subfamily contains a single nearctic species, *Allocórhynus slóssoni* Schaeffer, 3.5 to 4.2 millimeters in length, which occurs in southern Florida;

both adults and larvae feed on arrowroot. The adults have the elytra black, with an elongate reddish-yellow mark at each humerus.

—Subfamily *Tachygonìnae*—Toad Weevils — The toad weevils are less than 3 millimeters in length, broadly oval (about as broad as long) and somewhat toad-shaped. They are usually found on the foliage of oak or elm; at rest they usually hang downward from the leaves, hanging by means of their spiny hind femora. They characteristically walk about on the under sides of the leaves.

—Subfamily *Pterocolìnae*—Short-Winged Weevils— This group includes a single United States species, *Pterócolus ovàtus* (Fabricius). This beetle is broadly oval, indigo-blue in color, and 2.8 to 3.2 millimeters in length; the elytra are short and rounded apically, exposing the central portions of the last two or three abdominal terga. This species occurs from Florida to Canada, and is found principally on young oak trees, but has been collected on the foliage of plum, peach, and grape.

—Subfamily *Apionìnae*— The Apionìnae are small beetles, 4.5 millimeters in length or less, and somewhat pear-shaped. Most species occur on leguminous plants where the larvae bore into the seeds, stems, and other parts of the plant. Other species feed on various other plants, and there is one species (*Podàpion gallícola* Riley) that forms galls on pine trees.

—Subfamily *Curculionìnae*—Typical Snout Beetles— This is the largest subfamily of the Curculiónidae and contains about 2000 species in the United States. Many of these insects are important pests of various crops and trees.

The plum curculio, *Conotrachèlus nénuphar* (Herbst), is a serious pest of plum, cherry, peach, apple, and other fruits. The females lay their eggs in little pits they eat in the fruit, and then cut a crescent-shaped incision beside the pit containing the egg. The larvae develop in the fruit and pupate in the soil. The adult is about 6 millimeters in length, dark-colored, and has two prominent tubercles on each elytron (Figure 22-83).

The boll weevil, *Anthónomus grándis* Boheman, is a well-known and serious pest of cotton in the southern states. It entered the United States from Mexico about 1890 and has since spread over most of the cotton-growing sections in this country. The adults are about 6 millimeters in length, yellowish to brown in color, with a slender snout about half as long as the body. They feed on the seed pod or boll and lay their eggs in the holes made in feeding; the larvae feed inside the bolls and eventually destroy them. There are five or more generations a year.

The alfalfa weevil, *Hýpera pòstica* (Gyllenhal) (Figure 22-84 D), is an important pest of alfalfa and clover; the adults feed on the growing tips of the plant and skeletonize the leaves, and the larvae bore in the stalks and buds. The adult is 3 to 4 millimeters in length and dark grayish brown in color. The clover leaf weevil, *H. punctàta* (Fabricius), another species attacking clover, is about 8 millimeters in length and is dark brown speckled with black dorsally (Figure 22-84 C); its habits are similar to those of the alfalfa weevil.

The acorn and nut weevils, *Curcùlio* spp., are unique in having an extremely long and slender snout, which is often as long as the remainder of the body (Figure 22-82). They bore into acorns and nuts with their long snouts and deposit their eggs in some of these feeding holes. *C. nàsicus* Say is a common species breeding in hickory nuts.

The snout beetles in the genus *Líxus* are long and slender, with the curved beak nearly as long as the pronotum; they are common and widespread, and usually occur on the leaves of weeds near water. *L. concàvus* Say, which breeds in the stems of dock, sunflower, thistle, and occasionally rhubarb, is commonly called the rhubarb

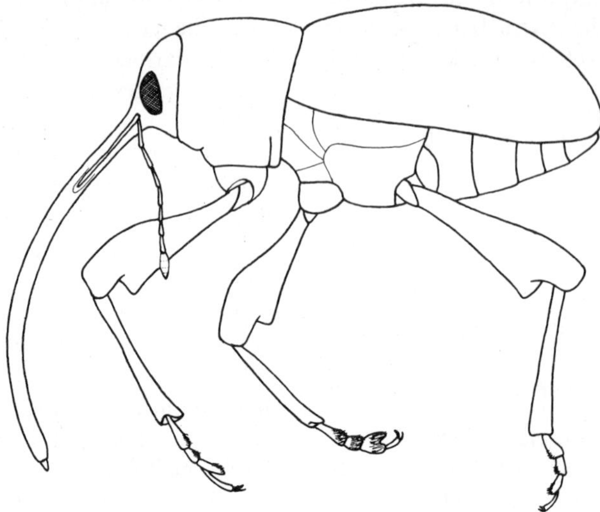

Fig. 22-82. A nut weevil, *Curcùlio* sp.

curculio; the adult is blackish and covered with a gray pubescence, and is 10.0 to 13.5 millimeters in length. About 50 species of the genus *Líxus* occur in the United States.

—Subfamily *Thecesternìnae* (*Brysopìnae*)— Bison Snout Beetles— This group includes only eight United States species, of which one occurs in the East. The eastern species, *Thecestérnus affínis* LeConte, is a dull-black beetle covered with brownish yellow scales and is 6.5 to 9.0 millimeters in length. When at rest, the head and beak are completely withdrawn into a large cavity in the prosternum. These beetles get their name from the fact that they were abundant in the West under dry buffalo dung; the eastern species occurs under dried cow dung or stones.

—Subfamily *Cossonìnae* — Broad-Nosed Bark Beetles— These beetles can usually be recognized by the broad short beak and the long curved spine at the apex of each front tibia. The tarsi are slender, with no dilated segments, and the third segment is not distinctly notched at the apex. Most species occur under the dead bark of trees or under logs or stones; a few occur under driftwood and debris along the seacoast. These beetles are 1.5 to 6.5 millimeters in length.

—Subfamily *Otiorhynchìnae* (including *Brachyrhìnae*—Scarred Snout Beetles or Short-Nosed Weevils— These snout beetles are small, usually dark-colored, and have the beak short and stout. The mandibles have a small appendage on the anterior edge; this soon breaks off, leaving a small oval scar (Figure 22-79 E). It is believed that these appendages or cusps on the mandibles aid the newly formed adult in cutting its way out of the old pupal skin. Most of the nearly 300 species of scarred snout beetles in the United States are flightless because the elytra are grown together along the suture and the rear wings are degenerate.

These beetles usually occur in low vegetation or on the ground, and some are important pests of various crops. The most important pest species in this group is the white-fringed beetle, *Graphógnathus leucolòma* (Boheman), which is a serious agricultural pest in the southern states. This beetle is about 12 millimeters in length, with the edges of the elytra whitish and with two white longitudinal stripes along the sides of the head and pronotum; it is flightless. No males of this species are known, and the females reproduce parthenogenetically, each female laying from 1000 to 1800 eggs. The larvae are subterranean and feed on newly planted seeds and roots.

Another flightless and extremely injurious weevil in this subfamily is the Fuller rose weevil, *Pantómorus gódmani* (Crotch), 7 to 9 millimeters in length, which is especially common in the Far West. It attacks roses and many greenhouse plants as well as citrus and other fruit trees, and the adults consume huge quantities of leaves. The larvae live in the soil and feed on the roots of the food plants. This species occurs throughout the United States and in some other countries as well.

Among the more common flightless species in this group are those belonging to the genus *Brachyrhìnus*. *B. ovàtus* (Linn.) is about 5 or 6 millimeters in length, black or dark brown in color, and often causes serious injury to strawberries and other plants.

—Subfamily *Calendrìnae* (*Calandrìnae*, *Rhynchophorìnae*) — Billbugs and Grain Weevils— These beetles are mostly stout-bodied and somewhat cylindrical and are of varying size; some of the largest snout beetles in our area belong to this group. One of the largest of the billbugs is *Rhynchóphorus cruentàtus* (Fabricius), which is 20 to 30 millimeters in length and occurs on palms. *Rhodobaènus tredecimpunctàtus* (Illiger), a common eastern billbug, is 7 to 11 millimeters in length; it is reddish with small black spots on the elytra, and the third tarsal segment is entirely hairy beneath. The genus *Sphenóphorus* (Figure 22-85) includes the corn billbugs, which occur on various grasses, including timothy and corn; the adults feed on the foliage and the larvae bore into the stalks.

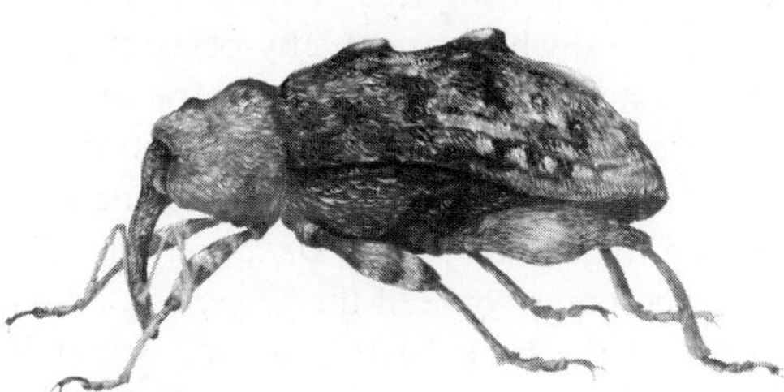

Fig. 22-83. The plum curculio, *Conotrachèlus nénuphar* (Herbst).

The most important pests in this subfamily are the granary weevil, *Sitóphilus granàrius* (Linn.), and the rice weevil, *S. orỳzae* (Linn.). These are small brownish insects, 3 to 4 millimeters in length, that attack stored grain (wheat, corn, rice, etc.); both adults and larvae feed on the grain, and the larvae develop inside the grains.

FAMILY **Platypódidae**—Pin-Hole Borers or Flat-Footed Ambrosia Beetles: The beetles in this group are elongate, slender, and cylindrical, with the head slightly wider than the pronotum; they are brownish in color and 4 to 6 millimeters in length. The tarsi are very slender, with the first segment longer than the remaining segments combined (Figure 22-10 K). Our only genus is *Plátypus*.

These beetles are wood-boring and bore in living trees, but they seldom attack a healthy tree; they generally attack deciduous trees. The larvae feed on fungi that are cultivated in their galleries.

FAMILY **Scolýtidae**—Bark or Engraver Beetles, and Ambrosia or Timber Beetles: The scolytids are small cylindrical beetles, rarely over 6 or 8 millimeters in length and usually brownish or black in color, that feed in the inner bark or wood of trees. The family contains two groups, the bark or engraver beetles and the ambrosia or timber beetles; these groups are very similar in appearance (Figure 22-86), but the bark beetles have a large spine or projection at the apex of the front tibiae.

The bark or engraver beetles live beneath the bark of trees, mining on the surface of the hardwood but not entering it. Both adults and larvae mine under the bark. The adults enter first and excavate a characteristic gallery or group of galleries in which

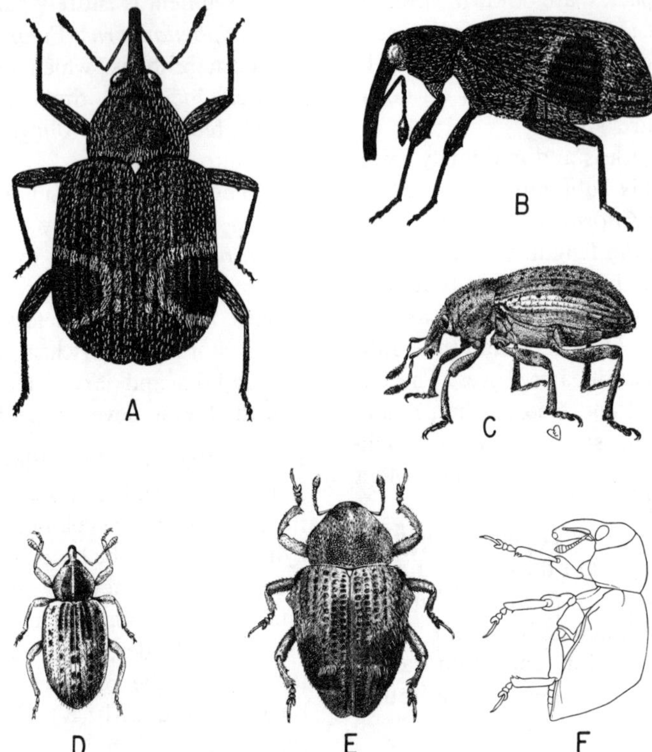

Fig. 22-84. Snout beetles (Curculioninae). A, the strawberry weevil, *Anthónomus signàtus* Say, female; B, same, male; C, cloverleaf weevil, *Hýpera punctàta* (Fabricius); D, alfalfa weevil, *Hýpera pòstica* (Gyllenhal); E, the beanstalk weevil, *Stérnechus paludàtus* (Casey), dorsal view; F, same, lateral view. (A and B, courtesy of Baerg and the Arkansas Agricultural Experiment Station; C-F, courtesy of USDA.)

the eggs are laid. These brood galleries may be made by a single pair, or a male may have a harem of two or more females, each of which excavates a brood gallery. The eggs are laid in little notches at intervals along the sides of the brood galleries. When the eggs hatch, the larvae excavate tunnels leading away from the brood gallery; these tunnels get larger as the larva gets farther from the brood gallery, and they form a characteristic pattern under the bark (Figure 22-87). The pattern of these tunnels varies in different species. These scolytids are often called engraver beetles because of the elaborate patterns they excavate beneath the bark. When the larvae complete their growth, they pupate at the ends of their tunnels, and emerge through a round hole eaten through the bark. These numerous emergence holes resemble the holes that would be made by a charge of small lead shot.

Different species of bark beetles attack different species of trees; some attack only recently cut or dead logs or branches, while others attack living trees. Those that attack living trees, which are chiefly pests of evergreens, may tunnel under the bark to such an extent that the tree is girdled and dies.

Most of the bark beetles attacking pine belong to genera *Íps* and *Dendróctonus*; the latter contains some of the largest scolytids. Some of the bark beetles are important in the transmission of tree diseases; Dutch elm disease is transmitted chiefly by the smaller European elm bark beetle, *Scólytus multis-*

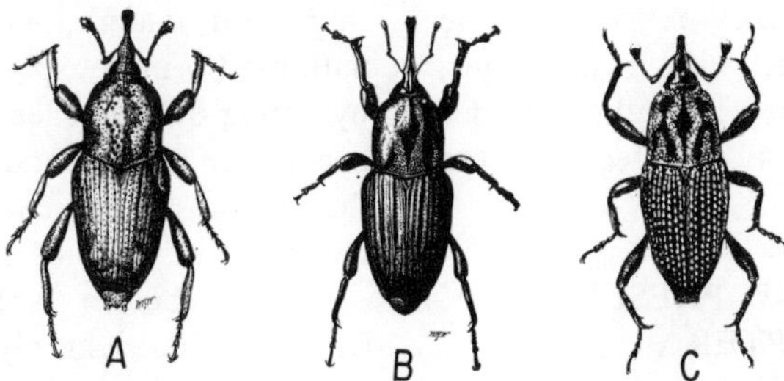

Fig. 22-85. Billbugs (Calendrìnae), 2 ×. A, the curlewbug, *Sphenóphorus callòsus* (Olivier); B, the maize billbug, *Sphenóphorus màidis* (Chittenden); C, the timothy billbug, *Sphenóphorus zèae* (Walsh). (Courtesy of USDA.)

triàtus (Marsham) (Figure 22-86 B), a species imported from Europe. These beetles have already caused the death of thousands of American elm trees east of Illinois, and in 1950 were collected by the hundreds in San Jose, California, having previously been recorded no farther west than Iowa. The clover-root borer, *Hylastìnus obscùrus* (Marsham), often causes serious damage to clover; the larvae tunnel in the roots of the clover and kill them.

The ambrosia or timber beetles bore into the hardwood of trees and feed on fungi that they cultivate in their galleries. They do not eat the wood, but do considerable damage by tunneling through it. The larvae develop in small cells adjoining the main galleries, and in most species the larvae are fed by the adults. Each species usually feeds on one particular type of fungus; when the females emerge and fly to another tree, they carry conidia of the fungus from the natal gallery to the new host and introduce the fungus into the gallery they excavate. After the eggs hatch, the females usually care for the larvae until they are full grown and

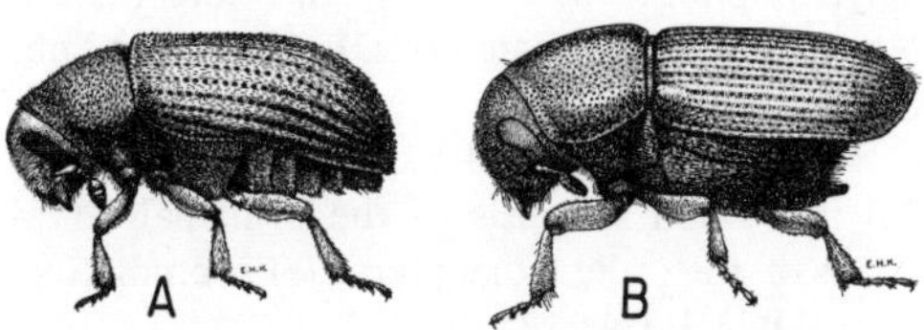

Fig. 22-86. Elm bark beetles (Scolýtidae); 12 ×. A, the native elm bark beetle, *Hylurgópinus rùfipes* (Eichhoff); B, the smaller European elm bark beetle, *Scólytus multistriàtus* (Marsham). (Courtesy of Kaston and the Connecticut Agricultural Experiment Station.)

Fig. 22-87. Semidiagrammatic drawing of a portion of a log containing galleries of bark beetles (Scolýtidae). The bark is cut through two entrance galleries, each with its accumulation of fine frass near the outside opening of the gallery. Three sets of galleries of different age are shown; in the one at the left the larvae are full grown and some have already pupated, and there is one empty pupal cell with its exit hole at the lower left corner of the cut-away section. Another entrance hole is evidenced by the frass accumulation on the bark at the left. (Courtesy of Kaston and the Connecticut Agricultural Experiment Station.)

pupate. To do this, they must keep the larval burrows supplied with fresh fungus, or "ambrosia," and they keep the galleries clean by carrying away the feces of the larvae.

COLLECTING AND PRESERVING COLEOPTERA

Since this is such a large and varied group, most of the methods discussed in Chapter 32 for collecting and preserving insects are applicable here. Several general collecting procedures, however, may be noted: (1) many species may be taken by sweeping in a variety of situations; (2) many species, often strikingly colored, may be taken on flowers; (3) a number of species, such as the carrion beetles and others, may be obtained by means of suitably baited traps; (4) a number of species are attracted to lights at night, and may be collected at lights or in a light trap; (5) beetles of many groups are to be found under bark, in rotting wood, under stones, and in similar situations; (6) many species may be obtained by sifting debris or leaf litter; and (7) many beetles are aquatic and may be collected by the various aquatic equipment and methods described in Chapter 32.

Most beetles are preserved pinned (through the right elytron) or on points. When a beetle is mounted on a point, it is important that it be mounted so that the ventral side of the body and the legs are visible; it may be mounted either on its side on the point or the tip of the point may be bent down and the specimen attached to this bent-down tip by the right side of the thorax. It may sometimes be desirable to mount two specimens on the same point (when one is sure they are the same species), one dorsal side up and the other ventral side up. Many of the more minute beetles must be preserved in alcohol (70 to 80 percent) and mounted on a microscope slide for detailed study.

REFERENCES ON THE COLEOPTERA

Arnett, Ross H., Jr. 1958. A list of beetle families. Coleop. Bull., 12:65-72.

Arnett, Ross H., Jr. 1960-1962. The beetles of the United States (a manual for identification). Introduction and Part I, Archestemata and Adephaga, 1960; Fasc. 1-9, xi+210 pp., illus. Part II, Suborder Myxophaga, Suborder Polyphaga (part), Series Staphyliniformia (part), Hydrophiloidea and Staphylinoidea; 1961: Fasc. 10-25, pp. 211-368, illus. Part III, Suborder Polyphaga (Cont.), Series Staphyliniformia (concl.), Scarabaeoformia, and Elateriformia; 1962; Fasc. 26-50, pp. 369-526, illus. Part IV, Suborder Polyphaga (Cont.), Series Elateriformia (Concl.), Bostrychiformia, and Cucujiformia; 1962; Fasc. 51-72, pp. 527-644, illus. Part V, Suborder Polyphaga (Cont.), Series Cucujiformia (Cont.); 1962; Fasc. 73-102, pp. 645-850, illus. Part VI, Suborder Polyphaga (Concl.), Series Cucujiformia (Concl.), Chrysomeloidea, Curculionoidea; 1962; Fasc. 103-110, pp. 851-1112, illus. Washington, D.C.: Catholic University of America Press.

Blatchley, W. S. 1910. An illustrated and descriptive catalogue of the Coleoptera or beetles (exclusive of the Rhynchophora) known to occur in Indiana. Indianapolis, Ind.: Nature Pub. Co. 1385 pp., 590 f.

Blatchley, W. S., and C. W. Leng. 1916. Rhynchophora or weevils of northeastern North America. Indianapolis, Ind.: Nature Pub. Co. 682 pp., 155 f.

Böving, A. G., and F. C. Craighead. 1930. An illustrated synopsis of the principal larval forms of the order Coleoptera. J. Entomol. Soc. Am., 11(1):1-351; 125 pl.

Bradley, J. Chester. 1930. A manual of the genera of beetles of America north of Mexico. Ithaca, N.Y.: Daw, Illiston, & Co. 360 pp.

Crowson, R. A. 1955. The natural classification of the families of Coleoptera. London: Nathaniel Lloyd & Co., Ltd. 187 pp., 212 f.

Dillon, E. S., and L. S. Dillon. 1961. A manual of common beetles of eastern North America. Evanston, Ill.: Row, Peterson & Company. viii+884 pp., 85 pl. (4 in color), 544 text f.

Edwards, J. Gordon. 1949. Coleoptera or Beetles East of the Great Plains. Ann Arbor, Mich.: J. W. Edwards, Publisher, Inc. 181 pp., 23 pl.

Edwards, J. Gordon. 1950. A bibliographical supplement to Coleoptera or Beetles East of the Great Plains, applying particularly to western United States, pp. 182-212. Published by the author, San Jose State College, San Jose, Calif.

Hatch, Melville H. 1927. A systematic index to the keys for the determination of the nearctic Coleoptera. J. N.Y. Entomol. Soc., 35(3):279-306.

Hatch, Melville H. 1953. The beetles of the Pacific Northwest. Part I: Introduction and Adephaga. Seattle, Wash.: University of Washington Press. vii+340 pp., 37 pl., 2 text f.

Hatch, Melville H. 1957. The beetles of the Pacific Northwest. Part II: Staphyliniformia. University of Wash. Publ. Biol., 16:1-384; illus.

Jaques, H. E. 1951. How to know the beetles. Dubuque, Iowa: Wm. C. Brown Company. iii+372 pp., 865 f.

Kissinger, David G. 1964. Curculionidae of America north of Mexico. A key to the genera. South Lancaster, Mass.: Taxonomic Publications. v + 143 p., 59 f.

Leech, H. B., and H. P. Chandler. 1956. Aquatic Coleoptera. In: Aquatic insects of California, ed. by Robert L. Usinger. Berkeley, Calif.: University of California Press. Pp. 293-371, 61 f.

Leech, H. B., and M. W. Sanderson. 1959. Coleoptera. In: Fresh-water biology, ed. by W. T. Edmondson. New York: John Wiley & Sons, Inc. Pp. 981-1023; 94 f.

Leng, C. W., *et al.* 1920-1948. Catalogue of the Coleoptera of America north of Mexico. Mt. Vernon, N.Y.: John D. Sherman. Original catalogue, 1920; x+470 pp. First supplement, 1927, by C. W. Leng and A. J. Mutchler, 78 pp. Second and third supplements, 1933, by C. W. Leng and A. J. Mutchler, 112 pp. Fourth supplement, 1939, by R. E. Blackwelder, 146 pp. Fifth supplement, 1948, by R. E. and R. M. Blackwelder, 87 pp.

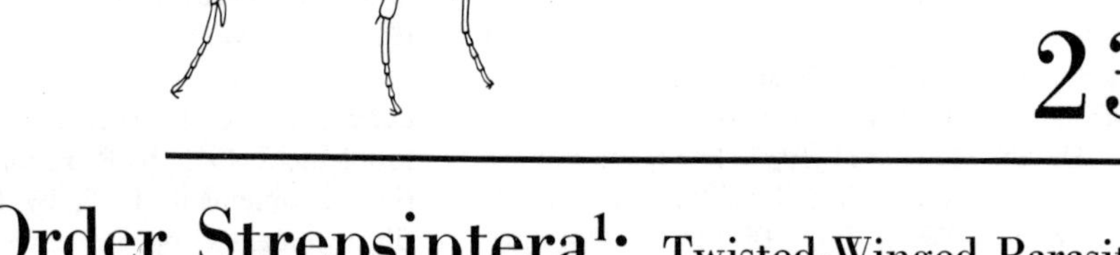

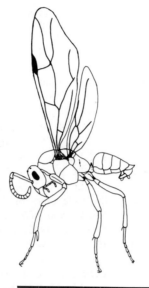

23

Order Strepsiptera[1]: Twisted-Winged Parasites

The Strepsiptera are minute insects, most of which are parasitic on other insects. The two sexes are quite different; the males are free-living and winged, while the females are wingless, often legless, and in the parasitic species, do not leave the host.

Male Strepsiptera (Figure 23-1 A-D) are somewhat beetlelike in appearance, with protruding eyes, and the antennae often have elongate processes on some segments; the front wings are reduced to clublike structures that resemble the halteres of the Diptera; the hind wings are large and membranous, fanlike, and have a reduced venation. The adult females of the free-living species (Figure 23-1 E) have a distinct head, with simple 4- or 5-segmented antennae, chewing mouth parts, and compound eyes. The females of the parasitic species usually lack eyes, antennae, and legs, the body segmentation is very indistinct, and the head and thorax are fused (Figure 23-1 G). The metamorphosis is complete.

The life history of the parasitic forms in this order is rather complex and involves hypermetamorphosis. A male, on emerging, seeks out and mates with a female, which never leaves its host. The female produces large numbers—up to several thousand—of tiny larvae, which escape from her body and the body of the host to the soil or to vegetation. These larvae, which are called triungulins, have well-developed eyes and legs (Figure 23-1 F) and are fairly active insects; they locate and enter the body of the host. Once there, the larva molts into a legless wormlike stage that feeds in the host's body cavity. After several molts, it pupates inside the last larval skin. The male, on emerging, leaves its host and flies about; the female remains in the host, with the

[1] Strepsiptera: *strepsi*, twisted; *ptera*, wings.

anterior part of its body protruding between the abdominal segments of the host; after the young are produced, it dies.

Various species of Orthoptera, Hemiptera, Homoptera, Hymenoptera and Thysanura serve as the hosts of Strepsiptera. The host is not always killed, but may be injured; the shape or color of the abdomen may be changed, or the sex organs may be damaged. The developing male strepsipteran usually causes more damage to its host than the female.

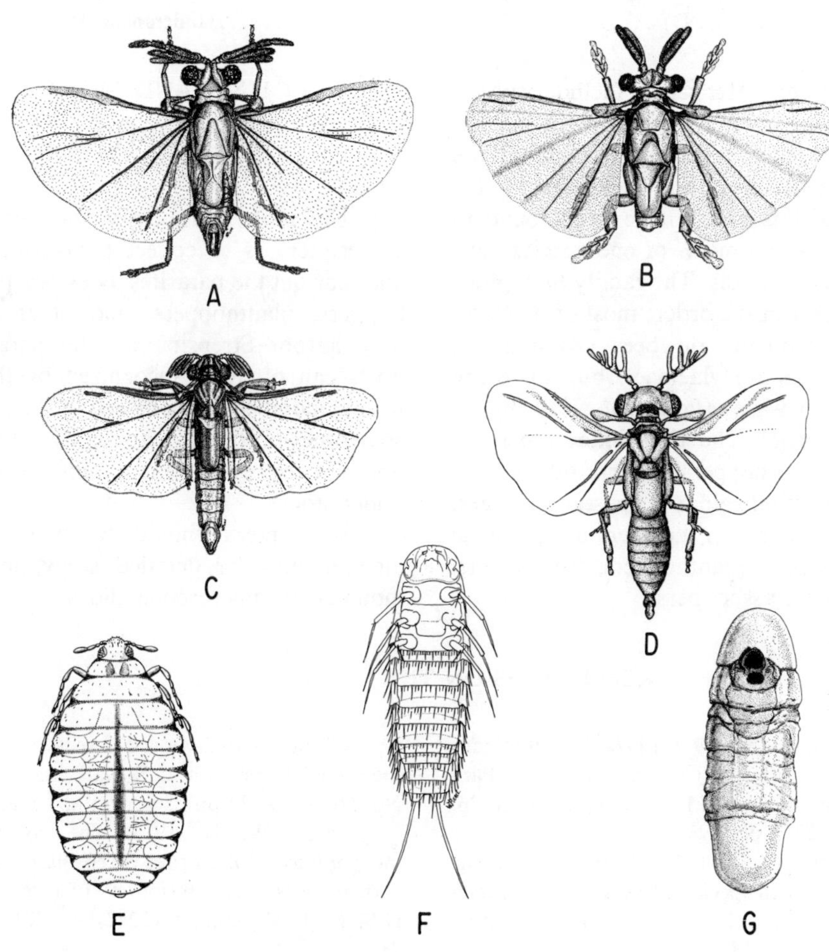

Fig. 23-1. Strepsiptera. A, *Triozócera mexicàna* Pierce (Mengèidae), male; B, *Neostỳlops shánnoni* Pierce (Stylópidae), male; C, *Halictóphagus oncometòpiae* (Pierce) (Halictophágidae), male; D, *Halictóphagus serràtus* Bohart (Halictophágidae), male; E, *Eoxènos laboulbénei* Peyerimhoff (Mengèidae), female; F, *Stỳlops califòrnica* Pierce (Stylópidae), triungulin, ventral view; G, *Halictóphagus oncometòpiae* (Pierce) (Halictophágidae), female, ventral view. (A-C, F, and G, courtesy of Pierce; D, courtesy of Bohart; E, courtesy of Parker and Smith; A-C, courtesy of the U.S. National Museum; D-E, courtesy of the Entomological Society of America; F-G, courtesy of the U.S. National Museum.)

The following key will separate the males of the four families of Strepsiptera known to occur in the United States.

KEY TO THE FAMILIES OF STREPSIPTERA

1.	Tarsi 5-segmented, with 2 claws (Figure 23-1 A). . . . . **Mengèidae**	p. 344
1′.	Tarsi with 4 or fewer segments, and without claws (Figure 23-1 B-D). . . . 2	
2(1′).	Tarsi 4-segmented; antennae 4- or 6-segmented (Figure 23-1 B) **Stylópidae**	p. 344
2′.	Tarsi 2- or 3-segmented; antennae 4- or 7-segmented (Figure 23-1 C, D). . 3	
3(2′).	Tarsi 2-segmented; antennae 4-segmented. . . . . **Elénchidae**	p. 344
3′.	Tarsi 3-segmented; antennae 7-segmented, the third, fourth, and fifth segments prolonged laterally, and the seventh segment elongate (Figure 23-1 C, D) . . . . **Halictophágidae**	p. 344

The family **Mengèidae** includes species that are free-living as adults, with the immature stages parasitizing Thysanura; the adults are usually found under stones. No females of this group have been found in this country, but males of one species have been taken in Texas. The family **Stylópidae** is the largest in the order; most of its members are parasitic on bees (Andrénidae, Halíctidae, and Hylaeìnae), but some are parasitic on wasps (Polistìnae, Eumenìnae, and Sphecìnae). The **Elénchidae** are parasitic on planthoppers (Fulgoròidea). The family **Halictophágidae** is the second largest in the order, and its members are parasitic on leafhoppers, planthoppers, treehoppers, and pygmy grasshoppers.

COLLECTING AND PRESERVING STREPSIPTERA

The most satisfactory way to collect Strepsiptera is to collect parasitized hosts and rear out the parasites. Bees, wasps, leafhoppers, planthoppers, and other insects may harbor Strepsiptera. The parasitized hosts can often be recognized by the distorted abdomen, and one end of the parasite sometimes protrudes between two of the abdominal segments. Some Strepsiptera occur under stones.

Strepsiptera should be preserved in alcohol, and for detailed study, must be mounted on microscope slides.

REFERENCES ON THE STREPSIPTERA

Bohart, R. M. 1936-1937. A preliminary study of the genus *Stylops* in California. Pan-Pacific Entomologist, 12(1):9-18, 1 pl., 1936. 13(1-2):49-57, 1 pl., 1937.

Bohart, R. M. 1941. A revision of the Strepsiptera with special reference to the species of North America. Calif. Univ. Publ., Entomol., 7(6):91-160; f. A-H.

Bohart, R. M. 1943. New species of *Halictophagus* with a key to the genus in North America (Strepsiptera, Halictophagidae). Ann. Entomol. Soc. Am., 36(3):341-359; 47 f.

Pierce, W. D. 1909. A monographic revision of the twisted-winged insects comprising the order Strepsiptera. U.S. Natl. Museum Bull. No. 66; xiii+232 pp., 3 f., 15 pl., 1 map.

Pierce, W. D. 1918. The comparative morphology of the order Strepsiptera together with records and descriptions of insects. Proc. U.S. Natl. Museum, 54(2242):391-501; pl. 64-78.

Sylvestri, F. 1942. Nuove osservazione sulla *Mengenilla parvula* Silvestri (Insecta Strepsiptera). Pontif. Acad. Sci., Acta Rome, 6:95-96.

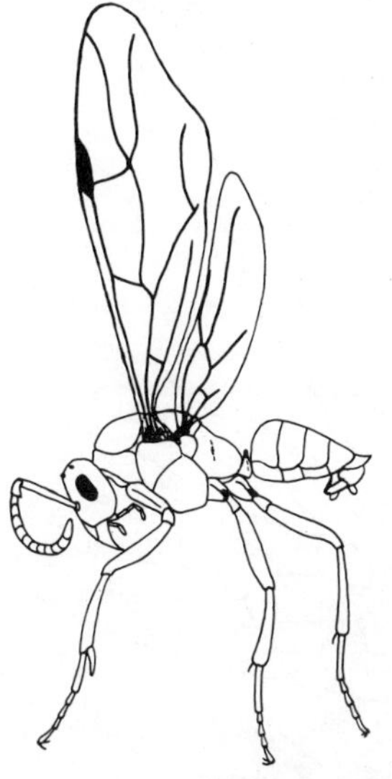

24

Order Mecoptera[1]: Scorpionflies

The scorpionflies are medium-sized, slender-bodied insects with a long-faced appearance (Figure 24-1). The mouth parts, which are of the chewing type, are prolonged ventrally to form a beaklike structure; this peculiar head shape (Figure 24-2) is one of the most characteristic features of the scorpionflies. Most of the Mecoptera have four long and narrow membranous wings; the front and hind wings are similar in size and shape and have a similar venation (Figure 24-4). The venation is rather generalized, with numerous cross-veins. The metamorphosis is complete, and the larvae (Figure 24-3) are usually eruciform (scarabaeiform in *Bòreus*).

Most of the scorpionflies are from $\frac{1}{2}$ to 1 inch in length, and are usually found in woods, ravines, and similar areas of dense vegetation. The eggs are generally laid on the ground, and the larvae live either in or on the surface of the soil, feeding chiefly on dead insects and other animal matter. The common name for these insects is derived from the structure of the male genitalia in the family Panórpidae, which are bulbous and recurved and look a little like the sting of a scorpion (Figure 24-1) Unlike scorpions, however, these insects are quite harmless to man.

[1] Mecoptera: *meco,* long; *ptera,* wings.

KEY TO THE FAMILIES OF MECOPTERA

1. Wings reduced, bristlelike in male and scalelike or completely absent in female (Figure 24-6); tarsi with 2 claws; dark-colored insects, 2 to 5 mm in length .... **Borèidae** p. 347

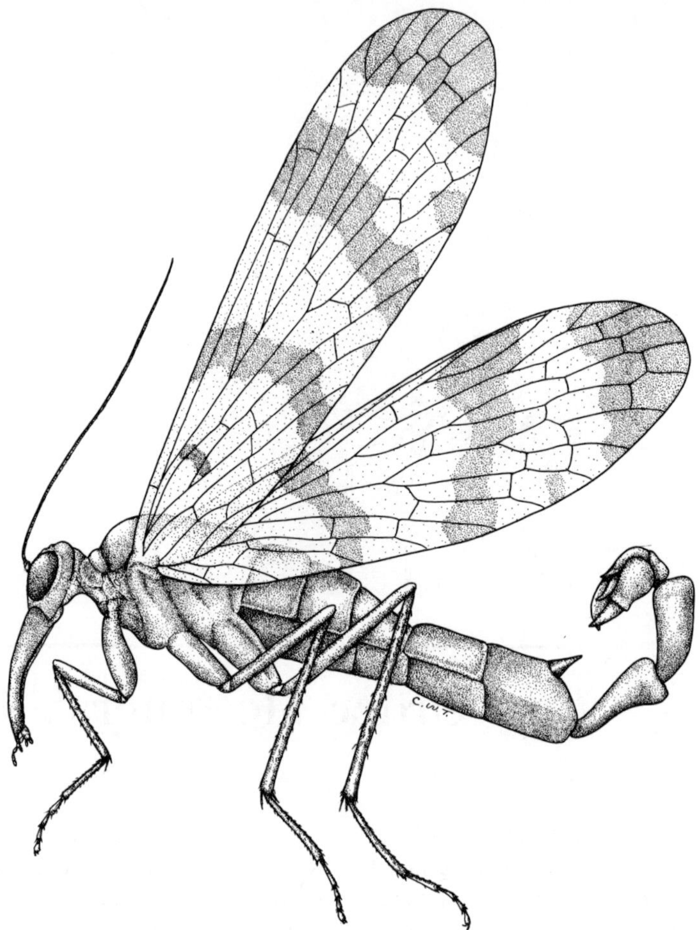

Fig. 24-1. A male scorpionfly, *Panórpa venòsa* Westwood.

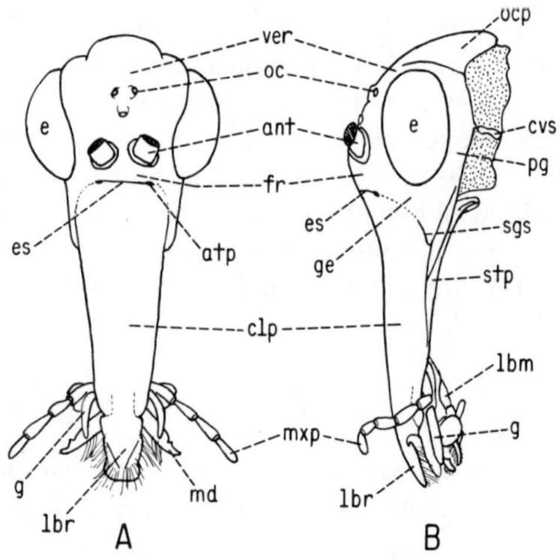

Fig. 24-2. Head of *Panórpa*. A, anterior view; B, lateral view. *ant*, antenna; *atp*, anterior tentorial pit; *clp*, clypeus; *cvs*, cervical sclerite; *e*, compound eye; *es*, epistomal suture; *fr*, frons; *g*, galea; *ge*, gena; *lbm*, labium; *lbr*, labrum; *md*, mandible; *mxp*, maxillary palpus; *oc*, ocelli; *ocp*, occiput; *pg*, postgena; *sgs*, subgenal suture; *stp*, stipes; *ver*, vertex. (Redrawn from Ferris and Rees.)

1′.	Wings well developed, or if absent (*Apterobìttacus*, western United States), the tarsi have only 1 claw 2	
2(1′).	Tarsi with 1 claw (Figure 24-5 B); fifth tarsal segment capable of being folded back on fourth; Rs 4-branched ....**Bittácidae**	p. 347
2′.	Tarsi with 2 claws (Figure 24-5 A); fifth tarsal segment not capable of being folded back on fourth; Rs usually with 5 or more branches..........3	
3(2′).	Ocelli present; M 4-branched; wings relatively long and narrow (Figure 24-4 A); a large and widespread group..................**Panórpidae**	p. 347
3′.	Ocelli absent; M with more than 4 branches; wings short and broad; a single rare species occurring in eastern United States......**Meropèidae**	p. 347

FAMILY **Borèidae**—Snow Scorpionflies: These insects are usually found in moss, on which they apparently feed; they are often found on the snow in the winter. The reduced and bristlelike wings of the male are used in grasping the female at the time of mating. Two species of the genus *Bòreus* occur in the East, *B, brumàlis* Fitch, a shiny black species, and *B. novoriúndus* Fitch, a dull brown species; *B. califòrnicus* Packard and *B. unicòlor* Hine occur in the West. Hinton (1958) puts this family in a separate order, the Neomecoptera.

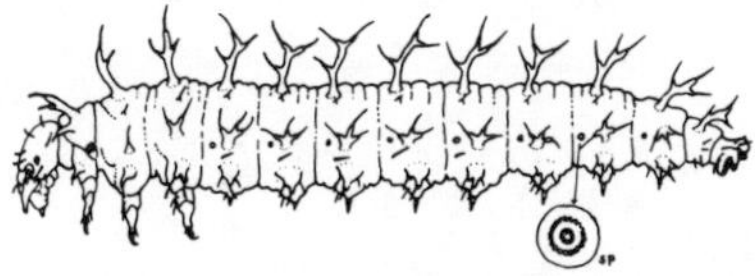

Fig. 24-3. Larva of a scorpionfly (*Bíttacus*). *sp*, spiracle. (Courtesy of Peterson. Reprinted by permission.)

FAMILY **Meropèidae**—Earwig Scorpionflies: This group is represented in the United States by a single species, *Mérope tùber* Newman, 10 to 12 millimeters in length, which has been reported from a number of East Coast states from Maine to Georgia, and in Michigan (Byers, 1954) and Minnesota (Barnes, 1956). The cerci of the male are forcepslike and resemble the cerci of earwigs. Very little is known of the habits of this rare insect; specimens have been taken at lights and under stones.

FAMILY **Panórpidae**—Common Scorpionflies: The male genitalia in this group are bulbous and recurved and resemble the sting of a scorpion (Figure 24-1). These scorpionflies are usually yellowish brown in color with spotted wings. The adults feed principally on dead or dying insects and occasionally on nectar and fruit. Two genera occur in the United States, *Panórpa* and *Brachypanórpa*; *Panórpa* is widely distributed throughout the central and eastern states and is represented by many species, while *Brachypanórpa* is represented by one species occurring in the Black Mountains of North Carolina and two species occurring in the West.

FAMILY **Bittácidae**—Hanging Scorpionflies, Hangingflies: The bittacids are yellowish brown and long-legged, about an inch in length or less, and look very much like crane flies. The wings are much narrower at the base than are those of the Panórpidae (Figure 24-4). One western species, *Apterobíttacus ápterus* (MacLachlan), is wingless. These insects spend most of their time hanging by their front legs from leaves and twigs. The adults are predaceous and capture their prey (while hanging) with their hind legs; the prey consists of small insects such as flies, aphids, caterpillars, and occasionally spiders. In captivity, bittacids are often cannibalistic.

Only a single genus, *Bíttacus,* with about half a dozen species, occurs in eastern United States. *B. apicàlis* Hagen, which has dark wing tips, hangs with its wings outstretched; the other species hang with the wings folded back over the abdomen.

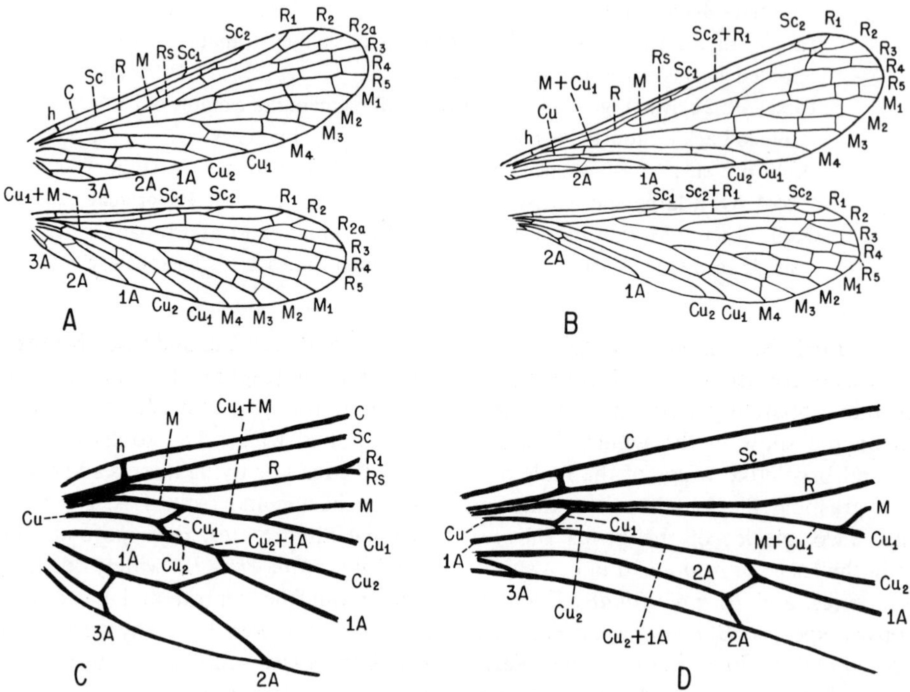

Fig. 24-4. Wings of Mecoptera. A, *Panórpa* (Panórpidae); B, *Bíttacus* (Bittácidae); C, base of hind wing of *Panórpa*; D, base of hind wing of *Bíttacus*.

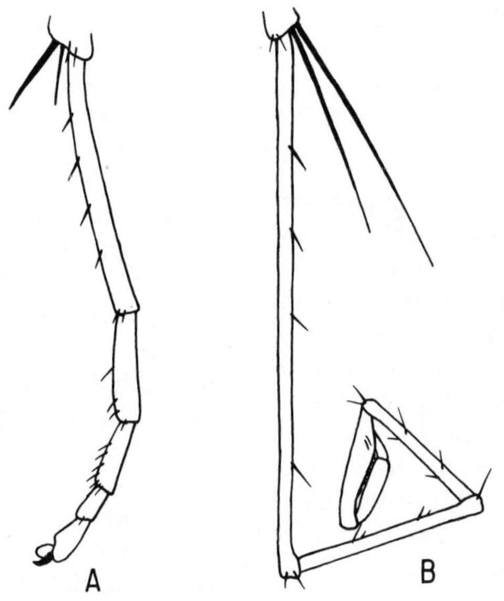

Fig. 24-5. Tarsi of Mecoptera. A, *Panórpa* (Panórpidae); B, *Bíttacus* (Bittácidae).

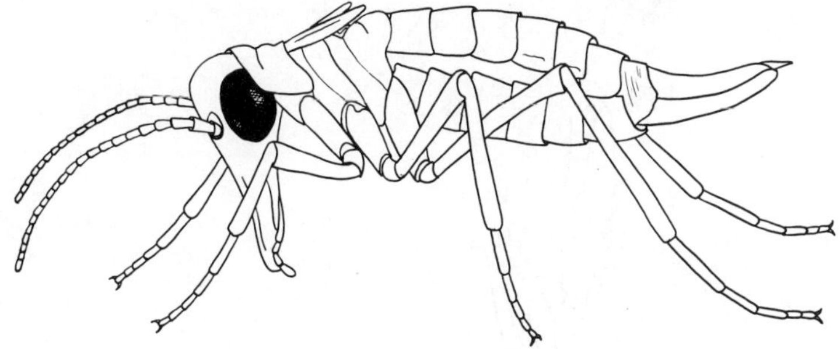

Fig. 24-6. A snow scorpionfly, *Bòreus brumàlis* Fitch, female.

REFERENCES ON THE MECOPTERA

Barnes, John W. 1956. Notes on Minnesota Mecoptera. Entomol. News, 57(7):191-192.

Byers, G. W. 1954. Notes on North American Mecoptera. Ann. Entomol. Soc. Am., 47(3):484-510; 17 f.

Byers, G. W. 1963. The life history of *Panorpa nuptialis* (Mecoptera: Panorpidae). Ann. Entomol. Soc. Am., 56(2):142-149; 6 f.

Carpenter, F. M. 1931. Revision of nearctic Mecoptera. Harvard Univ. Museum Compar. Zool. Bull. 72:205-277; 5 pl.

Carpenter, F. M. 1931. The biology of the Mecoptera. Psyche, 38(1):41-55.

Hinton, H. E. 1958. The phylogeny of the panorpoid orders. Ann. Rev. Entomol., 3:181-206.

Setty, L. R. 1940. Biology and morphology of some North American Bittacidae. Amer. Midland Naturalist, 23(2):257-353; 178 f.

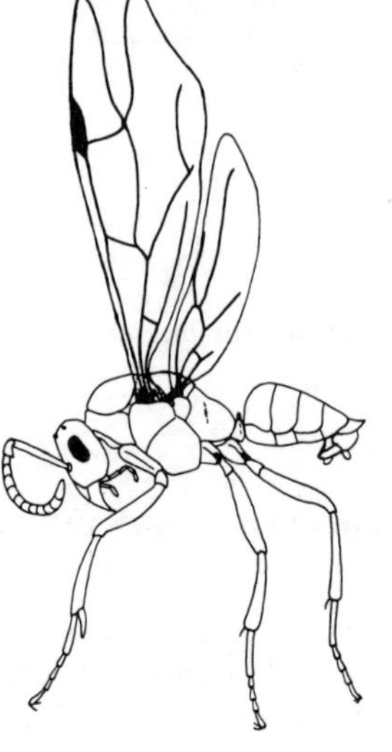

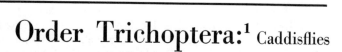

25

Order Trichoptera:[1] Caddisflies

The caddisflies are small to medium-sized insects somewhat similar to moths in general appearance. The four membranous wings are rather hairy (and occasionally bear scales also) and are usually held rooflike over the abdomen at rest. The antennae are long and slender. Most caddisflies are rather dull-colored insects, but a few are brightly patterned. The mouth parts are of the chewing type, with the palpi well developed but with the mandibles much reduced; the adults feed principally on liquid foods. Caddisflies undergo complete metamorphosis, and the larvae are aquatic.

Caddisfly larvae are caterpillarlike, with a well-developed head and thoracic legs, and a pair of hooklike appendages at the end of the abdomen; the abdominal segments bear filamentous gills (Figure 25-7). Caddisfly larvae occur in various types of aquatic habitats; some occur in ponds or lakes, and others occur in streams. One of the most interesting characteristics of these insects is the habit of most species of constructing cases, in which they live and in which they pupate. These cases vary considerably in form; some are straight and slender, some are oval, and some are coiled (Figure 25-6). The cases may be made of bits of leaves, twigs, sand grains, pebbles, or in some instances entirely of silk. The materials used in making the case are fastened together with silk, or they may be cemented together. Each species builds a very characteristic type of case, and in some species the young larvae build a case different from that made by older larvae. A number of species construct nets and feed on the materials caught in the nets. Most caddisfly larvae feed on plant materials, but a few (some of which do not construct cases) are predaceous.

[1] Trichoptera: *tricho,* hair; *ptera,* wings.

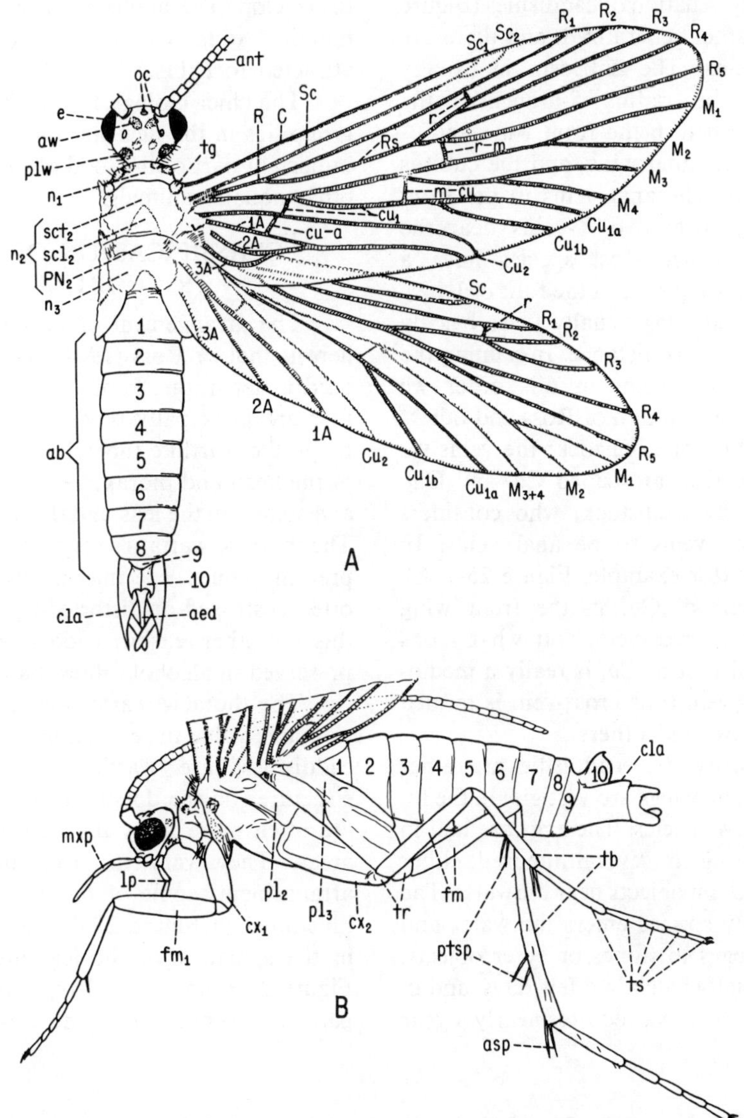

Fig. 25-1. Structure of a caddisfly. A, dorsal view; B, lateral view. *ab,* abdomen; *aed,* aedeagus; *ant,* antenna; *asp,* apical spur; *aw,* anterior wart; *cla,* clasper; *cx,* coxa; *e,* compound eye; *fm,* femur; *lp,* labial palpus; *mxp,* maxillary palpus; n_1, pronotum; n_2, mesonotum; n_3, metanotum; *oc,* ocelli; pl_2, mesopleuron; pl_3, metapleuron; *plw,* posterolateral wart; PN_2, postnotum of mesothorax; *ptsp,* preapical tibial spur; scl_2, mesoscutellum; sct_2, mesoscutum; *tb,* tibia; *tg,* tegula; *tr,* trochanter; *ts,* tarsus; 1-10, abdominal segments. (Redrawn from Ross.)

The larvae fasten their cases to some object in the water when they have completed their growth, seal the opening (or openings) in the case, and pupate in the case. When the pupa is fully developed, it cuts its way out of the case with its mandibles (which are well developed in this stage), swims to the surface, crawls out of the water onto a stone or stick or similar object, and the adult emerges.

The wing venation of caddisflies (Figure 25-1 A) is rather generalized, and there are few cross-veins. The subcosta is usually 2-branched, the radius 5-branched, the media 4-branched in the front wing and 3-branched in the hind wing, and the cubitus is 3-branched. The anal veins in the front wing usually form two **Y**-veins near the base of the wing. Most species have a characteristic wing spot in the fork of R_{4+5}. Cu_2 in the hind wing usually fuses basally with 1A for a short distance. In naming the cubital and anal veins in this order we follow the interpretation of Ross and others rather than that of Comstock; the veins we call Cu_{1a} and Cu_{1b} are called Cu_1 and Cu_2, respectively, by Comstock, who considers the remaining veins to be anal veins. In some groups (for example, Figure 25-1 A), the basal part of Cu_1 in the front wing appears like a cross-vein, and what looks like the basal part of Cu_1 is really a mediocubital cross-vein (this cross-vein is termed M_5 by Tillyard and others).

The majority of the caddisflies are rather weak fliers. The wings are vestigial in the females of a few species. The eggs are laid in masses or strings of several hundred, either in the water or on objects near the water. The adult in many species enters the water and attaches its eggs to stones or other objects. The eggs usually hatch in a few days, and in most species the larva requires nearly a year to develop. The adults usually live about a month. Adult caddisflies are frequently attracted to lights.

The chief biological importance of this group lies in the fact that the larvae are an important part of the food of many fish and other aquatic animals.

CLASSIFICATION OF THE TRICHOPTERA

The arrangement of families followed here is that of Ross (1944). The characters used in separating families of adult caddisflies are principally those of the maxillary palpi, the wartlike tubercles on the dorsum of the head and thorax, the ocelli, the spurs and spines on the legs, and the wing venation. The thoracic warts are very difficult to interpret in pinned specimens, since they are often destroyed or distorted by the pin; for this and other reasons, caddisflies should be preserved in alcohol rather than on pins.

The thoracic warts, which are of considerable value in separating the families of caddisflies, are wartlike or tuberclelike structures on the dorsum of the thorax and are often more hairy than the surrounding areas. They vary in size, number, and arrangement; some of these variations are illustrated in Figure 25-4. Some variations in the spination of the legs are shown in Figure 25-3, and several types of maxillary palpi are shown in Figure 25-5.

KEY TO THE FAMILIES OF TRICHOPTERA

1.	Mesoscutellum with posterior portion forming a flat triangular area with steep sides, and mesoscutum without warts; front tibiae never with more than 1 spur; small hairy insects, not over 6 mm in length. . **Hydroptìlidae**	p. 358
1′.	Either mesoscutellum evenly convex, without a triangular posterior portion set off by sharp sides, or mesoscutum with warts; length 5 to 40 mm. . 2	
2(1′).	Ocelli present 3	
2′.	Ocelli absent 8	
3(2).	Maxillary palpi 3-segmented; males. . . . . **Limnephìlidae**	p. 358
3′.	Maxillary palpi 4- or 5-segmented. 4	
4(3′).	Maxillary palpi 4-segmented (Figure 25-5 F); males. . . . . **Phryganèidae**	p. 358
4′.	Maxillary palpi 5-segmented. 5	

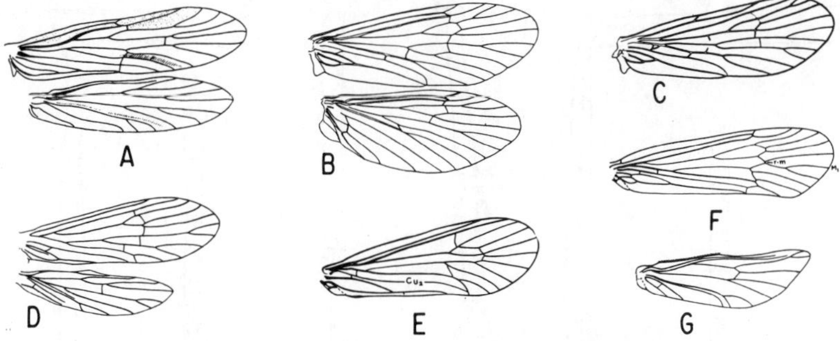

Fig. 25-2. Wings of Trichoptera. A, *Dibùsa angàta* Ross (Hydroptílidae); B, *Aphropsỳche àprilis* Ross (Hydropsýchidae); C, front wing of *Trentònius distínctus* (Walker) (Philopotámidae); D, *Psychomỳia nómada* (Ross) (Psychomyìidae); E, front wing of *Sericóstoma crassicórnis* (Walker) (Sericostomátidae); F, front wing of *Phanocèlia canadénsis* (Banks) (Limnephílidae); G, hind wing of *Helicopsỳche boreàlis* (Hagen) (Helicopsýchidae). (Courtesy of Ross and the Illinois Natural History Survey.)

5(4′). Maxillary palpi with fifth segment 2 or 3 times as long as fourth (Figure 25-5 B) .... **Philopotámidae** p. 356

5′. Maxillary palpi with fifth segment not more than 1⅓ times as long as fourth (Figure 25-5 C) 6

6(5′). Maxillary palpi with second segment short, subequal to first (Figure 25-5 C); labrum evenly rounded and fairly wide; males and females .... **Rhyacophílidae** p. 356

6′. Maxillary palpi with second segment much longer than first; labrum with a wide basal portion set off by a crease from a long tonguelike apex; females 7

7(6′). Front tibiae with 2 or more spurs; middle tibiae with 4 spurs (as in Figure 25-3 C) .... **Phryganèidae** p. 358

7′. Front tibiae with 1 spur or none; middle tibiae with 2 or 3 spurs .... **Limnephílidae** p. 358

8(2′). Maxillary palpi with 5 or more segments 9

8′. Maxillary palpi with less than 5 segments 11

9(8). Terminal segment of maxillary palpi much longer than the preceding segment and with close suturelike cross-striae that are not possessed by the other segments (Figure 25-5 G) 10

9′. Terminal segment of maxillary palpi without such striae and similar in general structure to the preceding segment and usually of the same length, or some segments with long hair brushes (Figure 25-5 A) 11

10(9). Mesoscutum without warts (Figure 25-4 A) .... **Hydropsýchidae** p. 357

10′. Mesoscutum with a pair of small warts (Figure 25-4 B) .... **Psychomyìidae** p. 357

11(8′, 9′). Middle tibiae without preapical spurs and with a row of black spines (Figure 25-3 B) 12

11′. Middle tibiae with preapical spurs, and with or without a row of spines (Figure 25-3 C-E) 16

12(11). Pronotum with a lateral pair of erect platelike warts separated by a wide mesal excavated collar that is usually hidden by the produced angulate margin of the mesonotum (Figure 25-4 C); mesonotum with the scutel-

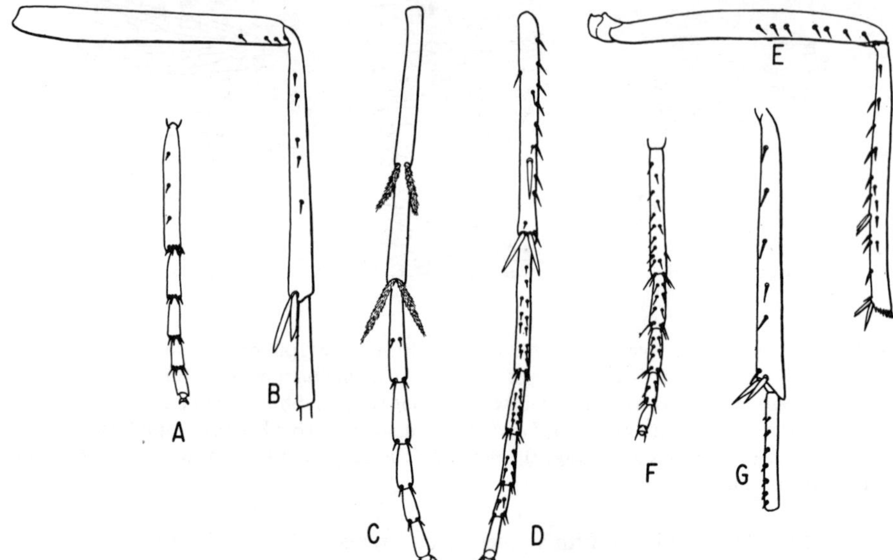

Fig. 25-3. Legs of Trichoptera. A, middle tarsus of *Beraèa górteba* Ross (Beraèidae); B, middle leg of *Beraèa górteba* Ross; C, middle tibia and tarsus of *Theliopsỳche coròna* Ross (Lepidostomátidae); D, middle tibia and tarsus of *Brachycéntrus numeròsus* (Say) (Brachycéntridae); E, middle leg of *Molánna unióphila* Vorheis (Molánnidae); F, middle tarsus of *Sericóstoma crassicórnis* (Walker) (Sericostomátidae); G, middle tibia of *Sericóstoma crassicórnis* (Walker). (Courtesy of Ross and the Illinois Natural History Survey.)

lum short and with the scutal warts represented by a long irregular line of setate spots; antennae very long and slender.......... **Leptocéridae** p. 360

12′. Pronotum with warts much closer together, not platelike, and usually prominent; mesonotum with scutal warts either small or absent; antennae relatively stout, or not longer than body 13

13(12′). Anterior margin of hind wing cut away beyond the middle, and with a row of hamuli along the straight basal portion of the margin (Figure 25-2 G) .... **Helicopsýchidae** p. 360

13′. Anterior margin of hind wing straight or evenly rounded 14

14(13′). Middle and hind tarsi with a crown of 4 black spines at apex of each segment, and only a few preapical spines arranged in a single row on basal tarsal segment (Figure 25-3 A); apical spurs of middle tibiae nearly half the length of basal tarsal segment (Figure 25-3 B).......... **Beraèidae** p. 360

14′. Middle and hind tarsi with apical spines more separated and not forming a crown, and with numerous preapical spines on all segments, arranged in a double row on the basal tarsal segment (Figure 25-3 F); apical spurs of middle tibiae not more than one-third the length of the basal tarsal segment (Figure 25-3 G) 15

15(14′). Mesoscutum with a deep anteromesal fissure, and with scutal warts near the meson (Figure 25-4 I); head with posterior warts diagonal and teardrop-shaped; front wing with a long cross-vein between R_1 and R_2 and with Cu_2 joining apex of Cu_{1b} directly (Figure 25-2 E).... **Sericostomátidae** p. 360

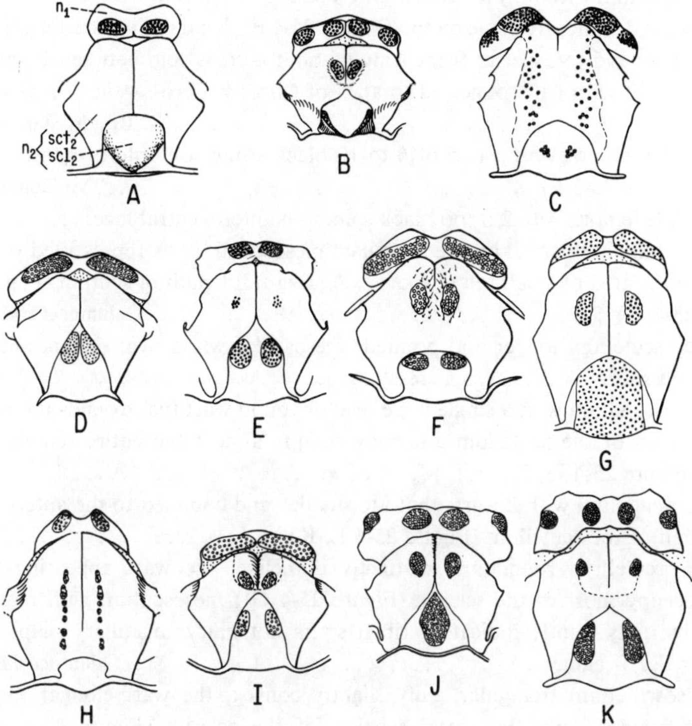

Fig. 25-4. Pro- and mesonota of Trichoptera. A, *Hydropsỳche símulans* Ross (Hydropsýchidae); B, *Psychomỳia flávida* Hagen (Psychomyìidae); C, *Anthripsòdes tarsi-punctàtus* (Vorheis) (Leptocéridae); D, *Beraèa górteba* Ross (Beraèidae); E, *Brachycéntrus numeròsus* (Say) (Brachycéntridae); F, *Helicopsỳche boreàlis* (Hagen) (Helicopsýchidae); G, *Psilotrèta frontàlis* Banks (Odontocéridae); H, *Ganonèma americànum* (Walker) (Calamocerátidae); I, *Sericóstoma crassicórnis* (Walker) (Sericostomátidae); J, *Goèra calcaràta* Banks (Goèridae); K, *Theliopsỳche* sp. (Lepidostomátidae). n_1, pronotum; n_2, mesonotum; scl_2, mesoscutellum; sct_2, mesoscutum. (Courtesy of Ross and the Illinois Natural History Survey.)

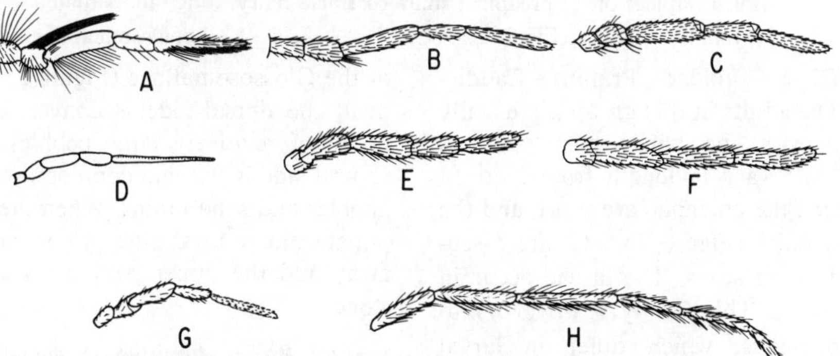

Fig. 25-5. Maxillary palpi of Trichoptera. A, *Psilotrèta* sp., male (Odontocéridae); B, *Dolóphilus shawnee* Ross, male (Philopotámidae); C, *Rhyacóphila lobífera* Betten, male (Rhyacophílidae); D, *Macronèmum zebràtum* (Hagen) (Hydropsýchidae); E, *Banksìola selìna* Betten, female (Phryganèidae); F, *Banksìola selìna* Betten, male (Phryganèidae); G, *Cyrnéllus marginàlis* (Banks) (Psychomyìidae); H, *Triaenòdes tárda* Milne, male (Leptocéridae). (Courtesy of Ross and the Illinois Natural History Survey.)

15′. Mesonotum with only a shallow anteromesal crease, and with scutal warts some distance from the meson (Figure 25-4 E); head with posterior warts linear and transverse; front wing without a cross-vein between R_1 and R_2 and with Cu_2 connected to apex of Cu_{1b} by a cross-vein.......... .... **Brachycéntridae** p. 360

16(11′). Middle femora with a row of 6 to 10 black spines on anteroventral face (Figure 25-3 E) .... **Molánnidae** p. 359

16′. Middle femora with 2 or no black spines on anteroventral face........17

17(16′). Mesoscutellum small and rectangular; mesoscutal warts represented by a linear area of small setate spots extending full length of scutum (Figure 25-4 H) .... **Calamocerátidae** p. 360

17′. Mesoscutellum longer and pointed; mesoscutal warts oval or lanceolate and short 18

18(17′). Mesoscutellum with a single large oval or round wart that extends the full length of the scutellum and may occupy almost the entire scutellum (Figure 25-4 G, J)..19

18′. Mesoscutellum with 2 warts that are smaller and confined to the anterior half of the scutellum (Figure 25-4 E, K) 20

19(18). Mesoscutellum round and distinctly domelike, the wart appearing to occupy most of the sclerite (Figure 25-4 G); mesoscutum with mesal line only faintly indicated; tibial spurs not hairy; maxillary palpi of males 5-segmented .... **Odontocéridae** p. 360

19′. Mesoscutellum triangular, only slightly convex, the wart elongate and occupying only the mesal portion of the sclerite (Figure 25-4 J); mesoscutum with a distinct mesal depression; tibial spurs hairy; maxillary palpi of males 3-segmented.......................... **Goèridae** p. 360

20(18′). Middle tibiae with an irregular row, middle tarsi with a long double row of spines; preapical spurs of tibiae bare, short, and situated about two-thirds of the distance from base of tibiae (Figure 25-3 D)........... .... **Brachycéntridae** p. 360

20′. Middle tibiae without spines, their tarsi with only a scattered few in addition to apical ones; preapical spurs of tibiae hairy, long, and situated at middle of tibiae (Figure 25-3 C) .... **Lepidostomátidae** p. 360

FAMILY **Rhyacophílidae**—Primitive Caddisflies: The adults in this group are usually brownish with the wings more or less mottled, and vary in length from 3 to 13 millimeters; the antennae are short, and the maxillary palpi (Figure 25-5 C) are 5-segmented in both sexes. The larvae occur in rapid streams. This family is divided into two subfamilies, which differ in larval habits; the larvae of the Rhyacophilìnae (Figure 25-7 B) are predaceous and do not make cases, while the larvae of the Glossosomatìnae are not predaceous and make saddlelike or turtle-shaped cases. The cases of the Glossosomatìnae (Figure 25-6 A) are oval; the dorsal side is convex and composed of relatively large pebbles, and the ventral side is flat and composed of smaller pebbles and sand grains. When these larvae pupate, the ventral side of the case is cut away and the upper part is fastened to a stone.

FAMILY **Philopotámidae**—Finger-Net Caddisflies or Silken-Tube Spinners: These caddisflies vary in length from 6 to 9 millimeters and have the last segment of the maxillary palpi elongate (Figure 25-5 B); they are usually brownish with gray wings.

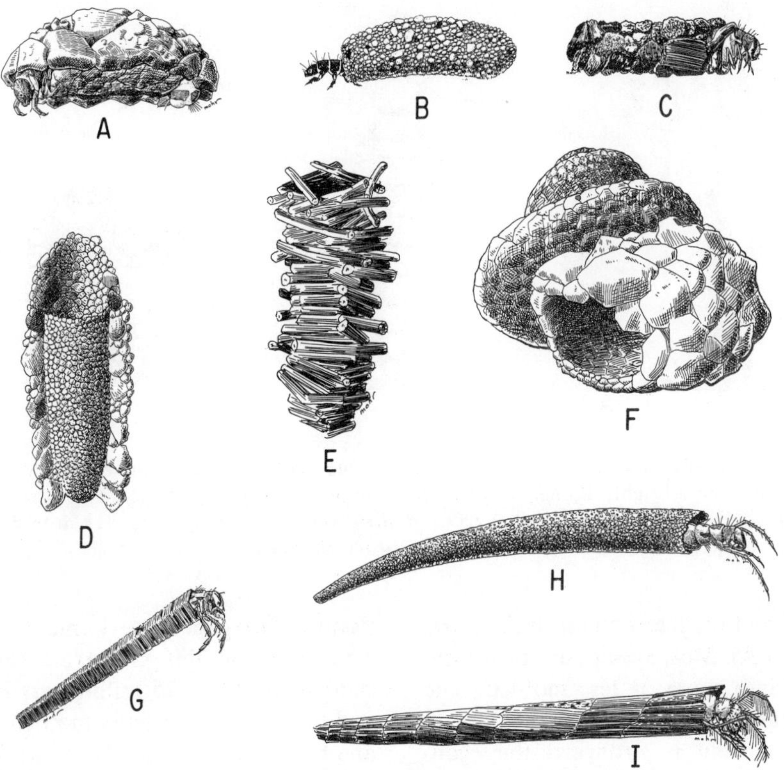

Fig. 25-6. Cases of caddisfly larvae. A, *Glossosòma intermèdium* (Klapálek) (Rhyacophílidae); B, *Ochrotríchia ùnio* (Ross) (Hydroptílidae); C, *Limnéphilus rhómbicus* (Linn.) (Limnephílidae); D, *Molánna unióphila* Vorheis (Molánnidae); E, *Oecètis cineráscens* (Hagen) (Leptocéridae); F, *Heliocopsỳche borealis* (Hagen) (Helicopsýchidae); G, *Brachycéntrus numeròsus* (Say) (Brachycéntridae); H, *Leptocélla álbida* (Walker) (Leptocéridae); I, *Triaenòdes tárda* Milne (Leptocéridae). (Courtesy of Ross and the Illinois Natural History Survey.)

Most females of *Trentònius distínctus* (Walker) have the wings vestigial. The larvae live in rapid streams and construct finger-shaped or tubular nets that are attached to stones. These tubes have a large opening at the upstream end and a smaller one at the other end. Many such nets are frequently attached close together. The larva stays in the net and feeds on the food caught there; pupation occurs in cases made of pebbles and lined with silk.

FAMILY **Psychomyìidae** (including Polycentrópidae)—Tube-Making and Trumpet-Net Caddisflies: These caddisflies vary in length from 4 to 11 millimeters; most of them are brownish with mottled wings. The larvae occur in a variety of aquatic situations; some occur in rapid streams, some occur in rivers, and others occur in lakes. Some (for example, *Polycéntropus*) construct trumpet-shaped nets which collapse rather rapidly when removed from the water; others (for example, *Phylocéntropus*) construct tubes in the sand at the bottoms of streams and cement the walls of these tubes to make a fairly rigid structure.

FAMILY **Hydropsýchidae** — Net-Spinning Caddisflies: This group is a large one, and many species are fairly common in small streams. The adults of both sexes have the maxillary palpi 5-segmented with the last segment elongate (Figure 25-5 D), ocelli

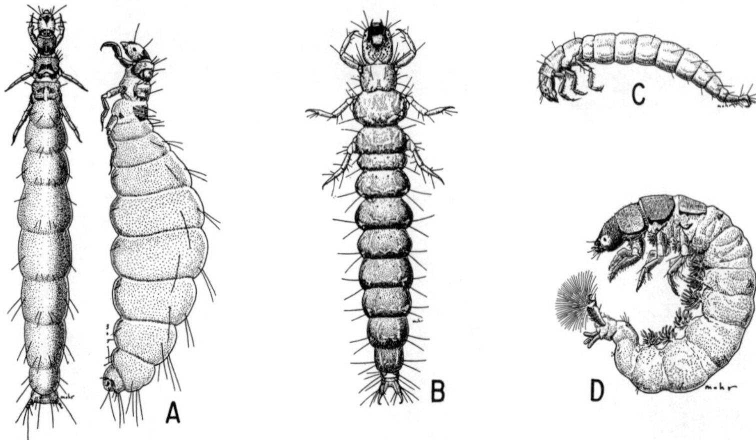

Fig. 25-7. Caddisfly larvae. A, *Hydróptila waubesiàna* Betten (Hydroptílidae), dorsal view at left, lateral view at right; B, *Rhyacóphila fenéstra* Ross (Rhyacophílidae); C, *Polycéntropus interrúptus* (Banks) (Psychomyìidae); D, *Hydropsŷche símulans* Ross (Hydropsýchidae). (Courtesy of Ross and the Illinois Natural History Survey.)

are absent, and the mesoscutum lacks warts (Figure 25-4 A). Most species are brownish, with the wings more or less mottled. The larvae occur in the parts of the stream where the current is strongest; they construct a caselike retreat of sand, pebbles, or debris, and near this retreat construct a cup-shaped net with the concave side of the net facing upstream. The larva feeds on materials caught in the net, and pupation occurs in the caselike retreat. These larvae are quite active, and if they are disturbed while feeding in the net, they back into their retreat very rapidly.

FAMILY **Hydroptílidae**—Micro-caddisflies: The members of this group vary in length from 1.5 to 6.0 millimeters; they are quite hairy (Figure 25-8 F), and most of them have a salt-and-pepper mottling. The larvae of most species occur in small lakes. These insects undergo a sort of hypermetamorphosis; the early instars are active and do not construct cases, while the later instars are case-making; the anal hooks are much larger in the active instars than in the later instars. The case is usually somewhat purse-shaped, with each end open (Figure 25-6 B).

FAMILY **Phryganèidae**—Large Caddisflies: The adults in this group are fairly large caddisflies (14 to 25 millimeters in length), and the wings are usually mottled with gray and brown (Figure 25-8 B, E); the maxillary palpi are 4-segmented in the males (Figure 25-5 F) and 5-segmented in the females (Figure 25-5 E). The larvae occur chiefly in marshes or lakes; only a few are found in streams. The larval case is usually long and slender and composed of narrow strips glued together in a spiral.

FAMILY **Limnephílidae**—Northern Caddisflies: This family is one of the largest in the order, with some 200 species in 20 genera occurring in North America; most species are northern in distribution. The adults vary in length from 7 to 23 millimeters, and most species are brownish with the wings mottled or patterned (Figure 25-8 A); the maxillary palpi are 3-segmented in the males and 5-segmented in the females. The larvae occur principally in ponds and slow-moving streams; the cases are made of a variety of materials, and in some species the cases made by the young larvae are quite different from those made by older larvae.

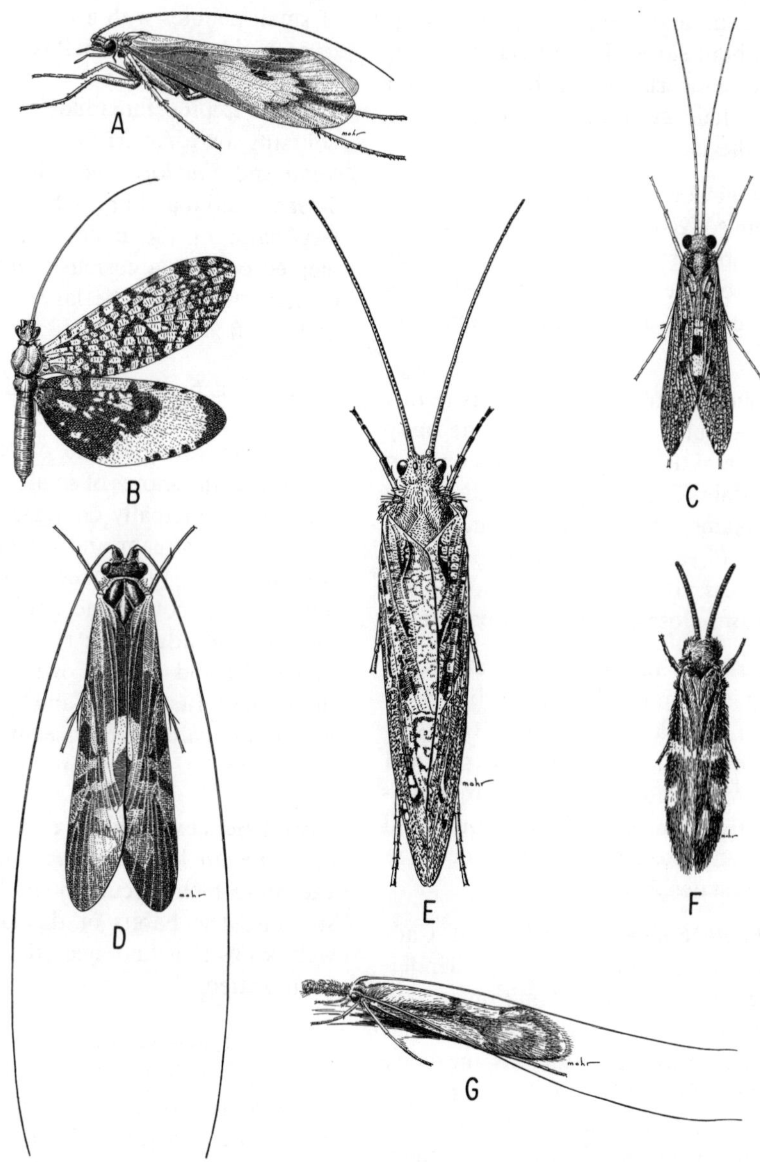

Fig. 25-8. Adult caddisflies. A, *Platycéntropus radiàtus* (Say), male (Limnephílidae); B, *Eubasilíssa pardàlis* (Walker), female (Phryganèidae); C, *Hydropsỳche símulans* Ross, male (Hydropsýchidae); D, *Macronèmum zebràtum* (Hagen), male (Hydropsýchidae); E, *Phrygànea cinèrea* Walker, male (Phryganèidae); F, *Hydróptila hamàta* Morton, male (Hydroptílidae); G, *Triaenòdes tárda* Milne, male (Leptocéridae). (Courtesy of Ross and the Illinois Natural History Survey.)

FAMILY **Molánnidae:** This group is small, and the known larvae live on the sandy bottoms of streams and lakes. The larval cases are shield-shaped and consist of a central cylindrical tube with lateral expansions (Figure 25-6 D). The adults, which are 10 to 16 millimeters in length, are usually brownish gray with the wings somewhat mottled, and have the palpi 5-segmented in both sexes. The adults at rest sit with the wings curled about the body, and the body is held at an angle to the surface on which the insect rests.

FAMILY **Beraèidae:** This family contains a single genus, *Beraèa,* with two North American species; very little is known of the habits of the larvae. The adults are brownish in color and about 5 millimeters in length.

FAMILY **Odontocéridae:** The adults in this group are about ½ inch in length, the body is blackish, and the wings are grayish brown with light dots. The larvae live in the riffles of swift streams, where they construct cylindrical cases of sand. When ready to pupate, large numbers attach their cases to stones, with the cases close together and parallel.

FAMILY **Calamocerátidae:** The adults of this group are orange-brown or brownish black, with the maxillary palpi 5- or 6-segmented. The larvae occur in both still and rapidly flowing water; their cases are cylindrical and are made of sand or small pebbles. Two species in this family occur in the eastern states.

FAMILY **Leptocéridae**—Long-Horned Caddisflies: These caddisflies are slender, often pale-colored, 5 to 17 millimeters in length, and have long slender antennae that are often nearly twice as long as the body (Figure 25-8 G). The larvae occur in a variety of habitats, and there is considerable variation in the types of cases they make. Some species make long, slender, tapering cases (Figure 25-6 H, I), some construct cases of twigs (Figure 25-6 E), and some construct cornucopia-shaped cases of sand grains.

FAMILY **Goèridae:** This group is represented in North America by three genera, *Goèra, Goerìta,* and *Pseudogoèra.* The maxillary palpi are 3-segmented in the males and 5-segmented in the females. The larvae occur in streams and construct cases of small pebbles with a larger pebble glued to each side to act as ballast.

FAMILY **Lepidostomátidae:** This group contains two American genera, *Lepidós-toma* and *Theliopsỳche.* The females have 5-segmented maxillary palpi, and the maxillary palpi of the males are either 3-segmented or have a curiously modified 1-segmented structure. The larvae occur principally in streams or springs.

FAMILY **Brachycéntridae:** This family contains two genera, *Brachycéntrus* and *Micrasèma.* The young larvae of *Brachycéntrus* occur near the shores of small streams where they feed principally on algae; older larvae move to midstream and attach their cases (Figure 25-6 G) to stones, facing upstream, and feed on both algae and small aquatic insects. The adults are 6 to 11 millimeters in length, and dark brown to black with the wings often tawny and checkered; the maxillary palpi are 3-segmented in the males and 5-segmented in the females.

FAMILY **Sericostomátidae:** This group contains the single genus *Sericóstoma,* the larvae of which occur in both lakes and streams. The habits of the larvae are not well known, as no nearctic species have been reared.

FAMILY **Helicopsýchidae**—Snail-Case Caddisflies: This family contains the single genus *Helicopsỳche,* the adults of which can usually be recognized by the short mesoscutellum with its narrow transverse warts (Figure 25-4 F), and the hamuli on the hind wings (Figure 25-2 G). The adults are 5 to 7 millimeters in length and are somewhat straw-colored, with the wings mottled with brownish color. The larvae construct cases of sand that are shaped like a snail shell (Figure 25-6 F). During development the larvae occur on sandy bottoms, and when ready to pupate, they attach their cases in clusters on stones. The cases are about ¼ inch wide.

COLLECTING AND PRESERVING TRICHOPTERA

Caddisfly adults are usually found near water. The habitat preferences of different species differ; hence one should visit a variety of habitats to get a large number of species. The adults can be collected by sweeping in the vegetation along the margins of and near ponds and streams, by checking the under side of bridges, and by collecting at lights. The best way of collecting the adults is at lights; blue lights seem more attractive than lights of other colors.

Caddisfly larvae can be collected by the various methods of aquatic collecting discussed in Chapter 32. Many can be found attached to stones in the water; others will be found among aquatic vegetation; still others can be collected with a dip net used to scoop up bottom debris or aquatic vegetation.

Both adult and larval caddisflies should be preserved in 80 percent alcohol. Adults may be pinned, but this frequently damages the thoracic warts that are used in separating families, and most dried specimens are more difficult to identify as to species than are specimens preserved in alcohol. When collecting at lights (for example, automobile headlights), large numbers can be easily collected by placing a pan containing about $\frac{1}{4}$ inch of alcohol directly below the light; the insects will eventually fly into the alcohol and be caught. Specimens attracted to lights may also be taken directly into a cyanide jar and then transferred to alcohol, or they may be picked off the light by dipping the index finger in alcohol and scooping up the insect rapidly but gently on the wet finger. An aspirator is a useful collecting device for the smaller species.

REFERENCES ON THE TRICHOPTERA

Betten, Cornelius. 1934. The caddis flies or Trichoptera of New York State. N.Y. State Museum Bull. 292; 570 pp., 61 text f., 67 pl.

Denning, D. G. 1956. Trichoptera. In Aquatic insects of California, ed. by Robert L. Usinger. Berkeley: University of California Press. Pp. 237-270; 37 f.

Krafka, Joseph, Jr. 1915. A key to the families of trichopterous larvae. Can. Entomologist, 47(7):217-225; 37 f.

Lloyd, John T. 1921. The biology of North American caddis fly larvae. Lloyd Libr. Bot., Pharm. and Materia Med. Bull. 21 (Entomo. Ser. No. 1); 124 pp. 197 f.

Pennak, Robert W. 1953. Fresh-water invertebrates of the United States. New York: The Ronald Press Company. ix+769 pp., 470 f.

Ross, H. H. 1944. The caddis flies or Trichoptera of Illinois. Illinois Nat. Hist. Survey, Bull. 23(1):1-326; 961 f.

Ross, H. H. 1959. Trichoptera. In: Freshwater biology, ed. by W. T. Edmondson. New York: John Wiley & Sons, Inc. Pp. 1024-1049; 17 f.

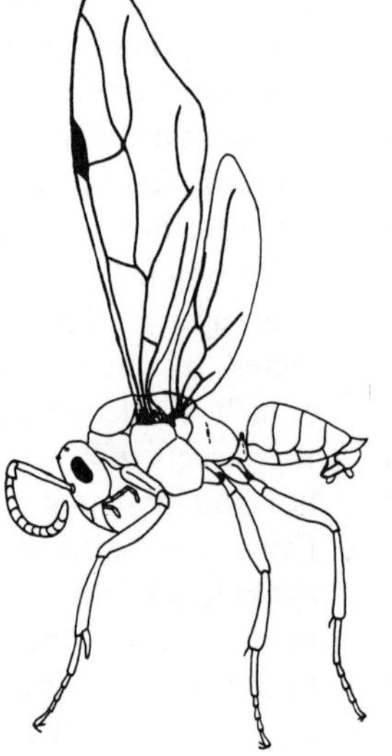

26

Order Lepidoptera[1]: Butterflies and Moths

The butterflies and moths are common insects and well known to everyone. They are most readily recognized by the scales on the wings (Figure 26-1), which come off like dust on one's fingers when the insects are handled; most of the body and legs are also covered with scales. This order is a large one, with about 11,000 species occurring in the United States and Canada; its members are to be found almost everywhere, often in considerable numbers.

The Lepidoptera are of considerable economic importance. The larvae of most species are phytophagous, and many are serious pests of cultivated plants; a few feed on various fabrics, and a few feed in stored grain or meal. On the other hand, the adults of many species are beautiful and are much sought after by collectors, and many serve as the basis of art and design. Natural silk is the product of a member of this order.

The mouth parts of a butterfly or moth are usually fitted for sucking; a few species have vestigial mouth parts and do not feed in the adult stage, and the mouth parts in one family (the Micropterýgidae) are of the chewing type. The labrum is small and is usually in the form of a narrow transverse band across the lower part of the face, at the base of the proboscis. The mandibles are nearly always lacking. The proboscis, when present, is formed by the galeae of the maxillae and is usually long and coiled. The maxillary palpi are generally small or lacking, but the labial palpi are nearly always well developed and usually extend forward in front of the face (Figure 26-2 B).

The compound eyes of a butterfly or moth are relatively large and composed of a large number of facets. Most moths have two ocelli, one on each side close to the margin of the compound eye.

[1] Lepidoptera: *lepido*, scale; *ptera*, wings.

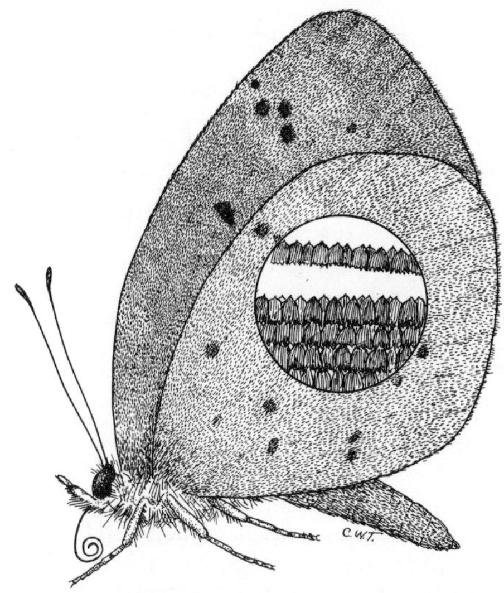

Fig. 26-1. Butterfly with a section of the wing enlarged to show the scales.

The members of this order undergo complete metamorphosis, and their larvae, usually called caterpillars, are a familiar sight. Many lepidopterous larvae have a grotesque or ferocious appearance, and some people are afraid of them, but the vast majority are quite harmless when handled. Only a few give off an offensive odor, and only a very few have stinging body hairs; the ferocious appearance is merely camouflage.

The larvae of Lepidoptera are usually eruciform (Figure 26-3), with a well-developed head and a cylindrical body of 13 segments (3 thoracic and 10 abdominal). The head usually bears 6 ocelli on each side just above the mandibles, and a pair of very short antennae. Each of the thoracic segments bears a pair of legs, and abdominal segments 3-6 and 10 usually bear a pair of prolegs. The prolegs are somewhat different from the thoracic legs; they are more fleshy and have a different segmentation, and they usually bear at their apex a number of tiny hooks called crochets. Some larvae, such as the measuringworms and loopers, have less than 5 pairs of prolegs. The only other eruciform larvae likely to be confused with those of the Lepidoptera are the larvae of sawflies. Sawfly larvae (Figure 29-29) have only 1 ocellus on each side, the prolegs do not bear crochets, and there are generally more than 5 pairs of prolegs; most sawfly larvae are an inch in length or less, whereas many lepidopterous larvae are considerably larger than this.

Most butterfly and moth larvae feed on plants, but different species feed in different ways. The larger larvae generally feed at the edge of the leaf and consume all but the larger veins; the smaller larvae skeletonize the leaf or eat small holes in it. Many larvae are leaf miners and feed inside the leaf; their mines may be linear, trumpet-shaped, or blotchlike. A few are gall makers, and a few bore in the fruit, stems, wood, or other parts of the plant. A very few are predaceous on other insects.

The larvae of Lepidoptera have well-developed silk glands, which are modified salivary glands that open on the lower lip. Many larvae use this silk in making a cocoon, and some use it in making shelters. Leaf rollers and leaf folders roll or fold up a leaf, tie it in place with silk, and feed inside the shelter so formed; other larvae tie a few leaves together and feed inside this shelter. Some of the gregarious species, such as the tent caterpillars and webworms, make a large shelter involving many leaves or even entire branches.

Pupation occurs in various situations. Many larvae form an elaborate cocoon and transform to the pupa inside it; others make a very simple cocoon, and still others make no cocoon at all. Many larvae pupate in some sort of protected situation. The pupae (Figure 26-4) are usually of the obtect type, with the appendages firmly attached to the body; moth pupae are usually brownish and relatively smooth, while butterfly pupae are variously colored and are often tuberculate or sculptured. Most of the butterflies do not make a cocoon, and their pupae are often called chrysalids (singular, chrysalis). The chrysalids of some butterflies (Danàidae, Nymphálidae, Satýridae, and Libythèidae)

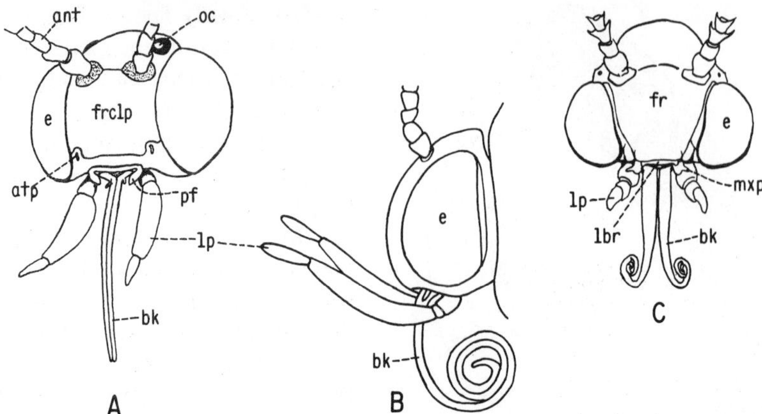

Fig. 26-2. Head structure in the Lepidoptera. A, *Sanninòidea* (Aegerìidae), anterior view; B, same, lateral view; C, *Hyphántria* (Arctìidae). *ant,* antenna; *atp,* anterior tentorial pit; *bk,* proboscis; *clp,* clypeus; *e,* compound eye; *fr,* frons; *frclp,* frontoclypeus; *lbr,* labrum; *lp,* labial palpus; *mxp,* maxillary palpus; *oc,* ocellus; *pf,* pilifer. (Redrawn from Snodgrass.)

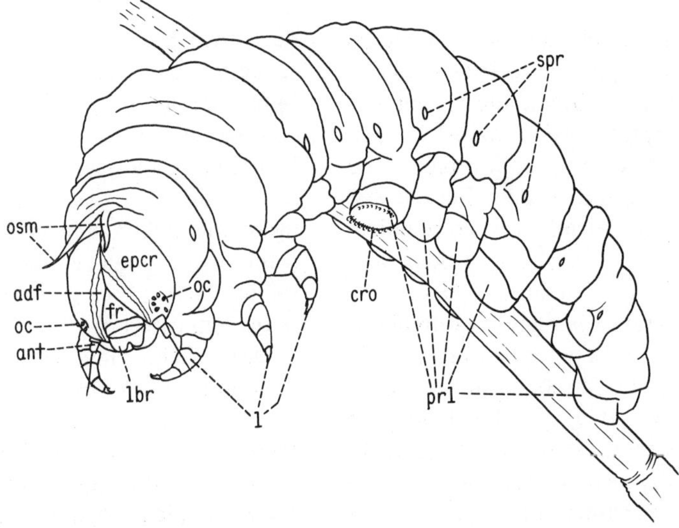

Fig. 26-3. The larva of *Papílio* (Papiliónidae). *adf,* adfrontal area; *ant,* antenna; *cro,* crochets; *epcr,* epicranium; *fr,* frons; *l,* thoracic legs; *lbr,* labrum; *oc,* ocelli; *osm,* osmeterium (scent gland); *prl,* prolegs; *spr,* spiracles.

are attached to a leaf or twig by the cremaster, a spiny process at the posterior end of the body, and hang head downward (Figure 26-4 B); in other cases (Lycaènidae, Piéridae, Riodínidae, and Papiliónidae) the chrysalis is attached by the cremaster, but is held in a more or less upright position by a silken girdle about the middle of the body (Figure 26-4 A).

Most of the Lepidoptera have one generation a year, usually overwintering as a larvae or pupa; a few species have two or more generations a year, and a few require two or three years to complete a generation.

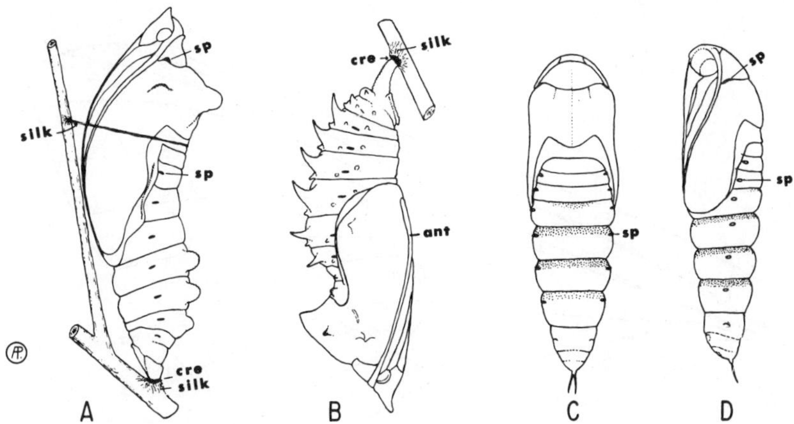

Fig. 26-4. Pupae of Lepidoptera. A, *Papílio* (Papiliónidae); B, *Nýmphalis* (Nymphálidae); C, *Helìothis* (Noctùidae), dorsal view; D, same, lateral view. *cre,* cremaster; *sp,* spiracle. (Courtesy of Peterson. Reprinted by permission.)

Many species overwinter in the egg stage, but relatively few overwinter as adults.

CLASSIFICATION OF THE LEPIDOPTERA

Most authorities divide this order into two suborders, the Jugàtae and the Frenàtae, on the basis of wing venation and the method of union of the two wings on each side. The Jugàtae have the front and hind wings similar in venation, and the two wings on each side are united by a small lobe at the base of the front wing, the jugum (Figure 26-5 *j*). The Frenàtae have the hind wing smaller than the front wing and with a reduced venation, and the two wings on each side are united by a frenulum (Figure 26-6 *f*) or by an expanded humeral angle of the hind wing (Figures 26-8 to 26-13). The Jugàtae are a small and relatively rare group; the vast majority of the Lepidoptera belong to the Frenàtae.

This order is sometimes divided into the suborders Rhopalócera and Heterócera. The Rhopalócera, which includes the butterflies and skippers, have knobbed antennae, lack a frenulum, and are generally small-bodied and day-flying; the Heterócera, or moths, have antennae of various sorts (usually not knobbed), usually have a frenulum, and are generally large-bodied and night-flying.

The Frenàtae are divided into a series of superfamilies on the basis of wing venation, the presence or absence of a frenulum, and other characters. Several of these superfamilies, comprising about half of the order, consist mainly of small to very small moths, and are often referred to as the Microlepidóptera.

A synopsis of the Lepidoptera occurring in the United States is given below. This synopsis follows the arrangement of McDunnough (1938-1939) and Forbes (1923, 1948, 1954), with a few changes based on more recent studies. Other names for the various groups are given in parentheses. The families marked with an asterisk are relatively rare or are unlikely to be taken by the general collector.

Suborder Frenàtae (Heteroneùra)
- Macrolepidóptera
  - Superfamily Papilionòidea—butterflies
    - Papiliónidae (incl. Parnassìidae)—swallowtails and parnassians
    - Piéridae (Ascìidae)—whites, sulfurs, and orange-tips

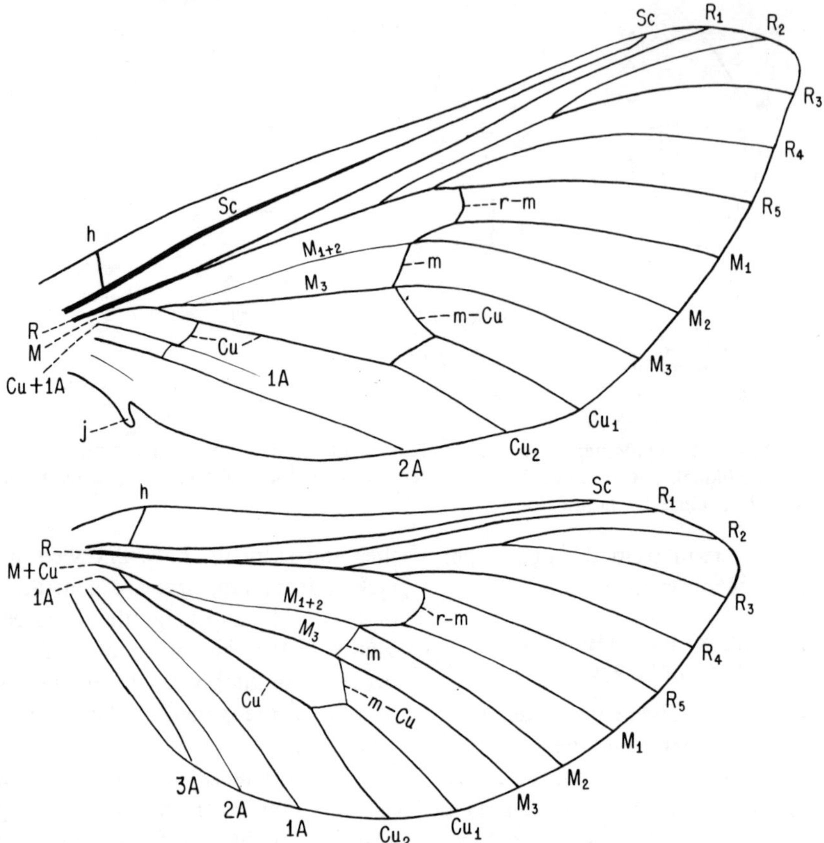

Fig. 26-5. Venation of a jugate moth, *Sthenòpis* (Hepiálidae). *j*, jugum.

Danàidae (Lymnádidae; Nymphálidae in part)—milkweed butterflies
Satýridae (Nymphálidae in part)—satyrs, wood nymphs, arctics
Heliconìidae (Nymphálidae in part)—heliconians
Nymphálidae (Aegyrèidae)—brush-footed butterflies: fritillaries, checker-spots, crescent-spots, anglewings, mourningcloaks, admirals, purples, and others
*Libythèidae (Nymphálidae in part)—snout butterflies
*Riodínidae (Erycínidae, Lemonìidae)—metal-marks
Lycaènidae (Cupidínidae, Rurálidae)—gossamer-winged butterflies: blues, coppers, hair-streaks, and harvesters
Superfamily Hesperiòidea—skippers
*Megathýmidae—giant skippers
Hesperìidae—skippers
Superfamily Sphingòidea
Sphíngidae (Smerínthidae)—sphinx or hawk moths, hornworms
Superfamily Saturniòidea
Saturnìidae—giant silkworm moths
Citheronìidae (Ceratocámpidae)—royal moths
Superfamily Noctuòidea
Amátidae (Syntómidae, Euchromìidae)—wasp moths, scape moths, ctenuchas, and others

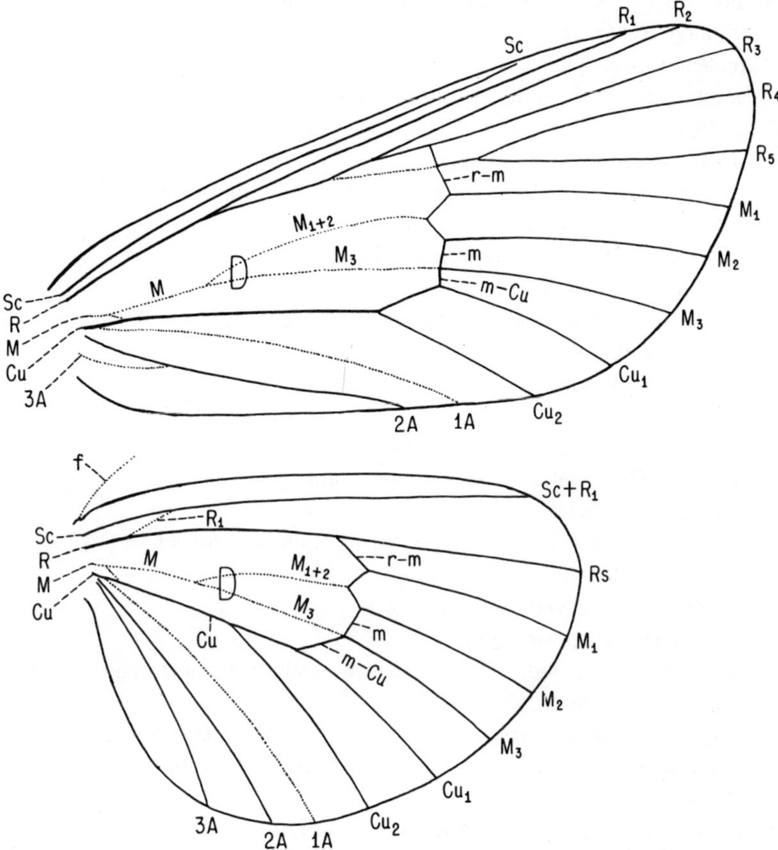

Fig. 26-6. Venation of a frenate (generalized). The veins shown by dotted lines are atrophied or lost in some groups in the suborder. *D*, discal cell; *f*, frenulum.

*Nólidae—nolid moths
Arctìidae (incl. Lithosìidae)—tiger moths, footman moths
Agarístidae—forester moths
Noctùidae (Phalaènidae; incl. Plusìidae and Hyblaèidae)—noctuid moths: underwings, cutworms, dagger moths, owlet moths, and others
*Pericópidae (incl. Hýpsidae)—pericopid moths
*Dióptidae—dioptid moths
Notodóntidae (Cerùridae)—prominents
Lipáridae (Lymantrìidae)—tussock moths, gypsy moth, brown-tail moth, and others
*Manidìidae (Semantùridae)—manidiid moths

Superfamily Bombycòidea

Lasiocámpidae—tent caterpillars and lappet moths
*Bombýcidae—silkworm moths
*Zanólidae (Eupterótidae; incl. Lemonìidae)—zanolid moths

Superfamily Drepanòidea

*Thyatíridae (Cymatophóridae)—thyatirid moths
Drepánidae—hook-tip moths

Superfamily Geometròidea

Geométridae—measuringworms, geometers, cankerworms, and others
Superfamily Uraniòidea
*Epiplémidae—epiplemid moths
*Lacosómidae (Perophóridae)—sack-bearers
Microlepidóptera
Superfamily Zygaenòidea (Psychodòidea)
Euclèidae (Limacódidae, Cochlidìidae)—slug caterpillars and saddle-back caterpillars
*Megalopýgidae (Lagòidae)—flannel moths
*Dalcéridae (Acrágidae)—dalcerid moths
*Epipyrópidae—planthopper parasites
*Pyromórphidae (Zygaènidae)—smoky moths, leaf skeletonizer moths
Superfamily Pyralidòidea
*Thyrídidae (Thýridae)—window-winged moths
Pyrálidae (Pyralídidae)—snout moths, grass moths, and others
Pterophóridae (incl. Agdístidae)—plume moths
*Alucítidae (Orneódidae)—many-plume moths
Superfamily Tortricòidea
Olethreùtidae—codling moth, oriental fruit moth, and others
Tortrícidae—leaf rollers, leaf tyers
*Phalonìidae (Conchýlidae)—webworms
*Carposínidae—carposinid moths
Cóssidae (incl. Hypóptidae and Zeuzéridae)—carpenter moths and leopard moths
Superfamily Gelechiòidea
*Cosmopterýgidae (Lavérnidae, Mómphidae)—cosmopterygid moths
*Epermenìidae (Yponomeùtidae in part)—epermeniid moths
Gelechìidae—gelechiid moths
Oecophóridae (Depressarìidae)—oecophorid moths
*Blastobásidae—blastobasid moths
*Stenómidae (Stenomátidae, Xyloríctidae, Uzùchidae)—stenomid moths
*Ethmìidae (Oecophóridae in part)—ethmiid moths
Superfamily Yponomeutòidea
*Glyphipterýgidae (Choreùtidae, Hemerophílidae)—glyphipterygid moths
Aegerìidae (Sesìidae)—clear-winged moths
*Heliodínidae (Tinaegerìidae)—heliodinid moths
*Plutéllidae (incl. Acrolepìidae)—diamond-back moths
Yponomeùtidae (incl. Argyresthesìidae)—ermine moths
*Scýthridae (Scythrídidae)—scythrid moths
Superfamily Cycnodiòidea (Elachistòidea)
*Heliozélidae—shield-bearers, leaf miners
*Douglasìidae—leaf miners
*Elachístidae (Cycnodìidae)—grass miners
Superfamily Tineòidea
Coleophóridae—casebearers
Gracilarìidae (incl. Phyllocnístidae)—leaf blotch miners
*Opostégidae—opostegid moths
*Lyonetìidae—lyonetiid moths
*Tischerìidae (Tinèidae in part)—the apple leaf miner and others
*Oinophílidae (Oenophílidae)—oinophilid moths

Psýchidae (incl. Talaeporiidae)—bagworms
*Acrolóphidae (Tinèidae in part)—burrowing webworms
Tinèidae (incl. Amydriidae and Setomórphidae)—clothes moths and others
Superfamily Nepticulòidea
*Nepticùlidae—leaf miners
Superfamily Incurvariòidea
*Incurvariidae—leaf miners
*Prodóxidae—yucca moths
*Adélidae—fairy moths
Suborder Jugàtae (Homoneùra)—jugate moths
*Eriocraniidae—eriocraniid moths
*Micropterýgidae (Eriocephálidae)—mandibulate moths
*Hepiálidae—ghost moths and swifts

CHARACTERS USED IN IDENTIFYING LEPIDOPTERA

The identification of adult Lepidoptera by means of keys is not easy, and as a result the beginning student is likely to identify most of his specimens by comparing them with pictures. Most of the larger and more common species of moths, and practically all the American species of butterflies, are illustrated in color in Holland's *Moth Book* and *Butterfly Book,* and these books are practically a "must" for students seriously interested in this order; Klots' field guide (1951) is an excellent reference on the butterflies. The identification of many of the moths from pictures is difficult and often inaccurate, for moths in different groups are often superficially very similar; the serious student should be able to run a member of this order through a key.

The principal characters used in keying adult Lepidoptera to family are those of the wing venation; other characters used include the character of the antennae, ocelli, method of wing union, mouth parts, legs, and abdomen. It is often necessary to bleach the wings in order to see the venation; sometimes one may carefully scrape a few scales from the under side of the wing to see critical venational characters.

WING VENATION: The wing venation in this order is relatively simple because there are few cross-veins and rarely extra branches of the longitudinal veins, and the venation is reduced in some groups. There are differences of opinion regarding the interpretation of certain veins in the lepidopterous wing; we follow here the interpretation of Comstock.[2]

The most generalized venation in the Lepidoptera is to be found in the suborder Jugàtae, in which the venation of the front and hind wings is similar. The members of this suborder have the subcosta simple or 2-branched; the radius 5-branched (occasionally 6-branched); the media 3-branched; the cubitus 2-branched; and there are usually three anal veins (Figure 26-5).

The Frenàtae have the venation in the hind wing reduced; the radius of the front wing usually has five branches (occasionally fewer), but in the hind wing the radial sector is unbranched and R_1 is usually fused with the subcosta. The basal portion of the media is atrophied in most of the Frenàtae, with the result that a large cell is formed in the central portion of the wing; this cell is commonly called the discal cell. The first anal vein in the front wing of many Frenàtae is atrophied. A somewhat generalized frenate wing venation is shown in Figure 26-6.

[2] The medio-cubital cross-vein of the Comstock terminology is called M_4 by some authorities; the three branches of the media according to Comstock are M_1, M_2, and M_3. According to these other authorities, Comstock's Cu_1 and Cu_2 are Cu_{1a} and Cu_{1b}, his 1A is Cu_2, his 2A is 1A, and his 3A is 2A.

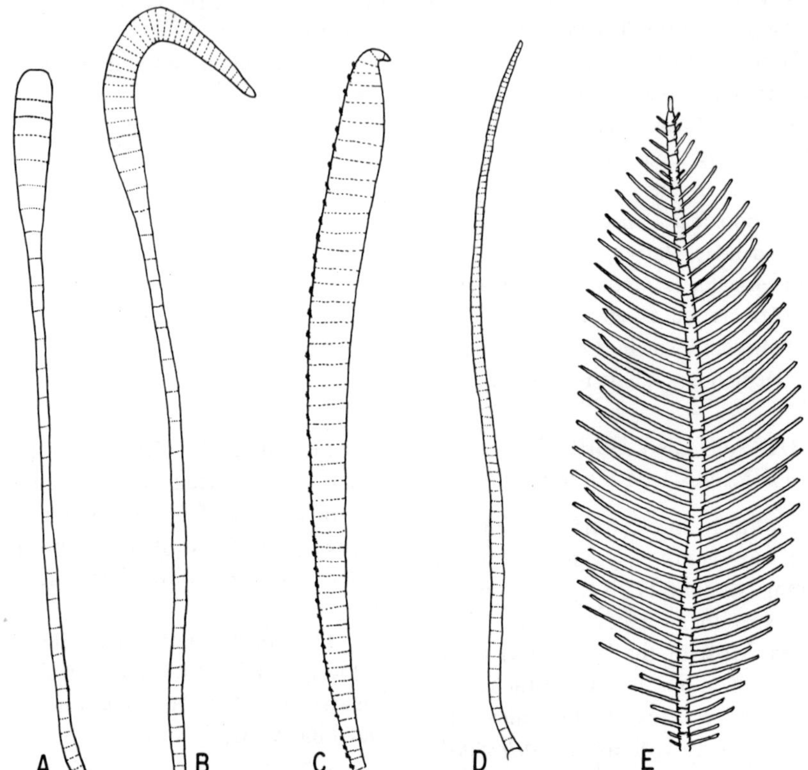

Fig. 26-7. Antennae of Lepidoptera. A, *Còlias* (Piéridae); B, *Epargýreus* (Hesperìidae); C, *Hémaris* (Sphíngidae); D, *Drastèria* (Noctùidae); E, *Callosàmia* (Saturnìidae).

The veins may fuse in various ways in the Frenàtae, and this fusing or stalking is made use of in the key. The subcosta in the front wing is always free of the discal cell and lies between it and the costa. The branches of the radius arise from the anterior side of the discal cell or from its anterior apical corner. Two or more branches of the radius are frequently stalked, that is, fused for a distance beyond the apex of the discal cell. Certain radial branches occasionally fuse again beyond their point of separation, thus forming accessory cells (for example, Figure 26-15 A, *acc*). The three branches of the media usually arise from the apex of the discal cell in both wings, though M_1 may be stalked with a branch of the radius for a distance beyond the apex of the discal cell (Figure 26-12 B). The point of origin of M_2 from the apex of the discal cell is an important character used in separating different groups; when it arises from the middle of the apex of the discal cell, as in Figure 26-18, or anterior to the middle, the vein (Cu) forming the posterior side of this cell appears 3-branched; when M_2 arises nearer to M_3 than to M_1 (Figures 26-21 to 26-26), then the cubitus appears 4-branched.

Variations in the venation of the hind wing in the Frenàtae involve principally the nature of the fusion of Sc + R_1 and Rs, and the number of anal veins. In the lower families R is separate from Sc at the base of the wing, and R_1 appears as a cross-vein between Rs and Sc somewhere along the anterior side of the discal cell (Figure 26-15 B). R_1 always fuses with Sc eventually, and judging from the pupal tracheation, the vein reaching the wing margin is Sc (the R_1 trachea is always small); however, this vein at the margin is usually called $Sc + R_1$. In many cases Sc and R are fused basally, or they may be separate at the base and fuse for a short distance along the anterior side of the discal cell (Figures 26-23 and 26-24).

OTHER CHARACTERS USED IN THE KEY: Another wing character used in the identification of the Lepidoptera is the nature of the wing union on each side. In the suborder Jugàtae there is a small lobe at the base of the front wing (the jugum), which overlaps the base of the anterior edge of the hind wing (Figure 26-5 *j*). In most of the moths of the suborder Frenàtae the wings are united by a frenulum; the frenulum is a large bristle, or group of bristles, arising from the humeral angle of the hind wing and fitting under a group of scales near the costal margin (on the lower surface) of the front wing (Figure 26-6 *f*). There is no frenulum in the butterflies and in some of the moths; the humeral angle of the hind wing is usually expanded in such forms, and fits up under the posterior margin of the front wing.

A few of the Microlepidoptera (for example, the Nepticulòidea and the Incurvariòidea) have minute hairlike spines under the scales of the wing; these are termed aculeae. The aculeae can be seen when the scales are bleached or removed; they are not movable at the base.

The head characters used are principally those of the antennae, ocelli, and mouth parts. The antennae of butterflies (Figure 26-7 A, B) are slender and knobbed at the tip; those of moths (Figure 26-7 C-E) are usually filiform, setaceous, or plumose. The basal segment of the antennae in some of the Microlepidoptera is enlarged, and when the antenna is bent down and back, this segment fits over the eye; such an enlarged basal antennal segment is called an eye-cap (Figure 26-28 B). Most of the moths have a pair of ocelli located on the upper surface of the head close to the margins of the compound eyes; these can often be seen only by separating the hairs and scales. The form of the maxillary or labial palpi is frequently used to separate the families of the Microlepidoptera.

The leg characters of value in identification include the form of the tibial spurs and the tarsal claws, the presence or absence of spines on the legs, and occasionally the structure of the epiphysis. The epiphysis is a movable pad on the inner side of the front tibia; it is probably used in cleaning the antennae. The front legs are very much reduced in some of the butterflies, particularly the Nymphálidae.

STUDYING WING VENATION IN THE LEPIDOPTERA

It is often possible to make out venational details in a butterfly or moth without any special treatment of the wings, or in some cases venational details may be seen by putting a few drops of alcohol, ether, or chloroform on the wings or by carefully scraping off a few of the wing scales. In many cases, however, it is necessary to bleach the wings in order to study all the details of wing venation. A method of bleaching and mounting the wings of Lepidoptera is described below.

The materials needed for clearing and mounting lepidopterous wings are as follows:

1. Three watch glasses, one containing 95 percent alcohol, one containing 10 percent hydrochloric acid, and one containing equal proportions of aqueous solutions of sodium chloride and sodium hypochlorite (Clorox serves fairly well in place of this mixture)
2. A preparation dish of water, preferably distilled water
3. Slides (preferably 2″ by 2″), masks, and binding tape
4. Forceps and dissecting needle

The procedure in clearing and mounting the wings is as follows:

1. Remove the wings from one side of the specimen, being careful not to tear them, or to break any connections such

as a frenulum between the front and hind wings.

2. Dip the wings in 95 percent alcohol for a few seconds to wet them.
3. Dip the wings in 10 percent hydrochloric acid for a few seconds.
4. Place the wings in the mixture of sodium chloride and sodium hypochlorite (or Clorox), and leave them there until the color is removed. This usually requires only a few minutes; if the wings are slow in clearing, dip them in the acid again and then return them to the bleaching solution.
5. Rinse the wings in water to remove the excess bleach.
6. Place the wings on the slide, centered and properly oriented (preferably with the base of the wings to the left); this is most easily done by floating the wings in water (for example, in a preparation dish) and bringing the slide up from underneath; the wings should be oriented on the slide while they are wet.
7. Allow the slide and wings to dry. If all the bleach has not been removed and some is deposited on the slide, place the slide again in water, carefully remove the wings, clean the slide, and remount the wings.
8. Place the mask on the slide around the wings (data, labeling, and the like should be put on the mask), put on the cover slide, and bind. Care should be taken before the slide is bound to make sure the wings are dry and that both slides are perfectly clean.

Such a slide, and the specimen from which the wings are removed, should always be labeled so that they can be associated. A wing slide of this sort will keep indefinitely and can be studied under the microscope or can be projected on a screen for demonstration. In the case of wings ½ inch in length or less, it is better not to use a mask, as the mask may be thicker than the wings and the wings may slip or curl after the slide is bound; the labeling can be put on a small strip of paper that is attached to the outside of the slide with cellophane tape.

The key to the families of Lepidoptera is designed primarily for the advanced student and includes all the families listed in the synopsis given above. Since it is based primarily on wing venation, it will often be necessary to bleach the wings of a specimen in order to run it through the key. The groups marked with an asterisk are relatively uncommon and are not likely to be encountered by the general collector; couplets containing these groups can often be skipped when running a specimen through the key.

KEY TO THE FAMILIES OF LEPIDOPTERA

1. Wings present and well developed 2

1′. Wings absent or vestigial (females only). 111

2(1). Front and hind wings dissimilar in venation and usually also in shape; Rs in hind wing unbranched; no jugum, the front and hind wings united by a frenulum or by an expanded humeral angle of the hind wing; mouth parts usually in the form of a coiled proboscis (suborder Frenàtae) 3

2′. Front and hind wings similar in venation and usually also in shape; Rs in hind wing 3- or 4-branched (Figures 26-5, 26-31 D); front and hind wings united by a jugum; no coiled proboscis (suborder Jugàtae). . 109*

3(2). Antennae threadlike and knobbed at tip (Figure 26-7 A, B); no frenulum; ocelli absent (butterflies and skippers). 4

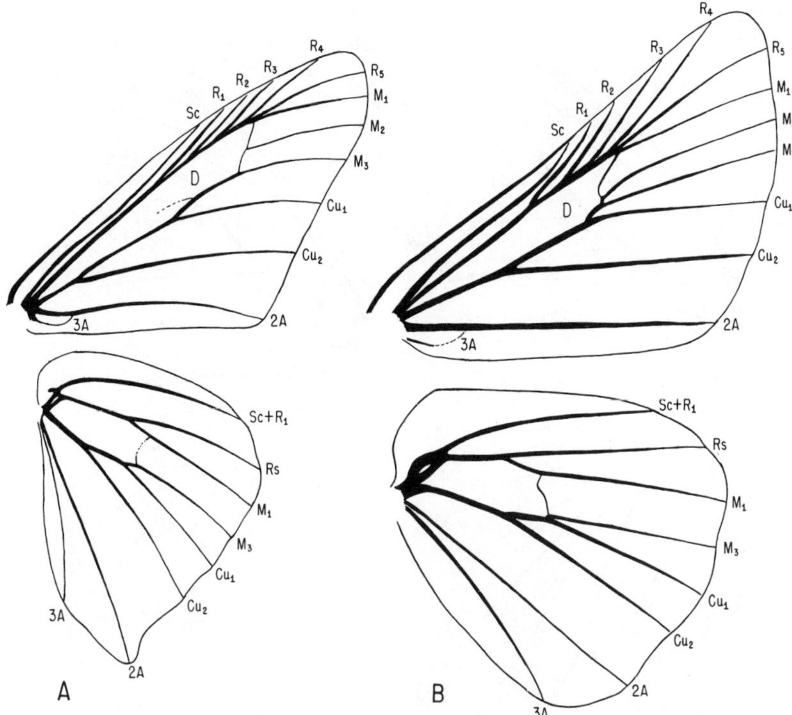

Fig. 26-8. Wings of Hesperìidae. A, *Epargỳreus* (Pyrgìnae); B, *Pseudocopaeòdes* (Hesperìinae). *D*, discal cell.

3′. Antennae of various forms, but usually not knobbed at tip (Figure 26-7 C-E); if antennae are clubbed, then a frenulum is present; ocelli present or absent (moths) 15

4(3). Radius in front wing 5-branched, with all the branches simple and arising from discal cell (Figure 26-8); antennae widely separated at base, and usually hooked at tip (Figure 26-7 B); hind tibiae usually with a middle spur; stout-bodied insects (skippers, superfamily Hesperiòidea)......5

4′. Radius in front wing with some branches stalked beyond discal cell, or with fewer than 5 branches (Figures 26-9 to 26-13); antennae close together at base and never hooked at tip (Figure 26-7 A); hind tibiae without a middle spur (butterflies, superfamily Papilionòidea)......6

5(4). Either the antennal club drawn out at tip and recurved (Figure 26-7 B), or the wingspread less than 30 mm; head as wide as or wider than thorax; hind tibiae usually with 2 pairs of apical spurs; widely distributed.... ....**Hesperìidae** p. 402

5′. Antennal club not drawn out at tip and recurved; wingspread 40 mm or more; head narrower than thorax; hind tibiae with 1 pair of apical spurs; southern and western United States............**Megathýmidae*** p. 402

6(4′). Cu in front wing apparently 4-branched (Figure 26-9); 1 anal vein in hind wing; front legs of normal size, not reduced; hind wings usually with tail-like prolongations ....**Papiliónidae** p. 394

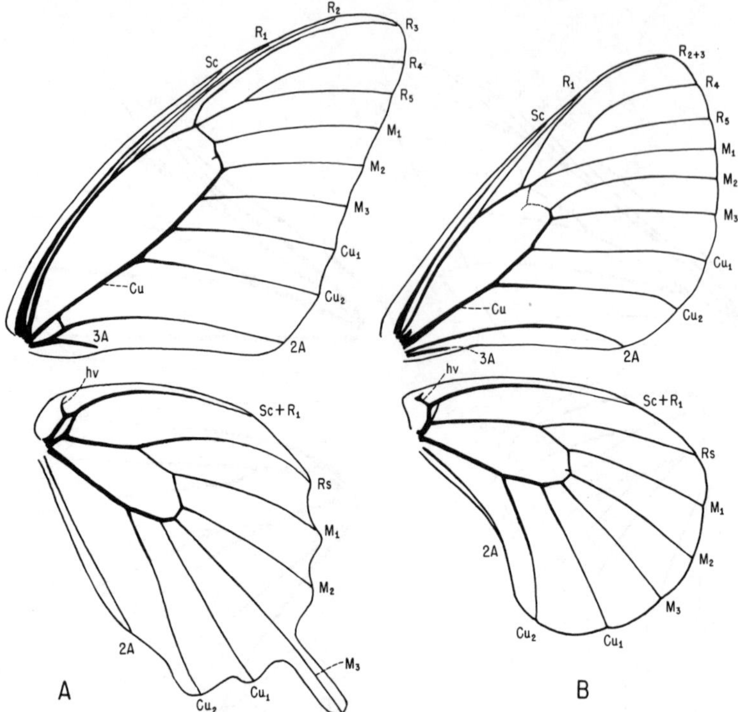

Fig. 26-9. Wings of Papiliónidae. A, *Papílio* (Papilionìnae); B, *Parnássius* (Parnassiìnae). *hv*, humeral vein.

6′. Cu in front wing apparently 3-branched (Figures 26-10 to 26-13); 2 anal veins in hind wing; front legs often reduced in size; hind wings with or without tail-like prolongations 7

7(6′). Labial palpi longer than thorax, thickly hairy, and extending forward . . . . **Libythèidae*** p. 400

7′. Labial palpi shorter than thorax 8

8(7′). Radius in front wing 5-branched (Figures 26-10 to 26-12 A); front legs usually reduced in size 9

8′. Radius in front wing 3- or 4-branched (Figures 26-12 B, 26-13); front legs, at least of females, of normal size, not reduced 13

9(8). Some veins in front wing greatly swollen at base (Figure 26-12 A); discal cell in hind wing closed; antennal club enlarging gradually; small to medium-sized butterflies, usually grayish or brownish and with eye spots in the wings (Figure 26-37) . . . . **Satýridae** p. 398

9′. No veins in front wing greatly swollen at base (Figures 26-10, 26-11); discal cell in hind wing open or closed; antennal club more abruptly swollen; size and color variable 10

10(9′). Antennae with scales, at least on upper surface; 3A in front wing lacking (Figure 26-10) 11

10′. Antennae without scales; 3A in front wing present but short (Figure 26-11); relatively large, brownish butterflies . . . . **Danàidae** p. 396

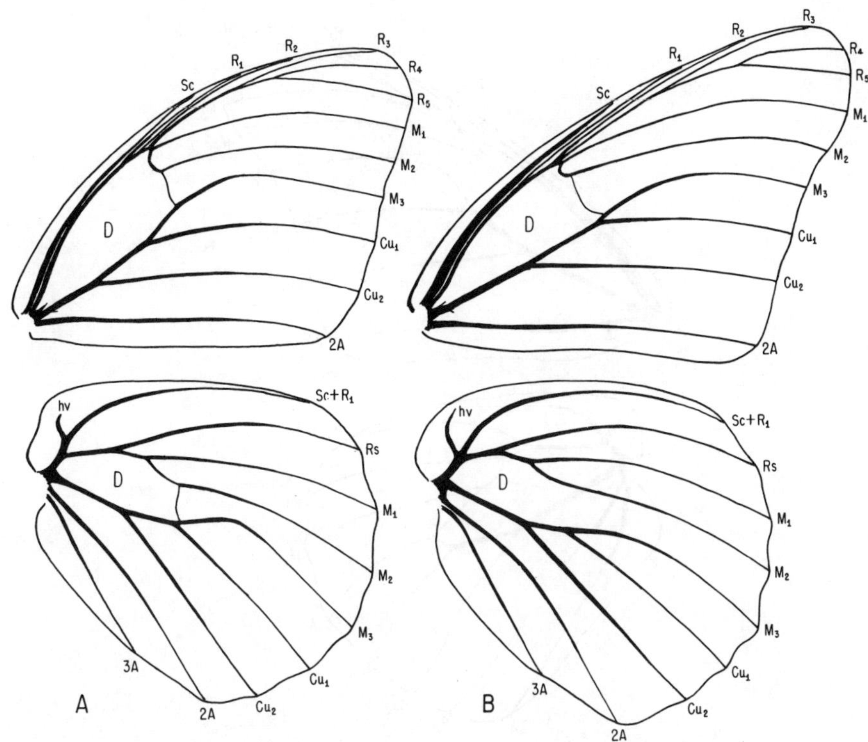

Fig. 26-10. Wings of Nymphálidae. A, *Speyéria* (discal cell in the hind wing closed by a vestigial vein); B, *Limenìtis* (discal cell in the hind wing open). *D*, discal cell; *hv*, humeral vein.

11(10). Front wings more than twice as long as wide; butterflies with brightly banded wings; southern United States.................. **Heliconiidae** p. 398

11′. Front wings less than twice as long as wide; size and color variable; widely distributed 12

12(11′). Front legs normal or only slightly reduced in size, their tarsal claws bifid; small butterflies, usually white with black and (or) orange markings (orange-tips).. **Piéridae** p. 395

12′. Front legs greatly reduced in size; size and color variable.... **Nymphálidae** p. 398

13(8′). Tarsal claws bifid; face as wide as long; M_1 in front wing stalked with a branch of R for a considerable distance beyond discal cell (Figure 26-12 B); color usually white, yellow, or orange, marked with black.. **Piéridae** p. 395

13′. Tarsal claws simple; face much longer than wide; M_1 in front wing not stalked with a branch of R beyond discal cell (Figure 26-13) (except in the harvester, Figures 26-39 B, 26-40); usually not colored as above.. 14

14(13′). Hind wings with costa thickened out to humeral angle, and Sc with a basal spur (the humeral vein) (Figure 26-13 A) .... **Riodínidae*** p. 400

14′. Hind wings with costa not thickened, and without a humeral vein (Figure 26-13 B) .... **Lycaènidae** p. 400

15(3′). Wings, especially hind wings, deeply cleft or divided into plumelike divisions (Figure 26-66); legs long and slender, with long tibial spurs.... 16

15′. Wings entire, or front wings slightly cleft........................ 17

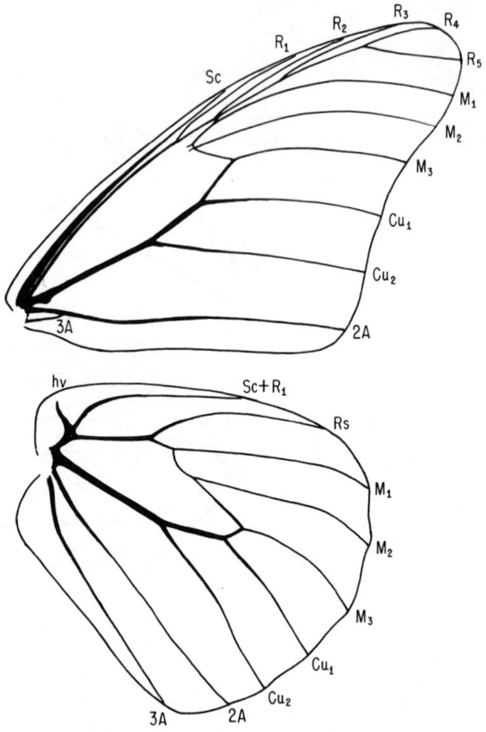

Fig. 26-11. Wings of *Dánaus* (Danàidae). *hv,* humeral vein.

16(15).	Each wing divided into 6 plumelike lobes . . . . **Alucítidae***	p. 422
16′.	Front wings divided into 2 to 4 lobes, hind wings divided into 3 lobes (Figure 26-66) . . . . **Pterophóridae**	p. 422
17(15′).	Under side of hind wings with a double series of enlarged and divergent scales along Cu; legs long and slender, with long spurs (*Agdístis*) . . . . **Pterophóridae**	p. 422
17′.	Under side of hind wings without such scales 18	
18(17′).	A large part of the wings, especially the hind wings, devoid of scales (Figure 26-74); front wings long and narrow, at least 4 times as long as wide (Figure 26-73); inner margin of front wings and costal margin of hind wings with a series of recurved and interlocking spines; wasplike day-flying moths . . . . **Aegeriidae**	p. 426
18′.	Wings scaled throughout, or if with clear areas, then the front wings are more triangular (not so long and narrow); wings without such interlocking spines 19	
19(18′).	Hind wings with 3 anal veins, or with a fringe of long hairs that is as wide as or wider than the wing; front wings usually with 2 anal veins reaching margin; hind wings often lanceolate (mostly Microlepidóptera) 20	
19′.	Hind wings with 2 or fewer anal veins, and without such a long fringe; front wings usually with only 1 anal vein; hind wings not lanceolate (mostly Macrolepidóptera) 33	
20(19).	Hind wings with veins $Sc + R_1$ and Rs fused for a varying distance beyond	

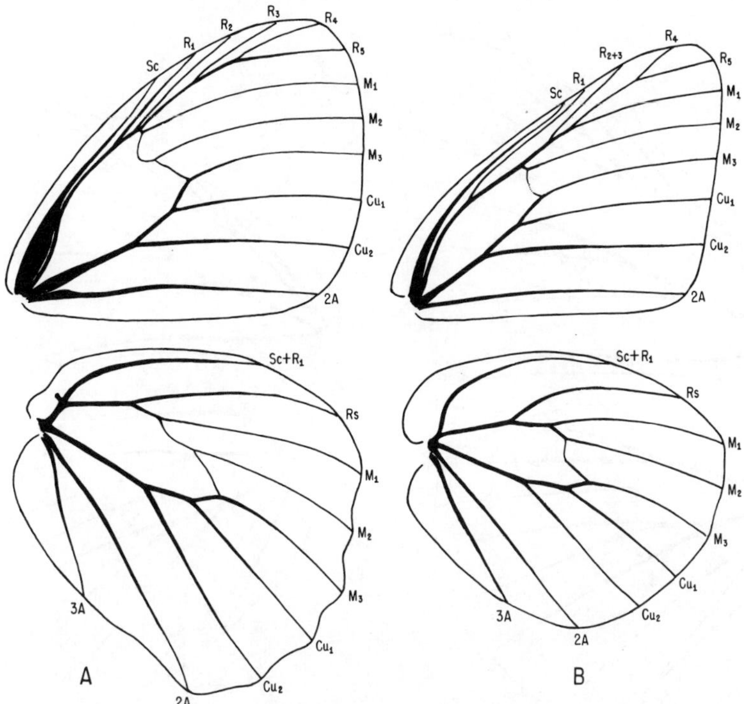

Fig. 26-12. A, wings of *Cercy̆onis* (Saty̆ridae); B, wings of *Còlias* (Piéridae).

apex of discal cell (Figure 26-14 A), or separate but very closely parallel (Figure 26-14 B) .... **Pyrálidae** p. 420

20′. Hind wings with veins $Sc+R_1$ and Rs widely separated beyond apex of discal cell 21

21(20′). Sc and Rs in hind wing fused to near end of discal cell, or at least fused beyond middle of cell (Figure 26-16 B) 22*

21′. Sc and Rs in hind wing separate from base, or fused for a short distance along basal half of discal cell 23

22(21). R_5 in front wing arising from discal cell; proboscis well developed; wings thinly scaled; small moths, mostly black or smoky in color.......... .... **Pyromórphidae*** p. 418

22′. R_5 in front wing stalked with R_4; proboscis vestigial or absent; wings densely clothed with soft scales and hair; medium-sized moths, light-colored or brown .... **Megalopy̆gidae*** p. 418

23(21′). Tibial spurs about as long as width of tibia; fringe on anal angle of hind wings not, or but slightly, longer than elsewhere 24

23′. Tibial spurs more than twice as long as width of tibia; fringe on anal angle of hind wings distinctly longer than elsewhere (Microlepidóptera) 62

24(23). Front wings with an accessory cell (Figure 26-15 A) 25

24′. Front wings without an accessory cell (Figure 26-15 B) 29

25(24). Mouth parts vestigial 26

25′. Mouth parts usually developed, with proboscis scaled; tibial spurs long; small to minute moths (Microlepidóptera) 62

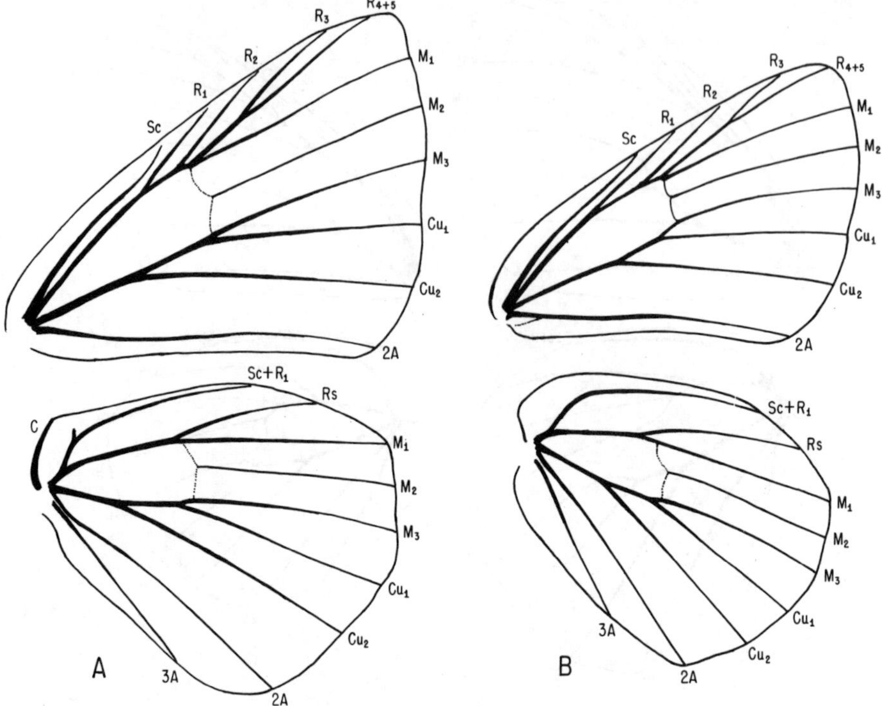

Fig. 26-13. A, wings of *Lephilísca* (Riodínidae); B, wings of *Lycaèna* (Lycaènidae).

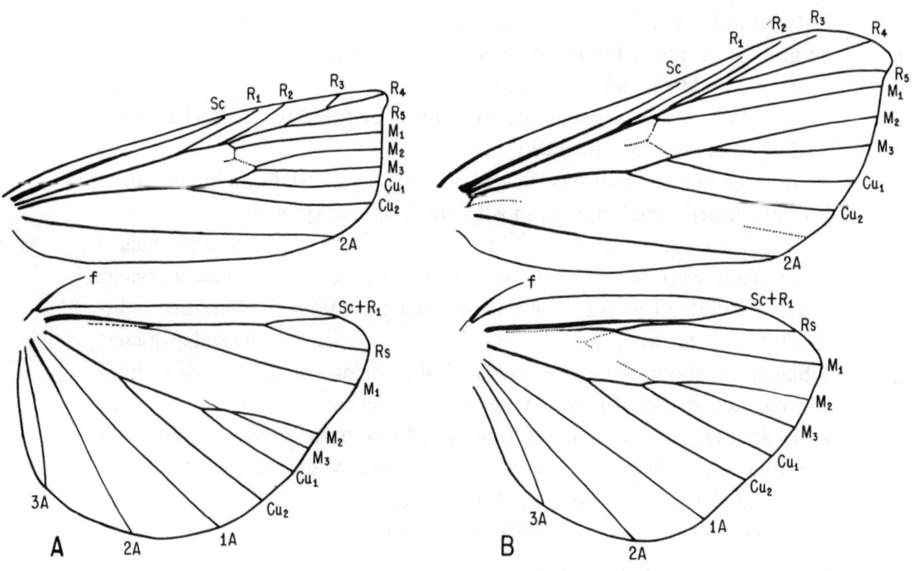

Fig. 26-14. Wings of Pyrálidae. A, *Crámbus* (Crambìnae); B, *Pýralis* (Pyralìnae). *f*, frenulum.

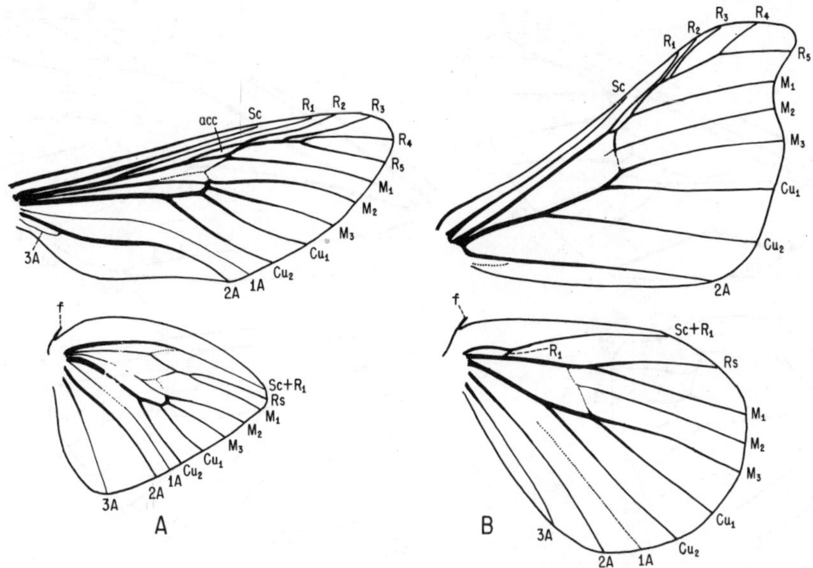

Fig. 26-15. A, wings of *Prionoxýstus* (Cóssidae); B, wings of *Bómbyx* (Bombýcidae). *acc*, accessory cell; *f*, frenulum.

26(25). Hind tibiae with 2 pairs of spurs; small moths, 9 to 18 mm in length; males (*Solenòbia*) .... **Psýchidae*** p. 430

26′. Tibial spurs short or absent 27

27(26′). Front wings with some branches of R stalked; accessory cell extending beyond discal cell (Figure 26-15 A) 28

27′. Front wings with no branches of R stalked; accessory cell not extending beyond discal cell; antennae bipectinate; small moths, the larvae parasitic on planthoppers .... **Epipyrópidae*** p. 418

28(27). Front wings subtriangular, about one-half longer than wide; abdomen not extending beyond hind wings; Arizona .... **Dalcéridae*** p. 418

28′. Front wings long and narrow; abdomen extending beyond hind wings (Figure 26-69); widespread .... **Cóssidae** p. 424

29(24′). M_2 in front wing arising about midway between M_1 and M_3, or closer to M_1, the cubitus appearing 3-branched (Figure 26-15 B); frenulum absent or vestigial; moderately large moths with broad hind wings 30*

29′. M_2 in front wing arising closer to M_3 than to M_1, the cubitus appearing 4-branched; frenulum present (if frenulum is absent in small moths with elongate wings, see couplet 53) 32

30(29). M_3 and Cu_1 in front wing stalked for a short distance beyond apex of discal cell; California .... **Dióptidae*** p. 412

30′. M_3 and Cu_1 in front wing not stalked beyond discal cell; widespread .. 31*

31(30′). Front wings with R_{2+3} and R_{4+5} stalked independently of R_1; Sc and Rs in hind wing not connected by a cross-vein .... **Lacosómidae*** p. 418

31′. Front wings with R_2, R_3, R_4, and R_5 united on a common stalk; Sc and Rs in hind wing connected basally by a cross-vein, R_1 (Figure 26-15 B) .... **Bombýcidae*** p. 415

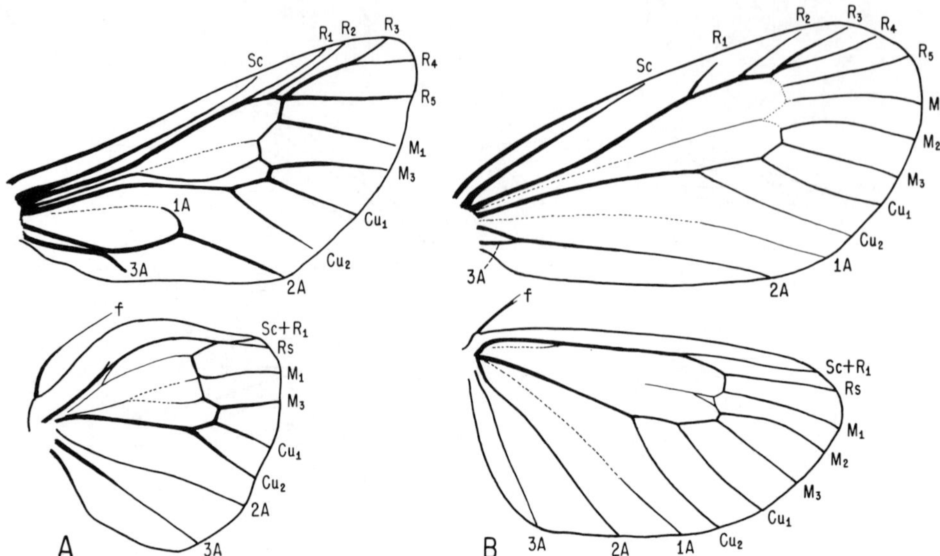

Fig. 26-16. A, wings of *Thyridópteryx* (Psýchidae); B, wings of *Málthaca* (Pyromórphidae). *f*, frenulum.

32(29′). All 5 branches of R in front wing arising from discal cell (*Hyblaèa*)...... .... **Noctùidae*** p. 410

32′. Some branches of R in front wing absent or fused beyond end of discal cell .... **Euclèidae** p. 418

33(19′). Front wings with 2 distinct anal veins, or with the anal veins more or less fused and appearing as a branched vein (Figure 26-16 A)..........34

33′. Front wings with a single complete anal vein, which is 2A; 1A at most represented by a fold, and 3A absent or meeting 2A basally so that the latter appears forked at base 35

34(33). Front wings with 2 distinct anal veins (*Harrisìna*)........ **Pyromórphidae*** p. 418

34′. Front wings with anal veins more or less fused and appearing as a branched vein (Figure 26-16 A) .... **Psýchidae** p. 430

35(33′). Antennae thickened, spindle-shaped (Figure 26-7 C); Sc and Rs in hind wing connected by a cross-vein near middle of discal cell, the two veins closely parallel to end of discal cell or beyond (Figure 26-17); stout, often large moths, with narrow wings (Figure 26-43)........ **Sphíngidae** p. 403

35′. Antennae variable, but rarely spindle-shaped; Sc and Rs in hind wing usually not connected by a cross-vein, or if such a cross-vein is present, then the 2 veins are strongly divergent beyond the cross-vein........36

36(35′). M_2 in front wing arising from middle, or anterior to middle, of end of discal cell (Figures 26-18 to 26-20), the cubitus appearing 3-branched (M_2 in front wings rarely absent)..............................37

36′. M_2 in front wing arising from posterior to middle of end of discal cell (Figures 26-21 to 26-26), the cubitus appearing 4-branched........47

37(36). Sc and Rs in hind wing fused to beyond middle of discal cell, swollen at base, then diverging; M_2 and M_3 in front wing absent; ocelli absent;

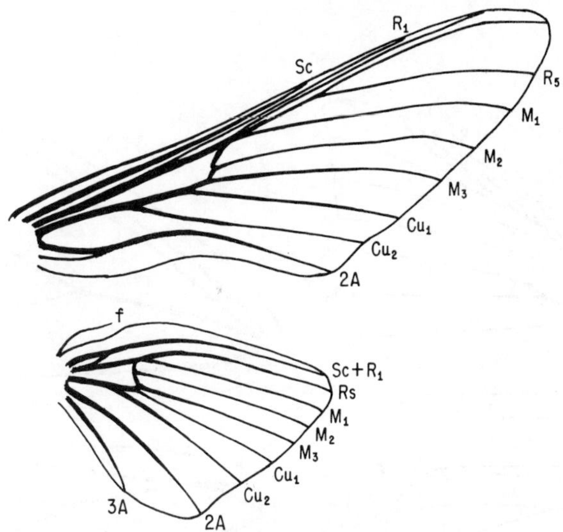

Fig. 26-17. Wings of *Hémaris* (Sphíngidae). *f*, frenulum.

small slender moths (subfamily Lithosiinae)................**Arctiidae** p. 408

37′. Sc and Rs in hind wing not fused at base, though they may be fused farther distad or connected by a cross-vein.............................38

38(37′). Sc in hind wing strongly angled at base, and usually connected to humeral angle by a strong brace vein; beyond bend, Sc fuses with or comes close to Rs for a short distance along the discal cell (Figure 26-18)......39

38′. Sc in hind wing straight or gently curving at base, not of the above conformation 40

39(38). Antennae dilated apically; eyes hairy; a single species occurring in Arizona...**Manidiidae*** p. 414

39′. Antennae not dilated apically, or if so, then eyes are bare; a large and widely distributed group.............................**Geométridae** p. 416

40(38′). Frenulum well developed...41

40′. Frenulum vestigial or absent; Sc and Rs in hind wing never fused, but sometimes connected by a cross-vein...........................45

41(40). M_3 and Cu_1 in front wing stalked for a short distance beyond apex of discal cell; California................................**Dióptidae*** p. 412

41′. M_3 and Cu_1 in front wing not stalked beyond discal cell; widespread..42

42(41′). $Sc+R_1$ in hind wing widely separated from Rs from near base of wing (as in Figure 26-20 B); M_1 in front wing stalked with R_5, which is well separated from R_4 ....**Epiplémidae*** p. 417

42′. $Sc+R_1$ in hind wing close to Rs, at least to middle of discal cell, often farther...43

43(42′). M_2 in hind wing arising nearer to M_3 than to M_1, the cubitus appearing 4-branched; M_1 in hind wing arising from discal cell, not stalked with Rs beyond the cell ....**Thyatíridae*** p. 416

43′. M_2 in hind wing absent, or arising midway between M_1 and M_3, or arising nearer to M_1, the cubitus appearing 3-branched; M_1 in hind wing stalked with Rs for a short distance beyond discal cell (Figure 26-19)..44

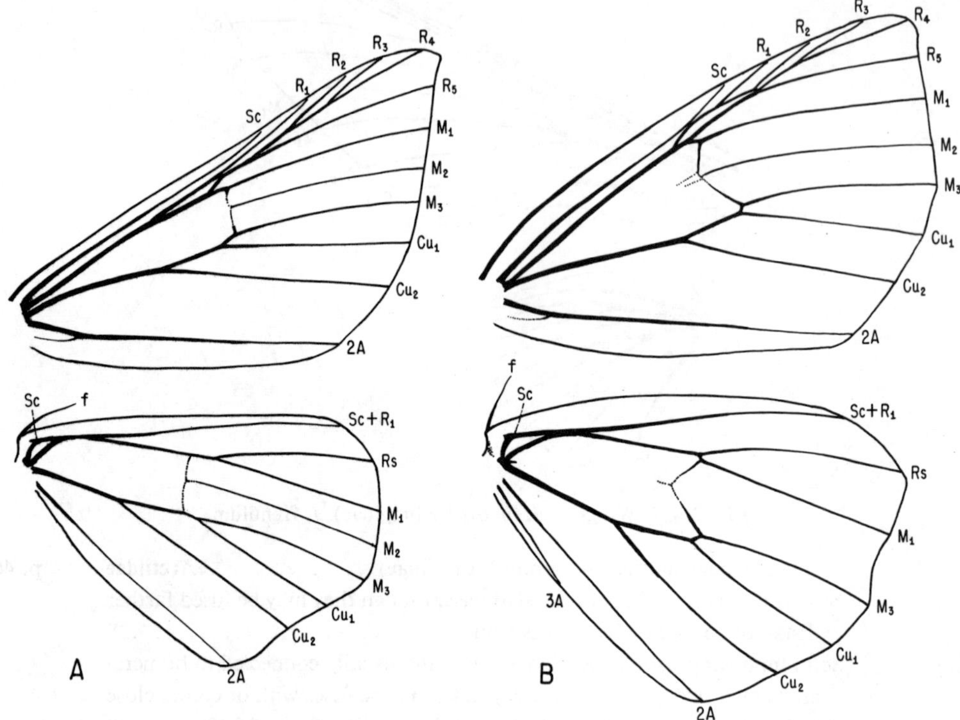

Fig. 26-18. Wings of Geométridae. A, *Haemátopis*; B, *Xanthótype*. *f*, frenulum.

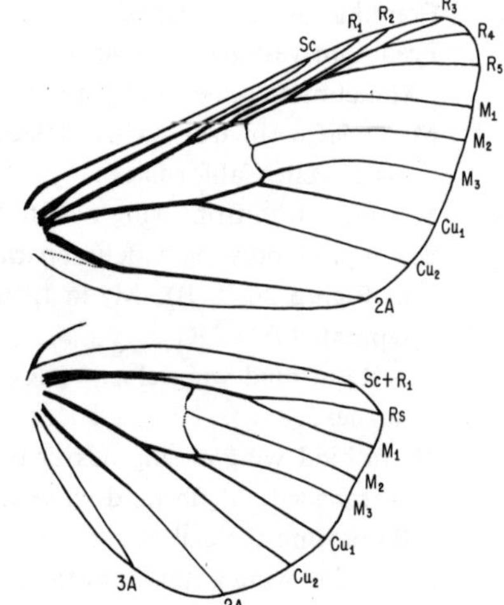

Fig. 26-19. Wings of *Datàna* (Notodóntidae).

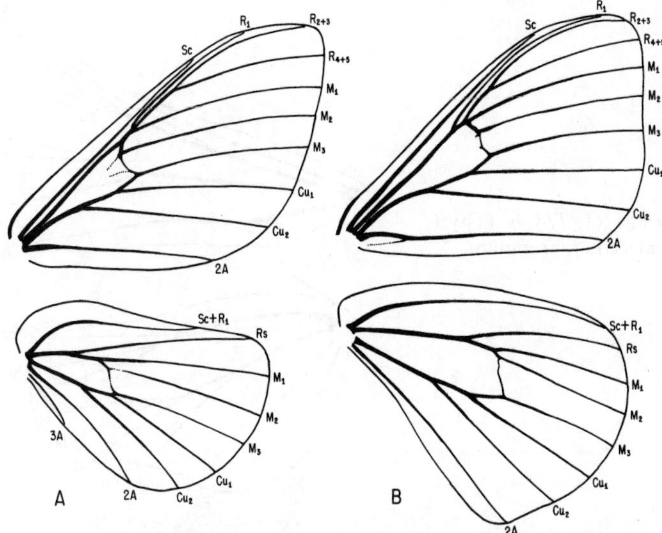

Fig. 26-20. A, wings of *Anisòta* (Citheronìidae); B, wings of *Autómeris* (Saturnìidae.)

44(43′). $Sc+R_1$ and Rs in hind wing close together and parallel along almost the entire length of the discal cell (Figure 26-19); proboscis usually present; front wings fully scaled; tarsal claws with a blunt tooth at base...... .... **Notodóntidae** p. 412

44′. $Sc+R_1$ and Rs in hind wing separating at about middle of discal cell; proboscis lacking; front wings with 1 or 2 small clear spots near tip; tarsal claws simple.................................. **Zanólidae*** p. 415

45(40′). Sc and Rs in hind wing connected by a cross-vein (Figure 26-15 B); white moths of medium size.............................. **Bombýcidae*** p. 415

45′. Sc and Rs in hind wing not connected by a cross-vein; color variable, but not white; size medium to large 46

46(45′). M_1 in front wing fused with R for a short distance beyond discal cell; hind wings with 2 anal veins (Figure 26-20 A); humeral angle of hind wings considerably expanded; wings without eye spots; discal cell in front wing closed .... **Citheroniidae** p. 407

46′. M_1 in front wing usually not fused with R beyond discal cell; usually only 1 anal vein in hind wing (Figure 26-20 B); humeral angle of hind wings but little expanded; wings usually with eye spots (Figure 26-45); discal cell in front wing variable, often open.................... **Saturnìidae** p. 405

47(36′). All the branches of R and M in front wing arising separately from the usually open discal cell (Figure 26-21); wings usually with clear spots.. .... **Thyrídidae*** p. 420

47′. Front wings with some branches of R and (or) M fused beyond discal cell 48

48(47′). Frenulum present and well developed 49

48′. Frenulum vestigial or absent 61

49(48). Antennae swollen apically; Sc in hind wing fused with Rs for only a short distance at base of discal cell (Figure 26-22 A); ocelli absent; moths

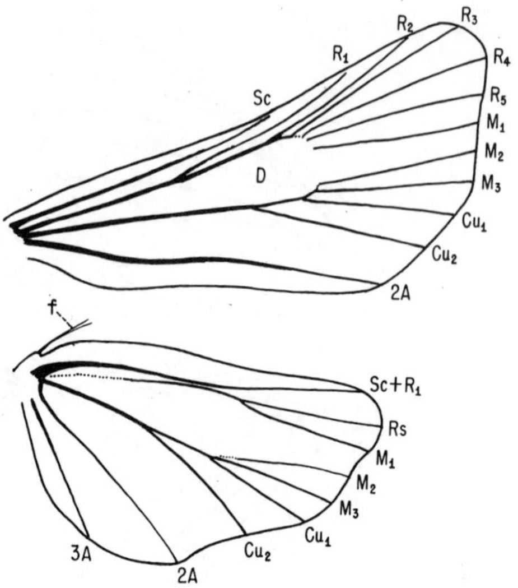

Fig. 26-21. Wings of *Thỳris* (Thyrídidae). *D*, discal cell; *f*, frenulum.

with a wingspread of about an inch, usually black with white or yellow spots in wings (Figure 26-50) .... **Agarístidae** p. 409

49′. Antennae usually not swollen apically; Sc in hind wing variable; ocelli present or absent 50

50(49′). $Sc+R_1$ in hind wing apparently absent (Figure 26-22 B); day-flying moths .... **Amátidae** p. 407

50′. $Sc+R_1$ in hind wing present 51

51(50′). Hind wings with Sc and Rs fused to near or beyond middle of discal cell, sometimes forming a small basal areole (Figure 26-23) 52

51′. Hind wings with Sc and Rs separate from base of wing, or if fused beyond base of wing, then the fusion is only for a short distance at or before middle of discal cell (Figure 26-24), or it is beyond the cell (Figure 26-14 A) 54

52(51). Ocelli present (subfamily Arctiinae) .... **Arctìidae** p. 408

52′. Ocelli absent 53

53(52′). Front wings with tufts of raised scales .... **Nólidae*** p. 408

53′. Front wings smoothly scaled (subfamily Lithosiinae) .... **Arctìidae** p. 408

54(51′). Sc in hind wing separate from Rs along discal cell, though sometimes bending toward it, or fusing with it near or beyond apex of cell (Figure 26-14) 55

54′. Sc in hind wing fused with Rs for a short distance before middle of discal cell (Figures 26-23 B, 26-24, 26-25) 58

55(54). Sc and Rs in hind wing connected by a cross-vein near middle of discal cell 56

55′. Sc and Rs in hind wing not connected by a cross-vein near middle of discal cell 57

56(55). Proboscis present; thorax and abdomen clothed with smooth scales.... .... **Noctùidae** p. 410

56′. Proboscis absent; thorax and abdomen hairy .... **Lipáridae** p. 413

57(55′). R_1 in front wing about as long as discal cell, or longer; outer margin of

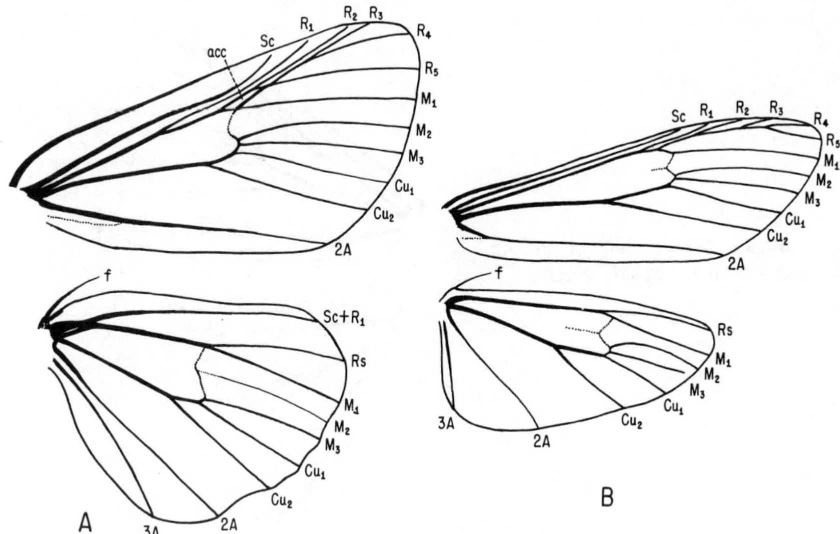

Fig. 26-22. A, wings of *Alýpia* (Agarístidae); B, wings of *Scépsis* (Amátidae). *acc*, accessory cell; *f*, frenulum.

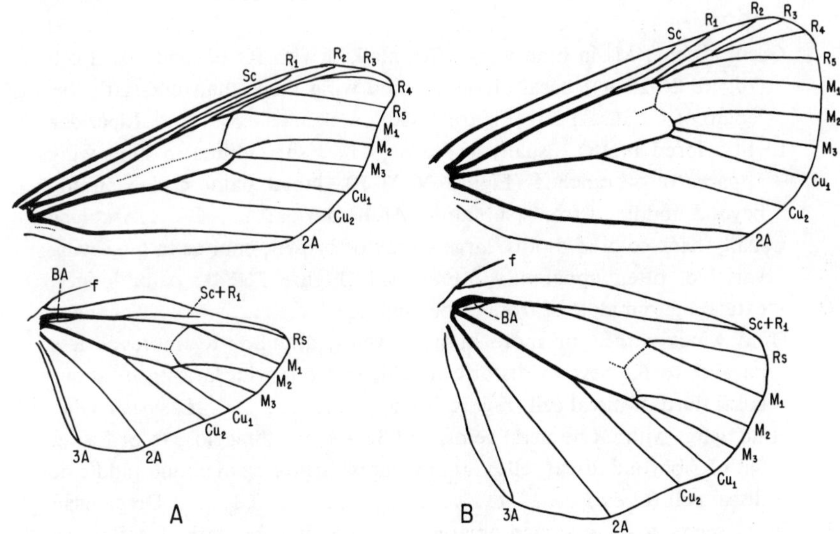

Fig. 26-23. Wings of Arctìidae (Arctiìnae). A, *Halisidòta*; B, *Apántesis*. *BA*, basal areole; *f*, frenulum.

front wing wavy .... **Drepánidae** p. 416

57′. R_1 in front wing much shorter than discal cell .... **Pyrálidae** p. 420

58(54′). Tympanal hoods (2 rounded prominences on dorsal surface of first abdominal segment) large and separated by about one-third the width of the abdomen; black moths with light markings on the wings, occurring in western United States and southern Florida...... **Pericópidae*** p. 412

58′. Tympanal hoods less conspicuous and more lateral; widely distributed..59

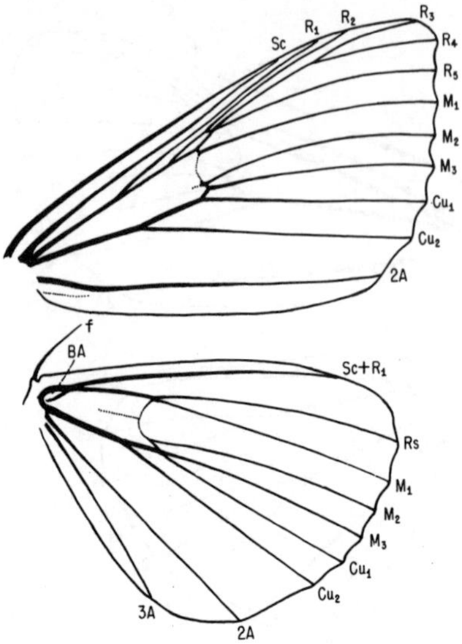

Fig. 26-24. Wings of *Catocàla* (Noctùidae). *BA*, basal areole; *f*, frenulum.

59(58′). Ocelli present; M_1 in hind wing free from Rs beyond discal cell, or fused with it for only a very short distance; basal areole in hind wing very small, less than one-sixth the length of the discal cell (Figures 26-23 B, 26-24) 60

59′. Ocelli absent; M_1 in hind wing often stalked with Rs beyond discal cell (Figure 26-25 A); basal areole in hind wing more than one-sixth the length of the discal cell (Figure 26-25) . . . . **Lipáridae** p. 413

60(59). Light-colored moths, usually white or yellowish; cubitus in hind wing apparently 4-branched (Figure 26-23 B); labial palpi not extending beyond middle of front (subfamily Arctiinae) . . . . **Arctiidae** p. 408

60′. Usually dark-colored moths, largely gray or brown; cubitus in hind wing variable, often apparently 3-branched (Figure 26-24); palpi longer, extending to middle of front or beyond . . . . **Noctùidae** p. 410

61(48′). Hind wings with 1 or more humeral veins, and $Sc+R_1$ more or less parallel to Rs beyond discal cell; Cu_2 in front wing arising in about basal third of discal cell (Figure 26-26) . . . . **Lasiocámpidae** p. 414

61′. Hind wings without humeral veins, and $Sc+R_1$ bending close to or fusing with Rs beyond discal cell; Cu_2 in front wing arising in about middle of discal cell (*Orèta*) . . . . **Drepánidae** p. 416

62(23′, 25′). Basal segment of antennae enlarged and concave beneath, forming an eye-cap (Figure 26-28 B) 63

62′. Basal segment of antennae not forming an eye-cap (Figure 26-28 A). . . .67

63(62). Maxillary palpi conspicuous, folded in a resting position. 64*

63′. Maxillary palpi porrect, or vestigial 65

64(63). Front wings with branched veins, and often a small discal cell (Figure 26-27 A); very small moths, wingspread 3 mm or less. . . . **Nepticùlidae*** p. 432

64′. Front wings with 3 or 4 simple veins only; hind wings linear; wingspread usually more than 3 mm . . . . **Opostégidae*** p. 430

65(63′). Venation complete, veins beyond discal cell in front wing more or less parallel; hind wings with a discal cell; wings not sharply pointed at apex

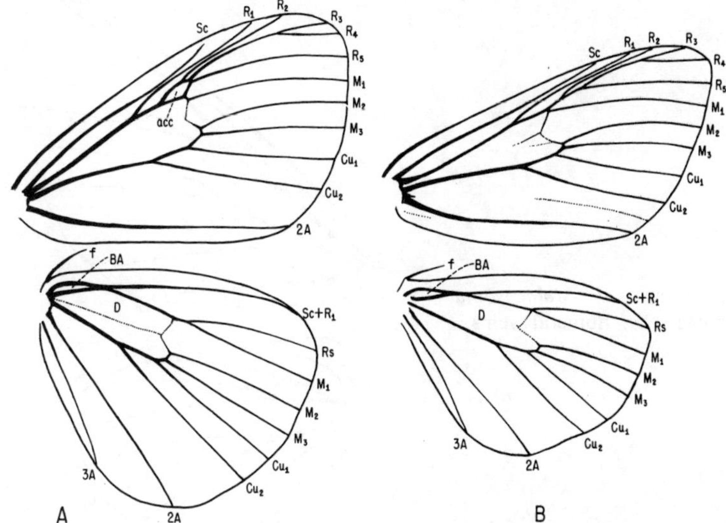

Fig. 26-25. Wings of Lipáridae. A, *Hemerocámpa*; B, *Porthètria*. *BA*, basal areole; *D*, discal cell; *f*, frenulum.

(*Calósima*) .... **Blastobásidae*** p. 426

65′. Venation reduced, veins beyond discal cell in front wing diverging; hind wings without a discal cell; wings sharply pointed at apex 66

66(65′). Labial palpi minute and drooping or absent .... **Lyonetìidae*** p. 430

66′. Labial palpi moderate in size and upcurved (*Phyllocnístis*) .. **Gracilarìidae** p. 429

67(62′). Maxillary palpi conspicuous, folded in a resting position 68

67′. Maxillary palpi porrect, or vestigial 73

68(67). R_5 in front wing extending to outer margin of wing (*Acrolèpia*) **Plutéllidae*** p. 427

68′. R_5 in front wing extending to costa, or absent 69

69(68′). Head tufted, at least on vertex; venation complete 70

69′. Head smooth; venation sometimes reduced; strongly flattened moths (*Phaeòses*, Louisiana and Mississippi) .... **Oinophílidae*** p. 430

70(69). Wing membrane aculeate (with minute hairlike spines under the scales); antennae smooth, often very long; female with a piercing ovipositor (superfamily Incurvarioìdea) 71*

70′. Wing membrane not aculeate; antennae usually rough, with a whorl of erect scales on each segment; ovipositor membranous, retractile .... **Tinèidae** p. 431

71(70). Antennae at least one-fourth longer than front wings .... **Adélidae*** p. 432

71′. Antennae little if any longer than front wings 72*

72(71′). Folded part of maxillary palpi half as long as width of head .... **Incurvarìidae*** p. 432

72′. Folded part of maxillary palpi two-thirds as long as width of head .... **Prodóxidae*** p. 432

73(67′). First segment of labial palpi as large as second, or larger .. **Acrolóphidae*** p. 431

73′. First segment of labial palpi smaller than second 74

74(73′). Upper face and usually vertex tufted with dense bristly hairs; third seg-

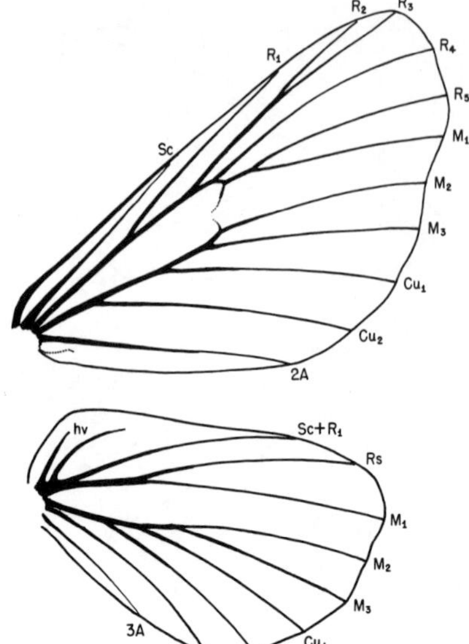

Fig. 26-26. Wings of *Malacosòma* (Lasiocámpidae). *hv*, humeral veins.

ment of labial palpi spindle-shaped and equal to second in length....75

74′. Upper face usually smooth, with short scales; third segment of labial palpi usually long and pointed (Figure 26-28 A), or very short in rough-scaled species...76

75(74). Wing membrane aculeate (see couplet 70); antennae long, often longer than body; female with a piercing ovipositor ....**Adélidae*** p. 432

75′. Wing membrane usually not aculeate; antennae usually short; female with ovipositor membranous and retractile ....**Tinèidae** p. 431

76(74′). Hind wings broad, rounded at apex or trapezoidal, usually broader than fringe, with anal region developed and venation usually complete (Figures 26-29 and 26-30 A, B); front wings sometimes rather square-cut at tip...77

76′. Hind wings lanceolate or linear, pointed at apex, much narrower than the fringe, and with venation often reduced (Figures 26-31 B, C and 26-32); front wings rounded or pointed at tip 90

77(76). Hind wings with M_1, and sometimes also M_2, absent......**Carposínidae*** p. 423

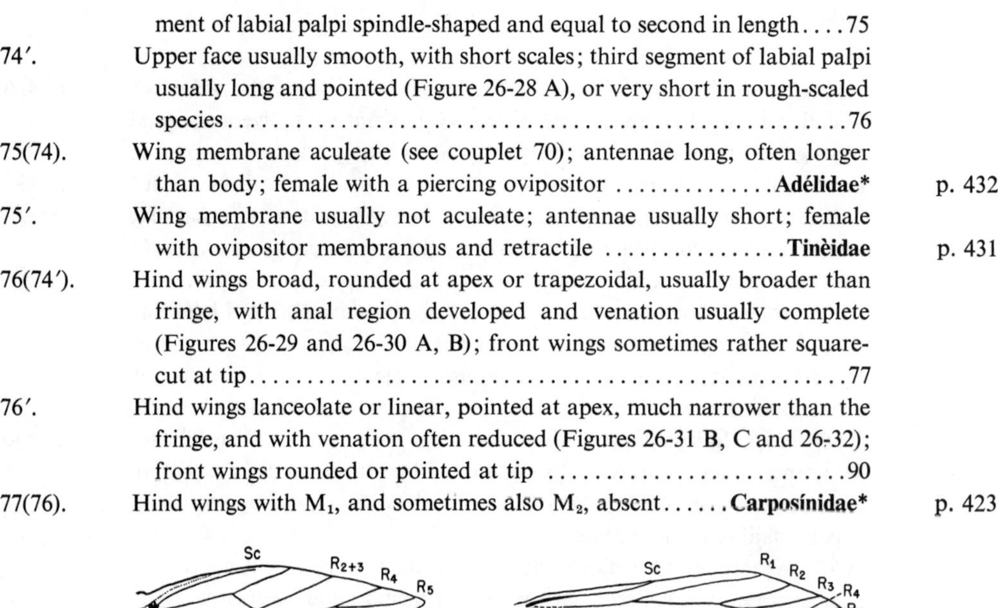

Fig. 26-27. A, wings of *Obrússa* (Nepticùlidae); B, wings of *Holcócera* (Blastobásidae). *f*, frenulum. (A, redrawn from Braun; B, redrawn from Comstock, after Forbes, by permission of Comstock Publishing Associates.)

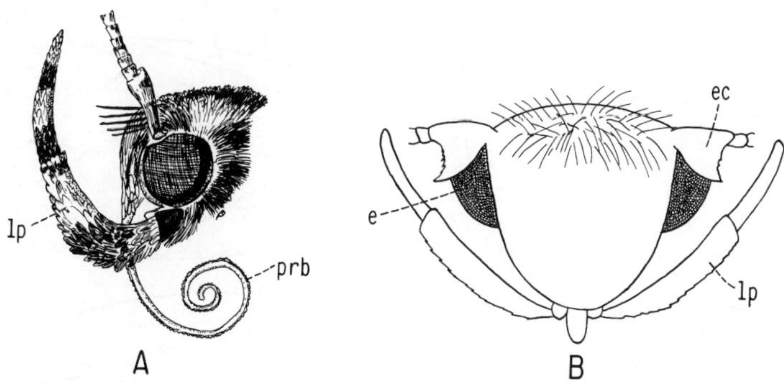

Fig. 26-28. Head structure in Microlepidoptera. A, *Pectinóphora* (Gelechìidae), lateral view; B, *Zenodòchium* (Blastobásidae), anterior view. *e,* compound eye; *ec,* eye-cap; *lp,* labial palpus; *prb,* proboscis. (A, redrawn from Busck; B, redrawn from Dietz.)

77′. Hind wings with M_1 present, or if absent (Gelechìidae), then the outer margin of the hind wings is more or less emarginate (Figure 26-29 C) 78

78(77′). Cu_2 in front wing arising in basal three-fourths of discal cell (Figure 26-29 A, B) 79

78′. Cu_2 in front wing arising in distal fourth of discal cell (Figure 26-29 C), or if not, then there is no fringe on the base of Cu 80

79(78). Upper side of hind wings usually with a fringe of long hairs on basal part of Cu; if this fringe is lacking, then M_1 and M_2 in front wing are close together at tip; front wings with R_4 and R_5 separate, or M_2, M_3, and Cu_1 strongly convergent distally .... **Olethreùtidae** p. 422

79′. Hind wings usually without a fringe of long hairs on basal part of Cu; if such a fringe is present, then R_4 and R_5 in front wing are stalked; M_2, M_3, and Cu_1 in front wing divergent or parallel .... **Tortrícidae** p. 423

80(78′). Front wings with 1A completely lacking (Figure 26-29 C) 81

80′. Front wings with 1A preserved, at least at wing margin (Figures 26-29 D, 26-30 A, B) 82

81(80). Labial palpi with third segment long and slender, usually tapering, the palpi upturned and extending to middle of front or beyond (Figure 26-28 A); R_5 in front wing stalked with R_4 and extending to costa (Figure 26-29 C) .... **Gelechìidae** p. 424

81′. Labial palpi with third segment short and blunt, the palpi beaklike; R_5 in front wing rarely stalked with R_4 and usually extending to outer wing margin .... **Phaloniidae*** p. 423

82(80′). Hind wings with Rs and M_1 close together, fused or stalked (Figure 26-29 D) 83*

82′. Hind wings with Rs and M_1 well separated at their origin, at least half as far apart as at wing margin 84

83(82). Wings narrow, the front wings sometimes sickle-shaped; maxillary palpi minute but porrect (*Ceróstoma*) .... **Plutéllidae*** p. 427

83′. Wings broad, not sickle-shaped; maxillary palpi of the folded type; front wings with Cu_1 and Cu_2 usually fused or stalked (Figure 26-29 D) .... **Stenómidae*** p. 426

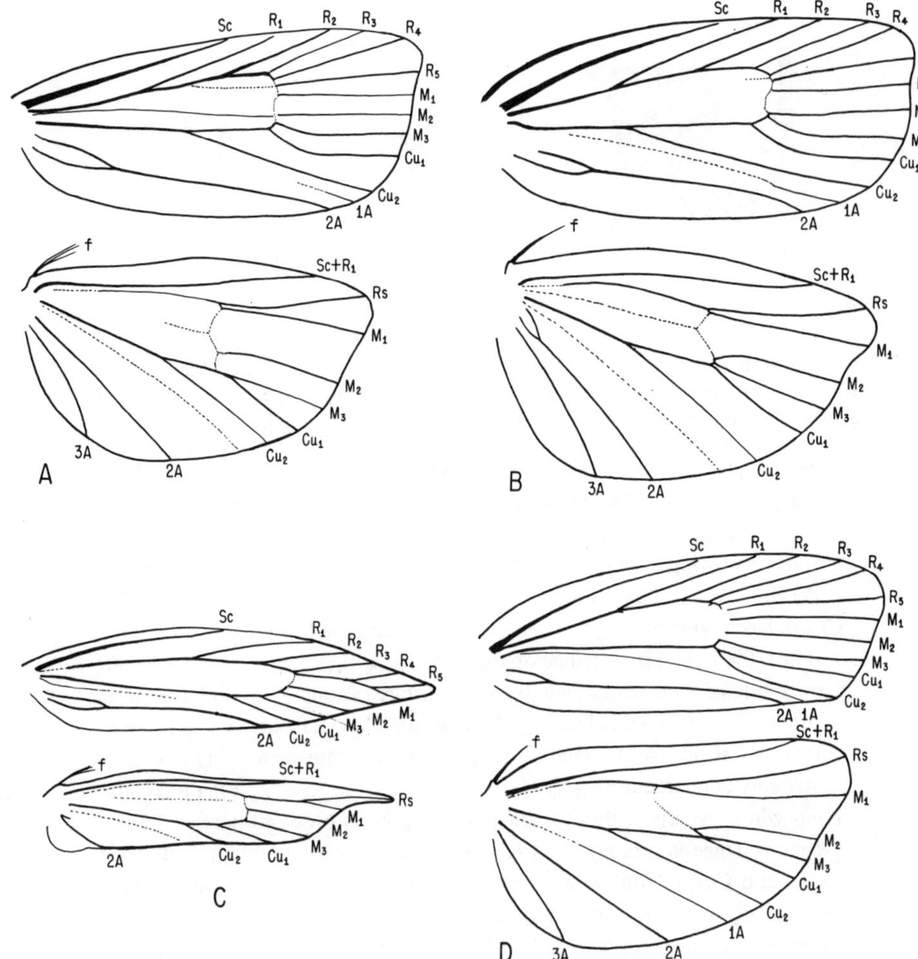

Fig. 26-29. Wings of Microlepidoptera. A, Olethreùtidae (*Carpocápsa*); B, Tortrícidae; C, Gelechìidae; D, Stenómidae (*Stenòma*). *f*, frenulum.

84(82′). Ocelli large and conspicuous; R_5 in front wing extending to outer margin of wing.. **Glyphipterýgidae*** p. 426

84′. Ocelli small or absent 85

85(84′). Labial palpi very small or vestigial (*Solenòbia*)................ **Psýchidae** p. 430

85′. Labial palpi long, often extending beyond vertex.................... 86

86(85′). R_5 in front wing extending to outer wing margin.................... 87

86′. R_5 in front wing stalked with R_4, and extending to costa 88

87(86). R_4 and R_5 in front wing stalked.. 88

87′. R_4 and R_5 in front wing separate 89

88(86′, 87). M_2 in hind wing arising closer to M_1 than to M_3........... **Ethmìidae*** p. 426

88′. M_2 in hind wing arising closer to M_3 than to M_1 (Figure 26-30 A)...... .... **Oecophóridae** p. 425

89(87′). M_1 and M_2 in hind wing stalked (*Plutélla*) .... **Plutéllidae*** p. 427

89′. M_1 and M_2 in hind wing separate (Figure 26-30 B)...... **Yponomeùtidae** p. 428

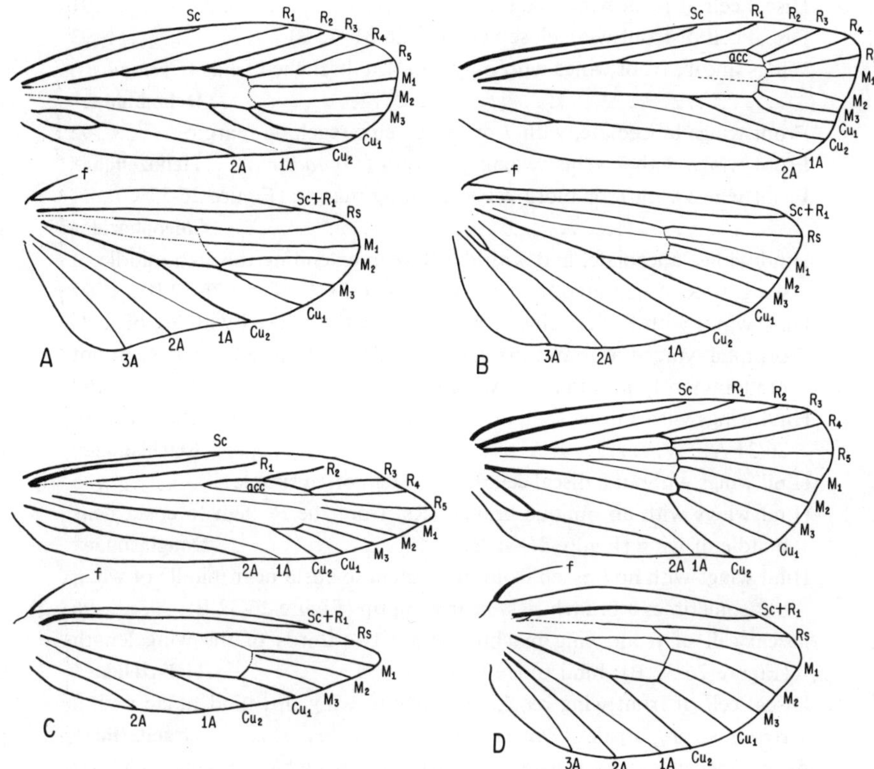

Fig. 26-30. Wings of Microlepidoptera. A, Oecophóridae (*Depressària*); B, Yponomeùtidae (*Átteva*); C, Tinèidae; D, Acrolóphidae (*Acrólophus*). *acc*, accessory cell; *f*, frenulum.

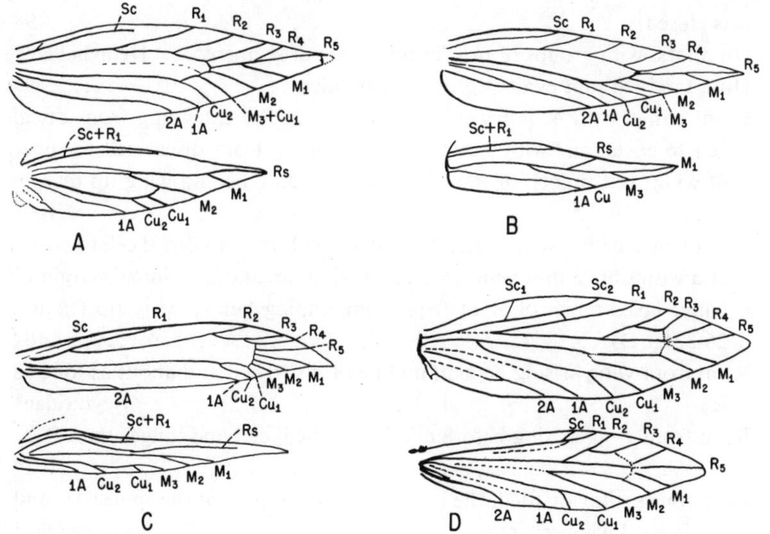

Fig. 26-31. Wings of Lepidoptera. A, Elachístidae (*Elachísta*); B, Douglasìidae (*Tinágma*); C, Gracilarìidae (*Gracilària*); D, Micropterýgidae (*Micrópteryx*). (Redrawn from Comstock by permission of Comstock Publishing Associates.)

90(76′). Discal cell of front wing open....................................91

90′. Discal cell of front wing closed (Figure 26-31 A, B) 93

91(90). Wings linear; front wings with only 3 or 4 unbranched veins (*Cycloplàsis*) .... **Heliodínidae*** p. 427

91′. Front wings lanceolate, with 7 or more veins reaching margin........92

92(91′). Front wings with 7 veins reaching margin (*Coptodísca*)....**Heliozélidae*** p. 428

92′. Front wings with 8 or more veins reaching margin (Figure 26-32 C).... ....**Coleophóridae** p. 429

93(90′). Hind wings lanceolate, and with the R stem extending through middle of wing, widely separated from Sc (Figures 26-31 A, B and 26-32 B)....94

93′. Hind wings with R stem closely associated with or fused with Sc, or lost; or, hind wings linear and the veins crowded or reduced, the R stem not predominantly in middle of wing 97

94(93). Hind wings with a discal cell, and the Cu stem at least 2-branched (Figure 26-31 A) ....**Elachístidae*** p. 429

94′. Hind wings without a discal cell, the Cu stem often simple............95

95(94′). Hind wings with an oblique branch (Rs) from the R stem to costa near middle of wing (Figure 26-31 B).....................**Douglasìidae*** p. 428

95′. Hind wings with no branch from the R stem to costa near middle of wing, but sometimes a branch (Rs) near wing tip (Figure 26-32 B)........96

96(95′). Discal cell of front wing reaching about two-thirds of the wing length (Figure 26-32 B); hind tibiae hairy....................**Heliozélidae*** p. 428

96′. Discal cell of front wing reaching nearly to wing tip; hind tibiae with a row of strong bristles (*Phyllocnístis*)...................**Gracilarìidae** p. 429

97(93′). Accessory cell very long, extending halfway to wing base (Figure 26-32 A); hind wings without a closed discal cell; male antennae heavily ciliate.. .... **Tischerìidae*** p. 430

97′. Accessory cell smaller, often absent (if long, then discal cell in hind wing is closed)...98

98(97′). Hind tarsi with groups of bristles near apex of segments....**Heliodínidae*** p. 427

98′. Hind tarsi without evident groups of bristles 99

99(98′). Front wings with 4 or fewer veins (including Sc) extending from discal cell to costa, and with 5 or 6 veins extending from discal cell to inner of wing; last branch of R in front wing ending behind wing tip margin 100*

99′. Front wings with 5 veins (including Sc) extending from discal cell to costa, and with only 3 or 4 veins extending from discal cell to inner margin of wing; last branch of R in front wing ending before wing tip (Figure 26-32 C, D) 102

100(99). R_1 in front wing arising beyond middle of discal cell and about as long as R_2 ....**Scýthridae*** p. 428

100′. R_1 in front wing arising before middle of discal cell and longer than R_2.. ....101*

101(100′). Hind tibiae stiffly bristled, the bristles usually in tufts at the spurs; M_1 and M_3 in hind wing separate...........................**Epermenìidae*** p. 424

101′. Hind tibiae with long loose hair; M_1 and M_2 in hind wing united or long-stalked (*Argyrésthia*)..............................**Yponomeùtidae*** p. 428

102(99′). Discal cell in front wing somewhat oblique, its apex closer to hind margin

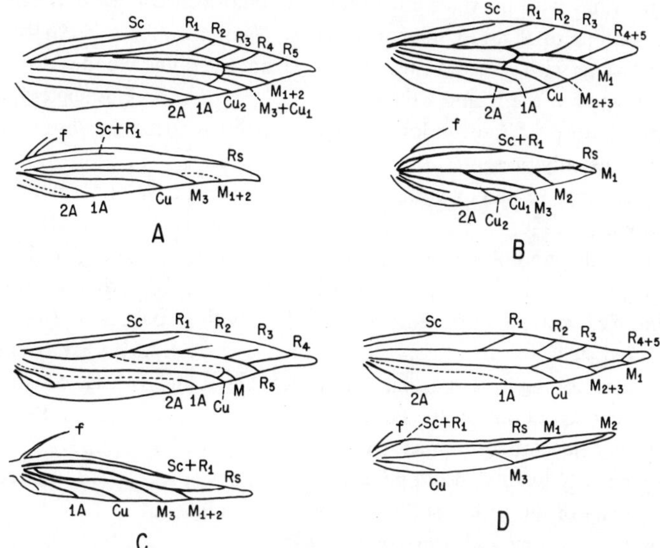

Fig. 26-32. Wings of Microlepidoptera. A, Tischerìidae (*Tischèria*); B, Heliozélidae (*Antíspila*); C, Coleophóridae (*Coleóphora*); D, Lyonetìidae (*Bedéllia*). *f*, frenulum. (Redrawn from Comstock by permission of Comstock Publishing Associates; A and B, after Spuler, D, after Clemens.)

of wing than to costa; Cu_2 in front wing usually short and oblique (Figure 26-27 B) 103

102′. Discal cell in front wing axial and central, its apex closer to costa than to hind margin of wing (Figure 26-32 D); Cu_2 in front wing usually longer and parallel to the veins anterior to it 105

103(102). Front wings with a long stigmal thickening between costa and R_1, and with R_2 arising nearer R_3 than R_1 and near end of discal cell (Figure 26-27 B); Sc and Rs in hind wing usually fused for a short distance near base .... **Blastobásidae*** p. 426

103′. Front wings without a stigma and with R_2 arising well before end of discal cell; Sc and Rs in hind wing not fused (Figure 26-32 C).......... 104

104(103′). Front tibiae slender, with the epiphysis small and apical or absent; antennae turned forward at rest .... **Coleophóridae** p. 429

104′. Front tibiae stouter, with the epiphysis at the middle; antennae turned backward at rest.............................. **Cosmopterýgidae*** p. 424

105(102′). Labial palpi minute and drooping; vertex tufted; hind wings linear (Figure 26-32 D) (*Bedéllia*) .... **Lyonetìidae*** p. 430

105′. Labial palpi larger, extending forward or upturned 106

106(105′). Labial palpi with third segment usually blunt; maxillary palpi extending forward, or absent; 2A not forked at base .... **Gracilarìidae** p. 429

106′. Labial palpi upturned, the third segment long, tapering, and pointed (Figure 26-28 A); 2A often forked at base...................... 107

107(106′). Front and hind wings with 1A preserved at margin and 2A forked at base (*Endròsis*) .... **Oecophóridae** p. 425

107′. Hind wings, and usually also front wings, lacking 1A 108

108(107′). Front wings with no veins emerging from end of discal cell between continuations of R and Cu stems (*Hélice, Theìsoa*) .... **Gelechìidae** p. 424

108′. Front wings with several veins emerging from the oblique end of the discal cell between the R and Cu stems.................. **Cosmopterýgidae*** p. 424

109(2′). Wing expanse 12 mm or less; maxillary palpi reduced or absent; tibial spurs usually present.......................................110*

109′. Wing expanse 15 mm or more; maxillary palpi well developed; tibial spurs absent ....**Hepiálidae*** p. 433

110(109). Functional mandibles present; middle tibiae without spurs; Sc in front wing forked near its middle (Figure 26-31 D)........**Micropterýgidae*** p. 433

110′. Mandibles vestigial or absent; middle tibiae with 1 spur; Sc in front wing forked near its tip ....**Eriocranìidae*** p. 432

111(1′). Moth developing in, and usually never leaving, a sack or case constructed and carried about by the larva ....**Psýchidae** p. 430

111′. Moth not developing in a sack constructed by the larva............112

112(111′). Body densely woolly; ocelli present ....**Arctìidae** p. 408

112′. Body scaly or hairy; if woolly, then without ocelli..................113

113(112′). Palpi usually long and projecting forward 114

113′. Palpi short and more or less concealed ....**Tortrícidae*** p. 423

114(113). Body stout, with short legs, and densely woolly (Figure 26-55 C)...... ....**Lipáridae** p. 413

114′. Body slender, with relatively long legs, and hairy or scaly (Figure 26-60 A) .... **Geométridae** p. 416

FAMILY **Papiliónidae** — Swallowtails and Parnassians: This family includes medium-sized to large butterflies, most of which have tail-like prolongations on the hind wings. The papilionids differ from other butterflies in that the cubitus in the front wing appears 4-branched, and there are two or three anal veins in the front wing and only one in the hind wing (Figure 26-9). This family is divided into two subfamilies, the Papilionìnae or swallowtails, and the Parnassiìnae or parnassians.

—Subfamily *Papilionìnae*—Swallowtails—These butterflies get their name from the fact that in most species there is a tail-like prolongation on the hind wing; a few species have two or three such prolongations. The larvae are usually smooth-bodied and possess an eversible forked scent gland, or osmeterium (Figure 26-3, *osm*); this gland is everted from the upper part of the prothorax when the larva is disturbed, and gives off a disagreeable odor. The chrysalis is attached to various objects by the cremaster and is held in a more or less upright position by means of a silken girdle about the middle of the body (Figure 27-4 A). The winter is passed as a chrysalis.

This group contains the largest and some of the most beautifully colored of the butterflies. In many species the two sexes are somewhat differently colored. Several species are fairly common in the eastern states. The black swallowtail, *Papílio polýxenes astérius* Stoll (Figure 26-33 C), is largely black, with two rows of yellow spots around the margin of the wings; the female has quite a bit of blue between the two rows of yellow spots in the hind wings. The larva feeds on carrots, parsley, and related plants. The tiger swallowtail, *Papílio glàucus* Linn. (Figure 26-33 B), is a large yellow swallowtail with black stripes in the front wings and black wing margins; in some individuals the wings are almost entirely dark. The larva feeds on cherry, birch, poplar, and various other trees and shrubs. The spicebush swallowtail, *Papílio tròilus* Linn., is

Fig. 26-33. Swallowtail butterflies. A, the zebra swallowtail, *Papílio marcéllus* Cramer; B, the tiger swallowtail, *Papílio glàucus* Linn.; C, the black swallowtail, *Papílio polýxenes astérius* Stoll, male; D, the giant swallowtail, *Papìlio cresphóntes* Cramer. About one-third natural size.

blackish, with a row of small yellowish spots along the margins of the front wings and extensive blue-gray areas in the rear half of the hind wings; the larva feeds on spicebush and sassafras. The zebra swallowtail, *Papílio marcéllus* Cramer (Figure 26-33 A), is striped with black and greenish white and has relatively long tails; the larva feeds on papaw. This species shows considerable variation, with the adults that emerge at different seasons differing slightly in their markings. The pipe-vine swallowtail, *Papílio phílenor* Linn., is largely black, with the hind wings shading into metallic green posteriorly; the larva feeds on the Dutchman's-pipe. The giant swallowtail or orange-dog, *Papílio cresphóntes* Cramer (Figure 26-33 D), is a large dark-colored butterfly with rows of large yellow spots on the wings; the larva feeds largely on citrus in the South and on prickly ash in the North.

Fig. 26-34. A parnassian, *Parnássius clòdius báldur* Edwards. About two-thirds natural size.

—Subfamily *Parnassìinae* — Parnassians— The parnassians are medium-sized butterflies without tail-like prolongations on the hind wings, and they have the radius in the front wing 4-branched (Figure 26-9 B) (5-branched in the Papilionìnae). They are usually white or gray with black markings on the wings (Figure 26-34); most of them have two small reddish spots in the hind wings. These butterflies pupate on the ground, among fallen leaves, in loose cocoonlike structures. The species in this group are principally western or mountain-dwelling.

FAMILY **Piéridae**—Whites, Sulfurs, and Orange-Tips: The pierids are medium-sized to small butterflies, usually white or yellowish in color, with black marginal wing markings, and with the radius in the front wing usually 3- or 4-branched (rarely 5-branched in some orange-tips). The front

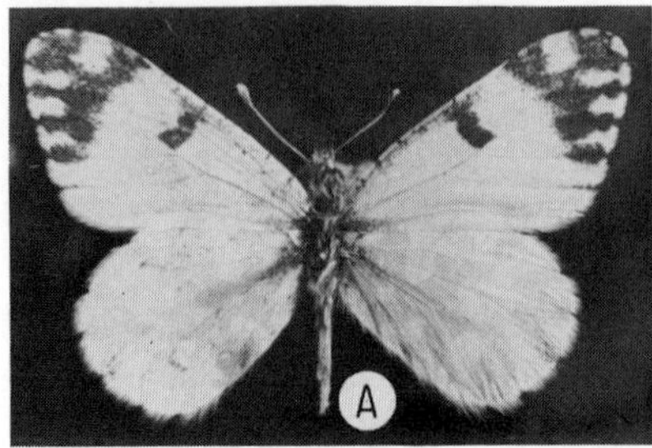

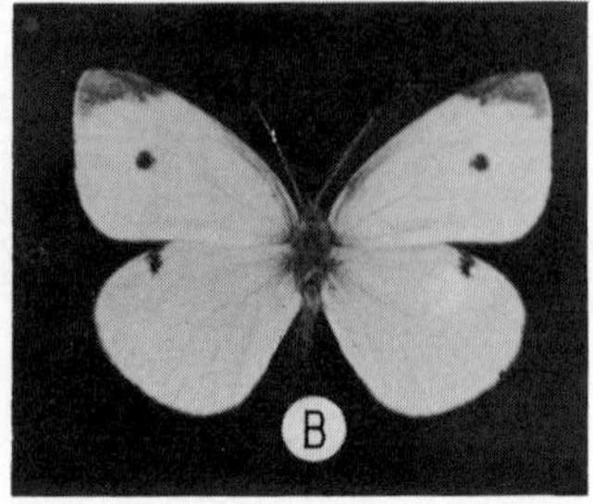

Fig. 26-35. Pierid butterflies. A, an orange-tip, *Eùchloe creùsa lótta* Beutenmüller; B, the cabbage butterfly, *Pìeris ràpae* (Linn.). A, slightly enlarged; B, slightly reduced.

legs are well developed, and the tarsal claws are bifid. The chrysalids are elongate and narrow and are attached by the cremaster and by a silken girdle around the middle of the body. Many pierids are very common and abundant butterflies. The members of this family are divided into three groups: the whites, the sulfurs or yellows, and the orange-tips.

The whites are white with black markings. One of the most common species in this group is the cabbage butterfly, *Pìeris ràpae* (Linn.) (Figure 26-35 B), the larva of which often does considerable damage to cabbage and related plants; it has two or more generations a year, and overwinters as a chrysalis.

The sulfurs or yellows are yellow or orange in color and have the wings margined with black; rarely, they may be white with black wing margins. Many species occur in two or more color forms. A common butterfly in this group is the orange sulfur or alfalfa butterfly, *Còlias eurýtheme* Boisduval; most individuals of this species are orange with black wing margins, but some females are white. The larva feeds on clovers and related plants and often does serious damage to clover crops. The common or clouded sulfur, *C. philódice* Latrielle, is yellow with black wing margins; it often occurs in large numbers around muddy pools along roadsides. The larva feeds on clovers. The females of these sulfurs have the black marginal band on the wings broader than in the males, and there are light spots in this band, particularly in the front wings.

The orange-tips are small white butterflies with dark markings (Figure 26-35 A); the under side of the wings is mottled with greenish, and the front wings of many species are tipped with orange. These butterflies are mainly western; only two species occur in the East, and they are relatively rare. The larvae feed on cruciferous plants.

FAMILY **Danàidae**—Milkweed Butterflies: The danaids are large and brightly colored butterflies, usually brownish with black and white markings; the front legs are very small, without claws, and are not used in walking. The radius in the front wing is 5-branched, the discal cell is closed by a well-developed vein, and there is a short third anal vein in the front wing (Figure 26-11). The larvae (Figure 26-36 B) feed on milkweed. The chrysalids are hung by the cremaster to leaves or other objects. The adults are "protected" by distasteful body fluids, and are seldom attacked by predators.

The most common species in this group is the monarch butterfly, *Dánaus plexíppus* (Linn.), which occurs throughout the United States and a large part of the remainder of the world. The monarch is a reddish-brown butterfly with the wings bordered by black; in most of the black marginal band, there are two rows of small white spots (Figure 26-36 A). The caterpillar is yellowish green banded with black, with two threadlike

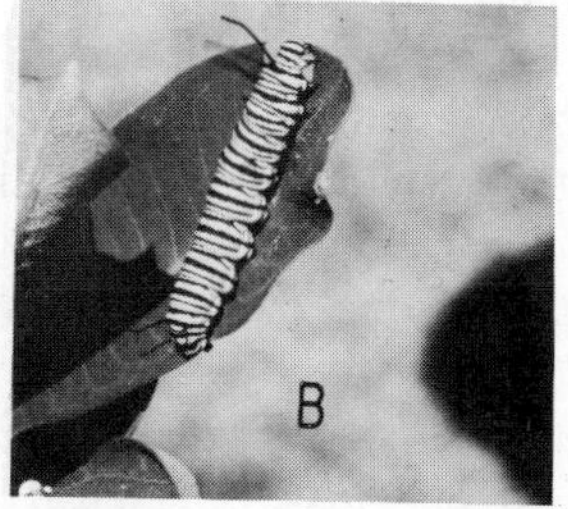

Fig. 26-36. The monarch, *Dánaus plexíppus* (Linn.). A, adult male; B, larva. About one-half natural size.

appendages at either end of the body (Figure 26-36 B); the chrysalis is pale green spotted with gold.

The monarch is one of the few butterflies that migrate; large numbers migrate South in the fall, and the species reappears in the North the following spring. The longest flight known for an adult monarch (based on a tagged individual) is over 1800 miles, from Ontario to Mexico. The butterflies that migrate South in the fall overwinter in the South, and usually start back North the following spring. They may reproduce in their wintering grounds, or after a short northward flight in the spring; the butterflies that arrive in the northern part of the country in the summer are not the same individuals that left there the preceding fall, but are the offspring of individuals that reproduced in the wintering grounds or en route north (see Urquhart, 1960).

The queen, *Dánaus gilíppus* Cramer, a common species in the southeastern states, is similar to the monarch but is darker, and lacks the dark lines along the veins; its larva also feeds on milkweed.

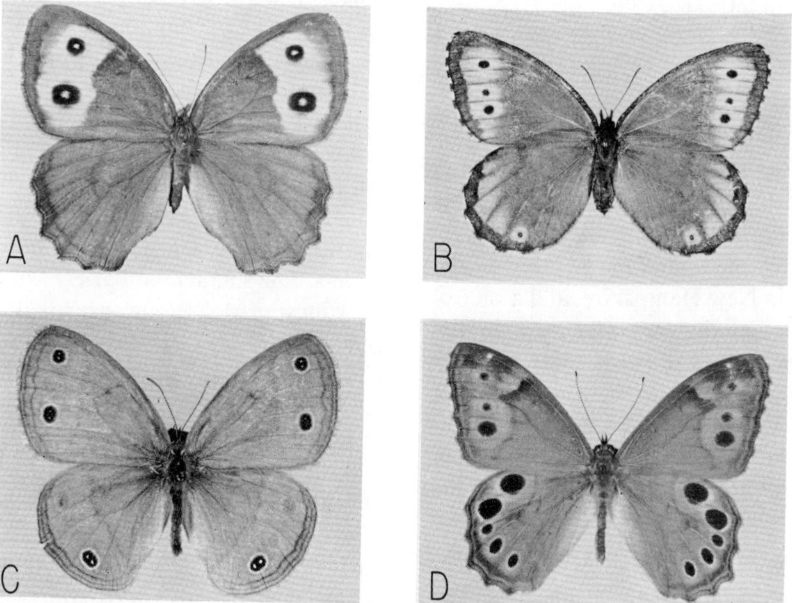

Fig. 26-37. Satyrid butterflies. A, the wood nymph, *Cercỳonis pégala* (Fabricius); B, the jutta arctic, *Oenèis jútta* Hübner; C, the little wood satyr, *Euptỳchia cỳmela* (Cramer); D, the pearly eye, *Lèthe* (*Enòdia*) *portlándica* Fabricius. A, slightly reduced; C, slightly enlarged; B and D, about natural size.

FAMILY **Satýridae**—Satyrs, Wood Nymphs, and Arctics: These butterflies are small to medium-sized, usually grayish or brown in color, and they usually have eyelike spots in the wings. The radius of the front wings is 5-branched, and some of the veins in the front wings (particularly Sc) are considerably swollen at the base (Figure 26-12 A). The larvae feed on grasses. The chrysalis is usually attached by the cremaster to leaves and other objects.

One of the most common species in this group is the wood nymph, *Cercyonis pégala* (Fabricius), a dark brown, medium-sized butterfly with a broad yellowish band across the apical part of the front wing; this band contains two black and white eye spots (Figure 26-37 A). Another common species is the little wood satyr, *Euptychia cymela* (Cramer), a brownish gray butterfly with prominent eye spots in the wings and with a wingspread of about an inch (Figure 26-37 C). The pearly eye, *Lèthe* (*Enòdia*) *portlándica* Fabricius (Figure 26-37 D), a brownish butterfly with a row of black eye spots along the border of the hind wings, is a woodland species with a quick flight and a habit of alighting on tree trunks. Among the most interesting species in this group are the arctics or mountain butterflies (*Oenèis*), which are restricted to the Arctic region and the tops of high mountains. A race of the melissa arctic, *O. melíssa semídea* (Say), is restricted to the summits of the White Mountains in New Hampshire, and a race of the polixenes arctic, *O. políxenes katáhdin* (Newcomb), occurs on Mt. Katahdin in Maine. The jutta arctic *O. jútta* Huebner (Figure 26-37 B), is a wide-ranging circumpolar species that occurs farther south than do most other arctics; it may be found in the sphagnum bogs of Maine and New Hampshire.

FAMILY **Heliconìidae**—Heliconians: The heliconians are brightly colored tropical butterflies with narrow and elongate front wings. As are the Danàidae, these butterflies are "protected" by distasteful body fluids and are therefore avoided by predators. The larvae feed on various species of passion flowers. Only a few species in this group occur in the southern states. Our most common heliconian is the zebra butterfly, *Helicònius charitònius* (Linn.), a black butterfly striped with yellow; this species occurs in the Gulf States, but is most common in Florida. The chrysalis, when disturbed, wriggles about in a characteristic manner and produces a creaking sound.

FAMILY **Nymphálidae**—Brush-Footed Butterflies: The members of this family have the front legs much reduced, without claws, and only the middle and hind legs are used in walking. This character also occurs in the Danàidae, Satýridae, Heliconìidae, and Libythèidae, and these groups are included in the Nymphálidae by some authorities. The radius in the front wing is 5-branched in nearly all the members of this family, and in most species the discal cell is either open or closed by a very weak vein. The chrysalids are usually suspended by the cremaster. This is a large group, and many of its members are common butterflies.

The fritillaries are brownish butterflies with numerous black markings consisting principally of short wavy lines and dots; the under side of the wings is usually marked with silvery spots. The larger fritillaries belong to the genus *Speyéria* (Figure 26-38 B); *Speyéria* larvae are nocturnal and feed on violets. The smaller fritillaries, 1 to 1½ inches in wingspread, belong principally to the genus *Bolòria*; their larvae also feed on violets.

The crescent-spots (*Phyciòdes*) are small brownish butterflies with black markings, and the wings (particularly the front wings) are usually margined with black (Figure 26-38 C). The larvae feed principally on various asters.

The anglewings (*Polygònia*) are small to medium-sized and brownish with black markings, and the wing margins are very irregularly notched and often bear tail-like prolongations (Figure 26-38 F); the under

Fig. 26-38. Brush-footed butterflies (Nymphálidae). A, the viceroy, *Limenìtis archippus* (Cramer); B, the great spangled fritillary, *Speyéria cýbele* (Fabricius); C, the pearl crescent-spot, *Phyciòdes thàros* Drury; D, the mourningcloak; *Nýmphalis antìopa* (Linn.); E, the red admiral, *Vanéssa atalánta* (Linn.); F, the comma, *Polygònia cómma* Harris. C, about natural size, the others slightly reduced.

side of the wings is darker and looks much like a dead leaf, and there is usually a small **C**-shaped silvery spot on the under side of the hind wing. The larvae feed principally on nettles, elm, hop-vine, and other Urticàceae.

The red admiral, *Vanéssa atalánta* (Linn.) (Figure 26-38 E), is a very common and widely distributed butterfly; the larva feeds principally on nettles, feeding in a shelter formed by tying a few leaves together. There are usually two generations a year.

Two very similar and fairly common species, the painted lady, *Vanéssa cárdui* (Linn.), and Hunter's butterfly (or the painted beauty), *V. virginiénsis* Drury, are orange-brown and brownish black above, with white spots in the front wings; the painted lady has four small eye spots on the under side of each hind wing, while Hunter's butterfly has two large eye spots on the under side of each hind wing. The larva of the painted lady feeds chiefly on thistles, while that of Hunter's butterfly feeds on everlastings.

The mourningcloak, *Nýmphalis antìopa* (Linn.), is a common butterfly that is brownish black with yellowish wing margins (Figure 26-38 D); the larvae are gregarious and feed chiefly on willow, elm, and poplar. This is one of the few butterflies that overwinter in the adult stage, and the adults appear early in the spring.

The admirals or sovereigns are medium-sized butterflies in which the antennal club is long and the humeral vein in the hind wing arises at the point of separation of $Sc + R_1$ and Rs (Figure 26-10 B). The viceroy, *Limenìtis archíppus* (Cramer), is a common species in this group and looks very much like the monarch; it differs in that it is slightly smaller, has a narrow black line across the hind wings, and has only a single row of white spots in the black marginal band of the wings (Figure 26-38 A). The resemblance of the viceroy to the monarch is a good example of protective mimicry; the monarch is "protected" by distasteful body fluids and is seldom attacked by predators, and the viceroy's resemblance to the monarch is believed to provide it with at least some protection from predators. The larva of the viceroy, a rather grotesque-looking caterpillar, feeds on willow, poplar, and related trees; it overwinters in a leaf shelter formed by tying a few leaves together with silk. The red-spotted purple, *L. árthemis astỳanax* (Fabricius), another common species in this group, is a blackish butterfly with pale bluish or greenish spots, and with reddish spots on the under side of the wings. The larva, which is similar to that of the viceroy, feeds on willow, cherry, and other trees; it overwinters in a leaf shelter. A similar butterfly, the banded purple, *L. árthemis* (Drury), occurs in the northern states; it has a broad white band across the wings.

FAMILY **Libythèidae**—Snout Butterflies: These are small brownish butterflies with long projecting palpi. The males have the front legs reduced, with only the middle and hind legs used in walking, while the females have the front legs longer and used in walking. One species, *Libýthea bachmánii* Kirtland, occurs in the eastern states; this is a reddish-brown butterfly with white spots in the apical part of the front wings, and with the outer margin of the front wings rather deeply notched; the larva feeds on hackberry.

FAMILY **Riodínidae**—Metalmarks: The riodinids are small, dark-colored butterflies that are somewhat similar to some of the lycaenids. They differ from the lycaenids in having the costa of the hind wing thickened out to the humeral angle, and in having a humeral vein in the hind wing (Figure 26-13 A). Most species in this group are tropical or western, and only two occur in the East. The little metalmark, *Lephelisca virginiénsis* (Guerin), with a wingspread of about 20 millimeters, occurs in the southern states, and the northern metalmark, *L. boreàlis* (Grote and Robinson), with a wingspread of 25 to 30 millimeters, occurs as far north as New York and Ohio; the little metalmark is fairly common in the South, but the northern metalmark is quite rare. The larvae feed on ragwort, thistle, and other plants.

FAMILY **Lycaènidae** — Gossamer-Winged Butterflies: The members of this group are small, delicate, and often brightly colored butterflies, some of which are quite common. The body is slender, the antennae are usually ringed with white, and there is a line of white scales encircling the eyes. The radius in the front wings is 3- or 4-branched. M_1 in the front wings arises at or near the apex of the discal cell, and there is no humeral vein in the hind wings (Figure 26-13 B). The front legs are normal in the female, but are shorter and lack tarsal claws in the male. Lycaenid larvae are flattened and sluglike; many secrete "honeydew," which attracts ants, and some live in ant nests. The chrysalids are fairly smooth and are attached by the cremaster, with a silken girdle about the middle of the body. The adults are rapid fliers. This family is divided into four subfamilies, the Theclìnae, Lycaenìnae (=Chrysophanìnae), Plebeiìnae (=Lycaenìnae), and Gerydìnae (=Spalgìnae).

—Subfamily *Theclìnae* — Hair-Streaks—The hair-streaks are usually dark gray or brownish, with delicate striping on the under side of the wings, and usually with small

Fig. 26-39. Lycaenid butterflies. A, the American copper, *Lycaèna phlèas americàna* Harris; B, the harvester, *Feníseca tarquínius* (Fabricius). Slightly enlarged.

reddish spots in the posterior part of the hind wings; there are generally two or three thin tails on the hind wings. These butterflies have a swift, darting flight, and are commonly found in meadows, along roadsides, and in other open areas. One of the most common eastern species is the gray hair-streak, *Strỳmon mélinus* (Hübner); the larva bores in the fruits and seeds of legumes and other plants. The great purple hair-streak, *Átlides hálesus* (Cramer), is the largest eastern species, with a wingspread of a little over an inch; it is brilliantly colored—blue, purple, and black—and quite iridescent; it occurs in the southern states. The elfins (*Incisàlia*) are small, brownish, early spring species which lack tails, but have the edges of the hind wings scalloped.

—Subfamily *Lycaenìnae*—Coppers— The coppers are small butterflies that are orange-red or brown (often with a coppery tinge) with black markings. They generally occur in open areas such as marshes and meadows and along roadsides. The American copper, *Lycaèna phlèas americàna* Harris (Figure 26-39 A), is one of the most common species in this group; the adults are quite pugnacious, and often "buzz" other butterflies (and even collectors!); the larva feeds on dock (*Rùmex*).

—Subfamily *Plebeiìnae*—Blues— The blues are small, delicate, slender-bodied butterflies with the upper surface of the wings blue. The females are usually darker than the males, and some species occur in two or more color forms. Many larvae secrete "honeydew," to which ants are attracted. One of the most common and widespread species is the spring azure, *Lycaenópsis argìolus* (Linn.); this species exhibits considerable geographic and seasonal variation in size and coloring. The tailed blues (*Evères*) have delicate tail-like prolongations on the hind wings.

—Subfamily *Gerydìnae*—Harvesters— The harvesters differ from the other lycaenids in having M_1 in the front wings stalked with a branch of R for a short distance beyond the discal cell (Figure 26-40). The wanderer or harvester, *Feníseca tarquínius* (Fabricius),

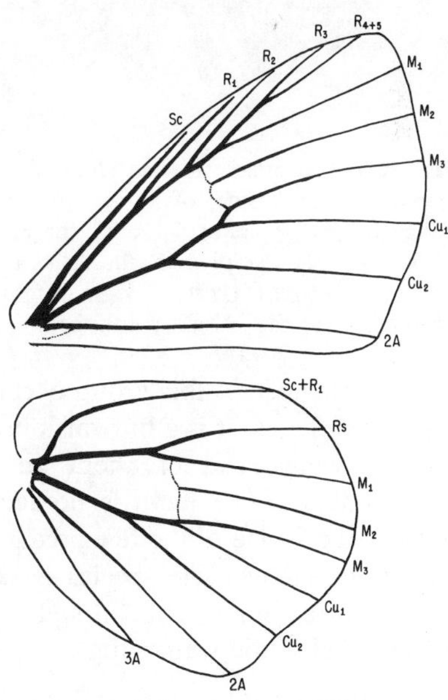

Fig. 26-40. Wings of *Feníseca tarquínius* (Fabricius).

Fig. 26-41. Skippers (Hesperìidae). A, the silver-spotted skipper, *Epargŷreus clàrus* Cramer (Pyrgìnae), underside of wings (natural size); B, the least skipper *Ancylóxipha nùmitor* Fabricius (Hesperiìnae), $1\frac{1}{2}$ ×; C, the Hobomok skipper, *Poànes hóbomok* Harris (Hesperiìnae), $1\frac{1}{3}$ ×; D, Peck's skipper, *Polìtes péckius* Kirby (Hesperiìnae), $1\frac{3}{4}$ ×; E, the checkered skipper, *Pýrgus commùnis* Grote (Pyrgìnae), $1\frac{1}{2}$ ×; F, the northern cloudy wing, *Thórybes pylàdes* Scudder (Pyrgìnae), slightly enlarged.

is the only member of this group occurring in the United States; it is a brownish butterfly with a wingspread of about an inch (Figure 26-39 B). The larva is predaceous on aphids, and is one of the few predaceous lepidopterous larvae. The species is rather local and not common, and (in spite of its name) does very little wandering.

FAMILY **Megathýmidae**—Giant Skippers: These skippers have a wingspread of $1\frac{1}{2}$ inches or more; they occur in the South and West. The antennal club is large, and the tip is not recurved as in many of the Hesperìidae. These skippers are stout-bodied, fast-flying, and when at rest, the wings are held vertically above the body. The larvae bore in the stems and roots of yucca and related plants; maguey worms (Figure 31-1) are the larvae of a megathymid.

FAMILY **Hesperìidae**—Skippers: The skippers are for the most part small and stout-bodied butterflies, and get their name from their fast and erratic flight. They differ from other butterflies (except the Megathýmidae) in having none of the five R branches in the front wings stalked, and all arise from the discal cell (Figure 26-8); the antennae are widely separated at the base, and the tips are usually recurved or hooked. Most skippers at rest hold the front and hind wings at a different angle. The larvae are smooth, with the head large and the neck constricted; they usually feed inside a leaf shelter, and pupation occurs in a cocoon made of leaves fastened together with silk. Most species overwinter as larvae, either in leaf shelters or in cocoons.

Over 200 species of skippers occur in the United States; most of these (including all the eastern species) belong to two subfamilies, the Pyrgìnae (Hesperiìnae of some authors) and the Hesperiìnae (Pamphilìnae of some authors); a third subfamily, the Pyrrhopygìnae, occurs in the West.

—Subfamily *Pyrgìnae*— In the front wings of the Pyrgìnae the discal cell is usually at least two-thirds as long as the wing, and M_2 arises midway between M_1 and M_3 and is not curved at the base (Figure 26-8 A); the middle tibiae lack spines. The males of some species have a costal fold, a long slitlike pocket near the costal margin of the front wing; this serves as a scent organ. Some species have scale tufts on the tibiae. Most of the skippers in this group are relatively large, grayish or blackish insects (Figure 26-41 A, E, F). The larvae feed principally on legumes.

One of the largest and most common species in this subfamily is the silver-spotted skipper, *Epargýreus clàrus* Cramer; it is dark brown with a large yellowish spot in the front wing and a silvery spot on the under side of the hind wing (Figure 26-41 A); the larva feeds on black locust and related plants; the species overwinters as a pupa.

—Subfamily *Hesperiìnae*—Tawny Skippers— These skippers have the discal cell in the front wings less than two-thirds as long as the wing; M_2 in the front wings is usually curved at the base and arises nearer to M_3 than to M_1 (Figure 26-8 B), and the middle tibiae are often spined. The tawny skippers (Figure 26-41 B-D) are usually brownish, with an oblique dark band (often called the stigma or brand) across the wing of the males; this dark band is composed of scales that serve as outlets for the scent glands. The larvae are chiefly grass feeders.

—Subfamily *Pyrrhopygìnae*— These skippers are similar to the Pyrgìnae in wing venation, but have the antennal club wholly reflexed. The group is principally tropical, but one species, *Apỳrrothrix aráxes* (Hewitson), occurs in southern Texas and Arizona; it is a large (wingspread a little over an inch), dark-colored skipper with light spots on the front wings, and the wings are held horizontally when at rest.

FAMILY **Sphíngidae**—Sphinx or Hawk Moths, Hornworms: The sphinx moths are medium-sized to large, heavy-bodied moths with long narrow front wings (Figure 26-43); some have a wingspread of 5 inches or more. The body is somewhat spindle-shaped, tapering and pointed both anteriorly

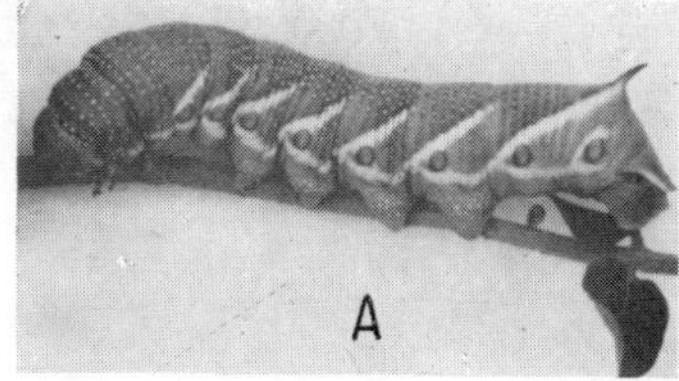

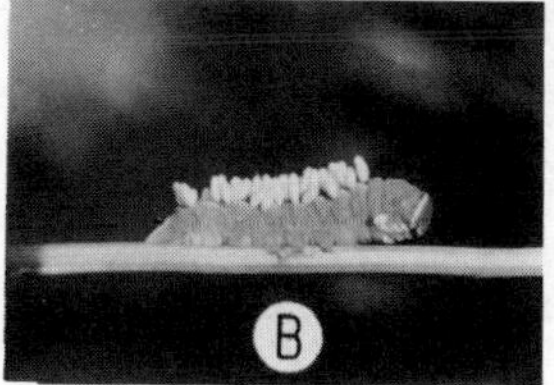

Fig. 26-42. A, the tomato hornworm, *Protopárce quinquemaculàta* (Haworth); B, a parasitized hornworm; the white objects on the back of the larva are cocoons of braconid parasites. (A, courtesy of the Ohio Agricultural Experiment Station.)

and posteriorly. The antennae are slightly thickened in the middle or toward the tip. The subcosta and radius in the hind wing are connected by a cross-vein (R_1) about opposite the middle of the discal cell (Figure 26-17). The proboscis in many species is very long, sometimes as long as the body or longer.

These moths are strong fliers and fly with a very rapid wing beat; some are day-fliers, but most of them are active at dusk or twilight. Most of them feed much like hummingbirds, hovering in front of a flower and extending their proboscis into it; these moths are sometimes called hummingbird moths, and in many species the body is about the size of a hummingbird. Some species (for example, *Hémaris*) have large areas in the wings devoid of scales, and are called clear-winged moths; these are not to be confused with the clear-winged moths of the family Aegerìidae, which are smaller and more slender and have the front wings much more elongate (compare Figures 26-43 B and 26-74).

The name "hornworm" is derived from the fact that the larvae of most species have a conspicuous horn or spinelike process on the dorsal surface of the eighth abdominal segment (Figure 26-42); the name "sphinx" probably refers to the sphinxlike position that some of these larvae occasionally assume. The larvae of most species pupate in the ground, in some cases forming pitcher-like pupae (the proboscis of the pupa looks like a handle); some species form a sort of cocoon among leaves on the surface of the ground.

One of the most common species in this group is the tomato hornworm, *Protopárce quinquemaculàta* (Haworth); the larva (Figure 26-42 A) is a large green caterpillar that feeds on tomato, tobacco, and potato; the larva of a similar species, *P. séxta* (Johannson), feeds on tobacco and other plants. The adults of these two species are large gray moths with a wingspread of about 4 inches; the hind wings are banded, and there are five (*quinquemaculàta*) or six (*séxta*) orange-yellow spots along each side

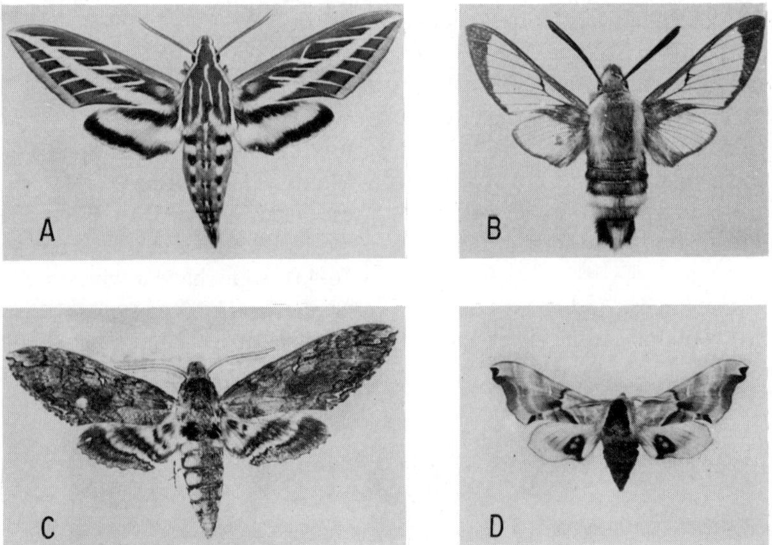

Fig. 26-43. Sphinx or hawk moths. A, the white-lined sphinx, *Celèrio lineàta* (Fabricius); B, a clear-winged sphinx, *Hémaris diffinis* Boisduval; C, adult of the tomato hornworm, *Protopárce quinquemaculàta* (Haworth); D, the twin-spot sphinx, *Smerínthus jamaicénsis* Drury.

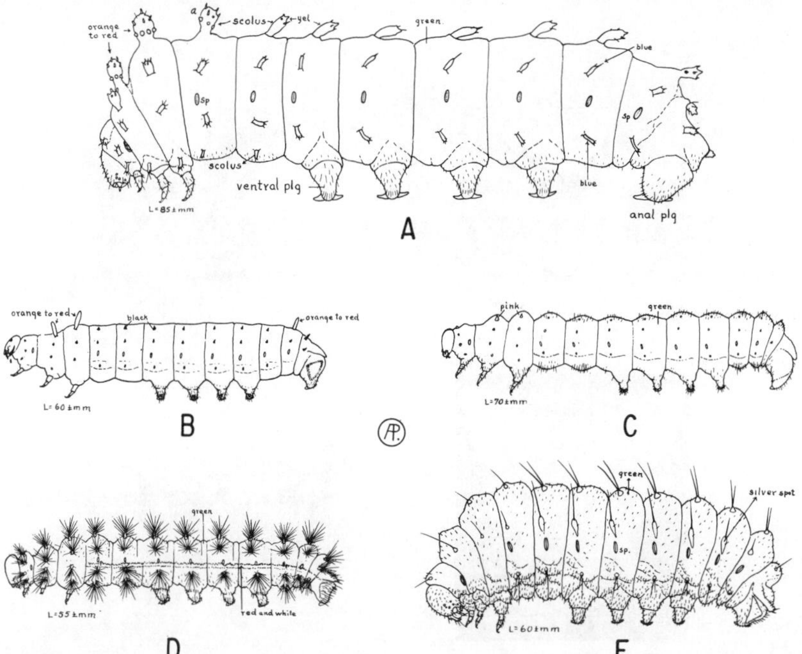

Fig. 26-44. Larvae of Saturnìidae. A, cecropia, *Hyalóphora cecròpia* (Linn.); B, promethea, *Callosàmia promèthea* (Drury); C, luna, *Áctias lùna* (Linn.); D, io, *Autómeris ìo* (Fabricius); E, polyphemus, *Antheraèa polyphèmus* (Cramer). *plg*, proleg. (Courtesy of Peterson. Reprinted by permission.)

of the abdomen (Figure 26-43 C). These hornworms often do considerable damage to the plants on which they feed. Hornworms are often attacked by braconid parasites, which form small white silken cocoons on the outside of the caterpillar (Figure 26-42 B).

FAMILY **Saturnìidae** — Giant Silkworm Moths: This family includes the largest moths in our area; some have a wingspread of 6 inches or more. This family includes some of the largest lepidopterans in the world; some species of *Áttacus* have a wingspread of about 10 inches. Many are conspicuously or brightly colored, and the wings usually have transparent eye spots. The antennae are bipectinate or feathery (Figure 26-7 E), and are larger in the male than in the female. The mouth parts are reduced and the adults do not feed.

The larvae of saturniids (Figure 26-44) are large caterpillars, and many are armed with conspicuous tubercles or spines. They spin silken cocoons, which are attached to the twigs or leaves of trees or shrubs or are formed among leaves on the ground. Most species overwinter in the pupal stage and have one generation a year. A few species in this group have been used for the production of commercial silk; some of the Asiatic species have provided a silk that makes strong and long-wearing fabrics, but none of the North American species has proved satisfactory for commercial silk production.

The largest saturniid in this country is the cecropia moth, *Hyalóphora cecròpia* (Linn.); most individuals have a wingspread of 5 or 6 inches. The wings are reddish brown, crossed in the middle with a white band; in the middle of each wing is a crescent-shaped white spot bordered with red (Figure 26-45 D). The larva (Figure 26-44 A) is a greenish caterpillar that reaches a length of about 4 inches; it has two rows of blue

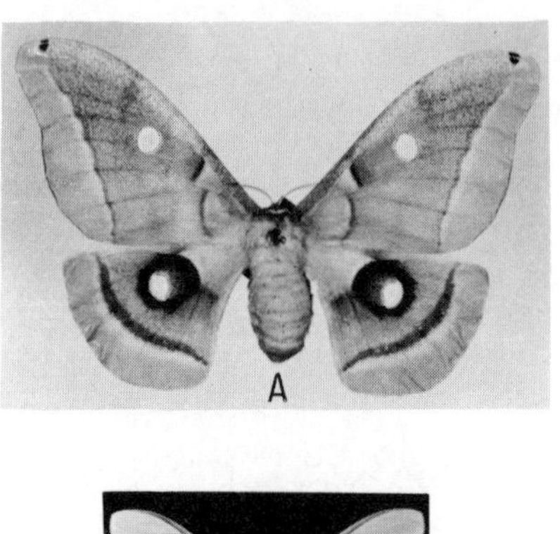

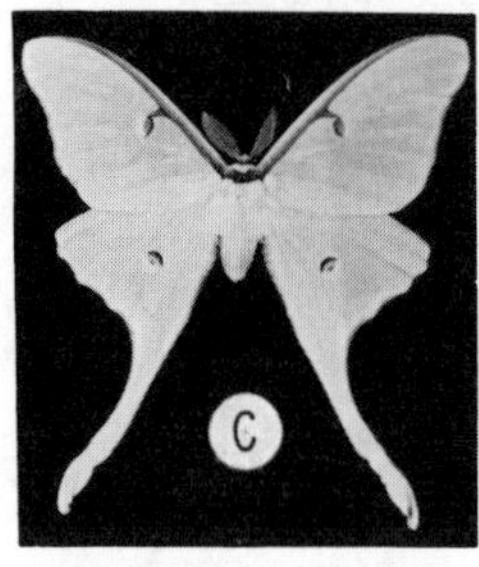

Fig. 26-45. Giant silkworm moths. (Saturnìidae). A, the polyphemus, *Antheraèa polyphèmus* (Cramer), $\frac{1}{2}\times$; B, the promethea, *Callosàmia promèthea* (Drury); male $\frac{1}{2}\times$; C, the luna, *Áctias lùna* (Linn.), $\frac{1}{3}\times$; D, the cecropia, *Hyalóphora cecròpia* (Linn.), $\frac{1}{4}\times$.

tubercles along each side, two rows of yellow tubercles down the back, and two pairs of large red tubercles on the thoracic segments. The cocoons are formed on twigs.

The promethea moth, *Callosàmia promèthea* (Drury), is sometimes called the spice-bush silk moth because the larva feeds on spice-bush, sassafras, and related plants. This moth is considerably smaller than the cecropia. The female is patterned a little like the cecropia, with the basal part of the wings dark brown and bordered by a white line; the outer portion of the wings is light brown. The males (Figure 26-45 B) are much darker, with a narrow marginal band of yellowish on the wings. The males often fly about during the day, and when on the wing, look a little like a large mourningcloak butterfly. The cocoon is formed in a leaf, which is prevented from falling off the twig by the petiole of the leaf being securely fastened with silk.

One of the most beautiful moths in this group is the luna, *Áctias lùna* (Linn.), a light-green moth with long tails on the hind wings and with the costal margin of the front wings narrowly bordered by dark brown (Figure 26-45 C). The larva (Figure 26-44 C) is greenish and feeds on walnut, hickory, and other trees, and the cocoon is formed in a leaf on the ground.

Another common moth in this group is the polyphemus, *Antheraèa polyphèmus* (Cramer), a large yellowish-brown moth with a windowlike spot in each wing (Figure 26-45 A). The larva (Figure 26-44 E) is similar to that of the luna and feeds on various trees; its cocoon is formed in a leaf on the ground.

The io moth, *Autómeris ìo* (Fabricius), is one of the smaller moths in this group; it has a wingspread of about 2 inches and is yellow with a large eye spot in each hind wing. The female is usually larger than the male, and its front wings are reddish brown. The larva is a spiny green caterpillar with a narrow reddish stripe, edged below with white, extending along each side of the body

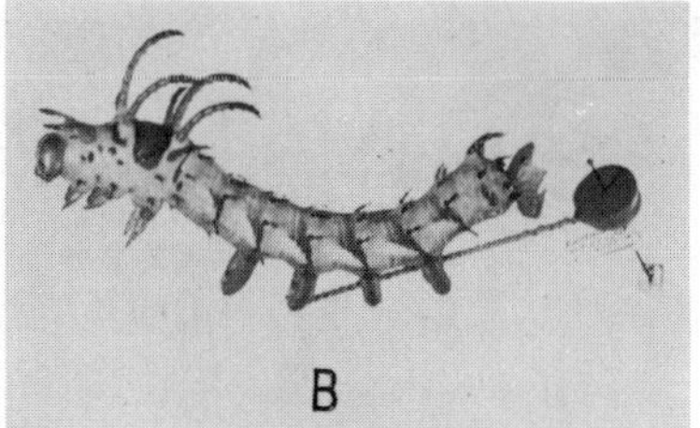

Fig. 26-46. The royal walnut or regal moth, *Citherònia regàlis* (Fabricius), $\frac{1}{2}\times$. A, adult; B, larva (the "hickory horned devil"). (B is a photograph of an inflated specimen.)

(Figure 26-44 D). This larva should be handled with care, for the spines sting.

FAMILY **Citheroniidae**—Royal Moths: The royal moths are medium-sized to large, stout-bodied moths with large wings. They are similar to Saturnìidae, but differ in several respects; they usually lack transparent spots in the wings, the antennae of the males are feathery for only a little more than half their length, the discal cell is closed (usually open in the saturniids), M_1 in the front wing separates from the radius beyond the apex of the discal cell, and there are two anal veins in the hind wing. The larvae are armed with horns or spines; they feed on various trees and pupate in the ground without forming a cocoon.

Our largest species in this group is the royal walnut, or regal, moth, *Citherònia regàlis* (Fabricius) (Figure 26-46), which sometimes has a wingspread of 5 or 6 inches. The front wings are gray or olive-colored spotted with yellow and with the veins reddish brown; the hind wings are orange-red spotted with yellow; the body is reddish brown with yellow bands. The larva is often called the hickory horned devil; when full grown, it is 4 or 5 inches in length and has long curved spines on the anterior part of the body (Figure 26-46 B); though quite ferocious in appearance this caterpillar is entirely harmless. It feeds principally on walnut, hickory, and persimmon.

The imperial moth, *Èacles imperiàlis* (Drury), is a large yellowish moth with dark peppered spots; each wing has a pinkish-brown diagonal band near the margin. The larva feeds on various trees and shrubs. The moths in the genus *Anisòta* are small, with a wingspread of about an inch and a half; most of them are brownish in color, but one species, *A. rubicúnda* (Fabricius), the rosy maple moth, is pale yellow banded with pink.

FAMILY **Amátidae**—Ctenuchas and Wasp Moths: The amatids are small day-flying moths, some of which are wasplike in appearance (but not so wasplike as the Aegerìidae). They can usually be recognized by the venation of the hind wings (Figure 26-22 B); the subcosta is apparently absent.

Ctenùcha virgínica (Charpentier), a common species in the Northeast, has brownish-black wings, a brilliant metallic bluish body, and an orange head; the larva is a woolly yellowish caterpillar that feeds on grasses; the cocoon is formed largely of the body hairs of the caterpillar. The yellow-collared scape moth, *Scépsis fulvicóllis* (Hübner) is somewhat smaller than the ctenucha, with narrower wings, and with the central portion of the hind wings lighter; the prothorax is yellowish (Figure 26-47). The

Fig. 26-47. The yellow-collared scape moth, *Scépsis fulvicóllis* (Hübner).

Fig. 26-48. Tiger moths (Arctiìnae). A, the virgin tiger moth, *Apántesis vírgo* (Linn.); B, adult of the salt-marsh caterpillar, *Estígmene acraèa* (Drury).

larva of this species feeds on grasses, and the adults frequent goldenrod flowers. The lichen moth, *Lycomórpha phòlus* (Drury), is a small blackish moth with the base of the wings yellowish; it looks a little like some of the lycid beetles. These moths occur in rocky places and the larvae feed on the lichens that grow on the rocks.

FAMILY **Nólidae:** The family Nólidae contains small moths that have ridges and tufts of raised scales on the front wings. *Célama ovílla* (Grote) is fairly common in Pennsylvania on the trunks of beeches and oaks; the larva feeds on the lichens growing on the tree trunks. *Nigétia formosàlis* Walker is a rather pretty mottled moth that is fairly common in southern Indiana. The larva of *Célama triquetràna* (Fitch), a gray moth with a wingspread of 17 to 20 millimeters, feeds on apple, but it is seldom numerous enough to do much damage.

FAMILY **Arctìidae**—Tiger Moths and Footman Moths: The arctiids are small to medium-sized moths, most of which are conspicuously and brightly spotted or banded. The wing venation is very similar to that in the Noctùidae, but Sc and Rs in the hind wing are usually fused to about the middle of the discal cell (Figure 26-23). The moths are principally nocturnal, and when at rest, hold the wings rooflike over the body. The larvae are usually hairy, sometimes very much so; the so-called woollybear caterpillars belong to this group. The cocoons are made largely from the body hairs of the larvae.

This family is divided into two subfamilies, the Lithosiìnae and the Arctiìnae; ocelli are present in the Arctiìnae and absent in the Lithosiìnae.

—Subfamily *Lithosiìnae*—Footman Moths — The footman moths are small and slender-bodied, and most of them are rather dull-colored. The larvae of most species feed on lichens. The striped footman moth, *Hypoprèpia miniàta* (Kirby), is a beautiful insect; it has the front wings pinkish with three gray stripes, and the hind wings are yellow and broadly margined with gray.

—Subfamily *Arctiìnae* — Tiger Moths— This subfamily contains the majority of the species in the family, and many of them are very common insects; a few are occasionally rather destructive to trees and shrubs.

The tiger moths in the genus *Apántesis* have the front wings black with red or yellow stripes, and the hind wings are usually pinkish with black spots. One of the largest and most common species in this genus is *A vírgo* (Linn.), which has a wingspread of about 2 inches (Figure 26-48 A); the larva feeds on pigweed and other weeds, and winters in the larval stage.

Estígmene acraèa (Drury) is another common tiger moth; the adults are white, with numerous small black spots on the wings, and the abdomen is pinkish with black spots (Figure 26-48 B); the male has the hind wings yellowish. The larva feeds

Fig. 26-49. The hickory tussock moth, *Halisidòta cáryae* (Harris). A, adult; B, larva. (Courtesy of Knull.)

on various grasses and is sometimes called the salt-marsh caterpillar.

One of the best known of the woollybear caterpillars is the banded woollybear, *Ísia isabélla* (J. E. Smith); this caterpillar is brown in the middle and black at each end, and the adult is yellowish brown with three rows of small black spots on the abdomen. These caterpillars are often seen scurrying across the highways in the fall; they overwinter as larvae and pupate in the spring. The larva feeds on various weeds. The amount of black in this larva in the fall is thought by some to indicate what sort of winter is ahead.

The larvae of some of the tiger moths feed on trees and shrubs and may often do serious damage. The fall webworm, *Hyphántria cùnea* (Drury), is a common species of this type; the larvae build large webs, often enclosing a whole limb of foliage, and feed within the web. These webs are common on many types of trees in late summer and fall. The adults are white with a few dark spots and have a wingspread of about an inch. The larvae of the hickory tussock moth, *Halisidòta cáryae* (Harris) (Figure 26-49), feed on hickory and other trees; the larva is somewhat similar to that of the tussock moths in the genus *Hemerocámpa*; the adults are light brown with white spots on the front wings.

FAMILY **Agarístidae**—Forester Moths: The foresters are usually black with two whitish or yellowish spots in each wing, and they have a wingspread of about an inch; the antennae are slightly clubbed. The wing venation (Figure 26-22 A) is similar to that

Fig. 26-50. The eight-spotted forester, *Alýpia octomaculàta* (Fabricius).

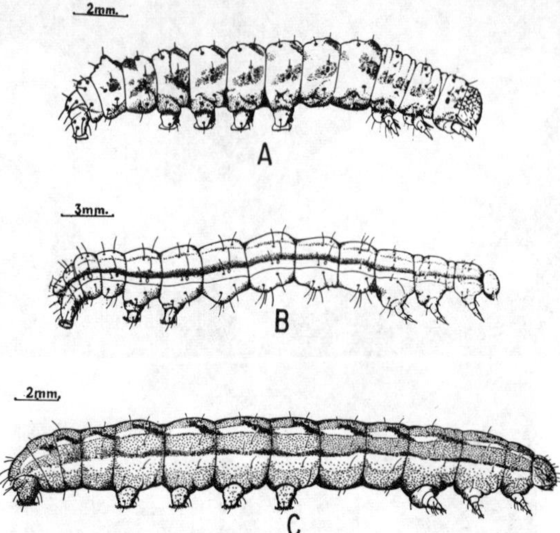

Fig. 26-51. Noctuid larvae. A, *Pálthis angulàlis* Hübner; B, *Autógrapha selécta* Walker (a looper; note the reduced number of prolegs); C, *Anomogỳna elimàta* Guenée. (Courtesy of Brown, McGuffin, MacKay, and *The Canadian Entomologist.*)

of the Noctùidae. The eight-spotted forester, *Alýpia octomaculàta* (Fabricius), is a common species in this group (Figure 26-50); the larvae feed on grape and Virginia creeper and sometimes defoliate them.

FAMILY **Noctùidae**—Noctuid Moths: The Noctùidae is the largest family in the order, and contains some 2700 species in the United States and Canada. These moths are mostly nocturnal in habit, and the majority of the moths that are attracted to lights at night belong to this group. The noctuids vary greatly in size and color, but most of them are of medium size (1 to 2 inches in wingspread) and dull color.

The noctuids are mostly heavy-bodied moths with the front wings somewhat narrower and the hind wings broadened (Figure 26-52). The labial palpi are usually long, the antennae are generally filiform (sometimes brushlike in the males), and in some species there are tufts of scales on the dorsum of the thorax. The wing venation (Figure 26-24) is rather characteristic: M_2 in the front wing arises closer to M_3 than to M_1, and the cubitus appears 4-branched; the subcosta and radius in the hind wing are separate at the base but fuse for a very short distance at the base of the discal cell; M_2 in the hind wing may be present or absent.

Noctuid larvae are usually smooth and dull-colored (Figure 26-51), and most of them have five pairs of prolegs. The majority feed on foliage, but some are boring in habit and some feed on fruits. A number of species in this group are serious pests of various crops.

The largest noctuid occurring in the United States is the black witch, *Érebus òdora* (Linn.), a blackish species with a wingspread of 4 or 5 inches (Figure 26-52 D). It breeds in the southern states, where the larva feeds on various leguminous trees; the adults sometimes appear in the northern states in late summer.

The armyworm, *Pseudalètia unipúncta* (Haworth), feeds on various grasses and frequently does serious damage to wheat and corn. The common name of this insect refers to the fact that the larvae frequently migrate in large numbers to a new feeding area. The moths are light brown with a single white spot in the middle of each front wing.

The corn earworm, *Helìothis zèa* (Boddie), is another serious pest; the larva

Fig. 26-52. Noctuid moths. A, adult of the cabbage looper, *Trichoplùsia nì* (Hübner); B, *Séptis árctica* Freyer; C, *Eùxoa excéllens* Grt. (the adult of one of the cutworms); D, the black witch, *Erebus òdora* (Linn.); E, *Euthisanòtia ùnio* Hübner; F, the darling underwing, *Catocàla càra* Guenée. D, $\frac{1}{3}$ ×; E, slightly enlarged; F, slightly reduced; other figures approximately natural size.

feeds on a number of plants, including corn, tomato, and cotton, and is sometimes called the tomato fruitworm or the cotton bollworm. When feeding on corn (Figure 26-53), the larva enters the end of the corn ear on the silks and eats the kernels from the tip of the cob; it burrows in the fruit of tomatoes and into the bolls of cotton. This is a very important pest species. The adults are light yellowish in color and exhibit some variation in their markings.

A few species in this group are called loopers because they have only three pairs of prolegs (Figure 26-51 B) and move like measuringworms. The cabbage looper, *Trichoplùsia nì* (Hübner) (= *Autógrapha brássicae* Riley), is a serious pest of cabbage, and the celery looper, *Anágrapha falcífera* (Kirby), attacks celery. The adults are dark brown with a wingspread of about $1\frac{1}{2}$ inches and have a small elongate silvery spot in the middle of each front wing (Figure 26-52 A).

The underwings (*Catocàla*) are relatively large and strikingly colored moths. They are forest or woodland species, and the larvae feed on the foliage of various trees. The hind wings are usually brightly colored with concentric bands of red, yellow, or orange (Figure 26-52 F). When at rest, the hind wings are concealed and the front wings are colored much like the bark of the trees on which these moths usually rest.

The larvae of many species in this group are commonly called cutworms because they feed on the roots and shoots of various herbaceous plants, and the plant is

Fig. 26-53. Larva of the corn earworm, *Helìothis zèa* (Boddie). (Courtesy of the Ohio Agricultural Experiment Station.)

often cut off at the surface of the ground. The cutworms are nocturnal in habit, and during the day hide under stones or in the soil. The more important cutworms belong to the genera *Agròtis, Hadèna, Perídroma, Féltia, Nephelòdes, Prodènia,* and *Eùxoa.*

The noctuids have a pair of tympanal auditory organs located at the base of the abdomen (such organs are present in many other families of moths, but not in all families); these consist of a pair of thin tympanic membranes directed obliquely backward. These organs are capable of detecting frequencies from 3 to over 100 kilocycles per second,[3] and they appear to function in the detection and evasion of bats. Bats are able to detect prey (and obstacles) in complete darkness by means of a sort of acoustic radar; they emit very high-pitched chirps (sometimes as high as 80 kilocycles per second), and locate objects from the echoes of these chirps.

FAMILY **Pericópidae:** The Pericópidae are medium-sized moths that are usually black with large white areas in the wings; these moths occur chiefly in the South and West. *Compòsia fidelíssima* Herrich-Schaeffer, a dark-blue moth marked with red and white, is found in southern Florida. Species in the genus *Gnophaèla* occur in western and southwestern United States.

FAMILY **Dióptidae:** The family Dióptidae is represented in the United States by a single species, *Phryganídia califórnica* Packard, which occurs in California. The adults are pale brown with dark veins and have a wingspread of 25 to 35 millimeters; the larvae feed on oak and often do serious damage.

FAMILY **Notodóntidae**—The Prominents: The prominents are usually brownish or yellowish moths that are similar to the Noctùidae in general appearance. The family name (*not,* back; *odont,* tooth) refers to the fact that in some species there are backward-projecting tufts on the hind margin of the wings, which protrude when the wings are folded (they are usually folded rooflike over the body when at rest), and the larvae have conspicuous tubercles on the dorsal surface of the body. The notodontids may be readily distinguished from the Noctùidae by the venation of the front wing (Figure 26-19); in the Notodóntidae, M_2 arises from the middle of the apex of the discal cell and the cubitus appears 3-branched, whereas in the Noctùidae, M_2 in the front wing arises closer to M_3 and the cubitus appears 4-branched (Figure 26-24).

Notodontid larvae feed on various trees and shrubs and are usually gregarious; when disturbed, they often elevate the anterior and posterior ends of the body and "freeze" in this position, remaining attached by the four pairs of prolegs in the middle of the body. The anal pair of prolegs is often rudimentary or modified into spinelike structures.

Most of the brownish moths in this group, which have narrow dark lines across the front wings, belong to the genus *Datàna*; these are sometimes called handmaid moths

[3] Three kilocycles (3000 cycles) per second is in the top octave of the piano; the average upper limit of hearing in man is about 15 kilocycles per second.

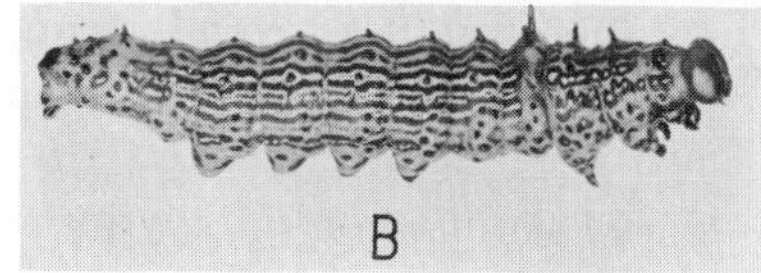

Fig. 26-54. Notodóntidae. A, *Datàna minístra* (Drury); B, the red-humped caterpillar, *Schizùra concínna* (J. E. Smith). (B, courtesy of the Ohio Agricultural Experiment Station.)

(Figure 26-54 A). The larvae are blackish with yellow longitudinal stripes. The yellow-necked caterpillar, *D. minístra* (Drury), feeds on apple and other trees; the walnut caterpillar, *D. integérrima* Grote and Robinson, feeds principally on walnut and hickory.

The red-humped caterpillar, *Schizùra concínna* (J.E. Smith), is a fairly common species in this group. The larva is black with yellow stripes, with the head and a hump on the first abdominal segment red (Figure 26-54 B). The adult has a wingspread of a little over an inch; the front wings are gray with brown markings, and the hind wings are white with a small black spot along the rear edge. The larva feeds on apple and other orchard trees, and on various shrubs.

FAMILY **Lipáridae**—Tussock Moths and Their Relatives: The liparids are medium-sized moths that are similar to the Noctùidae, but differ in that they lack ocelli and have the basal areole in the hind wing larger

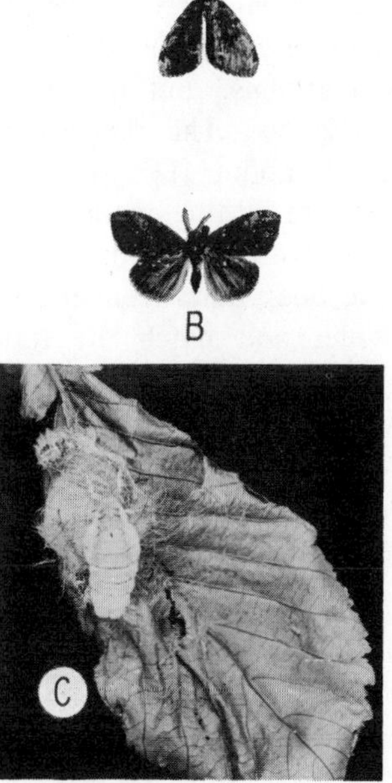

Fig. 26-55. The white-marked tussock moth, *Hemerocámpa leucostígma* (Abbott and Smith). A, larva; B, adult male; C, adult female. (Courtesy of the Ohio Agricultural Experiment Station.)

(Figure 26-25); in some species (Figure 26-25 A), M_1 in the hind wing is stalked with Rs for a short distance beyond the apex of the discal cell. The larvae are rather hairy and feed chiefly on trees. The tussock moths and the gypsy and brown-tail moths are serious pests of forest and shade trees; the tussock moths are native species, whereas the two latter were introduced from Europe.

The white-marked tussock moth, *Hemerocámpa leucostígma* (J.E. Smith) (Figure 26-55), is a common species throughout most of North America. The males are gray, with lighter hind wings and plumose antennae, and the females are wingless. The eggs are laid on tree trunks or branches, usually near the cocoon from which the female emerged, and the species overwinters in the egg stage. The larva (Figure 26-55 A) may be recognized by the characteristic tufts or brushes of hairs.

The gypsy moth, *Porthètria díspar* (Linn.), was introduced from Europe into Massachusetts about 1866; since then, it has become widely distributed throughout New England and has caused widespread damage to forest trees. The females are white with black markings, and the males are gray (Figure 26-56). The females have a wingspread of about 1½ to 2 inches, and the males are a little smaller. The eggs are laid on tree trunks, or similar places, in a mass of the body hairs from the female; they overwinter and hatch the following spring. The females are very weak fliers and seldom travel very far from the cocoon from which they emerge; the dispersal of the species is accomplished largely by the young larvae.

Fig. 26-56. The gypsy moth, *Porthétria díspar* (Linn.). Male above, female below.

The brown-tail moth, *Nýgmia phaeorrhoèa* (Donovan), is another serious pest of forest and shade trees that was introduced from Europe; it first appeared near Boston in the early 1890's, and has since spread throughout New England. The adults are white, have a wingspread of 1 to 1½ inches, and have brownish hairs at the end of the abdomen; the males are a little smaller than the females. This species passes the winter as a larva in a leaf shelter. Both sexes are winged. The hairs of the larva, when blown onto the skin of man, cause an irritating rash.

The satin moth, *Stilpnòtia sálicis* (Linn.), is a more recent introduction from Europe and may prove to be an important pest species.

FAMILY **Manidìidae:** This family is represented in the United States by a single species, *Anurápteryx crenulàta* Barnes and Lindsey, which occurs in Arizona.

FAMILY **Lasiocámpidae**—Tent Caterpillars and Lappet Moths: These moths are medium-sized and stout-bodied, with the body, legs, and eyes hairy. The antennae are somewhat feathery in both sexes, but the teeth of the antennae are longer in the male. There is no frenulum, and the humeral angle of the hind wing is expanded and provided with humeral veins (Figure 26-26). Most of these moths are brown or gray in color. The larvae feed on the foliage of trees, often causing serious damage; pupation occurs in a well-formed cocoon.

The eastern tent caterpillar, *Malacosòma americànum* (Fabricius) (Figure 26-57), is a common member of this group in eastern North America. The adults are yellowish brown and appear in midsummer; they lay their eggs in a bandlike cluster around a twig, and the eggs hatch the fol-

Fig. 26-57. The eastern tent caterpillar, *Malacosòma americànum* (Fabricius). Left, egg mass; center, larvae; right, adult female. (Courtesy of the Ohio Agricultural Experiment Station.)

lowing spring. The young that hatch from a given egg cluster are gregarious and construct a tentlike nest of silk near the eggs; this tent is used as a shelter, with the larvae feeding during the day in nearby branches. The larvae feed on a number of different trees, but seem to prefer cherry; the larvae are black and somewhat hairy and have a yellow stripe down the middle of the back. When full grown they wander off and spin their cocoons in sheltered places.

The forest tent caterpillar, *Malacosòma dísstria* Hübner, is widely distributed, but is probably more common in the South and Southwest, where it sometimes defoliates large areas. The caterpillars differ from those of the eastern caterpillar in that they have a row of keyhole-shaped spots (rather than a stripe) down the middle of the back; the adults are somewhat paler than those of the eastern tent caterpillar.

The lappet moths (*Tólype*) are bluish gray with white markings; the common name refers to the face that the larvae have a small lobe or lappet on each side of each segment. The larvae of *T. véllida* (Stoll) feed on apple, poplar, and syringa, and those of *T. láricis* (Fitch) feed on larch.

FAMILY **Bombýcidae**—Silkworm Moths: This family contains a single species, *Bómbyx mòri* (Linn.), a native of Asia that is sometimes reared in this country. This insect has long been reared for its silk, and it is one of the most important beneficial insects. After centuries of domestication it is now primarily a domestic species and probably does not exist in nature. Many different races of silkworms have been developed by breeding.

The adult moth is creamy white with several faint brownish lines across the front wings and has a wingspread of about 2 inches. The body is heavy and very hairy. The adults do not feed, they rarely fly, and usually they live only a few days. Each female lays 300 to 400 eggs. The larvae are naked, have a short anal horn, and feed principally on the leaves of mulberry; they become full grown and spin their cocoons in about six weeks. When used for commercial purposes, the pupae are killed before they emerge, since the emergence of the moth breaks the fibers in the cocoon. Each cocoon is composed of a single thread about 1000 yards long; about 3000 cocoons are required to make a pound of silk.

Sericulture is practiced in Japan, China, Spain, France, and Italy. The silk has a commercial value of from $200 to $500 million annually.

FAMILY **Zanólidae:** The Zanólidae are represented in North America by three species in the genus *Apatelòdes.* These moths are similar to the Notodóntidae, but usually have windowlike dots near the apex

Fig. 26-58. Tent of a tent caterpillar.

of the front wings; they have a wingspread of 1½ to 2 inches. The larvae feed on various shrubs and trees and pupate in the ground.

FAMILY **Thyatíridae:** The Thyatíridae are similar to the Noctùidae, but have the cubitus in the front wings appearing 3-branched; in the hind wings, the veins Sc + R_1 and Rs are more or less parallel along the anterior margin of the discal cell. The larvae of this small group feed on various trees and shrubs.

FAMILY **Drepánidae**—Hook-Tip Moths: These moths are small, slender-bodied, and usually dull-colored and can generally be recognized by the sickle-shaped apex of the front wings. The cubitus in the front wings appears 4-branched; in the hind wing, Sc + R_1 and Rs are separated along the discal cell; the frenulum is small or absent. The larvae feed on the foliage of various trees and shrubs. The most common species in this group is *Drépana arcuàta* Walker, a dirty white moth marked with dark brownish lines and with a wingspread of about an inch; it occurs in the Atlantic States.

FAMILY **Geométridae** — Measuringworms, Geometers: This family is the second largest in the order, with some 1200 species occurring in the United States and Canada. The moths in this group are mostly small, delicate, and slender-bodied; the wings are usually broad and are often marked with fine wavy lines. The two sexes are often different in color, and in a few species the

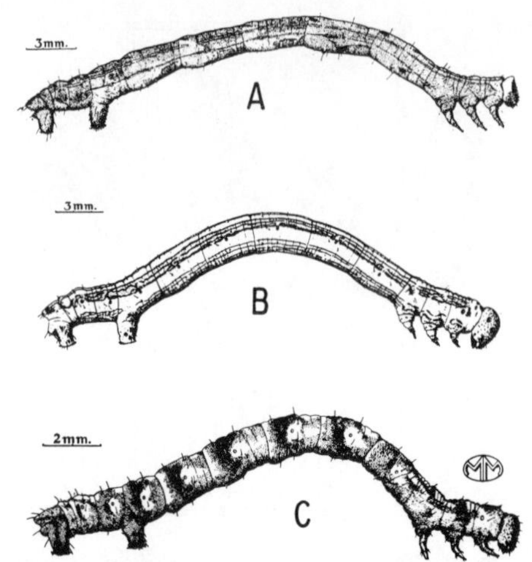

Fig. 26-59. Larvae of Geometridae. A, *Pèro morrisonàrius* (Hy. Edwards); B, *Nepỳtia canosària* Walker; C, *Protoboármia porcelària indicatòria* Walker. (Courtesy of McGuffin and MacKay, and *The Canadian Entomologist.*)

females are wingless or have only rudimentary wings. The geometers are principally nocturnal and are often attracted to lights. The most characteristic feature of the wing venation is the form of the subcosta in the hind wing (Figure 26-18); the basal part of this vein makes an abrupt bend into the humeral angle and is usually connected by a brace vein to the humeral angle. The cubitus in the front wing appears 3-branched.

The larvae of geometers are the familiar caterpillars commonly called inchworms or measuringworms (Figure 26-59). They have two or three pairs of prolegs at the posterior

Fig. 26-60. The fall cankerworm, *Alsóphila pometària* (Harris). A, adult female laying eggs; B, adult male. (Courtesy of the Ohio Agricultural Experiment Station.)

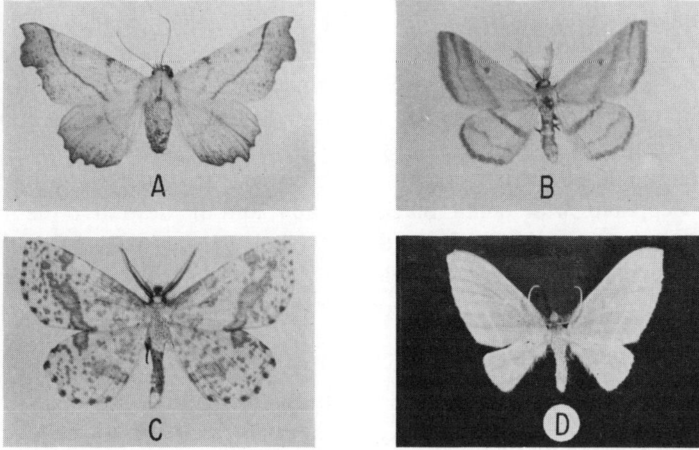

Fig. 26-61. Geometrid moths. A, the notch-wing geometer, *Énnomos magnàrius* Guenée; B, the chickweed geometer; *Haemátopis gratària* (Fabricius); C, the crocus geometer, *Xanthótype sóspeta* Drury; *D*, the bad-wing, *Dýspteris abortivària* Herrich-Schaeffer.

end of the body and none in the middle; locomotion is accomplished by placing the posterior end of the body near the thoracic legs and then moving the anterior end of the body, thus progressing in a characteristic looping fashion. Many measuringworms, when disturbed, stand nearly erect on the posterior prolegs and remain motionless, resembling small twigs.

This group contains the cankerworms, which feed on the foliage of various deciduous trees and often cause serious defoliation. The two common species are the spring cankerworm, *Paleácrita vernàta* (Peck), and the fall cankerworm, *Alsóphila pometària* (Harris) (Figure 26-60); the spring cankerworm overwinters in the pupal stage, and the female lays its eggs in the spring; the fall cankerworm overwinters in the egg stage. The larvae of the spring cankerworm have two pairs of prolegs; the larvae of the fall cankerworm have three pairs. The adult females of both species are wingless.

Many of the geometers are common moths, but only a few can be mentioned here. The chickweed geometer, *Haemátopis gratària* (Fabricius), is a reddish yellow moth with the margins of the wings and two bands near the margins pink (Figure 26-61 B); it has a wingspread of about an inch or less; the larva feeds on chickweed. One of the largest moths in this family is the notch-wing geometer, *Énnomos magnàrius* Guenée; it has a wingspread of $1\frac{1}{2}$ to 2 inches, and the wings are reddish yellow, with small brown spots, and shade to brown toward the outer margin (Figure 26-61 A); the larvae feed on various trees. Many of the geometers are light green in color; one of the common species of this type is the bad-wing, *Dýspteris abortivária* Herrich-Schaeffer (Figure 26-61 D); the front wings are large and triangular, and the hind wings are small and rounded. This moth has a wingspread of a little less than an inch; the larva rolls and feeds on the leaves of grape.

FAMILY **Epiplémidae:** The Epiplémidae are a small group of moths that are similar in size and general appearance to the Geométridae, but differ in wing venation; they have $Sc + R_1$ and Rs in the hind wing widely separated from near the base of the wing. The cubitus in the front wing appears 3-branched, and the veins M_1 and R_5 are stalked and well separated from R_4. The larvae are sparsely hairy and have five pairs of prolegs. Five species of this group occur in the United States; the moths are plain-colored and have a wingspread of about 20 millimeters.

FAMILY **Lacosómidae**—Sack-Bearers: The Lacosómidae are called sack-bearers because the larvae make cases from leaves and carry the cases about. *Cicínnus melsheìmeri* Harris, an eastern species, is a reddish-gray moth with a wingspread of about $1\frac{1}{4}$ inches; the wings are peppered with small black dots, and there is a narrow blackish band across both front and hind wings; the larva feeds on oak.

FAMILY **Euclèidae**—Slug Caterpillars: These insects are called slug caterpillars because the larvae are short, fleshy, and sluglike; the thoracic legs are small and there are no prolegs, and the larvae move with a creeping motion. Many of the larvae are curiously shaped or conspicuously marked. The cocoons are dense, brownish, and oval, and have at one end a lid that is pushed out by the emerging adult. The adult moths are small to medium-sized, robust, and hairy, and are usually brownish and marked with a large irregular spot of green, silver, or some other color.

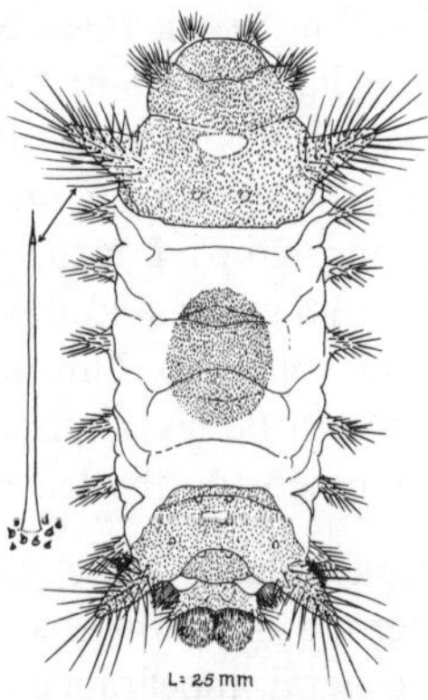

Fig. 26-62. The saddleback caterpillar, *Sibìne stimùlea* (Clemens). (Courtesy of Peterson. Reprinted by permission.)

One of the most common species in this group is the saddleback caterpillar, *Sibìne stimùlea* (Clemens). The larva (Figure 26-62) is green with a brown saddle-like mark on the back. These larvae have stinging hairs and can cause severe irritation to the skin. They feed principally on various trees.

FAMILY **Megalopýgidae**—Flannel Moths: These moths have a dense coat of scales mixed with fine curly hairs, which give the insect a somewhat woolly appearance; they are medium-sized to small, and usually brownish in color. The larvae are also hairy, and in addition to the usual five pairs of prolegs, they have two additional pairs that are suckerlike and lack crochets. The larvae have stinging hairs and can cause even more irritation than the saddleback caterpillars. The cocoons are tough and are provided with a lid as in the Euclèidae; they are usually formed on twigs. The crinkled flannel moth, *Megalopỳge crispàta* (Packard), is a common eastern species; it is a yellowish moth with brownish spots or bands on the wings and has a wingspread of a little over an inch; the larva feeds on blackberry, raspberry, apple, and other plants.

FAMILY **Dalcéridae**: This family is represented in the United States by two species that have been reported from Arizona. *Dalcérides ingénita* (Edwards) is an orange-yellow moth without markings and with a wingspread of about an inch; its larva is unknown. A Mexican species, *Pincònia còa* Schaus, has been reported from Arizona.

FAMILY **Epipyrópidae**: The Epípyrópidae are unique in that the larvae are parasitic on planthoppers (Fulgoròidea) and other Homoptera. The larva feeds on the dorsal surface of the abdomen of the planthopper, under the wings. These moths are relatively rare, and only two species are known from the United States.

FAMILY **Pyromórphidae**—Smoky Moths: The smoky moths are small, gray or black moths, usually with the prothorax reddish and often with other bright markings. The larvae have tufted hairs, and the commoner species feed on grape or Virginia creeper. The grape leaf skeletonizer, *Harrisìna americàna* (Guérin), is a common species in this group; the adult is a small, narrow-winged, smoky moth with a reddish collar,

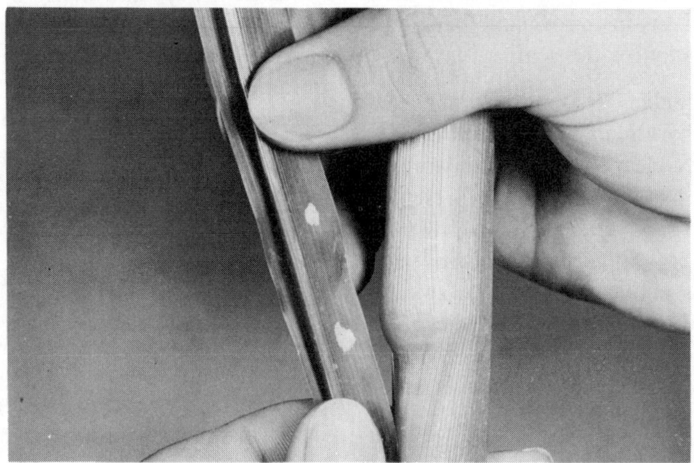

Fig. 26-63. The European corn borer, *Pyráusta nubilàlis* (Hübner). Top, egg masses on corn; center, larva; bottom, adults (male at left, female at right). (Courtesy of the Illinois Natural History Survey.)

and the larvae are yellow with black spots. A number of these larvae will feed on the same leaf, lined up in a row and backing up as they skeletonize the leaf.

FAMILY **Thyrídidae** — Window - Winged Moths: The thyridids are small and dark-colored and have clear spaces in the wings. All the branches of the radius are present, and they arise from the usually open discal cell (Figure 26-21). Some larvae burrow in twigs and stems and cause gall-like swellings; others feed on flowers and seeds. The most common eastern species is probably *Dysòdia oculatàna* Clemens, which occurs in the Ohio Valley.

FAMILY **Pyrálidae**—Pyralid Moths: This family is the third largest in the order, with over 1100 species occurring in the United States and Canada. Most of the pyralids are small and rather delicate moths; the front wings are elongate or triangular, with the cubitus appearing 4-branched, and the hind wings are usually broad. Veins Sc and R in the hind wing are usually close together and parallel opposite the discal cell (the base of R is usually atrophied), and are fused or closely parallel for a short distance beyond the discal cell (Figure 26-14). Since the labial palpi are often projecting, these moths are sometimes called snout moths.

The members of this family exhibit a great deal of variation in appearance, venation, and habits. The family is divided into a number of subfamilies, only a few of which can be mentioned here.

—Subfamily *Pyraustìnae*— This subfamily is a large group, and many of its members are relatively large and conspicuously marked. The most important species in this subfamily is the European corn borer, *Pyràusta nubilàlis* (Hübner), which was introduced into the United States about 1917 and has since spread over a large part of the central and eastern states. The larvae live in the stalks of corn and other plants and frequently do a great deal of damage. This species has one or two generations a year; it overwinters in the larval stage. The adult moths (Figure 26-63) have a wingspread of a little over an inch, and are yellowish brown with darker markings. The grape leaf folder, *Désmia funeràlis* (Hübner), is a black moth with two white spots in the front wing and one white spot in the hind wing; the larva feeds on grape leaves, folding the leaf over and fastening it with silk. The melonworm, *Diaphània hyalinàta* (Linn.), is a glistening white moth with the wings bordered with black; the larva feeds on the foliage and burrows in the stems of melons and related plants. Other important species in this subfamily are the pickleworm, *Diaphània nitidàlis* (Stoll), and the garden webworm, *Loxóstege similàlis* (Guenée).

The larvae of most *Nymphulìnae* are aquatic, breathing by means of gills, and feeding on aquatic plants. The waterlily leaf cutter, *Nýmphala obliteràlis* (Walker), lives on greenhouse water plants, in cases made of silk.

Fig. 26-64. A, the sugarcane borer, *Diatraèa saccharàlis* (Fabricius) (Pyrálidae, Crambìnae); B, the green cloverworm, *Plathypèna scábra* (Fabricius) (Noctùidae). (Courtesy of USDA.)

Fig. 26-65. The Mediterranean flour moth, *Anagásta kuehniélla* (Zeller). (Courtesy of the Ohio Agricultural Experiment Station.)

—Subfamily *Pyralìnae*— This subfamily is a small group of small moths; the larvae of most species feed on dried vegetable matter. One of the most important species in this subfamily is the meal moth, *Pýralis farinàlis* (Linn.); the larva feeds on cereals, flour, and meal, and makes silken tubes in these materials. The larvae of the clover hayworm, *Hypospỳgia costàlis* (Fabricius), occur in old stacks of clover hay.

—Subfamily *Crambìnae*—Close-Wings or Grass Moths— These are common moths in meadows, where the larvae (known as sod webworms) bore into the stems, crowns, or roots of grasses. Most of them feed about the base of grasses, where they construct a number of silken webs. The moths are usually whitish or pale-yellowish brown, and when at rest, hold the wings close about the body (hence the name close-wing). An important pest species in this subfamily is the sugarcane borer, *Diatraèa saccharàlis* (Fabricius), the larva of which bores in the stalks of sugarcane. Most of the species in this group belong to the genus *Crámbus.*

—Subfamily *Gallerìinae*— The best-known member of this subfamily is the bee moth or wax moth, *Gallèria mellonélla* (Linn.). The larva occurs in bee hives, where it feeds on wax; it often does considerable damage. The adult has brownish front wings and has a wingspread of about an inch.

—Subfamily *Phycitìnae*— The subfamily Phycitìnae is a large group, most of the members of which have long narrow front wings and broad hind wings; the larvae vary considerably in habits. The best-known species in this subfamily are those that attack stored grain, the Indian-meal moth, *Plòdia interpunctélla* (Hübner), and the Mediterranean flour moth, *Anagásta kuehniélla* (Zeller). The former is a gray moth with the apical two-thirds of the front wings dark brown, and the latter (Figure 26-65) is uniformly gray; both moths are rather small. The larvae of the Indian-meal moth feed on cereals, dried fruits, meal, nuts, and candies, and spin webs over these materials; they often cause enormous losses in stored food supplies. The Mediterranean flour moth attacks all types of grain products and is an important pest in granaries, warehouses, markets, and homes.

To this subfamily also belongs a moth that has been used for the deliberate destruction of plants; the cactus moth, *Cactoblástis cactòrum* (Berg), has been introduced into Australia to control the prickly pear cactus; this moth has successfully destroyed the dense cactus growth over many square miles of territory in New South Wales and Queensland (see page 657).

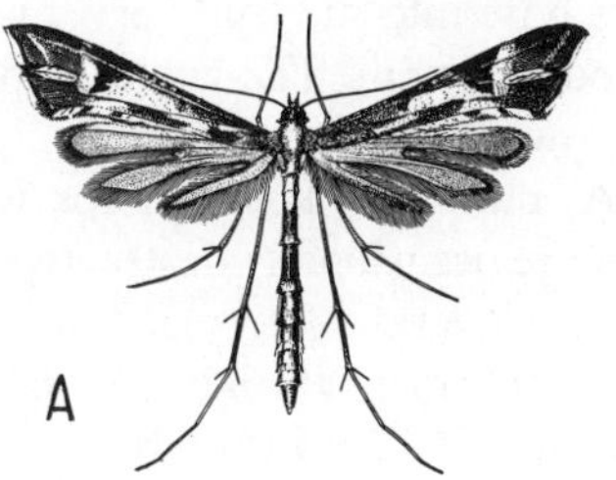

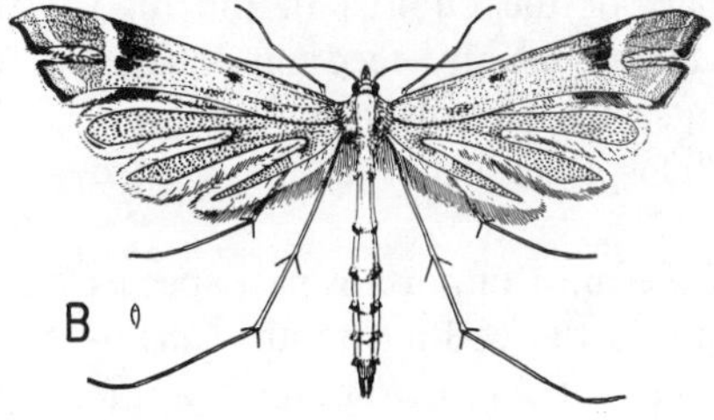

Fig. 26-66. Plume moths (Pterophóridae). A, *Platyptília bàuri* Lange, female; B, *P. grándis* (Walsingham), female. (Courtesy of Lange and *Hilgardia.*)

Another interesting species in this subfamily is the coccid-eating pyralid, *Laetília coccidívora* Comstock, the larva of which is predaceous on the eggs and young of various scale insects.

FAMILY **Pterophóridae** — Plume Moths: These moths are small, slender, usually gray or brownish, and have the wings split into two or three featherlike divisions (Figure 26-66). The front wing usually has two divisions; and the hind wing, three. The legs are relatively long. When at rest, the front and hind wings are folded close together and are held horizontally, at right angles to the body. The larvae of plume moths are leaf rollers and stem borers, and some may occasionally do serious damage. The grape plume moth, *Pteróphorus periscelidáctylus* Fitch, is common on grape vines; the larvae tie together the terminal portions of the leaves and feed inside this shelter.

FAMILY **Alucítidae**—Many-Plume Moths: The alucitids are similar to the pterophorids, but have the wings split into six plumelike divisions. Only one species in this family occurs in the United States, *Alùcita hùebneri* (Wallen); the adults have a wingspread of about half an inch. This species, which was introduced, occurs in the northeastern states.

FAMILY **Olethreùtidae:** These moths are small and brownish or gray in color, often with bands or mottled areas on the wings, and the front wings are rather square-tipped. Most species can be recognized as Olethreùtidae by the fringe of long hairs on the basal part of the cubitus in the hind wing. The larvae usually feed on foliage, fruits, or nuts. This family is a large one, and over 700 species occur in the United States.

One of the most important pest species in this family is the codling moth, *Carpocápsa pomonélla* (Linn.), a pest of apple and other fruits. This species was introduced into the United States from Europe and is now widely distributed. The front wings are gray with brownish cross-lines and a large coppery-brown spot across the apical portion of the wings (Figure 26-67). The adults appear in late spring and lay their eggs, which are flattened and transparent, on the surface of leaves. The young larvae crawl to young apples and chew their way into the fruit, usually entering by the blossom end. They are light-colored with a dark head. They complete their development in the fruit and pupate on the ground, under bark, or in similar protected situations. In the eastern portion of the United States there is a second generation in the latter part of the summer, with the full-grown larvae overwintering in cocoons under the bark of apple trees or in other protected places.

Fig. 26-67. The codling moth, *Carpocápsa pomonélla* (Linn.). (Courtesy of the Ohio Agricultural Experiment Station.)

The Oriental fruit moth, *Graphólitha molésta* (Busck), is an Oriental species that is widely distributed in this country; it is a serious pest of peaches and other fruits. It has several generations a year; the larvae of the first generation bore into the young green twigs, and the later generations of larvae bore into the fruit very much as does the codling moth. The winter is passed as a full-grown larva in a cocoon.

A number of other species in this family are occasionally destructive to various crops. The grape berry moth, *Polychròsis viteàna* (Clemens) (Figure 26-68 B), feeds in the larval stage in the berries of grapes; it has two generations a year. The strawberry leaf roller, *Áncylis comptàna fra-*

Fig. 26-68. Olethreutid moths. A, adults of the cloverleaf tyer, *Áncylis angulifasciàna* Zeller; B, the grape berry moth, *Polychròsis viteàna* (Clemens). (Courtesy of the Ohio Agricultural Experiment Station.)

gàriae (Walsh and Riley), attacks the foliage of strawberry and often does severe damage. The black-headed fireworm, *Rhopóbota naevàna* (Hübner), is a serious pest of cranberry plantings in the eastern states. The clover head caterpillar, *Graphólitha interstictàna* (Clemens), is a common pest that feeds in the heads of clover, destroying unopened buds and decidedly reducing the crop of seed; this insect has three generations a year and passes the winter as a pupa.

A species in this family, which is something of a curiosity, is the Mexican jumping-bean moth, *Laspeyrèsia sáltitans* (Westwood). The larva lives in the thin-walled seeds of *Sebastiàna,* and after consuming the inside of the seed, throws itself forcibly against the thin wall, causing the jumping movements of the seed.

FAMILY **Tortrícidae:** The tortricids are small moths, usually gray, tan, or brown with spots or mottled coloration, and they have the front wings rather square-cut at the tip; when at rest, the wings are held rooflike over the body. The larvae vary in habits, but many species are leaf rollers or leaf tyers; they may pupate in these leaf nests, or they may spin cocoons in debris or under bark. Most species feed on perennial plants. The adults usually differ from those of the preceding family in lacking the long fringe of hairs on the cubitus of the hind wing.

The fruit-tree leaf roller, *Árchips argyrospìla* (Walker), is a rather common tortricid that makes an unsightly leaf nest in fruit and forest trees and often causes serious defoliation. The spruce budworm, *Choristoneùra fumiferàna* (Clemens), is a very serious pest of spruce, fir, balsam, and other evergreens, and may completely defoliate and kill a tree.

FAMILY **Phaloniidae:** This family includes a number of species whose larvae are web spinners and borers; most of them attack herbaceous plants. The adults are similar to those of the two preceding families, but the vein 1A is completely lacking in the front wing, and Cu_2 in the front wing arises in the apical fourth of the discal cell; M_1 in the hind wing is usually stalked with Rs. *Phalònia rutilàna* Hübner attacks juniper, tying the leaves together to form a tube in which the larva lives. The adult of this species has a wingspread of about an inch, and the front wings are orange marked with four brownish cross-bands.

FAMILY **Carposínidae:** The Carposínidae differ from the three preceding families in lacking M_1, and usually also M_2, in the hind wing. Only seven species in this family occur

Fig. 26-69. The carpenter moth, *Prionoxýstus robíniae* (Peck). (Courtesy of the Ohio Agricultural Experiment Station.)

in the United States, and not much is known of their habits. The larvae of the currant fruitworm, *Carposìna fernaldàna* Busck, feed on the fruits of the currant; the infested fruit eventually drops, and the larvae pupate in the soil.

FAMILY **Cóssidae**—Carpenter Moths and Leopard Moths: The cossids are wood-boring in the larval stage; the adults are medium-sized and heavy-bodied, and the wings are usually spotted or mottled. The carpenterworm, *Prionoxýstus robíniae* (Peck), is a common species that attacks various trees; the adult (Figure 26-69) is a mottled gray and has a wingspread of about 2 inches; these insects may sometimes seriously damage trees. The leopard moth, *Zeùzera pyrìna* (Linn.), a slightly smaller moth with the wings pale and marked with large black dots, has similar habits. These moths require two or three years to complete their life cycle.

FAMILY **Cosmopterýgidae:** The Cosmopterýgidae are small moths with the wings long and narrow and often sharply pointed at the apex (Figure 26-71 B); the wingspread is seldom over half an inch, and some species are rather brightly colored. Most species are leaf miners in the larval stage. The larvae of the cat-tail moth, *Lymnaècia phragmitélla* Stainton, feed in the heads of cat-tails. The palm leaf skeletonizer, *Homáledra sabalélla* (Chambers), occurs in the southern states, where the larvae feed on the upper surface of the leaves of the saw palmetto; a group of larvae make a delicate silken cover over the injured portion of the leaf and cover it with their droppings. The larvae of *Pyrodérces rìleyi* (Walsingham) (Figure 26-71 B) feed in cotton bolls.

FAMILY **Epermenìidae:** The Epermenìidae are a small group of moths that were formerly placed in the family Scýthridae. The larvae of *Epermènia pimpinélla* Murtfeldt form puffy mines on *Pimpinélla integérrima* Benth and Hook, a species of parsley; the pupa is enclosed in a rather frail cocoon on the under side of a leaf or in an angle of a leaf stalk.

FAMILY **Gelechìidae:** This family is one of the largest of the Microlepidoptera, and many species are fairly common; the moths are all rather small. The labial palpi are long and upcurved, and the terminal segment is long and pointed (Figures 26-28 A and 26-71 A). Veins R_4 and R_5 in the front wing are stalked at the base (rarely, they are fused for their entire length), and 2A is forked at the base; the hind wing usually has the outer margin somewhat curved (Figure 26-29 C). Gelechiid larvae vary in habits; some are leaf miners, a few form galls, many are leaf rollers or leaf tyers, and one species is a serious pest of stored grain.

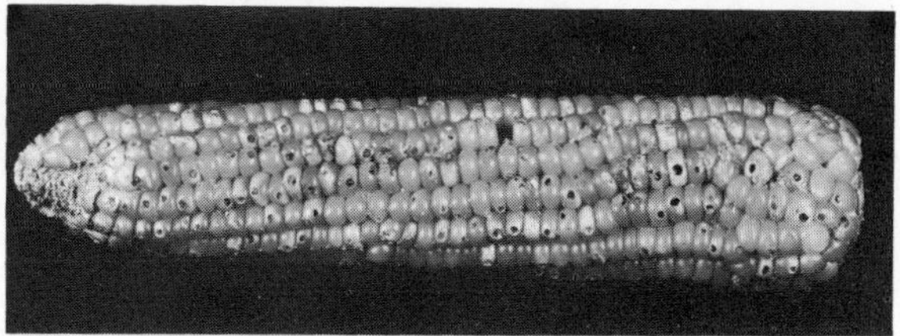

Fig. 26-70. Injury to corn by the Angoumois grain moth. (Courtesy of Davidson.)

The Angoumois grain moth, *Sitotròga cerealélla* (Olivier), is an important pest of stored grain. The larvae feed in the kernels of corn, wheat, and other grains, leaving a conspicuous emergence hole at one end of the kernel (Figure 26-70). The grain may become infested with this insect, either in the milk stage of the growing grain or in storage; stored grain may be completely destroyed by it. The adult moth is light grayish brown with a wingspread of about half an inch.

The pink bollworm, *Pectinóphora gossypiélla* (Saunders) (Figure 26-71 A), is a serious pest of cotton in the South and Southwest; the larvae attacks the bolls, and losses up to 50 percent of the crop are not uncommon in fields that are infested with this insect.

Many species in the genus *Gnorimoschèma* form galls in the stems of goldenrod, different species attacking different species of goldenrods. The galls are elongate and spindle-shaped, and rather thin-walled (Figure 26-72). The larva pupates in the gall, but before pupating, it cuts an opening (not quite completely through the wall) at the upper end of the gall; when the adult emerges, it can easily push out through this opening. Pupation occurs in mid- or late summer, and the adults emerge and lay their eggs on old goldenrod plants in the fall; the eggs hatch during the following spring.

Gnorimoschèma operculélla (Zeller), the potato tuberworm, is a pest of potatoes and related plants; the larvae mine in the leaves and bore into the tubers.

FAMILY **Oecophóridae:** The Oecophóridae are small and somewhat flattened moths, usually brownish in color, with the wings relatively broad and rounded apically. The venation (Figure 26-30 A) is complete, with 1A preserved in the front wing, R_4 and R_5 in the front wing stalked or coalesced throughout their length, and Rs and M_1 in the hind wing separate and parallel. The parsnip webworm, *Depressària heraclìana* (Linn.), attacks parsnips, celery, and related plants; the larvae web together and feed on the unfolding blossom heads and burrow

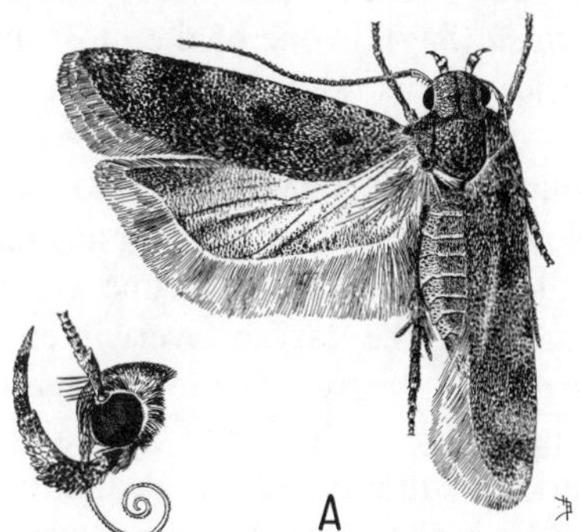

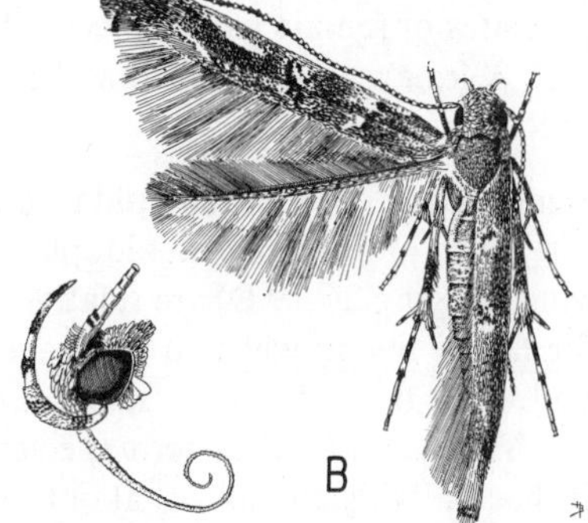

Fig. 26-71. A, the pink bollworm, *Pectinóphora gossypiélla* (Saunders) (Gelechìidae); B, *Pyrodérces rìleyi* Walsingham (Cosmopterýgidae). Inserts, lateral views of the head. (Courtesy of Busck and the USDA *Journal of Agricultural Research.*)

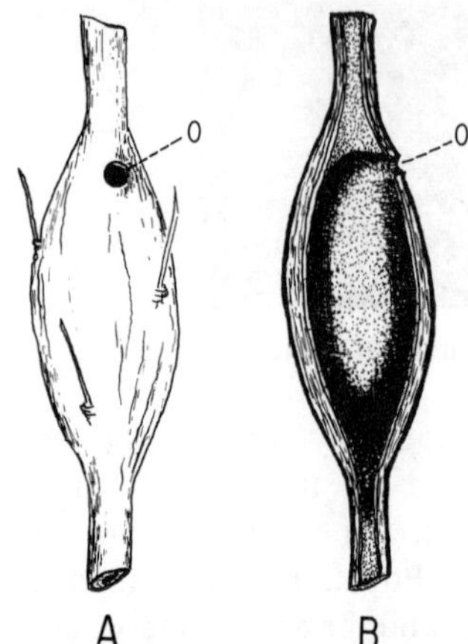

Fig. 26-72. Gall of the goldenrod gall moth, *Gnorimoschèma* (Gelechìidae). A, exterior view; B, a gall cut open. *o*, opening cut by the larva before pupating, through which the emerging adult escapes.

into the hollow stem to pupate; the adults appear in late summer and hibernate in protected situations.

FAMILY **Blastobásidae:** The Blastobásidae are small moths in which the hind wings are somewhat lanceolate and narrower than the front wings (Figure 26-27 B); the membrane of the front wing is slightly thickened along the costa. The larva of the acorn moth, *Valentínia glandulélla* Riley, feeds inside acorns that have been hollowed out by the larvae of acorn weevils; the larvae overwinter in the acorns, and the adults appear in the following summer. The larvae of *Zenodóchium coccivorélla* Chambers are internal parasites of female gall-like coccids of the genus *Kérmes*; this species has been found in Florida.

FAMILY **Stenómidae:** The Stenómidae are larger than most of the Microlepidoptera, and the wings (Figure 26-29 D) are relatively broad. The larvae live in webs on the leaves of oaks and other trees. *Stenòma schlaègeri* (Zeller) is a fairly common eastern species; the adult has a wingspread of about 30 millimeters; the wings are grayish white with dark markings, and when at rest, the moth resembles bird excrement.

FAMILY **Ethmìidae:** The Ethmìidae are small broad-winged moths somewhat similar to the Oecophóridae; the front wings are usually strikingly colored, often black and white. The larvae live in webs and feed mainly on bindweed and related plants (Borraginàceae). Most of the species in this family belong to the genus *Éthmia.*

FAMILY **Glyphipterýgidae:** The Glyphipterýgidae are small moths, some of which are similar in general appearance to the Tortrícidae. In the front wings, R_4 and R_5 are separate and Cu_2 arises near the apex of the discal cell; in the hind wing, 2A is forked at the base. These moths usually have large ocelli. The larvae are generally leaf tyers.

FAMILY **Aegerìidae**—Clear-Winged Moths: The greater part of one or both pairs of wings in this family is devoid of scalès, and many species bear a very striking resemblance to wasps (Figure 26-74). The front wings are long and narrow with the anal veins reduced, and the hind wings are broad with the anal area well developed (Figure 26-73). Many species are brightly colored, and most of them are active during the day. The two sexes are often differently colored, and in some cases they differ in the amount of clear area in the wings. The larvae bore in the roots, stems, canes, or trunks of plants or trees and often cause considerable damage.

The peach tree borer, *Sanninòidea exitiòsa* (Say), is one of the most important species in this family. The females lay their eggs on the trunks of peach trees near the ground, and the larvae bore into the tree just below the surface of the ground; they often girdle the tree. There is one generation a year, and the larvae overwinter in their burrows in the tree. The female has the front wings fully scaled, and the abdomen is marked with a broad orange band; the male has both the front and hind wings largely clear, and the abdomen is ringed with several narrow yellow bands (Figure 26-74). The adults are active through the summer.

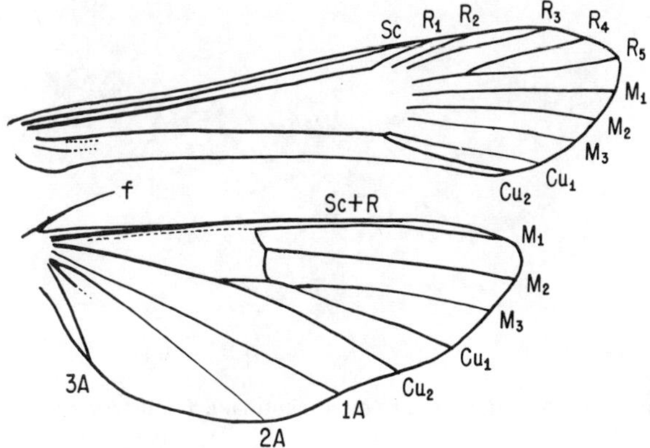

Fig. 26-73. Wings of *Synánthedon* (Aegerìidae). *f*, frenulum.

The lesser peach-tree borer, *Synánthedon píctipes* (Grote and Robinson), has similar habits, but the larvae generally bore into the trunk and the larger branches; both sexes resemble the male of *S. exitiòsa.*

The squash vine borer, *Melittia cucúrbitae* (Harris) is a serious pest of squash and related plants; the larvae bore into the stems and often destroy the plant. This species overwinters as a pupa in the soil. The adults are a little larger than those of the peach-tree borer and have the front wings olive green and the hind wings clear; the hind legs are heavily clothed with a long fringe of scales.

The imported currant borer, *Synánthedon tipulifórmis* (Linn.), is a small moth with a wingspread of about 18 millimeters; the larva bores in the stems of currants, and pupation occurs in the stems; the adults appear in early summer.

FAMILY **Heliodínidae:** The Heliodínidae are small moths that have the hind wings very narrow and lanceolate and with a broad fringe; the adult at rest usually holds the hind legs elevated above the wings. The family is a small one, and the known larvae vary in habits. The larvae of *Cyclóplasis panicifoliélla* Clemens mine in the leaves of panic grass, forming at first a linear mine that is later enlarged to a blotch; when full grown, the larva cuts a circular piece from the leaf, folds this piece over to make a case, then drops to the ground and pupates in the case. The larvae of *Schreckensteìnia* feed on sumac and species of *Rùbus. Euclemènsia bassettélla* Clemens is an internal parasite of female gall-like coccids of the genus *Kérmes.*

FAMILY **Plutéllidae**—Diamondback Moths: The Plutéllidae are similar to the Yponomeùtidae, but hold their antennae forward when at rest, and M_1 and M_2 in the hind

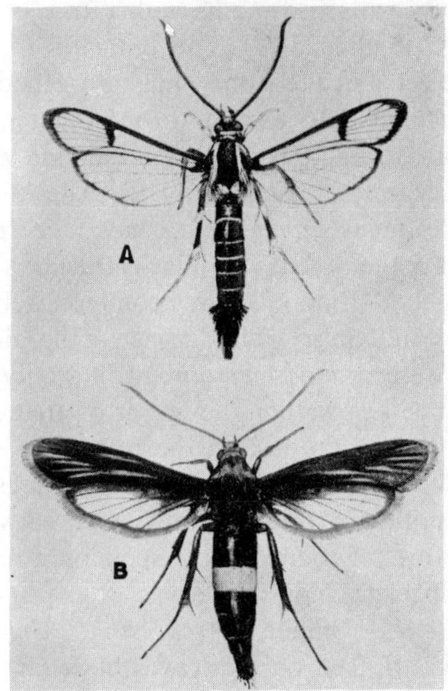

Fig. 26-74. The peach-tree borer, *Sanninòidea exitiòsa* (Say). A, male; B, female. (Courtesy of the Ohio Agricultural Experiment Station.)

Fig. 26-75. An ermine moth, *Átteva* sp. (Yponomeùtidae). (Courtesy of the Ohio Agricultural Experiment Station.)

wing are stalked. *Plutélla maculipénnis* (Curtis) is a pest of cabbage and other cruciferous plants; its larvae eat holes in the leaves and pupate in silken cocoons attached to the leaves. The name "diamondback" refers to the fact that the male wings when folded show a series of three yellow diamond-shaped marks along the line where the wings meet.

FAMILY **Yponomeùtidae**—Ermine Moths: The ermine moths are small and usually brightly patterned moths with rather broad wings (Figure 26-75). The branches of the main veins in the front wings are generally separate, and R_5 extends to the outer margin of the wing; Rs and M_1 in the hind wing are separate (Figure 26-30 B). The moths of the genus *Yponomeùta* have the front wings white dotted with black; the larvae of *Y. padélla* (Linn.) feed in a common web on apple and cherry. The larvae of the ailanthus webworm, *Átteva àurea* (Fitch), live in a frail silken web on the leaves of ailanthus and feed on the leaves; the pupae are suspended in loose webs. The front wings of the adult are bright yellow, marked with four rows of round yellow spots on a dark-blue background. The larvae of the arborvitea leaf miner, *Argyrésthia thuiélla* (Packard), feed on the leaves of cedar; the adults are white moths with the narrow front wings spotted with brown, and have a wingspread of about 8 millimeters.

FAMILY **Scýthridae:** The family Scýthridae is closely related to the Yponomeùtidae, and it contains the single genus *Scýthris.* The larvae of *S. magnatélla* Busck feed on willow herbs (*Epilòbium*), folding over a portion of the leaf for an individual cell.

FAMILY **Heliozélidae**—Shield Bearers: The heliozelids are small moths with lanceolate wings; the hind wings have no discal cell (Figure 26-32 B). The larvae of the resplendent shield bearer, *Coptodísca splendoriferélla* (Clemens), are both leaf miners and casebearers; the larvae make a linear mine in apple, wild cherry, and related plants, and this mine is later widened; when full grown, the larva makes a case from the walls of its mine, lines it with silk, and attaches it to a limb or to the trunk of the tree. There are two generations a year, with the larvae of the second generation overwintering in the cases. The front wings of the adult are dark gray at the base, with the outer portion bright yellow with brown and silver markings.

FAMILY **Douglasìidae:** The Douglasìidae are leaf miners in the larval stage, and the adults are small moths with lanceolate hind wings that lack a discal cell (Figure 26-31 B). Rs in the hind wing separates from the media near the middle of the wing. The ocelli are large. Only four species of douglasiids occur in this country; the larvae of *Tinágma obscurofasciélla* Chambers mine

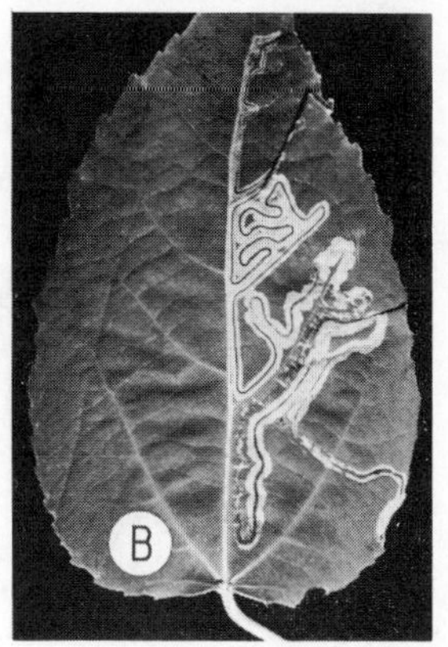

Fig. 26-76. Leaf mines of Gracilarìidae. A, the white oak leaf miner, *Lithocollètis hamadryadélla* Clemens; B, aspen leaf miner, *Phyllocnístis* sp. (A, courtesy of the Ohio Agricultural Experiment Station.)

in the leaves of plants in the family Rosàceae.

FAMILY **Elachístidae:** The Elachístidae are mainly leaf miners in grass. The adults have lanceolate hind wings that have a well-formed discal cell; the venation is but slightly reduced (Figure 26-31 A). The larvae make blotch mines in grasses; the larvae of some species leave the mines and pupate in suspended webs. Most of the species in this small family belong to the genus *Elachísta.*

FAMILY **Coleophóridae**—Casebearers: The moths in this family are small, with very narrow, sharply pointed wings. The discal cell of the front wing is oblique, and veins Cu_1 and Cu_2 (when present) are very short. There are no ocelli or maxillary palpi. About a hundred species of casebearers, all belonging to the genus *Coleóphora,* occur in this country. The larvae are usually leaf miners when young and casebearers when they become larger.

The pistol casebearer, *Coleóphora malivorélla* Riley, is a common pest of apple and other fruit trees. The larvae construct pistol-shaped cases composed of silk, bits of leaves, and excrement, which they carry about; by protruding their heads from these cases they eat holes in the leaves. They overwinter as larvae in the cases, and the moths appear in midsummer.

The cigar casebearer, *C. occidentàlis* Zeller, also attacks apple and other fruit trees. This species is similar to the preceding casebearer except that the young larvae are miners in the leaves for two or three weeks before making their cases.

FAMILY **Gracilarìidae**—Leaf Blotch Miners: This is a large group of small to minute moths with lanceolate wings; the front wing usually lacks an accessory cell, and the hind wing in some species has a hump along the costal margin near the base (Figure 26-31 C). The adult moths at rest have the anterior part of the body elevated, and the wing tips touch the surface on which the moth rests. The larvae usually make blotch mines, and the leaf is often folded.

The white oak leaf miner, *Lithocollètis hamadryadélla* Clemens, is a common eastern species that feeds on various types of oak. The mines are on the upper surface of the leaves, and each mine contains a single larva; many mines may occur on a single leaf (Figure 26-76 A). The larvae are flattened, with only rudiments of legs, and with the prothoracic segment enlarged. The larva pupates in a delicate cocoon inside the mine; it overwinters as a larva in dry leaves. The adult moth is white with broad irregular bronze bands on the front wings.

Some species of *Phyllocnístis* make winding serpentine mines in aspen leaves

Fig. 26-77. Bags of the evergreen bagworm. *Thyridópteryx ephemeraefórmis* (Haworth). (Courtesy of the Ohio Agricultural Experiment Station.)

(Figure 26-76 B). The larva usually starts near the tip of the leaf, mines toward the base, and often has to go out toward the edge of the leaf in order to get across a large vein; it pupates in a silken cocoon at the end of the mine, usually at the basal edge of the leaf.

FAMILY **Opostégidae :** The Opostégidae are small moths with linear hind wings and with the radius, media, and cubitus of the front wings unbranched; the first segment of the antenna forms a large eye-cap. The larvae are miners. This is a small group and contains the single genus *Opóstega.*

FAMILY **Lyonetìidae :** The Lyonetìidae are small moths with very narrow wings; the hind wings are often linear, with Rs extending through the center of the wing (Figure 26-32 D). Ocelli and maxillary palpi are usually lacking. The larvae are leaf miners or live in webs between the leaves. The apple bucculatrix, *Bucculàtrix pomifoliélla* Clemens, overwinters in rows of white, longitudinally ribbed cocoons on the twigs of apple; the adults emerge in the spring and oviposit on the lower surface of the leaves. The larvae enter the leaf and make a serpentine mine on the upper surface. Silken molting cocoons are made on the surface of the leaf before the pupal cocoons on the twigs are formed.

FAMILY **Tischerìidae :** The Tischerìidae are small moths in which the costal margin of the front wing is strongly arched and the apex is prolonged into a sharp point; the hind wings are long and narrow with a reduced venation (Figure 26-32 A). The maxillary palpi are small or absent. The larvae of most species make blotch mines in the leaves of oak or apple trees and blackberry or raspberry bushes. The apple leaf trumpet miner, *Tischèria malifoliélla* Clemens, is a common species in the East, and often does considerable damage; the larva makes a trumpet-shaped mine in the upper surface of the leaf, overwinters in the mine, and pupates in the spring; there are two or more generations a year.

FAMILY **Oinophílidae :** The family Oinophílidae is represented in the United States by a single species, *Phaeòses sabinélla* Forbes, which occurs in Louisiana and Mississippi. The adult is very flattened, shining gray-brown in color, and has a wingspread of about 9 millimeters. The larva feeds on decaying vegetable matter and fungi.

FAMILY **Psýchidae** — Bagworm Moths: These moths are so named because of the characteristic bags or cases that are made and carried about by the larvae; these bags are easily seen on trees during the winter after the leaves have fallen (Figure 26-77). The bags are composed of silk and portions of leaves and twigs; the larvae pupate in the bags, and most species overwinter as eggs in the bags. When the larvae hatch in the spring, they construct their cases and carry them about as they feed; when full

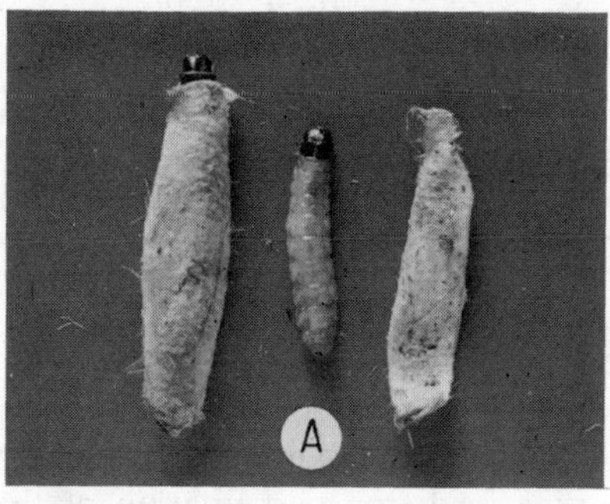

Fig. 26-78. The casemaking clothes moth, *Tínea pellionélla* (Linn.). A, larvae and cases; B, adult. (Courtesy of the Ohio Agricultural Experiment Station.)

grown, they attach the case to a twig and pupate inside it.

The adult males of this group are small, with well-developed wings, but the females are wingless, legless, and wormlike, and usually never leave the bag in which they pupate. The males on emergence fly about and locate a bag containing a female; mating takes place without the female leaving the bag. The eggs are later laid in the bag.

The evergreen bagworm, *Thyridópteryx ephemeraefórmis* (Haworth), is a common species, the larvae of which attack chiefly red cedar and arborvitae. The adult males are small, dark-colored, heavy-bodied moths with large clear areas in the wings.

FAMILY **Acrolóphidae**—Burrowing Webworms: The acrolophids are medium-sized moths that resemble the noctuids. The first segment of the labial palpi is as large as the second, or larger; the eyes are usually hairy; and the venation is complete, with three anal veins in both front and hind wings (Figure 26-30 D). The 40-odd species in this family are all placed in the genus *Acrólophus.* The larvae make a tubular web in the ground, sometimes extending as deep as 2 feet, into which they retreat when disturbed; they feed on the roots of grasses and also web in the blades at the surface. These insects often destroy entire young corn plants.

FAMILY **Tinèidae**—Clothes Moths and Their Relatives: This is a large group of small moths. The wing venation is rather generalized in most species (Figure 26-30 C), but in some it is reduced. The maxillary palpi are usually large and folded, and the labial palpi are short. The larvae of many species are casebearers; some are scavengers or feed on fungi, and some feed on woolen fabrics. Of the more than 130 species of tineids in the United States, three species that attack clothes and woolens are of considerable economic importance.

The most common clothes moth is the webbing clothes moth, *Tinèola bisselliélla* (Hummel). The adult is straw-colored, without dark spots on the wings, and has a wingspread of 12 to 16 millimeters. The larvae feed on hair fiber, woolens, silks, felt, and similar materials, and do not form cases. The larva when full grown forms a cocoon of fragments of its food material fastened together with silk.

Second in importance among the clothes moths is the casemaking clothes moth, *Tínea pellionélla* (Linn.) (Figure 26-78), which forms a case from silk and fragments of its food material. This case is tubular and open at each end; the larva feeds from within the case and pupates in it. The adult is brownish, with three dark spots on each front wing.

The clothes moth of least importance in the United States is the tapestry clothes moth or carpet moth, *Trichóphaga tapetzélla* (Linn.), which builds rather long silken tubes or galleries to go through certain fabrics which it may not feed upon. These tubes often have fragments of cloth woven in the silk. Where this species is found, it is quite destructive. The adult has a wingspread of 12 to 24 millimeters, and the front wings are black at the base and white in the apical portion.

FAMILY **Nepticùlidae:** The Nepticùlidae are minute moths, some species of which have a wingspread of only 3 millimeters. The wing venation is somewhat reduced, and the surface of the wings bears spinelike hairs or aculeae. The basal segment of the antennae is enlarged to form an eye-cap, the maxillary palpi are long, and the labial palpi are short. The male has a well-developed frenulum, but the frenulum of the female consists of only a few small bristles. Most species in this group are leaf miners in trees or shrubs; the mines are linear when the larvae are young, and are often broadened when the larvae become fully developed. The larvae usually leave the mines to pupate, spinning cocoons in debris on the surface of the soil. A few species in the genus *Ectoedèmia* are gall makers.

FAMILY **Incurvariidae:** The Incurvarìidae are small moths with the wing venation very little reduced and the wing surface aculeate; the females have a piercing ovipositor. The larvae of the maple leaf cutter, *Paracleménsia acerifoliélla* (Fitch), are leaf mining when young and become casebearers when older. The older larvae cut out two circular portions of the leaf and put these together to form the case; when the larva moves about, it carries this case with it and appears somewhat turtlelike. The winter is passed as a pupa inside the case. The adult moth is a brilliant steel blue or bluish green with an orange-colored head.

FAMILY **Prodóxidae:** The Prodóxidae are closely related to the preceding family; the wing surface is aculeate, and the females have a piercing ovipositor. The best-known moths in this group are the yucca moths (*Tegetícula*), of which four species are known. The yucca is pollinated solely by these insects. The female moth collects pollen from the yucca flowers by means of long, curled, spinelike maxillary tentacles, and then inserts her eggs into the ovary of another flower; after ovipositing, she thrusts the pollen she has collected into the stigma of the flower in which the eggs have been laid. This ensures fertilization and the development of the yucca seeds—on which the larvae feed; the perpetuation of the yucca is assured, as more seeds are developed than are needed for the larvae. The bogus yucca moths of the genus *Prodóxus* lack the maxillary tentacles and cannot pollinate yuccas; their larvae feed in the stems or fruit of these plants.

FAMILY **Adélidae**—Fairy Moths: The fairy moths are tiny moths in which the antennae of the males are extremely long and delicate; the antennae may be twice as long as the wings. This group is closely related to the three preceding families, and the wing surface is aculeate. The larvae are leaf miners when young and live in cases when older; they are found on herbaceous plants and shrubs. Most of the species in this family belong to the genus *Adèla.*

SUBORDER JUGÀTAE—JUGATE MOTHS

The jugate moths possess a small basal lobe on the posterior margin of the front wing, the jugum, with which the front and hind wings are united. The venation in the front and hind wings is very similar; the radius usually has as many branches in the hind wing as in the front wing.

FAMILY **Eriocraniidae:** The Eriocranìidae are small moths that are somewhat similar to clothes moths in general appearance. The subcosta of the front wing is forked near its tip, and the mandibles are vestigial. One of the best-known eastern species in this family is *Mnemónica auricyánea* Walsingham; the larvae make blotch mines in oak and chestnut and overwinter as pupae in the soil.

Fig. 26-79. A hepialid moth, *Sthenòpis argenteomaculàtus* Harris; 1.3 ×.

FAMILY **Micropterýgidae:** The Micropterýgidae are small moths that differ from all other Lepidoptera in that they have well-developed and functional mandibles; this family is sometimes placed in a separate order, the Zeugloptera. They differ from the Eriocranìidae in that their subcosta in the front wing is forked near the middle. This group contains only three North American species, one of which (*Micrópteryx auricrinélla* Walsingham) occurs in the East. The larvae whose habits are known feed on mosses and liverworts.

FAMILY **Hepiálidae:** The Hepiálidae, including the ghost moths or swifts, are medium-sized to large moths, with wingspreads of from 1 to 3 inches. Most of them are brown or gray with silvery spots on the wings. The jugum in this group is fingerlike and is reinforced by a branch of the third anal vein. The name "swift" refers to the fact that some of these moths have an extremely rapid flight; they superficially resemble some of the Sphíngidae. The larvae feed on the roots and woody tissues of plants. The smaller moths in this family, with a wingspread of 1 to 2 inches, belong to the genus *Hepìalus*; the larger moths belong to the genus *Sthenòpis*. The larva of *S. argenteomaculàtus* Harris (Figure 26-79) bores in the stems of alder, and the larva of *S. thùle* Strecker bores in willow.

COLLECTING AND PRESERVING LEPIDOPTERA

The Order Lepidoptera contains many large and showy insects, and many students begin their collecting with these insects. Lepidoptera are generally fairly easy to collect, but are more difficult to mount and preserve in good condition than insects in most other groups. Specimens must always be handled with great care because the scales—which give the specimens their color—are easily rubbed off, and in many species the wings are easily torn or broken.

Lepidoptera may be collected with a net, or they may be gotten directly into a killing jar without the use of a net. A net for collecting these insects should be of a fairly light mesh, light enough that the specimen can be seen through the net. Once netted, a specimen should be gotten into a killing jar or stunned as quickly as possible so that it will not damage its wings by fluttering and attempting to escape. Many collectors prefer to insert the killing jar into the net to get the specimen into the jar, without handling the specimen directly; the killing agent in the jar should be of sufficient toxic strength to stun the insect quickly. If the specimen is removed to the killing jar by hand, it should be grasped carefully through the net by the body, pinched slightly to stun it, and then placed in the killing jar.

Many moths can be taken directly into a killing jar without the use of a net. A wide-mouthed jar is simply placed over the specimen when it is resting on some flat surface. The jar should be strong enough to stun the insect quickly, before it can flutter about too much inside and damage its wings.

The best place to collect most Lepidoptera is on or near the plant on which the larva feeds. Many species, particularly butterflies, frequent flowers, and may be collected while feeding. To obtain a large number of species, one must visit a variety of habitats and collect at all seasons; many species occur only in certain types of habitats, may have a short adult life, and be on the wing only a short time each year.

Many of the moths are most easily collected at lights. They may be collected by traps, but specimens so collected are often in poor condition. Better specimens can be collected at lights if there is some flat white surface near the light on which the insect will land; the specimen can be taken from such a surface directly into the killing jar. Many interesting species can be obtained by sugaring (see Chapter 32).

One must take precautions to prevent the specimens from becoming damaged after they are placed in the killing jar. The jar should be strong enough to stun a specimen quickly. Large and heavy-bodied specimens should not be placed in a jar along with small and delicate ones. The jar should not be allowed to become too crowded; it is advisable to remove the specimens soon after they have been stunned and then to place them in paper envelopes.

The best way to obtain good specimens of many species is to rear them, either from larvae or from pupae. Suggestions for rearing are given in Chapter 33. By rearing, the collector not only obtains good specimens, but also can become acquainted with the larval stages of different species and the plants on which the larvae feed.

Specimens of Lepidoptera can be preserved in a collection in three ways—in paper envelopes (as in the case of Odonata and some other groups), spread and pinned, or spread and mounted under glass (in Riker or glass mounts). Envelopes are useful for temporary storage or in cases where the collection is large and space is not available for large numbers of spread specimens. If one desires to display his collection, the best type of mount is a Riker or glass mount. The best collections of Lepidoptera have the specimens spread and pinned.

All Lepidoptera that are pinned or mounted under glass should be spread. The beginning student or the person interested principally in displaying his collection is advised to spread his specimens in an upside-down position and mount them under glass; the advanced student or the person making a large collection of Lepidoptera should pin them. Methods of spreading and mounting Lepidoptera are described in Chapter 32 and need not be given here. It takes a little practice to become proficient in spreading these insects, and some of the smaller specimens will tax the skill and patience of the collector, but the resulting collection will be worth the effort.

In a large collection of pinned Lepidoptera, space can be saved by putting the pins into the bottom of the box at an angle, and overlapping the wings of adjacent specimens. A collection must be protected against museum pests by having naphthalene or some similar repellent in the boxes; it should be kept in the dark, for many specimens will fade if exposed to light for long periods.

REFERENCES ON THE LEPIDOPTERA

Braun, A. F. 1917. The Nepticulidae of North America. Trans. Entomol. Soc. Am., 43: 155-209.

Braun, A. F. 1948. Elachistidae of North America. Trans. Entomol. Soc. Am., 13:1-110; 26 pl.

Clarke, J. F. G. 1941. Revision of the North American moths of the family Oecophoridae. Proc. U.S. Nat. Museum, 90:33-286; 48 pl.

Dyar, H. G. 1902. A list of the North American Lepidoptera and a key to the literature to this order of insects. U.S. Natl. Museum Bull. No. 52; xx+723 pp.

Edwards, W. H. 1879-1897. The butterflies of North America. Boston: Houghton Mifflin Company. 3 vols., illus.

Englehardt, G. P. 1946. North American Aegeriidae. U.S. Nat. Museum Bull. 190:1-222; 32 pl.

Forbes, W. T. M. 1923. Lepidoptera of New York and neighboring states. N.Y. (Cornell) Agr. Expt. Sta., Mem. No. 68; 729 pp.

Forbes, W. T. M. 1948. Lepidoptera of New York and neighboring states. Part II, Geometridae, Sphingidae, Notodontidae, Lymantriidae. Cornell Univ. Agr. Expt. Sta., Mem. 274; 263 pp., 255 f.

Forbes, W. T. M. 1954. Lepidoptera of New York and neighboring states. Part III, Noctuidae. Cornell Univ. Agr. Expt. Sta., Mem. 329; 433 pp., 290 f.

Fracker, Stanley B. 1930 (2nd ed.). The classification of lepidopterous larvae. Contrib. Entomol. Lab. Univ. Illinois, No. 43. 161 pp., 112 f.

Hinton, H. E. 1958. The phylogeny of the panorpoid orders. Ann. Rev. Entomol. 3:181-206.

Holland, W. J. 1905. The moth book. New York: Doubleday & Co., Inc. xxiv+479 pp., 261 f., 48 col. pl.

Holland, W. J. 1949. The butterfly book. New York: Doubleday & Co., Inc. xii+424 pp., 198 f., 77 col. pl.

Klots, A. B. 1951. A field guide to the butterflies. Boston: Houghton Mifflin Company. xvi+349 pp., 8 text f., 40 pl.

Klots, A. B. 1958. The world of butterflies and moths. New York: McGraw-Hill Book Company, Inc., 207 pp., illus.

Lindsay, A. W., E. L. Bell, and R. C. Williams. 1913. Hesperioidea of North America. J. Sci. Labs. Denison Univ., 26:1-142; 33 pl.

McDunnough, J. 1938-1939. Check list of the Lepidoptera of Canada and the United States of America. Southern Calif. Acad. Sci., Mem. Part I, 1938, Macrolepidoptera, 274 pp. Part II, 1939, Microlepidoptera, 171 pp.

Mosher, Edna. 1916. A classification of the Lepidoptera based on characters of the pupa. Illinois Nat. Hist. Survey, Bull. 12(2):15-159; pl. 19-27.

Peterson, Alvah. 1948. Larvae of insects. Part I, Lepidoptera and plant infesting Hymenoptera. Ann Arbor, Mich.: J. W. Edwards. 315 pp., illus.

Scudder, S. H. 1889. Butterflies of Eastern United States and Canada. 3 vol., 1958 pp., 74 pl. Cambridge, Mass.

Seitz, A. 1906+. Macro-Lepidoptera of the world. Stuttgart: F. Lehmann. Several volumes. Vol. 5, 1924, The American Rhopalocera, viii+1139 pp., 203 col. pl.

Urquhart, F. A. 1960. The monarch butterfly. Toronto: University of Toronto Press. xxiv+361 pp., 79 f.

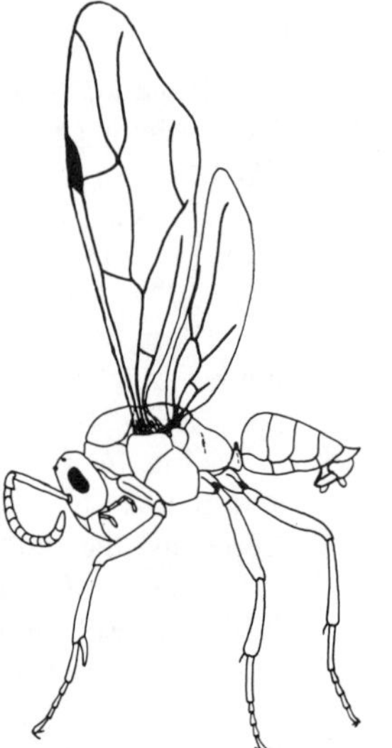

27

Order Diptera[1]: Flies

The Diptera constitute one of the largest orders of insects, and its members are abundant in individuals and species almost everywhere. Most of the Diptera can be readily distinguished from other insects to which the term "fly" is applied (sawflies, stoneflies, caddisflies, dragonflies, and others) by the fact that they possess only one pair of wings; these are the front wings, and the hind wings are reduced to small knobbed structures called halteres, which function as organs of equilibrium. There are occasional insects in a few other orders that have only one pair of wings (some mayflies, some beetles, male scale insects, and others), but none of these has the hind wings reduced to halteres. The Diptera are sometimes spoken of as the two-winged flies, to distinguish them from the "flies" in other orders. In the common names of Diptera, the "fly" of the name is written as a separate word, whereas in the common names of "flies" in other orders, the "fly" of the name is written together with the descriptive word.

The majority of the Diptera are relatively small and soft-bodied insects, and some are quite minute, but many are of great economic importance. The mosquitoes, black flies, punkies, horse flies, stable flies, and others are blood-sucking and constitute a serious pest of man and animals. Many of the blood-sucking flies, and some of the scavenging flies such as the house flies and blow flies, are important vectors of disease; the causative organisms of malaria, yellow fever, filariasis, dengue, sleeping sickness, typhoid fever, dysentery, and other diseases are carried and distributed by flies. Some flies, such as the hessian fly and the apple maggot, are important pests of cultivated plants. On the other hand, many flies are useful as scavengers, others are important predators or parasites of various insect pests, others aid in the pollination of useful plants, and some are enemies of noxious weeds.

[1] Diptera: *di*, two; *ptera*, wings.

The mouth parts of the Diptera are of the sucking type, but there is considerable variation in mouth-part structure within the order. In many flies, the mouth parts are piercing; in others they are sponging or lapping (pages 21-22), and in a few flies, the mouth parts are so poorly developed as to be nonfunctional.

The Diptera undergo complete metamorphosis, and the larvae of many are called maggots. The larvae are generally legless and wormlike; in the primitive families (Nematócera) the head is usually well developed and the mandibles move laterally; in the higher families (Brachýcera and Cyclórrhapha) the head is reduced and the mouth hooks move in a vertical plane. In some families (Brachýcera) the head of the larva is sclerotized and more or less retractile, while in others (Cyclórrhapha) there is no sclerotization of the head at all. The pupae of the Nematócera are of the obtect type, while those of the higher Diptera are coarctate; that is, the pupal stage is passed inside the next to the last larval skin, which is called a puparium.

Dipterous larvae occur in many kinds of habitats, but a large proportion of them live in water—in all sorts of aquatic habitats including streams, ponds, lakes, temporary puddles, brackish and alkaline water. The larvae that feed on plants generally live within some tissue of the plant, either as leaf miners, gall insects, stem borers, or root borers. The predaceous larvae live in many different habitats—in water, in the soil, under bark or stones, or on vegetation. Many species feed during the larval stage in decaying plant or animal matter. Some fly larvae live in rather unusual habitats; one species (*Psilòpa petròlei* Coquillett, family Ephýdridae) lives in pools of crude petroleum; other ephydrids breed in Great Salt Lake, and some will breed in formalin-soaked carcasses.

Adult Diptera feed on various plant or animal juices, such as nectar, sap, or blood; most species feed on nectar, but many are blood-sucking, and many are predaceous on other insects.

CLASSIFICATION OF THE DIPTERA

This order is divided into three suborders, the Nematócera, Brachýcera, and Cyclórrhapha. The Nematócera have many-segmented antennae, while the Brachýcera and Cyclórrhapha have five or fewer (usually three) antennal segments. The Brachýcera differ from the Cyclórrhapha in the way the adults emerge from the puparium; the Brachýcera emerge through a **T**-shaped opening, while the Cyclórrhapha emerge through a circular opening. Most Brachýcera (Figure 27-9)—all except the Dolichopódidae, many Empídidae, and some Stratiomýidae and Acrocéridae—have the vein R_{4+5} forked; none of the Cyclórrhapha has this vein forked. Some authorities combine the Brachýcera and Cyclórrhapha into a single suborder called the Brachýcera.

The muscoid flies (suborder Cyclórrhapha, Division Schizóphora, the flies with a frontal suture) are an extremely large group and make up about half of the order. Many are small, and their identification is often difficult. The muscoids fall into two principal groups, the calypterates and the acalypterates; these names refer to the development of the calypters, which are large and well developed in most of the calypterate muscoids and very small in the acalypterate muscoids. The two muscoid groups also differ (with a few exceptions) in the structure of the second antennal segment and the sutures on the dorsal surface of the thorax (see key, couplet 54). The division between some of the muscoid families is not always clear-cut, and many genera are placed in different families by different authorities.

The arrangement of suborders and families followed in this book is that which will be used in the forthcoming *Catalogue of the Diptera of North America North of Mexico,* and has been obtained through the kindness of the editor, Dr. Alan Stone. This arrangement is outlined below, with alternate names, spellings, and arrangements in parentheses. The groups marked with an asterisk are relatively rare or are unlikely to be taken by the general collector.

Suborder Nematócera (Nemócera; Orthórrhapha in part)—long-horned flies
- Trichocéridae (Trichocerátidae, Petaurístidae)—winter crane flies
- Tipùlidae (including Cylindrotómidae and Limonìidae = Limnobìidae)—crane flies
- *Tanydéridae—primitive crane flies
- Psychódidae—moth flies, sand flies
- Ptychoptéridae (Liriopèidae)—phantom crane flies
- *Blepharicéridae (Blepharocéridae, Blepharocerátidae)—net-winged midges
- *Nymphomyìidae—nymphomyiid flies
- *Deuterophlebiidae—mountain midges
- Díxidae—dixid midges
- Chaobóridae (Coréthridae; Culicidae in part)—phantom midges
- Culícidae—mosquitoes
- *Thaumalèidae (Orphnephílidae)—solitary midges
- Ceratopogónidae (Helèidae)—biting midges, punkies, no-see-ums
- Chironómidae (Tendipédidae)—midges
- Simuliidae (Melusínidae)—black flies, buffalo gnats
- Anisopódidae (Rhýphidae, Silvicólidae, Phrynèidae; including Mycetobìidae)—wood gnats
- Bibiónidae—march flies
- *Pachyneùridae (Anisopódidae in part)—pachyneurid gnats
- Mycetophílidae (including Sciophílidae, Bolitophílidae, Diadocìidae, Ditomyìidae, Ceroplátidae = Keroplátidae = Platyùridae, and Macrocerátidae; Fungivóridae in part)—fungus gnats
- Sciáridae (Lycorìidae; Fungivóridae in part)—dark-winged fungus gnats, root gnats
- *Hyperoscélidae (Corynoscélidae; Scatópsidae in part)—hyperoscelid gnats
- Scatópsidae—minute black scavenger flies
- Cecidomyìidae (Cecidomỳidae, Itonídidae)—gall gnats or gall midges

Suborder Brachýcera (Orthórrhapha; Brachýcera in part)—straight-seamed flies
- Xylophágidae (Erínnidae; including Coenomyìidae = Coenomyìdae and Rachicéridae = Rhachicéridae)—xylophagid flies
- Xylomỳidae (Xylomyiidae; Xylophágidae in part)—xylomyid flies
- Stratiomỳidae (Stratiomyìidae; including Chiromýzidae)—soldier flies
- *Pelecorhýnchidae (Tabánidae in part)—pelecorhynchid flies
- Tabánidae—horse flies, deer flies, greenheads
- Rhagiónidae (Léptidae)—snipe flies
- *Hilarimórphidae (Rhagiónidae in part)—hilarimorphid flies
- Therévidae—stiletto flies
- *Scenopínidae (Omphrálidae)—window flies
- *Apiocéridae (Apiocerátidae)—flower-loving flies
- Mỳdidae (Mydàidae, Mydásidae)—mydas flies
- Asílidae—robber flies
- *Nemestrínidae—tangle-veined flies
- *Acrocéridae (Acrocerátidae, Cýrtidae, Henópidae, Oncódidae)—small-headed flies
- Bombyliidae—bee flies
- Empídidae (Émpidae)—dance flies

Dolichopódidae (Dolichópidae)—long-legged flies
Suborder Cyclórrhapha (Brachýcera in part)—circular-seamed flies
Division Aschìza—Cyclórrhapha without a frontal suture
Lonchoptéridae (Musidóridae)—spear-winged flies
Phóridae—humpbacked flies
*Platypézidae (Clythìidae)—flat-footed flies
Pipuncùlidae (Dorilàidae, Dorylàidae)—big-headed flies
Sýrphidae—syrphid flies, flower flies
Conópidae—thick-headed flies
Division Schizóphora (including Pupípara)—Cyclórrhapha with a frontal suture, muscoid flies
Section Acalyptràtae—acalypterate muscoid flies
Micropézidae (including Tỳlidae and Calobátidae = Trepidarìidae)—stilt-legged flies
*Nerìidae—neriid flies
*Diópsidae—stalk-eyed flies
Psílidae—rust flies
*Tanypézidae (Micropézidae in part)—tanypezid flies
Richardìidae (Otítidae in part)—picture-winged flies
Otítidae (Ortálidae, Ortalídidae; including Ulidìidae = Chaetópsidae, Dorycéridae, Cephalìidae, and Ceroxýdidae)—picture-winged flies
Platystomátidae (Otítidae in part)—picture-winged flies
*Pyrgótidae—pyrgotid flies
Tephrítidae (Trypétidae, Trupanèidae, Trypanèidae, Euribìidae)—fruit flies, peacock flies
*Helcomýzidae (Dryomýzidae in part)—helcomyzid flies
*Ropaloméridae (Rhopaloméridae)—ropalomerid flies
Coelópidae (Phycodrómidae)—seaweed flies
*Dryomýzidae—dryomyzid flies
Sépsidae—black scavenger flies
Sciomýzidae (Tetanocéridae, Tetanocerátidae)—marsh flies
Lauxanìidae (Sapromýzidae)—lauxaniid flies
Chamaemyìidae (Chamaemỳidae, Ochthiphílidae)—chamaemyiid flies, aphid flies
*Periscélidae—periscelid flies
Piophílidae—skipper flies
*Thyreophóridae—thyreophorid flies
*Neottiophílidae—neottiophilid flies
*Palloptéridae (Sapromýzidae in part)—pallopterid flies
Lonchaèidae (Sapromýzidae in part)—lonchaeid flies
Sphaerocéridae (Sphaerocerátidae, Borbóridae, Cypsélidae; including Leptocerátidae)—small dung flies
*Bràulidae (Pupípara in part)—bee lice
Tethínidae (Opomýzidae in part)—tethinid flies
Milichìidae (Phyllomýzidae; including Cárnidae)—milichiid flies
*Canacèidae—canaceid flies
Ephýdridae (Hydréllidae, Notiophílidae)—shore flies
*Curtonótidae (Cyrtonótidae; Drosophílidae in part)—curtonotid flies
Drosophílidae—pomace flies, small fruit flies
*Diastátidae (Drosophílidae in part)—diastatid flies

*Camíllidae (Drosophílidae in part)—camillid flies
Chlorópidae (Oscínidae, Titanìidae)—frit flies, stem flies
*Odinìidae (Odínidae; Agromýzidae in part)—odiniid flies
Agromýzidae (Phytomýzidae)—leaf-miner flies
Clusiódidae (Clusìidae, Heteroneùridae)—clusiodid flies
*Acartophthálmidae (Clusiódidae in part)—acartophthalmid flies
Heleomýzidae (Helomýzidae)—heleomyzid flies
*Trixoscélidae (Trichoscélidae; Chyromỳidae in part)—trixoscelid flies
*Rhinotóridae—rhinotorid flies
Anthomýzidae (Opomýzidae in part)—anthomyzid flies
Opomýzidae (Geomýzidae)—opomyzid flies
*Chyromỳidae (Chyromyìidae)—chyromyid flies
*Aulacigastéridae (Aulacigástridae; Drosophílidae in part)—aulacigasterid flies
*Asteìidae (Astìidae)—asteiid flies
*Cryptochaètidae (Chamaemyìidae in part, Agromýzidae in part)—cryptochaetid flies

Section Calyptràtae—calypterate muscoid flies
Anthomyìidae (Anthomỳidae; Múscidae in part; including Scopeumátidae = Scopeùmidae = Cordylùridae = Cordilùridae = Scatophágidae = Scatomýzidae)—anthomyiid flies
Múscidae (including Glossínidae and Fannìidae)—muscid flies: house fly, face fly, horn fly, stable fly, tsetse fly, and others
*Gasterophílidae (Gastrophílidae)—horse bot flies
*Hippobóscidae (Pupípara in part)—louse flies
*Stréblidae (Pupípara in part)—bat flies
*Nycteribìidae (Pupípara in part)—bat flies
Calliphóridae (Metopìidae in part)—blow flies
Sarcophágidae (Stephanosomátidae; Metopìidae in part)—flesh flies
Tachínidae (Larvaevóridae; including Phasìidae = Gymnosomátidae, Dexìidae, and Rhinophóridae)—tachinid flies
*Cuterébridae—robust bot flies
*Oéstridae (including Hypodermátidae)—warble and bot flies

CHARACTERS USED IN THE IDENTIFICATION OF DIPTERA

The principal characters used in the classification and identification of Diptera are those of the antennae, legs, wing venation, and chaetotaxy (the arrangement of the bristles, chiefly on the head and thorax). Occasionally various other characters are used, such as the presence or absence of certain sutures, the shape of the head or abdomen, the form of the mouth parts, and the presence or absence of ocelli.

THE ANTENNAE: The antennae vary quite a bit in different families, and to some extent within a single family. In the suborder Nematócera the antennae are many-segmented (Figure 27-1 A, B) and the segments (except possibly the two basal ones) are similar. In the suborders Brachýcera and Cyclórrhapha the antennae are generally 3-segmented (Figure 27-1 C-H) with the two basal segments small and the third segment larger. In some of the Brachýcera the third segment of the antennae is annulated, that is, it is divided into subsegments (Figure 27-1 C, D, F); this annulation is sometimes difficult to see unless the antenna is properly illuminated; it may often be difficult to decide whether such antennae are 3-segmented or many-segmented, but the divisions of the third segment in such flies are never so

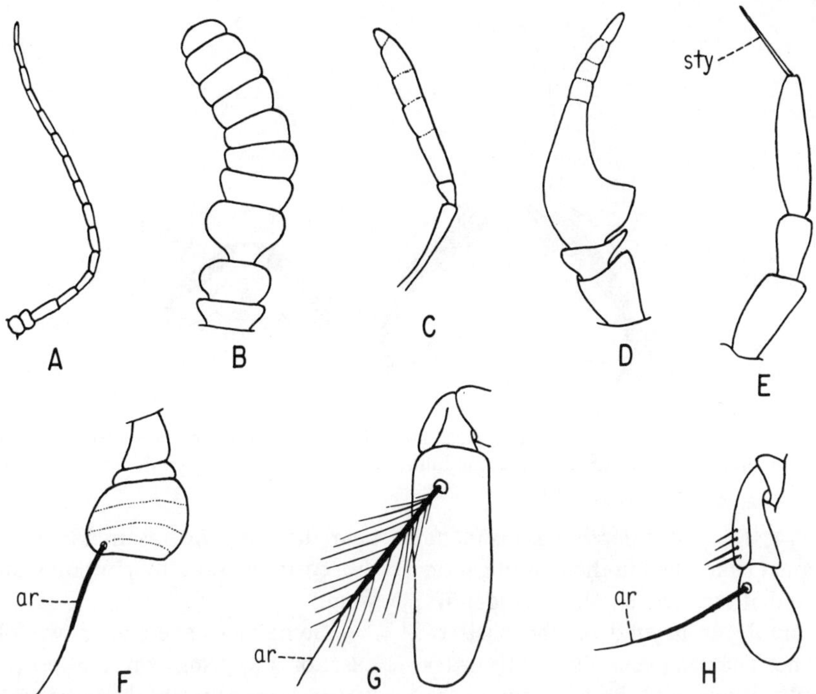

Fig. 27-1. Antennae of Diptera. A, Mycetophílidae (*Mycomỳa*); B, Bibiónidae (*Bíbio*); C, Stratiomỳidae (*Stratìomys*); D, Tabánidae (*Tabànus*); E, Asílidae (*Asìlus*); F, Stratiomỳidae (*Ptécticus*); G, Calliphóridae (*Callíphora*); H, Tachínidae (*Epálpus*). *ar*, arista, *sty*, style.

marked as the divisions between the three principal segments. Many of the Brachýcera bear an elongate process called a style at the end of the antenna (Figure 27-1 E); many bear a large bristle, the arista, on the third segment (Figure 27-1 G, H); the arista may be a simple bristle or it may be plumose. In some of the Cyclórrhapha the form of the second or third segment may serve to separate different groups; for example, the calypterate and acalypterate groups of muscoid flies differ in the structure of the second antennal segment.

THE LEGS: The principal leg characters used in separating families of flies are the structure of the empodium and the presence or absence of tibial spurs. The empodium (Figure 27-2, *emp*) is a structure arising from between the claws on the last tarsal segment; it is bristlelike or absent in most flies, but in a few families (Figure 27-2 B) it is large and membranous and resembles the pulvilli in appearance. The pulvilli are pads at the apex of the last tarsal segment, one at the base of each claw (Figure 27-2, *pul*). A fly may thus have two pads (the pulvilli), three pads (the pulvilli and a pulvilliform empodium), or no pads (pulvilli absent) on the last tarsal segment. Tibial spurs are spinelike structures, usually located at the distal end of the tibia (Figure 27-7, *tsp*). In some muscoid flies (Figure 27-26 B), there are bristles on the outer surface of the tibia just proximad of the apex; such bristles are spoken of as preapical tibial bristles (*ptbr*).

The body of most flies is more or less cylindrical, with the coxae situated very close together; in a few families the body is flattened and leathery, and the coxae are well separated (Figure 27-13). The coxae are generally short, but in some groups (for example, the fungus gnats, Figure 27-7) they are about as long as the femora.

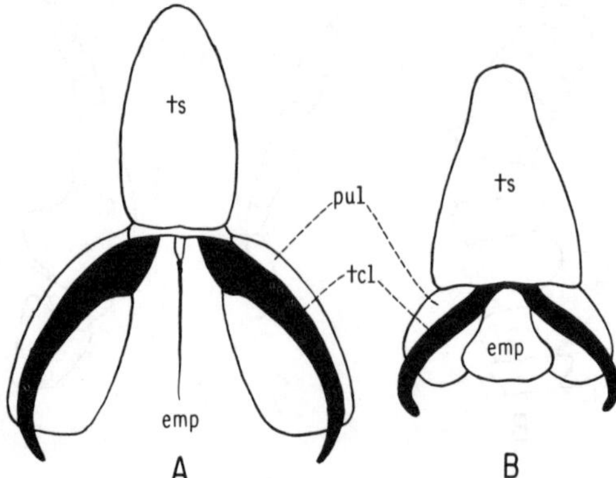

Fig. 27-2. Tip of tarsus, dorsal view. A, robber fly, with empodium bristlelike; B, horse fly, with empodium pulvilliform. *emp,* empodium; *pul,* pulvillus; *tcl,* tarsal claw; *ts,* last tarsal segment.

WING VENATION: Considerable use is made of venational characters in the identification of flies, and it is often possible to identify a fly to family or beyond on the basis of wings alone. The wing venation in this order is relatively simple, and the tendency in the higher families is toward a reduction in the number of veins.

There are two different terminologies of wing venation commonly used in this order. Most authorities use the Comstock-Needham system of naming the veins and cells (Figure 27-3 A), but not all agree with the Comstock-Needham interpretation of the venation. This interpretation has the media 3-branched; some authorities (Tillyard and others) say it is 4-branched, and label Cu_1 of the Comstock-Needham system vein as M_4; according to Tillyard, the Comstock-Needham Cu_2 is Cu_1, 1A is Cu_2, 2A is 1A, and 3A is 2A. All authorities do not agree in naming the branches of the radius. Many use terms of the older system (Figure 27-3 B), particularly for certain wing cells.

A closed cell is one that does not reach the wing margin (for example, the anal or 1A cell in Figure 27-3). When the thickening of the anterior edge of the wing (the costa) ends near the wing tip (as in Figure 27-6 B-F), the costa is said to extend only to the wing tip; where there is no abrupt thinning of the anterior margin of the wing near the wing tip (as in Figure 27-6 G-I), the costa is said to continue around the wing.

Some flies have one or two lobes at the base of the wing, on the posterior side, which fold beneath the base of the wing when the wing is folded back over the abdomen; these lobes are the calypters (also called alulae or squamae) (Figure 27-3, *cal*). The size of the calypters is frequently used to distinguish families or groups of families.

Many of the muscoid flies have one or two points in the costa where the sclerotization is weak or lacking or the vein appears to be broken; such points are termed costal breaks, and may occur near the end of R_1 and (or) the humeral cross-vein (Figures 27-22 A, B, and 27-23 C-E, *cbr*). Costal breaks are best seen with transmitted light. A few muscoids have a series of long hairs or bristles along the costa beyond the end of R_1 (Figure 27-22 H); the costa in such cases is said to be spinose.

CHAETOTAXY: In the identification of certain flies, particularly the muscoid groups, much use is made of the number, size, position, and arrangement of the larger bristles on the head and thorax. The terminology used in the chaetotaxy of flies is illustrated in Figures 27-4 and 27-5.

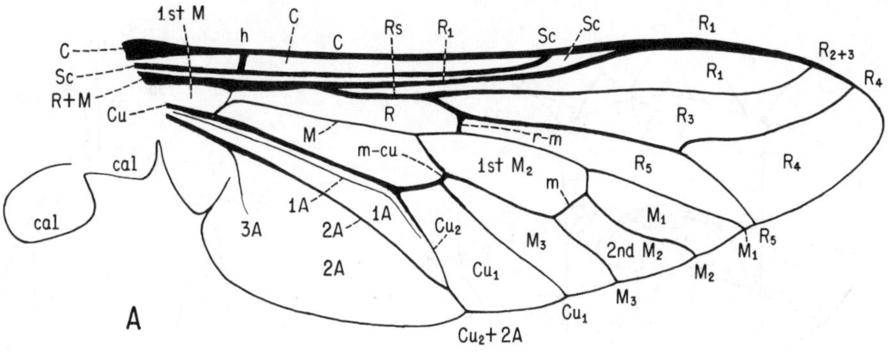

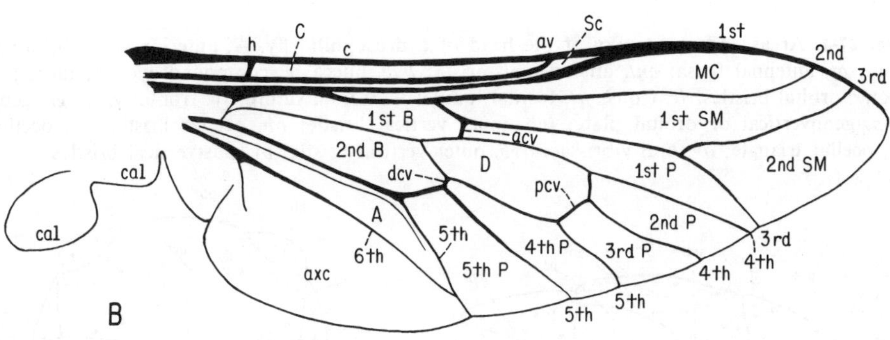

Fig. 27-3. Wing of a horse fly (*Tabànus*), showing venational terminologies. A, the Comstock-Needham system (for key to lettering, see page 15, Chap. 2); B, the older system, in which the longitudinal veins are numbered. Labeling in B: *A*, anal cell; *acv*, anterior cross-vein; *av*, auxiliary vein; *axc*, axillary cell; *B*, basal cells (first and second); *C*, costal cell; *c*, costal vein; *cal*, calypters; *D*, discal cell; *dcv*, discal cross-vein; *h*, humeral cross-vein; *MC*, marginal cell; *P*, posterior cells; *pcv*, posterior cross-vein; *Sc*, subcostal cell; *SM*, submarginal or apical cells (first and second).

HEAD AND THORACIC SUTURES: The principal head suture used in identification of flies is the frontal suture (Figure 27-4, *fs*). In the Cyclórrhapha the adult emerges from the puparium through a circular opening at the anterior end; this opening is made by pushing out the end of the puparium with a structure called the ptilinum. The ptilinum is a saclike structure that is everted from the front of the head, above the base of the antennae; after emergence the ptilinum is withdrawn into the head, and in most families of Cyclórrhapha, a suture remains through which the ptilinum was everted. This suture is called the frontal suture, and is usually in the shape of an inverted **U**. Between the apex of the **U** and the base of the antennae is a small crescent-shaped sclerite called the frontal lunule (*frl*). The presence of this suture distinguishes the muscoid flies from other flies. In cases where the complete suture is difficult to see, the flies possessing it can be recognized by the presence of a frontal lunule above the base of the antennae.

A transverse suture across the anterior part of the mesonotum (Figure 27-5, *trs*) separates most of the calypterate from the acalypterate muscoids. The calypterate muscoids usually have sutures in the lateroposterior portions of the mesonotum, which separate the posterior calli (Figure 27-5,

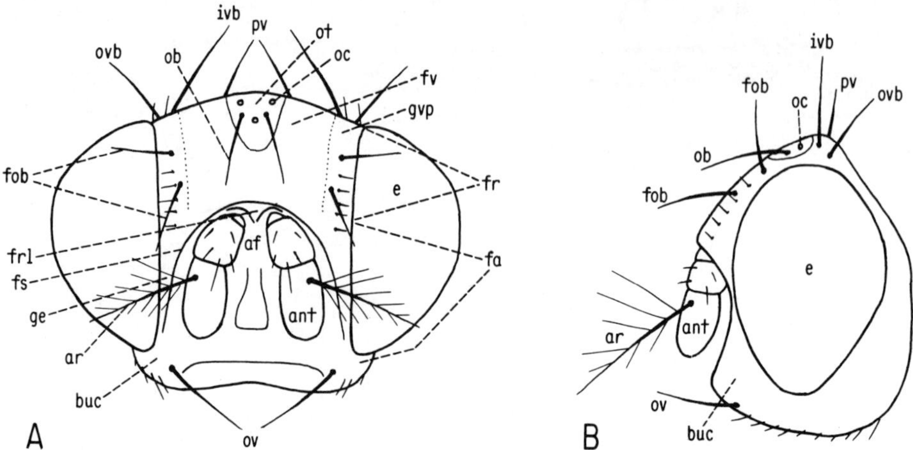

Fig. 27-4. Areas and chaetotaxy of the head of a drosophilid fly. A, anterior view; B, lateral view. *af*, antennal fossa; *ant*, antenna; *ar*, arista; *buc*, bucca; *e*, compound eye; *fa*, face; *fob*, fronto-orbital bristles; *fr*, frons; *frl*, frontal lunule; *fs*, frontal suture; *fv*, frontal vitta; *ge*, gena; *gvp*, genovertical or orbital plate; *ivb*, inner vertical bristle; *ob*, ocellar bristle; *oc*, ocellus; *ot*, ocellar triangle; *ov*, oral vibrissae; *ovb*, outer vertical bristle; *pv*, postvertical bristles.

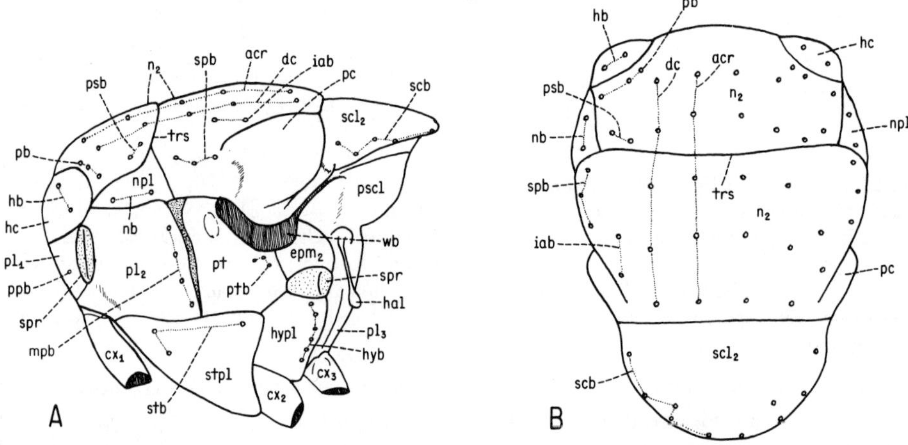

Fig. 27-5. Areas and chaetotaxy of the thorax of a blow fly. A, lateral view; B, dorsal view. *acr*, arostichal bristles; *cx*, coxae; *dc*, dorsocentral bristles; epm_2, mesepimeron; *hal*, haltere; *hb*, humeral bristles; *hc*, humeral callus; *hyb*, hypopleural bristles; *hypl*, hypopleuron; *iab*, intra-alar bristles; *mpb*, mesopleural bristles; n_2, mesonotum; *nb*, notopleural bristles; *npl*, notopleuron; *pb*, posthumeral bristles; *pc*, posterior callus; pl_1, propleuron; pl_2, mesopleuron; pl_3, metapleuron; *ppb*, propleural bristles; *psb*, presutural bristles; *pscl*, postscutellum; *pt*, pteropleuron; *ptb*, pteropleural bristles; *scb*, scutellar bristles; scl_2, mesoscutellum; *spb*, supra-alar bristles; *spr*, spiracle; *stb*, sternopleural bristles; *stpl*, sternopleuron; *trs*, transverse suture; *wb*, base of wing.

pc); these sutures are lacking in the acalypterate muscoids.

SIZE: In the keys and descriptions in this chapter "medium-sized" means about the size of a house fly or blue-bottle fly; "small" means smaller, and "large" means larger than this size. "Very small" or "minute" means less than 3 millimeters in length, and "very large" means an inch or more in length.

The following key includes all the families of flies occurring in the United States; the groups marked with an asterisk are relatively rare or are unlikely to be taken by the general collector, and couplets containing such groups may often be skipped in running a specimen through the key. The beginner is likely to encounter difficulty in some parts of the key, particularly in the couplets beyond 54, which deal with the muscoid flies, and he should become thoroughly familiar with the characters of these flies, particularly of head and thoracic structure and chaetotaxy, before attempting to run a specimen through this part of the key. We recommend that the beginner not worry too much if he is unable to key-out some of the smaller muscoids. A microscope of considerable magnification (90-120×) may be necessary to see the characters of some of the smaller flies. Many of the smaller Diptera other than muscoids can be recognized by wing venation alone, and the student is therefore advised to become familiar with the venational characters of this order.

KEY TO THE FAMILIES OF DIPTERA

1. Wings present and well developed 2

1′. Wings absent or greatly reduced 124*

2(1). Antennae composed of 6 or more freely articulated segments (Figure 27-1 A, B); in some males very long-plumose (Figures 27-32 B, D and 27-37 C) 3

2′. Antennae composed of 5 or fewer (usually 3) freely articulated segments, the third occasionally annulated and often bearing a style or arista (Figure 27-1 C-H), never long-plumose 27

3(2). Mesonotum with a **V**-shaped suture; legs long and slender (Figure 27-27 A) 4

3′. Mesonotum without a **V**-shaped suture 7

4(3). Ocelli present .... **Trichocéridae** p. 469

4′. Ocelli absent 5

5(4′). R 5-branched, all 5 branches reaching the wing margin; a cross-vein in the M_3 cell .... **Tanydéridae*** p. 470

5′. R with 4 or fewer branches reaching wing margin; M_3 cell without a cross-vein 6

6(5′). Only 1 anal vein reaching wing margin; R 4-branched; no closed discal cell (Figure 27-28 A); pulvilli present, empodium minute **Ptychoptéridae** p. 470

6′. Two anal veins reaching wing margin; R 2- to 4-branched; a closed discal cell usually present (Figure 27-28 B); pulvilli absent, empodium present .... **Tipùlidae** p. 469

7(3′). Wings large, broadest in basal fourth, densely covered with fine hairs; true veins almost absent, but a fanlike development of folds present; antennae very long, at least 3 times as long as body, and 6-segmented; ocelli and mouth parts absent; western United States .... **Deuterophlebìidae*** p. 471

7′. Not exactly fitting the above description 8

8(7′). Ocelli present 9

8′. Ocelli absent 19

9(8). Costa continuing around the wing, though weakened behind; venation reduced, with less than 9 veins reaching wing margin (Figure 27-6 A) .... **Cecidomyìidae** p. 478

9′. Costa ending at or near wing tip (Figures 27-6 C-F, 27-43) 10

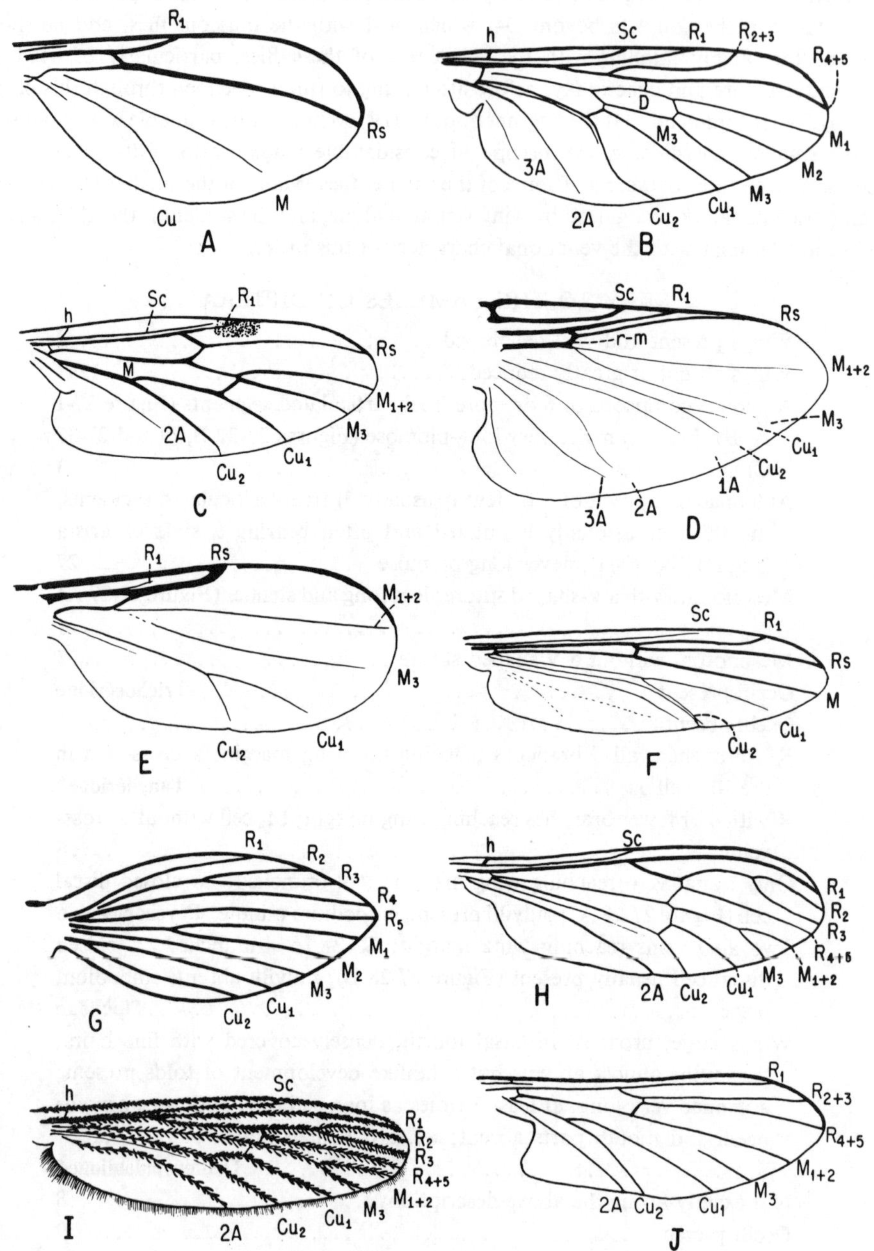

Fig. 27-6. Wings of Nematócera. A, Cecidomyìidae; B, Anisopódidae (*Anìsopus*); C. Bibiónidae (*Bíbio*); D, Simulìidae (*Simùlium*); E, Ceratopogónidae; F, Chironómidae; G, Psychódidae (*Psychòda*); H, Dixidae (*Díxa*); I, Culícidae (*Psoróphora*); J, Blephàricéridae (*Blepharícera*). *D*, discal cell.

10(9′). Discal (first M_2) cell present 11

10′. Discal cell absent (Figures 27-6 C-F, 27-43)......................12

11(10). Fourth posterior (M_3) cell open (Figure 27-6 B) (*Anìsopus*)..**Anisopódidae** p. 477

11′. Fourth posterior cell closed; medium-sized, elongate flies resembling sawflies (*Rachícerus*) ....**Xylophágidae*** p. 480

12(10′). Like a crane fly, with long legs; tibial spurs reduced or lacking; anal angle of wing projecting (Figure 27-6 J); wings sometimes with a network of delicate lines between the veins...........**Blepharicéridae*** p. 470

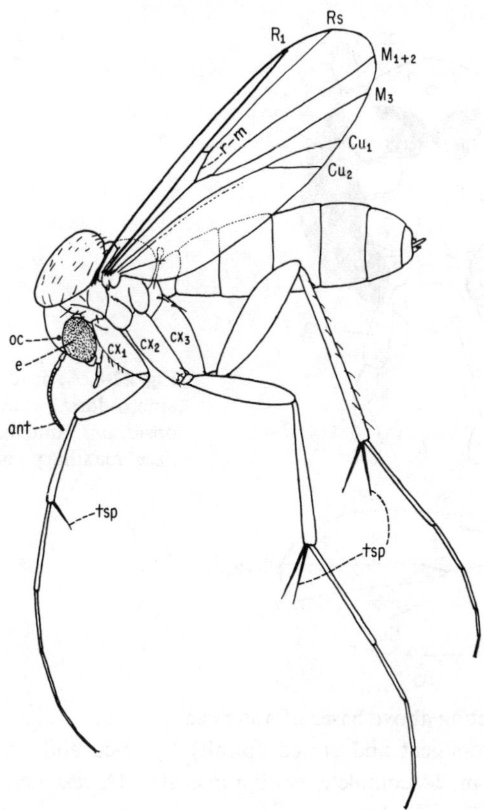

Fig. 27-7. A typical fungus gnat (Mycetophílidae). *ant,* antenna; *cx,* coxa; *e,* compound eye; *oc,* ocellus; *tsp,* tibial spurs.

12′. Legs and tibial spurs variable; wings variable, but if anal angle of wing is projecting, then the legs are short and the insect is not like a crane fly; wings without a network of delicate lines between the veins 13

13(12′). Pulvilli present; second basal (M) cell present (Figure 27-6 C); antennae usually shorter than thorax, rather stout (Figure 27-1 B), and arising low on face, below compound eyes (Figure 27-41); tibiae with apical spurs ....**Bibiónidae** p. 477

13′. Pulvilli absent or very minute; second basal cell absent or imperfectly developed (Figure 27-43); antennae variable in length, usually arising about middle of compound eyes or higher; tibial spurs present or absent 14

14(13′). Tibiae with apical spurs; coxae usually long (Figure 27-7); antennae usually longer than thorax 15

14′. Tibiae usually without apical spurs; coxae short; antennae short and stout; minute brown or black flies, 3 mm in length or less..........18

15(14). Rs 3-branched; R_2 appearing much like a cross-vein, extending from R_{2+3} to about the end of R_1 (*Axymỳia*).............. **Pachyneùridae*** p. 477

15′. Rs simple or 2-branched 16

16(15′). Eyes meeting above bases of antennae (Figure 27-8 A) ....**Sciáridae** p. 478

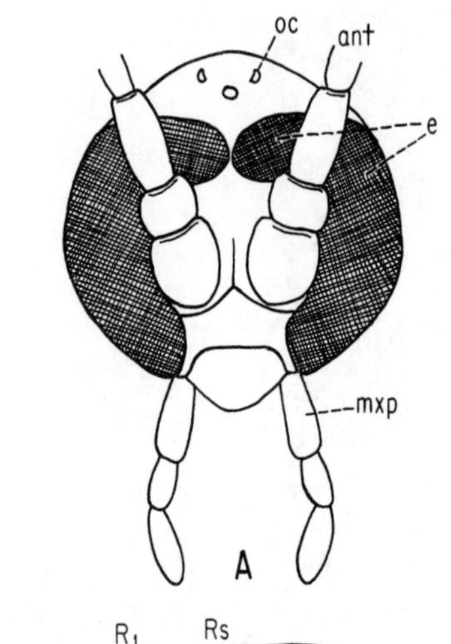

Fig. 27-8. A, head of *Scìara* (Sciáridae), antero-dorsal view; B, wing of a scatopsid. *ant,* antenna; *e,* compound eye; *mxp,* maxillary palpus; *oc,* ocellus.

16′. Eyes not meeting above bases of antennae 17

17(16′). Basal cells confluent and closed apically by m-cu and r-m; Rs forked opposite r-m; Sc complete, ending in costa; 2A reaching wing margin (*Mycetòbia*) ....**Anisopódidae*** p. 477

17′. Basal cells variable; Rs simple, or if forked, then the fork is distad of r-m or r-m is obliterated by the fusion of Rs and M; Sc and 2A variable; a large and widespread group........................**Mycetophílidae** p. 478

18(14′). Rs forked; costa extending beyond end of R_{4+5} and almost to wing tip; palpi 3- to 4-segmented; antennae 12-segmented......**Hyperoscélidae*** p. 478

18′. Rs not forked; costa extending only to end of Rs and, at most, only about three-fourths of the wing length (Figure 27-8 B); palpi 1-segmented; antennae 7- to 12-segmented ....**Scatópsidae** p. 478

19(8′). Costa ending at or near wing tip (Figures 27-6 B-F, 27-42, 27-43) 20

19′. Costa continuing around wing tip, though often weaker along hind margin of wing (Figure 27-6 G, I).............................22

20(19). Wings broad, the posterior veins weak (Figure 27-6 D); antennae about as long as head; dark-colored flies, rarely over 3 mm in length, with a somewhat humpbacked appearance and short thick legs....**Simulìidae** p. 476

20′. Wings narrower, the posterior veins usually stronger (Figure 27-6 E, F) 21

21(20′). M forked (Figure 27-6 E); metanotum rounded, without a longitudinal groove; front legs not lengthened; mouth parts fitted for piercing .... **Ceratopogónidae** p. 475

21′. M not forked (Figure 27-6 F); metanotum usually with a longitudinal groove or keel; front legs lengthened; mouth parts not fitted for piercing .... **Chironómidae** p. 475

22(19′). Wings short, broad, pointed apically, usually densely hairy and held rooflike over body (Psychodìnae) or together above body (Phlebotomìnae) when at rest; Rs 4-branched; no cross-veins except near base of wing (Figure 27-6 G) .... **Psychódidae** p. 470

22′. Wings usually long and narrow, or if broad, then not pointed apically (Figure 27-6 H, I); wings held flat over abdomen when at rest; wings not densely hairy, though there may be scales along the wing veins or the wing margin; Rs with 3 or fewer branches 23

23(22′). Venation reduced, with less than 7 veins reaching wing margin 24

23′. Venation not reduced, with at least 9 veins reaching wing margin (Figure 27-6 H, I) 25

24(23). Wings with 7 longitudinal veins; antennae about as long as head, with the 2 basal segments thick and globose, the 10 remaining segments bristlelike; small, bare, reddish yellow or brownish flies .... **Thaumalèidae*** p. 474

24′. Wings usually with fewer than 7 longitudinal veins (Figure 27-6 A); antennae usually very long, at least in species with 7 longitudinal veins, and with 10 to 36 similar segments .... **Cecidomyìidae** p. 478

25(23′). Rs and its branches arched (Figure 27-6 H); wing veins and wing margin not fringed with scales; body and legs not scaly .... **Díxidae** p. 471

25′. Rs and its branches straight or nearly so; wing margin, and often also wing veins, fringed with scales (Figure 27-6 I) 26

26(25′). Proboscis long, extending far beyond clypeus (Figure 27-32); scales present on wing veins and wing margin, and usually also on body .... **Culícidae** p. 471

26′. Proboscis short, extending little beyond clypeus; scales, when present, mostly confined to wing margin .... **Chaobóridae** p. 471

27(2′). Empodia pulvilliform, the tarsi with 3 pads (Figure 27-2 B) 28

27′. Empodia bristlelike or absent, the tarsi with not more than 2 pads (Figure 27-2 A) 35

28(27). Third antennal segment annulated (Figure 27-1 C, D, F) 29

28′. Third antennal segment not annulated (Figure 27-1 E, G, H), and usually bearing an elongate style (Figure 27-1 E) or arista (Figure 27-1 G, H) 33

29(28). Calypters large and conspicuous; R_4 and R_5 divergent, enclosing wing tip (Figure 27-3) 30

29′. Calypters small or vestigial; R_4 and R_5 variable 31

30(29). Anal vein (2A) slightly sinuate, the anal cell open; hind tibiae with apical spurs; abdomen of female posterior to fourth segment modified into a slender retractile postabdomen; face swollen below antennae, the antennae arising above middle of head; eyes densely hairy; Pacific Coast .... **Pelecorhýnchidae*** p. 481

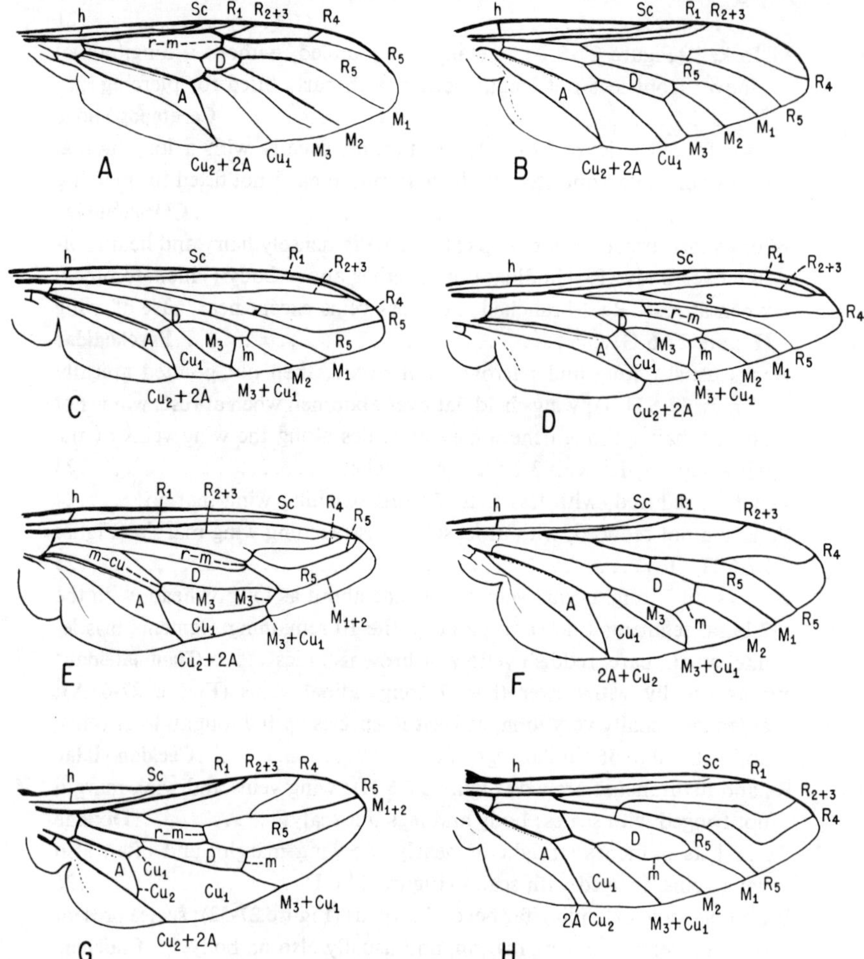

Fig. 27-9. Wings of Brachy̆cera. A, Stratiomy̆idae; B, Rhagiónidae; C, Asílidae (*Èrax*); D, Asílidae (*Prómachus*); E, Mýdidae (*My̆das*); F, Therévidae; G, Scenopínidae; H, Bombylìidae. *A*, anal (1A) cell; *D*, discal (first M_2) cell.

30′. Anal vein straight or gently curved, the anal cell closed at or before wing margin; hind tibiae with or without apical spurs; abdomen of female robust, not as above; antennae usually arising below middle of head; eyes usually bare; widely distributed .... **Tabánidae** p. 481

31(29′). At least middle tibiae with apical spurs; Rs usually arising distinctly proximal to base of discal cell; branches of R not crowded together near costal margin 32

31′. Tibial spurs lacking or, at most, middle tibiae with a slight apical spur; Rs arising opposite base of discal cell; branches of R sometimes crowded together near costal margin (Figure 27-9 A); R_5 (or R_{4+5} when it is not forked) ending before wing tip; M_3 cell open (the Pantophthálmidae, large robust tropical flies that may occur in extreme southern United

States, would key out here, but have R_5 ending beyond wing tip and the M_3 cell closed) .... **Stratiomỳidae** p. 481

32(31). M_3 cell closed; front tibiae without apical spurs .... **Xylomỳidae** p. 480

32′. M_3 cell open; front tibiae with an apical spur .... **Xylophágidae** p. 480

33(28′). Calypters very large; head very small and placed low down, and composed almost entirely of eyes; body appearing humpbacked (Figure 27-57); costa extending only to wing tip .... **Acrocéridae*** p. 486

33′. Calypters small or vestigial; head of normal size, the face or front broad; costa variable.. 34

34(33′). Costa usually ending at wing tip; venation peculiar, with many veins ending before wing tip; tibiae without apical spurs.... **Nemestrínidae*** p. 486

34′. Costa continuing around wing tip; venation normal (Figure 27-9 B); middle and hind tibiae usually with apical spurs.......... **Rhagiónidae** p. 482

35(27′). Wings rounded apically, with strong veins anteriorly and weak oblique veins posteriorly (Figure 27-10 G); antennae apparently 1-segmented, with a long arista; hind legs long, the femora flattened laterally; small or minute flies with a humpbacked appearance (Figure 27-61).. **Phóridae** p. 489

35′. Wings with normal venation or pointed at apex; antennae not as above 36

36(35′). R_{4+5} forked (Figure 27-9) or at least the radius appearing 4-branched (Figure 27-9 D) 37

36′. R_{4+5} not forked, the radius 3-branched (Figures 27-10 B-H, 27-11, 27-18, 27-22, 27-23) 44

37(36). Vertex sunken, the top of the head concave from anterior view, the eyes bulging (Figure 27-56 B) 38

37′. Vertex little or not at all sunken, the eyes not bulging................ 39

38(37). Body usually with hair or bristles, the face bearded; M_1 not ending before wing tip (Figure 27-9 C, D); 3 ocelli; antennae usually 3-segmented.. .... **Asílidae** p. 484

38′. Body and face usually bare; M_1 curved forward and ending at or before wing tip (Figure 27-9 E); 1 ocellus or none; antennae 4-segmented.... .... **Mỳdidae** p. 484

39(37′). Five posterior cells (Figure 27-9 F); abdomen long and tapering...... 40

39′. Four or fewer posterior cells (Figures 27-9 G, H and 27-10 A); abdomen usually oval or oblong.. 41

40(39). R_5 and M_1 curving forward and ending before wing tip; rare flies occurring in arid regions of the West .... **Apiocéridae*** p. 484

40′. R_5 and M_1 not curving forward, ending beyond wing tip (Figure 27-9 F); widely distributed .... **Therévidae** p. 484

41(39′). M_1 ending at or before wing tip; costa not continuing beyond wing tip; 3 posterior cells (Figure 27-9 G).................... **Scenopínidae*** p. 484

41′. M_1 ending beyond wing tip; costa usually continuing beyond wing tip; usually 4 posterior cells (Figures 27-9 H and 27-10 A) 42

42(41′). Anal cell open (Figure 27-9 H), or closed near wing margin; body usually hairy and robust (Figure 27-58) 43

42′. Anal cell closed far from wing margin (Figure 27-10 A), or absent; body not hairy and usually not robust (Figure 27-59)............ **Empídidae** p. 486

43(42). A closed discal cell present.............................. **Bombylìidae** p. 486

43′. No closed discal cell .... **Hilarimórphidae*** p. 483

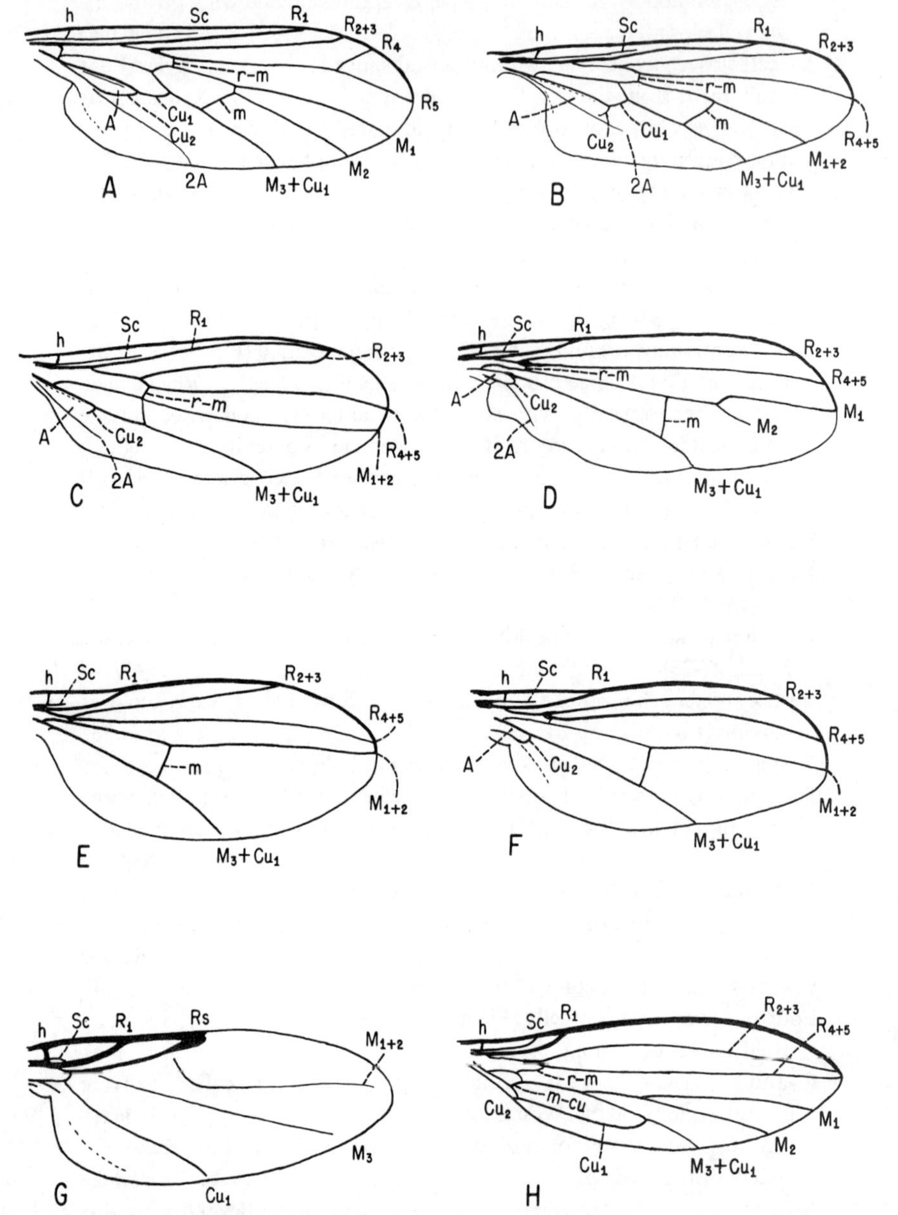

Fig. 27-10. Wings of Brachýcera and Cyclórrhapha. A-C, Empídidae; D-F, Dolichopódidae; G, Phóridae; H, Lonchoptéridae. *A*, anal (1A) cell.

44(36′). Wings pointed at apex and with no cross-veins except at base (Figure 27-10 H); small, slender, brownish or yellowish flies, 2 to 5 mm in length.... .... **Lonchoptéridae** p. 489

44′. Wings rounded at apex, almost always with cross-veins beyond base of wing (Figures 27-10 B-F, 27-11, 27-18, 27-22, 27-23)..............45

45(44′). Anal cell elongate, longer than second basal (M) cell, usually pointed apically and narrowed or closed near wing margin (Figure 27-11); no frontal suture (Figure 27-12); head bristles usually lacking. 46

45′. Anal cell usually shorter, closed some distance from wing margin, or lacking (Figures 27-10 C-F, 27-18, 27-22, 27-23); if the anal cell is elongate and pointed apically (Figure 27-22 C), then a frontal suture is present; head bristles usually present 50

46(45). Proboscis longer than head, slender, stiff, and often folding; face broad, with grooves below antennae; abdomen clavate, bent downward at apex (Figure 27-65); R_5 cell closed and pointed apically (Figure 27-11 D) . . . . **Conópidae** p. 490

46′. Proboscis small, rarely elongated; face narrow, without grooves below antennae; abdomen and R_5 cell variable 47

47(46′). R_5 cell closed; usually a spurious vein crossing r-m between R_{4+5} and M_1 (Figure 27-11 A-C) . . . .**Sýrphidae** p. 490

47′. R_5 cell open, though sometimes narrowed apically; no spurious vein. . 48

48(47′). Sc more or less reduced, and not reaching costa (Figure 27-10 B, C); proboscis slender and rigid; male genitalia terminal and not folded forward under abdomen (Figure 27-59) . . . .**Empídidae** p. 486

48′. Sc complete, ending in costa; proboscis small and soft; male genitalia usually folded forward under abdomen. 49

49(48′). Arista dorsal; head very large, hemispherical, the face very narrow (Figures 27-12 B and 27-62); hind tibiae and tarsi not dilated. . . . . **Pipuncùlidae** p. 490

49′. Arista terminal; head not unusually large, the face small and broad; hind tibiae and tarsi dilated, especially in male (Figure 27-26 C) **Platypézidae*** p. 489

50(45′). Frontal suture absent (Figure 27-12) 51

50′. Frontal suture present (Figures 27-4 A, 27-24, 27-25). 53

51(50). Head very large, hemispherical, the face very narrow (Figures 27-12 B and 27-62). . . . .**Pipuncùlidae** p. 490

51′. Head not unusually large; face variable. 52

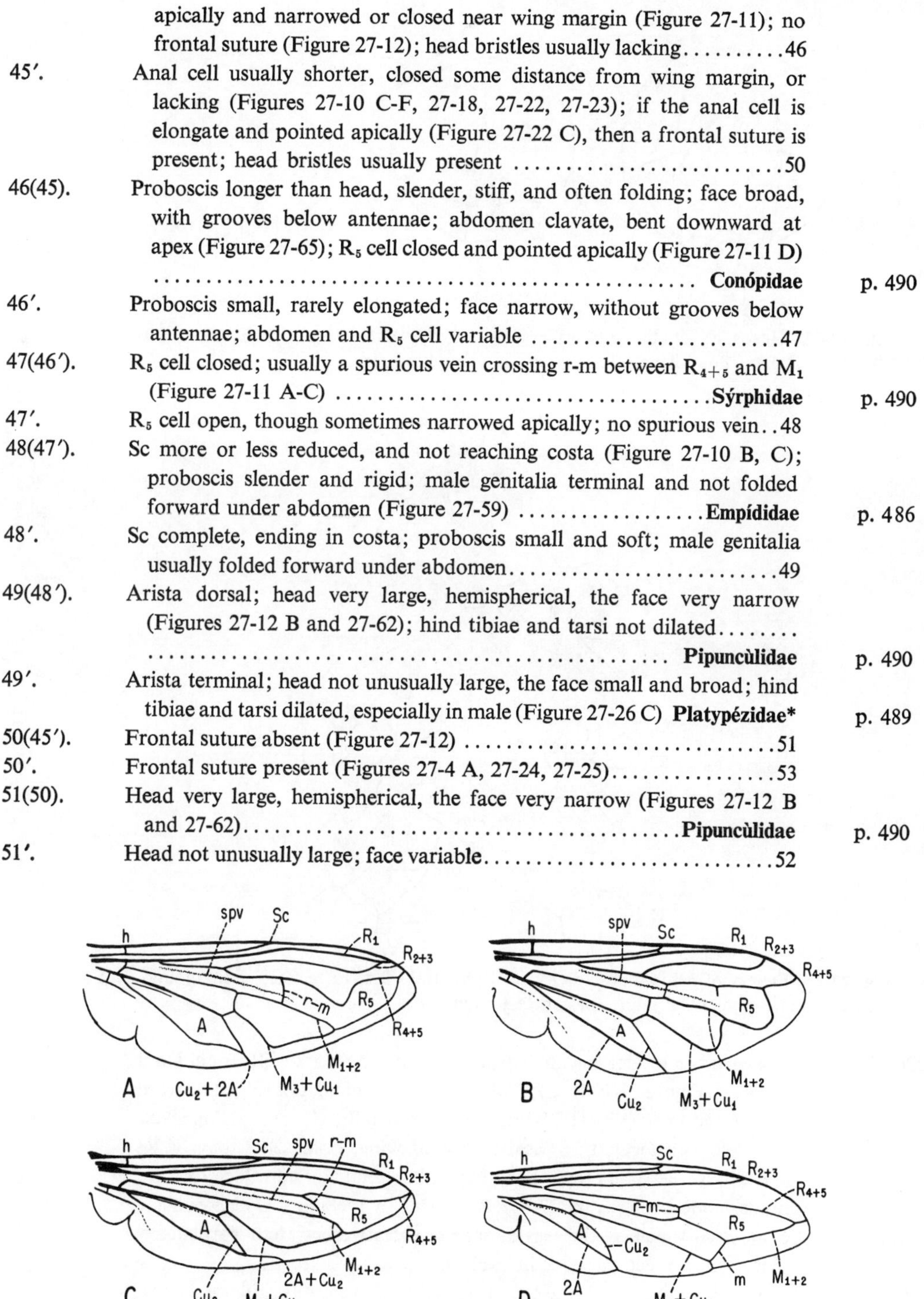

Fig. 27-11. Wings of Sýrphidae (A-C) and Conópidae (D). A, *Tubífera;* B, Mìcrodon; C, *Spilomỳia;* D, *Physocéphala.* A, anal (1A) cell. *spv,* spurious vein.

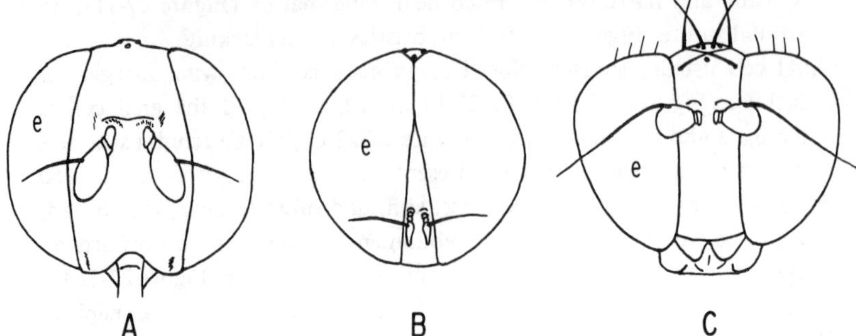

Fig. 27-12. Heads of Diptera, anterior view. A, Sýrphidae (*Metasýrphus*); B, Pipuncùlidae (*Dórilus*); C, Dolichopódidae (*Dolíchopus*). *e*, compound eye.

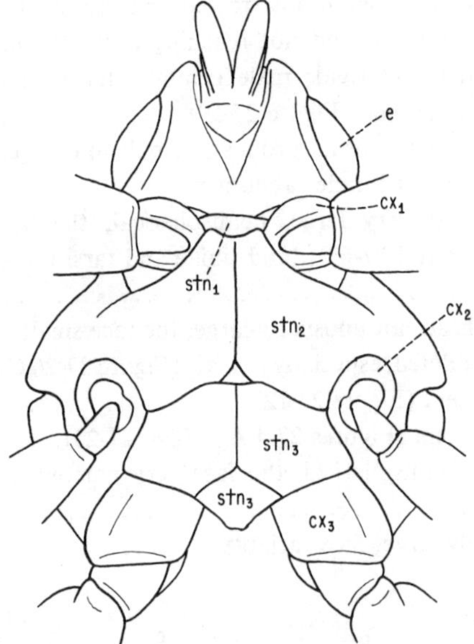

Fig. 27-13. Thorax of a hippoboscid (*Lýnchia*), ventral view. *cx*, coxae; *e*, compound eye; stn_1, prosternum; stn_2, mesosternum; stn_3, metasternum.

52(51′). Cross-vein r-m located beyond basal fourth of wing; fork of Rs usually not swollen (Figure 27-10 B, C); male genitalia terminal, not folded forward under abdomen (Figure 27-59); body not metallic..........**Empídidae** p. 486

52′. Cross-vein r-m located in basal fourth of wing, or absent; fork of Rs usually swollen (Figure 27-10 D-F); male genitalia often folded forward under abdomen (Figure 27-60); body usually metallic..**Dolichopódidae** p. 487

53(50′). Coxae close together, the legs attached ventrally; body not particularly flattened; not ectoparasitic in habit 54

53′. Coxae widely separated, the legs attached lateroventrally (Figure 27-13); ectoparasites of birds, mammals, or bees 123*

54(53). Second antennal segment with a longitudinal seam along upper outer side (Figure 27-14); thorax usually with a complete transverse suture (Figure

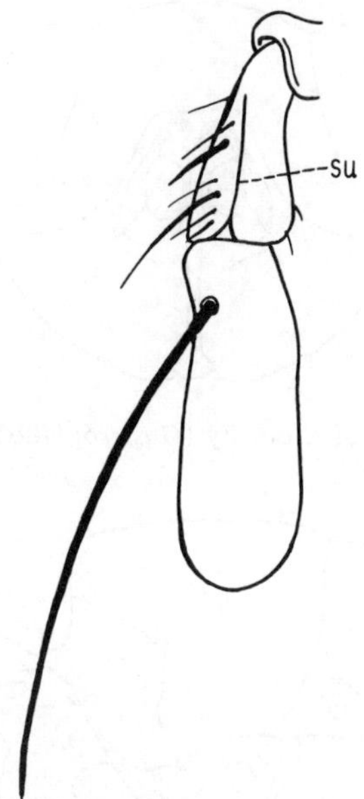

Fig. 27-14. Antenna of a tachinid, showing the suture (*su*) characteristic of the calypterate muscoid flies.

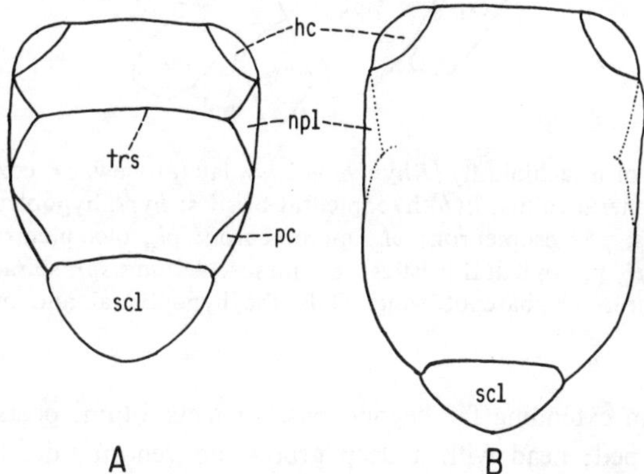

Fig. 27-15. Mesonota of muscoid flies. A, calypterate muscoid; B, acalypterate muscoid. *hc*, humeral callus; *npl*, notopleuron; *pc*, posterior callus; *scl*, scutellum; *trs*, transverse suture.

27-15 A); lower or innermost calypter usually large (calypterate muscoid flies, except *Loxócera*, family Psílidae) 55

54′. Second antennal segment without such a seam; thorax usually without a complete transverse suture (Figure 27-15 B); lower calypter usually small or rudimentary (acalypterate muscoid flies) 62

55(54). Mouth opening small, the mouth parts vestigial or lacking (Figure 27-16); body hairy, but not bristly (bot and warble flies) 56*

55′. Mouth opening normal, the mouth parts functional; body usually with bristles..57

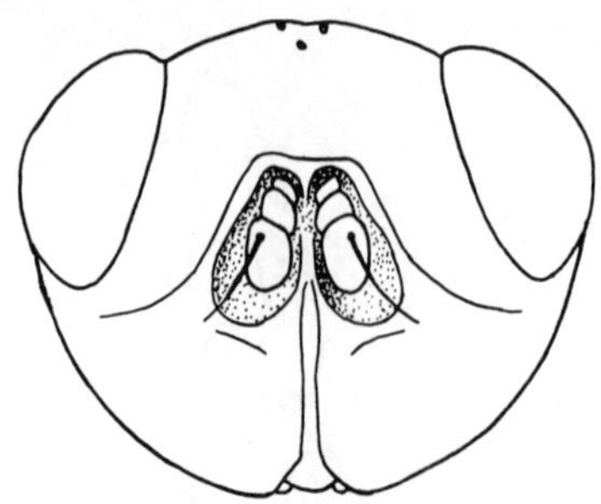

Fig. 27-16. Head of a bot fly (*Gasteróphilus*), anterior view.

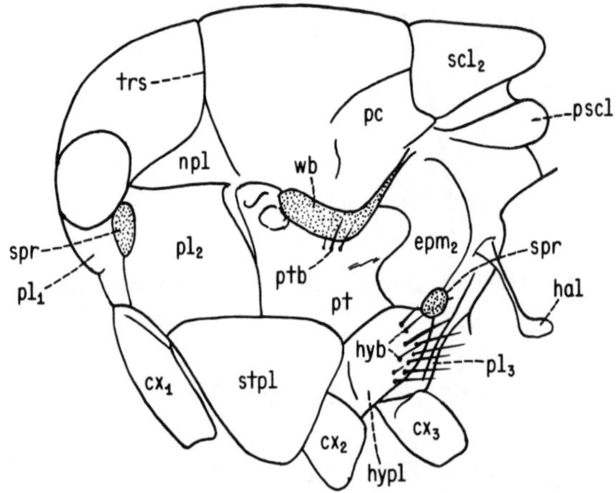

Fig. 27-17. Thorax of a tachinid fly (*Rhynchiodéxia*), lateral view. *cx,* coxa; *epm_2*, mesepimeron; *hal,* haltere; *hc,* humeral callus; *hyb,* hypopleural bristles; *hypl,* hypopleuron; *npl,* notopleuron; *pc,* posterior callus; *pl_1*, propleuron; *pl_2*, mesopleuron; *pl_3*, metapleuron; *pscl,* postscutellum; *pt,* pteropleuron; *ptb,* pteropleural bristles; *scl_2*, mesoscutellum; *spr,* spiracle; *stpl,* sternopleuron; *trs,* transverse suture; *wb,* base of wing. Only the hypopleural and pteropleural bristles are shown.

56(55). Scutellum extending far beyond base of metanotum; postscutellum not developed; head with a deep groove on ventral side, the palpi not visible; arista bare or plumose .... **Cuterébridae*** p. 507

56′. Scutellum very short; postscutellum usually well developed (see Figure 27-17, *pscl*); head apparently closed on ventral side, the palpi usually large; arista bare.. **Oéstridae*** p. 507

57(55′). Postscutellum developed (Figure 27-17, *pscl*); hypopleura and pteropleura with bristles (Figure 27-17, *hyb, ptb*); R_5 cell usually narrowed or closed apically (Figure 27-18 A); abdominal terga usually with strong bristles in addition to finer hairs; edges of abdominal terga overlapping sterna; arista usually bare .... **Tachínidae** p. 505

57′. Postscutellum not developed (Figure 27-5 A); hypopleura, R_5 cell, and abdominal terga variable; arista usually plumose, at least in part....58

58(57′). Hypopleura and pteropleura with bristles; R_5 cell narrowed or closed apically 59

58′. Hypopleura usually without bristles; if hypopleural bristles are present, then there are no pteropleural bristles, or the proboscis is rigid and fitted for piercing, or the R_5 cell is not narrowed apically..........60

59(58). Hindmost posthumeral bristle located laterad of presutural bristle, and usually 2 (rarely 3) notopleural bristles (Figure 27-19 A); arista usually plumose beyond basal half; propleura usually pubescent; body often metallic...**Calliphóridae** p. 504

59′. Hindmost posthumeral bristle located even with or mesad of presutural bristle, and usually 4 notopleural bristles (Figure 27-19 B); arista generally plumose only in basal half; propleura bare; body not metallic .... **Sarcophágidae** p. 505

60(58′). Oral vibrissae present; mesonotum with bristles 61

60′. Oral vibrissae absent; mesonotum without bristles except above the wings; third antennal segment longer than arista (Figure 27-20) (*Loxócera*).. .... **Psílidae** p. 491

61(60). Sixth vein (Cu_2+2A) reaching wing margin, at least as a fold (Figure 27-18 C); 1 sternopleural bristle (Figure 27-21 A, *stb*) or under surface of scutellum with fine erect hairs (a few exceptions); arista never pectinate on upper side only.........................**Anthomyìidae** p. 501

61′. Sixth vein never reaching wing margin (Figure 27-18 B, D); usually more than 1 sternopleural bristle; under surface of scutellum usually without fine erect hairs; arista variable, but may be pectinate on upper side only ....**Múscidae** p. 501

62(54′). Mouth parts vestigial, the mouth opening small (Figure 27-16); R_{4+5} and M_{1+2} diverging distally ....**Gasterophílidae*** p. 503

62′. Mouth parts normal, the mouth opening large; R_5 and M_{1+2} parallel or converging distally 63

63(62′). Posterior spiracle of thorax with at least 1 bristle (Figure 27-21 D, *spbr*); palpi vestigial; head spherical; abdomen elongate and usually narrowed at base (Figure 27-72) ....**Sépsidae** p. 495

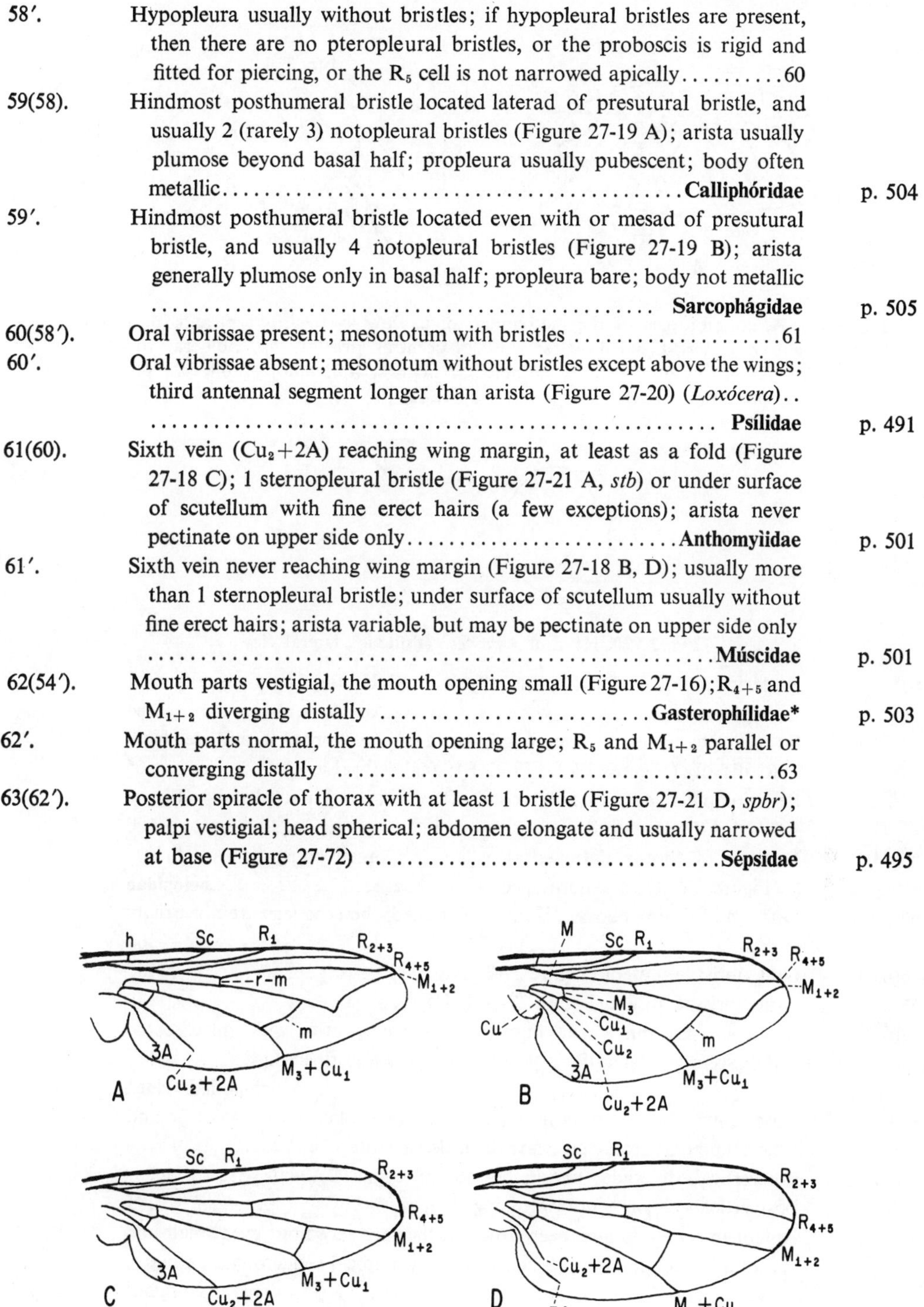

Fig. 27-18. Wings of calypterate muscoid flies. A, Tachínidae; B, Múscidae (*Musca*); C, Anthomyìidae (Scatomyzìnae); D, Múscidae (*Fánnia*).

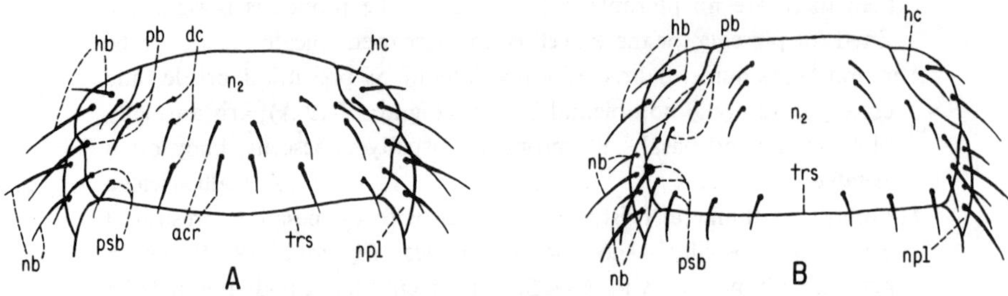

Fig. 27-19. A, anterior part of the mesonotum of a blow fly (*Callíphora*) and, B, a flesh fly (*Sarcóphaga*). *acr,* acrostichal bristles; *dc,* dorsocentral bristles; *hb,* humeral bristles; *hc,* humeral callus; n_2, mesonotum; *nb,* notopleural bristles; *npl,* notopleuron; *pb,* posthumeral bristles; *psb,* presutural bristles; *trs,* transverse suture.

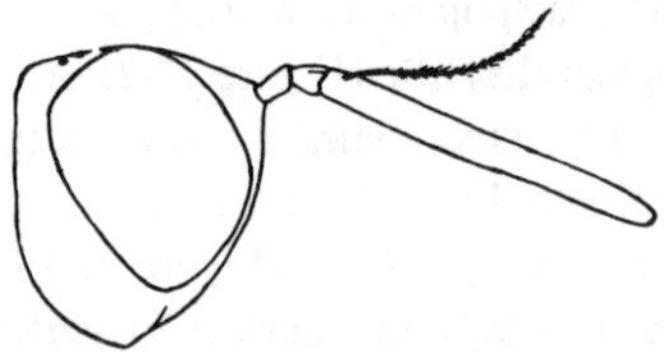

Fig. 27-20. Head of *Loxócera* (Psílidae), lateral view.

63′. Posterior spiracle of thorax usually without bristles; palpi usually well developed 64

64(63′). Sc complete or nearly so, ending in costa or just short of it, and free from R_1 distally (Figures 27-22, 27-23 F); anal cell present..............65

64′. Sc incomplete, not reaching costa, often fusing with R_1 distally (Figure 27-23 A-E); anal cell present or absent 100

65(64). Dorsum of thorax flattened; legs and abdomen conspicuously bristly (Figure 27-71); seashore species........................**Coelópidae** p. 494

65′. Dorsum of thorax convex; if rather flattened, then the legs are not bristly 66

66(65′). Oral vibrissae present (Figure 27-24 A-C, *ov*) 67

66′. Oral vibrissae absent (Figure 27-24 F-H) 78

67(66). Costa broken only near humeral cross-vein; eyes with microscopic pubescence; postverticals widely separated and diverging............ .... **Acartophthálmidae*** p. 499

67′. Costa entire, broken only near end of Sc, or broken near end of Sc and near humeral cross-vein; postverticals variable 68

68(67′). Postverticals diverging, parallel, or absent (Figure 27-24 A, B)........69

68′. Postverticals convergent or crossing (Figure 27-24 C)................75

69(68). Antennae retractile into deep grooves, the face receding; eyes small and round; scutellum long, flattened, with two apical setigerous tubercles.. .... **Thyreophóridae*** p. 495

69′. Antennae, face, and scutellum not as above........................70

70(69′). Second basal and discal cells confluent (Figure 27-22 A)............71*

70′. Second basal and discal cells separated (Figure 27-22 B) 72

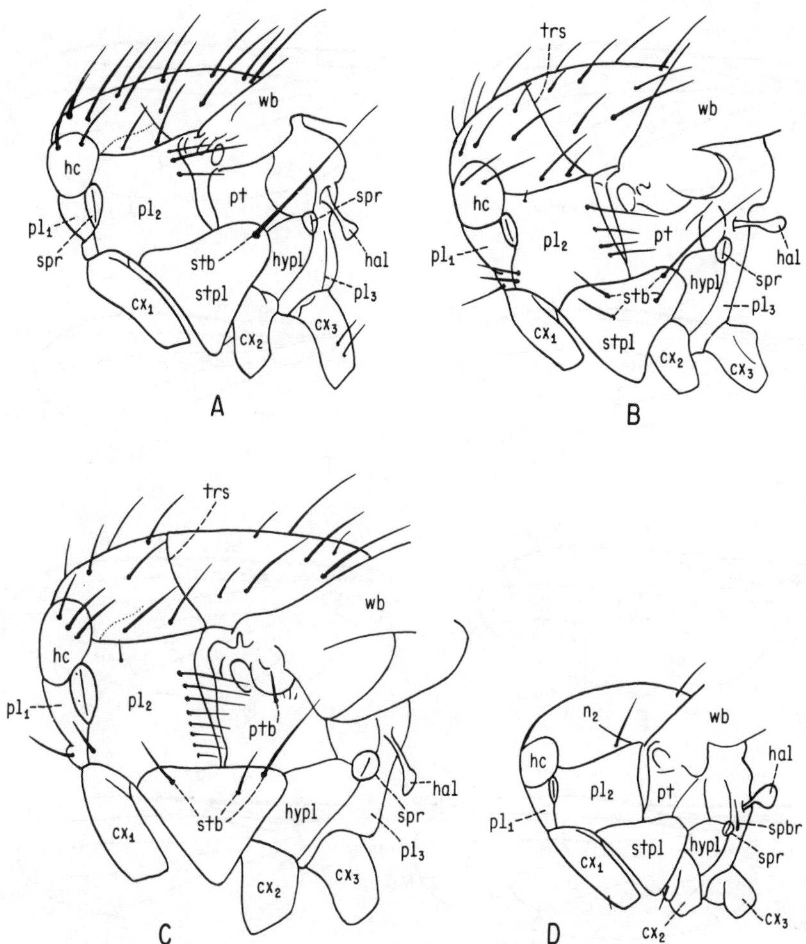

Fig. 27-21. Thorax of muscoid flies, lateral view. A, Anthomyìidae (*Scatóphaga*); B, Anthomyìidae (*Anthomỳia*); C, Múscidae (*Músca*); D, Sépsidae (*Themìra*). *cx,* coxa; *hal,* haltere; *hc,* humeral callus; *hypl,* hypopleuron; n_2, mesonotum; pl_1, propleuron; pl_2, mesopleuron; pl_3, metapleuron; *pt,* pteropleuron; *ptb,* pteropleural bristles; *spbr,* spiracular bristle; *spr,* spiracle; *stb,* sternopleural bristles; *stpl,* sternopleuron; *trs,* transverse suture; *wb,* base of wing.

71(70). Arista plumose; postverticals present and large; prescutellar acrostichal bristles strong .... **Curtonótidae*** p. 497

71′. Arista pubescent; postverticals lacking; prescutellar acrostichal bristles absent .... **Aulacigastéridae*** p. 501

72(70′). Two to 4 pairs of fronto-orbital bristles (Figure 27-24 A); second antennal segment usually with an angular projection on outer side; arista subapical (Figure 27-24 A) .... **Clusiódidae** p. 499

72′. At most 2 pairs of fronto-orbital bristles (Figure 27-24 B); second antennal segment without an angular projection on outer side; arista subbasal (Figure 27-24 B, H); small flies, rarely over 5 mm in length, usually shining black or metallic bluish 73

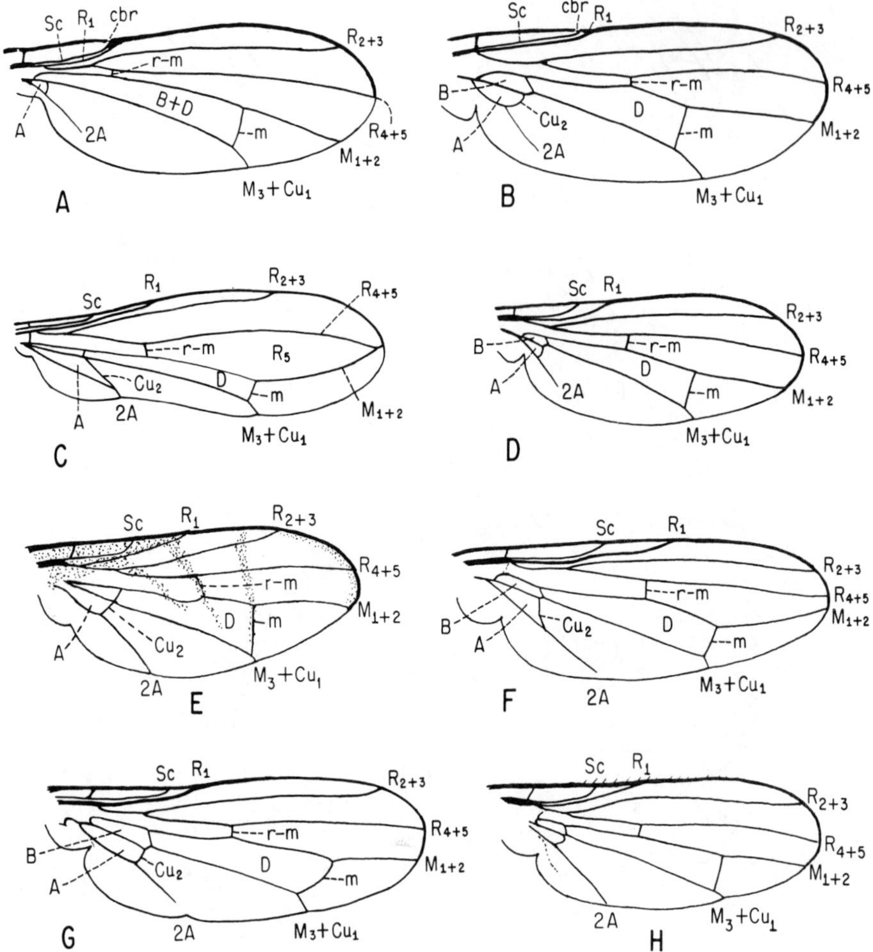

Fig. 27-22. Wings of acalypterate muscoid flies. A, Curtonótidae (*Curtonòtum*); B, Piophílidae (*Pióphila*); C, Micropézidae (*Taeniáptera*); D, Lauxanìidae (*Physegénua*); E, Platystomátidae (*Rivéllia*); F, Otítidae (*Acrosticta*); G, Sciomýzidae (*Sépedon*); H, Heleomýzidae (*Amoebalèria*). *A*, anal cell; *B*, second basal cell; *cbr*, costal break; *D*, discal (first M_2) cell.

73(72′). Eyes rounded (Figure 27-24 B); third antennal segment elongate-oval, not more than twice as long as wide 74

73′. Eyes semicircular (Figure 27-24 H); third antennal segment elongate, three or more times as long as wide; 2A usually undulate . . **Lonchaèidae** p. 497

74(73). Costa spinose (as in Figure 27-22 H); anal vein (2A) reaching wing margin; 4 to 5 sternopleurals; 2 pairs of fronto-orbitals; ocellar triangle large . . .. **Neottiophílidae*** p. 497

74′. Costa not spinose; anal vein not reaching wing margin (Figure 27-22 B); 2 sternopleurals; 0 to 2 pairs of fronto-orbitals; ocellar triangle of normal size .... **Piophílidae** p. 495

75(68′). Tibiae with dorsal preapical bristles; costa spinose (Figure 27-22 H); oral vibrissae well developed (Figure 27-24 C) 76

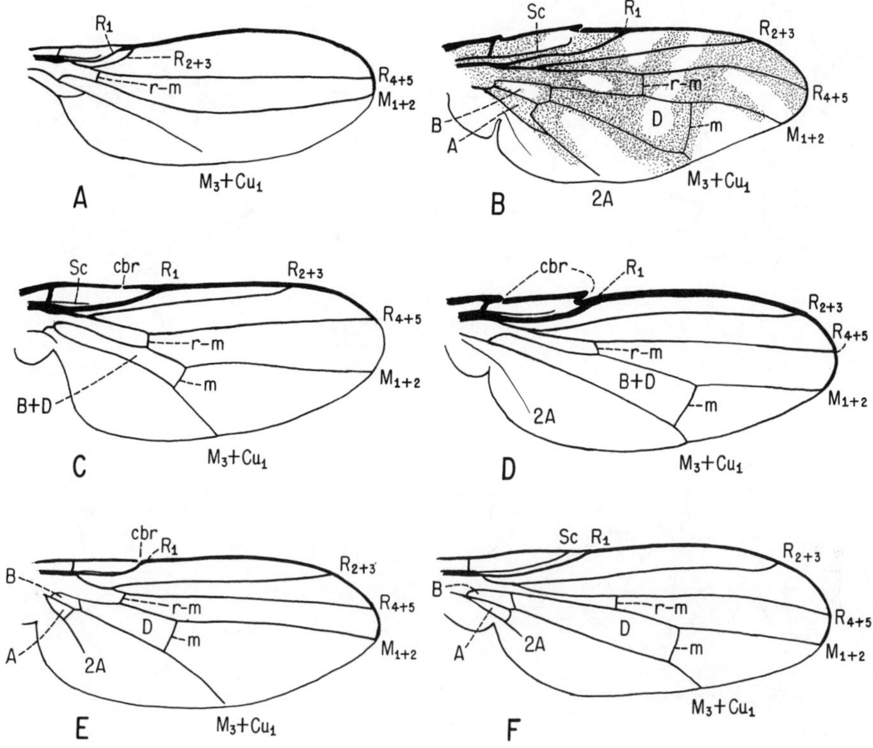

Fig. 27-23. Wings of acalypterate muscoid flies. A, Asteìidae (*Astèia*) (redrawn from Curran); B, Tephrítidae; C, Chlorópidae (*Epichlòrops*); D, Ephýdridae (*Éphydra*); E, Agromýzidae (*Agromỳza*); F, Chamaemyìidae (*Chamaemỳia*). *A*, anal cell; *B*, second basal cell; *cbr*, costal break; *D*, discal (first M_2) cell.

75′. Tibiae without dorsal preapical bristles; costa not, or but slightly, spinose; oral vibrissae variable 77

76(75). Orbital plates long, extending nearly to level of antennae; ocellar bristles laterad of median ocellus; 2 to 3 pairs of fronto-orbitals; 2A never reaching wing margin . . . . **Trixoscélidae*** p. 499

76′. Orbital plates short, not reaching level of antennae (Figure 27-24 C); ocellar bristles between median and lateral ocelli (Figure 27-24 C); 1 to 2 pairs of fronto-orbitals; 2A variable, sometimes (Figure 27-22 H) reaching wing margin . . . . **Heleomýzidae** p. 499

77(75′). Propleural bristle present; 2A reaching wing margin; oral vibrissae well developed; western Canada and Alaska (*Borborópsis* and *Oldenbergiélla*) . . . . **Heleomýzidae*** p. 499

77′. Propleural bristle absent; 2A not reaching wing margin; oral vibrissae poorly developed; widely distributed, but mainly southern United States . . . . **Chyromỳidae*** p. 500

78(66′). Costa broken only near humeral cross-vein; eyes with microscopic pubescence; postverticals widely separated and diverging . . . . **Acartophthálmidae*** p. 499

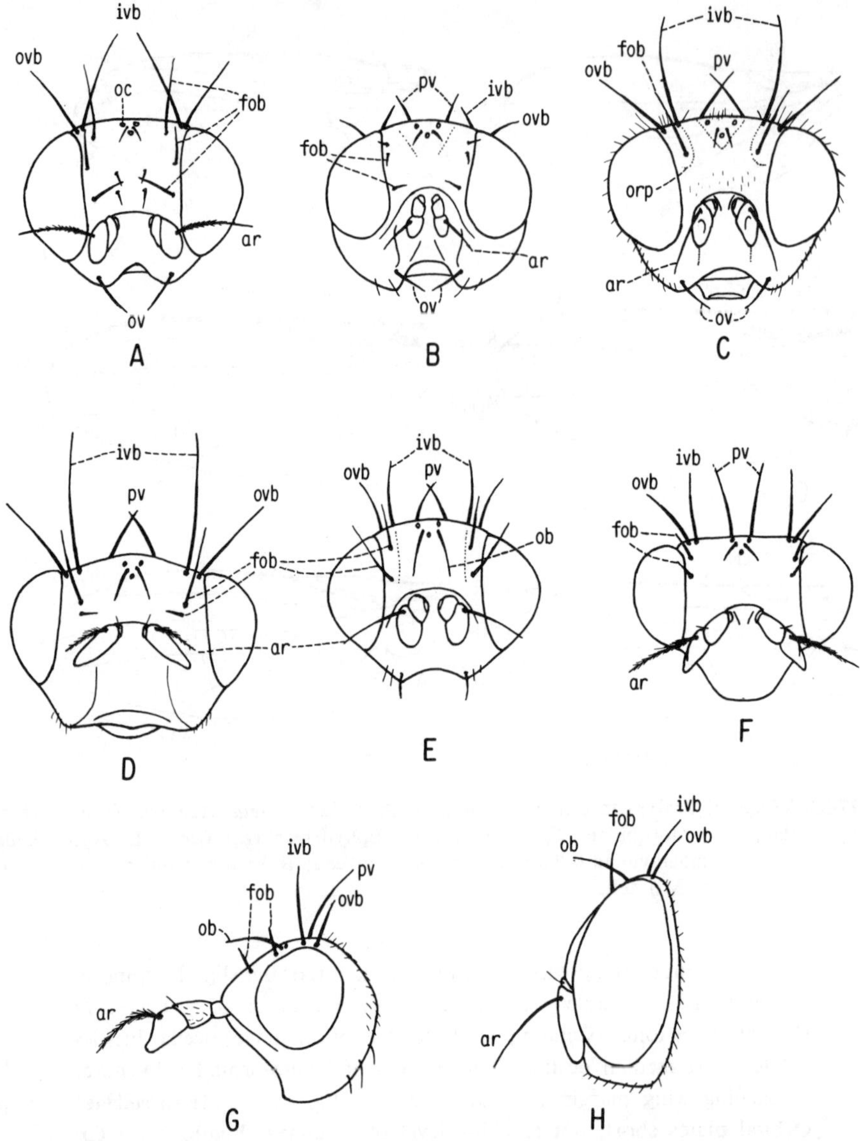

Fig. 27-24. Heads of acalypterate muscoid flies. A-F, anterior views; G-H, lateral views. A, Clusiódidae (*Clusiòdes*); B, Piophílidae (*Pióphila*); C, Heleomýzidae (*Heleomỳza*); D, Lauxanìidae (*Camptoprosopélla*); E, Chamaemyìidae (*Chamaemyìa*); F-G, Sciomýzidae (*Tetanócera*); H, Lonchaèidae (*Lonchaèa*). *ar,* arista; *fob,* fronto-orbital bristles; *ivb,* inner vertical bristles; *ob,* ocellar bristles; *oc,* ocellus; *orp,* orbital plate; *ov,* oral vibrissae; *ovb,* outer vertical bristles; *pv,* postvertical bristles.

78′. Costa entire, broken only near end of Sc, or broken near end of Sc and near humeral cross-vein; postverticals variable 79

79(78′). R_5 cell closed or much narrowed apically (Figure 27-22 C); legs usually long, slender, and stiltlike 80

79′. R_5 cell open and usually not narrowed apically; if narrower apically, then the legs are not unusually long and slender 83

80(79). Proboscis very long and slender, often elbowed; abdomen often clavate (Figure 27-65) and anal cell long and pointed (in *Stylogáster* the anal cell is very short, and the ovipositor is slender and as long as the remainder of the body) .... **Conópidae** p. 490

80′. Proboscis short, usually thick, not as above........................81

81(80′). Arista apical .... **Nerìidae*** p. 491

81′. Arista dorsal 82

82(81′). Head in profile higher than long; anal cell rounded apically; no sternopleural bristles .... **Tanypézidae*** p. 491

82′. Head in profile about as high as long or longer than high; anal cell square or pointed apically; 1 sternopleural bristle or none.... .... **Micropézidae** p. 491

83(79′). Eyes prominently bulging, the vertex sunken; scutellum often large and grooved; femora and usually also hind tibiae greatly enlarged; tropical flies 84*

83′. Eyes not prominently bulging, the vertex not sunken; widely distributed 85

84(83). R_1 ending far beyond Sc; R_5 cell narrowed distally; posterior thoracic spiracle with a group of bristles; palpi broad.......... **Ropaloméridae*** p. 493

84′. R_1 ending close to Sc; R_5 cell not narrowed distally; posterior thoracic spiracle without a group of bristles; palpi narrow ...... **Rhinotóridae*** p. 500

85(83′). Some or all tibiae with a preapical dorsal bristle (Figure 27-26 B); costa entire (Figure 27-22 D, G); body usually light-colored, at least in part 86

85′. Tibiae usually without a preapical dorsal bristle; if preapical tibial bristles are present, then either the ovipositor is long and sclerotized or R is setulose above or the vein forming the distal end of the anal cell is bent (Figure 27-22 F); costa entire or broken near end of Sc............89

86(85). Postverticals converging (Figure 27-24 D, *pv*); 2A short, not reaching wing margin (Figure 27-22 D); small flies, rarely over 6 mm in length.. .... **Lauxanìidae** p. 495

86′. Postverticals parallel, diverging, or absent; 2A reaching wing margin, at least as a fold...87

87(86′). Femora with bristles, and a characteristic bristle usually present near middle of anterior face of middle femora (Figures 27-26 B and 27-73); R_1 ending at middle of wing; antennae usually projecting forward, and the face usually produced (Figure 27-24 G); usually moderate-sized flies, brownish in color with patterned wings .... **Sciomýzidae** p. 495

87′. Femoral bristles not developed; R_1 ending beyond middle of wing; antennae usually not projecting forward.........................88*

88(87′). Third antennal segment spherical; antennae separated; palpi without apical bristles; oral margin not protruding........... **Helcomýzidae*** p. 493

88′. Third antennal segment longer than wide, more or less flattened laterally; antennae not separated; palpi with an apical bristle; oral margin protruding .... **Dryomýzidae*** p. 495

89(85′). Head produced on each side into a lateral process bearing the eye, with the antennae widely distant from each other on the eye stalks; scutellum bituberculate; mostly tropical .... **Diópsidae*** p. 491

89′. Head not so produced, the antennae arising on the front; scutellum not bituberculate 90

90(89′). Ocelli present 91

90′. Ocelli absent; medium- to large-sized flies, often with considerable coloring in the wings (Figure 27-67) .... **Pyrgótidae*** p. 492

91(90). Cu_2 bent distad in middle, the anal cell with an acute distal projection posteriorly (Figures 27-22 F and 27-23 B); wings usually patterned. .92

91′. Cu_2 straight or curved basad, the anal cell without an acute distal projection posteriorly (Figure 27-22 E); wing color variable 93

92(91). Lower fronto-orbital bristles present; costa broken near end of Sc; Sc apically bent toward costa at almost a right angle, and usually fading out before reaching costa (Figure 27-23 B) .... **Tephrítidae** p. 492

92′. Lower fronto-orbital bristles absent; costa broken near end of Sc or just beyond humeral cross-vein or entire; Sc apically bent toward costa at a less abrupt angle and usually reaching costa (Figure 27-22 F)...... .... **Otítidae** p. 492

93(91′). Costa broken near end of Sc 94

93′. Costa not broken near end of Sc (Figures 27-22 E, F, 27-23 F)........98

94(93). Sc apically bent toward costa at almost a right angle, and usually fading out before reaching costa (Figure 27-23 B); wings usually patterned (Figure 27-69)....................................... **Tephrítidae** p. 492

94′. Sc apically bent toward costa at a less abrupt angle, and usually reaching costa 95

95(94′). Second abdominal segment usually with lateral bristles; femora often thickened and spinose; wings usually pictured.......... **Richardìidae*** p. 492

95′. Second abdominal segment without lateral bristles; femora not thickened 96

96(95′). Cu_2 straight, the anal cell truncate apically; 3 to 5 pairs of fronto-orbital bristles; postverticals diverging .... **Canacèidae*** p. 497

96′. Cu_2 recurved, the anal cell rounded apically; 1 pair of fronto-orbital bristles; postverticals parallel or slightly diverging................97

97(96′). Head hemispherical in profile, the eyes large and oval or semicircular (Figure 27-24 H); third antennal segment elongate and cylindrical (Figure 27-24 H); postverticals divergent; 2A usually undulate; small, shining, blackish flies .... **Lonchaèidae** p. 497

97′. Head globular in profile, the eyes smaller and rounded; third antennal segment oval; postverticals parallel; 2A not undulate; usually pale-colored flies with patterned wings.................... **Palloptéridae*** p. 497

98(93′). Postverticals converging (Figure 27-24 E) or absent; R_1 bare above; small flies, usually gray in color .... **Chamaemyìidae** p. 495

98′. Postverticals diverging (rarely very small and difficult to see); R_1 usually setulose above, at least in apical third; small to medium-sized flies, usually dark and shining....................................99

99(98′). Anal cell relatively long, the anterior side more than one-fourth as long as posterior side of discal cell (Figure 27-22 E); sternopleural bristle lacking; propleural bristle weak or lacking; R_1 setulose; third antennal segment elongate, extending approximately to oral margin **Platystomátidae** p. 492

99′. Anal cell shorter, the anterior side usually less than one-fourth as long as

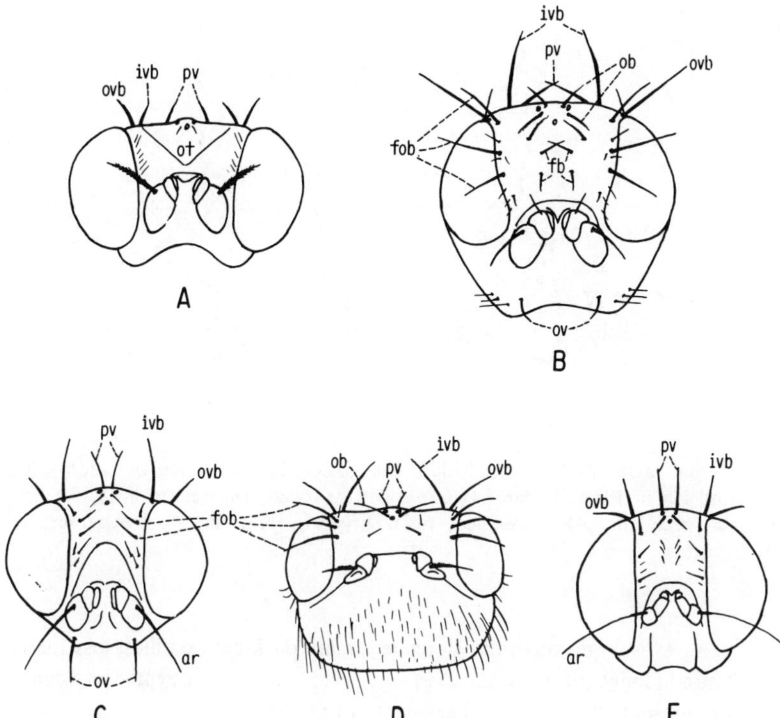

Fig. 27-25. Heads of acalypterate muscoid flies, anterior view. A, Chlorópidae (*Diplotóxa*); B, Tethínidae (*Tethìna*); C, Agromýzidae (*Agromŷza*); D, Ephýdridae (*Éphydra*); E, Milichìidae (*Milíchia*). *ar,* arista; *fb,* frontal bristles; *fob,* fronto-orbital bristles; *ivb,* inner vertical bristles; *ob,* ocellar bristles; *ot,* ocellar triangle; *ov,* oral vibrissae; *ovb,* outer vertical bristles; *pv,* postvertical bristles.

posterior side of discal cell; sternopleural bristles usually present, propleural bristle sometimes developed; R_1 bare or setulose; third antennal segment variable .... **Otítidae** p. 492

100(64′). Sc apically bent toward costa at almost a right angle and usually fading out beyond the bend (Figure 27-23 B); anal cell usually with an acute distal projection posteriorly; wings usually patterned (Figure 27-69).. .... **Tephrítidae** p. 492

100′. Sc and anal cell not as above; wing color variable.................. 101

101(100′). Basal segment of hind tarsi short and swollen, shorter than second segment (Figure 27-26 A); small black or brown flies...... **Sphaerocéridae** p. 497

101′. Basal segment of hind tarsi normal, not swollen, and usually longer than second segment 102

102(101′). R_{2+3} short, ending in costa close to R_1 (Figure 27-23 A); postverticals diverging .... **Asteìidae*** p. 501

102′. R_{2+3} longer, ending beyond middle of wing (Figure 27-23 C-F); postverticals variable 103

103(102′). Third antennal segment large, reaching almost to lower edge of head; arista absent but a short spine or tubercle at apex of third antennal seg-

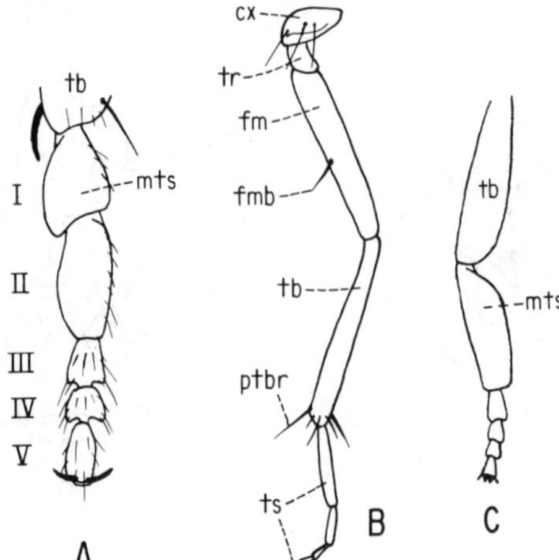

Fig. 27-26. A, hind tarsus of Sphaerocéridae (*Bórborus*); B, middle leg of Sciomýzidae (*Tetanócera*); C, hind leg of Platypézidae (*Agathomyia*). *cx,* coxa; *fm,* femur; *fmb,* femoral bristle; *mts,* first tarsal segment; *ptbr,* preapical tibial bristles; *tb,* tibia; *tr,* trochanter; *ts,* tarsus; *I-V,* tarsal segments.

ment; eyes large, vertically elongate; small, dark-colored flies, less than 2 mm in length; California........................**Cryptochaètidae*** p. 501

103′. Arista present; third antennal segment not as above................104

104(103′). Costa entire (Figure 27-23 F); oral vibrissae absent................105

104′. Costa broken near end of Sc (Figure 27-23 C-E), sometimes also near humeral cross vein (Figure 27-23 D); oral vibrissae variable........107

105(104). Arista plumose; postverticals divergent.................**Periscélidae*** p. 495

105′. Arista bare or pubescent; postverticals usually convergent..........106

106(105′). R_5 cell narrowed apically; legs long and slender; length 7-12 mm; southwestern United States, usually occurring on decaying cacti..**Nerìidae*** p. 491

106′. R_5 cell not narrowed apically; legs not unusually long and slender; length usually less than 7 mm; widely distributed, and usually not found on decaying cacti ....**Chamaemyìidae** p. 495

107(104′). Costa broken only near end of Sc or R_1 (Figure 27-23 C, E)........108

107′. Costa broken near end of Sc, and also near humeral cross vein (Figure 27-23 D) 117

108(107). Anal cell absent (Figure 27-23 C); ocellar triangle large (Figure 27-25 A); postverticals converging or absent......................**Chlorópidae** p. 498

108′. Anal cell present (Figure 27-23 E); ocellar triangle and postverticals variable...109

109(108′). No sternopleural bristles; postverticals divergent or absent..........110

109′. Sternopleural bristles present; postverticals variable................111

110(109). Oral vibrissae present; ocellar triangle large and shining, reaching nearly to base of antennae (as in Figure 27-25 A); small flies, not over 3.5 mm in length, occurring along the seashore..................**Canacèidae*** p. 497

110′. Oral vibrissae absent; ocellar triangle short; usually larger flies..**Psílidae** p. 491

111(109′). Eyes prominently bulging, the vertex sunken; scutellum usually tuberculate and medially grooved; front femora thickened; oral vibrissae present; no postvertical bristles; tropical flies ....**Rhinotóridae*** p. 500

111′. Eyes not prominently bulging, the vertex not sunken; scutellum not as above; front femora not enlarged; oral vibrissae and postvertical bristles variable 112

112(111′). Postverticals converging (Figure 27-25 B); oral vibrissae present, but sometimes weakly developed...................................113

112′. Postverticals diverging (Figure 27-25 C) or absent; oral vibrissae variable 115

113(112). Costa spinose (as in Figure 27-22 H); at least some fronto-orbital bristles reclinate ....**Trixoscélidae*** p. 499

113′. Costa not spinose; fronto-orbitals variable........................114

114(113′). All fronto-orbital bristles directed outward; presutural dorsocentral bristles present; mostly seashore species.................**Tethínidae** p. 497

114′. At least 1 pair of fronto-orbital bristles reclinate; presutural dorsocentral bristles absent ....**Anthomýzidae** p. 500

115(112′). Oral vibrissae present (Figure 27-25 C) 116

115′. Oral vibrissae absent ....**Opomýzidae** p. 500

116(113). Preapical tibial bristles present; 2 reclinate and 1 inclinate pairs of fronto-orbitals; 1 presutural and 3 postsutural dorsocentrals... **Odiniidae*** p. 499

116′. Preapical tibial bristles absent; fronto-orbital and dorsocentral bristles usually not as above ....**Agromýzidae** p. 499

117(107′). Antennae retractile into deep grooves, the face receding; eyes small and round; scutellum long, flattened, with two apical setigerous tubercles; postverticals diverging; oral vibrissae present ....**Thyreophóridae*** p. 495

117′. Not exactly fitting the above description..........................118

118(117′). Postverticals diverging (Figure 27-25 D); distinct oral vibrissae absent; anal cell absent (Figure 27-23 D)........................**Ephýdridae** p. 497

118′. Postverticals parallel or converging, rarely absent; oral vibrissae usually present; anal cell variable 119

119(118′). A pair of lower fronto-orbital bristles bent inward (Figure 27-25 E); oral vibrissae weakly differentiated.............................**Milichiidae** p. 497

119′. No fronto-orbitals bent inward (Figure 27-4); oral vibrissae usually well differentiated 120

120(119′). Costa usually spinose (as in Figure 27-22 H); mesopleura with bristles.. ....121*

120′. Costa not spinose; mesopleura rarely bristly.......................122

121(120). Proclinate fronto-orbital bristles in front of reclinate ones, both remote from eyes; arista long-plumose ....**Curtonótidae*** p. 497

121′. Proclinate fronto-orbital bristles behind the foremost reclinate pair, close to eyes; arista short-plumose..........................**Diastátidae*** p. 498

122(120′). Sternopleural bristle present; no mesopleural bristles; hind tibiae usually with preapical bristles; body usually not metallic........**Drosophílidae** p. 498

122′. Sternopleural bristle absent; mesopleura bristly; hind tibiae without preapical bristles; body metallic ....**Camíllidae*** p. 498

123(53′). Palpi slender and elongate, forming a sheath for the proboscis; wings with strong veins crowded anteriorly, the posterior veins weak or absent;

tarsal claws often toothed; eyes well developed, oval; ectoparasites of birds and mammals .... **Hippobóscidae*** p. 503

123′. Palpi broader than long, projecting leaflike in front of head; wings uniformly veined; tarsal claws simple; eyes small or vestigial; mostly ectoparasites of bats .... **Stréblidae*** p. 503

124(1′). Antennae 5-segmented, the third segment large, club-shaped, and annulated basally; head elongate, the mouth parts vestigial; legs long, slender, and widely separated; wings vestigial; found in rapid streams in New Brunswick .... **Nymphomyìidae*** p. 470

124′. Not exactly fitting the above description 125*

125(124′). Coxae separated (Figure 27-13); abdominal segmentation sometimes obscure 126*

125′. Coxae contiguous; abdomen distinctly segmented 129*

126(125). Mesonotum short, resembling the abdominal segments; scutellum absent; antennae inserted in lateral grooves; parasitic on the honey bee...... .... **Bráulidae*** p. 497

126′. Thorax and abdomen differentiated; scutellum present; parasitic on birds and mammals 127*

127(126′). Head small and narrow, folding back into a groove on mesonotum; spiderlike insects parasitic on bats .... **Nycteribìidae*** p. 503

127′. Head not folding back into a groove on mesonotum.............. 128*

128(127′). Head fitting into an emargination of the thorax; palpi elongate and forming a sheath for the proboscis, eyes oval or round...... **Hippobóscidae*** p. 503

128′. Head with a fleshy movable neck; palpi broad, projecting leaflike in front of head; eyes vestigial or absent........................ **Stréblidae*** p. 503

129(125′). Antennae consisting of 6 or more freely articulated segments; palpi usually segmented 130*

129′. Antennae consisting of 3 or fewer segments; palpi not segmented ..135*

130(129). Mesonotum with a **V**-shaped suture (as in Figure 27-27); female with a long sclerotized ovipositor............................ **Tipùlidae*** p. 469

130′. Mesonotum without a **V**-shaped suture; female without a sclerotized ovipositor.. 131*

131(130′). Eyes meeting above the antennae (Figure 27-8 A).................. 132*

131′. Eyes widely separated, not meeting above the antennae............ 134*

132(131). Abdomen enormously swollen, the four apical segments forming a slender projection; occurring in termite nests................ **Cecidomyìidae*** p. 478

132′. Abdomen not as above 133*

133(132′). Scutellum and halteres present; legs strong................ **Scatópsidae*** p. 478

133′. Scutellum and halteres absent; legs slender.................. **Sciáridae*** p. 478

134(131′). Halteres present; mesothorax large, forming a hood over the base of the head; abdomen constricted at base .... **Chironómidae*** p. 475

134′. Halteres absent; mesothorax small, not projecting over head; abdomen broadly joined to thorax (*Dáhlica*).................. **Mycetophílidae*** p. 478

135(129′). Antennae apparently consisting of a single globular segment, more or less sunk in cavities in head; hind femora robust and laterally flattened.... .... **Phóridae*** p. 489

135′. Antennae 2- or 3-segmented; hind femora not laterally flattened....136*

136(135′). No frontal suture; third antennal segment more or less tapering........

	.... **Empídidae***	p. 486
136′.	A frontal suture present; third antennal segment more or less ovate, with a dorsal arista 137*	
137(136′).	First segment of hind tarsi short and swollen, shorter than second segment (Figure 27-26 A) ....**Sphaerocéridae***	p. 497
137′.	First segment of hind tarsi not swollen, and longer than second segment.. ....138*	
138(137′).	Arista plumose.......................................**Drosophílidae***	p. 498
138′.	Arista pubescent or bare..............................**Heleomýzidae***	p. 499

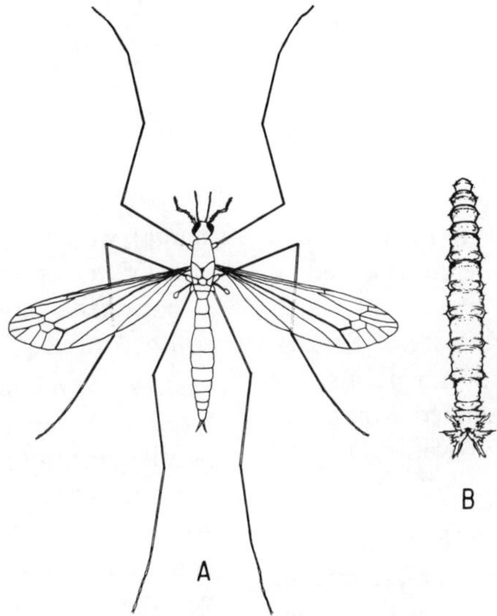

Fig. 27-27. A crane fly (*Típula* sp., family Tipùlidae). A, adult; B, larva. $1\frac{1}{2}\times$. (B, courtesy of Johannsen and the Cornell University Agricultural Experiment Station.)

FAMILY **Trichocéridae**—Winter Crane Flies: The members of this group are slender, medium-sized flies that are usually seen in the fall or early spring, and some may be seen on mild days in winter. They may be found in large swarms out of doors, or in cellars or caves. The larvae occur in decaying vegetable matter.

FAMILY **Tipùlidae**—Crane Flies: This family is by far the largest of the crane fly families, with several hundred species occurring in this country, and many of its members are common and abundant insects. Most of the tipulids resemble overgrown mosquitoes with extremely long legs, or daddy-long-legs with wings (Figure 27-27); the legs are very easily broken off. Some species are fairly large, reaching an inch or more in length, and have patterned wings. The members of this family differ from the Trichocéridae in that they lack ocelli; from the Tanydéridae, in that they have fewer than five radial branches; and from the Ptychoptéridae, in that they have two anal veins (Figure 27-28).

Crane flies occur chiefly in damp situations where there is abundant vegetation. The larvae of most species are aquatic or semiaquatic and feed on decaying vegetable matter; a few feed on living plant tissue and may damage cultivated plants, and a few are predaceous. Little is known of the feeding habits of the adults, but some are known to feed on flowers; crane flies do not bite man.

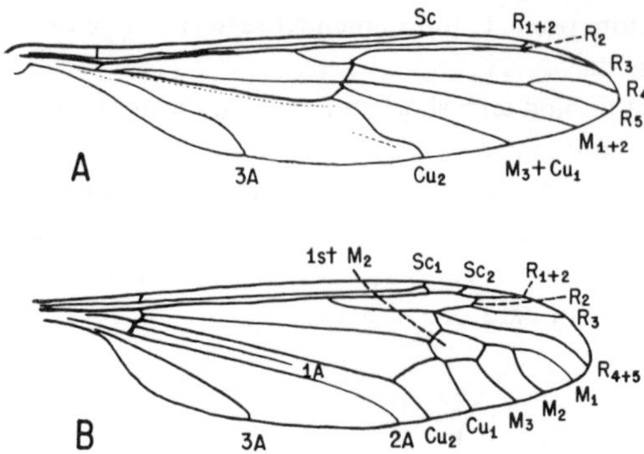

Fig. 27-28. Wings of crane flies. A, *Bittacomórpha* (Ptychoptéridae); B, *Típula* (Tipùlidae).

FAMILY **Tanydéridae**—Primitive Crane Flies: The tanyderids are represented in North America by three species, of which one, *Protoplàsa fítchii* Osten Sacken, occurs in the East. The tanyderids are medium-sized flies with banded wings, and their larval stages occur in wet, sandy soil at the margins of streams.

FAMILY **Psychódidae**—Moth Flies and Sand Flies: The psychodids are small to minute, usually very hairy, mothlike flies that, when at rest, hold the wings rooflike over the body or together above the body. The adults occur in shady places in the vicinity of water; they are sometimes extremely abundant in drains or sewers. The larvae occur in decaying vegetable matter, dung, or water.

Most of the northern species in this family (Psychodìnae) are harmless to man, but the species in the genus *Phlebótomus* (=*Flebótomus*) (Phlebotomìnae), often called sand flies, are blood-sucking; these occur in the southern states and in the tropics. Sand flies are known to act as vectors of several diseases in various parts of the world: pappataci fever (caused by a virus), which occurs principally in the Mediterranean region and in southern Asia; kala-azar and oriental sore (caused by leishmania organisms), which occur in South America, northern Africa, and southern Asia; espundia (caused by a leishmania), which occurs in South America; and oroya fever or verruga peruana (caused by a bartonella organism), which occurs in South America.

FAMILY **Ptychoptéridae**—Phantom Crane Flies: A fairly common species in this family, *Bittacomórpha clávipes* (Fabricius), has the long legs banded with black and white, and the first segment of the tarsi is conspicuously swollen; these flies often drift with the wind, with the long legs extended. Other species in this family (for example, *Ptychóptera*) resemble large fungus gnats. The larvae of the phantom crane flies live in the decaying vegetable matter in swamps and woods.

FAMILY **Blepharicéridae** — Net - Winged Midges: These midges are long-legged, mosquitolike insects that sometimes have a network of fine lines between the wing veins. They are found near fast-flowing streams, but are not common. The larvae live in swift water, clinging to rocks by means of a series of ventral suckers.

FAMILY **Nymphomyìidae**: This family was established for *Nymphomỳia álba* Tokunaga, which is found in the vicinity of rapid streams in Japan. The flies of this species are minute, elongate, with triangular wings that are fringed with long hairs and have almost no veins. Recently, a species (as yet undescribed) belonging to this family has

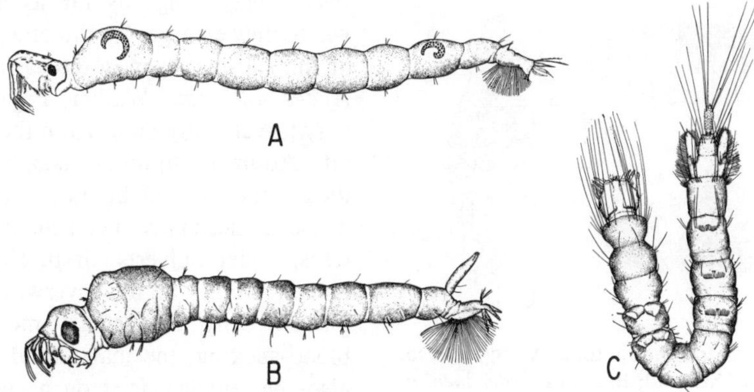

Fig. 27-29. Larvae of phantom (A-B) and dixid (C) midges. A, *Chaóborus flávicans* (Meigen); B, *Mochlónyx cinctipes* (Coquillet); C, *Paradíxa alíciae* (Johannsen). (Courtesy of Johannsen and the Cornell University Agricultural Experiment Station.)

been found in the rapid water of streams in New Brunswick, Canada, by Dr. F. P. Ide; the wings of the Canadian species are vestigial (or, possibly, broken off). Nymphomyiid larvae are as yet unknown, but are presumed to be aquatic.

FAMILY **Deuterophlebìidae** — Mountain Midges: These midges are peculiar in having broad, fanlike wings and extremely long antennae. Three species of *Deuterophlèbia* are known from the West (Colorado and California), where the larvae occur in swift-flowing mountains streams.

FAMILY **Díxidae**—Dixid Midges: The dixids are small, long-legged, mosquitolike insects that are similar to mosquitoes in wing venation but lack the scales on the wings; the adults do not bite. The larvae (Figure 27-29 C) are aquatic and are somewhat similar to the larvae of *Anópheles* mosquitoes, but do not have the thorax enlarged; they usually feed at the surface of the water like anopheline larvae, but the usual position is with the body bent into a **U**, and they move by alternately straightening and bending the body. The larvae feed on algae.

FAMILY **Chaobóridae**—Phantom Midges: These insects are very similar to mosquitoes, but differ in that they have a short proboscis and fewer scales on the wings; they do not bite. The larvae (Figure 27-29 A, B) are aquatic and predaceous, and have the antennae modified into prehensible organs. The larvae of *Chaóborus* (Figure 27-29 A) are almost transparent, giving rise to the name "phantom midges" for this group. The larvae of some species (for example, *Mochlónyx,* Figure 27-29 B) have a breathing tube and are very similar to mosquito larvae in appearance; others (for example, *Chaóborus*) do not have a mosquitolike breathing tube. The larvae occur in various sorts of pools, and are sometimes very abundant; they frequently destroy large numbers of mosquito larvae. This group is a small one, but its members are fairly common insects.

FAMILY **Culícidae** — Mosquitoes: This family is a large, abundant, well-known, and important group of flies. The larval stages are aquatic, and the adults can be recognized by the characteristic wing venation (Figure 27-6 I), the scales along the wing veins, and the long proboscis. Mosquitoes are very important from the standpoint of human welfare because the females are blood-sucking, many species bite man, and they serve as vectors in the transmission of several important human diseases.

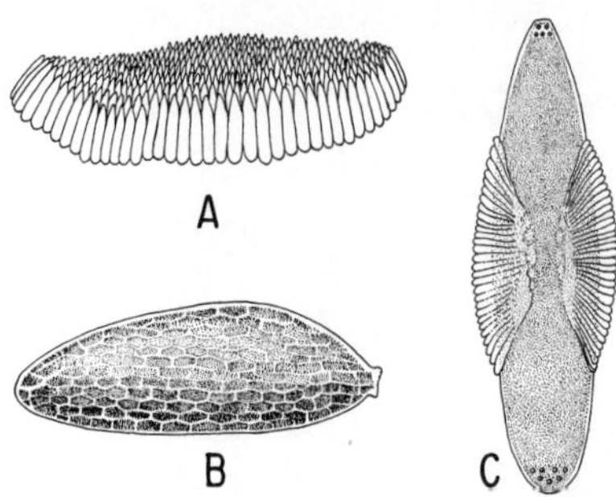

Fig. 27-30. Eggs of mosquitoes. A, egg raft of *Cùlex réstuans* Theobald; B, egg of *Aèdes taeniorhýnchus* (Wiedemann); C, egg of *Anópheles quadrimaculàtus* Say, showing floats. (Courtesy of USDA, after Howard, Dyar, and Knab.)

Mosquito larvae (Figure 27-31), or wrigglers, occur in a variety of aquatic situations—in ponds and pools of various sorts, in the water in artificial containers, in tree holes, and in other situations—but each species usually occurs only in a particular type of aquatic habitat. The eggs (Figure 27-30) are laid on the surface of the water, either in "rafts" (*Cùlex*) or singly (*Anópheles*), or near water (*Aèdes*). In the latter case the eggs usually hatch when flooded. The larvae of most species feed on algae and organic debris, but a few are predaceous and feed on other mosquito larvae. Mosquito larvae breathe principally at the surface, usually through a breathing tube at the posterior end of the body; the larvae of *Anópheles* lack a breathing tube and breathe through a pair of spiracular plates at the posterior end of the body.

Mosquito pupae (Figure 27-31 B) are also aquatic, and unlike most insect pupae, are quite active and are often called tumblers. They breathe at the surface of the water through a pair of small trumpetlike structures on the thorax.

Most adult mosquitoes do not travel far from the water in which they spent their larval stage. *Aèdes aegýpti* (Linn.), the vector of yellow fever and dengue, seldom travels more than a few hundred yards from where it emerges; some species of *Anópheles* may range as far as a mile from where they emerge. On the other hand, some of the salt-marsh mosquitoes (for example, *Aèdes sollícitans* Walker, Figure 27-35 A) may travel many miles from the larval habitat. Adult mosquitoes usually are active during the twilight hours or at night, or in dense shade; many spend the day in hollow trees, under culverts, or in similar resting places. Some adults overwinter in such places. Only the female mosquitoes are blood-sucking; the males (and occasionally also the females) feed on nectar and other plant juices.

The sexes of most mosquitoes can easily be determined by the form of the antennae (Figure 27-32); the antennae of the males are very plumose, while those of the females have only a few short hairs. In most mosquitoes other than *Anópheles* the maxillary palpi are very short in the female (Figure 27-32 A), but are longer than the proboscis in the male (Figure 27-32 B); the maxillary palpi are long in both sexes of *Anópheles*, but are clubbed in the male (compare Figure 27-32 C and D).

The mosquitoes constitute a large group containing many genera and species, but from man's point of view the most important genera are *Anópheles*, *Aèdes*, and *Cùlex*. The adults of *Anópheles* are rather easily distinguished; the maxillary palpi are long in both sexes (Figure 27-32 C, D) and clubbed in the male (usually short in the females of *Cùlex* and *Aèdes*, and not clubbed in the male), the scutellum is evenly rounded (trilobed in *Cùlex* and *Aèdes*), and the wings are usually spotted (not so in *Cùlex* and *Aèdes*). The wing spotting in *Anópheles* is due to groups of differently colored scales on the wing. In a resting position, an *Anópheles* mosquito has the proboscis and body in a straight line and at an angle to the surface on which the insect is resting (Figure 27-33 A, B); some species seem almost to "stand on their head" in a resting position. In a resting *Cùlex* or *Aèdes* the body is usually held parallel to the surface,

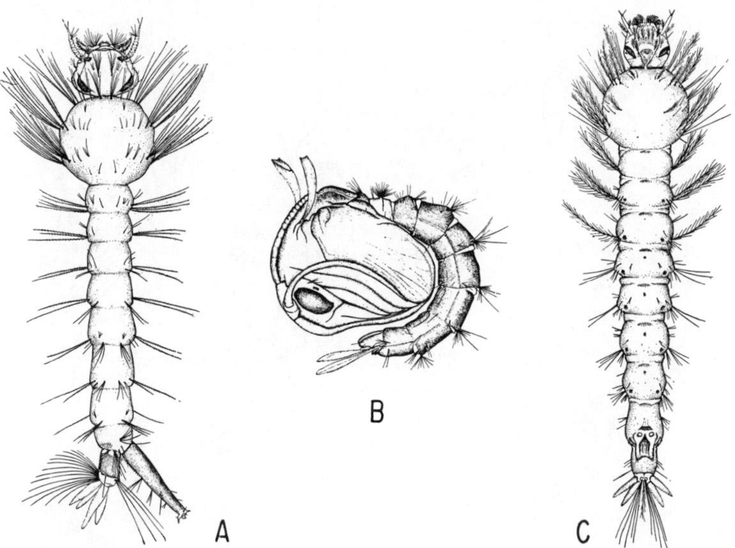

Fig. 27-31. Larvae and pupa of mosquitoes. A, larva of *Cùlex pípiens* Linn.; B, pupa of *C. pípiens*; C, larva of *Anópheles punctipénnis* Say. (After Johannsen, courtesy of the Cornell University Agricultural Experiment Station.)

with the proboscis bent down (Figure 27-33 C). The adults of *Cùlex* and *Aèdes* are not so easily separated; the best character is the presence (*Aèdes*) or absence (*Cùlex*) of postspiracular bristles. In *Aèdes* the tip of the abdomen of the female is usually pointed, with the cerci protruding, and the thorax often has silvery or white markings; in *Cùlex* the tip of the abdomen of the female is usually blunt, with the cerci retracted, and the thorax is usually dull-colored.

The larvae of these three genera are rather easily separated. *Anópheles* larvae (Figure 27-31 C) have no breathing tube, and when at rest, lie parallel to the surface of the water (Figure 27-34 A); *Cùlex* and *Aèdes* larvae have a breathing tube (Figure 27-31 A), and when at rest, have the body at an angle to the surface of the water (Figure 27-34 B). *Aèdes* larvae have only a single pair of hair tufts on the breathing tube, and the tube is relatively short and stout; *Cùlex* larvae have more than one pair of hair tufts on the breathing tube, and the tube is relatively long and slender.

Anópheles larvae occur chiefly in ground pools, marshes, and in places where there is considerable vegetation; *Aèdes* larvae occur in a variety of places, including artificial containers, woodland pools, borrow pits, and salt marshes; *Cùlex* mosquitoes breed in many places, but the most abundant species breed chiefly in artificial containers. The woodland species which are so troublesome early in the season, are largely species of *Aèdes* and have a single brood a year. Many species that breed in large bodies of water, borrow pits, or in artificial containers may continue breeding through the season as long as weather conditions are favorable.

Mosquitoes act as vectors of several very important diseases of man: malaria, caused by Protozòa of the genus *Plasmòdium,* and transmitted by certain species of *Anópheles*; yellow fever, caused by a virus and transmitted by *Aèdes aegýpti* (Linn.); dengue, caused by a virus and transmitted by *Aèdes aegýpti* (Linn.) and other species of *Aèdes*; filariasis, caused by a filarial worm and transmitted chiefly by species of

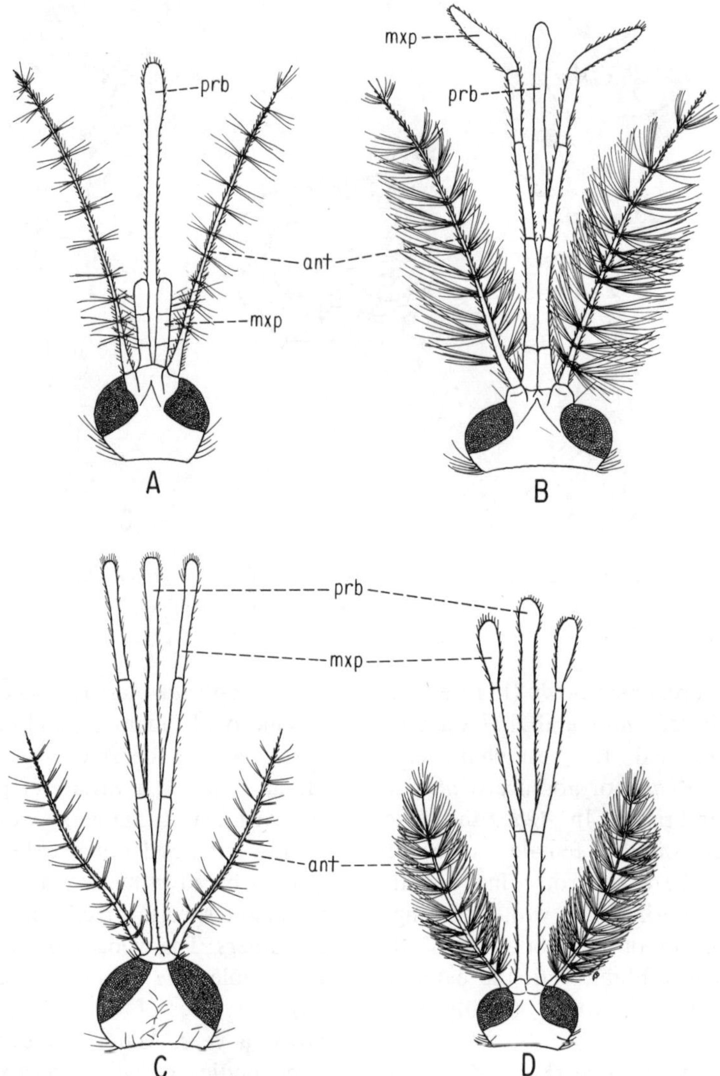

Fig. 27-32. Head structure in mosquitoes, showing sex characters. A, *Aèdes,* female; B, same, male; C, *Anópheles,* female; D, same, male. *ant,* antenna; *mxp,* maxillary palpus; *prb,* proboscis.

Cùlex; certain types of encephalitis, caused by a virus and transmitted by various species of mosquitoes (chiefly species of *Cùlex* and *Aèdes*).

Control measures against mosquitoes may be aimed at the larvae or at the adults. Measures aimed at the larvae may involve the elimination or modification of the larval habitats (for example, drainage), or may involve the treatment of the larval habitat with insecticides. Measures aimed at the adults may be in the nature of preventives (the use of protective clothing, screening, and the use of repellents), or insecticides (sprays or aerosols).

FAMILY **Thaumalèidae**—Solitary Midges: The members of this group are small, bare, reddish-yellow or brownish flies of rather peculiar appearance; only a few species

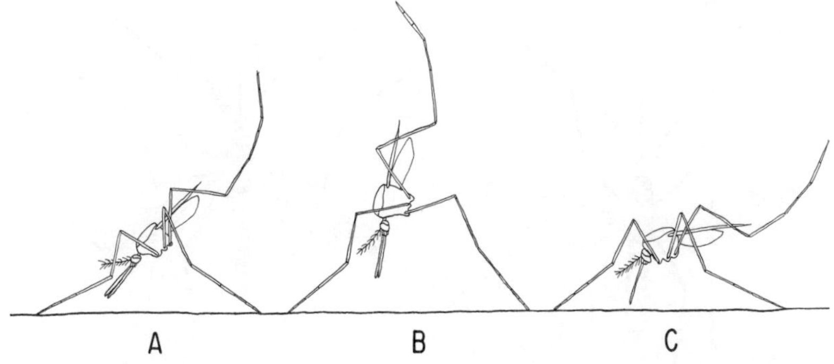

Fig. 27-33. Resting positions of mosquitoes. A and B, *Anópheles;* C, *Cùlex.* (Redrawn from King, Bradley, and McNeel.)

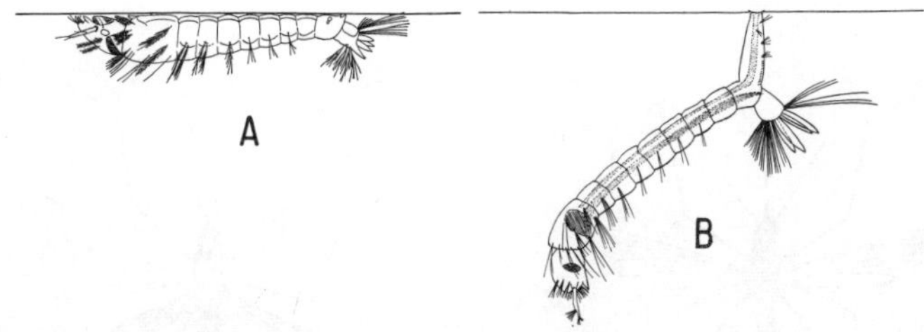

Fig. 27-34. Feeding positions of mosquito larvae. A, *Anópheles*; B, *Cùlex.* (Courtesy of USDA.)

occur in the United States, and these are rather uncommon. The adults are usually found along streams in which the larvae occur.

FAMILY **Ceratopogónidae**—Biting Midges, Punkies, or No-see-ums: These flies are very small, but are often serious pests because of their blood-sucking habits, particularly along the seashore or along the shores of rivers and lakes. Their small size is responsible for the name "no-see-ums," and their bite is all out of proportion to their size. Many species in this group attack other insects and suck blood from the insect host as an ectoparasite; punkies have been reported from mantids, walking sticks, dragonflies, alderflies, lacewings, certain beetles, certain moths, crane flies, and mosquitoes. Some of the larger species prey on smaller insects. Some species (Figure 27-36) have spotted wings. Most of the punkies that attack man belong to the genera *Culicòides* and *Leptocónops.* These insects apparently do not travel far from the place where the larvae occur, and one may often avoid punkie attacks by simply moving a few yards away.

The larvae of punkies are aquatic or semiaquatic, occurring in sand, mud, decaying vegetation, and the water in tree holes. Those occurring along the seashore apparently breed in the intertidal zone. The feeding habits of the larvae are not well known, but they are probably scavengers.

FAMILY **Chironómidae**—Midges: These insects are to be found almost everywhere. They are small (some are very small), delicate, somewhat mosquitolike in appearance (Figure 27-37 C), and the males usually have the antennae very plumose. They often occur in huge swarms, usually in the evening, and the humming of such a swarm may be audible for a considerable distance.

The larvae of most midges (Figure 27-38 B) are aquatic; a few occur in decaying matter, under bark, or in moist ground.

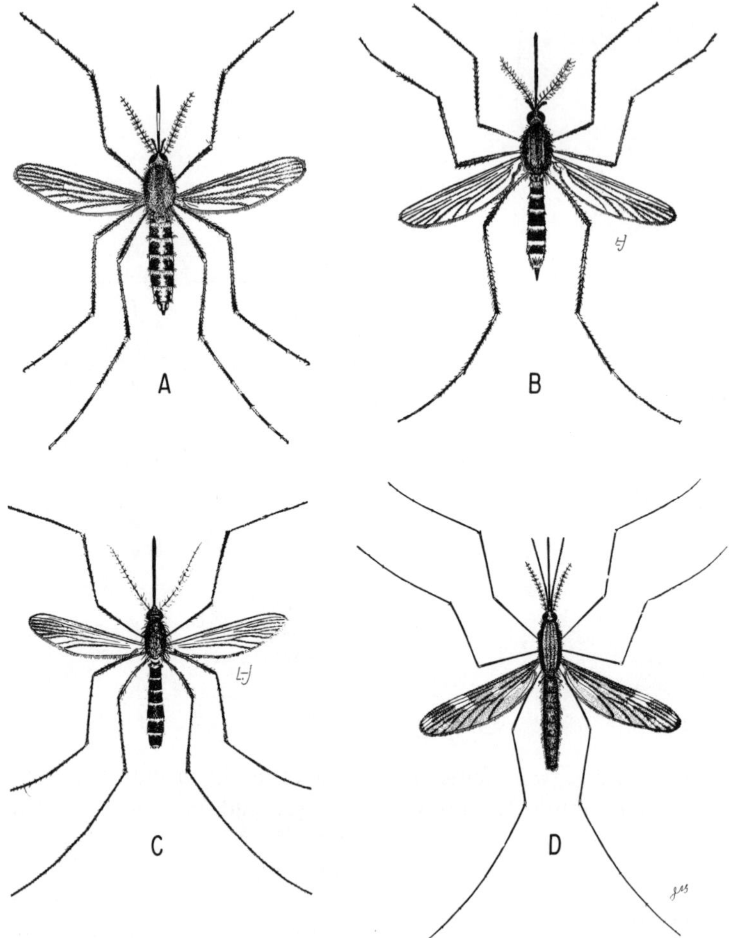

Fig. 27-35. Common mosquitoes. A, the salt marsh mosquito, *Aèdes sollícitans* (Walker); B, a woodland mosquito, *Aèdes stímulans* (Walker); C, the house mosquito, *Cùlex pípiens* Linn.; D, *Anópheles punctipénnis* (Say). (Courtesy of Headlee and the New Jersey Agricultural Experiment Station; after Smith.)

Most of them are scavengers. Many of the aquatic forms live in tubes or cases. The larvae of some species are red in color, due to the presence of haemoglobin in the blood, and are known as bloodworms. Midge larvae swim by means of characteristic whipping movements of the body, something like the movements of mosquito larvae. Midge larvae are often very abundant and are an important item of food for many freshwater fish and other aquatic animals.

FAMILY **Simulìidae**—Black Flies or Buffalo Gnats: The black flies are small, usually dark-colored insects with short legs, broad wings, and a humpbacked appearance (Figure 27-39). The females are blood-sucking. These insects are vicious biters and are serious pests in some sections of the country. The bites often cause considerable swelling and sometimes bleeding. Black flies sometimes attack livestock in such numbers and with such ferocity as to cause the death of the livestock, and there are records of human deaths caused by these insects. Black flies have a wide distribution, but are most numerous in the north temperate and sub-

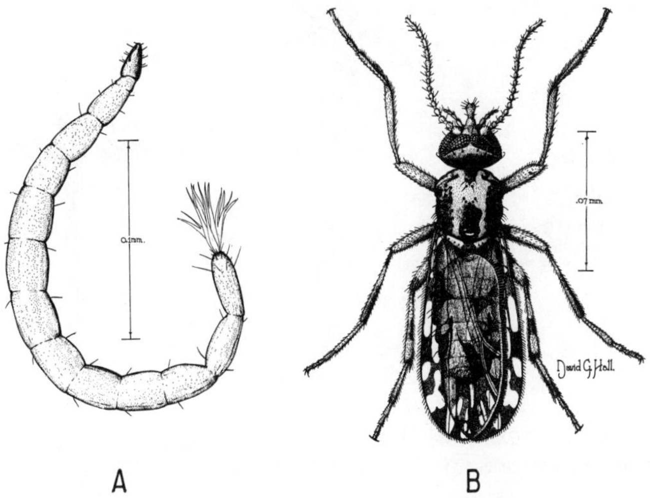

Fig. 27-36. The little gray punkie. *Culicòides fùrens* (Poey). (Ceratopogónidae). A. larva; B, adult female. (Courtesy of Dove, Hull, and Hull and the Entomological Society of America.)

arctic regions; the adults usually appear in late spring and early summer.

Black fly larvae occur in streams, where they attach to stones and other objects by means of a disclike sucker at the posterior end of the body. The larvae (Figure 27-40 C, G) are somewhat club-shaped, swollen posteriorly, and move about like a measuringworm; their locomotion is aided by silk spun from the mouth. They pupate in cone-shaped cases (Figure 27-40 B, E) attached to objects in the water. These larvae are sometimes extremely abundant. The adults are most frequently encountered near the streams where the larvae occur, but may occur at considerable distances from streams.

The black flies in the United States are not known to be vectors of any disease of man, but in Africa, Mexico, and Central America certain species in this group act as vectors of onchocerciasis, a disease caused by a filarial worm and characterized by large subcutaneous swellings; in some cases the worms may get into the eyes and cause partial or complete blindness.

FAMILY **Anisopódidae**—Wood Gnats: These gnats are usually found in moist places on foliage; some species occasionally occur in large swarms. The larvae live in or near decaying organic matter, fermenting sap, and similar materials, and the adults are often attracted to flowing sap. The most common species, which have faint spots on the wings, are in the genus *Anìsopus*.

FAMILY **Bibiónidae**—March Flies: The members of this group are small to medium-sized, usually dark-colored, stout-bodied flies with rather short antennae (Figure 27-41); many are marked with red or yellow. The adults are most common in the spring and early summer; they are frequently found on flowers, and may sometimes be quite abundant. The larvae feed on decaying vegetable matter and on the roots of plants.

FAMILY **Pachyneùridae:** The pachyneurid gnats are similar to the Anisopódidae, with which they were formerly classified, but differ in that they lack a closed discal cell and have R_{2+3} appearing like a cross-vein extending from R_{4+5} to about the end of R_1. A single rare species, *Axymỳia furcàta* McAtee, occurs in the East; it has been taken in low vegetation along mountain streams.

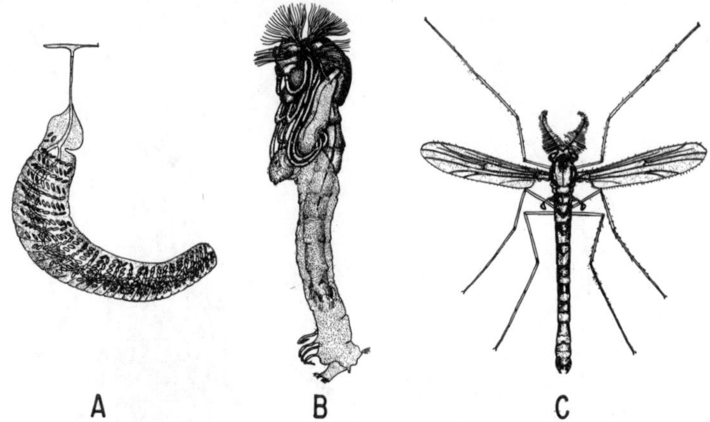

Fig. 27-37. A midge, *Chirónomus cristàtus* Fabricius. A, egg mass; B, pupa, lateral view, with the larval skin not completely shed; C, adult male. (Courtesy of Branch.)

FAMILY **Mycetophílidae**—Fungus Gnats: The fungus gnats are slender, delicate, mosquitolike insects with elongated coxae (Figures 27-7 and 27-42); they are found in damp places where there is an abundance of decaying vegetation or fungi and are usually fairly common insects. Most of them are about the size of mosquitoes, but a few are $\frac{1}{2}$ inch or more in length; these larger fungus gnats are occasionally found on flowers. The larvae live in moist soil, decaying vegetation, or fungi, and appear to feed on fungus growths. Some species are pests in mushroom cellars. This family is divided into a number of subfamilies.

FAMILY **Sciáridae**—Dark-Winged Fungus Gnats, Root Gnats: These gnats are similar to the Mycetophílidae, but have the eyes meeting above the bases of the antennae (Figure 27-8 A), and the r-m cross-vein is in line with the distal portion of Rs (Figure 27-43 C). The sciarids are small, usually blackish insects (Figure 27-44 A), which occur in moist shady places; the larvae of most species live in fungi and decaying plant materials, but a few attack the roots of plants. The larvae of some species occasionally become pests in mushroom cellars. The group is a small one, but its members are fairly common insects.

FAMILY **Hyperoscélidae:** This family is represented in North America by a single species, *Synneùron annùlipes* Lundström, which also occurs in Finland. Other species in this family occur in northern Europe, Chile and Patagonia, New Zealand, and Japan.

FAMILY **Scatópsidae**—Minute Black Scavenger Flies: These flies are black or brownish in color, 3 millimeters in length or less, and have short antennae; the veins near the costal margin of the wing (C, R_1, and Rs) are heavy, while the remaining veins are quite weak, and Rs ends in the costa at about one-half to three-fourths the wing length (Figure 27-8 B). The larvae breed in decaying material and excrement. The group is a small one, but its members are sometimes fairly abundant.

FAMILY **Cecidomyiidae**—Gall Midges or Gall Gnats: The gall midges are minute, delicate flies with relatively long antennae and legs, and with a reduced wing venation (Figures 27-6 A, 27-44 B, 27-46). The larvae of most species live in plants, where they form galls; some plant-feeding species do not form galls. Other larvae occur under bark, in decaying vegetation, or in fungi; a few are predaceous or parasitic on aphids, scale insects, and other small insects. Some

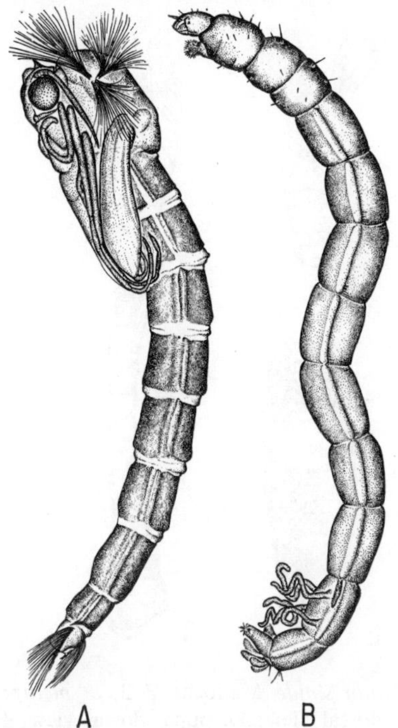

Fig. 27-38. Pupa (A) and larva (B) of *Chirónomus téntans* Fabricius. (Courtesy of Johannsen and the Cornell University Agricultural Experiment Station.)

of the gall-inhabiting species are merely inquilines; that is, they feed in a gall that has been caused by some other gall insect.

The larvae of gall midges are tiny maggots, with the head small and poorly developed and without mandibles, and in the last larval instar of most species there is a characteristic sclerotized structure called the "breast bone" on the ventral side of the prothorax. Many of the larvae are brightly colored—red, orange, pink, or yellow.

The galls formed by gall midges occur on all parts of plants and are usually more distinctive than the insects themselves. Each species of gall midge forms a characteristic gall on a particular part of a particular species of plant. In some galls, such as the pine-cone willow gall and the maple leaf spot (Figure 27-45), only one larva develops; in others, such as the stem gall of willow, many larvae develop.

A rather unusual type of reproduction occurs in *Miástor americàna* Felt, the larvae of which occur in decaying bark. In this species the larvae produce offspring—daughter larvae, which feed within the parent larva and eventually consume it and escape; these larvae may produce more larvae in a similar manner, through several generations, and the last larvae pupate. This type of reproduction, in which the larval stage of the animal reproduces, is called paedogenesis.

One of the most important pest species in this group is the hessian fly, *Phytóphaga destrúctor* (Say), which is a serious pest of wheat. This insect overwinters as a full-grown larva in a puparium, under the leaf sheaths of winter wheat; the larvae pupate and the adults emerge in the spring. These adults oviposit on wheat, and the larvae feed between the leaf sheath and the stem, weakening the shoot or even killing it. The larvae pass the summer in a puparium, and

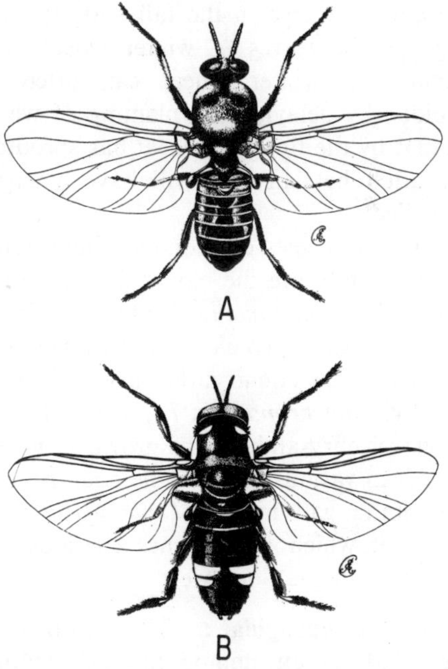

Fig. 27-39. A black fly, *Simùlium símile* Malloch. A, female; B, male. (Courtesy of Cameron and the Canadian Department of Agriculture.)

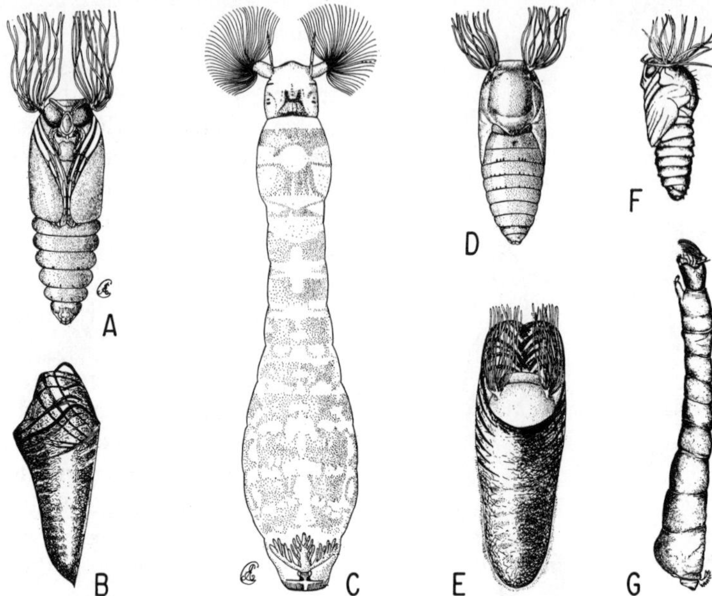

Fig. 27-40. Immature stages of a black fly. A-E, *Simùlium símile* Malloch; F-G, *S. pìcitipes* Hagen. A, pupa, ventral view; B, pupal case; C, larva, dorsal view; D, pupa, dorsal view; E, pupa in pupal case; F, pupa, lateral view; G, larva, lateral view. (A-E, courtesy of Cameron and the Canadian Department of Agriculture; F and G, courtesy of Johannsen and the Cornell University Agricultural Experiment Station.)

the adults emerge in the fall and lay their eggs on the leaves of winter wheat. The damage to winter wheat can often be avoided by delaying the planting of wheat so that by the time the wheat has sprouted, the adult hessian flies will have emerged and died.

Other species of economic importance in this family are the clover flower midge, *Dasyneùra leguminicola* (Lintner), which is a serious pest of red clover and white clover throughout the country; the chrysanthemum gall fly, *Diarthronomỳia hypogaèa* (Loew), a pest of chrysanthemums grown in greenhouses in various parts of the country; and the alfalfa gall midge, *Asphondỳlia wébsteri* Felt, which is sometimes a serious pest of alfalfa in the Southwest.

FAMILY **Xylophágidae:** The xylophagids are relatively uncommon flies of medium to large size; the larvae occur in decaying wood, under bark, or in the soil, and are probably predaceous. The flies in the genus *Xylóphagus* are slender and ichneumonlike; the other xylophagids are more robust. The flies in the genus *Coenomỳia* are large (14 to 25 millimeters in length), usually reddish or brownish in color, with the eyes pubescent and the second to fifth posterior cells about as wide as long. The flies in the genus *Rachícerus* are peculiar in having many-segmented serrate or somewhat pectinate antennae; they have the fourth posterior (M_3) cell closed, the eyes emarginate just above the antennae, and are 5 to 8 millimeters in length.

FAMILY **Xylomỳidae:** The most common flies in this group, belonging to the genus *Xylomỳia* (=*Sólva*), are slender and ichneumonlike; they differ from the xylophagids in the genus *Xylóphagus* (which are very similar in appearance) in that they lack an apical spur on the front tibiae and have the fourth posterior (M_3) cell closed. The larvae occur in decaying wood or under bark, and are probably predaceous.

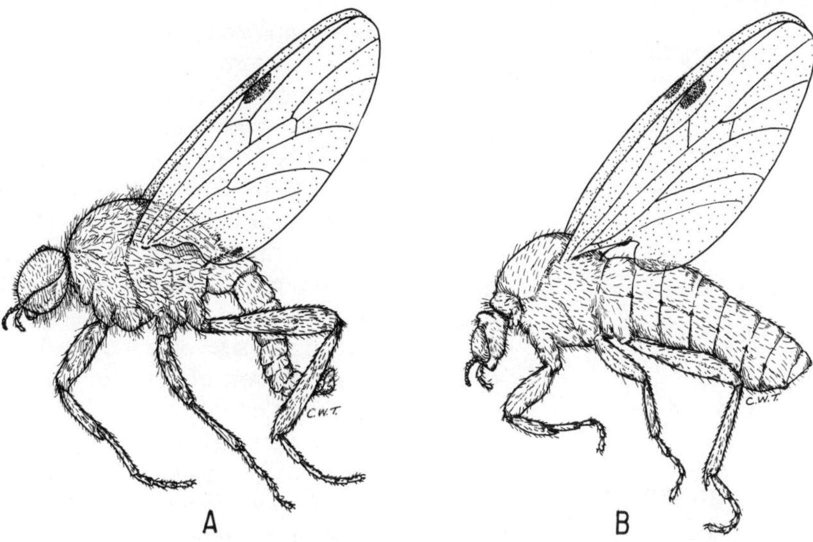

Fig. 27-41. A march fly, *Bíbio albipénnis* Say. A, male; B, female.

FAMILY **Stratiomỳidae**—Soldier Flies: Most of the soldier flies are medium-sized or larger and are usually found on flowers; many species are brightly colored and wasp-like in appearance. The larvae occur in a variety of situations; some are aquatic and feed on algae, decaying materials, or on small aquatic animals; some live in dung or other decaying materials; some occur under bark; others are found in other situations.

In some species of soldier flies (for example, *Stratìomys,* Figure 27-47 A) the abdomen is broad and flat, the wings at rest are folded back together over the abdomen, and the antennae (Figure 27-1 C) are long, with the third segment distinctly annulated. In other species (for example, in the genus *Ptécticus*) the abdomen is elongate, usually narrowed at the base, and the third antennal segment (Figure 27-1 F) appears globular, with an arista, and the annulations are very indistinct. Most soldier flies are dark-colored, with or without light markings, but some species are yellowish or light brown. The soldier flies are most easily recognized by their wing venation (Figure 27-9 A); the branches of the radius are rather heavy and are crowded together toward the costal margin of the wing, and the discal cell is small.

FAMILY **Pelecorhýnchidae:** This group, formerly considered a subfamily of the Tabánidae, is represented in the United States by a single species, *Bequaertomỳia anthracìna* Brennan, which occurs in the Pacific Coast States. This insect is 13 to 15 millimeters in length, and black with the wings smoky and the antennae and palpi orange.

FAMILY **Tabánidae**—Horse Flies and Deer Flies: The tabanids constitute a large group of flies, and many species are quite common; they are medium-sized to large, rather stout-bodied flies. The females are

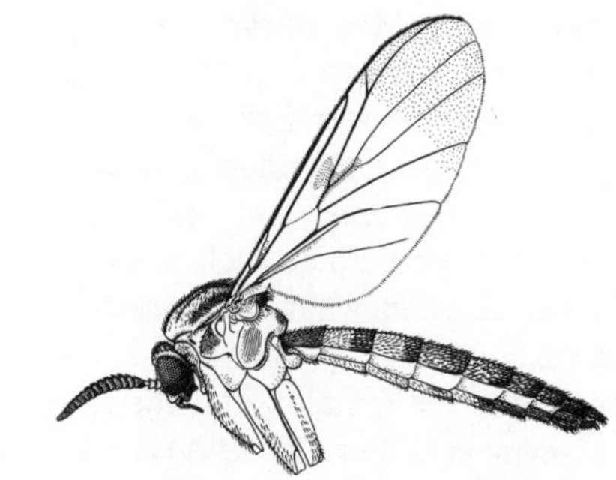

Fig. 27-42. A fungus gnat, *Platyùra fúltoni* Fisher; 8 ×. (Courtesy of Fulton and the Entomological Society of America.)

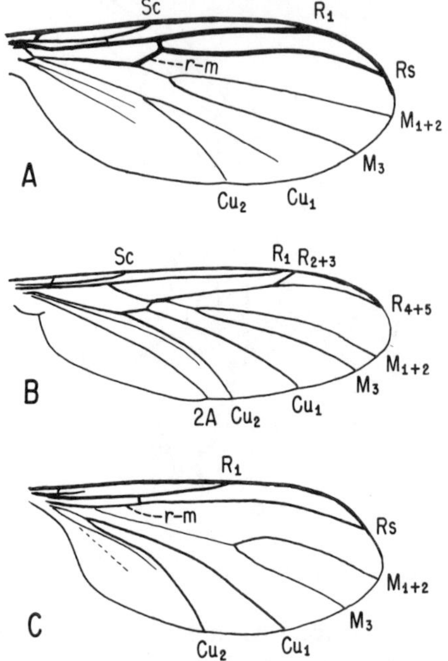

Fig. 27-43. Wings of fungus gnats. A and B, Mycetophílidae; C, Sciáridae.

blood-sucking and are often serious pests of livestock and man; the males feed chiefly on pollen and nectar and are often found on flowers. The two sexes are very easily separated by the eyes, which are usually contiguous in the males and separated in the females. The eyes are often brightly colored or iridescent. The larvae of most species are aquatic and predaceous, and the adults are generally encountered near swamps, marshes, ponds, and other situations where the larvae occur. Most horse flies are powerful fliers, and some species apparently have a flight range of several miles.

The two most common genera in this family are *Tabànus* and *Chrỳsops.* In *Tabànus* the hind tibiae lack apical spurs, the head is somewhat hemispherical in shape (usually slightly concave on the posterior side in the female), and the third antennal segment (Figure 27-49 A) has a toothlike process near the base. *Tabànus* is a very large genus, containing hundreds of species, and it includes some important pest species. One of the largest flies in the genus is *T. atràtus* Fabricius, a black insect an inch or more in length (Figure 27-48 E). The so-called greenheads, flies about $\frac{1}{2}$ inch in length with green eyes and a yellowish-brown body, are often serious pests on bathing beaches. In *Chrỳsops* the hind tibiae have apical spurs, the head is more rounded, and the third antennal segment (Figure 27-49 B) is elongate and lacks a basal toothlike process. Most members of this genus are about the size of a house fly or a little larger, brown or black in color, with dark markings on the wings (Figure 27-48 A, B). These tabanids are called deer flies; they are usually encountered near marshes or streams and frequently buzz around one's head or get in his hair.

The eggs of tabanids are usually laid in masses on leaves or other objects near or over water. Most species overwinter in the larval stage and pupate during the summer.

Some of the tabanids, particularly certain species of *Chrỳsops,* are known to serve as vectors of disease; tularemia and anthrax (and possibly other diseases) may be transmitted by tabanids in this country, and in Africa a disease caused by the filarial worm, *Lòa lòa* (Cobbold), is transmitted by deer flies.

FAMILY **Rhagiónidae**—Snipe Flies: The snipe flies are medium-sized to large, with the head somewhat rounded, the abdomen relatively long and tapering, and the legs rather long (Figure 27-50). Many species have spotted wings. The body may be bare or covered with short hair. Most snipe flies are brownish or gray, but some are black with spots or stripes of white, yellow, or green. They are common in woods, especially near moist places, and are usually found on foliage or grass. They are not particularly fast fliers. Both adults and larvae are predaceous on a variety of small insects. Most of the snipe flies do not bite, but several species of *Symphoromỳia* occur in the eastern states, and flies in this genus are common biting pests in the western mountains and coastal areas. Most snipe fly

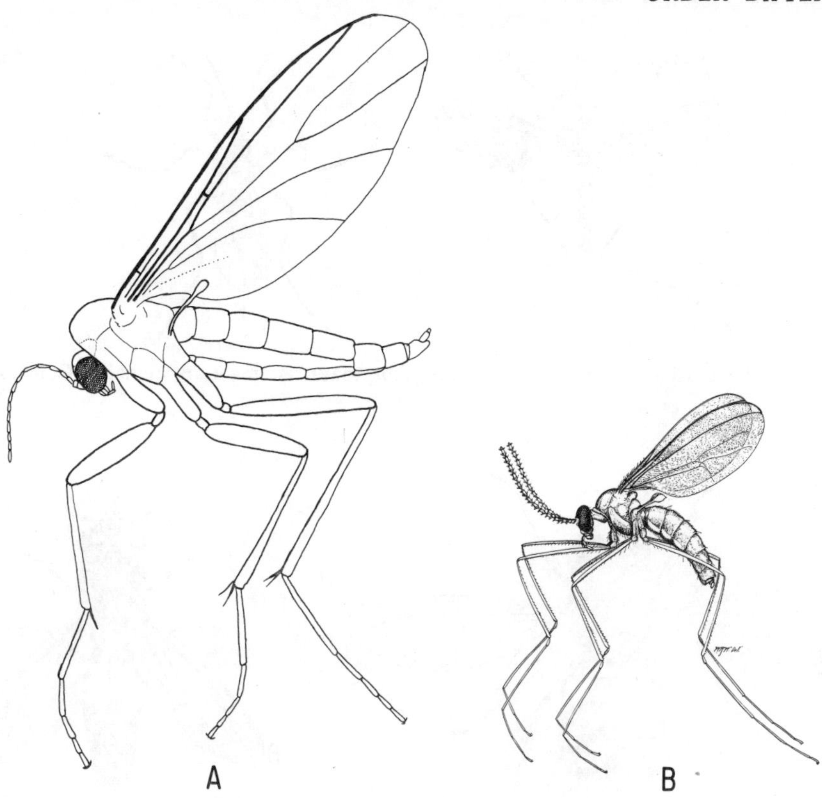

Fig. 27-44. A, a dark-winged fungus gnat, *Sciàra* sp., 15 ×; B, a cecidomyiid, *Aphidoléstes meridionàlis* Felt (which is predaceous on aphids). (B, courtesy of USDA.)

larvae occur in decaying vegetation or debris, where they prey upon various small insects. The larvae of the snipe flies in the genus *Athèrix* are aquatic; the adults lay their eggs in masses on twigs overhanging streams, into which the larvae fall after they hatch; the female remains on the egg mass and eventually dies there, and other females may lay their eggs on this mass until a ball of considerable size is formed—consisting of eggs and dead females.

FAMILY **Hilarimórphidae:** The hilarimorphids are small flies, 2.5 to 5 millimeters in length, and dark brown to blackish in color. The group is represented in the United States by three species of *Hilarimórpha,* all of which are quite rare; they have been recorded in New Hampshire, Vermont, Illinois, Colorado, California, and Oregon. These flies were formerly included in the family Rhagiónidae, but differ from them in that they lack a closed discal cell and empodia and have only four posterior cells.

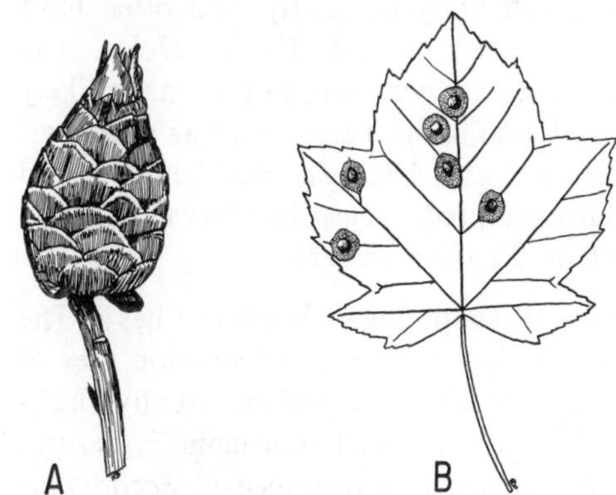

Fig. 27-45. Galls of cecidomyiids. A, the pine-cone willow gall, caused by *Rhabdóphaga strobilòides* (Walsh); B, the maple leaf spot, caused by *Cecidomỳia ocellàris* Osten Sacken (Redrawn from Felt.)

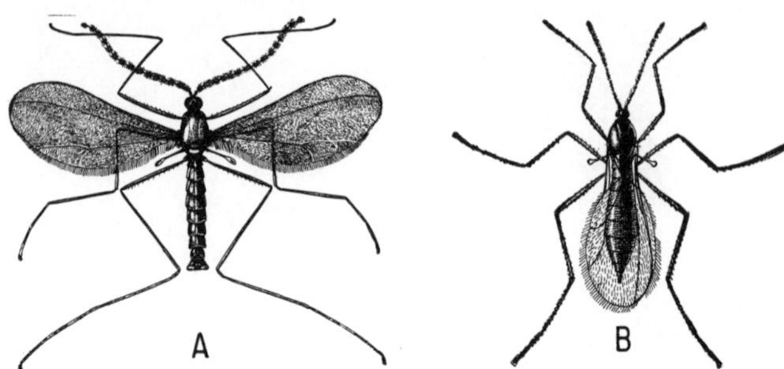

Fig. 27-46. The hessian fly, *Phytóphaga destrúctor* (Say). A, male; B, female. (Courtesy of USDA.)

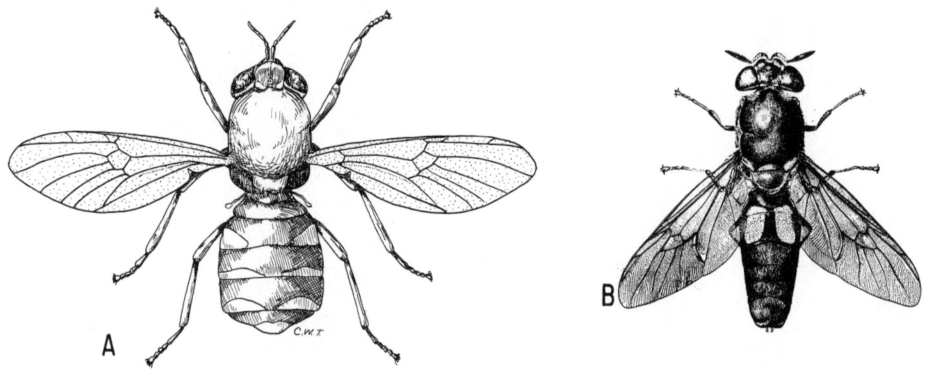

Fig. 27-47. Soldier flies. A, *Stratìomys láticeps* Loew; B, *Hermètia illùcens* (Linn.). (B, courtesy of USDA.)

FAMILY **Therévidae**—Stiletto Flies: The stilletto flies are of medium size, usually somewhat hairy or bristly, and often have the abdomen pointed (Figure 27-51). The adults are not common, but are most likely to be found in open areas such as meadows, pastures, and beaches. Both larvae and adults are predaceous. The larvae occur in soil or decaying materials.

FAMILY **Scenopínidae**—Window Flies: The window flies are rather uncommon flies of medium or small size and are usually blackish in color. The common name is derived from the fact that one species, *Scenópinus fènestràlis* (Linn.) (Figure 27-52), is sometimes common on windows; the larva of this species is said to feed on the larvae of carpet beetles. The larvae of other species occur in decaying wood and fungi.

FAMILY **Apiocéridae**—Flower-Loving Flies: The apiocerids are relatively large, elongate flies that are found on flowers. They occur in the arid regions of the West and are rather rare. Nothing is known of their immature stages. The group is a small one, with 17 known species in North America.

FAMILY **Mỳdidae**—Mydas Flies: The mydas flies are very large and elongate, with long, 4-segmented, clubbed antennae. A common species, *Mỳdas clavàtus* Drury (Figure 27-53), is black, with the second abdominal segment yellowish or orange. The adults are predaceous, and the larvae occur in decaying wood.

FAMILY **Asílidae**—Robber Flies: This is a large group, and some species are quite common. The adults are found in all sorts of places, but each species usually occurs in

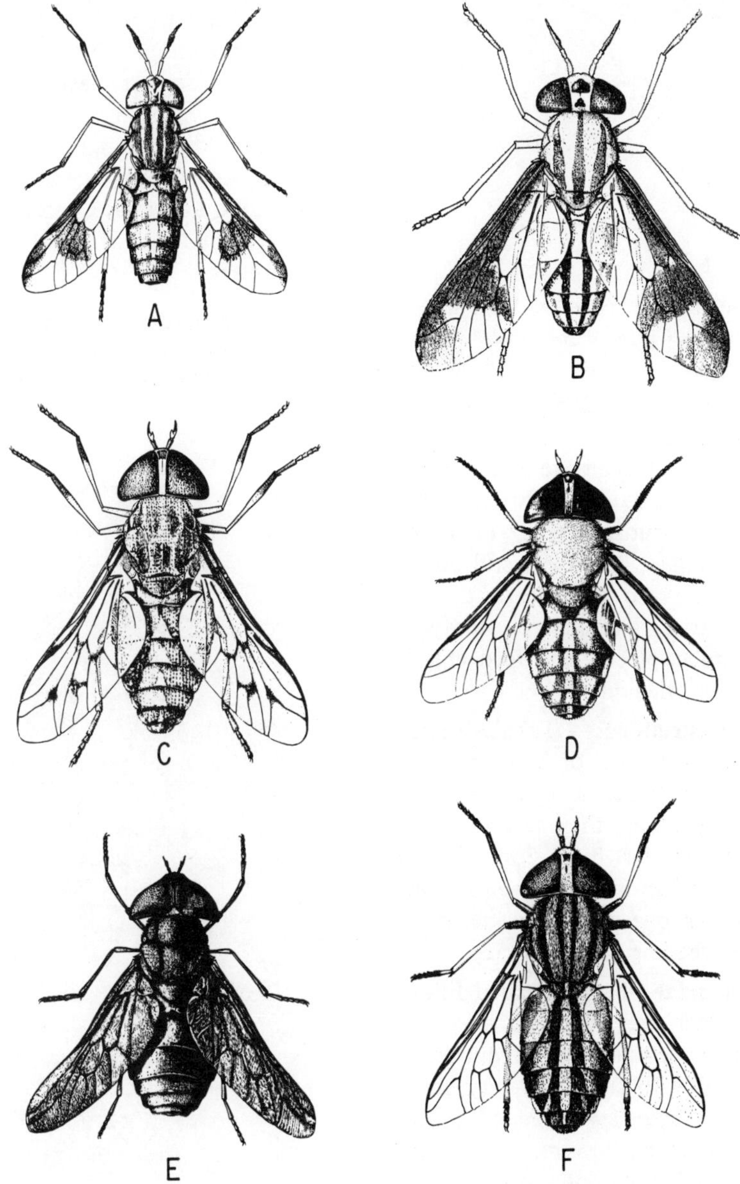

Fig. 27-48. Horse flies and deer flies (Tabánidae). A, *Chrỳsops wièdemanni* Krober; B, *Chrỳsops pìkei* Whitney; C, *Tabànus súlcifrons* Macquart; D, *Tabànus quinquevittàtus* Wiedemann; E, *Tabànus atràtus* Fabricius; F, *Tabànus linèola* Fabricius. (Courtesy of Schwardt and Hall and the Arkansas Agricultural Experiment Station.)

a characteristic type of habitat. The adults are highly predaceous and attack a variety of insects, including wasps, bees, dragonflies, grasshoppers, and other flies; they usually attack an insect as large as or larger than themselves. Some of the larger asilids can inflict a painful bite if carelessly handled.

The robber flies have the top of the head hollowed out between the eyes (Figure 27-56 B), the face more or less bearded, and they have a stout thorax with long, strong

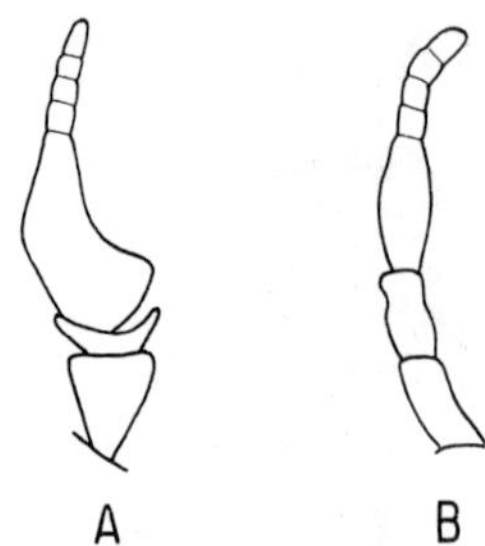

Fig. 27-49. Antennae of tabanids. A, *Tabànus atràtus* Fabricius; B, *Chrŷsops fuliginòsus* Wiedemann.

legs. Most of them are elongate, with the abdomen long and tapering (Figures 27-54 and 27-55 B); some species are stout-bodied and very hairy, and strongly resemble bumble bees, leafcutting bees, or other Hymenoptera (Figure 27-55 A); still others (Figure 27-56 A) are elongate and very slender. The larvae live in soil, decaying wood, and similar places, and feed chiefly on the larvae of other insects.

FAMILY **Nemestrínidae** — Tangle-Veined Flies: These flies are of medium size, stout-bodied, and occur in open fields of fairly high vegetation; they hover persistently, and are very fast fliers. Some species occur on flowers. Not much is known of the larval stages, but one species is known to parasitize root-feeding beetle larvae.

FAMILY **Acrocéridae**—Small-Headed Flies: These are rather rare flies of small to medium size with a somewhat humpbacked appearance and with the head very small (Figure 27-57). Some have a long, slender proboscis and feed on flowers; others have no proboscis and apparently do not feed in the adult stage. The larvae are internal parasites of spiders.

FAMILY **Bombyliidae**—Bee Flies: The bee flies are mostly stout-bodied, densely hairy flies of medium to large size; a few are slender-bodied, elongate, and not very hairy. Many have the proboscis very long and slender. The adults are found on flowers or hovering over or resting on the ground or grass in open sunny places. They often visit "water holes" in arid regions. The wings at rest are usually held outstretched. Most species are very fast fliers, and when caught in an insect net, buzz much like a bee. Many have banded or spotted wings (Figure 27-58). The larvae (as far as known) are parasitic and attack caterpillars, grubs, hymenopterous larvae, and the eggs of grasshoppers.

FAMILY **Empídidae**—Dance Flies: The dance flies are so named because the adults sometimes occur in swarms, flying with an

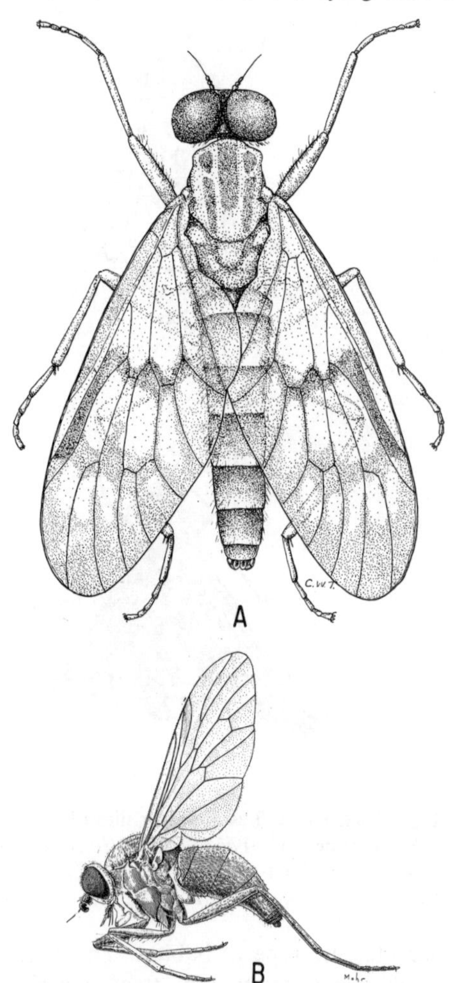

Fig. 27-50. Snipe flies. A, a common snipe fly, *Rhàgio mystàcea* Macquart; B, a blood-sucking snipe fly, *Symphoromŷia átripes* Bigot. (B, courtesy of Ross and the Entomological Society of America.)

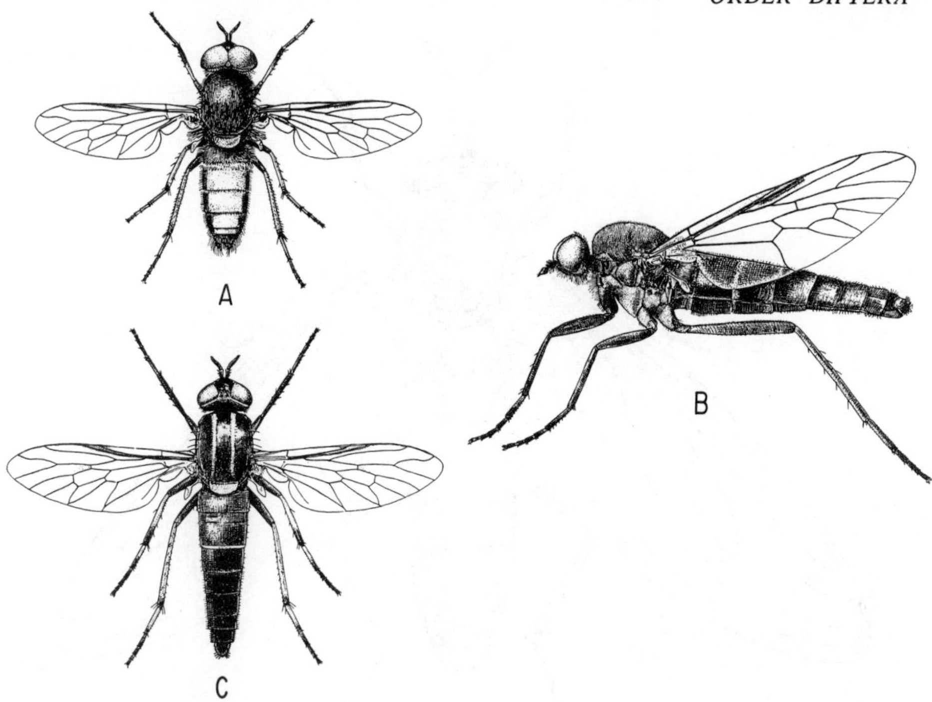

Fig. 27-51. Stiletto flies (Therévidae). A, *Psilocéphala áldrichi* Coquillett, female; B, *Caenòtus inornàtus* Cole, female; C, *Psilocéphala áldrichi* Coquillett, male. (Courtesy of Cole and the U.S. National Museum.)

up-and-down movement. This group is a large one, and many species are fairly common; all are small, and some are minute. The dance flies are found in a variety of situations, usually in moist places where there is an abundance of vegetation; they are predaceous on smaller insects, but occasionally frequent flowers. Most of them have a large thorax and a long tapering abdomen; the male genitalia are terminal and often are rather conspicuous (Figure 27-59).

Many species of dance flies have rather interesting mating habits. The males sometimes capture prey and use it to attract females; mating pairs may often be taken on the wing, the female still holding the prey which the male has given her.

Dance fly larvae occur in the soil, in decaying vegetation, under bark, or in water; they are believed to be predaceous or scavengers.

FAMILY **Dolichopódidae** — Long-Legged Flies: The dolichopodids are small to minute flies that are usually metallic in color —greenish, bluish, or coppery. The male genitalia are usually quite large and conspicuous and are usually folded forward under the abdomen (Figure 27-60); in the female the apex of the abdomen is pointed. The legs of the males are often peculiarly ornamented. The group is a large one, and its members are abundant in many places, particularly near swamps and streams, in

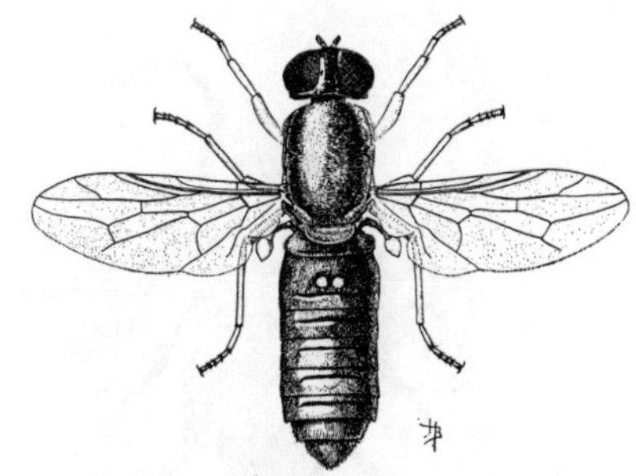

Fig. 27-52. A window fly, *Scenópinus fenestràlis* (Linn.). (Courtesy of USDA.)

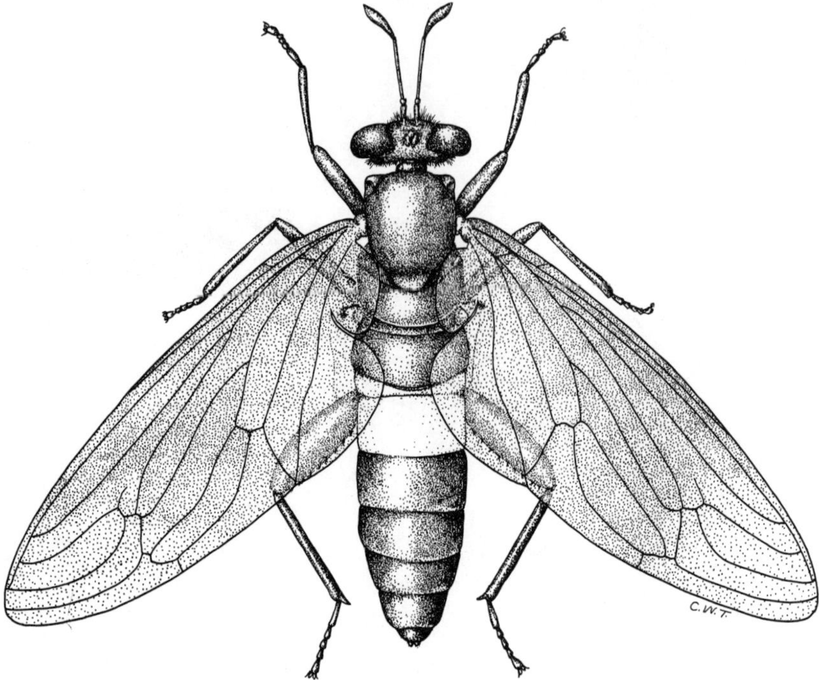

Fig. 27-53. A mydas fly, *Mỳdas clavàtus* Drury.

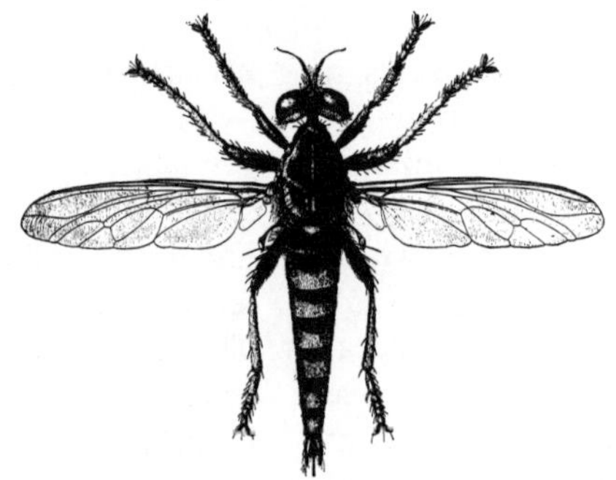

Fig. 27-54. A robber fly, *Prómachus vertebràtus* (Say). (Courtesy of USDA.)

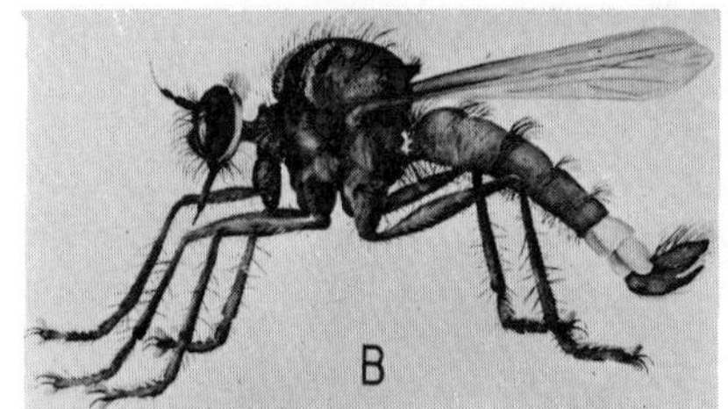

Fig. 27-55. Robber flies. A, *Bombomíma làta* (Macquart); B, *Èrax rufílabris* Macquart.

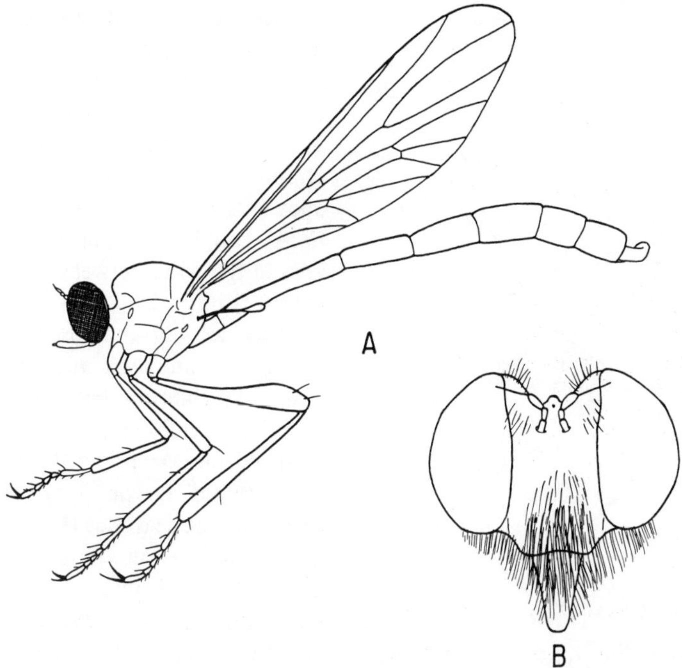

Fig. 27-56. A, a slender robber fly, *Leptogáster annulàtus* Say, 7½ ×; B, head of a robber fly (*Èrax*), anterior view.

woodlands, and in meadows. Many species occur only in a particular type of habitat. The adults are predaceous on smaller insects. The adults of many species engage in rather unusual mating dances. The larvae occur in mud, decaying wood, grass stems, and under bark; not much is known of their feeding habits, but at least some are predaceous. The larvae of the genus *Medèterus* live under bark and are predaceous on bark beetles.

FAMILY **Lonchoptéridae** — Spear-Winged Flies: The members of this group are slender, yellowish, or brownish flies less than 5 millimeters in length, with the wings somewhat pointed at the apex and with a characteristic venation (Figure 27-10 H). They are usually fairly common in moist shady or grassy places. The larvae occur in decaying vegetation. This small family contains the single genus *Lonchóptera.*

FAMILY **Phóridae**—Humpbacked Flies: The phorids are small or minute flies that are easily recognized by the humpbacked appearance (Figure 27-61), the characteristic venation (Figure 27-10 G), and the laterally flattened hind femora. The adults are fairly common in many habitats, but are most abundant about decaying vegetation. The habits of the larvae are rather varied; some occur in decaying animal or vegetable matter, some occur in fungi, some are internal parasites of various other insects, and some occur as parasites or commensals in the nests of ants or termites. A few of the species that occur in ant or termite nests have the wings reduced or lacking.

FAMILY **Platypézidae**—Flat-Footed Flies: These flies are so named because of the peculiarly shaped hind tarsi, which are often flattened or otherwise modified (Figure 27-26 C); the tarsi are generally more flattened in the females than in the males. The flat-footed flies are small, usually black or brown in color, and occur on low vegetation in wooded areas. The males frequently swarm in groups of up to 50 or more, the swarm dancing in midair several feet above

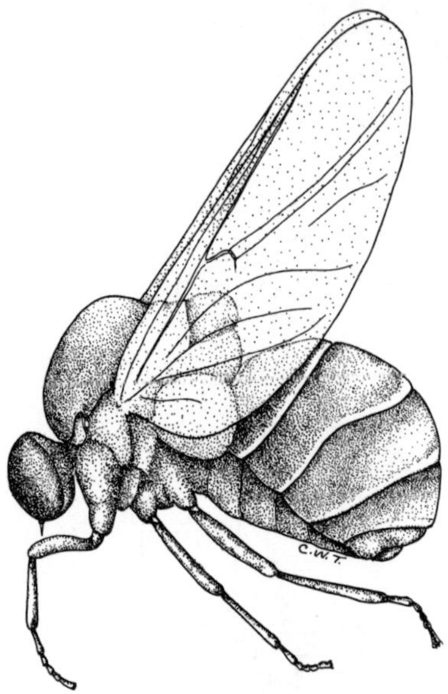

Fig. 27-57. A small-headed fly, *Ogcòdes* sp.

the ground, with the hind legs hanging down; if disturbed (for example, by a swinging net), they scatter and reform a little higher up (out of net reach). Adults of the genus *Microsània* are attracted to smoke, apparently reacting to the odor of the smoke. The larvae of flat-footed flies occur in fungi.

FAMILY **Pipuncùlidae**—Big-Headed Flies: The big-headed flies are small flies with the head very large and composed mostly of eyes (Figure 27-62). The group is a small one, and its members are seldom common. The larvae are parasitic, chiefly on leafhoppers and leaf bugs.

FAMILY **Sýrphidae**—Syrphid Flies or Flower Flies: This is a large group, and many species are very abundant. Syrphids may be found almost everywhere, but different species occur in different types of habitats. The adults are often common about flowers and frequently do a great deal of hovering. Different species vary quite a bit in appearance (Figure 27-63), but (with a few exceptions) can be recognized by the spurious vein in the wing between the radius and the media (Figure 27-11 A-C, *spv*). Many are brightly colored and resemble various bees or wasps; some look much like honey bees, others like bumble bees, others like wasps, and the resemblance is often very striking. None of the syrphids will bite man.

Syrphid larvae vary considerably in habits and appearance (Figure 27-64). Many are predaceous on aphids, others live in the nests of social insects (ants, termites, or bees), others live in decaying vegetation or rotting wood, others live in highly polluted aquatic habitats, and a few feed on growing plants. The larvae of *Tubífera,* which live in highly polluted water, have a very long breathing tube and are commonly called rat-tailed maggots; the adults of this genus (Figure 27-63 D) resemble bees. Rat-tailed maggots are sometimes responsible for intestinal myiasis in man.

FAMILY **Conópidae**—Thick-Headed Flies: The conopids are medium-sized, brownish flies, many of which superficially resemble small thread-waisted wasps (Figure 27-65). The abdomen is usually elongate and slender basally, the head is slightly broader than the thorax, and the antennae are long. All species have a very long and slender pro-

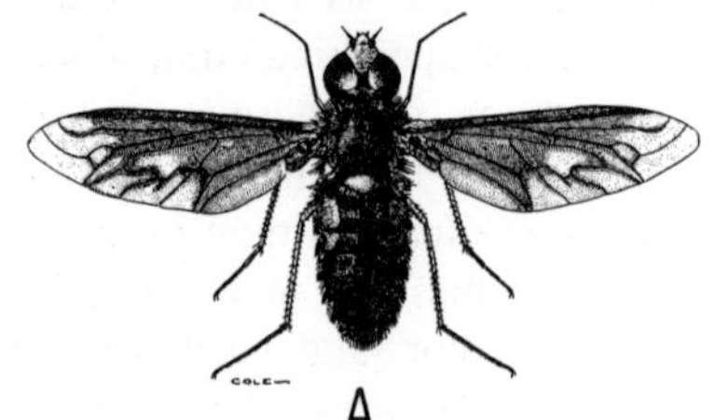

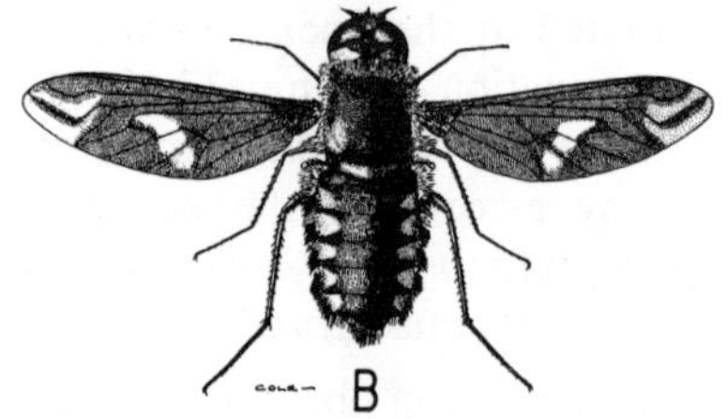

Fig. 27-58. Bee flies. A, *Ánthrax álpha* Osten Sacken; B, *Ánthrax yellowstònei* Cole. (Courtesy of Cole and the New York Entomological Society.)

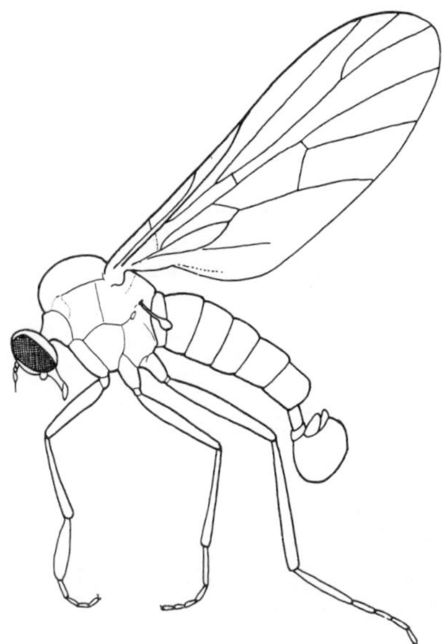

Fig. 27-59. A dance fly (Empídidae); 10 ×.

boscis; in some species the proboscis is elbowed. In one genus (*Stylogáster*) the abdomen is slender and in the female terminates in a very long ovipositor that is as long as the remainder of the body. The adults are usually found on flowers. The larvae are parasitic, chiefly on adult bumble bees and wasps, and the flies usually oviposit on their hosts during flight.

FAMILY **Micropézidae**—Stilt-Legged Flies: The members of this group are small to medium-sized, elongate flies with very long legs; the first posterior (R_5) cell is narrowed apically, and the anal cell is often long and pointed (Figure 77-22 C). The adults are found near moist places. Only a few species occur in North America, but the group is abundant in the tropics, where the larvae live in excrement.

FAMILY **Neriìdae:** This group is represented in the United States by a single species, *Odontoloxòzus longicòrnis* (Coquillet), which occurs in the Southwest from southern Texas to southern California. This species is slender, medium-sized, grayish with brown markings, and has long slender legs and relatively long porrect antennae. The larvae breed in decaying cacti, and the adults are usually found only on such cacti.

FAMILY **Diópsidae**—Stalk-Eyed Flies: The diopsids are small flies, and most species have the eyes situated on the ends of long stalks. The group is largely tropical, and only a single species, *Sphyracéphala brevicórnis* Say, occurs in North America. The eye stalks in this species are rather short; the adults are usually found on skunk cabbage; the immature stages are unknown.

FAMILY **Psílidae**—Rust Flies: The psilids are small to medium-sized flies, usually rather slender, with long antennae. They have a peculiar ridge or weakening across the basal third of the wing. In the genus *Loxócera* the third antennal segment is very long and slender (Figure 27-20). The larvae live in the roots or galls of plants, and one species, *Psíla ròsae* Fabricius, the carrot rust fly, often does considerable damage to carrots, celery, and related plants.

FAMILY **Tanypézidae:** The Tanypézidae are medium-sized flies with rather long and slender legs; they occur in moist woods and are quite rare. Nothing is known of their immature stages.

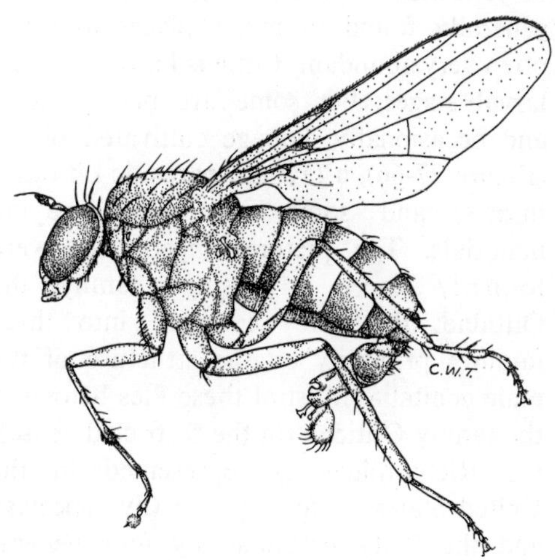

Fig. 27-60. A long-legged fly, *Dolíchopus pùgil* Loew.

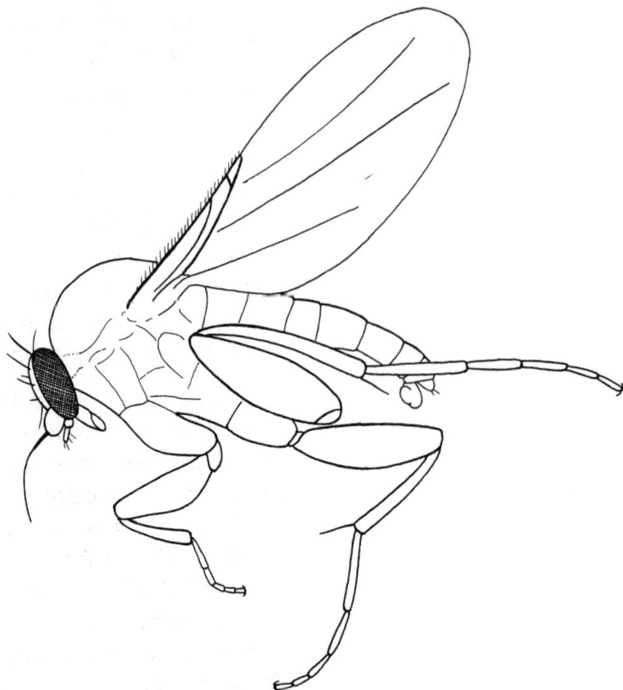

Fig. 27-61. A humpbacked fly (Phóridae); 50 ×.

FAMILIES **Richardiidae, Otítidae** AND **Platystomátidae**—Picture-Winged Flies: The picture-winged flies are a large group of small to medium-sized flies that usually have the wings marked with black, brown, or yellowish (Figure 27-66). These flies are generally found in moist places and are often very abundant. Little is known of their larval stages, but some are plant-feeding and occasionally damage cultivated plants (Figure 27-66), a few are parasitic on other insects, and some occur in decaying materials. The picture-winged flies were formerly placed in a single family, the Otítidae; they are separated into three families primarily on the structure of the male genitalia. Most of these flies belong to the family Otítidae (in the restricted sense); the Richardiidae is represented in the United States by four genera (five species), and the Platystomátidae by four genera; most of the species in these three families occur in the tropics.

FAMILY **Pyrgótidae:** The Pyrgótidae are rather elongate flies of medium to large size and often have considerable coloring in the wings; the head is prominent and rounded (Figure 27-67). The adults are mostly nocturnal and are frequently attracted to lights; the larvae are parasitic on adult June beetles.

FAMILY **Tephrítidae**—Fruit Flies, Peacock Flies: This is a large group of small to

Fig. 27-62. A big-headed fly, *Pipúnculus subviréscens* Loew, female. (Courtesy of Knowlton and the Utah Agricultural Experiment Station.)

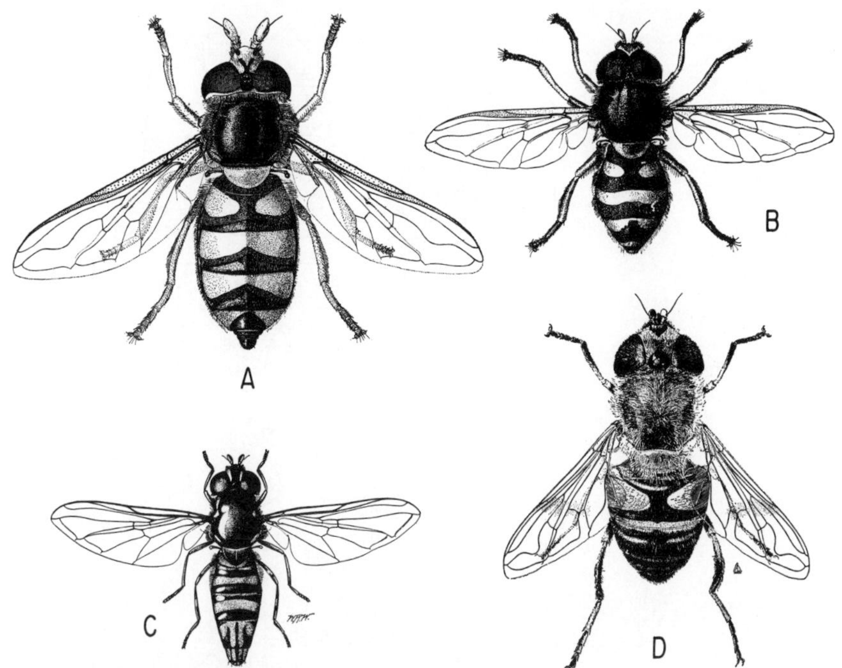

Fig. 27-63. Syrphid flies. A, *Dídea fúscipes* Loew; B, *Sýrphus tórvus* Osten Sacken; C, *Allográpta oblíqua* (Say); D, *Tubífera ténax* (Linn.). (A and B, courtesy of Metcalf and the Maine Agricultural Experiment Station; C and D, courtesy of USDA.)

medium-sized flies that usually have spotted or banded wings, the spotting often forming complicated or attractive patterns (Figures 27-68 and 27-69); many species are fairly common. The tephritids can be recognized by the structure of the subcosta, which apically bends forward at almost a right angle and then fades out (Figure 27-23 B). The adults are found on flowers or vegetation. Some species have a habit of slowly moving their wings up and down while resting on vegetation, and are often called peacock flies.

The larvae of most tephritids feed on plants, and some are rather serious pests. The larva of *Rhagóletis pomonélla* (Walsh), usually called the apple maggot, tunnels in the fruit of apple and other orchard trees (Figure 27-68); other species in this genus attack cherries. The Mediterranean fruit fly, *Cerátitis capitàta* (Wiedemann), attacks citrus and other fruits, and some years ago threatened to become a serious pest in the South; this species is now eradicated in Florida. Species of the genus *Euróst*a form stem galls on goldenrod (Figure 27-70); the galls are rounded and thick-walled, with a single larva in the center; in the fall, the larva cuts a tunnel to the surface, overwinters as a larva in the gall, and pupates in the spring. A few of the tephritids are leaf miners in the larval stage.

FAMILY **Helcomýzidae:** These flies are similar to the Dryomýzidae, with which they were formerly classified; they may be separated from the Dryomýzidae by the characters given in the key. The adults occur in moist places, and the larvae are aquatic; some species are abundant along the seashore, where the larvae breed in seaweeds.

FAMILY **Ropaloméridae:** This is a small group of about a dozen tropical species, most of them occurring in Central and

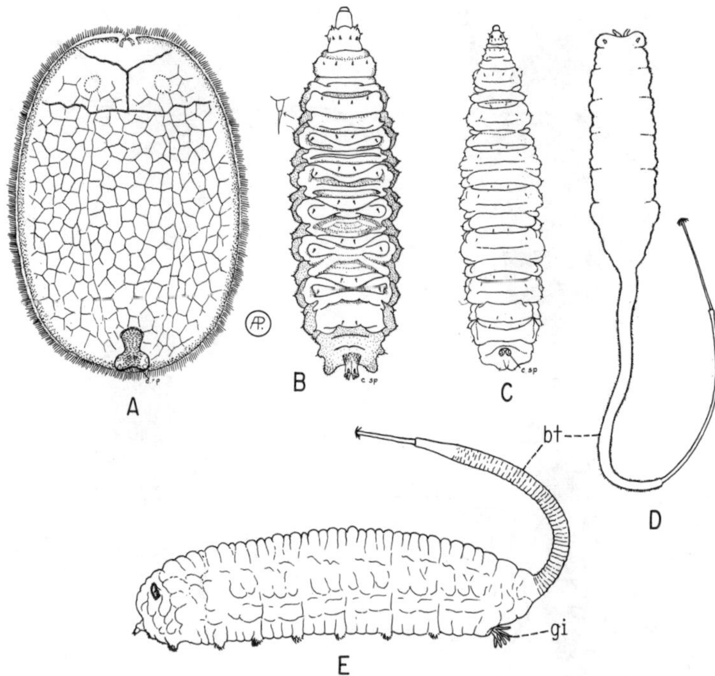

Fig. 27-64. Larvae of syrphid flies. A, *Mìcrodon* sp., 50 ×; B, *Pipìza femoràlis* Loew, 50 ×; C, *Sýrphus rìbesii vìttafrons* Shannon, 3½ ×; D and E, *Tubífera* spp. (D, 2 ×; E, 3½ ×). *bt*, breathing tube; *csp*, caudal spiracle; *gi*, gills. (Courtesy of Peterson. Reprinted by permission.)

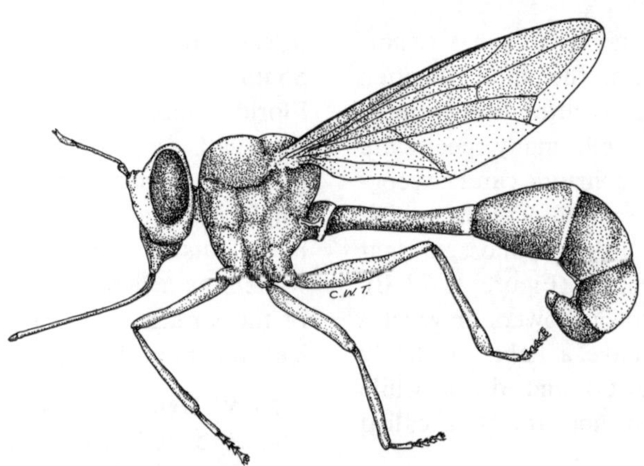

Fig. 27-65. A thick-headed fly, *Physocéphala furcillàta* Williston.

South America. They are of medium size, usually brownish or grayish in color, with the first posterior (R_5) cell narrowed apically, the femora thickened, and the hind tibiae often dilated. These flies occur along the seashore and along rivers; they are fast fliers, and frequently hover.

FAMILY **Coelópidae**—Seaweed Flies: The members of this family are medium-sized to small flies, usually dark brown or black in color, and have the dorsum of the thorax conspicuously flattened and the body and legs very bristly (Figure 27-71). These flies occur along the seashore and are particularly abundant where various seaweeds have washed up. The larvae breed in the seaweed in tremendous numbers, chiefly just above the high-tide mark in seaweed that has begun to rot. The adults swarming over the seaweed often attract large numbers of shore birds, which feed on them. Seaweed flies feed on flowers, and sometimes cluster so thickly on the flowers near the shore that a single sweep of a net may yield a hundred or more individuals.

FAMILY **Dryomýzidae:** The Dryomýzidae are similar to the marsh flies; the cross-veins are usually spotted. The adults are found in moist places or along the seashore, and the larvae are aquatic.

FAMILY **Sépsidae**—Black Scavenger Flies: The sepsids are small, shining black, or reddish flies that have the head rounded and the abdomen narrowed at the base (Figure 27-72). The larvae live in excrement, dung, and similar materials, and the adults are often numerous near such materials.

FAMILY **Sciomýzidae**—Marsh Flies: The members of this group are small to medium-sized flies that are usually yellowish or brownish with spotted wings and which have the antennae extending forward (Figure 27-73); most species are about the size of a house fly. Marsh flies are fairly common insects and occur along the banks of streams and ponds, in marshes, and in similar places. The larval stages feed on

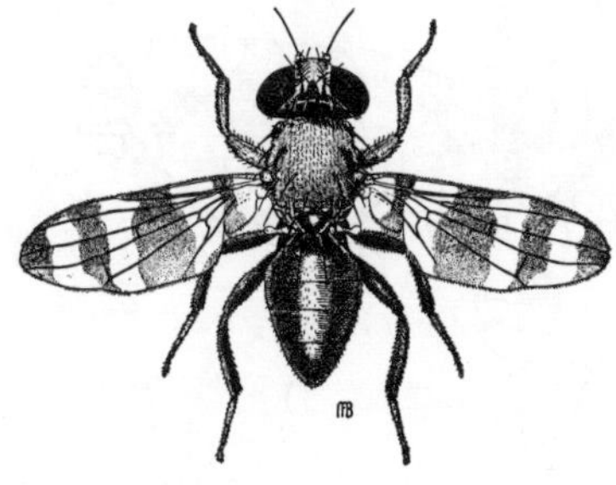

Fig. 27-66. A corn-infesting otitid, *Euxésta stigmátias* Loew; 6 ×. (Courtesy of Wolcott and the *Journal of Agriculture* of the University of Puerto Rico.)

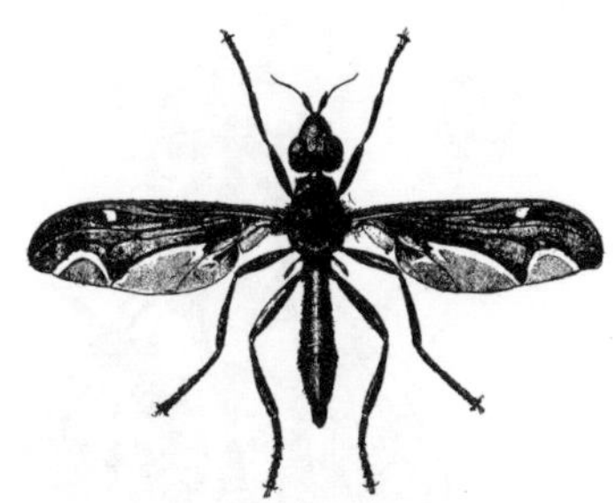

Fig. 27-67. *Pyrgòta undàta* Wiedemann (Pyrgotidae). (Courtesy of USDA.)

aquatic snails, generally as parasites, though some are predaceous.

FAMILY **Lauxanìidae:** The Lauxanìidae are small flies, rarely over 6 millimeters in length, and some have pictured wings. The adults may be found in many places, but often occur in large numbers in moist situations. The larvae of some species are leaf miners; others occur in decaying vegetation.

FAMILY **Chamaemyìidae:** The chamaemyiids are small flies that are usually grayish in color with black spots on the abdomen. The larvae of *Leucòpis* are predaceous on aphids.

FAMILY **Periscélidae:** The family Periscélidae is a small group resembling the Lauxanìidae; little is known of their immature stages.

FAMILY **Piophílidae**—Skipper Flies: The skipper flies are usually less than 5 millimeters in length and are rather metallic black or bluish (Figure 27-74 A). The larvae are mostly scavengers, and some live in cheese and preserved meats. The larvae of the cheese skipper, *Pióphila càsei* (Linn.), are often serious pests in cheese and meats; the name "skipper" refers to the fact that the larvae can jump. *P. càsei* has been recorded breeding in formalin-soaked human cadavers in medical schools.

FAMILY **Thyreophóridae:** This is a small group that occurs principally in Europe, Africa, and Australia. The most distinctive feature of these flies is the shape of the head; there are deep grooves below the an-

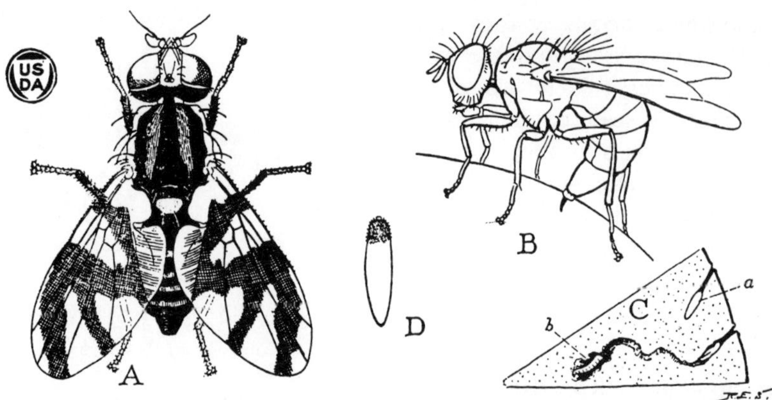

Fig. 27-68. The apple maggot, *Rhagóletis pomonélla* (Walsh) (Tephrítidae). A, adult female, 7 ×; B, female puncturing skin of apple preparatory to depositing an egg; C, section of an apple showing an egg inserted at *a,* and a young maggot tunneling into the pulp at *b*; D, an egg (greatly enlarged). (Courtesy of USDA.)

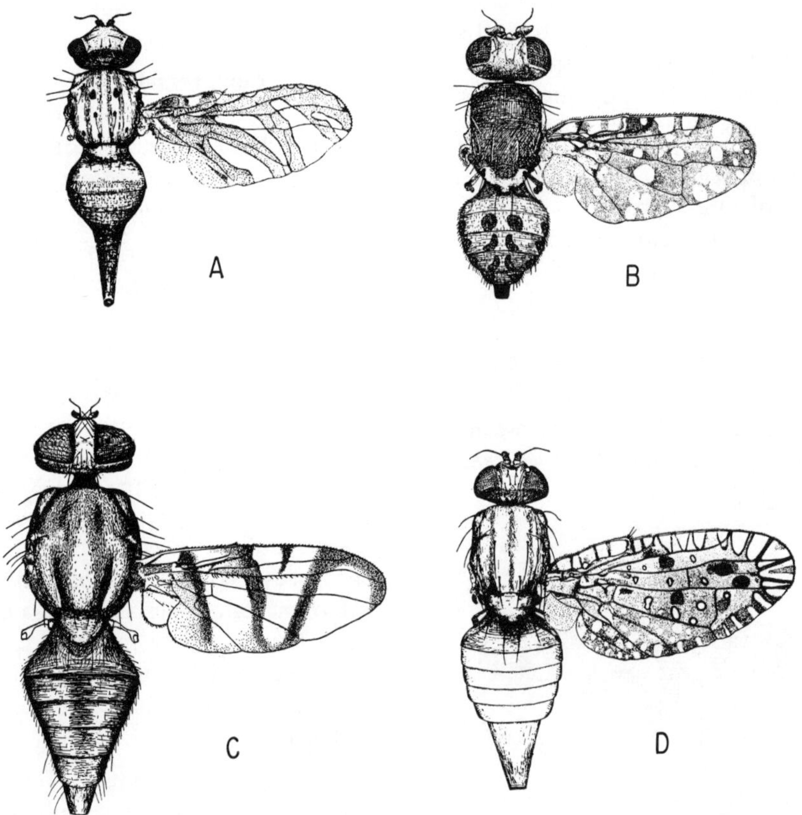

Fig. 27-69. Fruit flies (Tephrítidae). A, *Peronỳma maculàta* (Curran); B, *Acidogòna melanùra* (Loew); C, *Zonostémata elécta* (Say); D, *Paracántha cúlta* (Wiedemann). (Courtesy of USDA.)

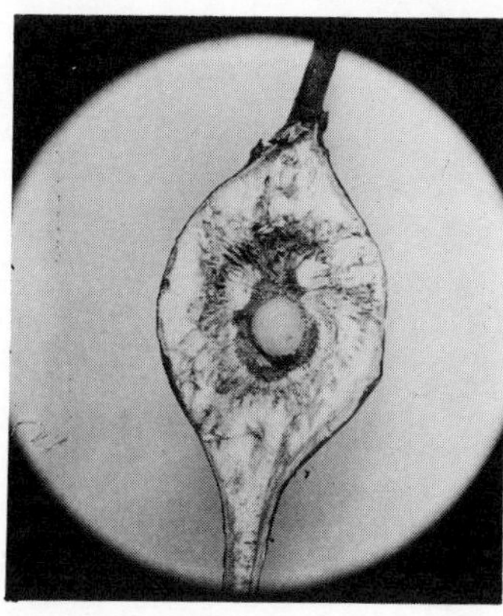

Fig. 27-70. A gall of a goldenrod gall fly, *Euròsta* sp. (Tephrítidae), cut open to show the larva. (Courtesy of the Illinois Natural History Survey.)

tennae, into which the antennae may be retracted, and the head in profile is more or less pointed in front of the eyes, with the face receding.

FAMILY **Neottiophílidae:** The members of this family are similar to the Piophílidae, from which they may be separated by the characters given in the key. The group is principally European, and the larvae are ectoparasites of nestling birds.

FAMILY **Pallоptéridae:** The Palloptéridae are medium-sized flies that usually have pictured wings; they are found in moist and shady places, usually on foliage, and along the seashore. They are not common, and little is known of their larval stages.

FAMILY **Lonchaèidae:** The Lonchaèidae are small, shining, blackish flies, the adults of which occur chiefly in moist or shady places. The larvae occur in decaying plants, under bark, and in fungi.

FAMILY **Sphaerocéridae**—Small Dung Flies: The sphaerocerids are very small, black or brown flies that can usually be recognized by the characteristic hind tarsi (Figure 27-26 A). They are found in swampy places near excrement, often in large numbers. The larvae live in excrement and refuse.

FAMILY **Bràulidae:** This family contains a single genus, *Bràula,* the members of which are parasitic on the honey bee. There is a single rare species in this country, *B. coèca* Nitzsch, a tiny insect about 1.5 millimeters in length.

FAMILY **Tethínidae:** The Tethinids are small to minute flies that occur chiefly in moist places. Most species occur along the seashore—in beach grass, salt marshes, and around seaweeds washed up along the shore —and the majority of the coastal species occur along the Pacific Coast.

FAMILY **Milichìidae:** The milichiids are small flies, usually black or silvery in color, and are usually fairly common in open areas.

FAMILY **Canacèidae:** The Canacèidae are very small flies, not over 3.5 millimeters in length. The adults occur along the seashore, and the larvae occur in brackish water. The group is a small one, with only three species known in the United States.

FAMILY **Ephýdridae**—Shore Flies: This is a large group, and some species are quite common. The shore flies are small to very small; most of them are dark colored, and a few have pictured wings. The adults are found in moist places—marshes, the shores of ponds and streams, and the seashore. The larvae are aquatic, and many species occur in brackish or even strongly alkaline water; one western species, *Psilòpa petròlei* Coquillett, breeds in pools of crude petroleum. These flies often occur in enormous numbers; pools along the seashore may sometimes be literally alive with the adults, which walk or cluster on the surface of the water (for example, *Éphydra ripària* Fallén, Figure 27-75). Along the shore of Great Salt Lake, ephydrids may arise from the ground literally in clouds, and a few sweeps of a net may yield a cupful; at one time the Indians gathered the puparia from the lake and ate them.

FAMILY **Curtonótidae:** This group is represented in the United States by a single species, *Curtonòtum hélva* Loew, which is found in the eastern states. It occurs in high

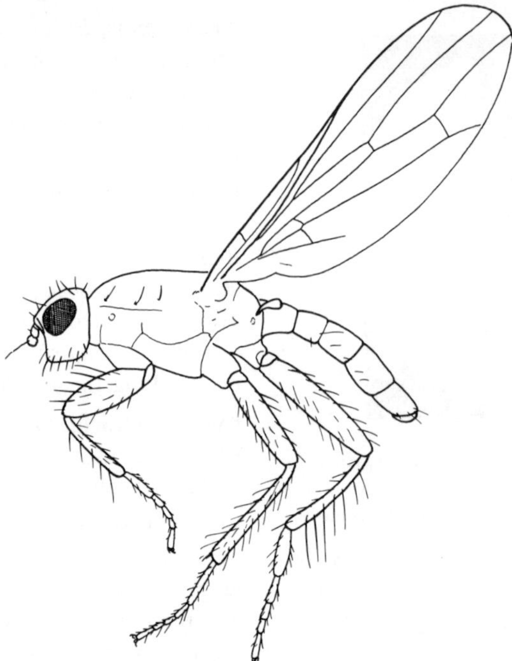

Fig. 27-71. A seaweed fly, *Coelòpa* sp. (Coelópidae); 10 ×.

grass in moist places; the habits of the larvae are not known.

FAMILY **Drosophílidae**—Pomace Flies or Fruit Flies: These flies are 3 to 4 millimeters in length and usually yellowish in color, and are generally found around decaying vegetation and fruit. This group is a large one, and many species are very common. The pomace flies are often pests in the household when fruit is present. The larvae of most species occur in decaying fruit and fungi; in the case of the larvae living in fruit, it has been shown that the larvae actually feed on the yeasts growing in the fruit. Several species in this group, because of their short life span and ease of culturing, have been used extensively in studies of heredity.

FAMILY **Diastátidae:** These flies resemble the Drosophílidae and Curtonótidae; they differ from the Drosophílidae in that they have the costa usually spinose and Sc somewhat more developed; they differ from the Curtonótidae in that they have the hairs on the arista shorter and the proclinate fronto-orbital bristles behind the foremost reclinate pair.

FAMILY **Camíllidae:** This is primarily an Old World group of flies, similar to the Drosophílidae but metallic in color, lacking sternopleural bristles, and with the anal cell open apically.

FAMILY **Chlorópidae**—Frit Flies: The frit flies are small and rather bare flies, and some species are brightly colored with yellow and black. They are very common in meadows and other places where there is considerable grass, though they may be found in a variety of habitats. The larvae of most species feed in grass stems, and some are serious pests of cereals; a few are scavengers, and a few are parasitic or predaceous. Some of the frit flies (for example, *Hippélates*), which breed in decaying vegetation and excrement, are attracted to animal secretions and feed on pus, blood, and similar materials; they are particularly attracted to the eyes and are sometimes called eye gnats. These flies may act as vectors of yaws and pinkeye.

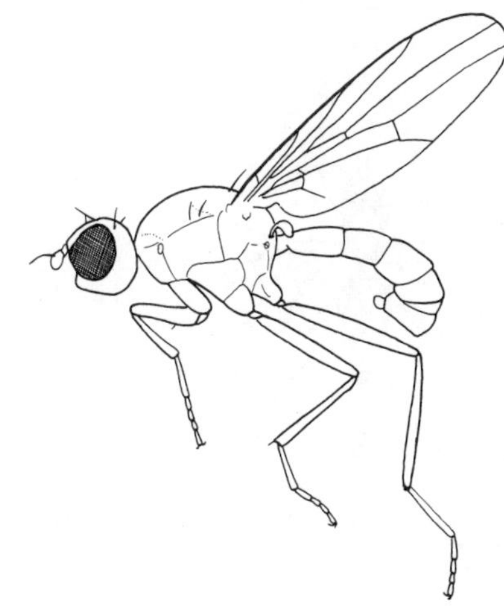

Fig. 27-72. A black scavenger fly (Sépsidae); 15 ×.

FAMILY **Odinìidae:** This is a small family of small flies that were formerly placed in the family Agromýzidae; they may be separated from the Agromýzidae by the characters given in the key. Most species have the wings pictured, or at least have the crossveins spotted with brownish. Five species in two genera (*Tráginops* and *Odínia*) occur in the eastern states.

FAMILY **Agromýzidae**—Leaf-Miner Flies: These flies are small and usually blackish or yellowish in color. The larvae are leaf miners, and the adults occur almost everywhere. Most species are more easily recognized by their mines than by the insects themselves. *Phytomỳza minúscula* Goureau is a fairly common species that makes a serpentine mine in the leaves of wild columbine (Figure 27-77 B); *Agromỳza parvicòrnis* Loew makes a blotch mine in corn and several species of grasses; *A. clàra* Melander mines in the leaves of catalpa (Figure 27-77 A). Most agromyzids make serpentine mines, that is, narrow winding mines that increase in width as the larva grows.

FAMILY **Clusiódidae:** The clusiodids are small (mostly 3 to 4 millimeters in length) and relatively uncommon flies in which the wings are often smoky or marked with brownish, especially apically. The body color varies from pale yellow to black; some species have the thorax black dorsally and yellowish laterally. The larvae occur in decaying wood and under bark; they are able to jump, much like the larvae of skipper flies.

FAMILY **Acartophthálmidae:** This family is represented in the United States by a single rare species, *Acartophthálmus nigrìnus* Zetterstedt, which has been recorded from Massachusetts, Idaho, and Washington; it is blackish, with the front coxae and halteres yellowish, and is 2 millimeters in length.

FAMILY **Heleomýzidae:** The heleomyzids are a fairly large group of small to medium-sized flies, most of which are brownish in color; many superficially resemble marsh flies, but they have well-developed oral vibrissae, the postverticals are converging, and the antennae are smaller and less prominent. They occur in shady or damp places, and the larvae occur in fungi, bird nests, the burrows of small mammals, and various other habitats.

FAMILY **Trixoscélidae:** The members of this family are small flies, mostly 2 to 3 millimeters in length, with the body yellow

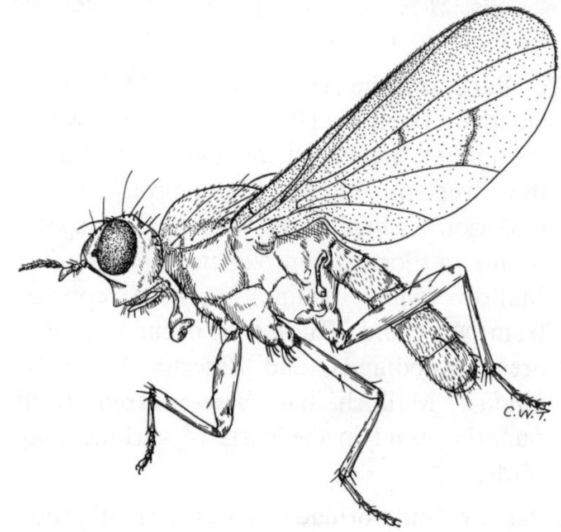

Fig. 27-73. A marsh fly, *Tetanócera vícina* Macquart; $7\frac{1}{2}$ ×.

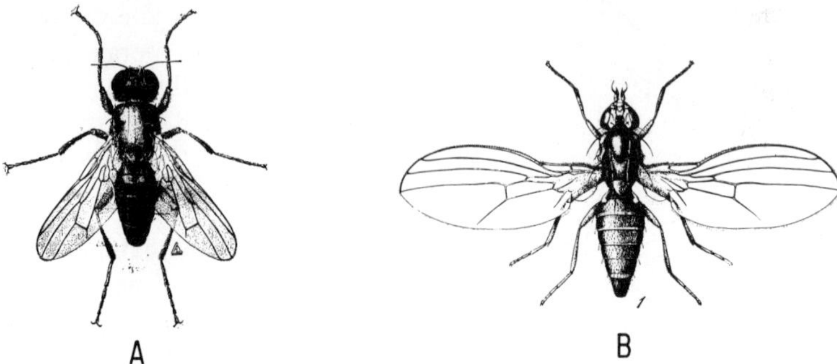

Fig. 27-74. A, adult of the cheese skipper, *Piópbila càsei* (Linn.); B, a leaf-miner fly, *Cerodónta dorsàlis* Loew (Agromýzidae). (Courtesy of USDA.)

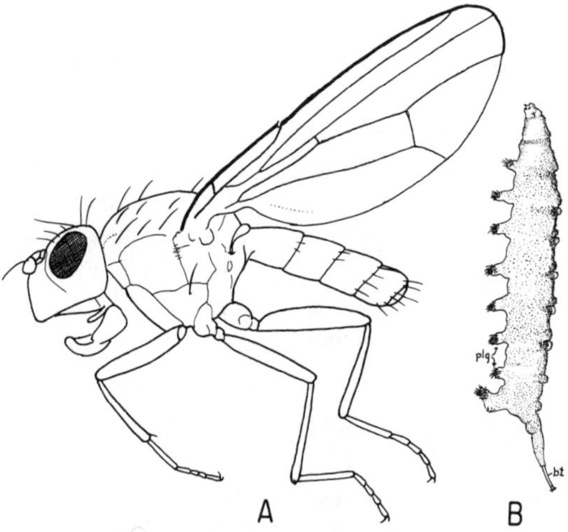

Fig. 27-75. A shore fly, *Éphydra ripària* Fallén. A, adult, 10 ×; B, larva, 4 ×. (B, courtesy of Peterson. Reprinted by permission.)

or dark and the wings hyaline, spotted, or clouded. Twenty-eight species are known in the United States, all but two occurring in the western states; *Spilochròa ornàta* (Johnson) (wings dark, with hyaline spots) occurs in Florida, and *Neóssos marylándica* Malloch (wings hyaline) has been reported from Maryland. These flies occur in grassy areas, woodlands, and deserts; *N. marylándica* Malloch has been reared from puparia found in the nests of various song birds.

FAMILY **Rhinotóridae:** This is a small group of tropical flies, similar in general appearance and habits to the Ropaloméridae (page 493); they differ from the ropalomerids in that the first posterior cell is not narrowed distally.

FAMILY **Anthomýzidae:** These flies are small and somewhat elongate, and occur chiefly in moist places and along the seashore; some species have pictured wings. Little is known of their larval stages.

FAMILY **Opomýzidae:** The opomyzids are small to minute flies that are usually found in grassy places; some species are leaf miners.

FAMILY **Chyromỳidae:** The chyromyids are small, rather uncommon flies that occur chiefly in the southern states along the seacoast. Very little is known of their habits.

FAMILY **Aulacigastéridae:** This group is represented in the United States by a single species, *Aulacigáster leucopèza* Meigen, which occurs from the East Coast west to Kansas and Texas. It was formerly placed in the family Drosophílidae, but has Sc complete or nearly so, the arista minutely pubescent, the postvertical bristles lacking, and the second basal and discal cells confluent. The adults occur about decaying plant materials, in which the larvae occur.

FAMILY **Asteìidae:** This family contains small to minute flies (usually 2 millimeters in length or less) and can be recognized by the peculiar venation—vein R_{2+3} ending in the costa close to R_1 (Figure 27-23 A). The group is a small one, with only 19 species occurring in the United States and Canada; little is known of the habits of these insects.

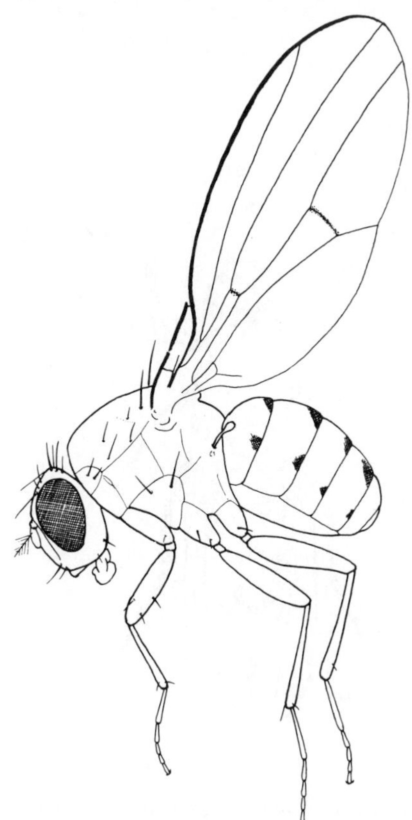

Fig. 27-76. A pomace fly, *Drosóphila* sp.; 20 ×.

FAMILY **Cryptochaètidae:** The flies in this group are superficially somewhat similar to black flies (Simulìidae), and have habits similar to those of eye gnats (*Hippélates,* family Chloröpidae; see page 498. They can usually be recognized by the enlarged third antennal segment, which reaches nearly to the lower edge of the head, and which lacks an arista but bears at its apex a short spine or tubercle. As far as known, the larvae are parasitic on scale insects of the family Margaródidae. The Cryptochaètidae are primarily Asiatic and Australian in distribution, but one species, *Cryptochaètum icéryae* (Williston), has been introduced into California from Australia; this insect is about 1.5 millimeters in length, stout-bodied, with the head and thorax dark metallic blue and the abdomen shiny green.

FAMILY **Anthomyìidae:** This family includes two subfamilies, the Anthomyiìnae and Scatomyzìnae, which are given family rank by some authorities. The Anthomyiìnae are generally dark-colored, and usually have fine erect hairs on the under surface of the scutellum and more than one sternopleural bristle; the Scatomyzìnae are often light-colored (yellowish or brownish) and lack the erect hairs on the under surface of the scutellum, and the generally have only one sternopleural bristle. The larvae of the Anthomyiìnae vary in habits; many feed on plants, and some of these (Figure 27-78) are serious pests of garden crops, others are scavengers, and still others are parasitic on other insects. The larvae of many of the Scatomyzìnae breed in cow dung, and are often quite common in pastures; some are plant-feeding, and others are parasitic on other insects. Many anthomyiids are very common flies.

FAMILY **Múscidae:** This family includes the house fly, stable fly, face fly, horn fly, tsetse fly, and many other species. The house fly, *Músca doméstica* Linn., breeds in filth

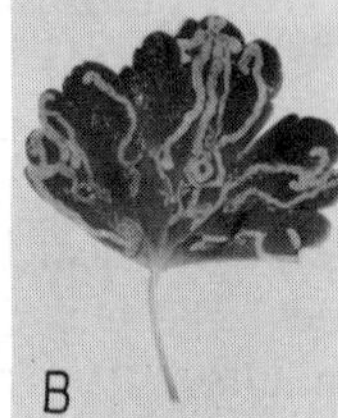

Fig. 27-77. Leaf mines of agromyzid flies. A, the catalpa leaf miner, *Agromỳza clàra* Melander; B, the columbine leaf miner, *Phytomỳza minúscula* Goureau. (Courtesy of the Ohio Agricultural Experiment Station.)

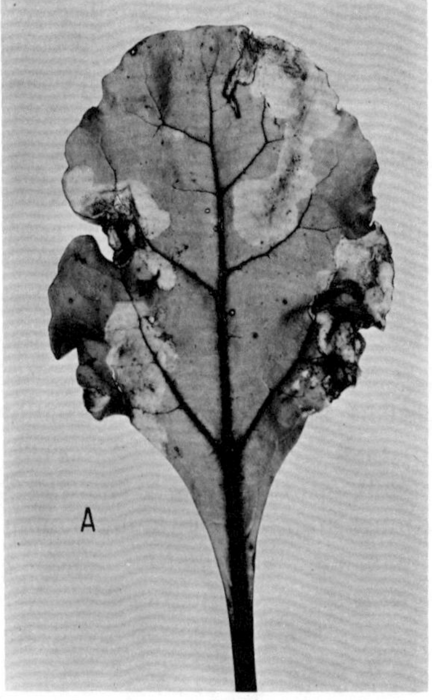

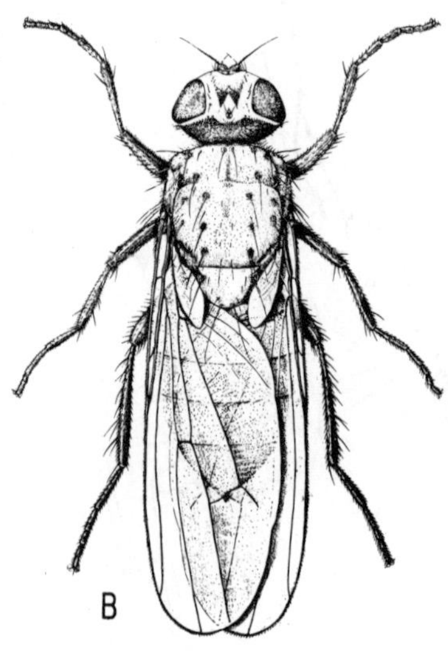

Fig. 27-78. A, mines of the spinach leaf miner, *Pegomỳia hyoscỳomi* (Panzer) (Anthomyìidae); B, adult female of the seed-corn maggot, *Hylemỳa cilicrùra* (Rondani), 8 × (Anthomyìidae). (A, courtesy of the Ohio Agricultural Experiment Station; B, courtesy of USDA.)

Fig. 27-79. Two common muscids, showing the difference in the shape of the proboscis. Left, stable fly; right, house fly. (Courtesy of the Illinois Natural History Survey.)

of all kinds and is often very abundant; it is known to be a vector of typhoid fever, dysentery, cholera, yaws, anthrax, and some forms of conjunctivitis; it does not bite. The stable fly, horn fly, and tsetse flies are biting flies; unlike the mosquitoes, black flies, and tabanids, both sexes bite. The stable fly, *Stomóxys cálcitrans* (Linn.) (Figure 27-80), is very similar to the house fly in appearance (Figure 27-79), and breeds chiefly in decaying vegetation. The horn fly, *Haematòbia írritans* (Linn.), which is similar to the house fly in appearance but is much smaller, is a serious pest of cattle; it breeds in fresh cow dung. The face fly, *Músca autumnàlis* DeGeer, an important pest of cattle in the East and Midwest, gets its name from its habit of clustering on the face of cattle. The tsetse flies, *Glossìna* spp., do not occur in this country, but in Africa they are vectors of the trypanosomes that cause sleeping sickness (African trypanosomiasis) and other diseases of man and animals.

Fánnia and its relatives, which differ from the other muscids in that they have 3A curving outward distally so that, if extended, Cu_2 + 2A would meet it (Figure 27-18 D), are sometimes placed in a separate family, the Fannìidae; these flies look very much like small house flies.

FAMILY **Gasterophílidae**—Horse Bot Flies: These flies are somewhat similar to honey bees in general appearance, and the larvae infest the alimentary tract of horses. These insects are often serious pests of horses. Three species occur commonly in this country, *Gasteróphilus intestinàlis* (DeGeer), *G. nasàlis* (Linn.), and *G. haemorrhoidàlis* (Linn.); a fourth species, *G. inérmis* Brauer, is very rare. In *G. intestinàlis* (Figure 27-86 A) the eggs are laid on the legs or shoulders of the horse and are taken into the mouth when the animal licks these parts; in *G. nasàlis* the eggs are usually laid on the under side of the jaw, and the larvae are believed to make their way through the skin into the mouth; in *G. haemorrhoidàlis* the eggs are laid on the lips of the horse. The larvae develop in the stomach (*intestinàlis*), duodenum (*nasàlis*) or rectum (*haemorrhoidàlis*); when ready to pupate, they pass out of the alimentary tract with the feces and pupate in the ground.

FAMILY **Hippobóscidae** — Louse Flies: This group includes both winged and wingless forms. Most of the winged forms are dark brownish in color and somewhat smaller than house flies; they are most likely to be found on birds. These flies are easily recognized by their flat shape and leathery appearance; they are the only flies likely to be found on living birds. The sheep ked, *Melóphagus ovìnus* Linn. (Figure 27-81), is a fairly common wingless louse fly; it is about 6 millimeters in length, reddish brown in color, and is a parasite of sheep.

FAMILIES **Stréblidae** AND **Nycteribìidae**—Bat Flies: The bat flies in the family Nycteribìidae are small, spiderlike, wingless insects that are parasitic on bats. The head is small, and when at rest, is folded back into a groove on the dorsum of the thorax. The eyes and ocelli are vestigial. This is a small and rare group. The bat flies in the family Stréblidae are somewhat similar to the

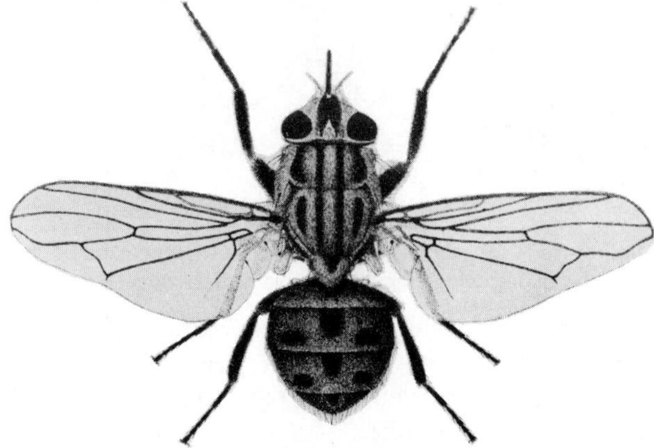

Fig. 27-80. The stable fly, *Stomóxys cálcitrans* (Linn.). (Courtesy of the Illinois Natural History Survey.)

nycteribiids, but the head is not bent back on the thorax; some species are winged, some have vestigial wings, and others are wingless.

FAMILY **Calliphóridae**—Blow Flies: The blow flies constitute a large group and are to be found practically everywhere; many species are of considerable economic importance. Most blow flies are about the size of a house fly or a little larger, and many are metallic blue or green (Figure 27-82). Blow flies are very similar to flesh flies (Sarcophágidae), and some authorities put the two groups in a single family, the Metopìidae. Blow flies are often metallic in color and have the arista of the antennae plumose to the tip, whereas flesh flies are blackish with gray thoracic stripes and have the arista bare or only the basal half plumose. In blow flies, the hindmost posthumeral bristle is usually more laterally located than is the presutural bristle, but in flesh flies, the hindmost posthumeral bristle is either on a level with or is nearer the midline than the presutural bristle (Figure 27-19); blow flies usually have two notopleural bristles and flesh flies usually have four.

Most blow flies are scavengers, the larvae living in carrion, excrement, and similar materials; the most common species are those that breed in carrion. These species lay their eggs on bodies of dead animals, and the larvae feed on the decaying tissues of the animal. To most people a dead animal teeming with maggots (mostly the larvae of blow flies) is a nauseating thing, but it should be remembered that these insects are performing a valuable service to man in helping to remove dead animals from the landscape. The larvae of some of the species that breed in carrion, particularly *Lucília sericàta* (Meigen) and *Phórmia regìna* (Meigen), when reared under aseptic conditions, have been used in the treatment of such diseases as osteomyelitis in man. On the other hand, many of these flies may act as mechanical

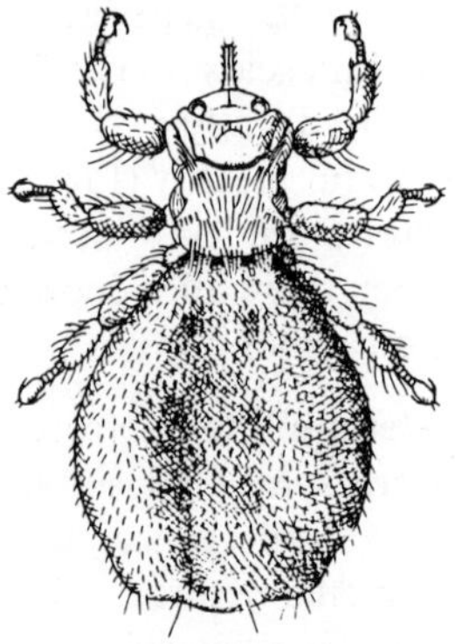

Fig. 27-81. The sheep ked or sheep-tick, *Melóphagus ovìnus* (Linn.). (Courtesy of Knowlton, Madsen, and the Utah Agricultural Experiment Station.)

Fig. 27-82. A blow fly, *Lucília caèsar* (Linn.).

vectors of various diseases; dysentery frequently accompanies high blow-fly populations.

Some blow flies lay their eggs in open sores of animals or man; in some cases the larvae feed only on decaying or suppurating tissue, but in other cases they may attack living tissue. The screw-worm fly, *Callitròga hominivòrax* (Coquerel) (Figure 27-83), is a species in the latter category; it lays its eggs in wounds or in the nostrils of its host, and its larvae may cause considerable damage. In recent years the number of screw-worm flies in the South and Southwest has been greatly reduced by releasing large numbers of sterile male flies; the females mate only once, and if a female mates with a sterile male, its eggs fail to hatch.

When fly larvae becomes parasitic on man or animals, the condition is spoken of as myiasis; the flies such as the screw-worm may develop in surface wounds and cause cutaneous myiasis, or in the nasal cavities and cause nasal myiasis; a few other flies in this group have been known to develop in the intestine of man and cause intestinal myiasis. Myiasis in man is relatively rare in this part of the world and is probably a more or less accidental occurrence; in the South and Southwest it has been very important in domestic animals.

FAMILY **Sarcophágidae**—Flesh Flies: Flesh flies are very similar to some blow flies in appearance and habits and are generally quite common. The species that breed in carrion usually give birth to young larvae. Most flesh flies are scavengers in the larval stage, but a few are parasitic on other insects, snails, earthworms, or other invertebrate animals. Certain species of *Wohlfáhrtia* parasitize mammals, including man.

FAMILY **Tachínidae**—Tachinid Flies: This family probably contains more species than any other family of muscoid flies, and many of its members are fairly large and common insects. Since all the tachinids are parasitic on other insects, this is probably the most beneficial family of Diptera.

The tachinids are usually relatively easy to recognize; both the hypopleural and pteropleural bristles are developed, and the postscutellum is prominent (Figure 27-17); the ventral sclerites of the abdomen are usually overlapped by the tergites, and the abdomen

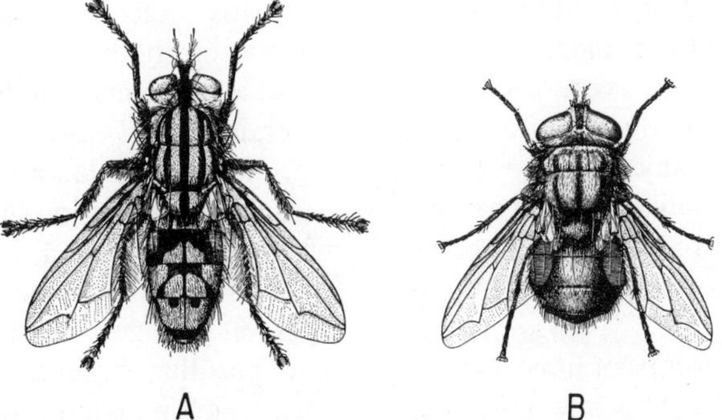

Fig. 27-83. A, a flesh fly, *Sarcóphaga haemorrhoidàlis* (Fallén); B, the screwworm fly, *Callitròga hominivòrax* (Coquerel). (Courtesy of USDA.)

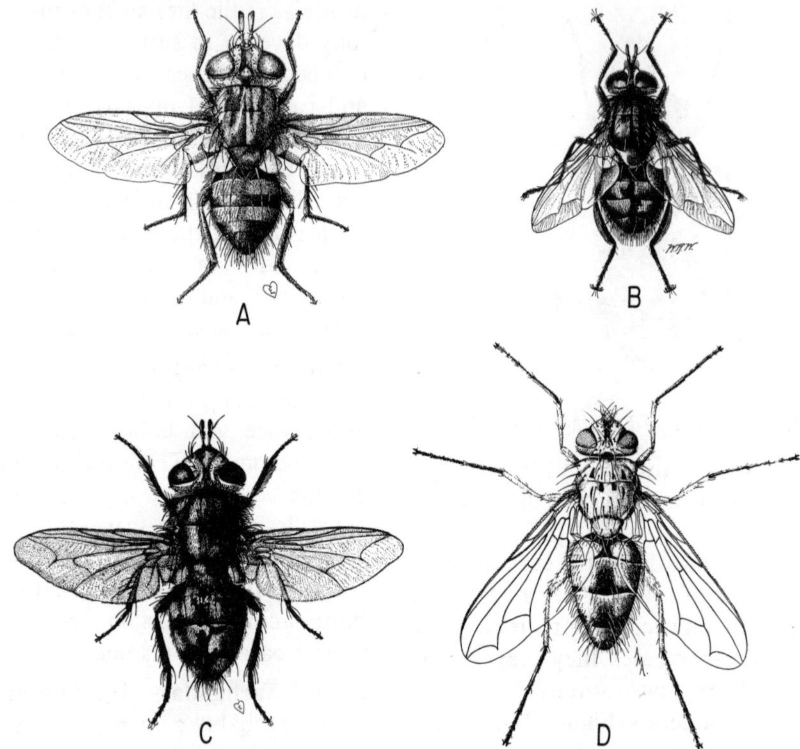

Fig. 27-84. Tachinid flies. A, *Phorócera claripénnis* Macquart; B, *Winthèmia quadripustulàta* (Fabricius); C, *Árchytas piliventris* Van der Wulp; D, *Déxia ventràlis* Aldrich. (Courtesy of USDA.)

usually has a large number of very large bristles in addition to the smaller ones. Within the group, however, there is much taxonomic confusion, and the group has been variously divided. Some authorities divide this group into two families, the Tachínidae proper (with the arista bare) and the Dexìidae (with the arista plumose), but this character is not always diagnostic.

Many tachinids are very similar in general appearance to house flies and flesh flies (Figure 27-84); many are large, bristly, and beelike or wasplike in appearance. They are to be found almost everywhere—on flowers, in grass or foliage, and in other places.

Many different groups of insects are parasitized by tachinids, and while most tachinids are more or less restricted to particular hosts, there are a few that may develop in a wide variety of hosts. Most tachinids parasitize the larvae of Lepidoptera, sawflies, or beetles, but some are known to attack Hemiptera, Orthoptera, and some other orders. A number of tachinids has been imported into this country to aid in the control of introduced pests.

Most tachinids deposit their eggs directly on the body of their host, and it is not at all uncommon to find caterpillars with several tachinid eggs on them. Upon hatching, the tachinid larva usually burrows into its host and feeds internally (Figure 27-85); when fully developed, it leaves the host and pupates nearby. Some tachinids lay their eggs on foliage; these eggs usually hatch into peculiar flattened larvae called planidia, which remain on the foliage until they can attach to a suitable host when it passes by. In other species that lay their eggs on

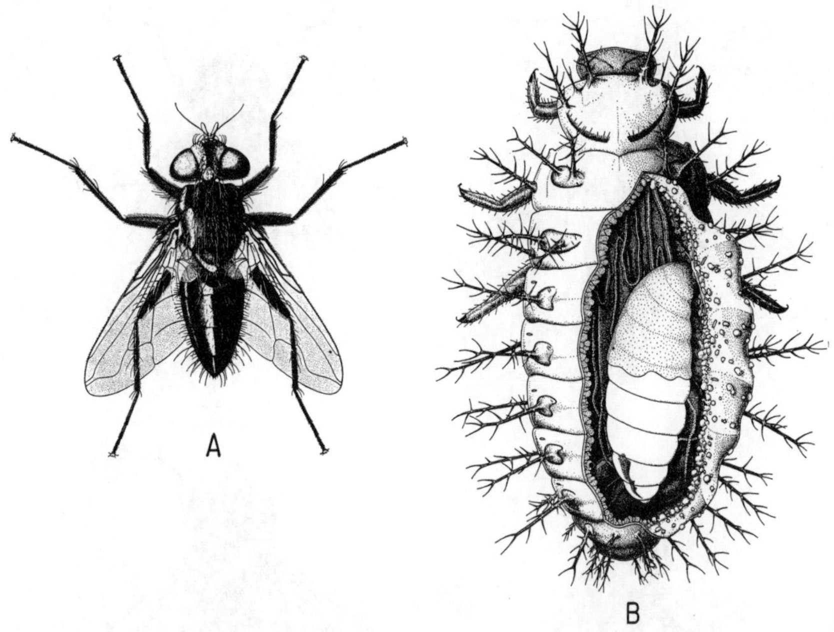

Fig. 27-85. The bean beetle tachinid, *Paradexòdes epiláchnae* Aldrich. A, adult; B, a bean beetle larva dissected to show a larva of this tachinid inside it. (Courtesy of USDA.)

foliage, the eggs hatch when they are ingested (along with the foliage) by a caterpillar; the tachinid larvae then proceed to eat the internal organs of the caterpillar. An insect parasitized by tachinids is practically always killed eventually.

FAMILY **Cuterébridae**—Robust Bot Flies: The robust bot flies are large, stout-bodied, rather hairy flies that resemble bees; the larvae of most species are parasitic on rodents. One tropical species, *Dermatòbia hóminis* (Linn.) (Figure 27-86 D), attacks man; this species lays its eggs on mosquitoes (principally mosquitoes in the genus *Psoróphora*), and the eggs hatch and the larvae penetrate the skin when the mosquito feeds on man. Stable flies and other muscids also serve as carriers of *D. hóminis* eggs to man.

FAMILY **Oéstridae**—Warble Flies and Bot Flies: The members of this group are large, stout-bodied flies that resemble bees, and the larvae are parasitic in various animals. The sheep bot fly, *Oéstrus òvis* Linn. (Figure 27-86 C), is viviparous and deposits its larvae in the nostrils of sheep (rarely, also in man); the larvae feed in the frontal sinuses of the sheep. The ox warble flies, *Hypodérma bòvis* (Linn.) and *H. lineàtum* (Villers) (Figure 27-86 B), are serious pests of cattle. The eggs of these species are usually laid on the legs of cattle, and the larvae penetrate the skin and migrate, often by way of the esophagus, to the back, where they develop in swellings or "warbles" just under the skin. When full grown, they escape through the skin and pupate in the ground. The adults of the ox warbles are very fast fliers, and although they do not bite or injure the cattle when they oviposit, they are very annoying to cattle. Ox warbles may seriously affect the health of cattle, and the holes made in the skin by the escaping larvae reduce the value of the hide when it is made into leather.

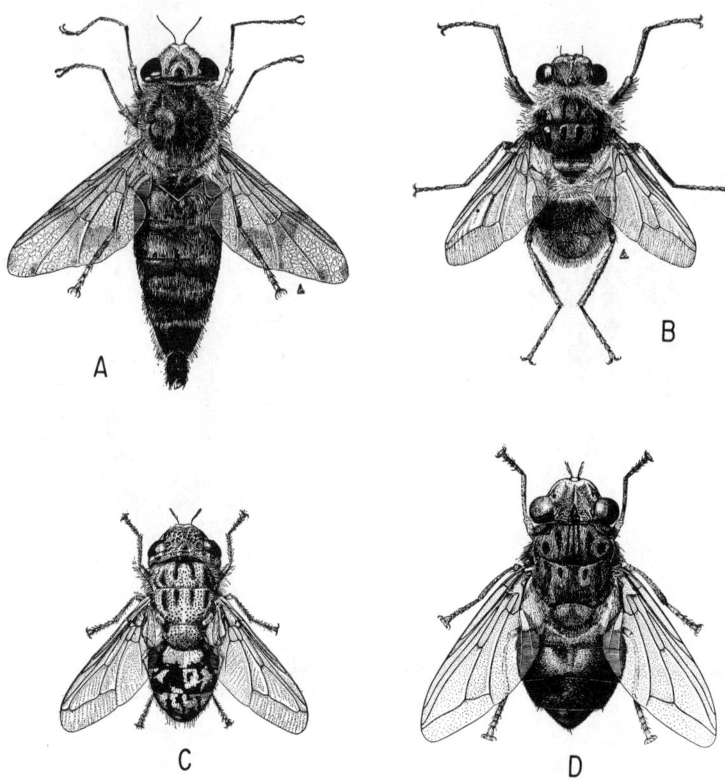

Fig. 27-86. Bot and warble flies. A, horse bot fly, *Gasteróphilus intestinàlis* (DeGeer), female; B, ox warble fly, *Hypodérma lineàtum* (Villers), female; C, sheep bot fly, *Oéstrus òvis* Linn., female; D, human bot fly, *Dermatòbia hóminis* (Linn.), female. (Courtesy of USDA.)

COLLECTING AND PRESERVING DIPTERA

The general methods of collecting Diptera are similar to those of collecting other insects; to secure a large variety, one must collect in a variety of habitats. Many of the smaller species can be best collected by sweeping, putting the entire catch into the killing bottle and examining it carefully later. Traps such as that shown in Figure 32-7 A, using various types of baits, are useful collecting devices.

Most Diptera, particularly the smaller specimens, should be mounted as soon as possible after they are captured because they dry quickly and are likely to be damaged in mounting if they have dried out very much; it is best to mount them within a few hours after they are captured. Many of the smaller and more delicate specimens, such as midges, mosquitoes, and similar forms, should be handled very carefully in order to avoid rubbing off the minute hairs and scales; these are often important in identification, particularly if the specimen is ever identified to species. The only way to get good specimens of many of these delicate forms is to rear them and to get them into a killing jar without using a net.

The larger Diptera are preserved on pins, and the smaller specimens are mounted on points or microscopic slides. In pinning a fly, particularly the muscoids, it is important that the bristles on the dorsum of the thorax be kept intact; the pin should be inserted to one side of the midline. Most Diptera less than $\frac{1}{4}$ inch in length, and some of the more slender forms longer than this, should be mounted on points, preferably on their side. Some of the more minute specimens must be mounted on microscope slides for detailed study.

REFERENCES ON THE DIPTERA

Aldrich, J. M. 1905. Catalogue of North American Diptera. Smithsonian Inst., Misc. Collections, 46(1444):1-680.

Alexander, C. P. 1919. The crane flies of New York. Part I. Distribution and taxonomy of the adult flies. N.Y. (Cornell) Agr. Expt. Sta., Mem. 25; pp. 771-993, 15 pl., 12 f.

Brues, C. T., A. L. Melander, and Frank M. Carpenter. 1954. Order Diptera. In Classification of Insects. Harvard Univ., Museum, Compar. Zool. Bull. 108:305-543; f. 465-764.

Carpenter, Stanley J., and Walter J. LaCasse. 1955. Mosquitoes of North America (north of Mexico). Berkeley, Calif.: University of California Press. vii+360 pp., 127 pl.

Coquillett, D. W. 1910. The type-species of North American genera of Diptera. Proc. U.S. Natl. Museum, 37(1719):499-647; Can. Entomol., 42(11):375-378.

Crampton, Guy C., C. H. Curran, C. P. Alexander, and R. B. Friend. 1942. Guide to the insects of Connecticut. Part VI. The Diptera or true flies of Connecticut. First Fasc. External morphology; key to families; Tanyderidae, Ptychopteridae, Trichoceridae, Anisopodidae, Tipulidae. Conn. State Geol. and Nat. Hist. Survey, Bull. 64; x+509 pp., 55 f., 4 pl.

Curran, C. H. 1934. The families and genera of North American Diptera. New York: published by the author. 512 pp., illus.

Felt, E. P. 1940. Plant galls and gall makers. Ithaca: Comstock Publishing Assoiates. viii+364 pp., illus.

Hall, David G. 1948. The blow flies of North America. Publication No. 4. Lafayette, Ind.: Thomas Say Foundation. v+477 pp., 5 col. pl., 46 pl., 9 text f.

James, Maurice T. 1959. Diptera. In: Fresh-water biology, ed. by W. T. Edmondson. John Wiley & Sons, Inc. Pp. 1057-1079; 32 f.

Johannsen, O. A. 1909-1912. Fungus gnats of North America. Maine Agri. Expt. Sta. Bull. 180, 192, 196, 200; 308 pp., illus.

Matheson, Robert. 1944. Handbook of the mosquitoes of North America. Ithaca, N.Y.: Comstock Publishing Associates. viii+314 pp., 42 f., 33 pl.

Meigen, J. W. 1800. Nouvelle classification des mouches à deux ailes (Diptera L.) d'après un plan tout nouveau. Paris.

Meigen, J. W. 1803. Versuch einer Gattungseintheilung der europaischen zweiflugligen Insekten. Illiger's Mag. f. Insekten, 2:259-281.

Pennak, Robert W. 1953. Fresh-water invertebrates of the United States. New York: The Ronald Press Company. ix+769 pp., 470 f.

Peterson, Alvah. 1951. Larvae of insects. Part II. Coleoptera, Diptera, Neuroptera, Siphonaptera, Mecoptera, Trichoptera. Ann Arbor, Mich.: Edwards Bros., Inc. v+519 pp., 104 f.

Stone, Alan. 1941. The generic names of Meigen 1800 and their proper application (Diptera). Ann. Entomol. Soc. Am., 34(2):404-418.

Williston, S. W. 1908 (3d ed.). Manual of the families and genera of North American Diptera. New Haven, Conn.: James T. Hathaway. 405 pp., 163 f.

Wirth, Willis W., and Alan Stone. 1956. Aquatic Diptera. In: Aquatic insects of California, ed. by Robert L. Usinger. Berkeley, Calif.: University California Press. Pp. 372-482, 64 f.

28

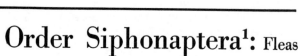

Order Siphonaptera[1]: Fleas

The fleas are small wingless insects that feed as adults on the blood of birds and mammals. Many species are very annoying because of their bites, a few act as vectors of disease, a few serve as the intermediate host of certain tapeworms, and a few burrow into the skin of man or other animals.

The body of an adult flea (Figures 28-1 A and 28-3 C) is strongly flattened laterally and is provided with numerous backward-projecting spines and bristles. Fleas are jumping insects and have long legs with the coxae greatly enlarged. The antennae are short and lie in grooves in the head. The mouth parts (Figure 2-15) are of the sucking type, with three piercing stylets (the epipharynx and two maxillary stylets), and both maxillary and labial palpi are well developed. Both sexes are blood-sucking. Eyes may be present or absent. The metamorphosis is complete.

Most fleas are active insects, moving freely over the body of their host, and frequently moving from one host to another. Many species, including those that attack man, are not very specific in their selection of a host and may feed on various animals. Many spend a large part of the time off the host. The adults are long-lived and may live a year or more; they are able to survive for several weeks off the host without feeding.

Fleas usually leave the host to lay their eggs, laying them in the dirt or in the nest of the host; the eggs may sometimes be laid on the host, but these eggs eventually fall off and develop on the ground or in the host's nest. The eggs hatch into tiny, whitish, legless larvae, which are sparsely covered with bristly hairs and have a pair of tiny hooks on the last body segment (Figure 28-1 B); the head is well developed, and the mouth parts are of the chewing type. The larvae feed on organic debris, on their own cast skins, and on the feces of adult fleas; this latter item is an important part of the

[1] Siphonaptera; *siphon,* a tube; *aptera,* wingless.

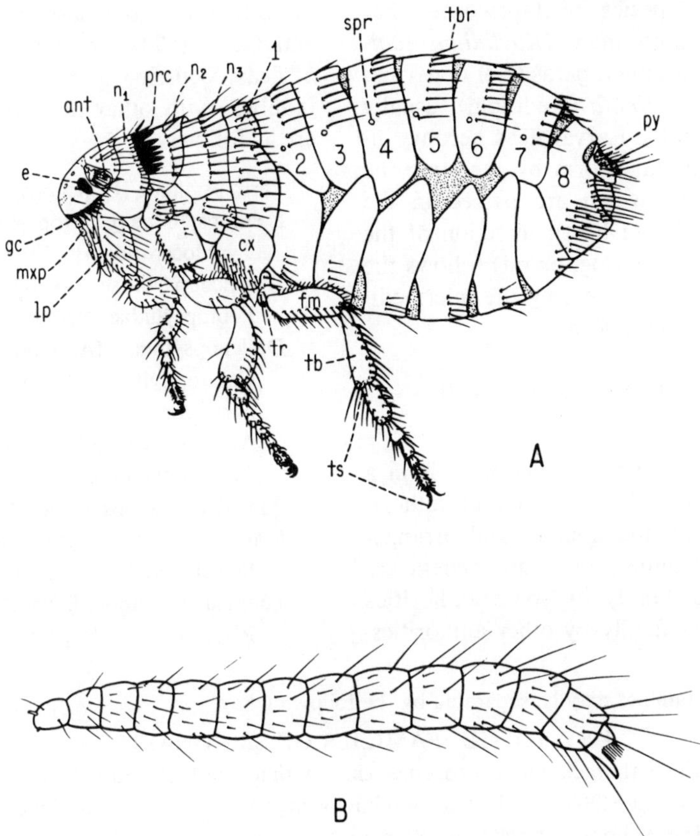

Fig. 28-1. A, an adult cat flea, *Ctenocephálides fèlis* (Bouché); B, larva of a flea. *ant*, antenna; *cx*, coxa; *e*, eye; *fm*, femur; *gc*, genal comb; *lp*, labial palpus; *mxp*, maxillary palpus; n_1, pronotum; n_2, mesonotum; n_3, metanotum; *prc*, pronotal comb; *py*, pygidium; *spr*, spiracle; *tb*, tibia; *tbr*, tergal or abdominal bristles; *tr*, trochanter; *ts*, tarsus; *1-9*, abdominal tergites.

food of the larvae. When fully developed, the larva spins a silken cocoon and pupates; particles of dirt usually adhere to the cocoon.

FLEAS AND DISEASE: The most important disease transmitted by fleas is plague, or black death, an acute infectious disease caused by the bacillus *Pasteurélla péstis* (Lehmann and Neumann). Three forms of plague occur in man—bubonic, pneumonic, and septicemic; the bubonic type is transmitted by fleas. Bubonic plague is a very serious disease because it often occurs in epidemic form and has a high mortality rate. Plague is primarily a disease of rodents and is spread from one rodent to another by fleas; rodents thus serve as a reservoir for the disease. The disease of wild rodents is often called sylvatic plague. Fleas may transmit plague in three ways: (1) by the regurgitation of the plague bacilli at the time of biting, due to a blocking of the digestive tract by the bacilli; (2) by infected feces of fleas being scratched into the skin; or (3) by the host ingesting an infected flea. Most plague transmission is by the first method.

Endemic typhus is a mild type of typhus caused by a *Rickéttsia*; it is primarily a disease of rodents (chiefly rats), but may be transmitted to man by fleas and to some extent by body lice.

Fleas serve as the intermediate host of

at least two species of tapeworms that occasionally infest man, *Dipylídium càninum* (Linn.) (usually a parasite of dogs) and *Hymenólepis diminùta* (Rudolphi) (usually a parasite of rats). Larval fleas become infested with the tapeworm by ingesting the tapeworm eggs (which are passed in the feces of an infested host); infection of the primary host (man, dog, or rat) follows the ingestion of a flea harboring the intermediate stage of the tapeworm.

CLASSIFICATION OF THE SIPHONAPTERA

The classification of this order is in a somewhat confused state; different authorities disagree on the number and arrangement of the families, and many genera are placed in one family by some authorities and in another family by other authorities. We follow here the classification of Jellison and Good (1942), who list seven families of fleas occurring in North America; these families, with other names in parentheses, are as follows:

Vermipsýllidae (Dolichopsýllidae in part)
Ischnopsýllidae (Ceratopsýllidae, Typhlocerátidae)
Hystrichopsýllidae (Ctenopsýllidae, Leptopsýllidae, Neopsýllidae)
Dolichopsýllidae (Anomiopsýllidae, Ceratophýllidae, Hystrichopsýllidae in part; including Rhadinopsyllìnae, Anomiopsyllìnae, Dolichopsyllìnae, and Ctenophthalmìnae)
Pulícidae (Xenopsýllidae, Archaeopsýllidae)
Malacopsýllidae (Megapsýllidae; Dolichopsýllidae in part)
Túngidae (Hectopsýllidae, Sarcopsýllidae, Rhynchopriónidae, Echidnophágidae)

These families may be separated by the following key.

KEY TO THE FAMILIES OF SIPHONAPTERA

1. The 3 thoracic tergites together shorter than the first abdominal tergite (Figure 28-2 E); sticktight and burrowing fleas .... **Túngidae** p. 515

1′. The 3 thoracic tergites together longer than the first abdominal tergite (Figures 28-1 A, 28-2 A-D, 28-3) 2

2(1′). Abdominal tergites 2 to 6, each with 1 row of bristles (Figure 28-1 A) . . 3

2′. Some of or all abdominal tergites 2 to 6 with 2 rows of bristles (Figure 28-3 C) 4

3(2). Eyes present and well developed; genal comb present (Figure 28-1 A) or absent .... **Pulícidae** p. 514

3′. Eyes absent or vestigial; genal comb absent (Anomiopsyllìnae)........ .... **Dolichopsýllidae** p. 513

4(2′). Genal comb present and consisting of 2 or 3 broad lobes on each side (Figure 28-3 A); head elongated; parasitic on bats.... **Ischnopsýllidae** p. 513

4′. Genal comb present or absent, but if present, usually not as above; head usually not elongated; parasitic on animals other than bats.......... 5

5(4′). Pronotal comb present 6

5′. Pronotal comb absent 7

6(5). An interantennal suture usually present on dorsal surface of head (Figure 28-3, *ias*); genal comb usually present; 2 or 3 rows of bristles on anterior part of head, forming cephalic combs; mostly parasites of rodents.... .... **Hystrichopsýllidae** p. 513

6′. No interantennal suture present on dorsal surface of head (Figure 28-3 C); genal comb usually absent; cephalic combs usually absent; parasites of various mammals and birds...................... **Dolichopsýllidae** p. 513

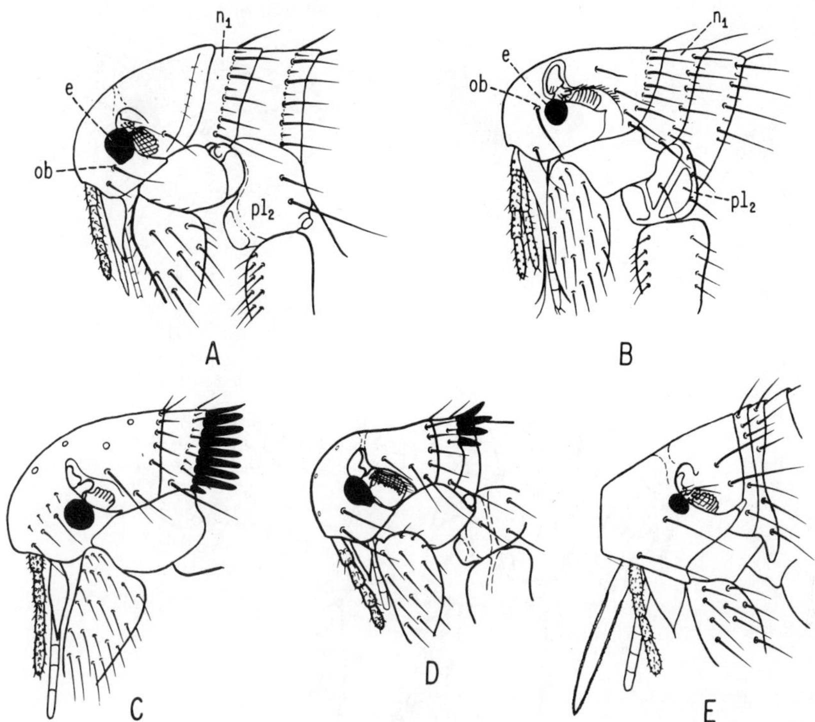

Fig. 28-2. Head and prothoracic characters of Siphonaptera. A, human flea, *Pùlex írritans* Linn. (Pulícidae); B, oriental rat flea, *Xenopsýlla cheòpis* (Rothschild) (Pulícidae); C, rat flea, *Nosopsýllus fasciàtus* (Bosc) (Dolichopsýllidae); D, rodent flea, *Hoplopsýllus anómalus* (Baker) (Pulícidae); E, sticktight flea, *Echidnóphaga gallinàcea* (Westwood) (Túngidae). *e*, eye; n_1, pronotum; *ob*, ocellar bristle (below eye in A, in front of eye in B); pl_2, mesopleuron (with a **V**-shaped thickening in B which is absent in A).

7(5′). One long antepygideal bristle on each side; parasitic on opossums and rats in the southern states .... **Malacopsýllidae** p. 515

7′. Antepygideal bristles absent; parasitic on bears, wolves, and other large carnivores .... **Vermipsýllidae** p. 513

FAMILY **Vermipsýllidae:** These fleas resemble certain of the Pulícidae (*Pùlex, Xenopsýlla*) in that they lack both genal and pronotal combs, but have two rows of setae on the abdominal tergites. This family is a small one, with only two North American genera. These fleas are parasitic on the larger carnivores such as bears, wolves, and coyotes.

FAMILY **Ischnopsýllidae:** The members of this family, which are parasitic on bats, can usually be recognized by the characteristic genal comb (Figure 28-3 A). They have a rather distinct interantennal suture on the dorsal surface of the head. The eyes are vestigial.

FAMILY **Hystrichopsýllidae:** The members of this small family are parasites of rats, mice, and shrews. The eyes are absent or vestigial. One of the mouse fleas, *Leptopsýlla ségnis* (Schonherr) (Figure 28-3 B), which is world-wide in distribution, is known to serve as a vector of endemic typhus.

FAMILY **Dolichopsýllidae:** Most of the fleas in this family have two or more rows of

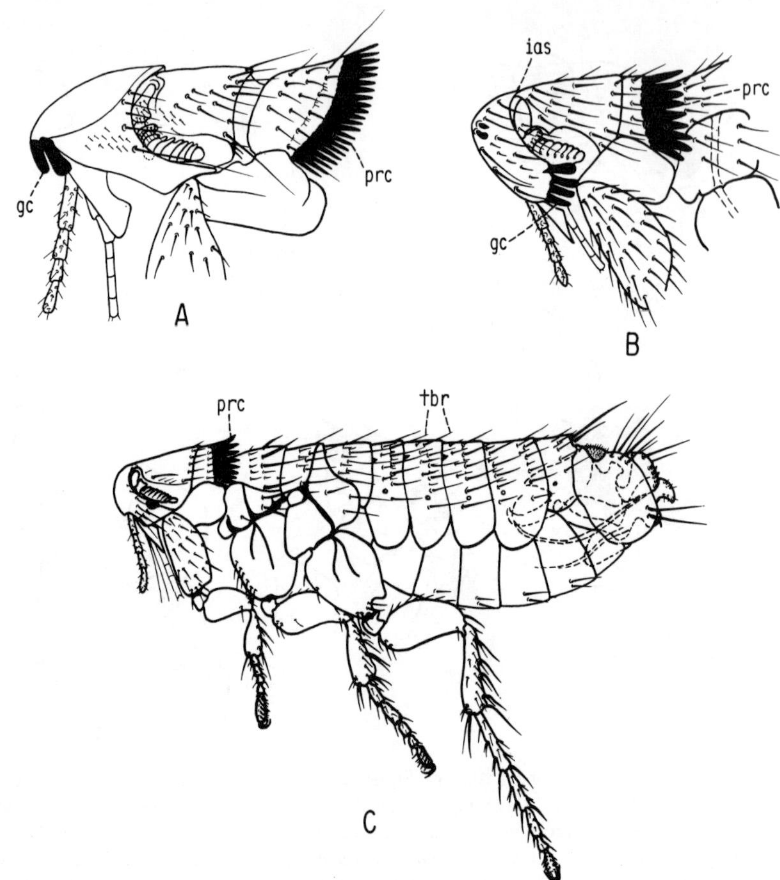

Fig. 28-3. A, head and prothorax of a bat flea, *Myodopsýlla insígnis* (Rothschild) (Ischnopsýllidae); B, head and prothorax of a mouse flea, *Leptopsýlla ségnis* (Schonherr) (Hystrichopsýllidae); C, a rodent flea, *Orchopèas leucòpus* (Baker) (Dolichopsýllidae). *gc*, genal comb; *ias*, interantennal suture; *prc*, pronotal comb; *tbr*, tergal bristles (two rows on most tergites).

bristles on the abdominal tergites (Figure 28-3 C); they have a pronotal comb, but usually lack a genal comb, and they usually lack cephalic combs; eyes may be present or absent. These fleas occur principally on various rodents and birds. The most important species in this group are those that attack rodents, for some of these serve as vectors of plague from one rodent to another. The rat flea, *Nosopsýllus fasciàtus* (Bosc) (Figure 28-2 C), has been shown capable of transmitting plague from rodents to man, but it is probably not an important vector; this flea may also transmit endemic typhus and serve as the intermediate host of the tapeworm *Hymenólepis diminùta* (Rudolphi). The fleas of the genus *Ceratophýllus* attack poultry; the European chicken flea, *C. gállinae* (Schrank), occurs in northern United States as well as in Europe.

FAMILY **Pulícidae:** This family is a large one and contains most of the fleas that attack man and domestic animals. These fleas are usually named after their principal host, but most species will attack a variety of hosts, including man. The most important genera of this family are *Ctenocep-*

hálides, Hoplopsýllus, Pùlex, and *Xenopsýlla.*

The genus *Ctenocephálides* includes the cat flea, *C. fèlis* (Bouché), and the dog flea, *C. cànis* (Curtis). These fleas, which possess both genal and pronotal combs (Figure 28-1 A), are common pests of cats, dogs, and man, and frequently occur in and about buildings or homes where cats and dogs are kept. The dog flea serves as the intermediate host of the dog tapeworm, *Dipylídium càninum* (Linn.).

The fleas in the genus *Hoplopsýllus* are usually called squirrel fleas, but may attack a variety of rodents. These fleas have a pronotal comb, but no genal comb (Figure 28-2 D).

In *Xenopsýlla* and *Pùlex,* both genal and pronotal combs are lacking (Figure 28-2 A, B). The oriental rat flea, *X. cheòpis* (Rothschild), is a widespread and important species; it is the principal vector of bubonic plague (from rat to rat, and from rat to man), it serves as a vector of endemic typhus, and it may serve as the intermediate host of the tapeworm *Hymenólepis diminùta* (Rudolphi). The human flea, *P. írritans* Linn., has a world-wide distribution and attacks man and various other animals; it is an important pest species to man because it may serve as a vector of plague.

FAMILY **Malacopsýllidae:** This family contains a single North American genus, *Rhopalopsýllus,* two species of which occur in the southern states from Florida and Georgia to Texas. These fleas have been recorded from opossums, rats, and dogs.

FAMILY **Túngidae:** The tungids are more or less permanent parasites in the adult stage. They have a small thorax, short legs, and the abdomen of the female when full of eggs is greatly enlarged. This group includes two important pest species, the sticktight flea and the chigoe flea.

The sticktight flea, *Echidnóphaga gallinàcea* (Westwood) (Figure 28-2 E), attacks domestic poultry and occasionally other birds and mammals. The adults tend to congregate in masses on the host, usually on the head, and often remain attached for several days or even weeks.

The chigoe flea or jigger, *Túnga pénetrans* (Linn.), occurs in the warmer sections of the country, principally in the southern United States. The males and virgin females of this species live like other fleas, feeding on a variety of mammalian hosts, but after mating, the female burrows into the skin of man or other animals, usually on the feet. Where the flea burrows into the skin, a painful ulcerlike sore develops. In this location and nourished by the surrounding tissues of the host, the abdomen of the flea swells (with the development of the eggs) and may get as large as a pea. The eggs are discharged to the outside and fall to the ground and develop; after all the eggs are discharged the body of the flea is usually expelled by the pressure of the surrounding tissues. These fleas usually burrow between the toes or under the toenails, and the sores, if untreated, may become gangrenous.

COLLECTING AND PRESERVING SIPHONAPTERA

Fleas can be most easily collected by capturing and examining the host; many species may be obtained from the nests or burrows of the hosts. In areas such as yards or buildings where fleas are particularly abundant, they may be collected by sweeping, or one may simply walk around in such an area and collect the fleas as they jump onto his clothing; in the latter case, the fleas are most easily seen if one wears white clothing.

Fleas may be picked up with forceps, an aspirator, or with a moistened camel's-hair brush; they should be preserved in 70 to 80 percent alcohol. Fleas may be mounted on points, but for detailed study, they should be mounted on microscope slides.

REFERENCES ON THE SIPHONAPTERA

Fox, Irving. 1940. Fleas of Eastern United States. Ames, Iowa: Iowa State College Press. vii+191 pp., 166 f., 31 pl.

Fox, Irving, and H. E. Ewing. 1943. The fleas of North America. USDA Misc. Pub. No. 500, 128 pp., 10 pl.

Holland, G. P. 1949. The Siphonaptera of Canada. Canada Dept. Agr. Pub. 817, Tech. Bull. 70; 306 pp., 350 f.

Hubbard, C. A. 1947. Fleas of western North America. Ames, Iowa: Iowa State College Press. ix+533 pp., 230 f.

Jellison, W. L., and N. E. Good. 1942. Index to the literature of Siphonaptera of North America. U.S. Public Health Serv., Nat. Inst. Health, Bull. 178; 193 pp.

Snodgrass, R. E. 1946. The skeletal anatomy of fleas (Siphonaptera). Smithsonian Inst. Publs., Misc. Collections, 104(18):1-89; 21 pl., 8 text f.

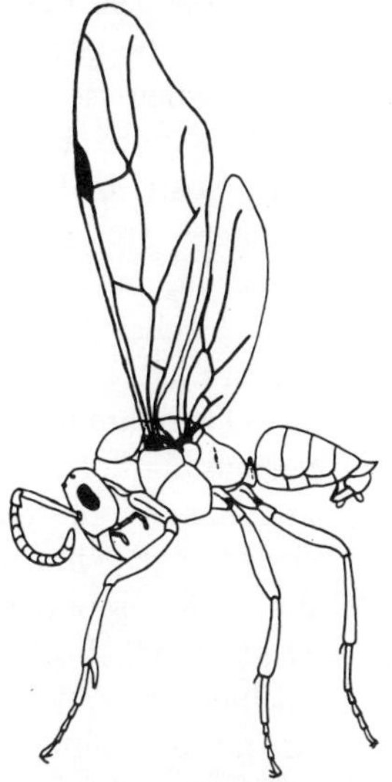

29

Order Hymenoptera[1]: Sawflies, Ichneumons, Chalcids, Ants, Wasps, and Bees

From man's standpoint, this order is probably the most beneficial in the entire insect class; it contains a great many insects that are of value as parasites or predators of various insect pests, and it contains the most important insects (the bees) that are involved in the pollination of plants. Biologically the Hymenoptera are a very interesting group, for they exhibit a great diversity of habits and complexity of behavior culminating in the social organization of the wasps, bees, and ants.

The winged members of this order have four membranous wings; the hind wings are smaller than the front wings and have a row of tiny hooks on their anterior margin by which the hind wing attaches to the front wing. The wings contain relatively few veins, and in some minute forms, there are almost no veins at all. The mouth parts are of the chewing or chewing-sucking type; in the higher forms, especially the bees, the labium and maxillae form a tonguelike structure through which liquid food is taken. The antennae usually contain ten or more segments and are generally fairly long. The tarsi are usually 5-segmented. The ovipositor is usually well developed; in the higher forms in the order, it is modified into a sting, which functions as an effective organ of offense and defense; only females can sting. The metamorphosis is complete, and in most of the order, the larvae are grublike or maggotlike; the larvae of most of the sawflies and related forms (suborder Sýmphyta) are eruciform and differ from those of the Lepidoptera in that they have more than five pairs of prolegs that lack crochets and usually have only a single pair of ocelli. The pupae are of the exarate type

[1] Hymenoptera: *hymeno*, membrane; *ptera*, wings.

and may be formed in a cocoon, in the host (in the case of parasitic species) or in special cells.

Sex in most Hymenoptera is determined by the fertilization of the egg; fertilized eggs develop into females, and unfertilized eggs usually develop into males.

CLASSIFICATION OF THE HYMENOPTERA

The order Hymenoptera is divided into two suborders, each of which is further divided into superfamilies. In the suborder Sýmphyta, the abdomen is broadly joined to the thorax, the trochanters are 2-segmented, and there are at least three closed cells at the base of the hind wing (Figure 29-1); nearly all the Sýmphyta are phytophagous. In the suborder Apócrita, the basal segment of the abdomen is fused with the thorax and separated from the remainder of the abdomen by a constriction; the abdominal segment that is fused with the thorax is called the propodeum. The term "abdomen," when used in this chapter in speaking of the Apócrita, refers to that part of the body posterior to the propodeum. The trochanters are 1- or 2-segmented in the Apócrita, and there are not more than two closed cells at the base of the hind wing (Figure 29-3).

There are differences of opinion among various authorities about the arrangement and naming of the families in this order; the arrangement followed here is essentially that of Muesebeck *et al.* (1951) and Krombein *et al.* (1958). In the outline below, alternate spellings, synonyms, and other arrangements are given in parentheses. The groups marked with an asterisk are relatively rare or are unlikely to be taken by the general collector.

Suborder Sýmphyta (Chalastogástra)—sawflies and horntails
  Superfamily Megalodontòidea—primitive sawflies
    *Xyélidae—xyelid sawflies
    *Pamphilìidae (Lýdidae)—leaf-rolling and web-spinning sawflies
  Superfamily Tenthredinòidea—sawflies
    *Pérgidae (Acordulecéridae)—pergid sawflies
    Árgidae (Hylotómidae)—argid sawflies
    Cimbícidae—cimbicid sawflies
    Dipriónidae (Lophýridae)—conifer sawflies
    Tenthredínidae—typical sawflies
  Superfamily Siricòidea—horntails and wood wasps
    *Syntéxidae (Syntéctidae)—cedar wood wasps
    Sirícidae (Urocéridae)—horntails
    *Xiphydrìidae—wood wasps
    *Orússidae (Orýssidae)—parasitic wood wasps
  Superfamily Cephòidea—stem sawflies
    Céphidae—stem sawflies
Suborder Apócrita (Clistogástra, Petiolàta)
  Superfamily Ichneumonòidea—parasitic Hymenoptera
    *Stephánidae—stephanids
    Bracónidae—braconids
    Ichneumónidae—ichneumons
  Superfamily Chalcidòidea—chalcids
    Mymáridae—fairyflies
    Trichogrammátidae—trichogrammatids
    Eulóphidae—eulophids

*Elásmidae—elasmids
*Thysánidae (Encýrtidae in part; Signiphóridae)—thysanids
*Eutrichosomátidae (Encýrtidae in part)—eutrichosomatids
*Tanaostigmátidae (Encýrtidae in part)—taeniostigmatids
Encýrtidae—encyrtids
Eupélmidae—eupelmids
*Eucharítidae (Eucharídidae, Eucháridae)—eucharitids
Perilámpidae—perilampids
*Agaónidae (Agaóntidae)—fig insects
Torýmidae (Callimómidae; incl. Podagriónidae in part)—torymids
*Ormýridae—ormyrids
Pteromálidae (incl. Cleonýmidae in part and Miscogastéridae)—pteromalids
Eurytómidae—eurytomids, seed chalcids
*Chalcedéctidae (Podagriónidae in part)—chalcedectids
Chalcídidae (Chálcidae)—chalcidids
*Leucóspidae (Leucospídidae)—leucospids

Superfamily Cynipòidea—gall wasps and their relatives
*Ibalìidae—ibaliids
*Lioptéridae—liopterids
Figítidae—figitids
Cynípidae—gall wasps and others

Superfamily Proctotrupòidea (Serphòidea)—parasitic Hymenoptera
Evanìidae—ensign wasps
Gasteruptìidae (Gasteruptiónidae; incl. Aulácidae)—gasteruptiids
Pelecínidae—pelecinids
*Vanhornìidae—vanhorniids
*Roproniìdae—roproniids
*Helóridae—helorids
Proctotrùpidae (Sérphidae)—proctotrupids
Ceraphrónidae (Callicerátidae)—ceraphronids
Diaprìidae (incl. Cinétidae = Belýtidae)—diapriids
Scelionidae—scelionids
Platygastéridae (Platygástridae)—platygasterids

Superfamily Bethylòidea—parasitic Hymenoptera
Chrysídidae (incl. Cléptidae)—cuckoo wasps
Bethýlidae—bethylids
*Sclerogíbbidae—sclerogibbids
Drýinidae (incl. Embolémidae)—dryinids
*Trigonálidae—trigonalids

Superfamily Scoliòidea—parasitic wasps and ants
Tiphìidae (incl. Anthobóscidae, Methóchidae, Myrmósidae, Thýnnidae, and Brachycistidìnae of Mutíllidae)—tiphiid wasps
*Sierolomórphidae—sierolomorphid wasps
Mutíllidae—velvet ants
*Rhopalosomátidae (Rhopalosómidae)—rhopalosomatid wasps
Scolìidae—scoliid wasps
*Sapýgidae—sapygid wasps
Formícidae—ants

Superfamily Vespòidea—vespoid wasps
  Véspidae (incl. Euménidae)—paper wasps, potter wasps, and their relatives
  Pompílidae (Psammochâridae)—spider wasps
Superfamily Sphecòidea—sphecoid wasps
  *Ampulícidae—ampulicid wasps
  Sphècidae—sphecid wasps
Superfamily Apòidea—bees
  Collétidae (incl. Hylaèidae)—plasterer and yellow-faced bees
  Andrénidae—mining bees
  Halíctidae—mining bees
  *Melíttidae—melittid bees
  Megachílidae—leafcutting bees
  Ápidae (incl. Anthophóridae, Nomádidae, Eucéridae, Ceratínidae, Xylocópidae, and Bómbidae)—mining bees, digger bees, cuckoo bees, carpenter bees, bumble bees, honey bees

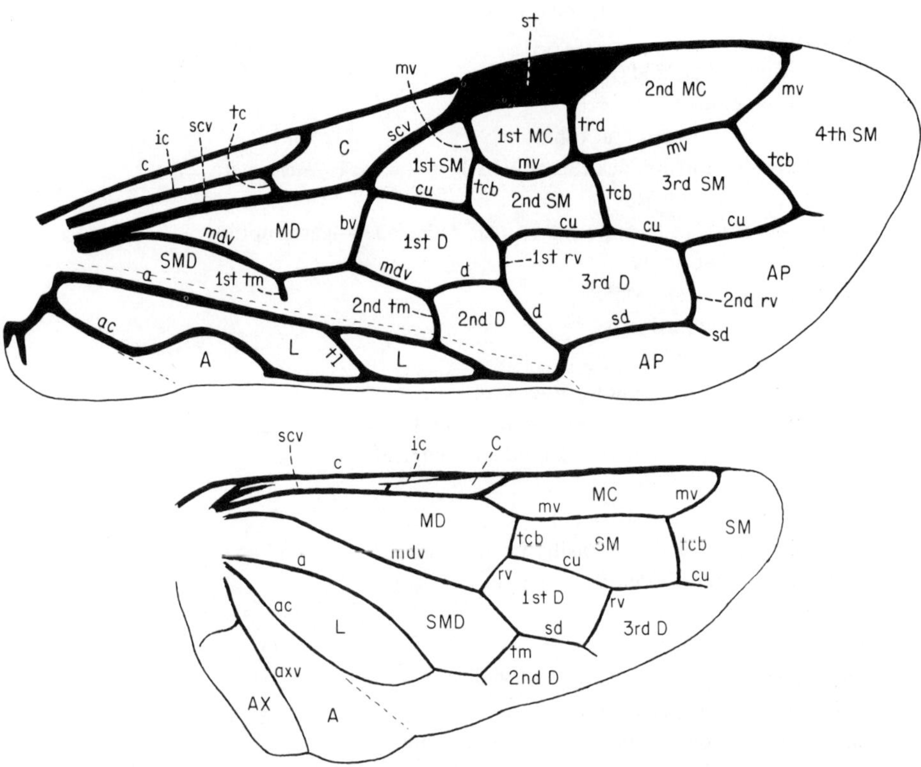

Fig. 29-1. Wings of *Acanthólyda* (Pamphilìidae), showing the old system of terminology (veins are shown by small letters, cells by capitals). Veins: *a*, anal; *ac*, accessory, lanceolate, or subanal; *axv*, axillary; *bv*, basal; *c*, costal; *cu*, cubital; *d*, discoidal; *ic*, intercostal; *mdv*, median; *mv*, marginal or radial; *rv*, recurrent; *scv*, subcostal; *sd*, subdiscal or subdiscoidal; *st*, stigma; *tc*, transverse costal; *tcb*, transverse cubitals; *tl*, transverse lanceolate; *tm*, transverse median; *trd*, transverse radial or transverse marginal. Cells: *A*, anal; *AP*, apical of posterior; *AX*, axillary; *C*, costal; *D*, discoidal; *L*, lanceolate; *MC*, marginal; *MD*, median; *SM*, submarginal; *SMD*, submedian. The basal cells (hind wing) are *MD*, *SMD*, and *L*.

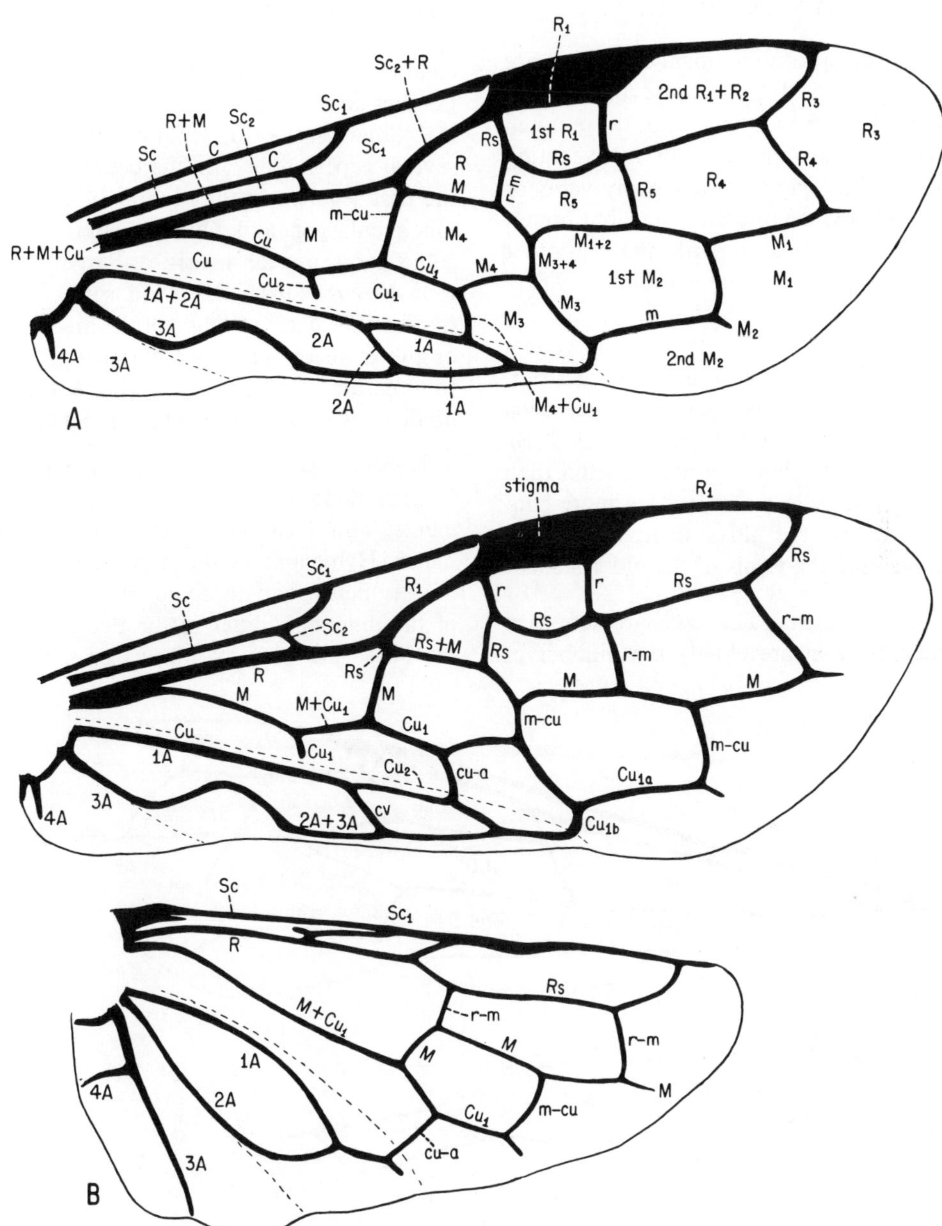

Fig. 29-2. Wings of *Acanthólyda* (Pamphiliidae), showing (A) the Comstock terminology, and (B) the terminology of Ross.

CHARACTERS USED IN THE IDENTIFICATION OF HYMENOPTERA

WING VENATION: Venational characters are used a great deal to separate the various groups of Hymenoptera, and the student should become familiar with the venation in this order. There are not many veins or cells in the hymenopteran wings, but homologizing this venation with that in other orders has proved to be a problem. There are two basic terminologies in use for the venation of the Hymenoptera, an old system (Figures 29-1 and 29-3) and that of Comstock (Figure 29-2 A); the latter has been modified by Ross (1936) (Figure 29-2 B). Ross's interpretation is probably better than that of Comstock, but it is often more convenient to use the old system; in our key we have used the terms of the old system.

LEG CHARACTERS: The leg characters used in identification are chiefly the number of trochanter segments, the number and form of the tibial spurs, and the form of the tarsal segments. In the Sýmphyta and some superfamilies of the Apócrita there are two trochanter segments (Figure 29-10 A). The number and form of the apical spurs on the tibiae serve to separate families in several superfamilies. In the bees (Apòidea) the first segment of the hind tarsi is usually much enlarged and flattened and may in some cases appear nearly as large as the tibia (Figure 29-11 B, C). In some superfamilies the size and shape of the hind coxae or the form of the tarsal claws may serve to separate families. Some of the Chalcidòidea have less than five tarsal segments.

ANTENNAL CHARACTERS: The antennae of Hymenoptera vary in form, number of segments, and location on the face. In the higher Hymenoptera the number of antennal segments, and in some cases the form of the antennae, differ in the two sexes; in the bees and many of the wasps the male

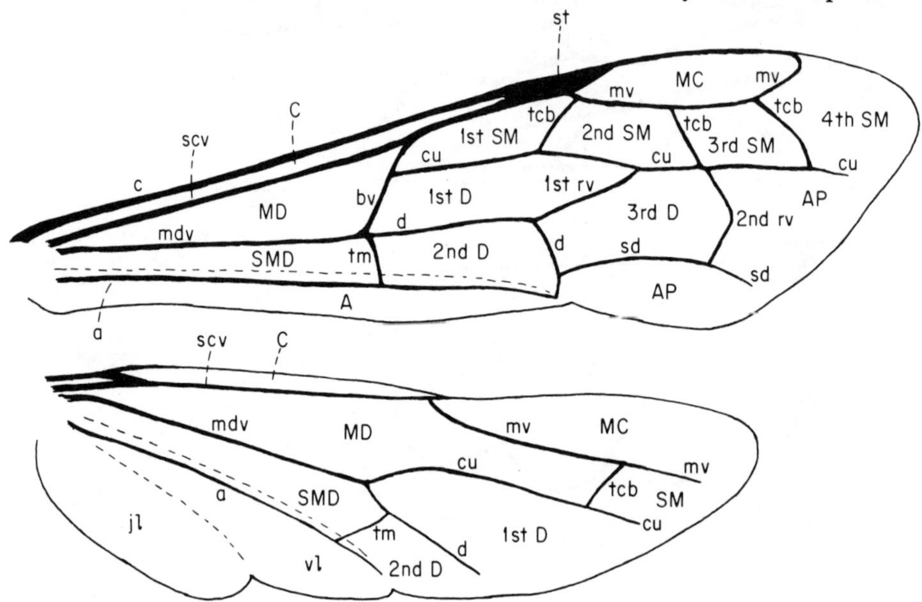

Fig. 29-3. Wings of *Mỳzinum* (Tiphìidae), showing the old system of terminology (veins are shown by small letters, cells by capitals). Veins: *a*, anal; *bv*, basal; *c*, costal; *cu*, cubital; *d*, discoidal; *mdv*, median; *mv*, marginal or radial; *rv*, recurrent; *scv*, subcostal; *sd*, subdiscal or subdiscoidal; *st*, stigma; *tcb*, transverse cubitals; *tm*, transverse median. Cells: *A*, anal; *AP*, apical or posterior; *C*, costal; *D*, discoidal; *MC*, marginal; *MD*, median; *SM*, submarginal; *SMD*, submedian. The basal cells (hind wing) are *MD* and *SMD*. Lobes of hind wing: *jl*, jugal lobe; *vl*, vannal lobe.

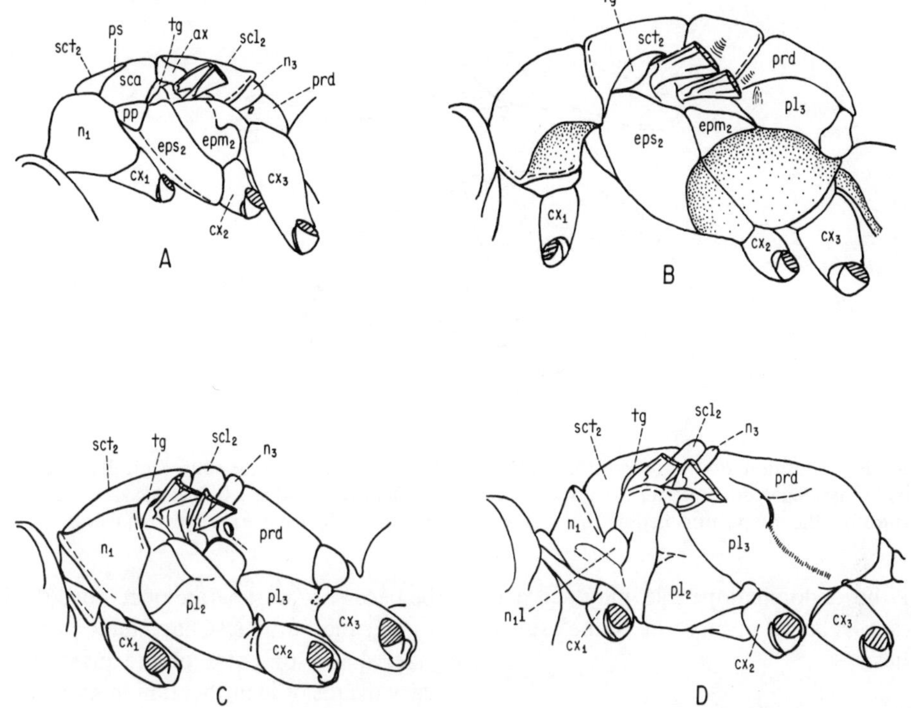

Fig. 29-4. Thorax of Hymenoptera, lateral view. A, chalcid (Torýmidae); B, cuckoo wasp (Chrysídidae); C, paper wasp (Véspidae); D, thread-waisted wasp (Sphècidae). *ax*, axilla; *cx*, coxa; *epm*, empimeron; *eps*, episternum; *n*, notum; n_1l, pronotal lobe; *pl*, pleuron; *pp*, prepectus; *prd*, propodeum; *ps*, parapsidal suture; *sca*, scapula or parapsis; *scl*, scutellum; *sct*, scutum; *tg*, tegula.

has 13 antennal segments and the female has 12; in the ants the antennae are much more distinctly elbowed in the queens and workers than in the males.

THORACIC CHARACTERS: The thoracic characters used in identifying Hymenoptera involve principally the form of the pronotum and of certain mesothoracic sclerites and sutures. In the Ichneumonòidea, Cynipòidea, Proctotrupòidea, most Scoliòidea, Vespòidea, and some Bethylòidea, the pronotum appears to be more or less triangular when viewed from the side, with its apex extending back to the base of the front wing (Figure 29-4 C); in the Sphecòidea and Apòidea the pronotum is more collarlike and bears a rounded lobe on each side that does not extend to the base of the front wing (Figure 29-4 D); in the Chalcidòidea and some Bethylòidea the pronotum is somewhat collarlike and does not extend to the base of the front wing, it lacks a rounded lobe on each side, and in the Chalcidòidea a prepectus is present in the lateral wall of the thorax (Figure 29-4 A, B). The presence or absence of parapsidal sutures or notauli (Figure 29-17, *ps*) often serves to separate related families.

ABDOMINAL CHARACTERS: In the superfamilies Ichneumonòidea, Cynipòidea, and Chalcidòidea the ovipositor issues from the abdomen anterior to the apex, on the ventral side, and is not withdrawn into the body when not in use (Figure 29-5 A); in most of the remaining Apócrita the ovipositor issues from the apex of the abdomen and is withdrawn into the body when not in use (Figure 29-5 B). The shape of the abdomen

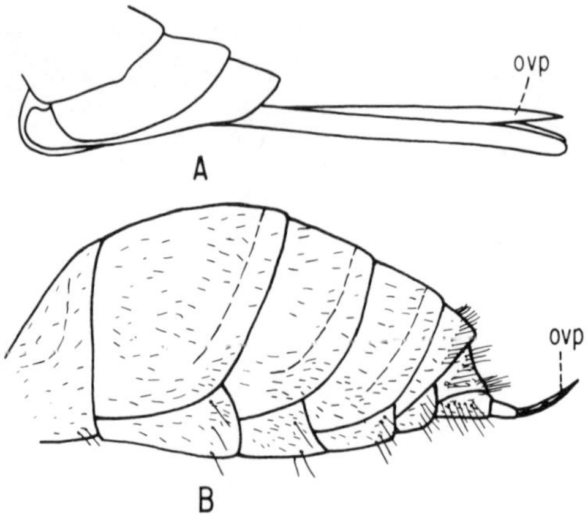

Fig. 29-5. Position of the ovipositor in Hymenoptera. A, last sternite split ventrally, the ovipositor issuing from anterior to apex of abdomen (Ichneumónidae); B, last sternite not split ventrally, the ovipositor issuing from apex of abdomen (Sphècidae). *ovp*, ovipositor.

or of the abdominal petiole may serve to separate related groups in some superfamilies.

OTHER CHARACTERS: In some of the wasps the shape of the compound eyes or ocelli differs in different families. The mouth-part structures used to separate groups of Hymenoptera are chiefly the form of the mandibles and the structure of the tongue (see page 535 and Figure 29-15). The tongue provides some excellent characters for identification in the bees, but because it is usually folded up under the head in specimens of bees and is not easily studied, we have avoided the use of tongue characters as much as possible in our key. The head and thoracic characters that involve the form of sclerites and sutures are usually easy to see except when the specimen is very small or very hairy; in the latter case, it may be necessary to separate or remove the hairs to see the sutures. Characters such as the size, shape, or color of the insect provide easy means of identification in many groups. "Minute" means 2 millimeters in length or less; "small" means 2 to 7 millimeters in length.

The principal difficulties likely to be encountered in keying out a specimen in this order are those due to the small size of some specimens; the larger specimens should not cause a great deal of difficulty. We have included here a key to all the families of Hymenoptera represented in the United States, though we realize that the student is likely to have some difficulty in keying out the smaller specimens. Groups that are relatively rare are marked with an asterisk, and couplets containing such groups may often be skipped over by the beginning student.

The old system of venational terminology (Figures 29-1 and 29-3) is used in this key, and unless otherwise indicated all venational characters refer to the front wings. The number of marginal or submarginal cells refers to the number of *closed* cells.

KEY TO THE FAMILIES OF HYMENOPTERA

1. Base of abdomen broadly joined to thorax (Figures 29-30 to 29-34); trochanters 2-segmented; hind wings with at least 3 closed cells at the base of the wing (Figures 29-1, 29-2, 29-6) (suborder Sýmphyta)....2

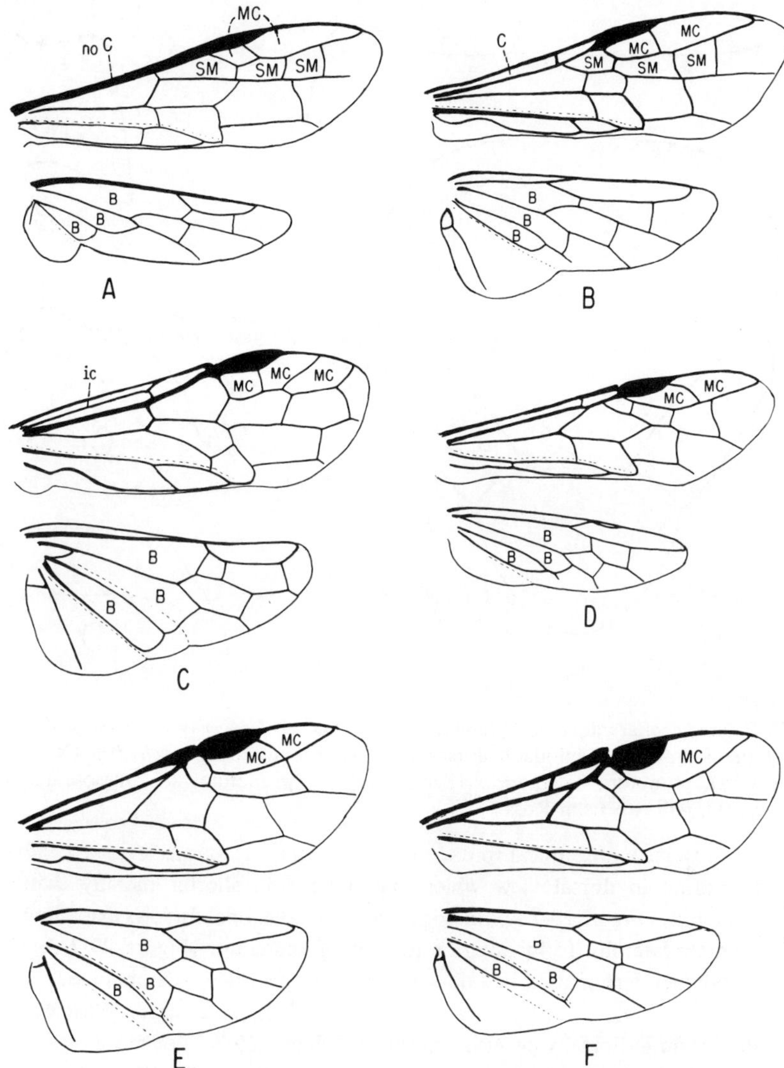

Fig. 29-6. Wings of Sýmphyta. A, Céphidae (*Cèphus*); B, Xiphydríidae (*Xiphýdria*); C, Xyélidae (*Macroxỳela*); D, Tenthredínidae (*Tenthrèdo*); E, Tenthredínidae (*Dólerus*); F, Tenthredínidae (*Amauronématus*). *B*, basal cell; *C*, costal cell; *ic*, intercostal vein; *MC*, marginal cell; *SM*, submarginal cell.

1′. Base of abdomen constricted, the abdomen more or less petiolate; trochanters 1- or 2-segmented; hind wings with 2 or fewer closed cells at the base of the wing (Figures 29-3, 29-13, 29-14, 29-16, 29-21, 29-24, 29-26, 29-66, 29-67, 29-68) (suborder Apócrita) 13

2(1). Antennae inserted on a frontal ridge below eyes, just above mouth; 1 submarginal cell . . . . **Orússidae*** p. 552

2′. Antennae inserted above base of eyes, near middle of face; usually 2 or 3 submarginal cells 3

3(2′). Front tibiae with 1 apical spur 4

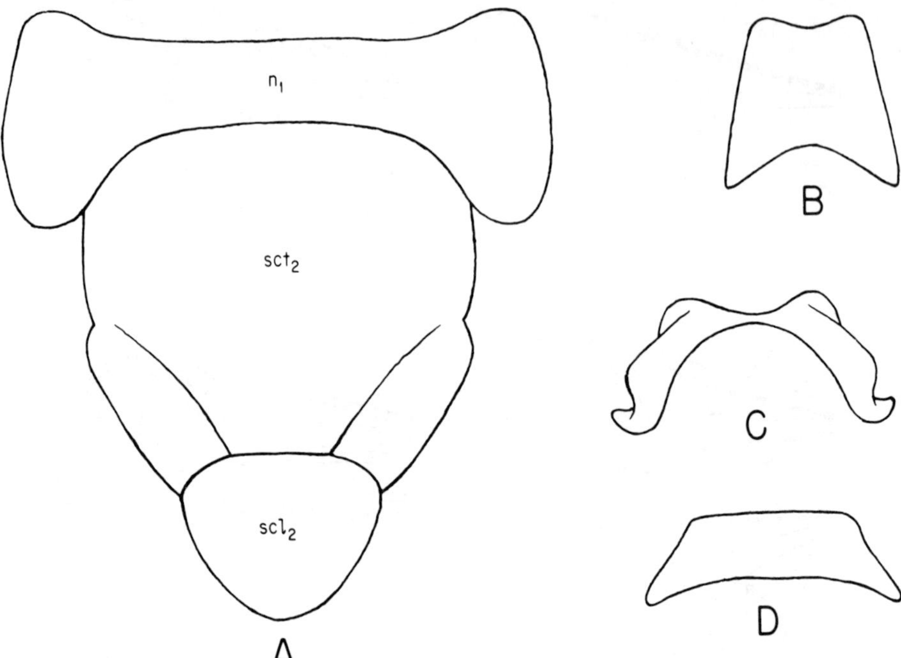

Fig. 29-7. Thoracic characters of Sýmphyta. A, thorax of *Uróceru*s (Sirícidae), dorsal view; B, pronotum of *Hártiga* (Céphidae), dorsal view; C, pronotum of *Xiphýdria* (Xiphydrìidae), dorsal view; D, pronotum of *Syntéxis* (Syntéxidae). n_1, pronotum; scl_2, mesoscutellum; sct_2, mesoscutum. (D, redrawn from Ross.)

3′. Front tibiae with 2 apical spurs 7

4(3). Pronotum in dorsal view wider than long, and shorter mesally than laterally (Figure 29-7 A); mesonotum with 2 diagonal furrows extending antero-laterally from anterior margin of scutellum (Figure 29-7 A); abdomen terminating in a dorsally located, spearlike plate or spine. . . . . **Sirícidae** p. 552

4′. Pronotum in dorsal view either **U**-shaped (Figure 29-7 C) or more or less quadrate (Figure 29-7 B, D); mesonotum without diagonal furrows; abdomen not terminating in a dorsally located spear or spine 5

5(4′). Pronotum in dorsal view **U**-shaped, the posterior margin deeply curved, and very short along the midline (Figure 29-7 C); costal cell and transverse costal vein present (Figure 29-6 B); abdomen cylindrical. . . . . **Xiphydrìidae*** p. 552

5′. Pronotum in dorsal view not **U**-shaped, the posterior margin straight or only slightly curved (Figure 29-7 B, D); costal cell present or absent; transverse costal vein absent; abdomen more or less flattened laterally. 6

6(5′). Costal cell present and distinct; apical spur on front tibiae pectinate on inner margin; pronotum in dorsal view much wider than long (Figure 29-7 D); southern California . . . . **Syntéxidae*** p. 552

6′. Costal cell absent (Figure 29-6 A) or very narrow; apical spur of front tibiae not pectinate on inner margin; pronotum in dorsal view about as

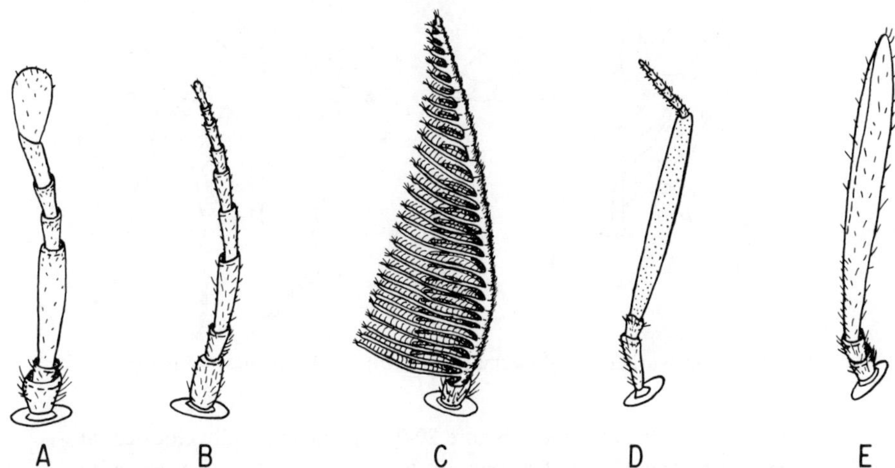

Fig. 29-8. Antennae of Sýmphyta. A, Cimbícidae (*Címbex*); B, Tenthredínidae (*Leucopelmònus*); C, male Dipriónidae (*Neodíprion*); D, Xyélidae (*Macroxȳela*); E, Árgidae (*Árge*).

long as or longer than wide (Figure 29-7 B); widely distributed . **Céphidae** p. 553

7(3′). Antennae 3-segmented, the third segment very long (Figure 29-8 E), sometimes lyre-shaped .... **Árgidae** p. 550

7′. Antennae with 4 or more segments 8

8(7′). Third antennal segment very long, longer than the remaining segments combined (Figure 29-8 D); 3 (rarely 2) marginal cells, and an intercostal vein, in front wings (Figure 29-6 C) .... **Xyélidae*** p. 550

8′. Third antennae segment short (Figure 29-8 A-C); 1 or 2 marginal cells in front wings (Figure 29-6 D-F); intercostal vein in front wings usually absent 9

9(8′). Antennae clubbed, with 7 or fewer segments (Figure 29-8 A); large, robust sawflies resembling bumble bees (Figure 29-30) .... **Cimbícidae** p. 550

9′. Antennae filiform (Figure 29-8 B), serrate, or pectinate (Figure 29-8 C), rarely slightly clubbed 10

10(9). Antennae 6-segmented; scutellum with anterior margin sinuate. . **Pérgidae*** p. 550

10′. Antennae with more than 6 segments; scutellum with anterior margin **V**-shaped 11

11(10′). Front wings with an intercostal vein and 2 transverse median veins (Figures 29-1 and 29-2); antennae with 13 or more segments........ .... **Pamphilìidae*** p. 550

11′. Front wings without an intercostal vein and with only 1 transverse median vein (Figure 29-6 D-F); antennae variable 12

12(11′). Antennae 7- to 10-segmented, and usually filiform (Figure 29-8 B); 1 or 2 marginal cells (Figure 29-6 D-F) .... **Tenthredínidae** p. 550

12′. Antennae with 13 or more segments, and either serrate or pectinate (Figure 29-8 C); 1 marginal cell .... **Dipriónidae** p. 550

13(1′). First abdominal segment (sometimes the first 2 abdominal segments) bearing a dorsal hump or node, and strongly differentiated from the

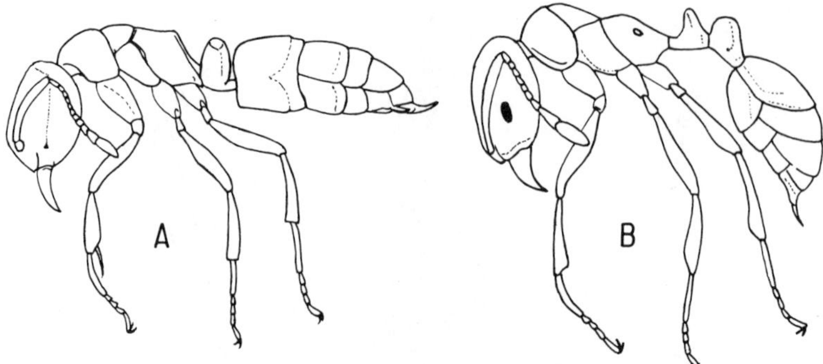

Fig. 29-9. Ant workers. A, Ponerìnae (*Ponèra*); B, Myrmicìnae (*Solenópsis*).

remainder of the abdomen (Figure 29-9); antennae usually elbowed, at least in the female, with first segment long................**Formícidae** p. 575

13′. First abdominal segment not as above, or antennae not elbowed......14

14(13′). Wings vestigial or lacking 15

14′. Wings well developed 36

15(14). Hind trochanters 2-segmented (Figure 29-10 A); ovipositor issuing from anterior to tip of abdomen and provided with a pair of narrow exserted sheaths as long as ovipositor (Figure 29-5 A) 16

15′. Hind trochanters 1-segmented (Figure 29-10 B); ovipositor issuing from tip of abdomen, usually as a sting, and without a pair of exserted sheaths (Figure 29-5 B) (the ovipositor is often withdrawn into the abdomen and not visible) 23*

16(15). Antennae elbowed and often clubbed (Figures 29-19 and 29-20); prepectus well developed and triangular (Figure 29-4 A, *pp*) (wingless chalcids)..17

16′. Antennae filiform; prepectus, if present, elongate and less well differentiated..21*

17(16). Head with a deep triangular impression anteriorly; males 18*

17′. Head without such an impression 19

18(17). Abdomen much drawn out to a point apically, or broadened at tip; antennae short and stout, 3- to 9-segmented (see also couplet 50).... ....**Agaónidae*** p. 564

18′. Abdomen not pointed or enlarged apically ....**Torýmidae*** p. 564

19(17′). Tarsi 4-segmented (see also couplet 49′) ....**Eulóphidae*** p. 562

19′. Tarsi 5-segmented..20

20(19′). Mesopleura with an oblique femoral groove or impression (Figure 29-20) 57

20′. Mesopleura large and convex, without a femoral groove (Figure 29-19 B, C) 52

21(16′). Petiole of abdomen cylindrical, rarely very short; abdomen compressed; antennae often swollen apically (wingless Cynipòidea)............75*

21′. Petiole of abdomen, if well developed, curved toward tip; antennae never swollen apically (wingless Ichneumonòidea) 22*

22(21′). Abdomen petiolate, the petiole curved and expanded apically.......... ....**Ichneumónidae*** p. 557

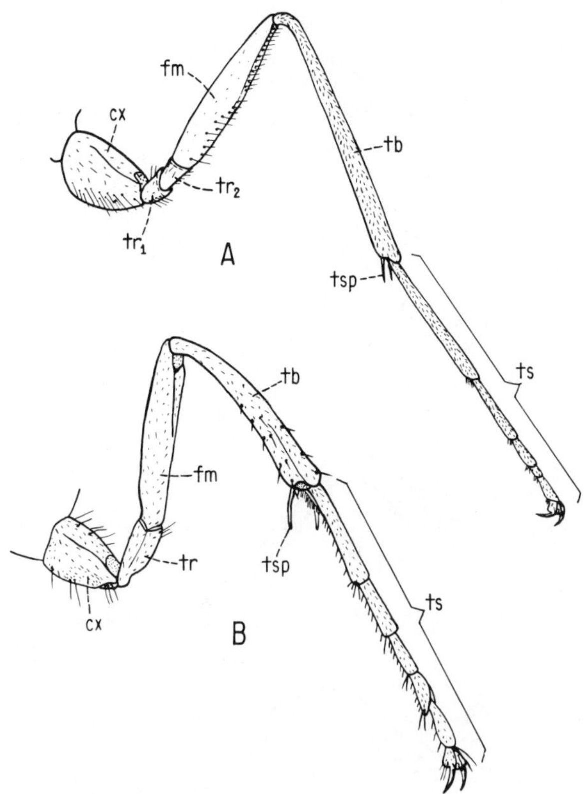

Fig. 29-10. Legs of Hymenoptera. A, Ichneumónidae; B, Sphècidae. *cx,* coxa; *fm,* femur; *tb,* tibia; *tr,* trochanter; *ts,* tarsus; *tsp,* tibial spurs.

22′. Abdomen sessile, or if petiolate, then the petiole is not curved or expanded apically .... **Bracónidae*** p. 554

23(15′). Dorsum of thorax without sutures, or with only 1 suture separating pronotum from rest of thorax; no scutellum; females 24*

23′. Dorsum of thorax with 3 sclerites separated by sutures or constrictions, or with 2 sclerites separated by a constriction; scutellum usually present.. .... 25*

24(23). Pronotum separated from remainder of thoracic dorsum by a suture (Myrmosìnae) .... **Tiphìidae*** p. 574

24′. Dorsum of thorax without sutures (Apterogynìnae) .... **Mutíllidae*** p. 574

25(23′). Antennae with 22 or more segments; females .... **Sclerogíbbidae*** p. 572

25′. Antennae with 15 or fewer segments.............................. 26*

26(25′). Antennae inserted on a frontal shelf or prominence (Figure 29-25 A); females 27*

26′. Antennae not inserted on a frontal shelf or prominence 28*

27(26). First abdominal segment forming a distinct petiole; antennae 12- (Diapriìnae) or 13-segmented (Belytìnae) .... **Diaprìidae*** p. 571

27′. First abdominal segment without a distinct petiole; antennae 10-segmented (Embolemìnae) .... **Drýinidae*** p. 573

28(26′). Abdomen with sharp lateral margins 29*

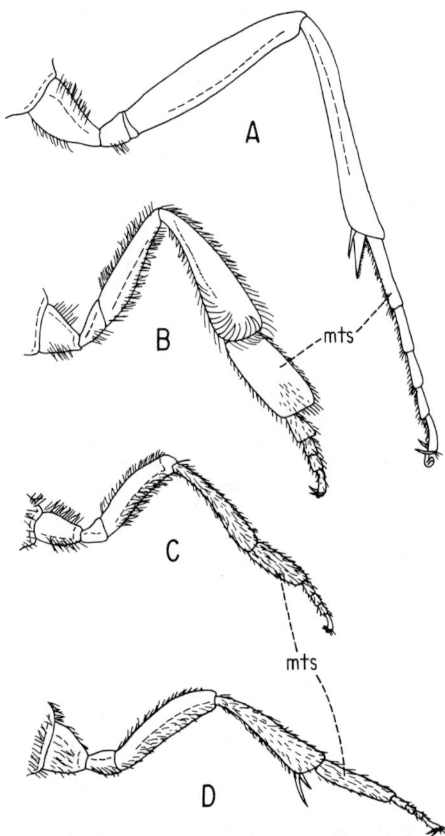

Fig. 29-11. Hind legs of Sphecòidea (A) and Apòidea (B-D). A, Sphècidae (*Sphéx*); B, Ápidae (*Ápis*), C, Andrénidae (*Andrèna*); D, Ápidae (*Nómada*). *mts*, first tarsal segment.

28′. Abdomen without sharp lateral margins........................30*

29(28). Antennae with 10 or fewer segments; males............**Platygastéridae*** p. 572

29′. Antennae usually 11- or 12-segmented; females............**Sceliónidae*** p. 572

30(28′). Antennae inserted at middle of face, far above clypeus; females........ ....**Proctotrùpidae*** p. 571

30′. Antennae inserted low on face, near margin of clypeus.............31*

31(30′). Antennae 10- or 11-segmented 32*

31′. Antennae 12- or 13-segmented 33*

32(31). Males with 10-segmented antennae; females with front tarsi pincerslike.. ....**Drýinidae*** p. 573

32′. Males with 11-segmented antennae; females with front tarsi not pincerslike ....**Ceraphrónidae*** p. 571

33(31′). Head elongate, usually longer than wide; front femora usually thickened in middle; body usually conspicuously flattened; females..**Bethýlidae*** p. 572

33′. Head not elongate, usually oval and broader than high.............34*

34(33′). Wings present but greatly reduced; tegulae normally developed; thorax normal, divided by sutures 35*

34′. Wings entirely absent; tegulae absent or indicated only by minute tubercles; thorax often abnormal, usually divided by constrictions;

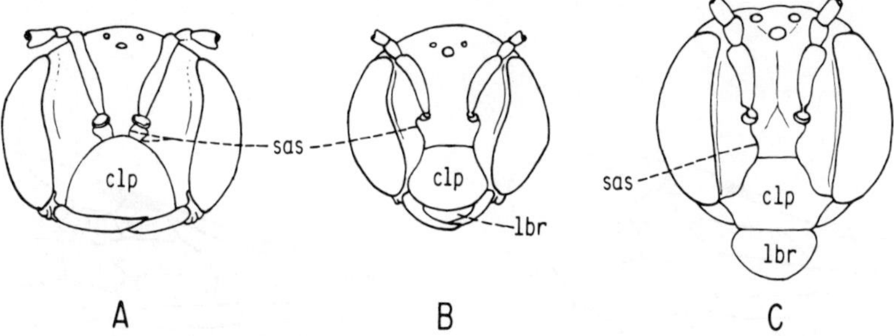

Fig. 29-12. Heads of bees, anterior view. A, Andrénidae (*Andrèna*); B, Megachílidae (*Ósmia*); C, Ápidae (*Triepèolus*, Anthophorìnae). *clp*, clypeus; *lbr*, labrum; *sas*, subantennal suture.

females (Brachycistidìnae and Methochìnae) .... **Tiphìidae*** p. 574

35(34). Antennae 13-segmented; males .... **Mutíllidae*** p. 574

35′. Antennae 12-segmented; females .... **Pompílidae*** p. 582

36(14′). Pronotum short, more or less collarlike, not extending laterally to tegulae, and with a rounded lobe on each side posteriorly (Figure 29-4 D); venation complete (Figures 29-13, 29-14, 29-66—29-68) 37

36′. Pronotum without a rounded lobe on each side posteriorly, and sometimes extending to tegulae (Figure 29-4 B, C); venation variable, sometimes reduced 44

37(36). All body hairs unbranched; first segment of hind tarsi slender, not broadened or thickened, and usually bare (Figure 29-11 A); abdomen often petiolate (superfamily Sphecòidea) 38

37′. Some body hairs, especially those on thorax, branched or plumose; first segment of hind tarsi elongate, usually thickened or flattened, and often hairy (Figure 29-11 B-D); abdomen not petiolate (superfamily Apòidea) 39

38(37). Mesosternum produced into a forked process posteriorly; parapsidal sutures distinct and complete; pronotum long, conically produced anteriorly, usually with a median groove (Figure 29-64); abdomen of male with 4 to 6 exposed tergites .... **Ampulícidae*** p. 583

38′. Mesosternum not so produced; parapsidal sutures indistinct or absent; abdomen of male usually with 7 exposed tergites .... **Sphècidae** p. 583

39(37′). Two subantennal sutures below each antennal socket (Figure 29-12 A); jugal lobe in hind wings usually as long as or longer than submedian cell (Figure 29-13 A, B) .... **Andrénidae** p. 597

39′. Only 1 subantennal suture below each antennal socket (Figure 29-12 B, C); jugal lobe in hind wings variable, sometimes absent 40

40(39′). Jugal lobe in hind wings as long as or longer than submedian cell (Figure 29-13 C-E) 41

40′. Jugal lobe in hind wings shorter than submedian cell (Figures 29-13 F and 29-14 A, C-F), or lacking (Figure 29-14 B) 42

41(40). Basal vein strongly arched (Figure 29-13 C); glossa pointed. . **Halíctidae** p. 598

41′. Basal vein straight or feebly arched (Figure 29-13 D, E); glossa bilobed or truncate (Figure 29-15 C) .... **Collétidae** p. 597

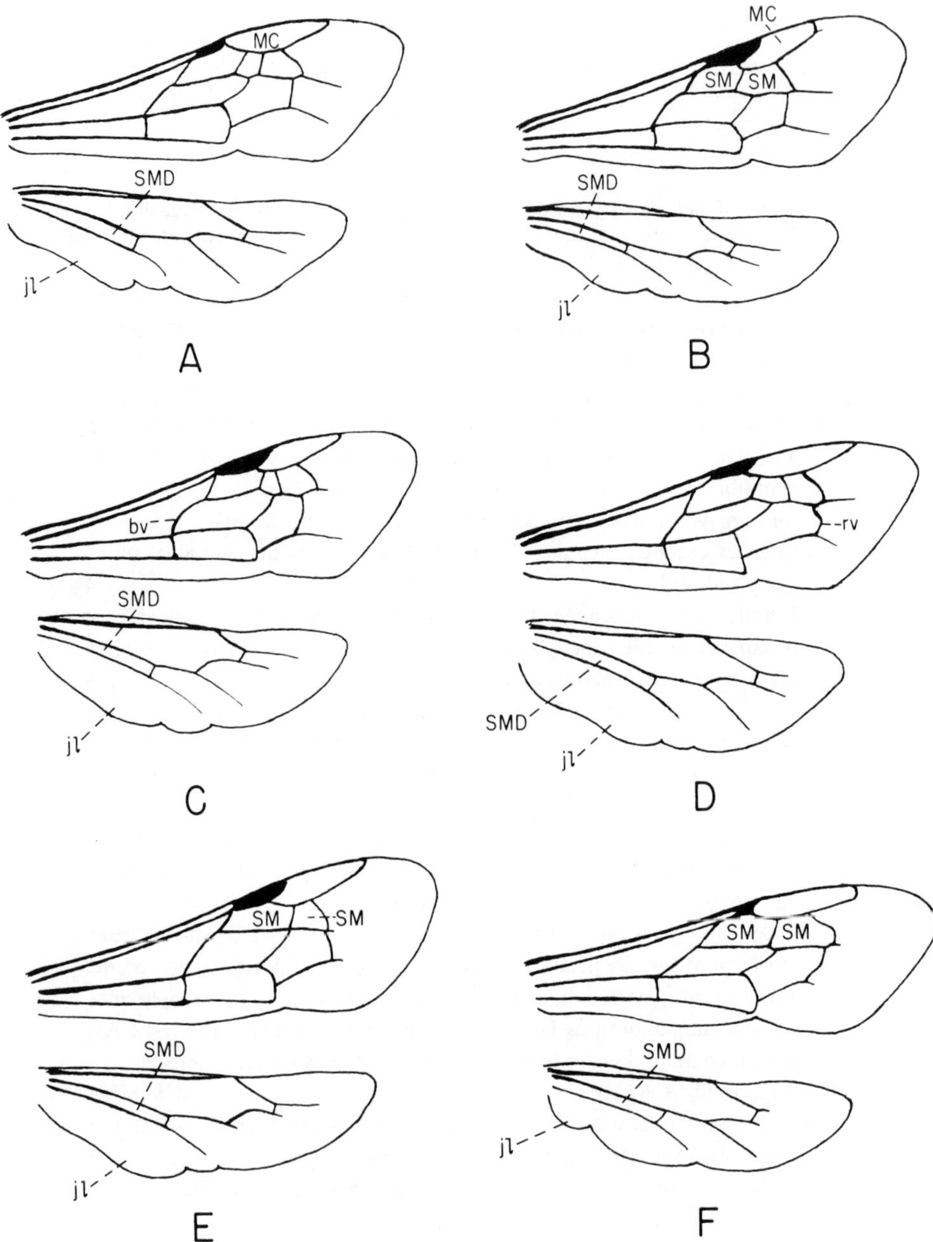

Fig. 29-13. Wings of Apòidea. A, *Andrèna* (Andrenìnae, Andrénidae); B, *Panúrga* (Panurgìnae, Andrénidae); C, *Sphecòdes* (Halíctidae); D, *Collètes* (Colletìnae, Collétidae); E, *Hylaèus* (Hylaeìnae, Collétidae); F, *Coelióxys* (Megachílidae). *bv*, basal vein; *jl*, jugal lobe; *MC*, marginal cell; *rv*, second recurrent vein; *SM*, submarginal cells; *SMD*, submedian cell.

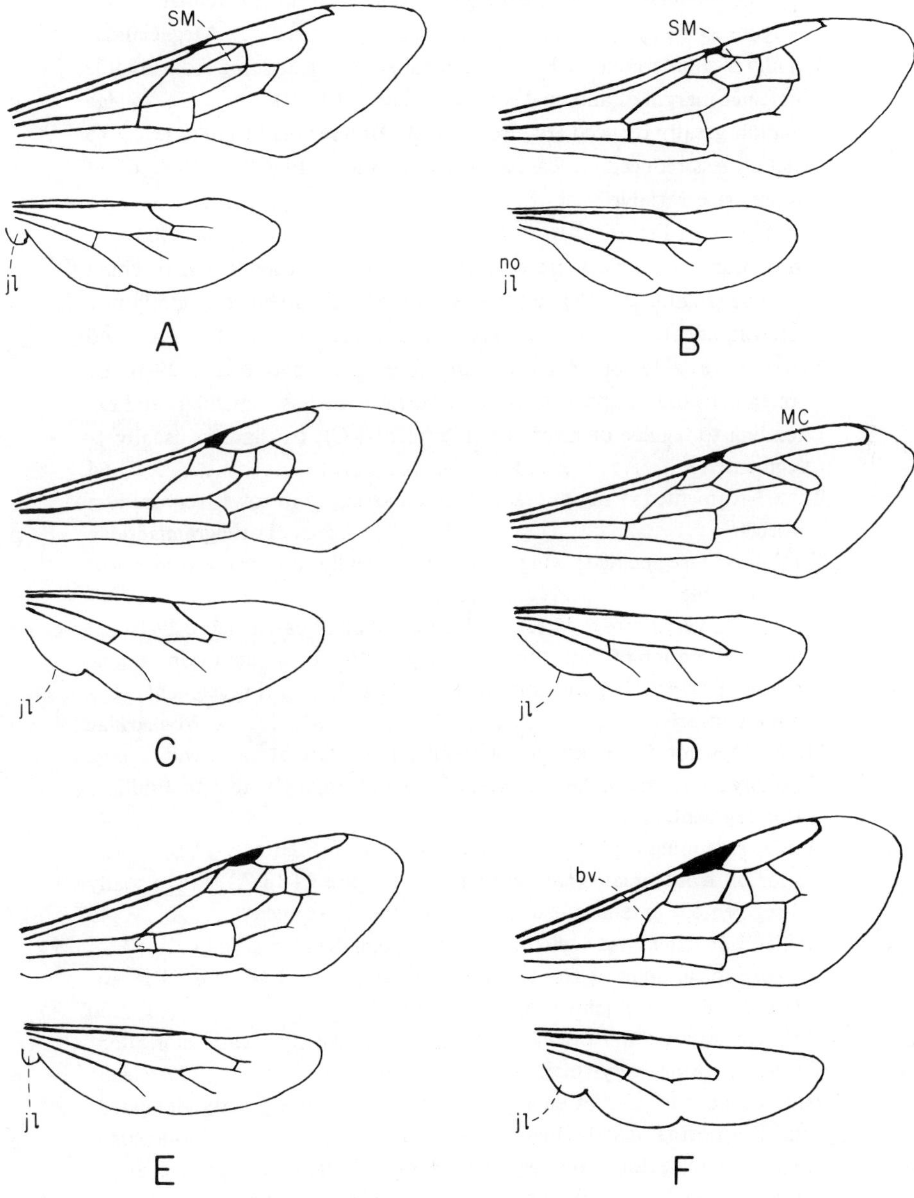

Figs. 29-14. Wings of Ápidae. A, *Xylócopa* (Xylocopìnae); B, *Bómbus* (Apìnae); C, *Melissòdes* (Anthophorìnae); D, *Àpis* (Apinae); E, *Nómada* (Anthophorìnae); F, *Cerátina* (Xylocopìnae). *bv,* basal vein; *jl,* jugal lobe; *MC,* marginal cell; *SM,* second marginal cell.

42(40′). Labial palpi with segments similar and cylindrical (as in Figure 29-15 C, D); galeae short; rare bees .... **Melíttidae*** p. 599

42′. Labial palpi with the first 2 segments long and sheathlike (Figure 29-15 A); galeae elongate; common bees 43

43(42′). Two submarginal cells, the second nearly as long as the first (Figure 29-13 F); subantennal sutures extending from outer margin of antennal sockets (Figure 29-12 B) .... **Megachílidae** p. 599

43′. Usually 3 submarginal cells; subantennal sutures extending from middle or inner margin of antennal sockets (Figure 29-12 C) .... **Ápidae** p. 599

44(36′). Venation greatly reduced (Figure 29-16 B-D); size small to minute.... 45

44′. Venation less reduced, at least as many veins as in Figure 29-16 A, often more; size variable 66

45(44). Venation as in Figure 29-16 B, or even more reduced; antennae elbowed; pronotum in profile more or less quadrate, and usually not reaching tegulae (Figure 29-4 A); trochanters usually 2-segmented (superfamily Chalcidòidea) 46

45′. Venation variable, but usually with more veins than Figure 29-16 B; antennae variable; pronotum in profile more or less triangular, and extending to tegulae or nearly so (Figure 29-4 C); trochanters usually 1-segmented 66

46(45). Tarsi 3-segmented; wing pubescence often arranged in rows; very minute insects .... **Trichogrammátidae** p. 561

46′. Tarsi 4- or 5-segmented; wing pubescence usually not arranged in rows; size variable 47

47(46′). Hind wings very narrow, linear, with a long stalk at base (Figure 29-16 C); wings with a long fringe, the front wings without a stigmal vein; antennae with scape short and compressed, and without a ring segment; very minute insects .... **Mymáridae** p. 561

47′. Hind wings not so narrow and without a long stalk at base; wing fringe usually short; antennae with scape long and usually with 1 to 3 minute ring segments 48

48(47′). Axillae extending cephalad to or beyond tegulae (Figure 29-17 B); apical spur on front tibiae small and straight (Figure 29-18 A); tarsi usually 4-segmented; antennae usually with 9 or fewer segments 49

48′. Axillae not extending cephalad to or beyond tegulae (Figure 29-17 A, C-E); apical spur of front tibiae large and curved (Figure 29-18 B); tarsi usually 5-segmented; antennae variable 50

49(48). Hind coxae large and disclike; marginal vein usually greatly elongated; tarsi very long; very small, usually blackish insects .... **Elásmidae*** p. 563

49′. Hind coxae normal, not enlarged; marginal vein not greatly elongated; tarsi of normal length (Figure 29-18 A) .... **Eulóphidae** p. 562

50(48′). Head of female long, oblong, with a deep longitudinal groove above (males wingless); occipital margin usually with a small tubercle or spine; front and hind legs stout, their tibiae much shorter than their femora, the middle legs slender .... **Agaónidae*** p. 564

50′. Head and legs not as above 51

51(50′). Mesopleura large and convex, usually without a femoral groove (Figure

29-19 B, C); axillae usually meeting at their inner basal angles; apical spur of middle tibiae usually very large and stout (Figure 29-18 F)..52

51′. Mesopleura with a groove for the reception of the femora (Figures 29-19 D and 29-20); apical spur of middle tibiae normal, not enlarged....56

52(20′, 51). Mesonotum more or less convex, parapsidal sutures lacking or indistinct 53

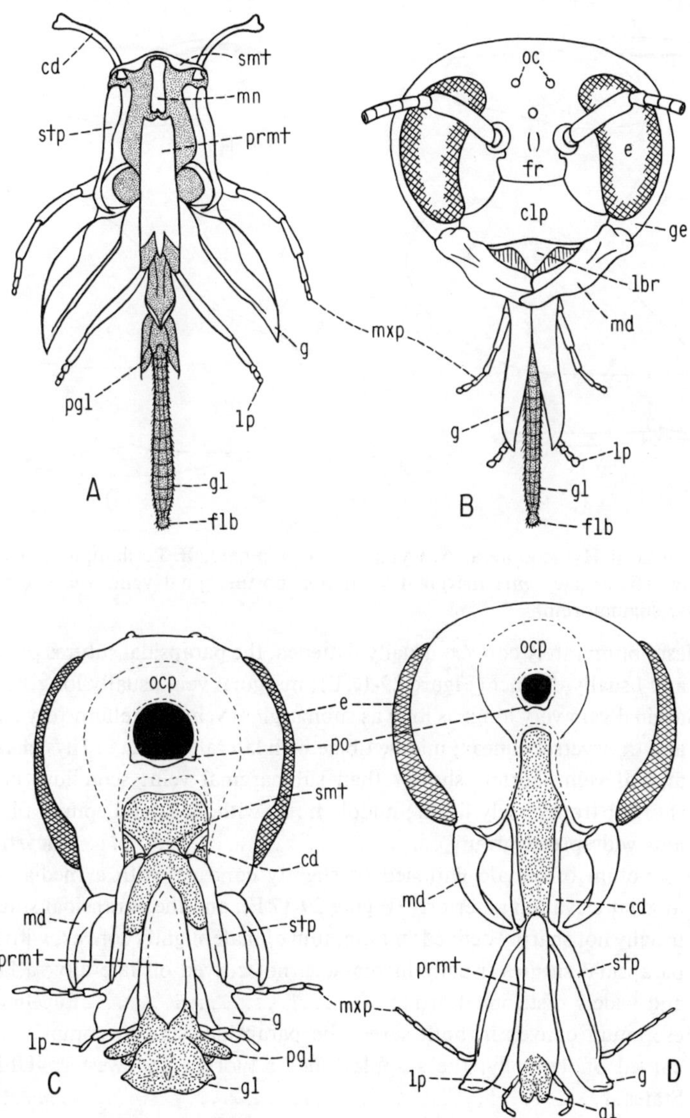

Fig. 29-15. Head and mouth-part structure in bees. A, mouth parts of *Xylócopa* (Ápidae, Xylocopìnae), posterior view; B, same, anterior view; C, mouth parts of *Hylaèus* (Collétidae, Hylaeìnae), posterior view; D, mouth parts of *Sphecòdes* (Halíctidae), posterior view. *cd,* cardo; *clp,* clypeus; *e,* compound eye; *flb,* flabellum; *fr,* frons; *g,* galea; *ge,* gena; *gl,* glossa; *lbr,* labrum; *lp,* labial palpus; *md,* mandible; *mn,* mentum; *mxp,* maxillary palpus; *oc,* ocelli; *ocp,* occiput; *pgl,* paraglossa; *po,* postocciput; *prmt,* prementum; *smt,* submentum; *stp,* stipes.

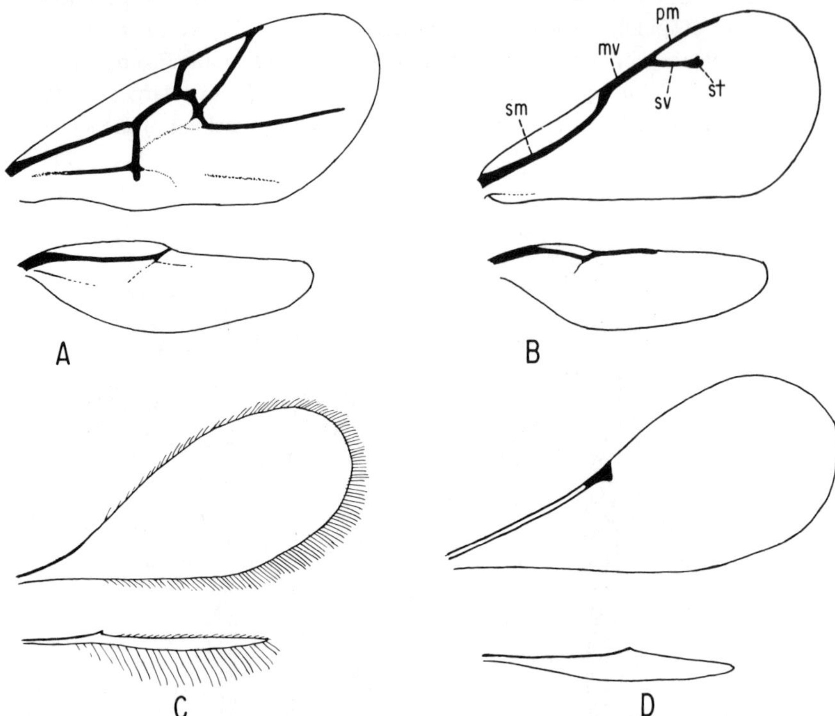

Fig. 29-16. Wings of Hymenoptera. A, Cynípidae (Cynipìnae); B, Perilámpidae; C, Mymáridae; D, Diaprìidae (Diapriìnae). *mv,* marginal vein; *pm,* postmarginal vein; *sm,* submarginal vein; *st,* stigma; *sv,* stigmal vein.

52′. Mesonotum rarely convex, usually flattened, the parapsidal sutures present and usually distinct (Figure 29-17 E); marginal vein usually long. . . . 54

53(52). Marginal vein very long, as long as submarginal vein; scutellum very short and transversely linear; middle tibiae with lateral spurs. . . . **Thysánidae*** p. 563

53′. Marginal vein shorter, shorter than submarginal vein; scutellum never short or transversely linear; middle tibiae without lateral spurs; a large and widespread group . . . . **Encýrtidae** p. 563

54(52′). Mesonotum of female flattened or slightly concave, with a median triangular elevation anteriorly (Figure 29-17 E), and the parapsidal sutures usually not sharply defined; mesonotum of male slightly convex, with the parapsidal sutures usually incomplete, not curved off laterally; a large and widely distributed group . . . . **Eupélmidae** p. 563

54′. Mesonotum convex in both sexes, the parapsidal sutures complete and curved off laterally, the scapulae short; Florida and western United States. 55*

55(54′). First antennal segment of female more or less dilated or compressed; flagellum of antennae of male with 4 branches; recorded from Florida, Arizona, and California . . . . **Tanaostigmátidae*** p. 563

55′. First antennal segment of female slender, not dilated or compressed; flagellum of antennae of male filiform, without branches; recorded from Texas and Montana . . . . **Eutrichosomátidae*** p. 563

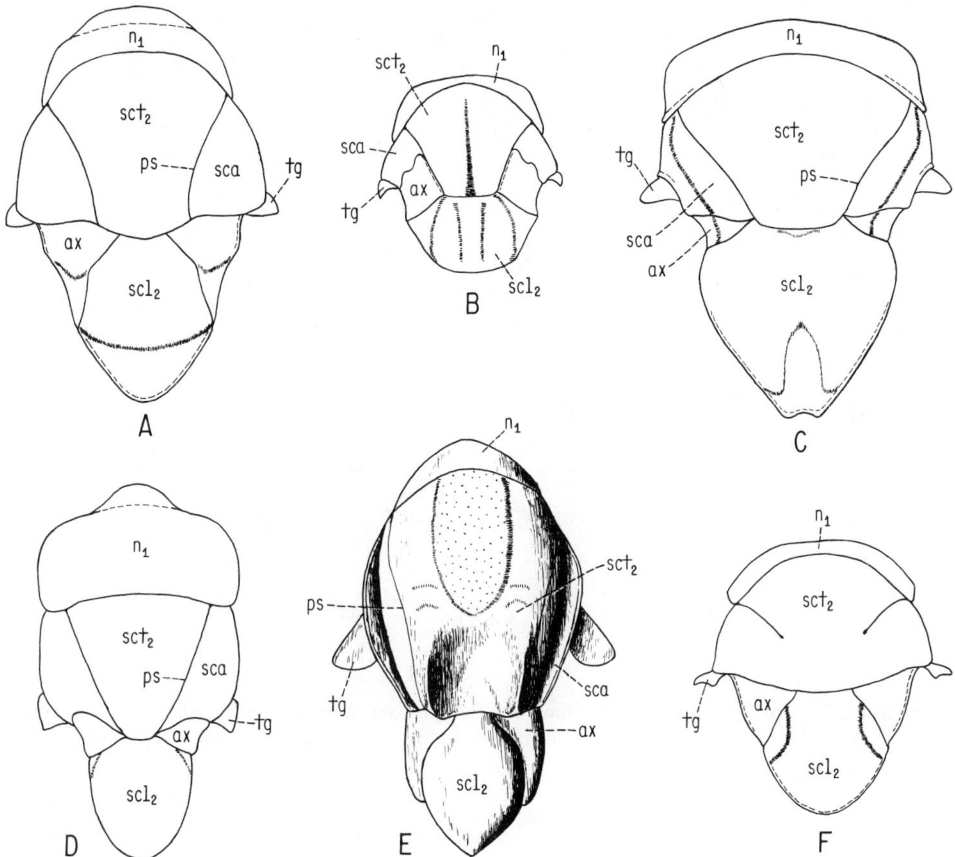

Fig. 29-17. Thorax of Chalcidòidea, dorsal view. A, Torýmidae (*Tórymus*); B, Eulóphidae; C, Perilámpidae (*Perilámpus*); D, Eurytómidae (*Eurýtoma*); E, Eupélmidae; F, Pteromálidae (*Pterómalus*). *ax,* axilla; n_1, pronotum; *ps,* parapsidal suture; *sca,* scapula; scl_2, mesoscutellum; sct_2, mesoscutum; *tg,* tegula.

56(51′). Mandibles sickle-shaped, with 1 or 2 teeth on inner side; thorax strongly elevated, the pronotum with only an anterior face and not visible from above (Figure 29-19 D); axillae contiguous; scutellum large and produced posteriorly; abdomen compressed, the second segment very large; stigmal vein not developed .... **Eucharítidae*** p. 564

56′. Mandibles stout, not sickle-shaped, and with 3 or 4 teeth at apex; thorax not elevated; axillae usually separated 57

57(20, 56′). Hind tibiae with 2 apical spurs (1 of which may be small) (Figure 29-18 D), rarely with only 1; if with only 1 apical spur on hind tibiae, then stigmal vein terminates in a large rounded stigma; ovipositor very long.... 58

57′. Hind tibiae with 1 apical spur (Figure 29-18 C); ovipositor usually short (if long, then the stigma is small); hind coxae rarely larger than front coxae; axillae separated; mandibles usually stout, with 3 or 4 teeth at apex; minute (1 to 2 mm in length), black, metallic, or iridescent insects .... **Pteromálidae** p. 566

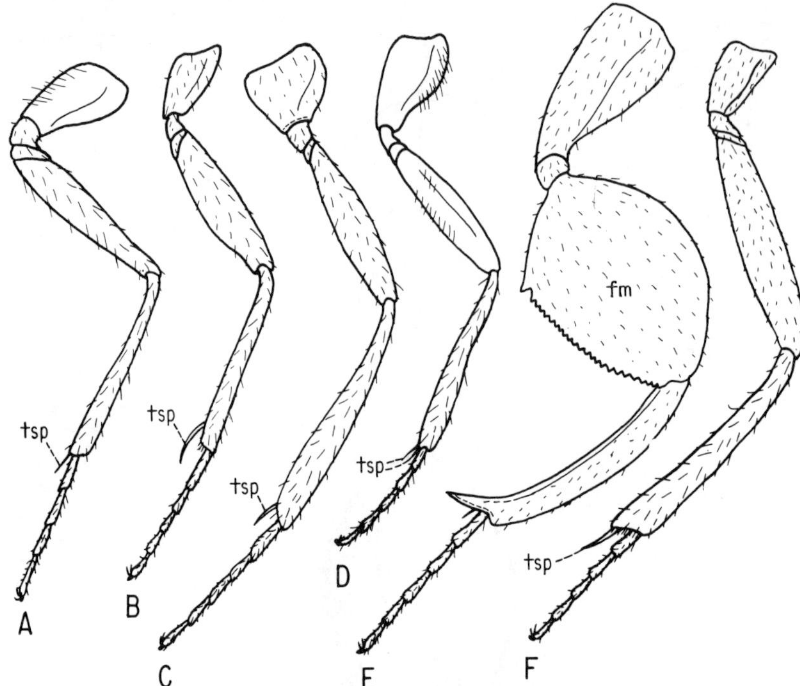

Fig. 29-18. Legs of Chalcidòidea. A, front leg, Eulóphidae; B, front leg, Pteromálidae; C, hind leg, Pteromálidae; D, hind leg, Eurytómidae; E, hind leg, Chalcídidae; F, middle leg, Encýrtidae. *fm,* femur; *tsp,* tibial spur.

58(57).	Hind femora much swollen, and usually toothed or denticulate beneath (Figure 29-18 E); hind tibiae usually arcuate 59	
58′.	Hind femora not, or but slightly, swollen; either not toothed beneath or with only 1 or 2 teeth 62	
59(58).	Hind coxae considerably larger than front coxae....................60	
59′.	Hind coxae little if any larger than front coxae ....**Chalcedéctidae***	p. 566
60(59).	Hind coxae long and cylindrical.................................61	
60′.	Hind coxae triangular in cross-section (Podagrioninae) ......**Torýmidae***	p. 564
61(60).	Front wings folded longitudinally when at rest; ovipositor usually long and curving upward and forward over dorsal side of abdomen; usually black and yellow insects, 10 mm or more in length......**Leucóspidae***	p. 566
61′.	Front wings not folded longitudinally when at rest; ovipositor usually short and not up-curved; usually 7 mm in length or less....**Chalcídidae**	p. 566
62(58′).	Hind coxae considerably larger than front coxae (Figure 29-44 B)....63	
62′.	Hind coxae little if any larger than front coxae (Figure 29-20 B-D)....64	
63(62).	Parapsidal sutures present (Figure 29-17 A); ovipositor exserted and usually very long (Figure 29-44 B); abdomen not pitted or punctured; body metallic ....**Torýmidae**	p. 564
63′.	Parapsidal sutures absent or very indistinct; ovipositor short and hidden; abdomen of female conical and elongate (of male, oblong) and usually with rows of deep pits or large punctures in both sexes ....**Ormýridae***	p. 565
64(62′).	Pronotum wide, more or less quadrate, as wide as mesonotum (Figure	

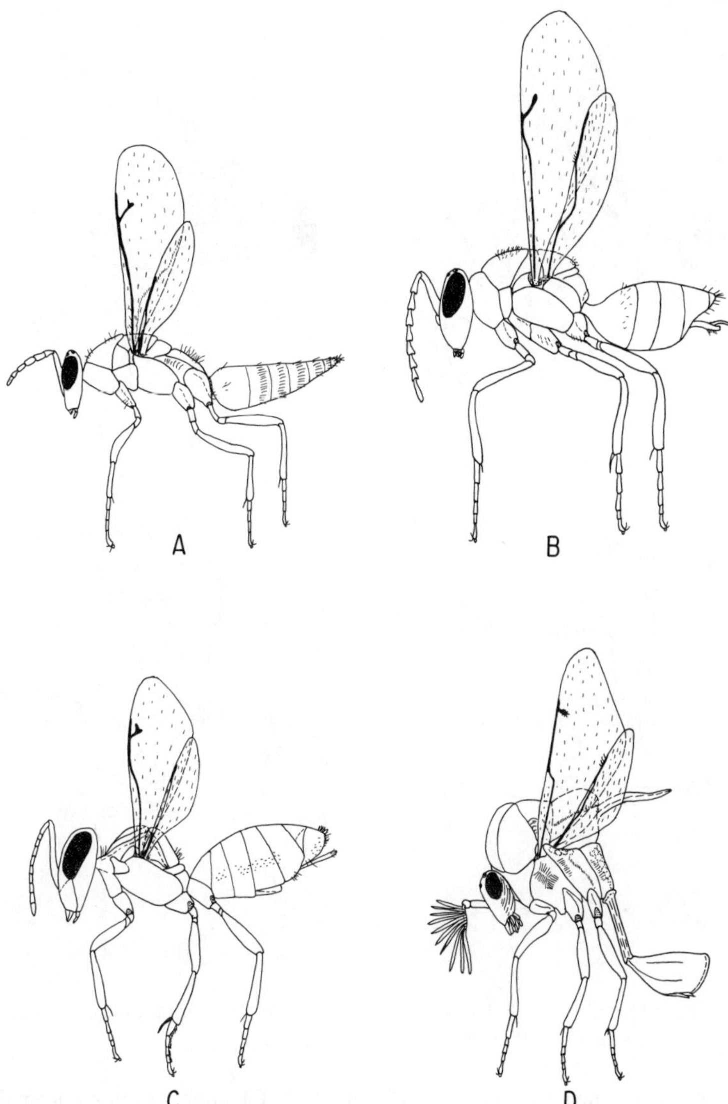

Fig. 29-19. Chalcidòidea. A, Eulóphidae; B, Encýrtidae; C, Eupélmidae; D, Eucharítidae.

29-17 C, D); mesonotum usually very coarsely sculptured..........65

64′. Pronotum somewhat conical and usually much narrowed in front, or short and transversely linear, rarely as wide as mesonotum (Figure 29-17 F); mesonotum usually finely sculptured ....**Pteromálidae** p. 566

65(64). Pronotum short, wider than long (Figure 29-17 C); abdomen of female subtriangular, the second tergite (or the fused second and third tergites) covering most of its surface (Figure 29-20 B); thorax very robust; often metallic insects ....**Perilámpidae** p. 564

65′. Pronotum more or less quadrate, nearly as long as wide (Figure 29-17 D); abdomen of female rounded or ovate, more or less compressed, the

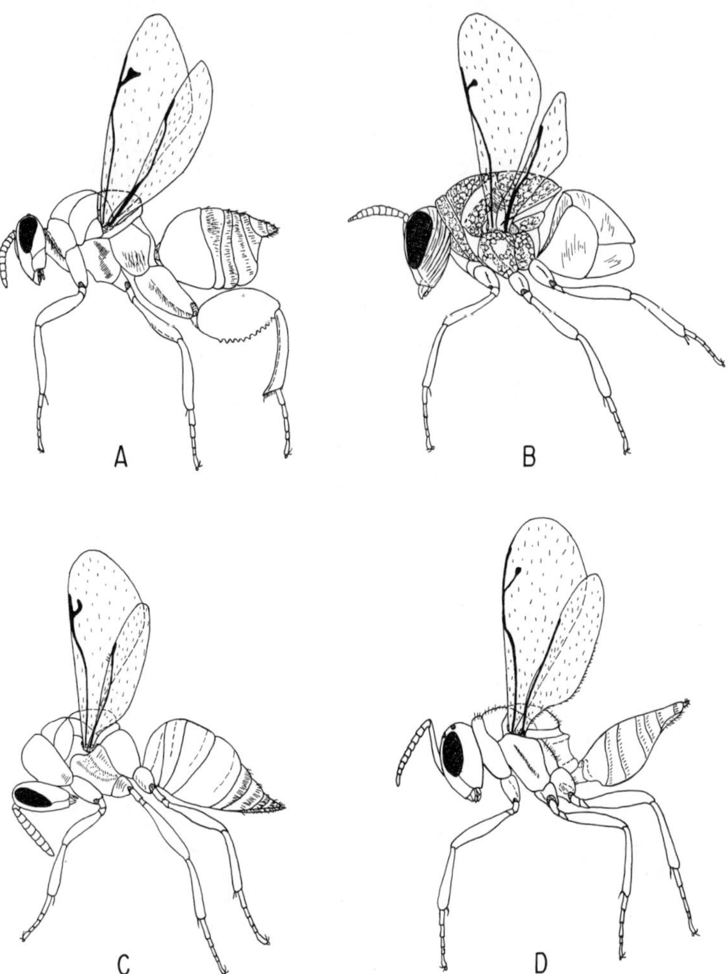

Fig. 29-20. Chalcidòidea. A, Chalcídidae (*Brachymèria*); B, Perilámpidae (*Perilámpus*); C, Eurytómidae (*Eurýtoma*); D, Pteromálidae (*Pterómalus*).

second tergite never very large (Figure 29-20 C); thorax of more normal proportions; black or yellowish insects, thorax not metallic........ .... **Eurytómidae** p. 566

66(44′, 45′). Hind trochanters 2-segmented, or venation as in Figure 29-16 A......67

66′. Trochanters 1-segmented; venation variable........................74

67(66). Antennae usually with 14 or fewer segments, rarely more; front wings with a reduced venation and usually without a stigma (as in Figure 29-16 A, or with even fewer veins)............................68

67′. Antennae usually with 16 or more segments; front wings with venation usually well developed and with a more or less well-defined stigma (Figure 29-21); abdomen usually elongate, sometimes shining......69

68(67). Antennae 11-segmented, elbowed; hind femora greatly thickened; front wings folded longitudinally when at rest; body yellow and black, usually 10 mm or more in length, with the head and prothorax deflexed; ovi-

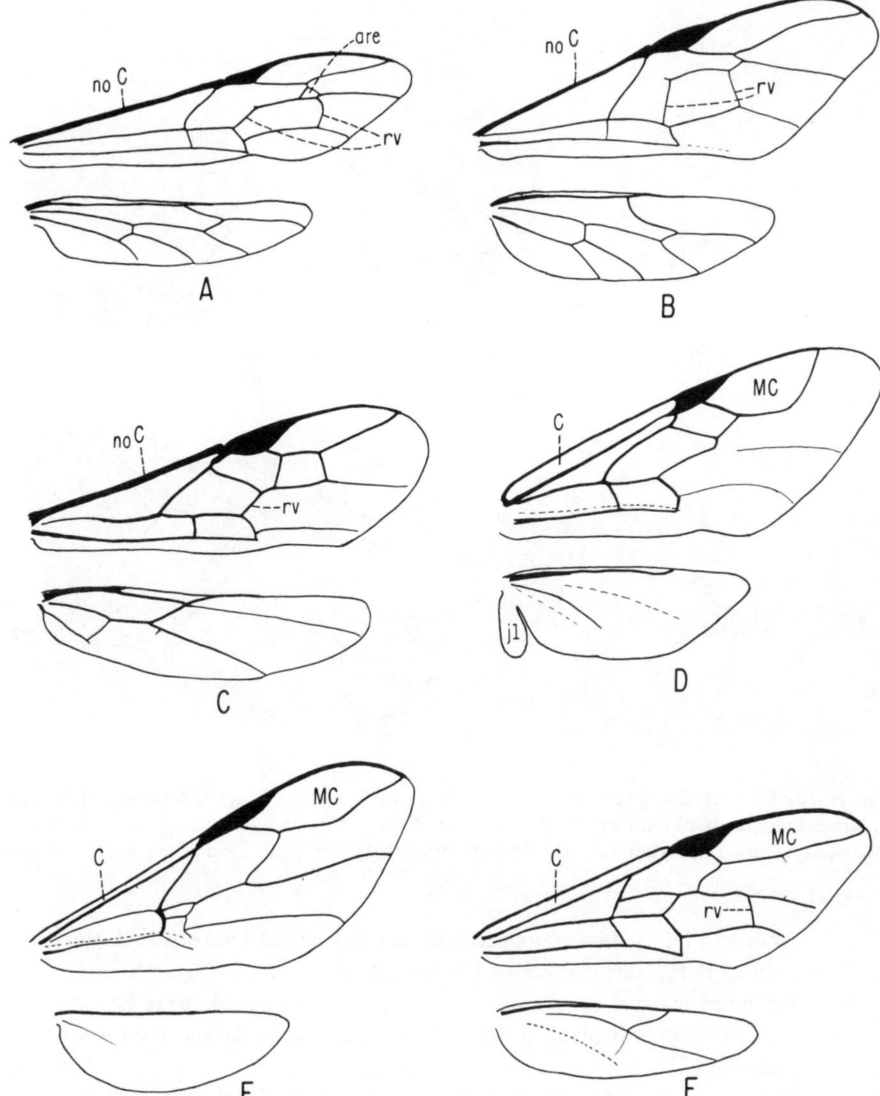

Fig. 29-21. Wings of Hymenoptera. A, Ichneumónidae (*Megarhýssa*); B, Ichneumónidae (*Óphion*); C, Bracónidae; D, Evanìidae (*Prosevània*); E, Gasteruptìidae (Gasteruptìinae); F, Gasteruptìidae (Aulacìnae). *are*, areolet; *C*, costal cell; *jl*, jugal lobe; *MC*, marginal cell; *rv*, recurrent vein.

positor of female curving upward and forward over dorsal side of abdomen .... **Leucóspidae*** p. 566

68′. Antennae with 12 or more segments; hind femora not thickened; front wings not folded longitudinally when at rest; body color variable, but usually black and shining; ovipositor not as above (superfamily Cynipòidea) 75

69(67′). A costal cell present (Figure 29-21 D-F) 70

69′. Costal cell absent (Figure 29-21 A-C) 73

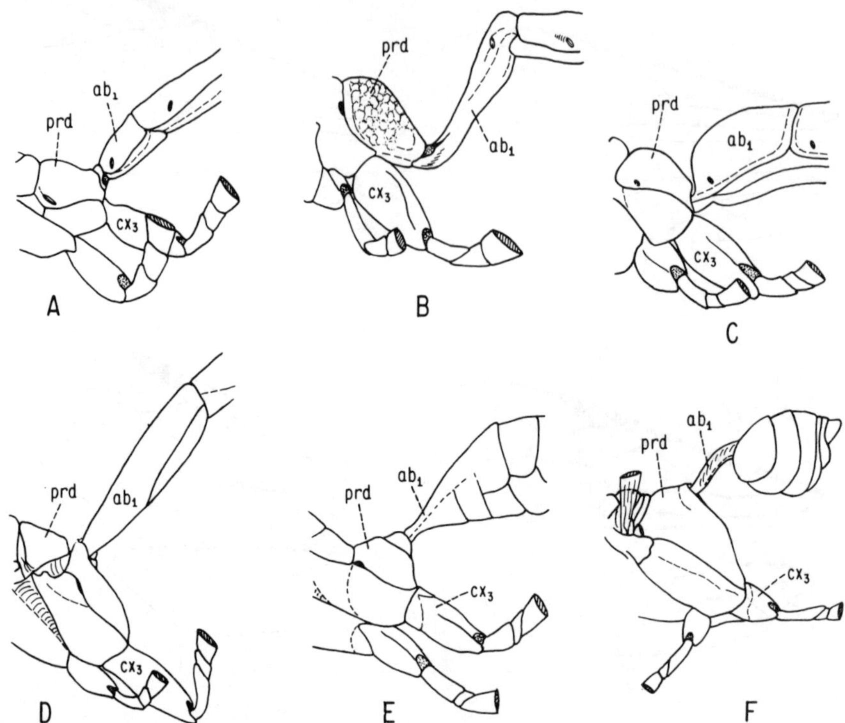

Fig. 29-22. Base of the abdomen in parasitic Hymenoptera. A, Ichneumónidae (Pimplìnae); B, Ichneumónidae (Ophionìnae); C, Bracónidae; D, Gasteruptìidae (Gasteruptìinae); E, Gasteruptìidae (Aulacìnae); F, Evanìidae. ab_1, first abdominal segment; cx_3, hind coxa; *prd*, propodeum.

70(69). Abdomen inserted on propodeum far above bases of hind coxae (Figure 29-22 D-F); antennae 13- or 14-segmented 71

70′. Abdomen inserted on propodeum between bases of hind coxae or only slightly above them (as in Figure 29-22 A-C); antennae with 18 or more segments 72*

71(70). Prothorax long and necklike; abdomen long and slender (Figure 29-22 D); marginal cell long and pointed (Figure 29-21 E, F) .... **Gasteruptiidae** p. 570

71′. Prothorax short, not necklike; abdomen short, oval, and flaglike, born on a cylindrical petiole (Figures 29-22 F and 29-48); marginal cell broad apically (Figure 29-21 D), or absent .... **Evanìidae** p. 569

72(70′). One submarginal cell or none .... **Stephánidae*** p. 554

72′. Two or 3 submarginal cells........................... **Trigonálidae*** p. 573

73(69′). Two recurrent veins (Figure 29-21 A, B), or if with only 1, then with abdomen 3 times as long as remainder of body and with tip of propodeum prolonged beyond hind coxae; size variable, from a few millimeters up to 40 mm or more in length (excluding ovipositor)........ .... **Ichneumónidae** p. 557

73′. One recurrent vein (Figure 29-21 C) or none; abdomen not greatly elongate; propodeum not prolonged beyond hind coxae; mostly small

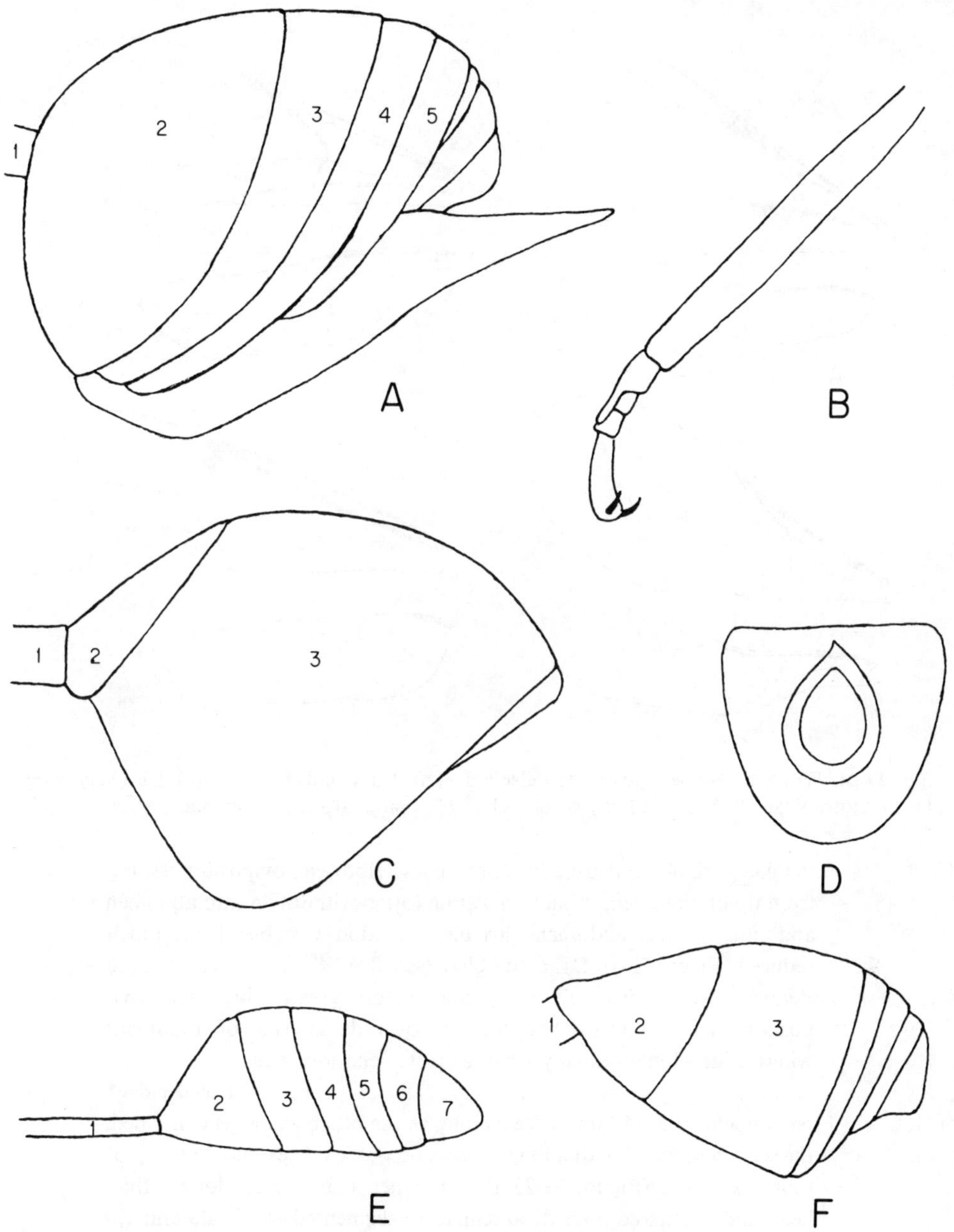

Fig. 29-23. Characters of Cynipòidea. A, abdomen of *Diplólepis* (Cynipìnae, Cynípidae); B, hind tarsus of *Ibàlia* (Ibalìidae); C, abdomen of *Callaspídia* (Aspiceratìnae, Figítidae); D, scutellum of Eucoilìnae (Cynípidae); E, abdomen of *Anácharis* (Anacharitìnae, Figítidae); F, abdomen of Figitìnae (Figítidae). The abdominal tergites are numbered.

insects, rarely over 12 mm in length .... **Bracónidae** p. 554

74(66′). Antennae filiform; ovipositor issuing from anterior to tip of abdomen; abdomen oval, usually shining (Figure 29-46); venation somewhat reduced (Figure 29-16 A) (superfamily Cynipòidea) 75

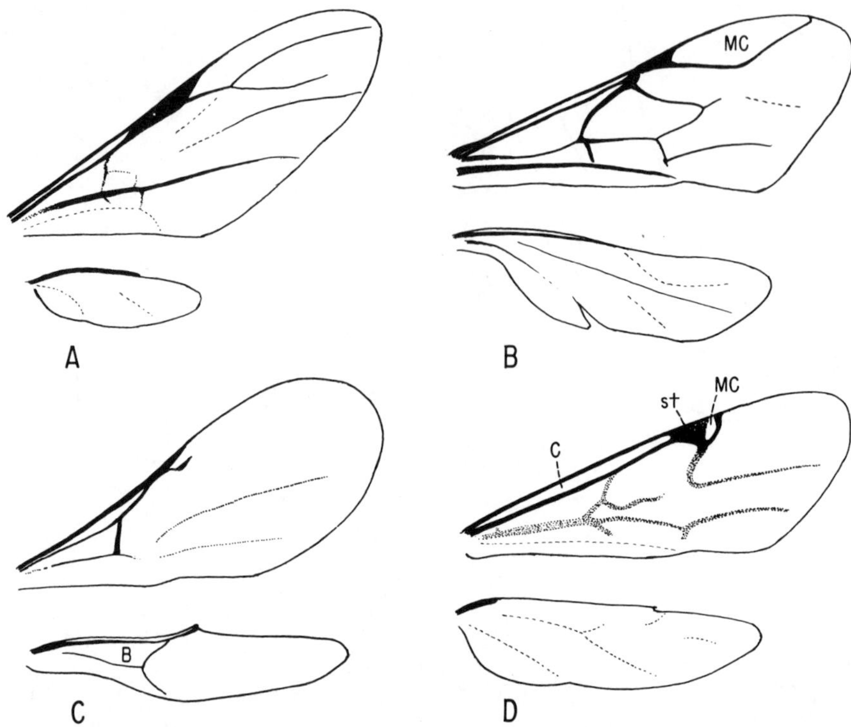

Fig. 29-24. Wings of Hymenoptera. A, Pelecínidae; B, Chrysídidae; C, Diaprìidae (Belytìnae); D, Proctotrùpidae. *B*, basal cell; *C*, costal cell; *MC*, marginal cell; *st*, stigma.

74′. Antennae variable, but usually more or less elbowed; ovipositor issuing from tip of abdomen, usually as a sting (often withdrawn into abdomen and not visible); abdomen variable; venation variable, from much reduced (Figure 29-16 D) to complete (see also 74″) 80

74″. Antennae 11-segmented, elbowed; hind femora greatly thickened; ovipositor curving upward and forward over dorsal side of abdomen; wings folded longitudinally when at rest; venation reduced.. **Leucóspidae*** p. 566

75(21, 68′, 74). First segment of hind tarsi twice as long as the other segments combined, the second segment with a long process on outer side extending to tip of fourth segment (Figure 29-23 B); abdomen compressed, longer than head and thorax combined; antennae 13-segmented in female and 15-segmented in male; 7 to 16 mm in length ....**Ibalìidae*** p. 566

75′. First segment of hind tarsi much shorter, the second segment without a long process on outer side; antennae variable, but usually 13-segmented in female and 14-segmented in male; usually 8 mm in length or less..76

76(75′). Abdomen petiolate and attached far above bases of hind coxae; propodeum with a median furrow; fourth abdominal tergite much lengthened; recorded from Texas and California........**Lioptéridae*** p. 567

76′. Abdomen variable in shape, but attached at apex of propodeum between bases of hind coxae 77

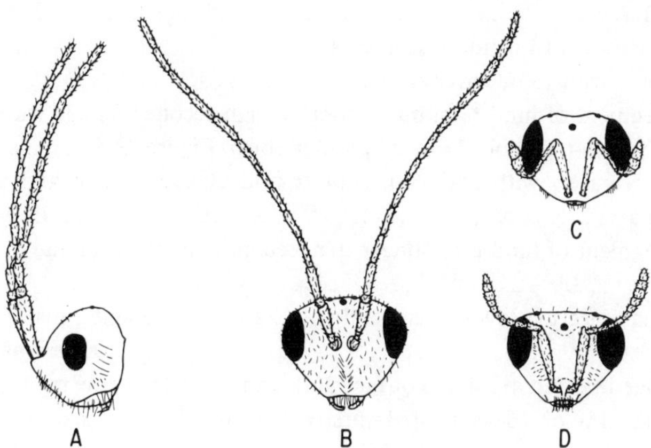

Fig. 29-25. Head structure in the Proctotrupòidea. A, Diaprìidae; B, Proctotrùpidae; C, Platygastéridae; D, Sceliónidae. A, lateral view; B-D, anterior views.

77(76′). Dorsal surface of scutellum with a rounded or oval elevation or keel in center (Figure 29-23 D); cubital vein in front wings arising from base of basal vein; second abdominal tergite longer than third; antennae 11- to 16-segmented, usually 13-segmented in female and 15-segmented in male (Eucoilìnae) .... **Cynípidae** p. 568

77′. Dorsal surface of scutellum not as above; venation, abdominal terga, and antennae variable 78

78(77′). Second abdominal tergite narrow, tongue-shaped, shorter than third (Figure 29-23 C); cubital vein arising from base of basal vein (Aspiceratìnae) .... **Figítidae** p. 567

78′. Second abdominal tergite not tongue-shaped or (some Cynipìnae) tongue-shaped but much longer than third 79

79(78′). Second abdominal tergite at least half as long as abdomen (Figure 29-23 A), or if shorter, then the cubital vein arises from middle of basal vein (Charipìnae and Cynipìnae) .... **Cynípidae** p. 568

79′. Second abdominal tergite less than half as long as abdomen (Figure 29-23 E, F); cubital vein arising from base of basal vein, or lacking (Anacharitìnae and Figitìnae) .... **Figítidae** p. 567

80(74′). Hind wings with venation reduced and without closed cells (Figures 29-16 D and 29-24 A, B, D) 81

80′. Hind wings with normal venation and at least 1 closed cell (Figures 29-24 C and 29-26) 95

81(80). Antennae inserted far above clypeus on a frontal shelf or prominence (Figure 29-25 A); small or minute, usually black insects 82

81′. Antennae usually not inserted on a frontal shelf or prominence and arising either just above clypeus or near middle of face 83

82(81). Marginal cell small or not developed; discoidal vein absent; antennae 11- to 14-segmented, usually clubbed in female; hind wings without a jugal lobe (Figure 29-16 D) (Diapriìnae) .... **Diapriidae** p. 571

82′. Marginal cell large, though not always completely closed; discoidal vein present; antennae 10-segmented; hind wings with a jugal lobe (Emboleminae) .... Dryínidae* p. 573

83(81′). Antennae with 14 or more segments 84

83′. Antennae with 13 or fewer segments 87

84(83). First segment of hind tarsi much shorter than second; female with abdomen very long (about 1½ inches) and filiform (Figure 29-49); male (which is very rare), with abdomen shorter and clavate; black and shining insects .... Pelecínidae p. 570

84′. First segment of hind tarsi longer than second; small or minute insects.. .... 85*

85(84′). Antennae inserted low on face and with 22 to 40 segments; males...... .... Sclerogíbbidae* p. 572

85′. Antennae inserted at middle of face and with 14 to 16 segments...... 86*

86(85′). Antennae 15- or 16-segmented; first discoidal cell triangular; abdomen not compressed (Figure 29-50)........................ Helóridae* p. 571

86′. Antennae 14-segmented; first discoidal cell irregularly 6-sided; abdomen strongly compressed .... Roproniidae* p. 571

87(83′). Mandibles widely separated, not meeting when closed, and when open with tips directed laterally; abdomen with 2 (females) or 4 (males) visible tergites, the first covering most of abdomen...... Vanhorniidae* p. 570

87′. Mandibles normal, the tips meeting when closed.................... 88

88(87′). Antennae inserted at middle of face and 13-segmented (Figure 29-25 B); front wings with a broad stigma and a small marginal cell (Figure 29-24 D); abdomen with a short cylindrical petiole and the second segment much longer than the others........................ Proctotrùpidae p. 571

88′. Antennae inserted near mouth, close to margin of clypeus 89

89(88′). Hind wings with the vannal lobe separated by a deep slitlike incision (Figure 29-24 B) 90

89′. Hind wings narrow, the vannal lobe not separated by a deep incision.. 93

90(89). Antennae 10-segmented; front tarsi of female usually pincerslike........ .... Dryínidae* p. 573

90′. Antennae 12- or 13-segmented; front tarsi not pincerslike........... 91

91(90′). Abdomen with 3 or fewer (4 in males of *Parnòpes*) visible tergites, the last often dentate apically; venter of abdomen concave; body metallic blue or green and with coarse sculpturing.................... Chrysídidae p. 572

91′. Abdomen with 4 to 7 visible tergites; venter of abdomen convex 92*

92(91′). Abdomen with 6 (females) or 7 (males) visible tergites; head usually oblong and elongate .... Bethýlidae* p. 572

92′. Abdomen with 4 (females) or 5 (males) visible tergites (Cleptìnae)...... .... Chrysídidae* p. 572

93(89′). Abdomen rather sharply keeled laterally 94

93′. Abdomen rounded laterally, not keeled .... Ceraphrónidae p. 571

94(93). Antennae with not more than 10 segments; front wings with neither marginal nor stigmal veins, often without any venation; some individuals (females of *Inostémma*, Figure 29-52) with a long handlelike process arising on dorsum of first abdominal segment and extending forward over thorax............................ Platygastéridae p. 572

94′. Antennae usually 11- or 12-segmented; if 7- or 8-segmented, the antennal club is unsegmented; front wings usually with marginal and stigmal

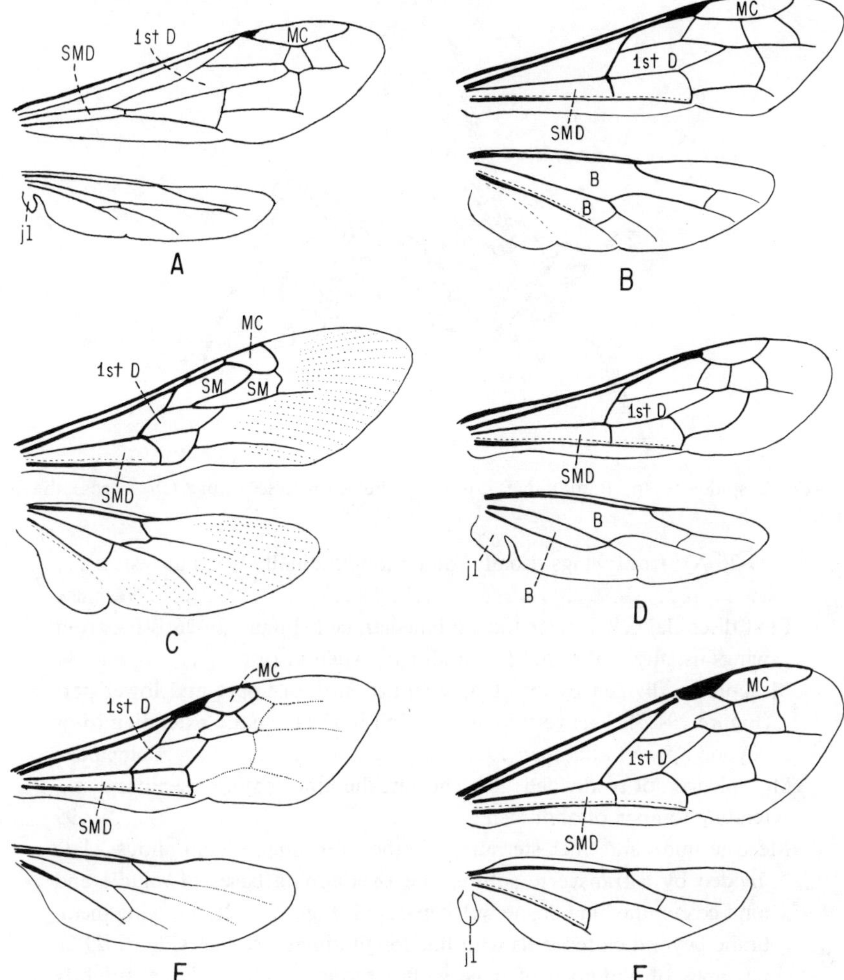

Fig. 29-26. Wings of Vespòidea (A) and Scoliòidea (B-F). A, Véspidae (*Polístes*); B, Tiphìidae (*Mỳzinum*); C, Scolìidae (*Scòlia*); D, Pompílidae; E, Mutíllidae (*Dasymutílla*); F, Tiphìidae (Myrmosìnae). *B*, basal cell; *D*, discoidal cell; *jl*, jugal lobe; *MC*, marginal cell; *SM*, submarginal cell; *SMD*, submedian cell.

	veins; abdomen without a handlelike process as described above.. **Sceliónidae**	p. 572
95(80′).	Antennae with 14 or more segments.............................96	
95′.	Antennae 13-segmented in males and 12-segmented in females........97	
96(95).	Antennae 14- or 15-segmented; usually no closed submarginal cells; 1 closed cell in hind wings (Figure 29-24 C); small black or brown insects (Belytìnae) ....**Diapriidae**	p. 571
96′.	Antennae with 16 or more segments; 2 or 3 submarginal cells; 2 closed cells in hind wings; moderate-sized, often brightly colored insects, with the head large and quadrate ....**Trigonálidae***	p. 573
97(95′).	First discoidal cell very long, much longer than submedian cell (Figure	

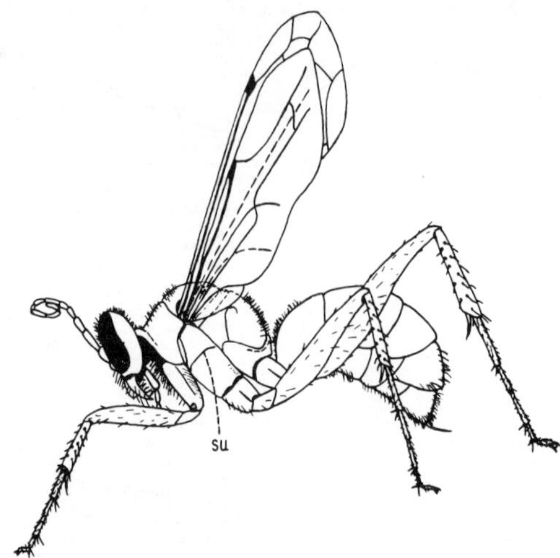

Fig. 29-27. A spider wasp (Pompílidae), showing the transverse suture (*su*) across the mesopleuron.

29-26 A); front wings usually folded longitudinally when at rest...... .... **Véspidae** p. 579

97′. First discoidal cell shorter than submedian cell (Figure 29-26 B-F); front wings usually not folded longitudinally when at rest 98

98(97′). Mesopleura divided by an oblique suture into an upper and lower part (Figure 29-27); legs very long, the hind femora usually extending to or beyond apex of abdomen ....**Pompílidae** p. 582

98′. Mesopleura not so divided; legs shorter, the hind femora usually not extending to apex of abdomen 99

99(98′). Mesosternum and metasternum together forming a continuous plate divided by a transverse suture, and overlapping bases of middle and hind coxae, the hind coxae well separated (Figure 29-28 A); wing membrane beyond closed cells with fine longitudinal wrinkles (Figure 29-26 C); apex of abdomen of male with 3 retractile spines; large, brightly colored wasps..**Scolìidae** p. 574

99′. Mesosternum and metasternum not forming such a plate, though there may be a pair of plates overlying bases of middle coxae; hind coxae contiguous or nearly so; wing membrane beyond closed cells usually not wrinkled; apex of abdomen of male without 3 retractile spines 100

100(99′). Segments of antennal flagellum long and slender, and each segment bearing 2 apical spines; transverse median vein more than two-thirds its length distad of basal vein; second to fourth tarsal segments of female dilated .... **Rhopalosomátidae*** p. 574

100′. Segments of antennal flagellum without apical spines; transverse median vein opposite basal vein, or nearly so (Figure 29-26 E, F); tarsal segments not dilated..101

101(100′). Mesosternum with 2 lobelike extensions behind, which project between and partially cover bases of middle coxae (Figure 29-28 B, *msl*) (Brachycistidìnae, Tiphiìnae, Myzinìnae, and Anthoboscìnae) **Tiphìidae** p. 574

101′. Mesosternum without such lobes, at most a pair of minute, toothlike pro-

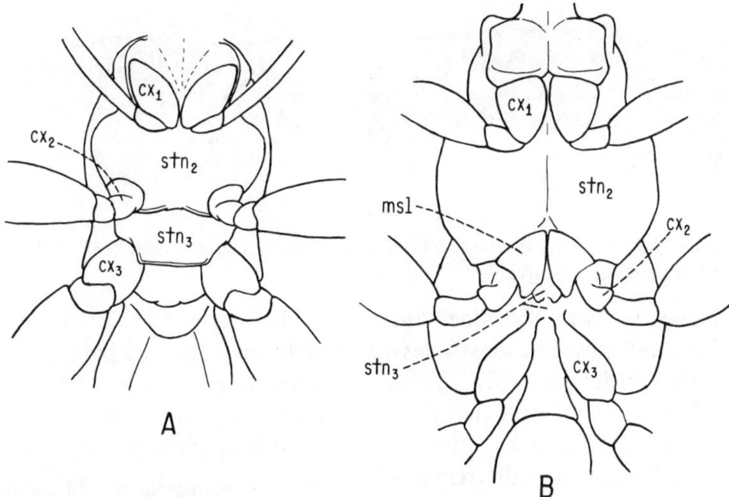

Fig. 29-28. Thorax, ventral view. A, Scolíidae (*Scòlia*); B, Tiphìidae (*Típhia*). *cx*, coxae; *msl*, mesosternal lobe; stn_2, mesosternum; stn_3, metasternum.

jections behind 102

102(101′). Hind wings with a distinct jugal lobe (Figure 29-26 F) 103

102′. Hind wings without a distinct jugal lobe (Figure 29-26 E) 105

103(102). Abdominal segments separated by strong constrictions; eyes usually not emarginate; males (Myrmosìnae and Methochìnae) . . . . **Tiphiidae** p. 574

103′. Abdomen without such constrictions; eyes sometimes emarginate 104

104(103′). Body bare, marked with yellow or white; eyes deeply emarginate . . . . **Sapýgidae*** p. 575

104′. Body usually very hairy; color and eyes variable; males (Apterogynìnae and Pseudophotopsidìnae) . . . . **Mutíllidae** p. 574

105(102′). Shining black wasps, 4.5 to 6.0 mm in length; males and females . . . . **Sierolomórphidae*** p. 574

105′. Body usually very hairy and brightly colored; size variable, but mostly over 6 mm in length; males . . . . **Mutíllidae** p. 574

SUBORDER SÝMPHYTA

The members of this suborder, except for the family Orússidae, are phytophagous, and the majority are external feeders on foliage. The larvae of the external feeders are eruciform (Figure 29-29) and differ from the larvae of the Lepidoptera in that they have more than five pairs of prolegs that lack crochets and usually have only one pair of ocelli. The larvae of a few species bore in stems, fruit, wood, or leaves (leaf miners); these larvae usually have the prolegs reduced or absent. All the Sýmphyta have a well-developed ovipositor, which is used in inserting the eggs into the tissues of the host plant; in the Tenthredinòidea the ovipositor is somewhat sawlike, hence the common name "sawflies" for the members of this group.

Most of the Sýmphyta have a single generation a year and overwinter as a full-grown larva or as a pupa, either in a cocoon or in some sort of protected place; most of the external feeders overwinter in a cocoon or cell in the soil, while boring species usually overwinter in their tunnels in the host plant. Some of the larger species may require more than a year to complete their development.

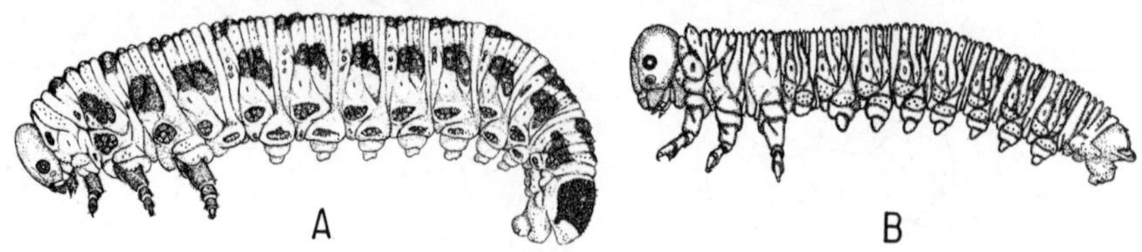

Fig. 29-29. Sawfly larvae. A, *Neodíprion lecóntei* (Fitch) (Dipriónidae); B, *Allántus cínctus* (Linn.) (Tenthredínidae). (Courtesy of USDA.)

FAMILY **Xyélidae:** The Xyélidae are medium-sized to small sawflies, mostly less than 10 millimeters in length, which differ from other sawflies in having three marginal cells (Figure 29-6 C) and the third antennal segment very long (longer than the remaining segments combined) (Figure 29-8 D). Unlike that of all the other sawflies except the Pamphilìidae, the costal cell is divided by a longitudinal vein. The larvae of the xyelids feed on hickory, elm, and in the staminate flowers of pine. This group is a small one, and none of its members is of very great economic importance.

FAMILY **Pamphilìidae**—Web-Spinning and Leaf-Rolling Sawflies: These sawflies are stout-bodied and usually less than 15 millimeters in length. The larvae tie leaves together with silk or roll up a leaf and feed in the shelter so formed. This group is small, and only a few species are of much economic importance. One web-spinning species, *Neurótoma inconspícua* (Norton), feeds on plum; a leaf-rolling species, *Pamphílius pérsicum* MacGillivray, feeds on peach.

FAMILY **Pergidae:** These sawflies have the antennae 6-segmented. This family contains a single genus, *Acordulécera*, the larvae of which are external feeders on the leaves of oak and hickory.

FAMILY **Árgidae:** The Árgidae are a small group of medium-sized to small, stout-bodied sawflies, easily recognized by the characteristic antennae (Figure 29-8 E); a few species have the last antennal segment **U**-shaped or **Y**-shaped. Most of the argids are black or dark-colored. The larvae feed chiefly on various kinds of trees, but one species, *Árge humeràlis* (Beauvois), feeds on poison ivy, and another, *Sphacóphilus cellulàris* (Say), feeds on sweet potato.

FAMILY **Cimbícidae:** The Cimbícidae are large, robust, bumblebeelike sawflies with clubbed antennae. The most common species is the elm sawfly, *Címbex americàna* Leach, a dark-blue insect 18 to 25 millimeters in length (Figure 29-30); the female has four small yellow spots on each side of the abdomen. The full-grown larva of this species is about 1½ inches long, with the diameter of a lead pencil, and is greenish yellow with black spiracles and a black stripe down the back; when at rest or when disturbed, it assumes a spiral position; often, when disturbed, it will eject a fluid, sometimes for a distance of several inches, from glands just above the spiracles. This species has one generation a year and overwinters as a full-grown larva in a cocoon in the ground; it pupates in the spring, and the adults appear in early summer. The larva feeds chiefly on elm and willow.

FAMILY **Dipriónidae**—Conifer Sawflies: These are medium-sized sawflies with 13 or more antennal segments; the antennae are serrate in the female and pectinate or bipectinate in the male (Figures 29-8 C, 29-31). The larvae feed on conifers and may sometimes do serious damage. These insects are relatively rare in the Midwest, but are fairly common elsewhere.

FAMILY **Tenthredínidae**—Typical Sawflies: This is a very large group, and probably

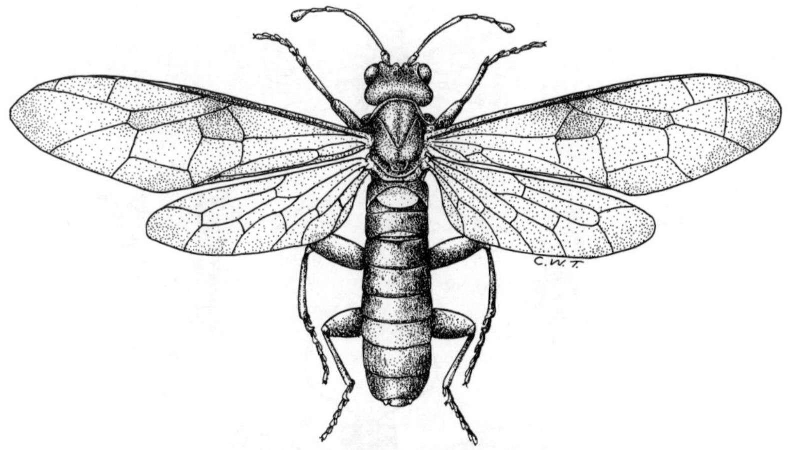

Fig. 29-30. The elm sawfly, *Címbex americàna* Leach, male.

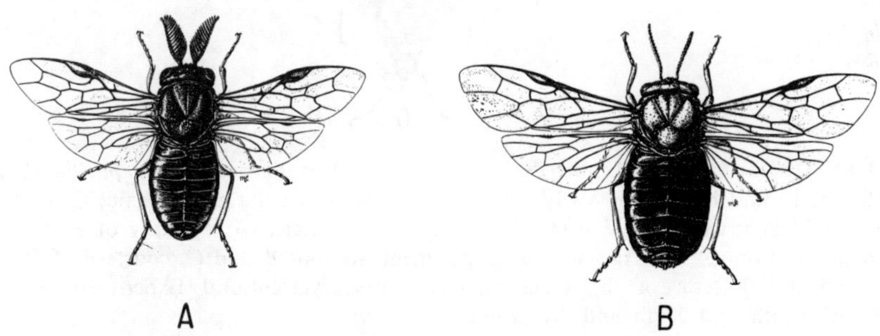

Fig. 29-31. The red-headed pine sawfly, *Neodíprion lecóntei* (Fitch) (Dipriónidae). A, male; B, female. (Courtesy of USDA.)

nine out of ten of the sawflies the general collector is likely to encounter will belong to this family. The adults are wasplike insects, often brightly colored, and are usually found on foliage or flowers; they are medium-sized to small, rarely over 20 millimeters in length. The larvae are eruciform, and most of them are external feeders on foliage; when feeding, they usually have the body (or the posterior part of it) coiled over the edge of the leaf. There is usually a single generation a year, and the insect overwinters in a pupal cell or cocoon, either in the ground or in a protected situation.

Sawfly larvae feed chiefly on various trees and shrubs, and some of them are very destructive. The larch sawfly, *Pristíphora erichsònii* (Hartig), is a very destructive pest of larch and, when numerous, may cause extensive defoliation over large areas. The imported currantworm, *Nématus rìbesii* (Scopoli), is a serious pest of currants and gooseberries.

A few species in this group are gall makers, and a few are leaf miners. Species of the genus *Euùra* form galls on willow, one of the commonest being a small oval gall on the stem. The birch leaf miner (Figure 29-32 A), *Fenùsa pusílla* (Lepeltier), which makes blotch mines in birch, is a serious pest in the northeastern states; it has two or three generations a year and

Fig. 29-32. Typical sawflies (Tenthredínidae). A, birch leaf miner, *Fenùsa pusílla* (Lepeltier), male; B, cherry and hawthorn sawfly, *Profenùsa canadénsis* (Marlatt), female; C, same, male; D, raspberry leaf sawfly, *Prióphorus mòrio* (Lepeltier), female. (A, courtesy of Friend and the Bulletin of the Connecticut Agricultural Experiment Station; B and C, courtesy of Parrot and Fulton and the Bulletin of the Geneva, New York, Agricultural Experiment Station; D, courtesy of Smith and Kido and *Hilgardia.*)

pupates in the ground. The elm leaf miner, *Fenùsa úlmi* Sundevall, mines in elm leaves and frequently does quite a bit of damage.

The family Tenthredínidae is divided into a number of subfamilies, chiefly on the basis of wing venation. The two sexes are differently colored in many species.

FAMILY **Syntéxidae**—Cedar Wood Wasps: This family is represented in the United States by a single species, *Syntéxis libocèdrii* Rohwer, which occurs in California. The adult female is black and 8 millimeters in length; the larva bores in the wood of the incense cedar.

FAMILY **Sirícidae**—Horntails: Horntails are fairly large insects, usually an inch or more in length, and the larvae are wood-boring. Both sexes have a horny spearlike plate on the last abdominal tergite, and the female has a long ovipositor. The most common eastern species is *Trèmex colúmba* (Linn.), a brown and black insect about $1\frac{1}{2}$ inches in length (Figure 29-33 A); the larvae burrow in maple, elm, beech, and other trees, but are seldom sufficiently numerous to do a great deal of damage. Pupation occurs in the burrow made by the larva (Figure 29-33 B).

FAMILY **Xiphydrìidae**—Wood Wasps: The wood wasps are moderate-sized (12 to 20 millimeters in length) cylindrical insects, somewhat similar to the horntails, but lack the horny plate at the apex of the abdomen. The larvae bore in dead and decaying wood of deciduous trees.

FAMILY **Orússidae**—Parasitic Wood Wasps: This is a small group of rare insects, the adults of which are somewhat similar to

A

B

Fig. 29-33. A, an adult horntail, *Trèmex colúmba* (Linn.); B, horntail pupa in the larval gallery. (A, courtesy of Knull; B, courtesy of the Ohio Agricultural Experiment Station.)

the horntails but are considerably smaller (8 to 14 millimeters in length). The larvae as far as known are parasitic on the larvae of the metallic wood-boring beetles (Bupréstidae).

FAMILY **Céphidae**—Stem Sawflies: These are slender, compressed sawflies (Figure 29-34); the larvae bore in the stems of grasses and berries. *Cèphus cínctus* Norton, an insect about 9 millimeters in length, bores in the stems of wheat and is often called the wheat stem sawfly (Figure 29-34 C); the adult is shining black, banded and spotted with yellow. *C. cínctus* is an important wheat pest in the western states; *C. pygmaèus* (Norton), a similar species, occurs in the East. *Jànus ínteger* (Norton) bores in the stems of currants; the adult is shining black and about 13 millimeters in length; there is a single generation a year, and the insect overwinters in a silken cocoon inside the plant in which the larva feeds.

SUBORDER APÓCRITA

The Apócrita differ from the Sýmphyta in having the base of the abdomen constricted, the thorax appearing 4-segmented (with the propodeum representing the first abdominal segment fused with the thorax), and the hind wings with not more than two basal cells. The larval stages are usually grublike or maggotlike and vary in feeding habits. The larvae of some species are parasitic or predaceous on other insects, but many are plant feeders. The adults feed chiefly on flowers, sap, and other plant materials; some of the parasitic species occasionally feed on the body fluids of the host.

A great many species in this suborder are parasitic in the larval stage on other insects (or other invertebrate animals), and because of their abundance are very important from the standpoint of keeping other insects in check. Most of the parasitic Apócrita lay their eggs on or in the body of the host, and many have a long ovipositor with which hosts in cocoons, burrows, or other protected situations may be reached. In some cases only a single egg is laid on a host, while in others several to many eggs may be laid on the same host. A single parasite attacking a host usually pupates inside that host; where there are many parasites in the same host, they may pupate inside it, on the outside of it (Figure 29-37), or even entirely away from it. Some species are parthenogenetic. Polyembryony occurs in a few species; that is, a single egg develops into many larvae. Some of the parasitic Apócrita are hyperparasites; that is, they parasitize an insect that is a parasite of another insect.

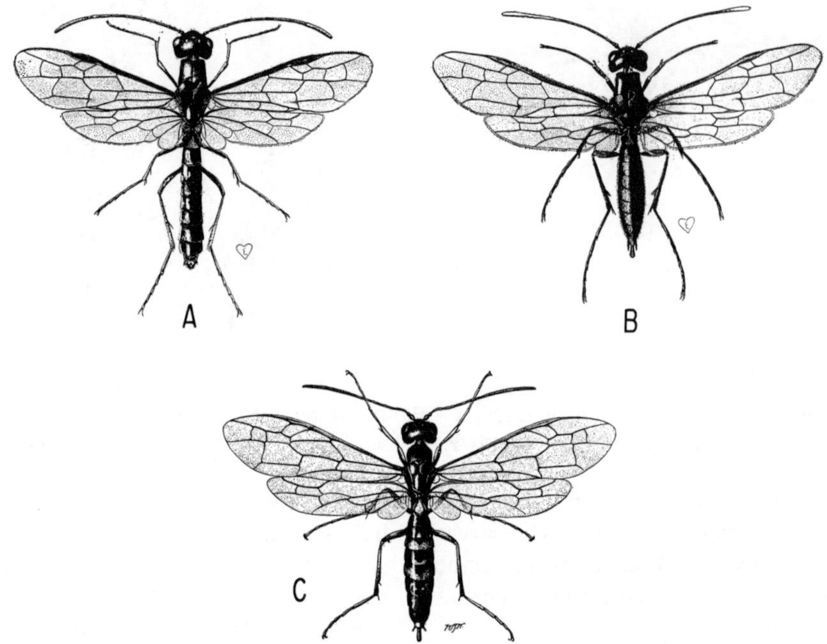

Fig. 29-34. Stem sawflies (Cèphidae). A, *Tràchelus tábidus* (Fabricius), male; B, same, female; C, the wheat stem sawfly; *Cèphus cínctus* Norton, female. (Courtesy of USDA).

All adult female Apócrita are equipped with a piercing ovipositor, but as a rule the females in the superfamilies Ichneumonòidea, Chalcidòidea, Cynipòidea, Proctotrupòidea, and Bethylòidea do not sting man, but the females of the Scoliòidea, Vespòidea, Sphecòidea, and Apòidea usually do. The term "wasp" is often applied to all the Apócrita except the ants (Formícidae) and bees (Apòidea); sometimes this term is used only for the Scoliòidea (excluding the ants), Vespòidea, and Sphecòidea.

SUPERFAMILY ICHNEUMONÒIDEA: This is a very large and important group, and its members are all parasitic on other insects or other invertebrate animals. These insects are wasplike in appearance, but (with rare exceptions) do not sting.

FAMILY **Stephánidae**: The Stephánidae are a small group of rare insects which, so far as known, are parasitic on the larvae of wood-boring Coleoptera. The adults are 5 to 19 millimeters in length and are rather queer-looking insects; the head is spherical and set out on a long neck, and bears a crown of teeth.

FAMILY **Bracónidae**—Braconids: This is a large and beneficial group of parasitic Hymenoptera. The adults are all relatively small (rarely over 15 millimeters in length), and a great many are more stout-bodied than the ichneumons (Figures 29-35, 29-36). They resemble ichneumons in lacking a costal cell, but differ in that they have not more than one recurrent vein (Figure 29-21 C). Many species in this family have been of considerable value in the control of insect pests.

The habits of the braconids are similar to those of the ichneumons. Unlike the ichneumons, however, many of them pupate in silken cocoons on the outside of the body of the host (Figure 29-37) and others spin silken cocoons entirely apart from the host (often many cocoons in a mass). Polyem-

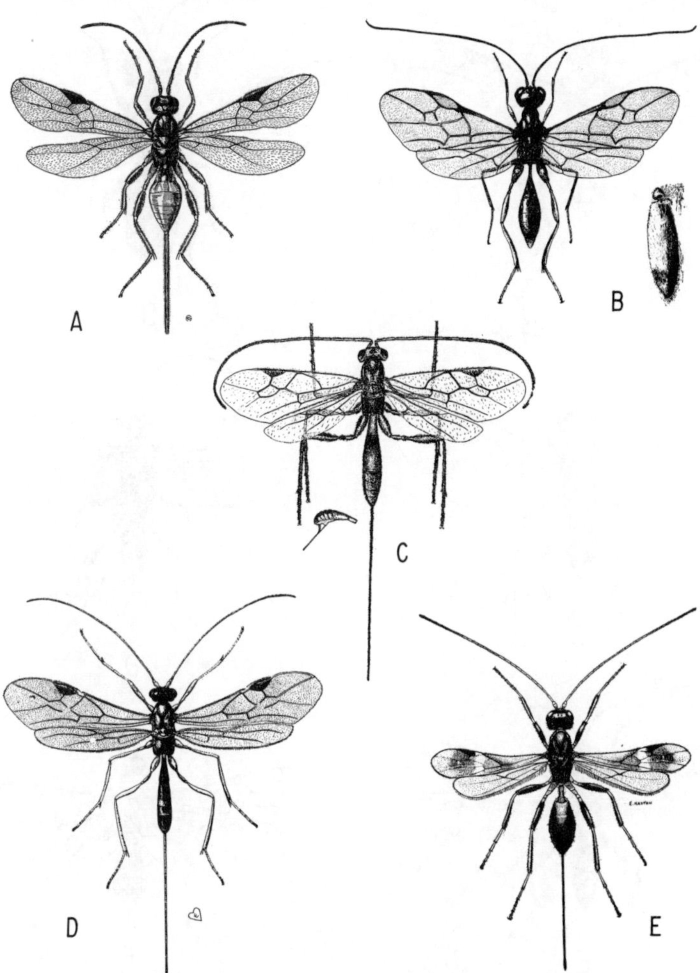

Fig. 29-35. Bracónidae. A, *Coelòides dendróctoni* Cushman, female (Braconìnae), a parasite of bark beetles (Scolýtidae); B, *Metèorus nigricóllis* Thomson, male (Euphorìnae), a parasite of the European corn borer (insert shows cocoon); C, *Macrocéntrus ancylívorus* Rohwer, female (Macrocentrìnae) (insert, lateral view of abdomen), a parasite of various tortricid moths; D, *Macrocéntrus gifuénsis* Ashmead, female, a parasite of the European corn borer; E, *Spàthius canadénsis* Ashmead, female, a parasite of bark beetles (Scolýtidae). (A, courtesy of DeLeon and the New York Entomological Society; B, courtesy of Parker and the Entomological Society of Washington; C and D, courtesy of USDA; E, courtesy of Kaston and the Connecticut Agriculture Experimental Station.)

bryony occurs in a few species, chiefly in the genus *Macrocéntrus* (Figure 29-35 C, D); each egg of *M. gifuénsis* Ashmead, a parasite of the European corn borer, develops into from 16 to 24 parasite larvae.

The family Bracónidae is divided into about 20 subfamilies, some of which may be mentioned here. The Macrocentrìnae, Agathidìnae, Chelonìnae, Microgasterìnae, and Rogadìnae (Rhogadìnae) are chiefly parasites of lepidopterous larvae. The gregarious forms of the Macrocentrìnae are polyembryonic; in the Chelonìnae the egg is laid in the host egg, and the parasite matures when the host reaches maturity. *Chélonus texànus* Cresson (Figure 29-36 B) is a para-

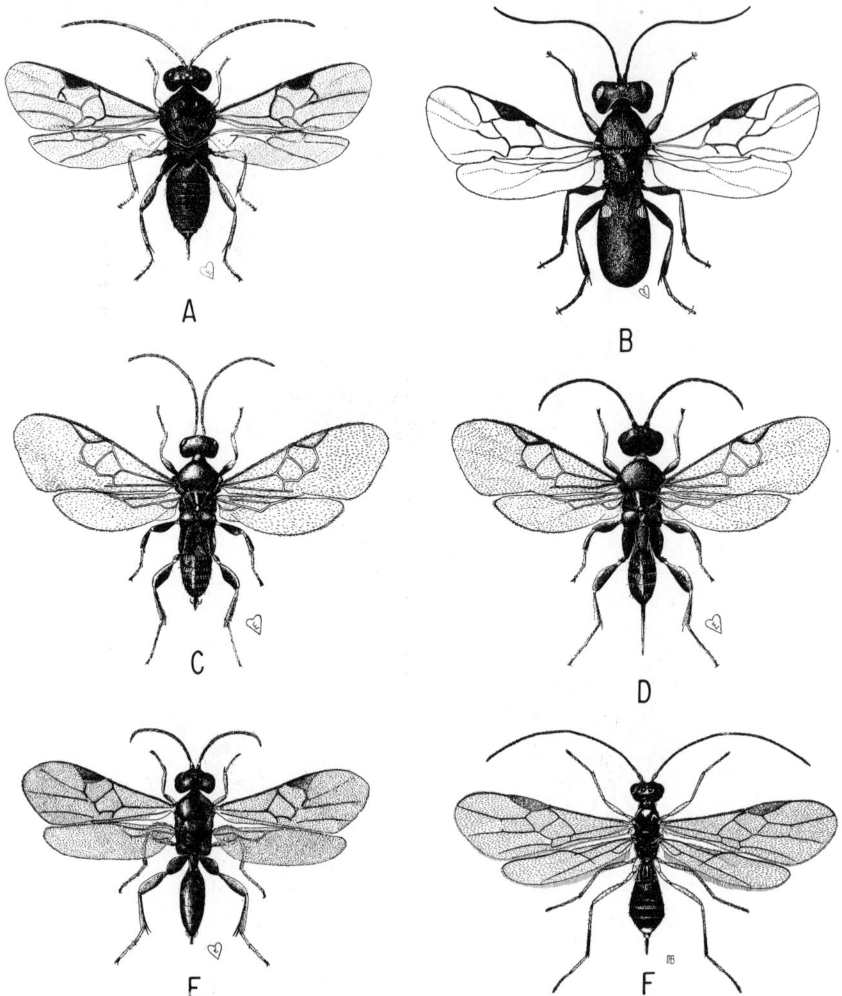

Fig. 29-36. Bracónidae. A, *Microgáster tibiàlis* Nees, female (Microgasterìnae), a parasite of the European corn borer; B, *Chélonus texànus* Cresson (Chelonìnae), a parasite of various noctuid moth larvae; C, *Apánteles diatraèae* Muesebeck, male (Microgasterìnae), a parasite of the southwestern corn borer, *Diatraèa grandiosélla* Dyar; D, same, female; E, *Apánteles thómpsoni* Lyle, female, a parasite of the European corn borer; F, *Phanómeris phyllótomae* Muesebeck, female (Rogadìnae), a parasite of birch leaf-mining sawflies. (A, courtesy of Vance and the Entomological Society of America; others, courtesy of USDA.)

site of the larvae of various noctuid moths; species of *Apánteles* (Microgasterìnae) (Figure 29-36 C-E) are parasitic on the corn borer and similar pests; *Phanómeris phyllótomae* Muesebeck (Figure 29-36 F) is a parasite of the birch leaf-mining sawflies. The Helconìnae, Spathiìnae, and Doryctìnae are parasitic on beetle larvae, the Helconìnae attacking chiefly wood-boring beetles; *Spàthius canadénsis* Ashmead (Figure 29-35 E) is a parasite of bark beetles (Scolýtidae). The Ichneutìnae are parasites of sawflies; the Dacnusìnae, Alysiìnae, and Opiìnae are parasitic on Diptera; the Opiìnae parasitize chiefly flies in the families Tephrítidae and Agromýzidae. Other braconids parasitize ants, bugs, or other insects.

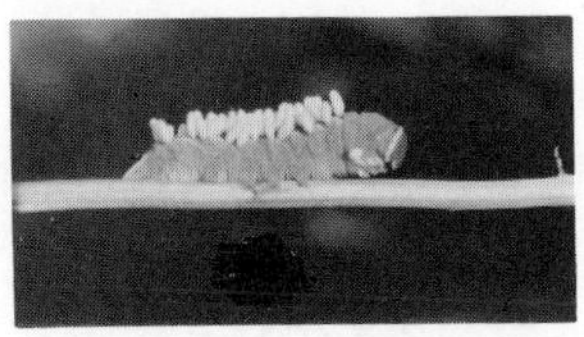

Fig. 29-37. A parasitized sphinx moth larva; the white objects on the larva are cocoons of braconids, probably *Apánteles* sp.

FAMILY **Ichneumónidae**—Ichneumons: This family is one of the largest in the entire insect class, with four or five thousand species occurring in the United States, and its members are to be found almost everywhere. The adults vary considerably in size, form, and coloration, but the majority resemble slender wasps (Figures 29-38, 29-39). They differ from the wasps that sting (Scoliòidea, Vespòidea, and Sphecòidea) in that they have the antennae longer and with more segments (16 or more in ichneumons, usually 12 or 13 in wasps), have the trochanters 2-segmented (one-segmented in the stinging wasps), and lack a costal cell in the front wings. In many ichneumons (Figure 29-38 A) the ovipositor is quite long, often longer than the body, and it arises anterior to the tip of the abdomen and is permanently extruded; in the stinging wasps, the ovipositor issues from the tip of the abdomen and is withdrawn into the abdomen when not in use. In most ichneumons the first submarginal cell is fused with the first discoidal cell, owing to the loss of a part of the cubital vein, and the second submarginal cell, lying opposite the second recurrent vein, is often quite small (Figure 29-21 A, *are*); this small submarginal cell (called the areolet) is lacking in some ichneumons (Figure 29-21 B). The ichneumons differ from the braconids in having two recurrent veins; the braconids have only one or none (Figure 29-21 C). In many species there is a considerable difference in the appearance of the two sexes; they may differ in color, size, body form, or even in the presence of wings.

The ichneumons attack a great variety of hosts, though most individual species attack only a few types of hosts. There are few groups of insects that are not parasitized by some ichneumon, and some species in this family attack spiders. Most ichneumons are internal parasites of the immature stages of the host. The parasite may complete its development in the stage of the host in which the egg is laid, or in a later stage.

The family Ichneumónidae is divided into over a dozen subfamilies; no attempt will be made here to distinguish these subfamily groups, since there are differences of opinion about the exact limits of some subfamilies. We note here only some of the more important or striking types in the family.

The largest ichneumons in the United States belong to the tribe Rhyssìni of the subfamily Pimplìnae (Ephialtìnae); some of these may be $1\frac{1}{2}$ inches or more in body length, and the ovipositor may be twice as long as the body. These insects are parasitic on the larvae of horntails, wood wasps, and various wood-boring Coleoptera; the long ovipositor is used in getting the eggs of the ichneumon into the tunnels of the host, and the ovipositor may sometimes penetrate a half-inch or more of wood. It is a little difficult to imagine the hairlike ovipositor of these insects being pushed through wood, but the process takes place nevertheless. The genus *Megarhýssa* contains several species that parasitize horntails; *Rhyssélla nítida* (Cresson) (Figure 29-38 A) attacks wood wasps (Xiphydrìidae).

Some of the other Pimplìnae are parasitic on lepidopterous larvae, some (especially those in the tribe Polysphinctìni) are parasitic on spiders, and some parasitize wood-boring Coleoptera.

Most of the ichneumons in the subfamily Tryphonìnae are parasitic on sawflies; *Phytodiètus vulgàris* Cresson (Figure 29-38 C) is a parasite of tortricid moths. Some members of this subfamily carry their eggs on the ovipositor, attached by short

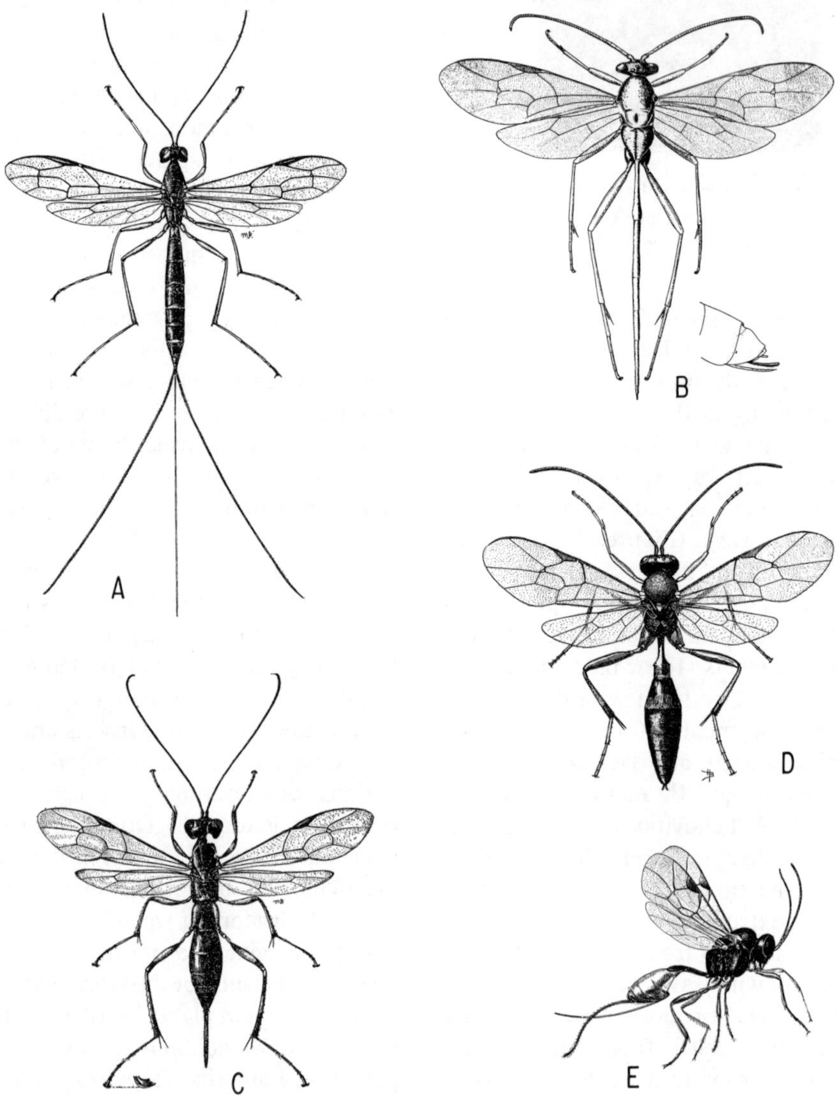

Fig. 29-38. Ichneumónidae. A, *Rhyssélla nítida* (Cresson), female (Pimplìnae, Rhyssìni); B, *Casinària texàna* (Ashmead), female (Ophionìnae) (insert shows tip of abdomen in lateral view); C, *Phytodiètus vulgàris* Cresson, female (Tryphonìnae); D, *Phobocámpe dísparis* (Viereck), female (Ophionìnae); E, *Tersílochus conotràcheli* (Riley), female (Ophionìnae). (A and C, courtesy of Rohwer; B, courtesy of Walley; D and E, courtesy of USDA; A, courtesy of the U.S. National Museum; B, courtesy of *Scientific Agriculture*; C, courtesy of the U.S. National Museum.)

stalks; when a suitable host is found, the eggs are attached to the skin of the host by a stalk, and if no host is found, the eggs may be discarded. The parasite larvae usually complete their development in the cocoon of the host.

The members of the subfamily Cryptìnae (Gelìnae) are mostly external parasites of pupae in cocoons; a few are parasitic on wood-boring beetle larvae, a few attack dipterous larvae, and a few are hyperparasites of braconids or other ichneumons. The

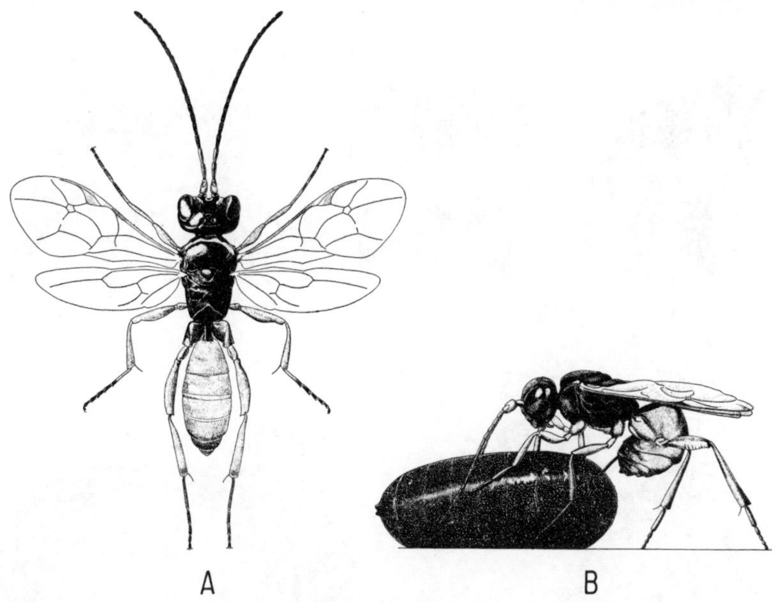

Fig. 29-39. A hyperparasitic ichneumon, *Phygadeùon subfúscus* Cresson (Cryptìnae). A, adult male; B, female ovipositing in puparium of host. The host of this ichneumon is a tachinid fly, *Paradexòdes epiláchnae* Aldrich, which is parasitic on the Mexican bean beetle, *Epiláchna varivéstis* Mulsant (see Fig. 27-85). (Courtesy of USDA.)

members of the subfamily Ichneumonìnae (Joppìnae, Phaeogenìnae) are internal parasites of Lepidoptera; they oviposit in either the host larva or pupa, but always emerge from the host pupa. Most species in this subfamily have the two sexes quite different in appearance. The Lissonotìnae (Banchìnae) are internal parasites of caterpillars; the Scolobatìnae (Mesoleiìnae) are chiefly parasites of sawflies, ovipositing in the host larva and emerging from its cocoon; the Plectiscìnae (Microleptìnae) are parasitic on fungus gnats (Mycetophílidae and Sciáridae); the Diplazonìnae are parasitic on Sýrphidae, laying their eggs in the egg or young larva of the host and emerging from the puparium of the host.

Many members of the subfamily Ophionìnae have a very compressed abdomen and a short, very sharp ovipositor. Most ichneumons when handled will attempt to sting by poking at one's fingers with their ovipositor, but in most cases this can scarely be felt. However, the ovipositor of some of the Ophionìnae can actually penetrate one's skin, and the effect is much like a sharp pin prick. The larger ichneumons of this group are thus able to "sting."

The majority of the Ophionìnae are parasites of lepidopterous larvae. *Casinària texàna* (Ashmead) (Figure 29-38 B) is a parasite of the saddleback caterpillar, *Síbine stimùlea* Clemens; *Phobocámpe dísparis* (Viereck) (Figure 29-38 D) is a parasite of the gypsy moth. *Tersílochus conotràcheli* (Riley) (Figure 29-38 E) is a parasite of the plum curculio.

SUPERFAMILY CHALCIDÒIDEA — Chalcids: The chalcids constitute a very large and important group of insects. Nearly all are very small, and some are quite minute; some of the Mymáridae, for example, are less than 0.5 millimeter in length. Chalcids are to be found almost everywhere, but because of their small size they are frequently overlooked—or discarded—by the beginning student. The majority of the chalcids are only about 2 or 3 millimeters in length, though a few (for example, some of the

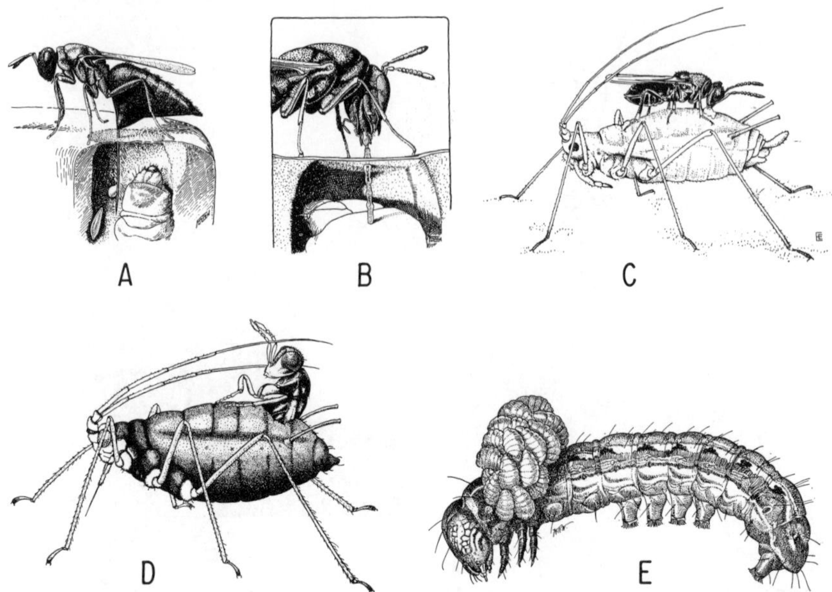

Fig. 29-40. Feeding and emerging chalcids. A, *Habrócytus* (Pteromálidae) ovipositing; B, *Habrócytus* feeding at the tube made by her ovipositor; C, *Zarhópalus inquísitor* (Howard) (Encýrtidae) feeding at an oviposition puncture made in the abdomen of an aphid; D, adult of *Aphelìnus jucúndus* Gahan (Eulóphidae) emerging from an aphid; E, a colony of *Euplèctrus* larvae (Eulóphidae) feeding on a caterpillar. (A and B, courtesy of Fulton and the Entomological Society of America; C and D, courtesy of Griswold and the Entomological Society of America; E, courtesy of USDA.)

Leucóspidae) may reach 10 or 15 millimeters in length. The members of this group occur in a variety of situations, chiefly on flowers and foliage, and it is seldom that one can sweep through vegetation without coming up with a few of them. They generally hold the wings flat over the abdomen when at rest, and many appear to jump when they take flight.

The chalcids can generally be recognized by the characteristic wing venation (Figure 29-16 B); the antennae are usually elbowed and never contain more than 13 segments; the pronotum is somewhat collarlike and does not reach the tegulae, and there is usually a prepectus present in the side of the thorax (Figure 29-4 A). Most of the chalcids are dark-colored, and many are metallic blue or green in color. Most species are clear-winged. There is a great deal of variation in body shape in this group (Figures 29-19, 29-20, 29-41—29-45), and some chalcids have rather peculiar, even grotesque, shapes. The wings are reduced or lacking in some of the chalcids.

Most of the chalcids are parasitic on other insects, attacking chiefly the egg or larval stage of the host. Most of the hosts are in the orders Lepidoptera, Diptera, Coleoptera, and Homoptera, and since these orders contain most of the crop pests, it can be seen that the chalcids are a very beneficial group in that they aid in keeping pests in check. Many species have been imported into this country to act as a means of controlling various insect pests.

This superfamily is divided into a number of families; some families consist of distinctive-looking insects and are easily recognized, but in most cases the separation

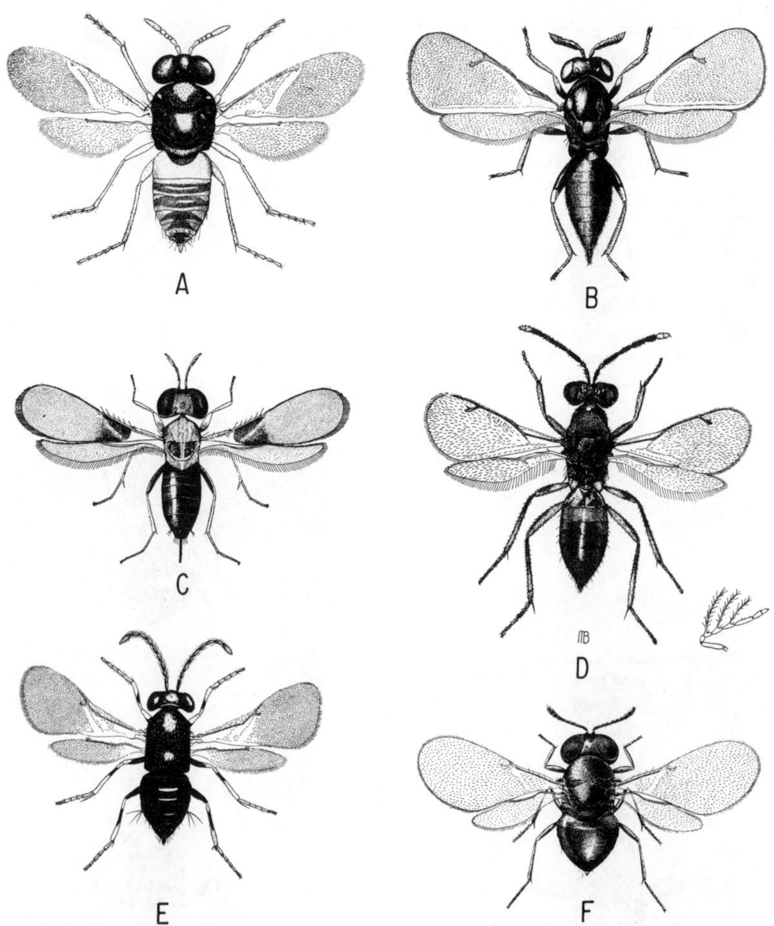

Fig. 29-41. Chalcidòidea; A-D, Eulóphidae; E, F, Encýrtidae. A, *Aphelìnus jucúndus,* Gahan, female, a parasite of aphids; B, *Tetrástichus bruchóphagi* Gahan, a parasite of the clover seed chalcid, *Bruchóphagus gíbbus* (Boheman); C, *Centródora speciosíssima* (Girault), female, a parasite of the cecidomyiids and chalcids which attack wheat; D, *Hemiptársenus aneméntus* (Walker), female, a parasite of leaf-mining sawflies; E, *Zarhópalus inquísitor* (Howard), male, a parasite of aphids and mealybugs; F, *Ooencýrtus kuwánai* (Howard), female, an imported parasite of the gypsy moth. (A and E, courtesy of Griswold and the Entomological Society of America; others, courtesy of USDA.)

of families is very difficult. There are differences of opinion among entomologists about the limits of some of the families.

FAMILY **Mymáridae**—Fairyflies: The fairyflies are very tiny insects, mostly less than a millimeter in length, with the hind wings linear (Figure 29-16 C). All are egg parasites, and some species parasitize the eggs of aquatic insects. This group contains some of the smallest insects known; one species of *Aláptus* has a body length of 0.21 millimeter (about a hundredth of an inch).

FAMILY **Trichogrammátidae:** The Trichogrammátidae are very tiny insects, 0.3 to 1.0 millimeter in length, and may be recognized by the 3-segmented tarsi, the microscopic hairs of the wings usually being arranged in rows, and the rather short head that is somewhat concave behind. The members of this group are egg parasites. Some species have

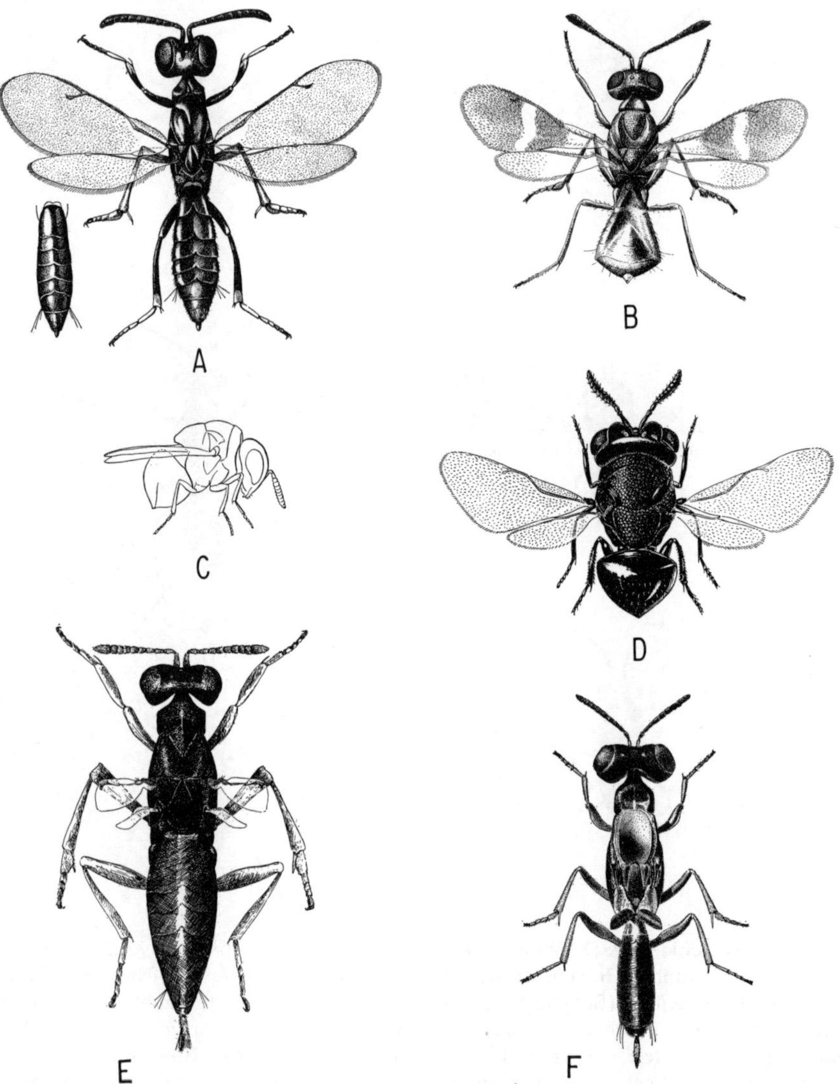

Fig. 29-42. Chalcidòidea; A, B, E, F, Eupélmidae; C, D, Perilámpidae. A, *Eupélmus allýnii* (French), female (insert is abdomen of male), a parasite of the hessian fly; B, *Anastàtus bifasciàtus* Fonscolomb, an imported egg parasite of the gypsy moth; C, *Perilámpus platygáster* Say, a hyperparasite attacking *Metèorus dimidiàtus* Cresson, a braconid parasite of the grape leaf folder, *Désmia funeràlis* Hübner (Pyrálidae), lateral view; D, same, dorsal view; E, *Eupélmus atropurpùreus* Dalman, female, a parasite of the hessian fly; F, *Eupelmélla vesiculàris* (Retzius), female, which parasitizes insects in the orders Coleoptera, Lepidoptera, and Hymenoptera. (Courtesy of USDA.)

been reared in large numbers to aid in the control of certain orchard pests.

FAMILY **Eulóphidae:** The Eulóphidae are a large group of rather small insects (1 to 3 millimeters in length); they are parasitic on a wide variety of hosts, including a number of major crop pests (Figures 29-40 D, E and 29-41 A-D). They may be recognized by the 4-segmented tarsi (Figure 29-18 A),

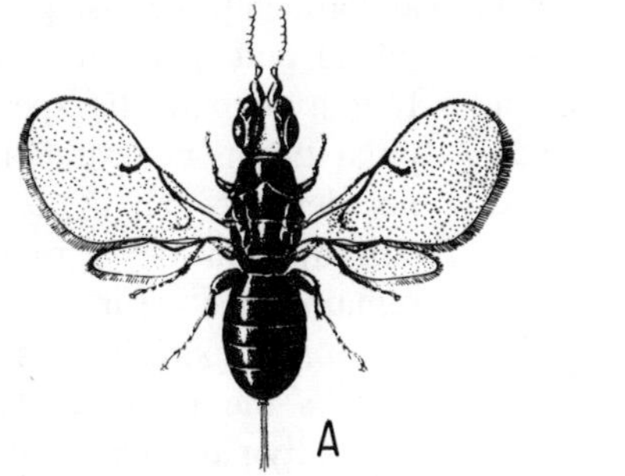

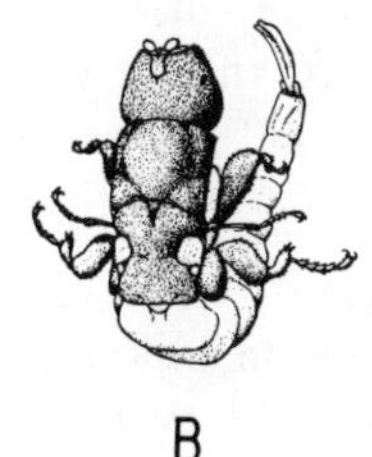

Fig. 29-43. The fig wasp, *Blastóphagus psènes* (Linn.). A, female; B, male. (Courtesy of Condit and the California Agricultural Experiment Station.)

and the axillae extending forward beyond the tegulae (Figure 29-17 B); many have a brilliant metallic coloring, and the males of many species have pectinate antennae.

Some of the eulophids are hyperparasites, and there are some interesting phenomena regarding hyperparasitism and sex in the eulophids that attack scale insects. In the genus *Coccóphagus,* the females develop as parasites of scale insects, while the males develop as hyperparasites attacking parasites of scale insects, often females of their own species!

FAMILY **Elásmidae:** The Elásmidae are small, black or brown, elongate insects that are somewhat triangular in cross-section. They are parasites of lepidopterous larvae, or hyperparasites, attacking ichneumons or braconids that parasitize lepidopterous larvae.

FAMILY **Thysánidae:** The Thysánidae are small stout-bodied chalcids that are parasitic on scale insects, whiteflies, and other Homoptera or hyperparasites of the chalcids parasitizing Homoptera.

FAMILY **Eutrichosomátidae** AND **Tanaostigmátidae:** The families Eutrichosomátidae and Tanaostigmátidae are small groups and have been recorded only from the West and from Florida. These chalcids are parasitic on snout beetles (Curculiónidae).

FAMILY **Encýrtidae:** The Encýrtidae are a large and widespread group. The encyrtids are 1 to 2 millimeters in length and can usually be recognized by the broad convex mesopleura (Figure 29-19 B); in most of the chalcids the mesopleura have a groove for the femora, but this groove is lacking in the encyrtids (also lacking in the thysanids, eutrichosomatids, tanaostigmatids, and eupelmids). The encyrtids differ from the eupelmids in that they have the mesonotum convex and lack or have incomplete the parapsidal furrows. Most of the encyrtids are parasitic on aphids, scale insects, and whiteflies, but the group contains species that attack insects in other orders [for example, *Ooencýrtus kuwánai* (Howard), Figure 29-41 F, is a parasitic of the gypsy moth]. A few are hyperparasites. Polyembryony occurs in a number of species, with from ten to over a thousand young developing from a single egg.

FAMILY **Eupélmidae:** The Eupélmidae are a large group, and some species are fairly common. They are similar to the encyrtids, but have the mesonotum flatter and parapsidal furrows are present (Figure 29-42 A, B, E, F). Some of them are wingless or have very short wings (Figure 29-42 E, F). Many of the eupelmids are good jumpers and often tumble about after jumping, before gaining a foothold; their jumping seems to be aided by their ability to bend the head and abdomen up over the thorax, much as do the click beetles. The wingless or short-winged forms, when killed in a cyanide bottle, usually die with the head and abdomen bent up over the thorax. The members of this group parasitize a wide variety of hosts; a number of species are known which attack hosts in several different orders. A few are parasitic on spiders.

FAMILY **Eucharítidae:** The Eucharítidae, though not very common, are rather distinctive-looking insects with very interesting habits. They are fair-sized (at least for a chalcid), black or metallic blue or green in color, with the abdomen petiolate and the scutellum often spined; the thorax often appears somewhat humpbacked (Figure 29-19 D). These chalcids are parasitic on the pupae of ants. The eggs are laid, usually in large numbers, on leaves or buds and hatch into tiny flattened larvae called planidia. These planidia simply lie in wait on the vegetation or on the ground and attach to passing ants, which carry them to the ant nest. Once in the ant nest, the planidia leave the worker ant that brought them there and attach to ant larvae; they do little or no feeding on the larvae of the ant, but feed after the larva has pupated.

FAMILY **Perilámpidae:** The Perilámpidae are stout-bodied chalcids with the thorax large and coarsely punctate, and the abdomen small, shiny, and triangular (Figures 29-20 B and 29-42 C, D). Some are metallic green in color and resemble cuckoo wasps (Chrysídidae), and others are black; they are frequently found on flowers. Most of the perilampids are hyperparasites, attacking the Diptera and Hymenoptera that parasitize caterpillars; a few are parasitic on free-living insects in various orders. *Perilámpus platygáster* Say (Figure 29-42 C, D) is a hyperparasitic species; it attacks *Metèorus dimidiàtus* Cresson, a braconid parasite of the grape-leaf folder. The perilampids, like the eucharitids, lay their eggs on foliage, and the eggs hatch into larvae of the planidium type (small, flattened, able to go without feeding for a considerable time); these planidia remain on the foliage and attach to a passing host (usually a caterpillar) and penetrate into its body cavity. If a hyperparasitic species enters a caterpillar that is not parasitized, it usually does not develop, but if the caterpillar is parasitized, then the perilampid larva usually remains inactive in the caterpillar until the caterpillar parasite has pupated, and then attacks the parasite. The perilampids are generally parasites of the pupae of tachinids, braconids, or ichneumons.

FAMILY **Agaónidae**—Fig Insects: This group is represented in the United States by two species, *Blastóphagus psènes* (Linn.) and *Secundeisènia mexicàna* (Ashmead); the former occurs in California and Arizona, and the latter in Florida. *B. psènes* (Figure 29-43) was introduced into the United States to make possible the production of certain varieties of figs. The Smyrna fig, which is grown extensively in California, produces fruit only when it is pollinated with pollen from the wild fig, or caprifig, and the pollination is done entirely by fig insects. The fig insect develops in a gall at the base of the caprifig flowers; the female, in emerging from the gall, becomes covered with caprifig pollen. The female visits a number of flowers, including those of the Smyrna fig, but lays its eggs only in the flowers of the wild fig. Fig growers usually aid in the process of Smyrna fig pollination by placing in their fig trees branches of the wild fig; when the fig insects emerge from the wild fig, they are almost certain to visit the flowers of the Smyrna fig and thus pollinate them.

FAMILY **Torýmidae:** The torymids are somewhat elongate, metallic-green insects 2 to 4 millimeters in length, with a long ovipositor; the hind coxae are very large, and there are distinct parapsidal sutures on the thorax (Figures 29-17 A and 29-44 A-C). This group includes both parasitic and phytophagous species; the Torymìnae, Erimerìnae, and Monodontomerìnae parasitize gall insects and caterpillars; the

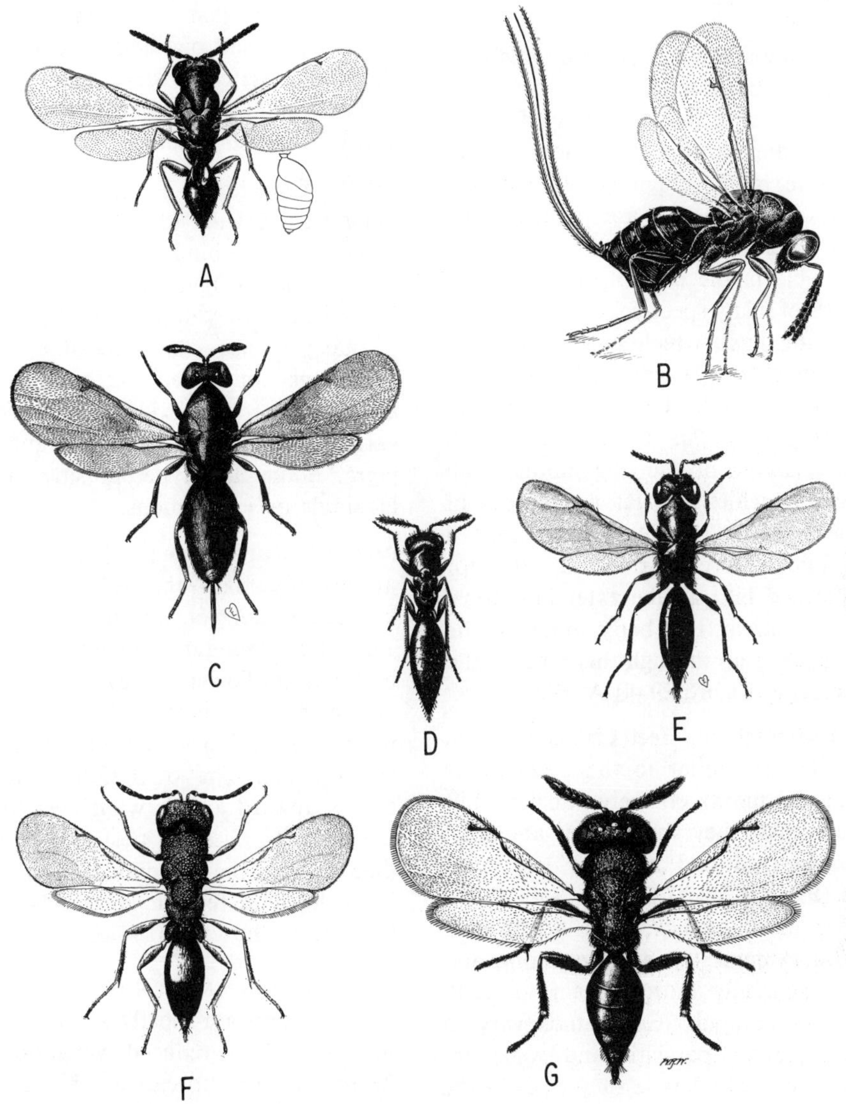

Fig. 29-44. Chalcidòidea; A-C, Torýmidae; D-G, Eurytómidae. A, *Tórymus drupàrum* Boheman, the apple seed chalcid, male (insert is lateral view of abdomen); B, same, female; C, *Liodontómerus perpléxus* Gahan, female, a parasite of the clover seed chalcid (G in this figure); D, *Harmólita grándis minùta* (Howard), the wheat straw-worm, a wingless female; E, *Harmólita trítici* (Fitch), female, the wheat jointworm; F, *Eurýtoma phoèbus* Girault, female, a parasite of the hessian fly and the wheat jointworm (E in this figure); G, the clover seed chalcid, *Bruchóphagus gíbbus* (Boheman). (Courtesy of USDA.)

Podagrionìnae are parasites of mantid eggs; and the Idarnìnae and Megastigmìnae attack seeds.

FAMILY **Ormýridae:** The Ormýridae are similar to the Torýmidae, but have the parapsidal sutures indistinct or lacking and have a very short ovipositor. They are parasitic on gall insects.

FAMILY **Pteromálidae:** The Pteromálidae are a large group of minute black or metallic-green or bronze insects, many of which have the abdomen appearing more or less triangular in profile (Figures 29-20 D and 29-40 A). These insects are parasitic and attack a wide variety of hosts; many are very valuable in the control of crop pests. The adults of many species feed on the body fluids of the host, which exude from the puncture made by the parasite's ovipositor (as in Figure 29-40 C); in the case of *Habrócytus cerealéllae* (Ashmead), which parasitizes larvae of the angoumois grain moth and in which the larvae are out of reach of the adult parasite (in the seed), a viscous fluid is secreted from the ovipositor and is formed into a tube extending down to the host larva. The body fluids of the host are sucked up through this tube by the adult parasite (Figure 29-40 A, B).

FAMILY **Eurytómidae**—Seed Chalcids: The eurytomids are similar to the perilampids in having the thorax coarsely punctate, but differ in that they have the abdomen rounded or oval and more or less compressed (Figures 29-20 C and 29-44 D-G). They are usually black, with the thorax, head, and antennae often rather hairy, and they are generally more slender in build than the perilampids. Eurytomids vary in habits; some are parasitic and some are phytophagous. The larvae of species in the genus *Harmólita* (Figure 29-44 D, E) feed in the stems of grasses, sometimes producing galls on the stems; some of these insects are often serious pests of wheat. The clover seed chalcid, *Bruchóphagus gibbus* (Boheman) (Figure 29-44 G), infests the seeds of clover and other legumes. A few species in this group are hyperparasites.

FAMILY **Chalcedéctidae:** The Chalcedéctidae are similar to the Chalcídidae and Leucóspidae in having the hind femora swollen and toothed, but they differ from them in that they have the hind coxae little, if any, larger than the front coxae. This group is a small one and is represented in the United States by four species that occur in Texas and California; the larvae are parasitic on buprestid beetles.

FAMILY **Chalcídidae:** The Chalcídidae are fair-sized chalcids (2 to 7 millimeters in length) with the hind femora greatly swollen and toothed (Figures 29-18 E, 29-20 A, 29-45 I), and they differ from the leucospids in that they have the ovipositor short and the wings not folded longitudinally when at rest. The chalcidids are parasitic on various Lepidoptera, Diptera, and Coleoptera. Some are hyperparasitic, attacking tachinids or ichneumons.

FAMILY **Leucóspidae:** The Leucóspidae are usually black-and-yellow insects, and they are parasitic on various bees and wasps. They are rather rare, but may occasionally be found on flowers. They are stout-bodied and have the wings folded longitudinally when at rest, and look a little like a small yellowjacket. The ovipositor is long and curves upward and forward over the abdomen, ending over the posterior part of the thorax. Like the chalcidids, the leucospids have the hind femora greatly swollen and toothed on the ventral side.

SUPERFAMILY CYNIPÒIDEA: The members of this group are mostly small or minute insects with a reduced venation (Figure 29-16 A); most species are black, and the abdomen is usually shiny and somewhat compressed. The antennae are filiform, the pronotum extends back to the tegulae, and the ovipositor issues from anterior to the apex of the abdomen. Of the nearly 800 species in this group in the United States, over 600 (all in the subfamily Cynipìnae) are gall makers or gall inquilines; the others, as far as is known, are parasitic.

FAMILY **Ibalìidae:** The ibaliids are relatively large (7 to 16 millimeters in length) and have the abdomen somewhat elongate;

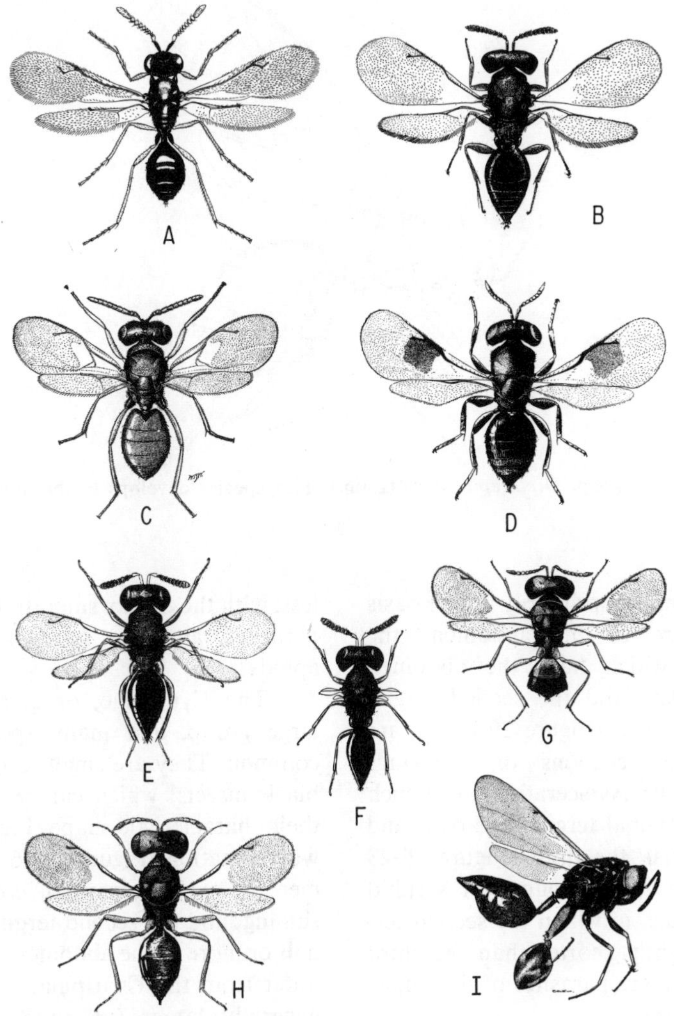

Fig. 29-45. Chalcidòidea; A-H, Pteromálidae; I, Chalcídidae. A, *Ásaphes americànus* Girault, male, a parasite of aphids; B, *Bubékia fállax* Gahan, female, a parasite of the hessian fly; C, *Pterómalus eùrymi* Gahan, a parasite of the alfalfa caterpillar, *Còlias eurýtheme* Boisduval; D, *Merisóporus chalcidóphagus* (Walsh and Riley), female, a parasite of the hessian fly; E, *Eupterómalus subápterus* (Riley), female, a parasite of the hessian fly; F, same, a subapterous female; G, *Callítula bìcolor* Spinola, male, a parasite of various flies and platygasterids; H, same, female; I, *Spilachálcis flavopícta* (Cresson), a parasite of various Coleoptera, Lepidoptera, and Hymenoptera. (A, courtesy of Griswold and the Entomological Society of America; others, courtesy of USDA.)

they are parasitic on horntails, and are not very common.

FAMILY **Lioptéridae:** These insects have the abdomen petiolate and attached far above the bases of the hind coxae. Three rare species occur in Texas and California; their immature stages are unknown.

FAMILY **Figítidae:** The members of this group are parasites of the pupae of lacewings and Diptera. The family is divided

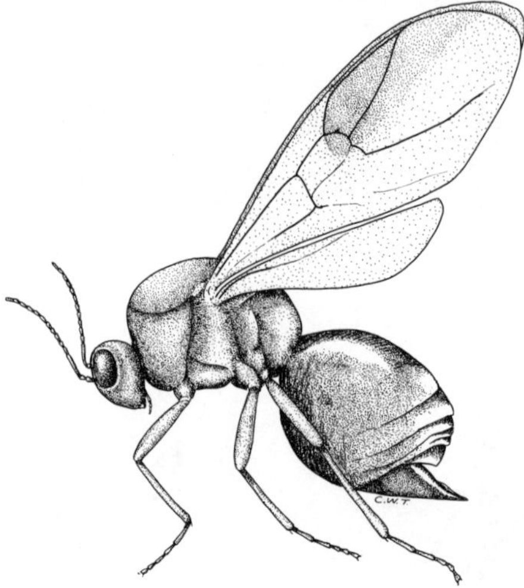

Fig. 29-46. A gall wasp, *Diplólepis ròsae* (Linn.). This species develops in the mossy rose gall (Fig. 29-47 D).

into three subfamilies, primarily on the basis of the structure of the abdomen; the Anacharitìnae, which have the abdomen distinctly petiolate and the second tergite longer than the third (Figure 29-23 E), are parasitic in the cocoons of lacewings (Chrysópidae); the Aspiceratìnae, in which the second abdominal tergite is narrow and much shorter than the third (Figure 29-23 C), are parasites of the pupae of syrphid flies; the Figitìnae, in which the second tergite is only slightly shorter than the third (Figure 29-23 F), are parasites of the pupae of various Diptera.

FAMILY **Cynípidae**—Gall Wasps and Others: This family is divided into three subfamilies, of which two (the Eucoilìnae and Charipìnae) are parasitic and the third (Cynipìnae) are gall makers or gall inquilines; a little over a hundred species of the first two subfamilies occur in the United States, compared with over 600 Cynipìnae.

The Eucoilìnae can be recognized by the rounded elevation on the scutellum (Figure 29-23 D); they are parasites of the pupae of various flies. The Charipìnae are minute insects, 2 millimeters in length or less, with the thorax smooth; they are hyperparasites, attacking braconids parasitic in aphids.

The Cynipìnae, or gall wasps, are a large group, and many species are quite common. They are small to minute, usually black insects, which can be recognized by their characteristic shape (Figure 29-46) and wing venation (Figure 29-16 A). The abdomen is oval, somewhat compressed and shining, and the second tergite covers about half or more of the abdomen. The Cynipìnae differ from the Charipìnae in that they are generally larger (up to 8 millimeters in length), and the thorax usually has coarse sculpturing.

Each species of gall maker forms a characteristic gall on a particular part of a particular plant; the galls are much more often noticed than are the insects. Many of the gall wasps form galls on oak. Some galls harbor a single insect, while many insects develop in others. The inquilines among the gall wasps live in galls made by some other gall insect. Most of the gall wasps are of little economic importance, but some of their galls have been used as a source of tannic acid, and others

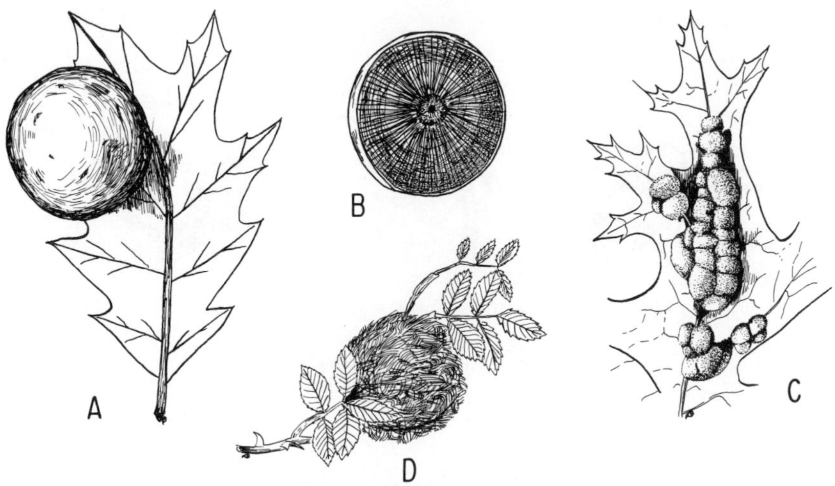

Fig. 29-47. Galls of Cynípidae. A, an oak-apple gall, caused by *Amphíbolips* sp.; B, another oak-apple, cut open to show the interior and the central capsule in which the gall wasp larva develops; C, the woolly oak gall, caused by *Callirhỳtis lanàta* (Gillette); D, the mossy rose gall, caused by *Diplólepis ròsae* (Linn.). (Redrawn from Felt.)

have been used as a source of certain dyes.

Many gall wasps have a rather complex life history, with two quite different generations a year. One generation, which develops during the summer in one type of gall, emerges in the fall and consists entirely of females that reproduce parthenogenetically; the eggs of this generation hatch and develop in a different type of gall, and the adults that emerge in the early part of the following summer consist of males and females. Both the adult insects and the galls of these two generations may be quite different in appearance.

SUPERFAMILY PROCTOTRUPÒIDEA: All the members of this group are parasitic on the immature stages of other insects. Most of them are small or minute, black and often shiny, and are likely to be confused with the cynipids, chalcids, or some of the scolioid or bethyloid wasps; a few (particularly the Gasteruptìidae) may be confused with ichneumons. The smaller members of this group have a much-reduced wing venation, similar to that of the chalcids, but may be distinguished from the chalcids by the structure of the thorax and ovipositor; the pronotum in the proctotrupoids extends laterally to the tegulae, and the ovipositor usually issues from the end of the abdomen rather than from anterior to the tip. The larger members of this group can be recognized by the characters given in the key.

There are differences of opinion about the limits of this superfamily, and some groups here included in it are often placed in other superfamilies; and some groups that we have placed in other superfamilies are sometimes included in the Proctotrupòidea.

The proctotrupoids are not so common as the chalcids or ichneumons, and some are quite rare. Many have the abdomen flattened, with the lateral edges rather sharp.

FAMILY **Evanìidae**—Ensign Wasps: The ensign wasps are black, somewhat spider-like insects 10 to 15 millimeters in length (Figure 29-48). The abdomen is very small and oval and is attached by a slender petiole to the propodeum considerably above the base of the hind coxae (Figure 29-22 F); it is carried almost like a flag, and hence the common name for this family. The ensign wasps are parasitic in the egg capsules of roaches and are likely to be found in building or other places where roaches occur.

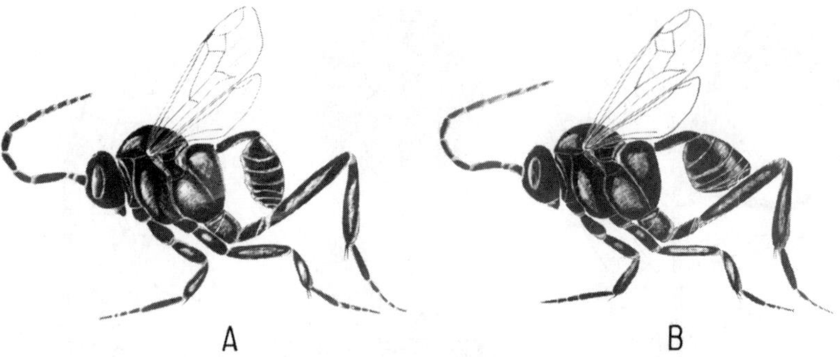

Fig. 29-48. An ensign wasp, *Prosevània punctàta* (Brullé). A, male; B, female. (Courtesy of Edmunds.)

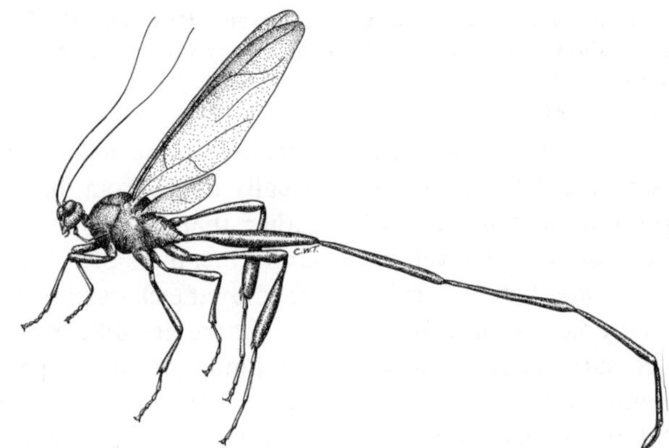

Fig. 29-49. A pelecinid, *Pelecìnus polyturàtor* (Drury), female; $1\frac{1}{2}\times$.

FAMILY **Gasteruptìidae:** The Gasteruptìidae are slender ichneumonlike insects, the females of which have an ovipositor about as long as the body. They are usually blackish (Gasteruptiìnae) or black with a reddish abdomen (Aulacìnae). They are not very common. The Gasteruptiìnae, which have one recurrent vein or none and one submarginal cell or none (Figure 29-21 E), are usually found on flowers, particularly wild parsnip, wild carrot, and related species; the larvae are parasitic on solitary wasps and bees. The Aulacìnae, which have two recurrent veins and usually two submarginal cells (Figure 29-21 F), parasitize the larvae of wood-boring beetles and xiphydriid wood wasps; they are usually found around logs in which the hosts occur.

FAMILY **Pelecínidae:** The family Pelecínidae is represented in North America by a single species, *Pelecìnus polyturàtor* (Drury), which is a large and striking insect. The female is 2 inches or more in length, shining black, with the abdomen very long and slender (Figure 29-49); the male, which is extremely rare in this country, is about an inch long and has the posterior part of the abdomen swollen. The females do not sting. This insect is parasitic on the larvae of June beetles.

FAMILY **Vanhornìidae:** The family Vanhornìidae includes a single North American species, *Vanhórnia eucnemídarum* Crawford, which is parasitic on the larvae of eucnemid beetles.

FAMILY **Roproniidae:** This family contains three rather rare North American species; the adults are about 8 millimeters in length and have a rounded and petiolate abdomen and a fairly complete wing venation. The immature stages are unknown.

FAMILY **Helóridae:** The family Helóridae contains a single North American species, *Helòrus paradóxus* (Provancher), a black insect about 4 millimeters long with a fairly complete wing venation (Figure 29-50). This species is parasitic on the larvae of lacewings (Chrysópidae), and the adult helorid emerges from the host cocoon.

FAMILY **Proctotrùpidae:** Most of the Proctotrùpidae range in length from 3 to 6 millimeters (some are larger); they may be recognized by the large stigma in the front wing, beyond which is a very small marginal cell (Figure 29-24 D). Very little is known of their habits, but a few are parasitic on beetles.

FAMILY **Ceraphrónidae:** The Ceraphrónidae are a fairly large group, and members of it have been reared from a variety of hosts. Some of the ceraphronids are hyperparasitic, attacking the braconid or chalcid parasites of aphids or scale insects. Wingless forms in this group can often be collected by sifting soil litter.

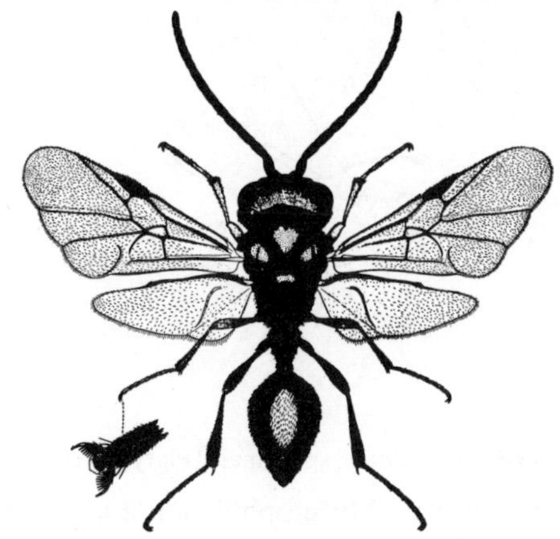

Fig. 29-50. *Helòrus paradóxus* (Provancher), female (Helóridae), showing tarsal comb. (Courtesy of Clancy and the University of California.)

FAMILY **Diaprìidae:** The diapriids are small to minute black insects, most of which are parasitic on immature Diptera. They can usually be recognized by the form of the head; the antennae arise on a shelflike protuberance in about the middle of the face (Figure 29-25 A). The family contains two subfamilies, which are designated as families by some authorities, the Diapriìnae and the Belytìnae (=Cinetìnae). The Diapriìnae are small to minute and have a very much reduced wing venation with no closed cell in the hind wings (Figure 29-16 D); the Belytìnae are usually larger and have a closed cell in the hind wings (Figure 29-24 C). These insects are usually collected by sweeping; the Belytìnae are most common in wooded areas, for they are parasitic on

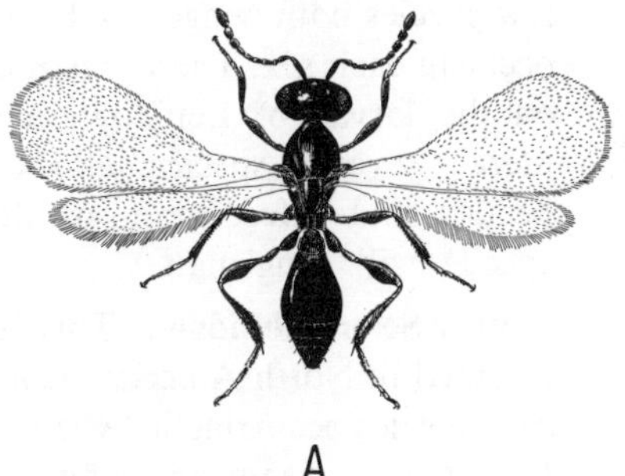

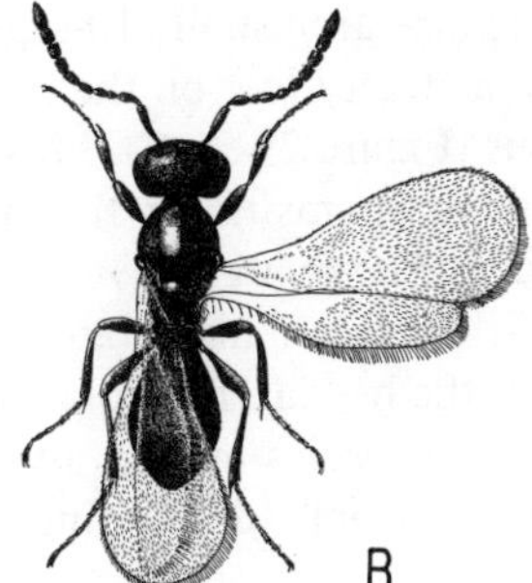

Fig. 29-51. Platygastéridae. A, *Xestonotídea érror* (Fitch), female; B, *Platygáster hiemàlis* Forbes, female. (Courtesy of USDA.)

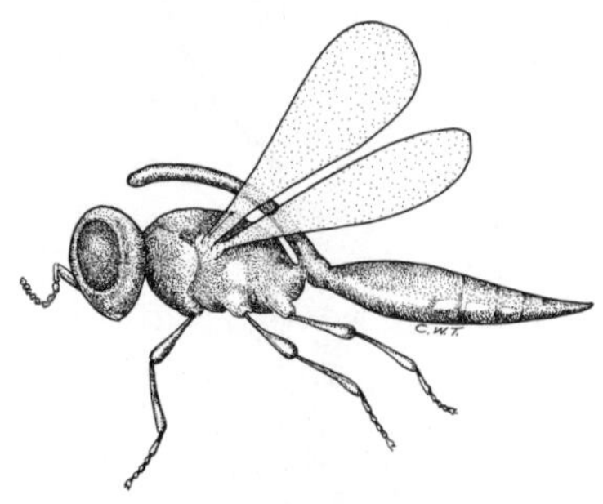

Fig. 29-52. *Inostémma* sp., female (Platygastéridae).

fungus gnats (Mycetophílidae) and other flies breeding in fungi.

FAMILY **Sceliónidae:** The Sceliónidae are small insects that are parasitic in insect or spider eggs; some of them have been successfully utilized in the control of crop pests. The females of some of the scelionids, particularly those that parasitize the eggs of grasshoppers or mantids, attach themselves to the female of the host species and ride on it until the host lays its eggs, whereupon the parasite leaves the host and attacks the eggs; in a few such cases the female scelionid may do some feeding on the adult of the host, but usually the adult host merely serves as a means of transportation. This phenomenon of one insect attaching itself to another for transportation is called phoresy; it occurs also in the chalcid family Eucharítidae, discussed above.

FAMILY **Platygastéridae:** The Platygastéridae are minute, shining-black insects with reduced wing venation (much as in chalcids); the antennae are usually 10-segmented and are attached very low on the face, next to the clypeus (Figure 29-25 C). Most of the platygasterids are parasitic on the larvae of Cecidomyìidae; *Platygáster hiemàlis* Forbes (Figure 29-51 B) is an important agent in the control of the hessian fly. Polyembryony occurs in several species in this family, with as many as 18 young developing from a single egg.

Most of the platygasterids are normal-looking insects, but the females of the genus *Inostémma* are peculiar in that they have a long handlelike process arising from the dorsum of the first abdominal segment and extending forward over the thorax (Figure 29-52); this structure serves as a receptacle for the ovipositor when it is not in use.

SUPERFAMILY BETHYLÒIDEA: Most of the members of this group are parasitic on other insects. The only common insects in this group are the cuckoo wasps (Chrysídidae); the others are quite rare.

FAMILY **Chrysídidae**—Cuckoo Wasps: The cuckoo wasps are small insects, rarely over 12 millimeters in length, and are metallic green or blue in color and usually have the body coarsely sculptured. Some of the chalcids and bees are of a similar size and coloration, but the cuckoo wasps can be recognized by the wing venation (Figure 29-24 B)—a fairly complete venation in the front wing but no closed cells in the hind wing—and the structure of the abdomen; the abdomen consists of only three or four visible segments and is hollowed out ventrally. When a cuckoo wasp is disturbed, it usually curls up in a ball. Most of the cuckoo wasps are external parasites of full-grown wasp or bee larvae; the species in the genus *Cléptes* are parasitic on sawfly larvae, and those in *Mesitiópterus* are parasitic on the eggs of walking sticks.

FAMILY **Bethýlidae:** The Bethýlidae are small to medium-sized, usually dark-colored wasps; the females of many species are wingless and antlike in appearance. In a few species both winged and wingless forms occur in each sex. These wasps are parasitic on the larvae of Lepidoptera and Coleoptera; several species attack moths or beetles that infest grain or flour. A few species will sting man.

FAMILY **Sclerogíbbidae:** This family is represented in North America by a single, very rare species occurring in Arizona, *Probéthylus schwárzi* Ashmead. A few sclerogibbids (occurring in other parts of the world) are known to be parasites of Embioptera.

FAMILY **Dryínidae:** The Dryínidae are rare wasps, and in most species the two sexes are quite different in appearance. The antennae are 10-segmented, and the front tarsi of the female are usually pincerslike. The peculiar front tarsi of some females in this family are used in holding the host during oviposition. The dryinids whose life histories are known are parasitic on nymphs and adults of the homopterous groups Fulgoròidea, Cicadéllidae and Membrácidae. Dryinid larvae feed internally on their host, although during most of their development a part of the body of the larva protrudes from the host in a saclike structure. The parasite, when full grown, leaves the host and spins a silken cocoon nearby. Polyembryony occurs in *Aphelòpus thèliae* Gahan, which parasitizes the treehopper *Thèlia bimaculàta* (Fabricius), with 40 to 60 young developing from a single egg.

FAMILY **Trigonálidae:** The trigonalids are a small group of rather rare insects; they are medium-sized, usually brightly colored, and rather stout-bodied; they look much like other wasps, but have the antennae very long and many-segmented.

The trigonalids are parasitic on social Véspidae or on the parasites of caterpillars. The very minute eggs are laid in considerable numbers on foliage. In the case of the species attacking caterpillar parasites, the eggs hatch when eaten by a caterpillar, and the trigonalid larva attacks the ichneumon, tachinid, or other parasite larva present in the caterpillar. In the species that parasitize vespid larvae, it is thought that the eggs are eaten by a caterpillar, which is in turn eaten by a vespid wasp, which in regurgitating the caterpillar and feeding it to its young transfers the trigonalid larvae from the caterpillar to the wasp larvae.

SUPERFAMILY SCOLIÒIDEA: This group contains a series of families that are very similar to the Vespòidea (and are placed in the Vespòidea by some authorities), but differ in habits. The Scoliòidea and Vespòidea have a similar thoracic structure; the pronotum in lateral view appears more or less triangular, with the lateral angles extending back to, or nearly to, the tegulae (Figure 29-4 C); in the Sphecòidea the pronotum is more collarlike, usually not particularly triangular in lateral view, and there is generally a rounded lobe on each side posteriorly which does not reach the tegula (Figure 29-4 D). The wasps in the superfamily Scoliòidea are parasitic, much as those in the preceding superfamilies of Apócrita; the female lays its eggs on

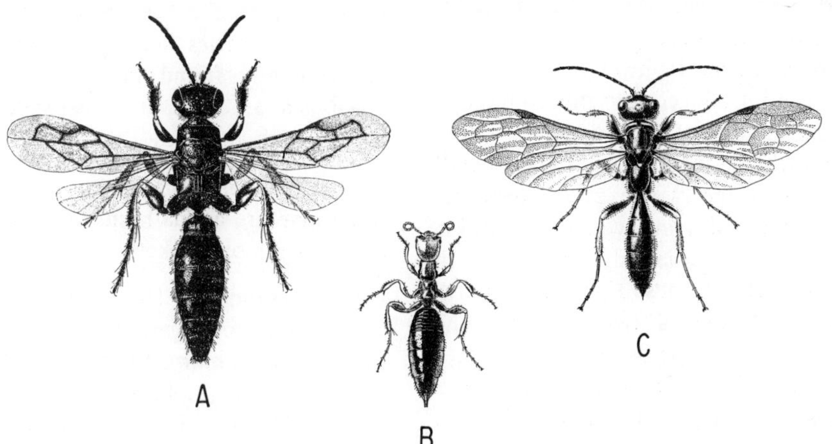

Fig. 29-53. Tiphiid wasps. A, *Típhia popilliávora* Rohwer, male; B, *Neozelobòria próximus* Turner, female; C, same, male. (A, courtesy of USDA, B and C, courtesy of Burrell and the New York Entomological Society.)

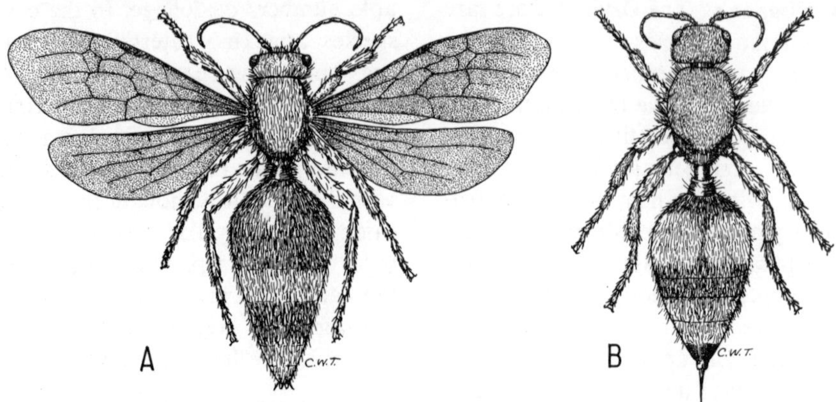

Fig. 29-54. A velvet ant, *Dasymutílla occidentàlis* (Linn.). A, male; B, female.

its host, usually without particularly injuring the host in the process, and then goes on its way to lay eggs on other hosts; the wasp larva feeds as an external parasite of its host. The wasps in this group usually do not construct a nest, as do the wasps in the Vespòidea.

FAMILY **Tiphìidae:** This family is divided into several subfamilies, some of which are often considered as families. Most of the members of the Tiphìinae are fair-sized, black, and somewhat hairy wasps with short legs (Figure 29-53 A); the Myzinìnae are brightly colored, black and yellow, and an inch or more in length. These tiphiids are parasitic on the larvae of scarabaeid beetles and are a very beneficial group. One species, *Típhia popilliávora* Rohwer (Figure 29-53 A), has been introduced into this country to aid in the control of the Japanese beetle. The Methochìnae (Methocìnae) are a small group in which the two sexes are very dissimilar; the females are wingless, antlike, and much smaller than the males (as in Figure 29-53 B, C); these tiphiids are parasitic on the larvae of tiger beetles. The Myrmosìnae are parasitic on various bees and wasps. The Brachycistidìnae and Anthoboscìnae are mainly western; little is known of their immature stages.

FAMILY **Sierolomórphidae:** The Sierolomórphidae are a small but widely distributed group of shining black wasps 4.5 to 6.0 millimeters in length; they are quite rare, and nothing is known of their immature stages.

FAMILY **Mutíllidae**—Velvet Ants: These wasps are so called because the females are wingless and antlike, and are covered with a dense pubescence (Figure 29-54). The males are winged and usually larger than the females, and are also densely pubescent. Most species are brightly colored, with red, orange, or yellow markings. The females have a very painful sting. Most of the mutillids whose life histories are known are external parasites of the larvae and pupae of various wasps and bees; a few are parasitic on certain beetles and flies. The mutillids are generally found in open areas. This group is a large one, and most species occur in the South and West.

FAMILY **Rhopalosomátidae:** The Rhopalosomátidae are a small and rare group; they are parasitic on crickets.

FAMILY **Scolìidae:** The Scolìidae are somewhat similar to the males of the Mutíllidae; they are large, hairy, and usually black with a yellow band (or bands) on the abdomen (Figure 29-55). These wasps are external parasites of the larvae of scarabaeid beetles; the adults are commonly found on flowers. The females burrow into the ground to

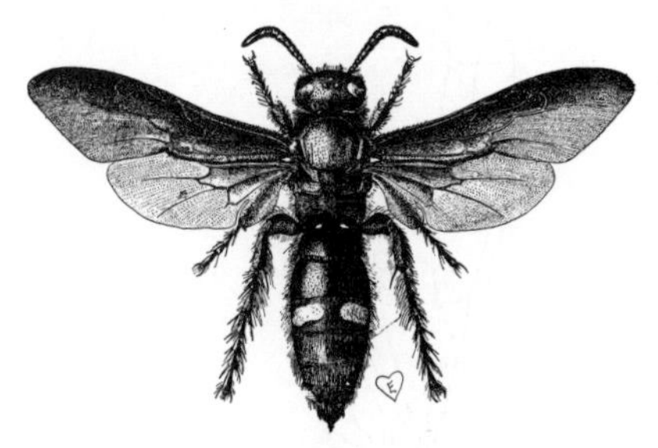

Fig. 29-55. *Scòlia dùbia* Say (Scolìidae), a parasite of the green June beetle. (Courtesy of Davis and Luginbill and the North Carolina Agricultural Experiment Station.)

locate a host; when they find a grub, they sting it and paralyze it, and then burrow deeper into the soil and construct a cell around the grub. Many grubs may be stung without the wasp ovipositing; such grubs usually never recover.

FAMILY **Sapýgidae:** The Sapýgidae are a small and rare group; the adults are of moderate size, usually black spotted or banded with yellow, and with short legs. They are parasitic in the nests of leafcutting bees (Megachílidae).

FAMILY **Formícidae**—Ants: This is a very common and widespread group, well known to everyone. The ants are probably the most successful of all the insect groups; they occur practically everywhere in terrestrial habitats and outnumber in individuals most other terrestrial animals. The habits of ants are often very elaborate, and a great many studies have been made of ant behavior.

Though most ants are easily recognized, there are a few other insects that strongly resemble ants, and some of the winged forms of ants resemble wasps. The most distinctive structural feature of ants is the form of the pedicel of the abdomen, which is 1- or 2-segmented and nodiform or scale-like (Figures 29-9, 29-56); the antennae are usually elbowed, and the first segment is often very long.

All ants are social insects, and each colony contains three castes—queens, males, and workers (Figure 29-56).[2] The queens are larger than the members of the other castes and are usually winged, though the wings are shed after the mating flight. The queen usually starts a colony and does most of the egg-laying in the colony. The males are winged and usually considerably smaller than the queens; they are short-lived and die soon after mating. The workers are sterile wingless females and make up the bulk of the colony. In the smaller ant colonies there are usually just the three types of individuals, but in many of the larger colonies there may be two or three types within each caste; these may vary in size, shape, or other characters.

Ant colonies vary greatly in size, from a dozen or more up to many thousands of individuals. Ants nest in all sorts of places; some nest in various types of cavities in plants (in stems, in nuts or acorns, in galls, and so on), some (for example, the carpenter ants) excavate galleries in wood, but perhaps the majority of ants nest in the ground. The ground nests of ants may be small and relatively simple, or they may be quite large and elaborate, consisting of a maze of tunnels and galleries. The galleries of some of the larger mound nests may extend several feet underground. Certain chambers in such underground nests may serve as brood chambers, others as chambers for the storage of food, and others may be used in some other way; most ants will shift their brood from one part of the nest to another when conditions change.

Males and queens in most ant colonies are produced in numbers at certain seasons; these emerge and engage in mating flights. Shortly after mating, the male dies, and the queen either starts a new colony or gets into an already established colony. This established colony may be of her own or of an alien species; in the latter case her offspring may be spoken of as temporary or permanent parasites, as the case may be. The queen sheds her wings immediately after

[2] In a few species there is no worker caste.

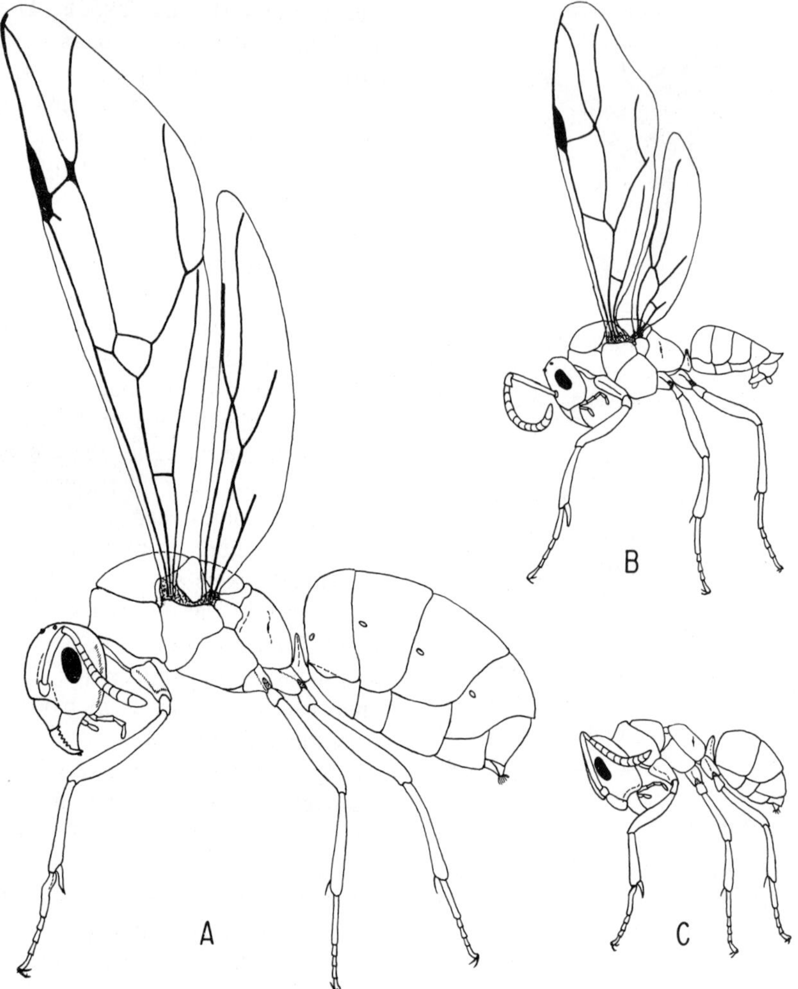

Fig. 29-56. Castes of an ant (*Formica* sp.); A, queen; B, male; C, worker.

the mating flight, usually locates a suitable nesting site, makes a small excavation, and produces her first brood. This first brood is fed and cared for by the queen and consists of workers; once the first workers appear, they take over the work of the colony—nest construction, caring for the young, gathering food, and the like—and henceforth the queen does little more than lay eggs. The queens of some species may live for several years. There may be more than one queen in some colonies. In some species of ants, certain castes or types of individuals may not be produced until the colony is several years old.

The feeding habits of ants are rather varied. Some are carnivorous, feeding on the flesh of other animals (living or dead), some feed on plants, some feed on fungi, and many feed on sap, nectar, honeydew, and similar substances. Ants in the nest often feed on the excretions of other individuals, and the exchange of food between individuals (trophallaxis) is a common occurrence. Many ants are serious pests in houses, greenhouses, and other places, owing to their feeding on foodstuffs, plants, or other materials.

Ants have various means of defense; many species (all except the Dolichoderìnae and Formicìnae) can sting, many can bite rather severely, and a few (Dolichoderìnae and some Myrmicìnae) give off or eject a foul-smelling secretion.

The family Formícidae is divided into seven subfamilies, the workers of which may be separated by the following key.

KEY TO THE SUBFAMILIES OF FORMÍCIDAE (WORKERS)

1.	Abdominal pedicel consisting of 2 segments (Figure 29-9 B) 2	
1′.	Abdominal pedicel consisting of 1 segment (Figures 29-9 A and 29-56). .4	
2(1).	Frontal carinae located very close together and not covering the antennal insertions; southern United States 3	
2′.	Frontal carinae not placed close together, and often expanded laterally and more or less concealing the antennal insertions when the head is viewed from above; clypeus usually prolonged back between the frontal carinae; the largest subfamily of ants. . . . . *Myrmicìnae*	p. 578
3(2).	Eyes very large, more or less oval, and occupying almost half the side of the head; ocelli usually present . . . .*Leptaleìnae* (*Pseudomyrmìnae*)	p. 578
3′.	Eyes absent, or vestigial and ocelluslike; no ocelli . . . . *Dorylinae*	p. 577
4(1′).	Gaster with a distinct constriction between the first and second segments (Figure 29-9 A), or if this constriction is faint, the mandibles are linear and the petiole bears a conical dorsal spine; sting well developed; integument highly sclerotized 5	
4′.	Gaster without a constriction between the first and second segments; sting rudimentary or absent 6	
5(4).	Antennal scape short and stout, flattened or with a greatly reduced tip that bears a prominent lateral furrow; with a pygidium bearing distinct spines on its lateral and posterior borders; rare ants occurring in Texas and Arizona . . . . *Cerapachyìnae*	p. 577
5′.	Antennal scape usually long and slender, but if short and enlarged at tip, at least the basal third is slender; without a pygidium; a widely distributed group . . . .*Ponerìnae*	p. 577
6(4′).	Cloacal orifice circular and usually surrounded by a fringe of hairs; a large group . . . .*Formicìnae*	p. 578
6′.	Cloacal orifice slitlike and not surrounded by a fringe of hairs. . . . . *Dolichoderìnae*	p. 578

—Subfamily *Dorylìnae*— The Dorylìnae are the legionary ants or army ants; they are mostly tropical, but one genus (*Éciton*) occurs in the southern and southwestern sections of the United States. These ants are nomadic and often travel in distinct files or "armies"; they are highly predaceous. The queens in this group are wingless.

—Subfamily *Cerapachyìnae*— This subfamily is represented in North America by only three very rare forms occurring in Arizona and Texas. The colonies are usually small, consisting of a few dozen individuals or less. These ants are predaceous.

—Subfamily *Ponerìnae*— In the subfamily Ponerìnae the pedicel of the abdomen is 1-segmented, but there is a distinct constriction between the first and second segments of the gaster (that part of the abdomen posterior to the pedicel) (Figure 29-9 A).

The only common genus in the East is *Ponèra*; the workers are 2 to 4 millimeters in length, and the queens are only a little larger. These ants form small colonies and nest in rotten logs or stumps, or in the soil beneath various objects; they are carnivorous.

—Subfamily *Leptaleìnae*— The Leptaleìnae are very slender ants that nest in hollow twigs, galls, or other cavities in plants, and are largely arboreal in habit. The single genus that occurs in the United States, *Pseudomýrma,* is largely restricted to the southern states.

—Subfamily *Myrmicìnae*— The subfamily Myrmicìnae is the largest and most common subfamily of ants, and its members can usually be recognized by the fact that the pedicel of the abdomen is 2-segmented (Figure 29-9 B). The myrmicine ants vary considerably in habits. The ants in the genera *Pogonomýrmex* and *Pheidòle* are often called harvester ants or agricultural ants; they feed on seeds, and store seeds in their nests. The fungus ants of the genus *Trachymýrmex* feed on fungi, which they cultivate in the nest. *Monomòrium pharaònis* (Linn.), the Pharaoh ant, is a small light-yellowish ant that is a common pest in houses. The leaf-cutting ants (*Átta*) cut large pieces of leaves and carry them to the nest; *A. texàna* (Buckley) is common in some parts of the South and Southwest, and sometimes does considerable damage. Some of the ants in this group are parasitic or inquilines; they live in the nests of other species and have no worker caste.

The imported fire ant, *Solenópsis saevíssima ríchteri* Forel, a species introduced into this country from South America, is an important pest in the South, from Georgia and Florida to Texas. It builds large mounds in open areas, and feeds on young plants and seeds, and it often attacks young animals. It has a painful sting, and the after effects of the sting are severe in some individuals. The workers are reddish to blackish in color, and from 3 to 6 millimeters in length. A related native species, *S. molésta* (Say), the thief ant, is a common house-infesting species in the South and West. Ants of the genus *Solenópsis* may be distinguished from other myrmicine ants by the fact that the antennae are 10-segmented, with a 2-segmented club.

—Subfamily *Dolichoderìnae*— In this and the following subfamily, the pedicel of the abdomen consists of a single segment, and there is no constriction between the first and second segments of the gaster (Figure 29-56). In the Dolichoderìnae the cloacal orifice is slitlike and is located ventrally. This is a small group, and most of its members occur in the southern part of the United States; most of them are rather small, the workers being less than 5 millimeters in length. These ants possess anal glands that secrete a foul-smelling fluid, which can sometimes be forcibly ejected from the anus for a distance of several inches. One species, the Argentine ant, *Iridomýrmex hùmilis* (Mayr), is a common household pest in the southern states.

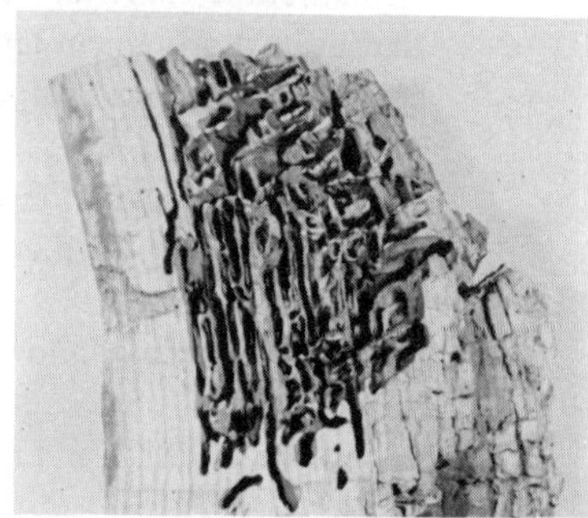

Fig. 29-57. Tunneling of carpenter ants.

—Subfamily *Formicìnae*— This is the second largest subfamily of ants and is widespread in distribution; it differs from the preceding subfamily in that the anal orifice is terminal and circular. There is considerable variation in habits in this group. The genus *Camponòtus* includes the carpenter ants, some of which are the largest ants in North America; *C. hercu-*

leànus pennsylvánicus (DeGeer) is a large black ant that excavates a series of anastomosing galleries in wood (Figure 29-57) for its nest. The ants in the genus *Polyérgus* are slave-makers and are entirely dependent on slaves. When a *Polyérgus* queen starts a new colony, she raids a nest of another species, usually a *Formìca*, kills the queen in that colony, and the *Formìca* workers usually adopt the *Polyérgus* queen; to maintain the colony, the *Polyérgus* ants make raids on *Formìca* colonies, killing the workers and carrying off the pupae.

The worker caste of *Polyérgus* is given to fighting, whereas the slaves take over the activities of nest-building, brood-rearing, foraging, and the like. The *Polyérgus* ants are often called amazons; *P. lùcidus* Mayr, a brilliant red species, is fairly common in eastern United States. The genus *Làsius* contains a number of small field ants that make small mound nests and feed largely on honeydew; many of them tend aphids, storing the aphid eggs through the winter and placing the young aphids on their food plant in the spring.

The genus *Formìca* is a very large genus, containing over a hundred species. Many are mound-building; the mounds of *F. exsectòides* Forel, a common species in eastern United States, are sometimes 2 or 3 feet high and several feet across. The United States varieties of *F. sanguínea* Latrielle are slave-makers, somewhat similar in habits to the amazons; they periodically raid the nests of others species of *Formìca* and carry off worker pupae; some of these are eaten, but others are reared and take their place in the *sanguínea* colony. The honey ants of the genus *Myrmecocýstus*, which occur in southwestern United States, are of interest in that some of the individuals (termed "repletes") serve as reservoirs for the honeydew collected by other workers.

SUPERFAMILY VESPÒIDEA: Most of the Vespòidea can be recognized as wasps by the single-segmented trochanters, the ovipositor issuing from the apex of the abdomen, and the antennae 12- or 13-segmented; they differ from the sphecoid wasps in the form of the pronotum (Figure 29-4 C, D).

Adult wasps generally feed on nectar, sap, or similar materials, and the larvae are fed other insects or spiders. In most of the solitary vespoid wasps the adult constructs a nest of some sort, usually in the ground or in some natural cavity, or of mud, and then goes out and finds suitable prey, stings it and paralyzes it, brings it back to the nest, lays an egg on it, seals up the nest or cell, and then repeats the process until it has prepared a number of cells, each with food for a young. The social vespoids construct a nest of a papery material and feed the young during their growth. Some of the spider wasps attack a spider in its own cell or burrow and do not move it after stinging and ovipositing on it.

FAMILY **Véspidae:** The members of this large group can usually be recognized by the very long first discoidal cell in the front wings (Figure 29-26 A) and the fact that the wings are usually folded longitudinally when at rest. This family is divided into seven subfamilies; the Vespìnae, Polistìnae, and Polybiìnae are social wasps, while the remaining subfamilies consist of solitary wasps.

The subfamilies of the Véspidae may be separated by the following key.

KEY TO THE SUBFAMILIES OF VÉSPIDAE

1. Two submarginal cells; antennae clavate; western and southwestern United States .... *Masarìnae* p. 582

1′. Three submarginal cells..2

2(1′). Transverse median vein elongate, the second discoidal cell 4-sided; jugal lobe of hind wing half as long as submedian cell, or longer; southwestern United States . . . . *Euparagiìnae* p. 582

2′. Transverse median vein short, the second discoidal cell triangular; jugal lobe of hind wing less than half as long as submedian cell, or absent . . 3

3(2′). Middle tibiae with 1 apical spur; tarsal claws toothed or bifid; solitary wasps 4

3′. Middle tibiae with 2 apical spurs; tarsal claws simple; social wasps 5

4(3). Mandibles short and broad; clypeus wider than long; thorax narrowed in front of tegulae, much narrower than head; southeastern United States . . . . *Zethìnae* p. 582

4′. Mandibles elongate and knifelike, often crossing; clypeus as long as, or longer than, wide; thorax not strongly narrowed in front of tegulae, and about as wide as head; a large and widely distributed group . . . . *Eumenìnae* p. 582

5(3′). Clypeus broadly truncate and more or less emarginate at apex; hind wings without a jugal lobe . . . . *Vespìnae* p. 581

5′. Clypeus pointed at apex, rarely rounded or straight; hind wings usually with a jugal lobe (Figure 29-26 A) 6

6(5′). First abdominal segment often stalklike; propodeum with a broad oval

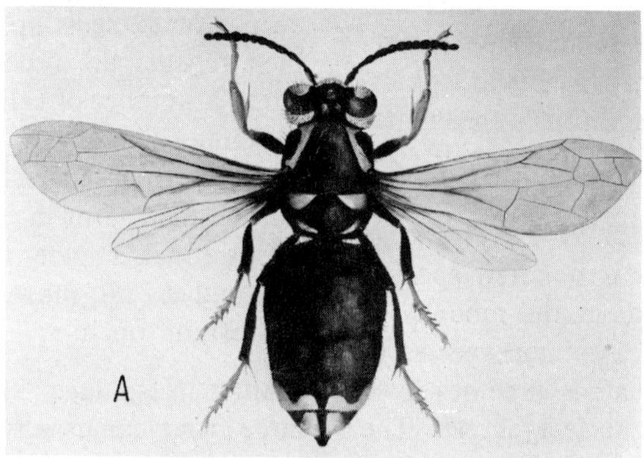

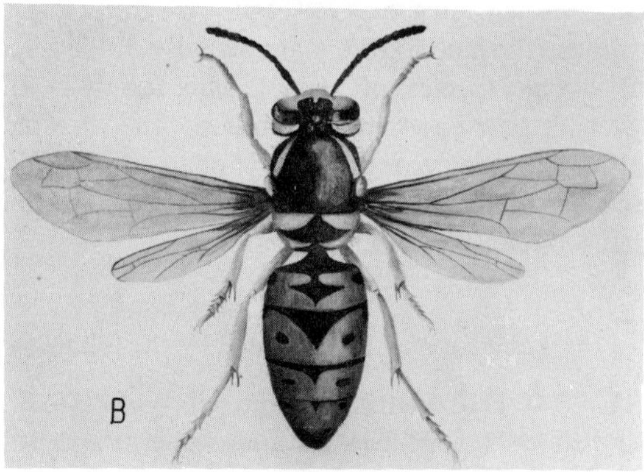

Fig. 29-58. Paper wasps (Vespìnae). A, the bald-faced hornet, *Véspula maculàta* (Linn.); B, a yellowjacket, *Véspula macùlifrons* (Buysson).

cavity marking the insertion of the extensor muscle of the abdomen; southern United States .... *Polybiìnae* p. 582

6′. First abdominal segment never stalklike (Figure 29-60); propodeum with a narrow slit marking the insertion of the extensor muscle of the abdomen; a widely distributed group .... *Polistìnae* p. 581

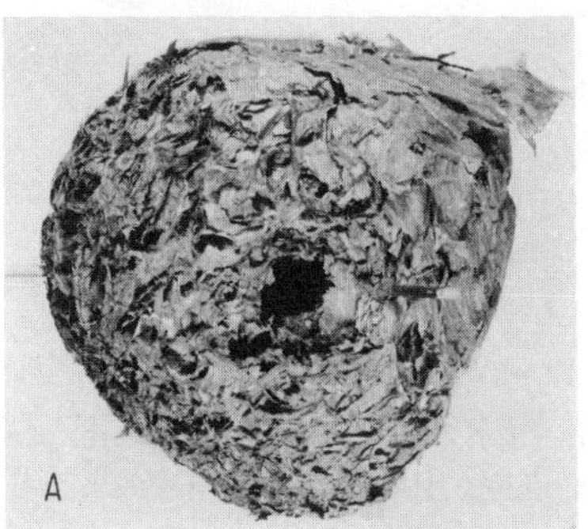

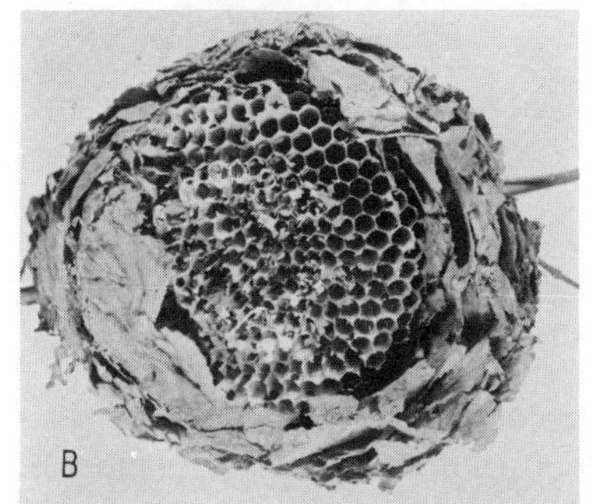

Fig. 29-59. Nests of a bald-faced hornet, *Véspula maculàta* (Linn.). A, nest as seen from below, showing entrance opening; B, lower part of outer envelope removed to show a tier of cells.

The social vespids, or paper wasps, include the yellowjackets and hornets, with which most people are familiar. As are other truly social insects, the individuals of a colony are of three castes—queens, workers, and males. Queens and workers are females and have a very effective sting—to which anyone who has ever gotten too familiar with these insects can testify. In some species there is very little difference between the queen and workers, and in a few parasitic species the worker caste is not differentiated.

The social vespids construct a nest out of a papery material that consists of wood or foliage chewed up and elaborated by the insect. The colonies in temperate regions exist for just a single season; only the queens overwinter, and in the spring each queen starts a new colony. The queen begins construction of a nest (or she may use a nest built in a previous year) and raises her first brood, which consists of workers; the workers then assume the duties of the colony, and thenceforth the queen does little more than lay eggs. The larvae are fed chiefly on insects and other animals.

—Subfamily *Vespìnae*— Most of our species of Vespìnae belong to the genus *Véspula*; this group includes the insects commonly called yellowjackets. The nests of these wasps consist of several to many tiers of hexagonal paper cells, all enclosed in a papery envelope. Some species build their nests in the open, attached to branches, under a porch, or beneath any projecting surface; other species build their nests in the ground. The most common exposed nests, which may sometimes be nearly a foot in diameter (Figure 29-59), are made by the bald-faced hornet, *Véspula maculàta* (Linn.), an insect that is largely black with yellowish-white markings (Figure 29-58 A). Most of the black-and-yellow paper wasps that are commonly called yellowjackets (Figure 29-58 B) nest in the ground.

—Subfamily *Polistìnae*— The Polistìnae are elongate and slender with a spindle-shaped abdomen and are usually reddish or

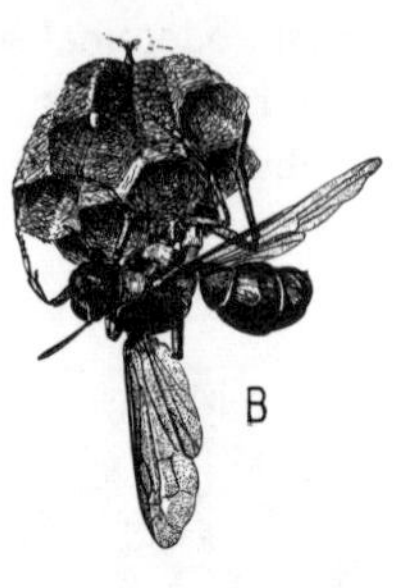

Fig. 29-60. A paper wasp, *Polístes fuscàtus pállipes* Lepeltier. A, adult female; B, adult at nest. (B, courtesy of USDA.)

brown in color (Figure 29-60). Their nests (Figure 29-60 B) consist of a single more or less circular horizontal comb of paper cells, attached to a support by a slender stalk. The cells are open on the lower side while the larvae are growing and are sealed when the larvae pupate. The North American species in this subfamily belong to the genus *Polístes.*

—Subfamily *Polybiìnae*— The Polybiìnae are principally tropical, but a few species occur in the southern states. The nests of these wasps are similar to those of *Polístes.*

The solitary vespids vary considerably in their nesting habits, but most of them provision their nests with caterpillars. Some species utilize cavities in twigs or logs for a nest, others burrow in the ground, and others make a nest of mud or clay. Most of the solitary vespids are black marked with yellow, and they vary in size from about 10 to 25 millimeters in length.

—Subfamily *Zethìnae*— The Zethìnae are black wasps about an inch long that have the abdomen petiolate (much as in Figure 29-61 A); they are not common. In some species several females may construct a colony of cells of leaves or plant fibers pasted together. The food of the larvae consists of caterpillars.

—Subfamilies *Masarìnae* and *Euparagiìnae*— These groups are uncommon, and occur only in the West. The Masarìnae are relatively slender, 10 to 20 millimeters in length, and provision their nests with pollen and nectar. The Euparagiìnae are more stocky, and 6 to 7 millimeters in length.

—Subfamily *Eumenìnae*— The Eumenìnae, the mason or potter wasps, are a large and widespread group, and many species are very common. The species in the genus *Eùmenes* construct juglike nests of mud, which are attached to twigs and are provisioned with caterpillars (Figure 29-61). The other species in this subfamily nest in various sorts of mud or clay nests, in burrows, in cavities in twigs or logs, or in the abandoned nests of other wasps. Most species provision their nests with caterpillars; some provision their nests with the larvae of chrysomelid beetles. Most of these wasps do not lay their eggs on the insects with which the cells are provisioned, but suspend their eggs on slender threads from the ceiling or side of the cells.

FAMILY **Pompílidae**—Spider Wasps: The spider wasps are slender wasps with long spiny legs and a characteristic suture across the mesopleura (Figures 29-27, 29-63). The commoner members of this group are from $\frac{1}{2}$ inch to an inch in length, but some of the western spider wasps are about 2 inches in length. Most of them are dark-colored, with smoky or yellowish wings; a few are

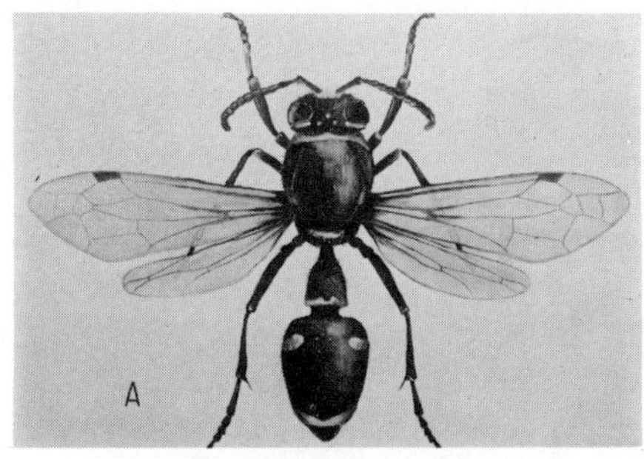

Fig. 29-61. A potter wasp, *Eùmenes fratérnus* Say. A, adult; B, nest.

brightly colored. The adults are usually found on flowers or on the ground in search of prey. The larvae of most species feed on spiders (hence the common name), although these are not the only wasps that attack spiders. The spider wasps generally capture and paralyze a spider and then prepare a cell for it—in the ground, in rotten wood, or in a suitable crevice in rocks; some spider wasps construct a cell first, then hunt for a

Fig. 29-62. A mason wasp, *Rýgchium dorsàle dorsàle* (Fabricius). This species nests in small colonies in vertical burrows in the ground.

spider to store in the cell. A few species attack the spider in its own cell or burrow and do not move it after stinging and ovipositing on it; a few species oviposit on spiders that have been stung by another wasp. The spider wasps are fairly common insects, and the females have a very efficient sting.

SUPERFAMILY SPHECÒIDEA: These wasps can be distinguished from other wasps by the structure of the pronotum, which terminates laterally in a rounded lobe that does not reach the tegula (Figure 29-4 D). All are solitary wasps, though large numbers of some species (for example, Bembicìni) may nest in a small area.

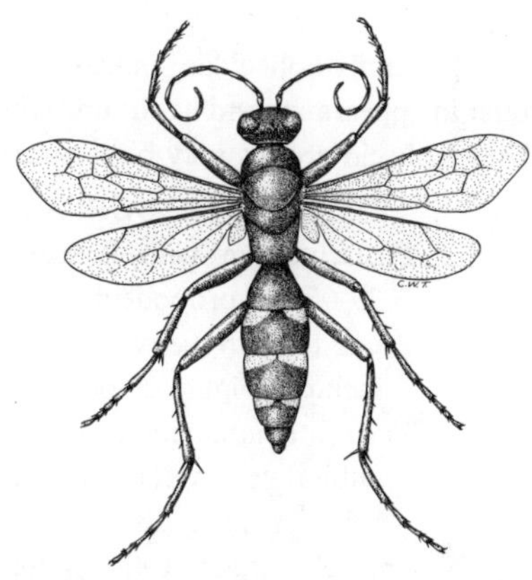

Fig. 29-63. A spider wasp, *Episýron quinquenotàtus* (Say); $2\frac{1}{2}\times$.

FAMILY **Ampulícidae:** The ampulicids are small, black, rather rare wasps (Figure 29-64). They nest in twigs, under bark, and under leaf litter on the ground, and provision their nests with immature roaches. Three species occur in North America.

FAMILY **Sphècidae:** The members of this large group are solitary wasps, and the adults are commonly found on flowers. They nest in a variety of situations, but the majority nest in wood, in burrows in the ground, or construct cells of mud. Each group within the family is usually restricted to a particular type of food for the larvae.

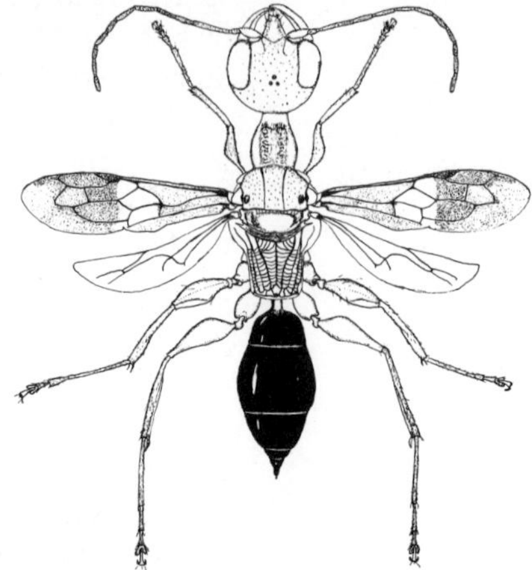

Fig. 29-64. An ampulicid wasp, *Rhinópsis ferrugínea* Bradley. (Courtesy of Strandtmann and the Entomological Society of America.)

The family Sphècidae, as treated here, contains a number of subfamilies and tribes that differ in appearance and habits and which are considered distinct families by some authorities. These sphecid groups may be separated by the following key.

KEY TO THE SUBFAMILIES AND TRIBES OF SPHÈCIDAE

1. Postscutellum with 2 scalelike backward-projecting processes (Figure 29-65 B); propodeum with a median spine or forked process; base of cubital vein, between first submarginal and first discoidal cells, weak or lacking (Figure 29-68 C) (Oxybelìni) .... *Crabronìnae* p. 594

1′. Postscutellum, and usually also propodeum, simple and not as above; cubital vein well developed between first submarginal and first discoidal cells 2

2(1′). One submarginal cell (Figure 29-66 A, B), or if with more than 1, then the eyes are deeply emarginate 3

2′. Two or 3 submarginal cells (Figures 29-66 C-F, 29-67, 29-68 A-D); eyes

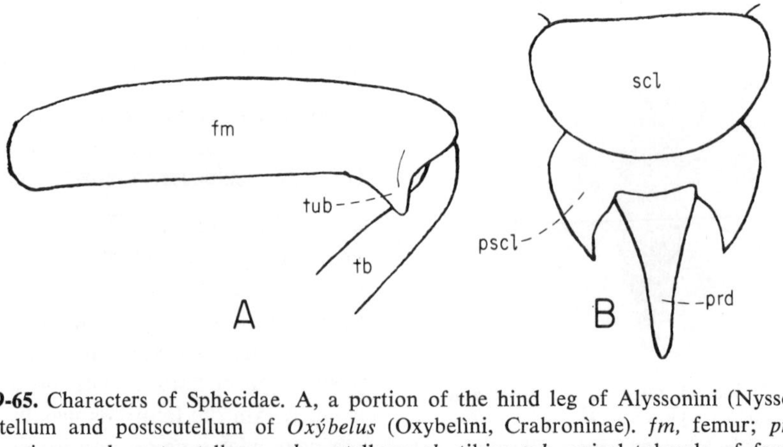

Fig. 29-65. Characters of Sphècidae. A, a portion of the hind leg of Alyssonìni (Nyssonìnae); B, scutellum and postscutellum of *Oxýbelus* (Oxybelìni, Crabronìnae). *fm,* femur; *prd,* propodeal spine; *pscl,* postscutellum; *scl,* scutellum; *tb,* tibia; *tub,* apical tubercle of femur.

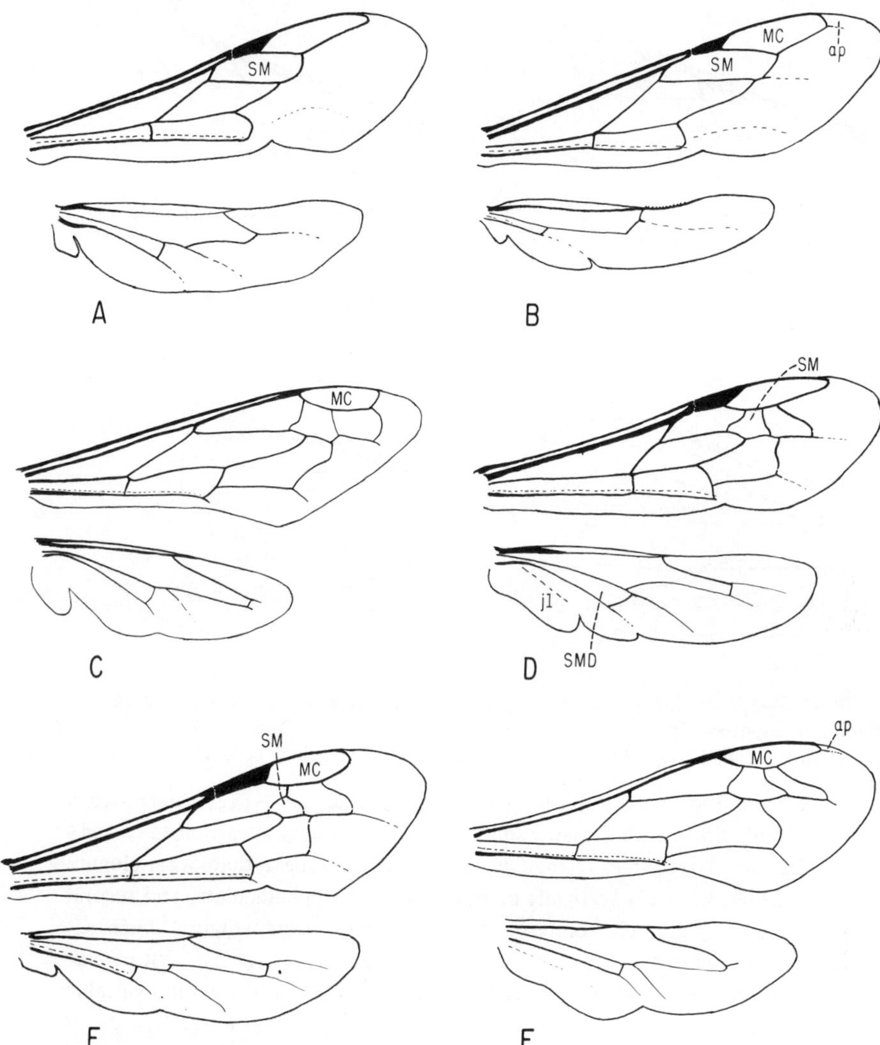

Fig. 29-66. Wings of Sphècidae. A, *Trypóxylon* (Trypoxylonìnae); B, *Crábro* (Crabronìni, Crabronìnae); C, *Microbémbex* (Bembicìni, Nyssonìnae); D, *Philánthus* (Philanthìni, Philanthìnae); E, *Cérceris* (Cercerìni, Philanthìnae); F, *Táchysphex* (Tachytìni, Larrìnae). *ap,* appendiculate marginal cell; *jl,* jugal lobe; *MC,* marginal cell; *SM,* submarginal cell; *SMD,* submedian cell.

not emarginate, or only slightly so 5

3(2). Eyes deeply emarginate (Figure 29-69 A); medium-sized, slender, black wasps (Figure 29-72) ....*Trypoxylonìnae* p. 590

3′. Eyes not emarginate (Figure 29-69 E)............................4

4(3′). Marginal cell appendiculate (Figure 29-66 B); head large and quadrate; antennae arising low on face (Figure 29-69 E); usually black wasps with yellow markings (Crabronìni)........................*Crabronìnae* p. 594

4′. Marginal cell not appendiculate (Pemphredonìni) ......*Pemphredonìnae* p. 591

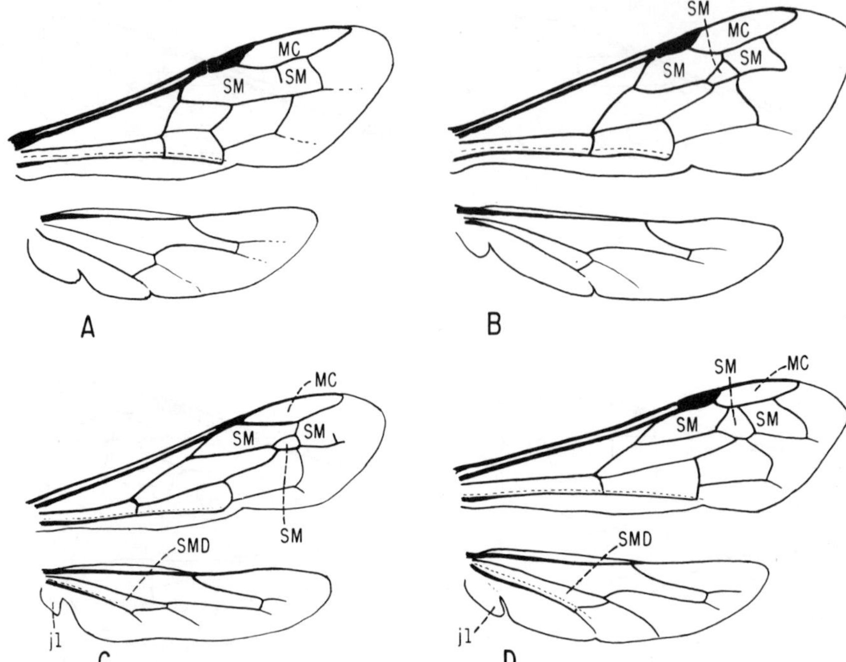

Fig. 29-67. Wings of Sphècidae. A, *Pémphredon* (Pemphredonìni, Pemphredonìnae); B, *Psén* (Psenìni, Pemphredonìnae); C, *Nýsson* (Nyssonìni, Nyssonìnae); D, *Gorỳtes* (Gorytìni, Nyssonìnae). *jl*, jugal lobe; *MC*, marginal cell; *SM*, submarginal cell; *SMD*, submedian cell.

5(2′). Middle tibiae with 1 apical spur 6

5′. Middle tibiae with 2 apical spurs 14

6(5). Labrum large, free, triangular, as long as or longer than wide (Figure 29-69 B); ocelli vestigial; marginal cell not appendiculate, and second submarginal cell receiving both recurrent veins (Figure 29-66 C) (Bembicìni) . . . . *Nyssonìnae* p. 592

6′. Labrum small, usually concealed by clypeus; ocelli and venation variable 7

7(6′). Abdomen not petiolate, and a strong constriction, both dorsally and ventrally, between first and second segments (Figure 29-70 A, B); relatively robust wasps, usually black with yellow markings (Figure 29-77) . . . . *Philanthìnae* 8

7′. Abdomen either petiolate or without a strong constriction between first and second segments 9

8(7). Second submarginal cell 4-sided and touching marginal cell (Figure 29-66 D); inner margins of eyes slightly emarginate, and clypeus with a median upward-projecting lobe (Figure 29-69 C); mesopleura with a vertical furrow below front wing, separating a prepectus from rest of mesopleuron; hind femora simple at apex (*Philánthus*, Philanthìni). . . . . *Philanthìnae* p. 594

8′. Second submarginal cell more or less triangular, and usually not touching marginal cell (Figure 29-66 E); eyes, clypeus, and mesopleura not as above; hind femora reniform at apex (Cercerìni). . . . . *Philanthìnae* p. 594

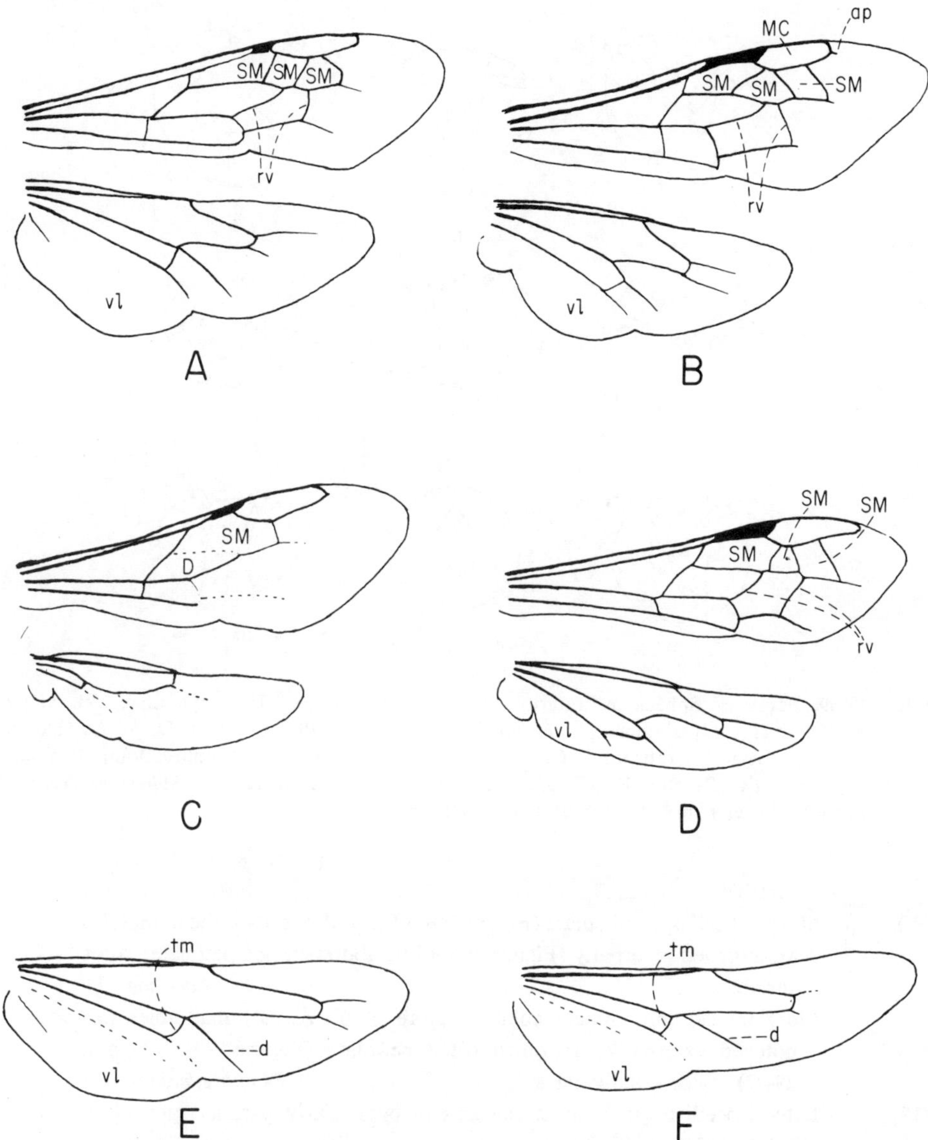

Fig. 29-68. Wings of Sphècidae. A, *Chlorìon* (Chlorionìni, Sphecìnae); B, *Astàta* (Astatìnae); C, *Oxýbelus* (Oxybelìni, Crabronìnae); D, *Méllinus* (Mellinìni, Nyssonìnae); E, *Scéliphron*, hind wing (Sceliphronìni, Sphecìnae); F, *Sphéx* (Sphecìni, Sphecìnae). *ap*, appendiculate marginal cell; *d*, discoidal vein; *D*, first discoidal cell; *MC*, marginal cell; *rv*, recurrent vein; *SM*, submarginal cell; *tm*, transverse median vein; *vl*, vannal lobe.

9(7′). Hind femora produced below at apex as a flattened tubercle overlying base of tibiae (Figure 29-65 A); second submarginal cell petiolate (as in Figures 29-66 E and 29-67 C); abdomen not petiolate (Alyssonìni).... .... *Nyssonìnae* p. 592

9′. Hind femora simple at apex, without projection; second submarginal cell

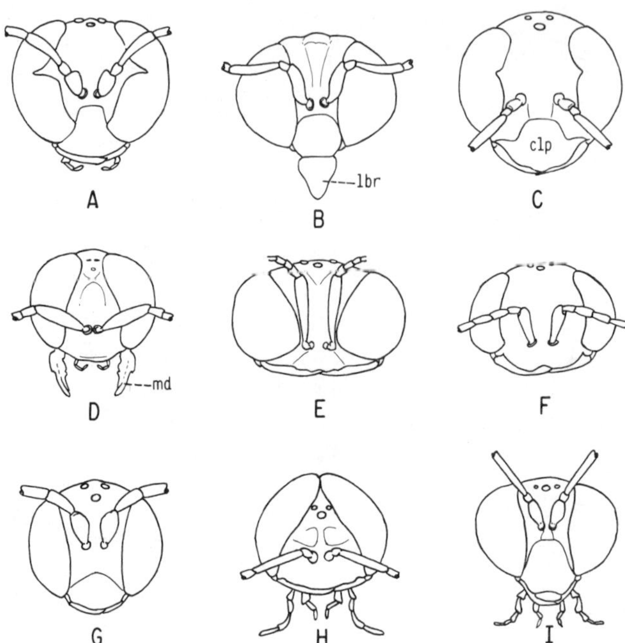

Fig. 29-69. Faces of Sphècidae, anterior view. A, *Trypóxylon* (Trypoxylonìnae); B, *Microbémbex* (Bembicìni, Nyssonìnae); C, *Philánthus* (Philanthìni, Philanthìnae); D, *Mòtes* (Larrìni, Larrìnae); E, *Crábro* (Crabronìni, Crabronìnae); F, *Pémphredon* (Pemphredonìni, Pemphredonìnae); G, *Psén* (Psenìni, Pemphredonìnae); H, *Astàta* (Astatìnae); I, *Sphècius* (Gorytìni, Nyssonìnae). *clp*, clypeus; *lbr*, labrum; *md*, mandible.

variable 10

10(9′). Marginal cell appendiculate (Figure 29-66 F), or if not, then the mandibles are notched externally (Figure 29-69 D); abdomen not petiolate; color variable.. *Larrìnae* 11

10′. Marginal cell not appendiculate (Figure 29-67 A, B); mandibles not notched externally; abdomen often petiolate (Figures 29-70 D and 29-73); color usually black .... *Pemphredonìnae* 13

11(10). Lateral ocelli normal; inner margins of eyes nearly parallel; pronotum trilobed (Miscophìni) .... *Larrìnae* p. 590

11′. Lateral ocelli distorted or deformed; inner margins of eyes converging above; pronotum simple 12

12(11′). Lateral ocelli small and transversely elongate (Figure 29-69 D); a transverse ridge below median ocellus (Larrìni).................. *Larrìnae* p. 590

12′. Lateral ocelli oblique to nearly longitudinal in position; no transverse ridge, but a more or less dome-shaped swelling below median ocellus (Tachytìni) .... *Larrìnae* p. 590

13(10′). One or 2 submarginal cells (Figure 29-67 A); antennae arising low on face, near base of eyes (Figure 29-69 F) (Pemphredonìni).... *Pemphredonìnae* p. 591

13′. Three submarginal cells (Figure 29-67 B); antennae arising near middle of face, above base of eyes (Figure 29-69 G) (Psenìni).... *Pemphredonìnae* p. 591

14(5′). Hind femora produced below at apex as a flattened tubercle overlying base of tibiae (Figure 29-65 A); second submarginal cell petiolate (as in Figures 29-66 E and 29-67 C); abdomen not petiolate (Alyssonìni) .... *Nyssonìnae* p. 592

14′. Hind femora simple at apex, without projection; second submarginal cell variable 15

15(14′). Vannal lobe of hind wing large, strongly projecting posteriorly (Figure 29-68 A, B, E, F, *vl*); mesonotum not expanded laterally into laminae, which overlie bases of tegulae 16

15′. Vannal lobe of hind wing smaller, not strongly projecting posteriorly (Figures 29-67 C, D and 29-68 D); mesonotum often expanded laterally into laminae, which overlie bases of tegulae 21

16(15). Abdomen with a distinct, usually long, cylindrical petiole (Figure 29-70 E); marginal cell pointed or narrowly rounded apically and not appendiculate (Figure 29-68 A); eyes widely separated .... *Sphecìnae* 17

16′. Abdomen not petiolate; marginal cell truncate at apex and appendiculate (Figure 29-68 B); eyes of male very large and contiguous above (Figure 29-69 H) .... *Astatìnae* p. 590

17(16). Second and third submarginal cells each receiving a recurrent vein (Figure 29-68 A) 18

17′. Second submarginal cell receiving both recurrent veins (as in Figures 29-67 D and 29-68 B) 19

18(17). Antennae arising in middle of face; tarsal claws with 1 to 6 teeth beneath; tibiae usually strongly spinose; widely distributed, common wasps (Chlorionìni) .... *Sphecìnae* p. 591

18′. Antennae arising below middle of face; tarsal claws without teeth beneath or, at most, with a small tooth near middle; tibiae smooth, not spinose; rare wasps, mostly southern (Podiìni) .... *Sphecìnae* p. 591

19(17′). Discoidal vein in hind wing arising distinctly beyond anterior end of transverse median vein (Figure 29-68 F); abdomen elongate, the petiole usually 2-segmented (Figure 29-74 B) (Sphecìni) .... *Sphecìnae* p. 591

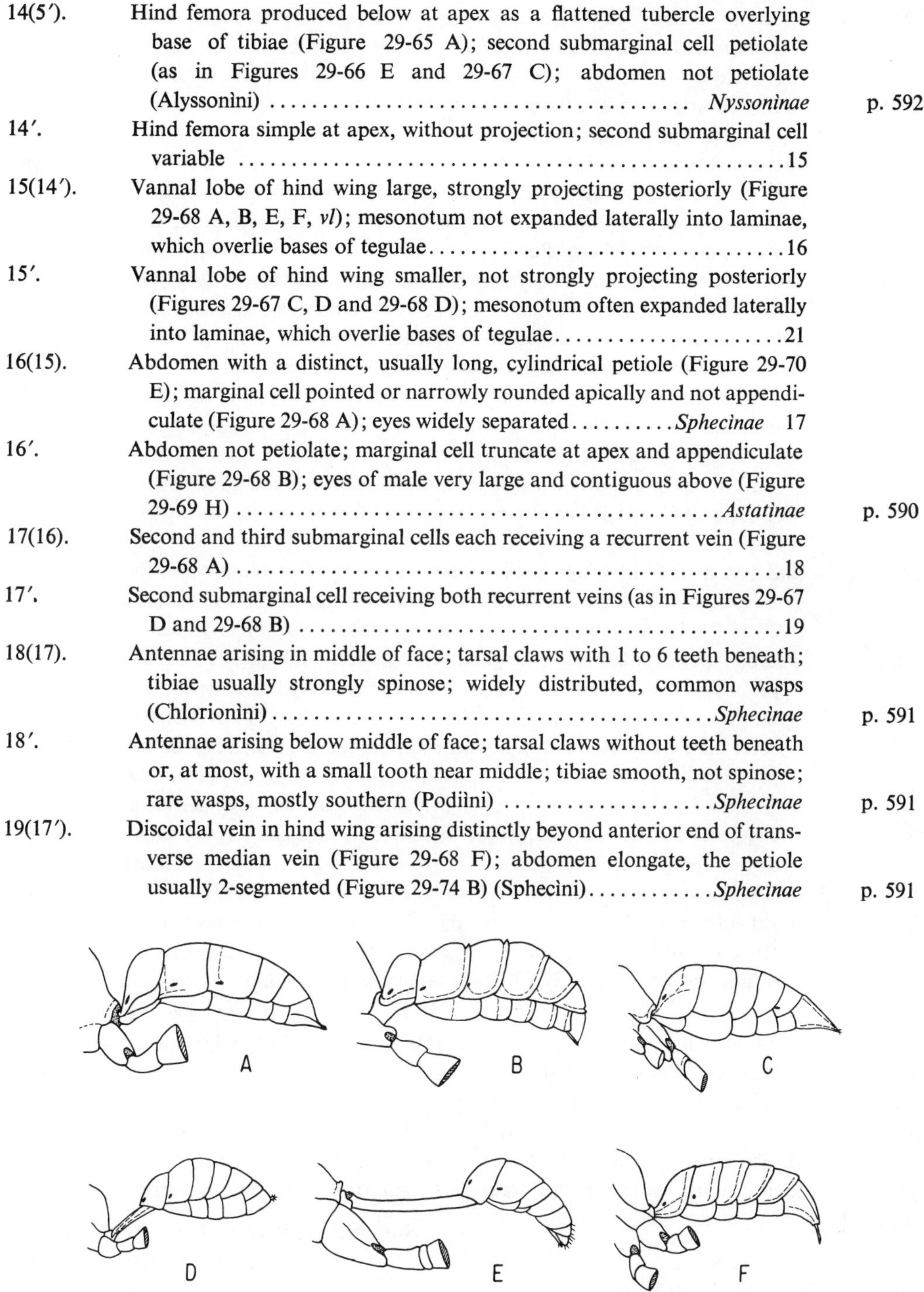

Fig. 29-70. Abdominal structure in the Sphècidae, lateral view. A, *Philánthus* (Philanthìni, Philanthìnae); B, *Cérceris* (Cercerìni, Philanthìnae); C, Larrìnae; D, *Psén* (Psenìni, Pemphredonìnae); E, *Scéliphron* (Sphecìnae); F, *Sphècius* (Gorytìni, Nyssonìnae).

19′. Discoidal vein in hind wing arising at or just beyond anterior end of transverse median vein (Figure 29-68 E); petiole of abdomen 1-segmented (Figure 29-70 E) 20

20(19′). Antennae arising in middle of face; propodeum with a dorsal **U**-shaped area; mesopleura not longer than height of thorax; widely distributed, common wasps (Sceliphronìni) ....*Sphecìnae* p. 591

20′. Antennae arising far below middle of face; propodeum without a dorsal **U**-shaped area; mesopleura much longer than height of thorax; rare wasps, mostly southern (Podiìni) ....*Sphecìnae* p. 591

21(15′). Second submarginal cell not receiving a recurrent vein (Figure 29-68 D); first abdominal segment long, slender, swollen apically, and separated from second by a distinct constriction (Mellinìni)..........*Nyssonìnae* p. 592

21′. Second submarginal cell receiving one or both recurrent veins; first abdominal segment stout, not particularly swollen apically, and separated from second by a less distinct constriction; more common wasps....22

22(21′). Basal vein in front wings distant from stigma by less, generally much less, than twice the distance between apex of marginal cell and apex of wing (Figure 29-67 C, D); last abdominal tergite of male simple, not trilobed 23

22′. Basal vein in front wings distant from stigma by 2 or more times the distance between apex of marginal cell and apex of wing (as in Figure 29-66 C); last abdominal tergite of male trilobed (Stizìni)..*Nyssonìnae* p. 592

23(22). Second submarginal cell triangular and petiolate (Figure 29-67 C); propodeum with upper hind angles acute or produced as sharp spines; thorax coarsely punctate (Nyssonìni)....................*Nyssonìnae* p. 592

23′. Second submarginal cell not as above, usually quadrate (Figure 29-67 D); propodeum and thorax variable...............................24

24(23′). Jugal lobe in hind wing about as long as submedian cell or longer (as in Figure 29-66 D); eyes widely separated, and the clypeus with a median upward-projecting lobe (Figure 29-69 C); thorax coarsely punctate (*Aphilánthops*, Philanthìni) ....*Philanthìnae* p. 594

24′. Jugal lobe in hind wing not more than half as long as submedian cell (Figure 29-67 D); eyes closer together, and the entire clypeus projecting upward (Figure 29-69 I); thorax smooth (Gorytìni)..*Nyssonìnae* p. 592

—Subfamily *Astatìnae* (*Dimorphìnae*)— Varicolored Wasps— These wasps are rather stout-bodied, about $\frac{1}{2}$ inch in length, and are either all black or black with the abdomen red. They nest in the ground and provision their nests with Hemiptera, especially Pentatómidae and Lygaèidae.

—Subfamily *Larrìnae* — Sand-Loving Wasps— These are for the most part rather dull-colored wasps of small to medium size (Figure 29-71); most of them nest in burrows in sandy places. The Miscophìni (Dinetìni, Nitelìni), which are rather small and rare insects, provision their nests with spiders or small Hemiptera. The Tachytìni and Larrìni provision their nests with various Orthoptera, chiefly grasshoppers (Tachytìni) or crickets (Larrìni).

—Subfamily *Trypoxylonìnae* (*Trypoxylìnae*) — Organ-Pipe Mud-Daubers— The organ-pipe mud-daubers are elongate, slender, usually shining-black wasps with a single submarginal cell (Figure 29-72 A) and with the inner margins of the eyes deeply

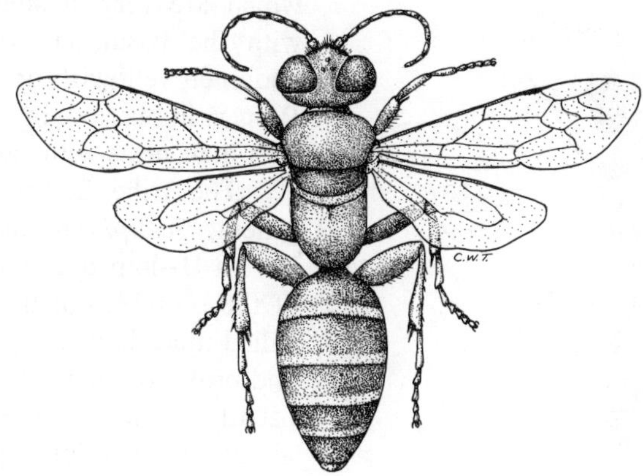

Fig. 29-71. A sand-loving wasp, *Táchytes mandibulàris* Patton (Tachytìni, Larrìnae); 3 ×.

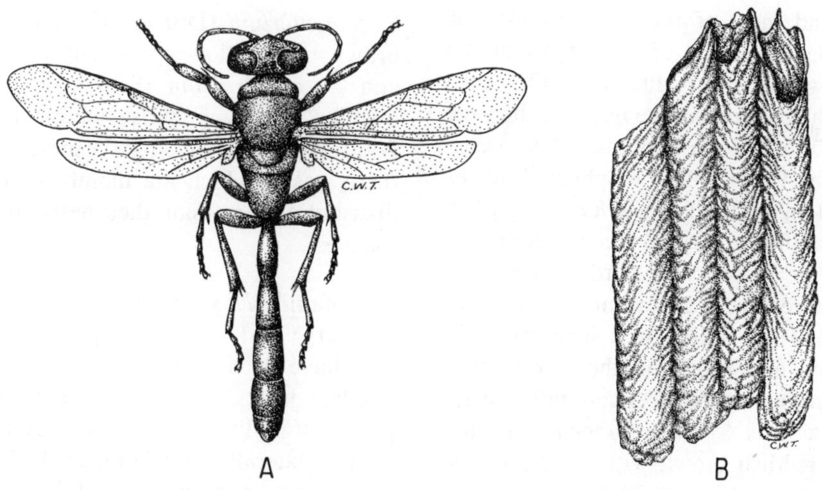

Fig. 29-72. An organ-pipe mud-dauber. A, adult of *Trypóxylon clavàtum* Say, $3\frac{1}{2}$ ×; B, nest of *T. polítum* (Say), $\frac{1}{2}$ ×.

emarginate (Figure 29-69 A); they vary in length from about $\frac{1}{2}$ inch to an inch or more. Some species make their nests of mud, with the cells arranged in the form of a long tube; hence the common name for this group. In species that construct this type of nest, the male usually guards the nest while the female is absent. Some species nest in hollow twigs, abandoned beetle galleries, or other similar cavities. These wasps provision their nests with spiders.

—Subfamily *Pemphredonìnae* — Aphid Wasps— The aphid wasps are small, slender, usually black wasps (Figure 29-73) that nest in cavities in twigs or logs (a few nest in the ground) and provision their nests with various Homoptera. Most of the Psenìni provision their nests with various hoppers (Cercópidae, Membrácidae, and Cicadéllidae); a few species in this tribe provision their nests with aphids or psylliids. Most of the Pemphredonìni nest in the ground and provision their nests with aphids.

—Subfamily *Sphecìnae* — Thread-Waisted Wasps— These wasps are very common

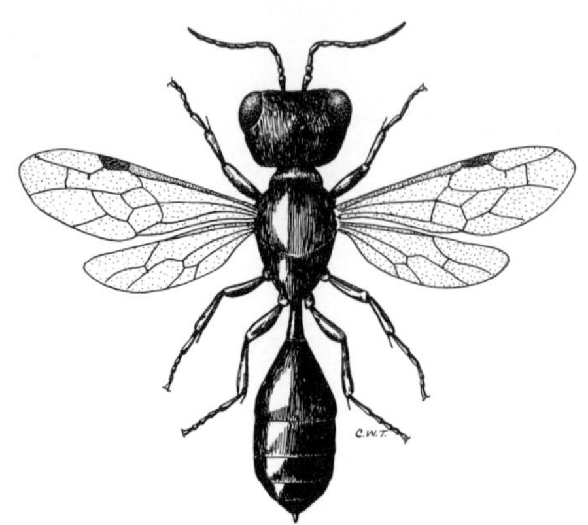

Fig. 29-73. An aphid wasp, *Pémphredon inornàtus* Say.

insects, and most of them are an inch or more in length; some of the largest of the sphecid wasps are included in this subfamily. The common name refers to the very slender petiole of the abdomen. The wasps in the tribe Chlorionìni (=Sphecìni), all of which belong to the genus *Chloriòn* (*Sphéx* of many authors), may be recognized by the fact that the second and third submarginal cells each receive a recurrent vein (Figure 29-68 A). These wasps nest in burrows in the ground and provision their nests with grasshoppers or crickets. A common species in this group is *C. ichneumòneum* (Linn.), which is reddish brown with the tip of the abdomen black (Figure 29-75). The wasps in the tribe Sphecìni (=Ammophilìni), which are very slender and usually black with the basal half or two-thirds of the abdomen yellowish or orange (Figure 29-74 B), nest in burrows in the ground and provision their nests with caterpillars.

The tribe Sceliphronìni contains two genera, *Scéliphron* and *Chalýbion,* which have a **U**-shaped area on the dorsal surface of the propodeum; these wasps, commonly called mud-daubers, construct nests of mud and provision them with spiders. Their nests usually consist of a number of cells, each about an inch long, placed side by side. Mud-dauber nests are quite common on the ceilings and walls of old buildings. The two most common species of mud-daubers are *S. cementàrium* (Drury), which is blackish brown with yellow spots and yellow legs, and *C. califórnicum* (Saussure), which is metallic blue with bluish wings. The tribe Podiìni contains a single genus, *Pòdium*; these wasps, which are mainly southern in distribution, provision their nests with cockroaches.

—Subfamily *Nyssonìnae*— The Nyssonìnae is a large and varied group, and its members have been variously classified by different workers. Nearly all the members of this subfamily have the mesonotum expanded laterally into laminae, which more or less overlie the bases of the tegulae, and the anal lobe of the hind wing is shorter than

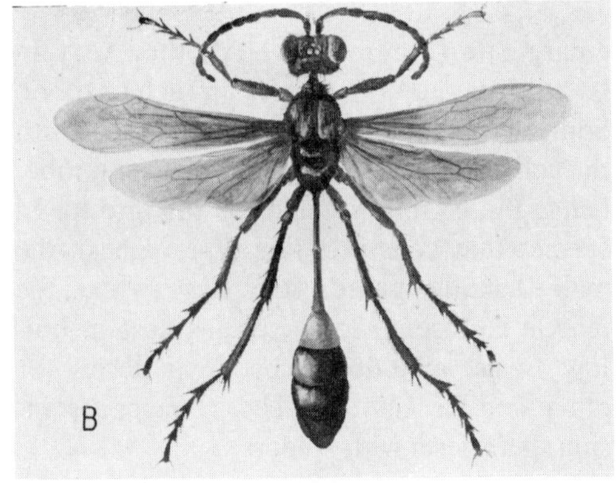

Fig. 29-74. Thread-waisted wasps (Sphecìnae). A, *Chloriòn aeràrium* (Patton); B, *Sphéx nígricans* (Dahlbom); $1\frac{1}{2}\times$.

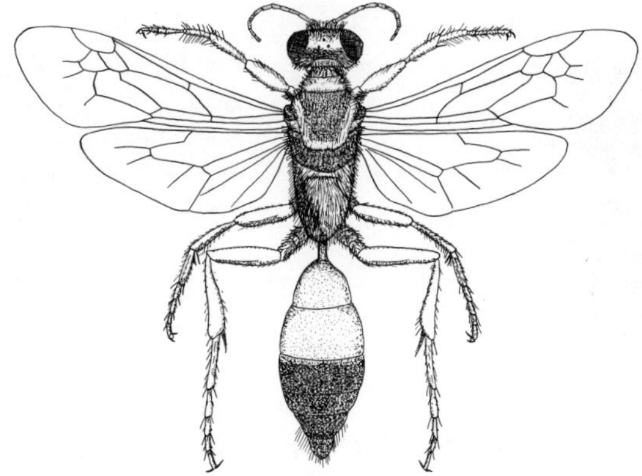

Fig. 29-75. A common thread-waisted wasp, *Chloriòn ichneumòneum* (Linn.); $1\frac{1}{2}\times$.

the submedian cell; all except the Bembicìni have two apical spurs on the middle tibiae. This subfamily is usually divided into six tribes, the Mellinìni, Alyssonìni (Alysonìni), Nyssonìni, Gorytìni, Stizìni, and Bembicìni.

The Mellinìni nest in the ground and provision their nests with adult flies; these wasps are small and rare. The Alyssonìni are also rather rare; little is known of their nesting habits, but some species nest in the ground and provision their nests with leafhoppers. The Nyssonìni are a small and not very common group; most species are inquilines in the nests of other sphecoid wasps and bees.

Most of the Gorytìni are small wasps, about $\frac{1}{2}$ inch long or less, with black and yellow markings; they nest in burrows in the ground and provision their nests with various Homoptera, chiefly Cercópidae, Cicadéllidae, and Membrácidae. One species in this group, *Sphècius speciòsus* (Drury), commonly known as the cicada-killer, is a very large and striking insect (Figure 29-76 A); it varies in length from about 1 to $1\frac{1}{2}$ inches and is black or rusty in color with yellow bands on the abdomen. Cicada-killer wasps nest in burrows in the ground and provision their nests with cicadas.

The Stizìni are a small group; most species nest in the ground; some provision their nests with meadow grasshoppers and others with leafhoppers. The species in the genus *Stizòides* are "cuckoo" wasps, laying

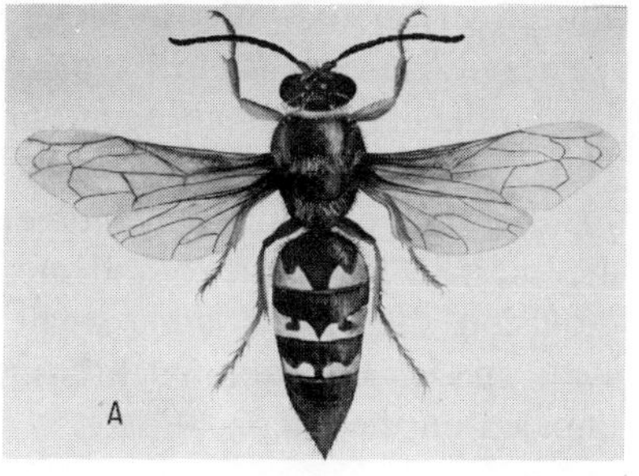

Fig. 29-76. Nyssonine wasps. A, the cicada-killer wasp, *Sphècius speciòsus* (Drury), about natural size; B, a sand wasp, *Epibémbex spinòlae* (Lepeltier), slightly enlarged.

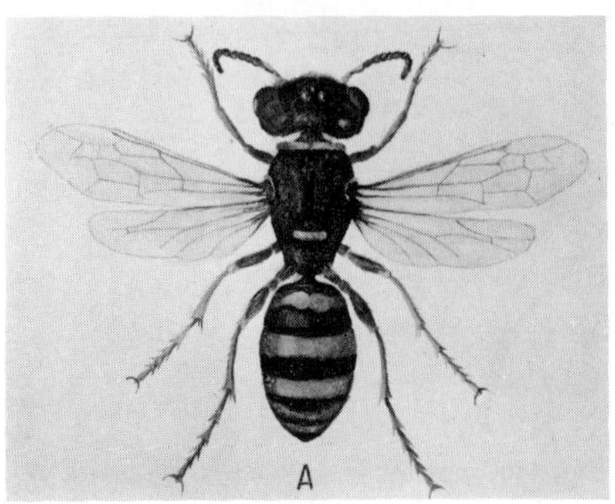

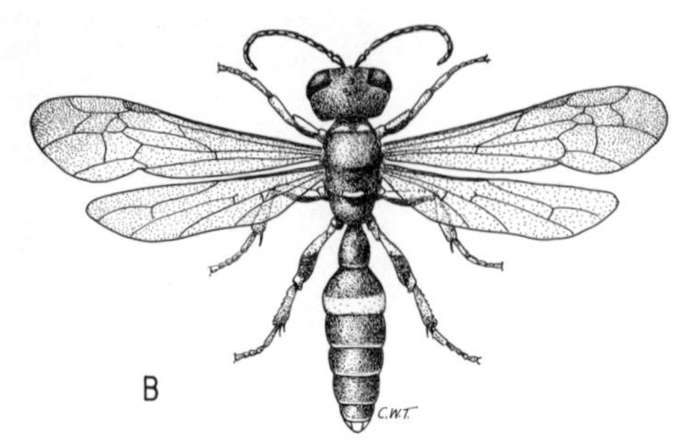

Fig. 29-77. Philanthine wasps. A, a bee-killer wasp, *Philánthus ventílabris* Fabricius; B, a weevil wasp, *Cérceris clypeàta* Dahlbom; 2 ×.

their eggs on the grasshopper prey of certain thread-waisted wasps.

The Bembicìni, or sand wasps, are rather stout-bodied wasps of moderate size (Figure 29-76 B) which are most easily recognized by the elongate and triangular labrum (Figure 29-69 B). They nest in burrows in the sand and differ from most of the other sphecoid wasps in that a great many burrows may be made in a small area—to form what amount to colonies—and the adults continue to feed the larvae during their growth. The food of the larvae consists mainly of flies; a few species feed their young nymphal Hemiptera, adult Lepidoptera, or bees. *Microbémbex monodónta* (Say) is a common sand wasp occurring in the Northeast and along the seashore; it is largely black with greenish-white markings. *Bémbix carolìna* (Fabricius), an insect about an inch long and black with yellow markings, is fairly common in the South; it often hunts for flies near horses, and is called the "horse guard." Other sand wasps are black with yellow, white, or pale-green markings.

—Subfamily *Philanthìnae*— The Philanthìnae are digger wasps of medium size, usually black with yellow markings, which have a distinct constriction between the first and second abdominal segments (Figure 29-70 A, B). The Philanthìni, or bee-killer wasps (Figure 29-77 A), provision their nests with bees or winged ants; the Cercerìni, or beetle wasps (Figure 29-77 B), provision their nests with various types of beetles (Chrysomélidae, Bupréstidae, and Curculiónidae). These wasps are fairly common.

—Subfamily *Crabronìnae*— The Crabronìnae are another group of digger wasps. The Crabronìni, or square-headed wasps, are fairly common insects that vary in length from about 6 to 20 millimeters and are usually black with yellow markings (Figure 29-78 A). They are easily recognized by the large and quadrate head, with the inner margins of the eyes straight and converging ventrally (Figure 29-69 E), and the single submarginal cell (Figure 29-66 B). The square-headed wasps vary in their nesting habits; some nest in hollow stems or in abandoned galleries in wood (Figure 29-78 B), and others burrow in the ground. The principal prey utilized by these wasps is flies, but some species utilize various other types of insects. The adults are commonly found on flowers. The Oxybelìni, or spiny digger wasps, are a small group of rather uncommon wasps; they nest in sandy areas, and most species provision their nests with small flies; in some species the captured flies are carried impaled on the sting.

SUPERFAMILY APÒIDEA—BEES: The bees are abundant in both species and indivi-

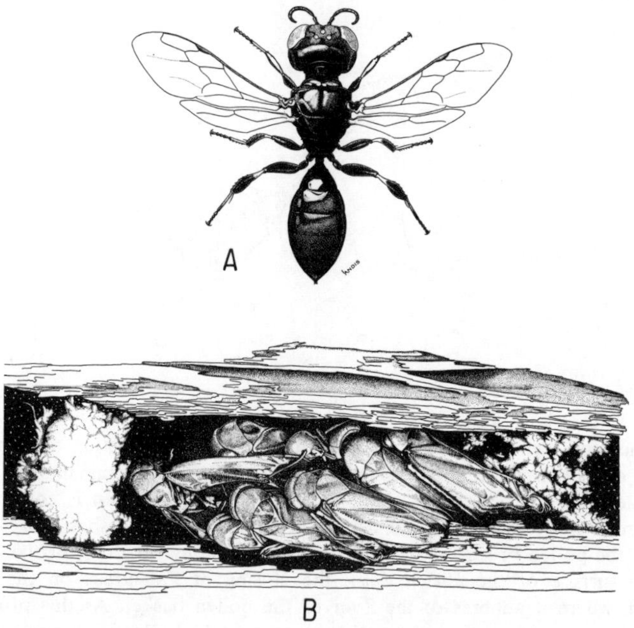

Fig. 29-78. A square-headed wasp, *Crossócerus ambíguus* (Dahlbom), A, adult, 2 ×; B, a section of a rotting log in which this wasp has stored leafhoppers. (Courtesy of Davidson and Landis and the Entomological Society of America.)

duals and are to be found almost everywhere, particularly on flowers. They differ from most of the wasps in that the young are fed honey and pollen rather than animal food, and the honey is collected in the form of nectar from flowers and elaborated into honey in the crop of the bee.

The bees resemble the sphecoid wasps in having the pronotum terminating laterally in rounded lobes that do not reach the tegulae. The most distinctive feature that separates the bees from the wasps is the form of the body hairs; in the bees, at least some of the body hairs, particularly those on the thorax, are branched or plumose, whereas the body hairs of wasps are simple and unbranched. Those bees that are parasitic—that is, which live as inquilines in the nests of other bees—are usually wasplike in appearance with relatively little body hair and without a pollen-collecting apparatus, and can be recognized as bees only by a very careful examination of the body hairs. The bees that are not parasitic, which construct a nest and collect pollen and have a pollen-collecting apparatus, are usually easily distinguished from wasps.

The distinctive structures of the nonparasitic bees have to do largely with the pollen-collecting apparatus (Figure 29-79). Most bees are quite hairy, and as they visit flowers a certain amount of pollen more or less accidentally sticks to their body hairs. This pollen is periodically combed off and carried either on the ventral side of the abdomen (Megachílidae) or on the hind legs (other bees; see Figure 29-80). The bees that carry pollen on their hind legs have the first segment of the hind tarsi enlarged and more or less flattened. The pollen-collecting apparatus thus consists of brushes of hairs (called scopae), located either on the hind legs or on the ventral side of the abdomen

The maxillae and labium of bees form a tonguelike structure through which the insect sucks up nectar. There is some development of such a tongue in other Hymenoptera, but in most bees the tongue

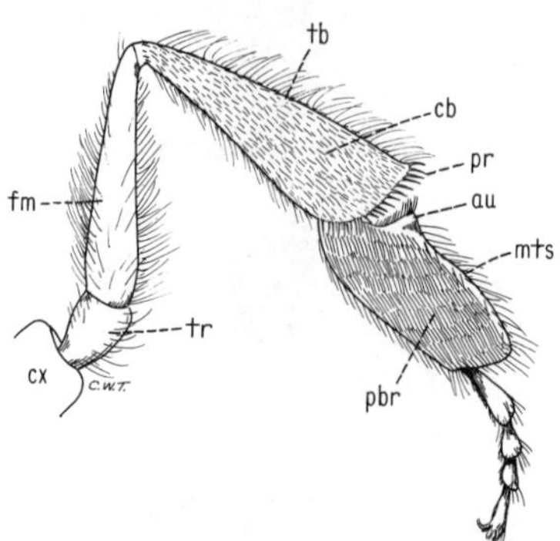

Fig. 29-79. The hind leg of a honey bee, showing the pollen-collecting apparatus. *au,* auricle; *cb,* corbicula or pollen basket; *cx,* coxa; *fm,* femur; *mts,* first tarsal segment; *pbr,* pollen brush; *pr,* pollen rake or pecten; *tb,* tibia; *tr,* trochanter. The pollen is collected off the body hairs by the front and middle legs and deposited on the pollen brushes *(pbr)* of the hind legs. The pollen on the pollen brush of one leg is raked off by the rake (*pr*) of the other, the pollen falling on the surface of the auricle (*au*); the closing of the tarsus on the tibia forces the pollen upward, where it adheres to the floor of the pollen basket. As this process is repeated, first on one side and then on the other, the pollen is packed into the lower ends of the pollen baskets until both are filled (see also Fig. 29-80).

is elongate and the bee is thus able to reach the nectar in flowers with a deep corolla. The structure of the tongue differs considerably in different bees and provides characters that are used in classification.

The two sexes of bees differ in the number of antennal segments and abdominal tergites. The males have 13 antennal segments and 7 visible abdominal tergites; the females have only 12 antennal segments and 6 visible abdominal tergites.

The pollen-collecting bees play an extremely important role in the pollination of plants. Some of the higher plants are self-pollinating, but a great many are cross-pollinated; that is, the pollen of one flower must be transferred to the stigma of another. Cross-pollination is brought about by two principal agencies, the wind and insects. Wind-pollinated plants include the grasses (such as the cereal grains, timothy, and the like), many trees (such as the willows, oaks, hickories, elms, poplars, and conifers), and many wild plants. The insect-pollinated plants include most of our orchard fruits, berries, many vegetables (particularly the cucurbits), many field crops (such as the clovers, cotton, and tobacco), and many flowers. Most of the pollination is done by bees, often chiefly honey bees and bumble bees, but a great deal of pollinating is done by certain solitary bees. Many growers, by bringing in hives of honey bees when the plants are in bloom, have been able to get greatly increased yields of orchard fruits, clover seed, and other crops that are dependent on bees for pollination. When it is realized that the annual value of the insect-pollinated crops in this country is about $4½ billion, it will be apparent that the bees are extremely valuable insects.

The bees are very similar to the wasps in their nesting habits. Most species are solitary and nest in burrows in the ground, in cavities in plants, or in similar situations. The nests are always provisioned with honey and pollen. A number of bees (often called cuckoo bees) build no nest of their own, but lay their eggs in the nests of other bees; these are the parasitic bees, or in-

Fig. 29-80. A honey bee collecting pollen. Note the large mass of pollen on the hind leg of this bee. (Courtesy of Teale.)

quilines. Two types of bees in the United States, honey bees and bumble bees, are social, and the colonies consist of a queen, workers, and drones (males).

There has been a great deal of difference of opinion about the classification of bees, and practically every book on insects has a somewhat different arrangement of families. The arrangement followed here is that of Michener (1944).

FAMILY **Collétidae**—Plasterer Bees and Yellow-Faced Bees: This is a rather primitive group of bees, with the tongue short and either truncate or bilobed at the apex (Figure 29-15 C). The family is divided into two subfamilies, the Colletìnae and the Hylaeìnae.

—Subfamily *Colletìnae*—Plasterer Bees—These bees burrow into the ground to nest, and line their burrows with a thin translucent substance. They are of moderate size and are quite hairy, with bands of pale pubescence on the abdomen; there are three submarginal cells, and the second recurrent vein is sigmoid (Figure 29-13 D). Most of the species in this subfamily belong to the genus *Collètes*.

—Subfamily *Hylaeìnae* (*Prosopìnae*)—Yellow-Faced Bees— The Hylaeìnae are small, black, very sparsely hairy bees, usually with yellowish markings on the face (Figure 29-81) and with only two submarginal cells (Figure 29-13 E). They are very wasplike in appearance, and the hind legs of the females do not have pollen brushes. They nest in various sorts of cavities and crevices, in plant stems, or in burrows in the ground. Our species belong to the genus *Hylaèus*.

FAMILY **Andrénidae**—Mining Bees: The andrenids are medium-sized bees that can be recognized by the two subantennal sutures below each antennal socket (Figure 29-12 A). They nest in burrows in the ground; the main tunnel is usually vertical, with lateral tunnels branching off from it and each terminating in a single cell. Some-

Fig. 29-81. A yellow-faced bee, *Hylaèus modéstus* Say; 10 ×.

times large numbers of these bees will nest close together, usually in areas where the vegetation is sparse.

Three subfamilies of andrenids occur in the United States: the Andrenìnae, Panurgìnae, and Oxaeìnae. In the Andrenìnae the apex of the marginal cell is pointed or narrowly rounded and on the costal margin of the wing (Figure 29-13 A); in the other two subfamilies the apex of the marginal cell is truncate or bent away from the costal margin of the wing. The Panurgìnae have two submarginal cells and a well-developed stigma in the front wings (Figure 29-13 B); the Oxaeìnae have three submarginal cells and the stigma is virtually absent. The Andrenìnae is a large and widely distributed group, most of the species of which are in the genus *Andrèna*; the Panurgìnae is a smaller and less common group, but is widely distributed; the Oxaeìnae are restricted to southwestern United States.

FAMILY **Halíctidae**—Mining Bees: The halictids are small to moderate-sized bees, often metallic, and can usually be recognized by the strongly arched basal vein (Figure 29-13 C). Most of them nest in burrows in the ground, either on level ground or in banks, and the burrows are similar to those of the andrenids. Large numbers of these bees often nest close together, and many bees may use the same passageway to the outside.

Three subfamilies of halictids occur in the United States: the Halictìnae (the largest and most common of the three subfamilies), Nomiìnae, and Dufoureìnae. The Dufoureìnae, represented by the genus *Dufóurea*, differ from the other two subfamilies in that they have only two submarginal cells, and have the clypeus short, usually not longer than the labrum, and in profile strongly convex and protruding. The Nomiìnae, represented by the genus *Nòmia*, have the first and third submarginal cells about the same length; these bees are often of considerable importance in the pollination

Fig. 29-82. Mining bees. A, *Andrèna wilkélla* (Kirby) (Andrénidae); B, *Agapóstemon viréscens* (Fabricius) (Halíctidae).

of plants. In the Halictìnae the third submarginal cell is shorter than the first; this subfamily contains several genera of fairly common bees. In *Agapóstemon* (Figure 29-82 B), *Augochloròpsis*, and *Augochlòra*, the head and thorax are a brilliant metallic blue; these bees are small, 14 millimeters in length or less, and some of the bees in the genus *Augochlòra* are only a few millimeters in length. The other two fairly common genera of Halictìnae are *Halíctus* and *Sphecòdes*; these usually have the head and thorax black (in some species of *Halíctus* the head and thorax are metallic); in *Halíctus* the abdomen has bands of pale pubescence, and in *Sphecòdes* the abdomen is red. The bees in the genus *Sphecòdes* are rather wasplike in appearance and are parasitic. Some of the small members of the genus *Halíctus* are frequently attracted to people who are perspiring, and are called sweat bees.

FAMILY **Melíttidae:** The melittids are small, dark-colored, rather rare bees, similar in nesting habits to the Andrénidae. They differ from the bees in the preceding families in that they have the jugal lobe of the hind wing shorter than the submedian cell; they differ from the following families in that they have the segments of the labial palpi similar and cylindrical; the labial palpi of the Megachílidae and Ápidae have the first two segments elongate and flattened. Three subfamilies of Melíttidae occur in the United States: the Macropidìnae (with two submarginal cells and a very broad stigma), Dasypodìnae (with two submarginal cells and a narrow stigma), and Melittìnae (with three submarginal cells).

FAMILY **Megachílidae**—Leafcutting Bees: The leafcutting bees are mostly moderate-sized, fairly stout-bodied bees (Figure 29-83). They differ from most other bees in having two submarginal cells of about equal length (Figure 29-13 F), and the females of the pollen-collecting species have the pollen brushes on the ventral side of the abdomen rather than on the hind legs. The common name of these bees is derived from the fact that in many species the cells are lined with pieces cut from leaves; these pieces are usually very neatly cut out, and it is not uncommon to find plants from which neat circular pieces have been cut by these bees. A few species in this family are parasitic. The nests are made in various places, occasionally in the ground but more often in some natural cavity, frequently in wood.

This family is divided into two subfamilies, the Lithurgìnae and the Megachilìnae; the former is represented by a single genus, *Lithúrge*, which occurs chiefly in the South, and its members feed largely on cactus flowers; the Megachilìnae form a large group of widespread distribution. Some of the more common genera of Megachilìnae are *Anthídium, Dianthídium, Stèlis, Herìades, Hóplitis, Ósmia, Megachìle,* and *Coelióxys*; the bees in the genera *Stèlis* and *Coelióxys* are parasitic. In *Coelióxys* the abdomen is somewhat conical and tapers posteriorly almost to a point.

FAMILY **Ápidae:** This family is divided into three subfamilies: the Anthophorìnae,

Fig. 29-83. A leafcutting bee, *Megachìle latimànus* Say; 3 ×.

Fig. 29-84. A cuckoo bee, *Triepèolus lunàtus* (Say) (Anthophorìnae); 3 ×.

Xylocopìnae, and Apìnae. The Apìnae have the maxillary palpi vestigial and the hind tibiae without apical spurs (honey bees), the genal areas broad (bumble bees), or the scutellum produced posteriorly (Euglossìni); the other two subfamilies have the maxillary palpi well developed, the hind tibiae with spurs, the genal areas very narrow, and the scutellum not produced posteriorly. The Anthophorìnae have the clypeus somewhat protuberant, the front coxae little broader than long, and the last abdominal tergite usually (at least in females) with a triangular platelike area; the Xylocopìnae do not have the clypeus protuberant, the front coxae are transverse, and the last abdominal tergite lacks a triangular platelike area.

—Subfamily *Anthophorìnae*—Mining or Digger Bees and Cuckoo Bees— The parasitic species in this group (the cuckoo bees) belong to the tribes Nomadìni, Biastìni, Townsendiellìni, Ammobatìni, Holcopasitìni, Neolarrìni, Melictìni, Epeolìni, Protepeolìni and Epeoloidìni. They are usually wasplike in appearance and have very few hairs on the body. Some of them (for example, members of the genus *Nómada*) are usually reddish and of medium or small size; others (for example, *Epèolus* and *Triepèolus*) (Figure 29-84), are fair-sized (½ to ¾ inch in length) and dark-colored, with small patches of short pale pubescence. The pollen-collecting bees in this group belong chiefly to the tribes Emphorìni, Eucerìni, and Anthophorìni; they are mostly fair-sized, robust, hairy bees (Figure 29-85 A). They nest in burrows in the ground or in banks, and the cells are lined with a thin wax or varnishlike substance.

—Subfamily *Xylocopìnae*—Carpenter Bees — These bees make their nests in wood or plant stems. The two genera in this group, *Ceràtina* and *Xylócopa*, differ somewhat in habits, and their members differ considerably in size. The small carpenter bees (*Ceràtina*) are dark bluish green and about 6 millimeters in length; they are superficially similar to some of the halictids, particularly since the basal vein is noticeably arched, but may be distinguished from a halictid by the much smaller jugal lobe in the hind wings (Figures 29-13 C and 29-14 F). These bees excavate the pith from the stems of various bushes and nest in the tunnels so produced (Figure 29-87). The large carpenter bees (*Xylócopa*) are robust bees about an inch in length, similar in appearance to bumble bees, but have the dorsum of the abdomen largely bare (Figure 29-86 A), and the second submarginal cell

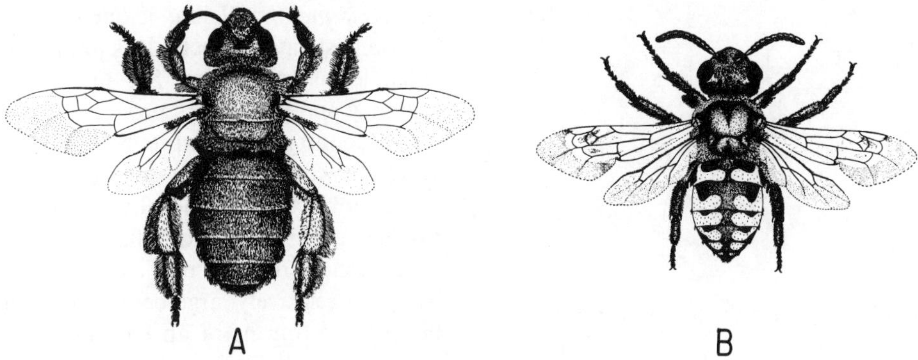

Fig. 29-85. Anthophorine bees. A, a digger bee, *Anthóphora occidentàlis* Cresson, 2 ×; B, a cuckoo bee, *Melícta califórnica miránda* Fox, 2 ×, an inquiline of *A. occidentàlis.* (Courtesy of Porter.)

Fig. 29-86. A, a large carpenter bee, *Xylócopa virgínica* (Linn.) (Xylocopìnae); B, a bumble bee, *Bómbus americanòrum* (Fabricius) (Bombini, Apinae). $1\frac{1}{2}$ ×.

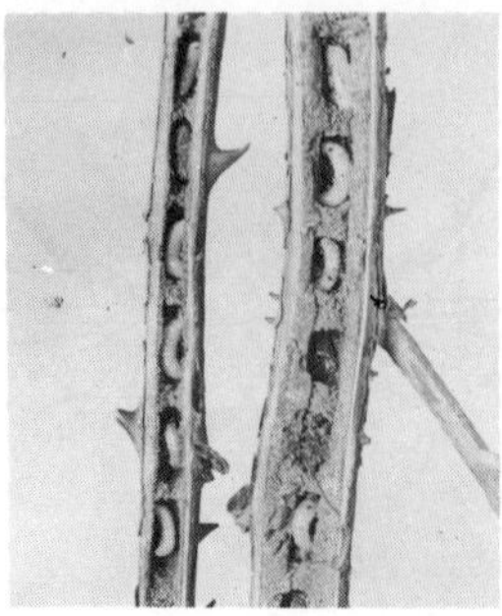

Fig. 29-87. Nest of the small carpenter bee, *Cerátina dùpla* Say.

is triangular (Figure 29-14 A); these bees excavate galleries in solid wood.

—Subfamily *Apìnae*—Social Bees— Three tribes of this subfamily occur in the United States: the Bombìni, or bumble bees (*Bómbus* and *Psíthyrus*); the Apìni, or honey bees (*Àpis*); and the Euglossìni, a tropical group represented by a single species in southern Texas. The bumble bees (except for those in the genus *Psíthyrus*, which are inquilines of *Bómbus* bumble bees) and honey bees differ from the other bees in this country in being social. The social bees are common and well-known insects, and they are the most important bees in the pollination of plants. The honey bee, *Àpis mellífera* Linn., is one of the very few domesticated insects; it is an extremely valuable insect, as some $50 million worth of honey and beeswax is produced annually in this country by it, and its pollinating activities are worth 15 or 20 times this amount.

Bumble bees can usually be recognized by their robust shape and black and yellow coloration; a few are marked with orange. They are relatively large bees, most of them being three-fourths of an inch in length or more. The hind wings lack a jugal lobe (Figure 29-14 B), and there is a distinct space (the genal space) between the eye and the base of the mandible. Honey bees may be recognized by their golden brown coloration and characteristic shape (Figures 29-80 and 29-88), the form of the marginal and submarginal cells in the front wings (Figure 29-14 D), and the absence of spurs on the hind tibiae.

The bumble bees of the genus *Bómbus* nest in the ground, usually in a deserted mouse nest or bird nest or similar situation. The colonies are annual (at least in temperate regions), and only the fertilized queens overwinter. In the spring, the queen selects a nest site and begins construction of the

Fig. 29-88. The honey bee, *Àpis mellífera* Linn.; 5 ×.

nest; the first brood raised by the queen consists of workers. Once the workers appear, they take over all the duties of the colony except egg-laying; they enlarge the nest, collect food and store it in little saclike "honey pots," and care for the larvae. Later in the summer, males and queens are produced, and in the fall all but the queens die.

Bumble bees are very important in the pollination of certain kinds of clover because of their very long tongues.

The bumble bees of the genus *Psíthyrus* differ from those of *Bómbus* in having the outer surface of the hind tibiae convex and hairy (flat or concave and largely bare in *Bómbus*). These bees have no worker caste; they invade the nests of *Bómbus* and lay their eggs, leaving their young to be reared by the *Bómbus* workers. In the absence of a worker caste, the males of *Psíthyrus* can usually be readily distinguished in the field from the queens by their smaller size.

Only a single species of honey bee occurs in this country, *Àpis mellífera* Linn.; this is an introduced species, and most of its colonies are in man-made hives; escaped swarms usually nest in a hollow tree. The cells in the nest are in vertical combs, two cell layers thick. Honey-bee colonies are perennial, with the queen and workers overwintering in the hive; a queen may live several years. Unlike the bumble bee queen, the honey-bee queen is unable to start a colony by herself. As in most of the Hymenoptera, the sex of a bee is determined by the fertilization of the egg; fertilized eggs develop into females, and unfertilized eggs develop into males. Whether a larval honey bee destined to become a female becomes a worker or queen depends on the sort of food it is fed. There is normally only one queen in a honey-bee colony; when a new one is produced, it may be killed by the old queen, or one of the queens (usually the old queen) may leave the hive in a swarm, along with a group of workers, and build a nest elsewhere. The new queen mates during a mating flight, and thereafter never leaves the hive except to swarm. The males serve only to fertilize the queen, and only one of them is able to carry out this function; they do not remain in the colony long, as they are eventually killed by the workers.

Honey bees have a very interesting "language," a means of communicating with one another. When a worker goes out and discovers a flower with a good nectar flow, she returns to the hive and "tells" other workers about it: the type of flower, its direction from the hive, and how far away it is. The type of flower involved is communicated by means of its odor, either on the body hairs of the bee that discovered the flower or in the honey it brings back from the flower. The distance and direction of the flower from the hive are "told" by means of a peculiar sort of dance put on by the returning worker. Many social insects undoubtedly have a "language" or a means of communication, but its exact nature is known in very few cases.

The Euglossìni are brilliant metallic, nonsocial bees that are tropical in distribution. They differ from the honey bees in that they have apical spurs on the hind tibiae, lack the jugal lobe in the hind wings, and have the scutellum produced posteriorly over the abdomen. One species in this group has been recorded from Brownsville, Texas.

COLLECTING AND PRESERVING HYMENOPTERA

Most of the general collecting methods described in Chapter 32 will apply to the insects in this order. Species of Hymenoptera are to be found almost everywhere, and to secure a large variety of species, one should examine all available habitats and use all available methods of collecting. Many of the larger and more showy Hymenoptera are common on flowers. The parasitic species may be reared from parasitized hosts, or they may be taken by sweeping. Many insects in this order are attracted to lights or to various types of molasses baits.

Since many of the Hymenoptera sting, it is well to exercise a certain amount of care in removing them from the net. The simplest way is to get the insect into a fold of the net and stun it by pinching the thorax; then it may be transferred to the killing bottle. If one has a pair of forceps, he can grasp the insect through the net with the forceps and transfer it to the killing bottle. A third method, which is considerably slower, is to get the insect into a fold of the net and then put this fold into the killing jar until the insect is stunned. Some of the large ichneumons that have the abdomen laterally flattened (subfamily Ophioninae) are able to "sting" by jabbing with their short sharp ovipositor; such insects should be grasped through the net by the *abdomen*; this way, since the insect cannot move its abdomen, it cannot jab with the ovipositor. Many stinging Hymenoptera feeding on flowers can be collected directly into a killing jar without the use of a net.

The smaller Hymenoptera should be mounted on their side on a point, or if they are extremely minute, they should be preserved in liquid or mounted on a microscope slide; it is usually necessary to mount the more minute forms on microscope slides for detailed study. Some of the best characters for the identification of bees are in the mouth parts; hence the mouth parts of these insects should be extended if possible. All specimens, whether pinned or mounted on points, should be oriented so that the leg and thoracic characters and venation can be easily seen. The Hymenoptera are generally harder-bodied than the Diptera and are less likely to be damaged in handling.

REFERENCES ON THE HYMENOPTERA

Ashmead, W. H. 1904. Classification of the chalcid flies or the superfamily Chalcidoidea, with descriptions of new species in the Carnegie Museum. Carnegie Museum Mem., 1(4):225-551; illus.

Bischoff, H. 1927. Biologie der Hymenopteren. Berlin: Verlag Julius Springer. 598 pp., 224 f.

Clausen, C. P. 1940. Entomophagous insects. New York: McGraw-Hill Book Co., Inc. x+688 pp., 257 f. Hymenoptera, pp. 3-342, f. 2-156.

Creighton, W. S. 1950. The ants of North America. Harvard Univ., Museum Compar. Zool. Bull. 104:1-585; illus.

Dalla Torre, K. W. 1891-1898. Catalogus Hymenopterorum. Leipzig: Engelmann. 10 vol. Vol. 1, 1894, Tenthredinidae incl. Uroceridae (Phyllophaga and Xylophaga), x+459 pp. Vol. 2, 1893, Cynipidae, 140 pp. Vol. 3, 1891-1892, Trigonalidae, Megalyridae, Stephanidae, Ichneumonidae, Agriotypidae, Evaniidae, Pelecinidae, viii+1141 pp. Vol. 4, 1898, Braconidae, 323 pp. Vol. 5, 1898, Chalcididae and Proctotrupidae, x+598 pp. Vol. 6, 1892, Chrysididae (Tubulifera), x+118 pp. Vol. 7, 1893, Formicidae (Heterogyna), 289 pp. Vol. 8, 1897, Fossores (Sphegidae), x+749 pp. Vol. 9, 1894, Vespidae (Diploptera), 181 pp. Vol. 10, 1896, Apidae (Anthophila), x+643 pp.

Duncan, Carl D. 1939. A contribution to the biology of the North American vespine wasps. Stanford Univ. Publs., Univ. Ser., Biol. Sci., 8(1):1-272; 54 pl.

Grout, Roy A. (ed.). 1949. The hive and the honey bee. Hamilton, Ill.: Dadant & Sons. xviii+652 pp., 305 f.

Kinsey, A. C. 1936. The origin of the higher categories in *Cynips*. Indiana Univ., Cont. Dept. Zool., No. 242 (Entomol. Ser. No. 10); 334 pp., 172 f.

Krombein, Karl V., *et al.* 1958. Hymenoptera of America north of Mexico; synoptic catalogue. U.S. Dep. Agr., Agr. Monog. No. 2, First Supplement. 305 pp.

Michener, C. D. 1944. Comparative external morphology, phylogeny, and a classification of the bees (Hymenoptera). Amer. Museum Nat. Hist. Bull. 82(6):151-326; 13 diag., 246 f.

Michener, C. D., and M. H. Michener.

1951. American social insects. New York: D. Van Nostrand Co. xiv+267 pp., 109 f.

Muesebeck, C. F. W., Karl V. Krombein, Henry K. Townes, *et al.* 1951. Hymenoptera of America north of Mexico. Synoptic catalogue. U.S. Dep. Agr., Agr. Monog. No. 2; 1420 pp.

Peckham, G. W., and E. G. Peckham. 1905. Wasps, social and solitary. Boston: Houghton Mifflin Co. xvi+311 pp., illus.

Rau, Phil, and N. L. Rau. 1918. Wasp studies afield. Princeton, N.J.: Princeton University Press. 372 pp.

Root, A. I., and E. R. Root. 1929. The ABC and XYZ of bee culture. Medina, Ohio: The A. I. Root Company. vii+815 pp., illus.

Ross, H. H. 1936. The ancestry and wing venation of the Hymenoptera. Ann. Entomol. Soc. Am., 29(1):99-111; 2 pl.

Ross, H. H. 1937. A generic classification of nearctic sawflies (Hymenoptera, Symphyta). Illinois Biol. Monog., 15(2):1-173; 1 chart, 424 f.

Smith, M. R. 1943. A generic and subgeneric synopsis of the male ants of the United States. Am. Midland Naturalist, 30(2):273-321; 7 f.

Smith, M. R. 1947. A generic and subgeneric synopsis of the United States ants, based on workers (Hymenoptera, Formicidae). Am. Midland Naturalist, 37(3):521-647; 85 f.

Snodgrass, R. E. 1941. The male genitalia of Hymenoptera. Smithsonian Inst. Misc. Collections, 99(14):1-86; 33 pl., 6 text f.

Townes, Henry and Marjorie. 1959. Ichneumon-Flies of America north of Mexico: 1. Subfamily Metopiinae. U.S. Natl. Museum Bull. 216; ix+318 pp., 196 f.

Townes, Henry and Marjorie, *et al.* 1960. Ichneumon-Flies of America north of Mexico: 2. Subfamilies Ephialtinae, Xoridinae, Acaenitinae. U.S. Natl. Museum Bull. No. 216, Part 2; vii+676 pp., 378 f.

Townes, Henry and Marjorie. 1962. Ichneumon-Flies of America north of Mexico: 3. Subfamily Gelinae, Tribe Mesostenini. U.S. Natl. Museum Bull. 216, Part 3; viii+602 pp., 400 f.

Viereck, H. L., *et al.* 1916. The Hymenoptera, or wasp-like insects, of Connecticut. Conn. State Geol. and Nat. Hist. Survey, Bull. 22; 824 pp., 15 f., 10 pl.

Wheeler, W. M. 1910. Ants, their structure, development, and behavior. New York: Columbia University Press. xxvi+663 pp., 286 f.

Wheeler, W. M. 1928. The social insects, their origin and evolution. New York: Harcourt, Brace & Co., Inc. xviii+378 pp., 79 f.

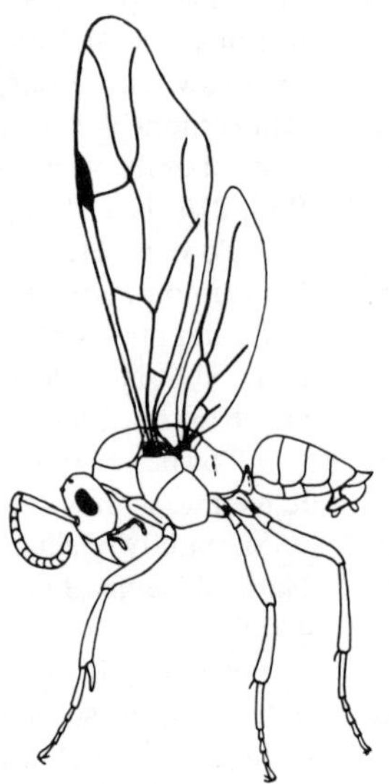

30

Arthropods Other Than Insects

Although we are concerned in this book primarily with insects, it seems appropriate to include some account of the animals most closely related to them—the other arthropods. Many other arthropods are very similar to the insects and are often mistaken for them.

The members of the Phylum Arthrópoda have a segmented body with the segments usually grouped into two or three more or less distinct body regions, paired segmented appendages, a chitinous exoskeleton that is periodically shed and renewed as the animal grows, and certain characteristic internal organs. The annelid worms (Phylum Annélida), which are closely related to the Arthrópoda, differ in that they lack segmented appendages and a chitinous exoskeleton, and their internal organs are somewhat different. Some arthropods, such as certain insect larvae, lack segmented appendages and superficially resemble certain annelids; such forms may be recognized as arthropods by their internal organization. The annelids lack tracheae and malpighian tubules, they have a well-developed and closed circulatory system, and their excretory organs consist of paired, segmentally arranged, ciliated tubes called nephridia; most of the arthropods have tracheae and malpighian tubules, have an open circulatory system, and (except for the Onychóphora, which are usually considered a separate phylum) do not have ciliated nephridia.

The various groups of arthropods are classified differently by different authorities; a synopsis of the groups as they are treated here is given below, with alternate names or arrangements in parentheses.

Subphylum Trilóbita—trilobites
Subphylum Mandibulàta—mandibulate arthropods
- Crustaceans
  - Class Crustàcea—crustaceans
- Myriapods
  - Class Diplópoda—millipedes

Class Chilópoda—centipedes
Class Paurópoda—pauropods
Class Sýmphyla—symphylids
Insects
Class Insécta (Hexápoda)—insects
Subphylum Cheliceràta—chelicerate arthropods
Class Xìphosùra—horseshoe crabs or king crabs
Class Pycnogónida—sea spiders
Class Tardigràda—water bears
Class Linguatùlida (Pentastómida)—tongueworms
Class Aráchnida—spiders, mites, scorpions, harvestmen, and others

The trilobites are primitive aquatic arthropods known only from fossils; they lived during the Palaeozoic era, but were most abundant during the Cambrian and Ordovician periods. They had a pair of antennae, with the remaining appendages similar and leglike. The preoral part of the body and the first four postoral segments were covered by a carapace, and the body had three rather distinct longitudinal divisions.

The mandibulate arthropods have one or two pairs of antennae, and a pair of mandibles; the number of legs and the character of the body regions vary in different mandibulate groups.

The chelicerate arthropods lack antennae and generally have six pairs of appendages; the first or anterior pair (the chelicerae) are jawlike; the second pair (the pedipalps) vary in form, but are usually not leglike; and the remaining four pairs are legs. There are usually two body regions, the cephalothorax (which bears the appendages) and the abdomen.

CLASS CRUSTÀCEA[1]—CRUSTACEANS

The crustaceans form a rather heterogeneous group, but nearly all are aquatic and breathe by means of gills. The head and thoracic portions of the body are often fused into a cephalothorax; the cephalothorax in many crustaceans is partly or entirely covered by a shieldlike portion of the body wall called the carapace. The appendages vary in number, but there are two pairs of antennae, a pair of appendages on each segment of the cephalothorax, and (in the subclass Malacóstraca) appendages on the abdominal segments. Most of the appendages in the Crustàcea are biramous; that is, they consist of a basal segment bearing

[1] Crustàcea: from the Latin, referring to the crustlike exoskeleton possessed by many of these animals.

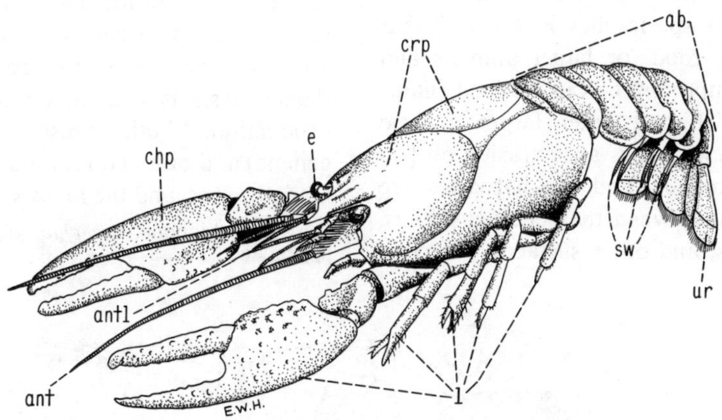

Fig. 30-1. A crayfish (*Cámbarus* sp.), natural size. *ab,* abdomen; *ant,* antenna; *antl,* antennule; *chp,* cheliped; *crp,* carapace; *e,* eye; *l,* legs (including the cheliped); *sw,* swimmerets; *ur,* uropod.

two terminal branches. One of the two branches may be lost in some specialized appendages.

Most present students of this group recognize five major subclasses of the Crustacea; four of these (the Cirripèdia, Branchiópoda, Ostrácoda, and Copépoda) are sometimes placed in a single subclass, the Entomóstraca. The five subclasses may be separated by the following key.

KEY TO THE SUBCLASSES OF CRUSTACEA

1. All body segments except the last (the telson) bearing appendages, 7 to 8 pairs on the thorax, and 6 (rarely more) on the abdomen (Figures 30-1 and 30-7 to 30-9); mostly over 5 mm in length.......... **Malacóstraca** p. 610

1′. All body segments except the last few (the abdomen) bearing appendages, the number of appendages variable (Figures 30-2 to 30-6); size variable, but mostly less than 5 mm in length............................. 2

2(1′). Free-swimming, or parasitic on fish; marine and freshwater forms...... 3

2′. Sessile forms, with the body enclosed in a shell (Figure 30-6), or parasitic on decapods or molluscs; marine .... **Cirripèdia** p. 610

3(2). Thoracic appendages flattened, often leaflike (Figures 30-2 and 30-3); mostly freshwater forms .... **Branchiópoda** p. 608

3′. Thoracic appendages slender and cylindrical (Figures 30-4 and 30-5); marine and freshwater forms.................................. 4

4(3′). Body short, unsegmented, and covered by a bivalved carapace; 4 pairs of head appendages and 3 pairs of thoracic legs (Figure 30-5).. **Ostrácoda** p. 610

4′. Body elongate and distinctly segmented, not covered by a bivalved carapace; 5 pairs of head appendages and 4 to 6 pairs of thoracic legs (Figure 30-4) .... **Copépoda** p. 610

The smaller crustaceans, particularly those in the subclasses Branchiópoda, Copépoda, and Ostrácoda, are abundant in both salt and fresh water. The chief importance of most species lies in the fact that they serve as food for larger animals and thus are an important link in the food chains leading to fish and other larger aquatic animals. A few species are parasitic on fish and other animals, and the barnacles are often a nuisance when they encrust pilings, boat bottoms, and other surfaces. Many of the smaller crustaceans can easily be maintained in indoor aquaria, and are frequently reared as food for other aquatic animals.

SUBCLASS BRANCHIÓPODA:[2] Most members of this subclass occur in fresh water. Males are uncommon in many species, and parthenogenesis is a common method of reproduction; both unisexual (parthenogenetic) and bisexual reproduction occurs in many species, and the factors controlling the

[2] Branchiópoda: *branchio*, gill; *poda*, foot or appendage.

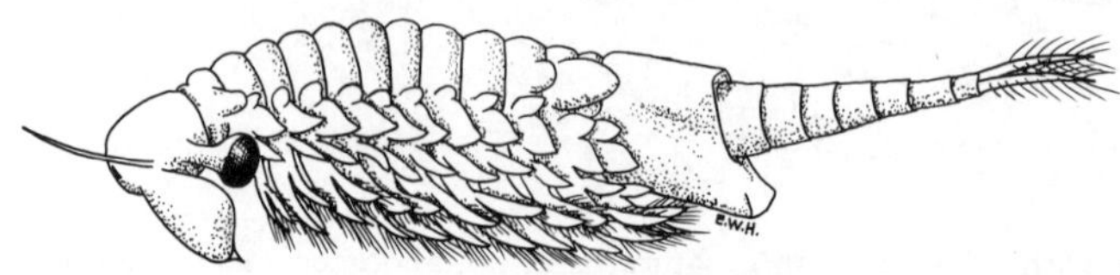

Fig. 30-2. A fairy shrimp, *Eubránchipus* (Subclass Branchiópoda, order Anóstraca); 6 ×.

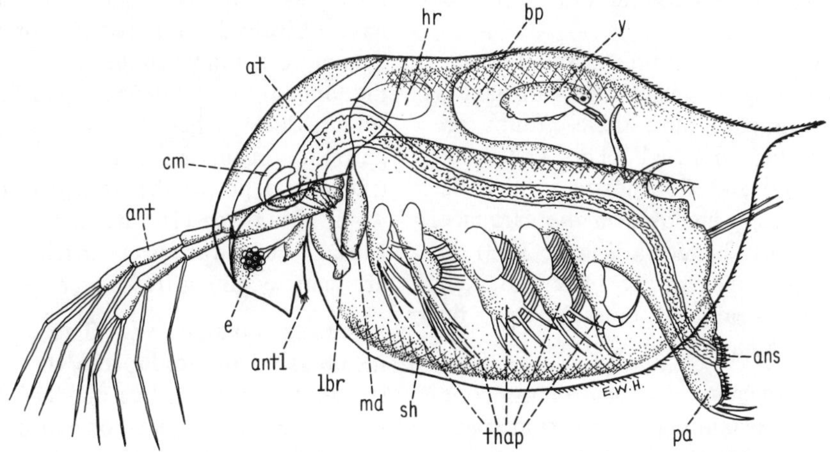

Fig. 30-3. A water flea or cladoceran, *Dáphnia* sp.; 25 ×. *ans,* anus; *ant,* antenna; *antl,* antennule; *at,* alimentary tract; *bp,* brood pouch; *cm,* caecum; *e,* compound eye; *hr,* heart; *lbr,* labrum; *md,* mandible; *pa,* postabdomen; *sh,* bivalved shell; *thap,* thoracic appendages; *y,* developing young.

production of males are not well understood.

There are differences of opinion regarding the classification of these crustaceans, but four fairly distinct groups are usually recognized, the Anóstraca, Notóstraca, Conchóstraca, and Cladócera. The first two or three of these are sometimes placed in a group called the Phyllópoda.

The Anóstraca,[3] or fairy shrimps (Figure 30-2), have the body elongate and distinctly segmented, without a carapace, with 11 pairs of swimming legs, and the eyes are stalked; the fairy shrimps are often abundant in temporary pools. The Notóstraca,[4] or tadpole shrimps, have an oval convex carapace covering the anterior part of the body, 35 to 71 pairs of thoracic appendages, and 2 long filamentous caudal appendages; these animals range in size from about $\frac{1}{2}$ to 2 inches, and are restricted to the western states. The Conchóstraca,[5] or clam shrimps, have the body somewhat flattened laterally and entirely enclosed in a bivalved carapace, and have 10 to 32 pairs of legs; most species are 10 millimeters in length or less. The Cladócera,[6] or water fleas (Figure 30-3), have a bivalved carapace, but the head is not enclosed in the carapace; there are 4 to 6 pairs of thoracic legs. The water fleas are 0.2 to 3.0 millimeters in

[3] Anóstraca: *an,* without; *ostraca,* shell.
[4] Notóstraca: *not,* back; *ostraca,* shell.
[5] Conchóstraca: *conch,* shell or shellfish; *ostraca,* shell.

[6] Cladócera: *clado,* branch; *cera,* horn (referring to the antennae).

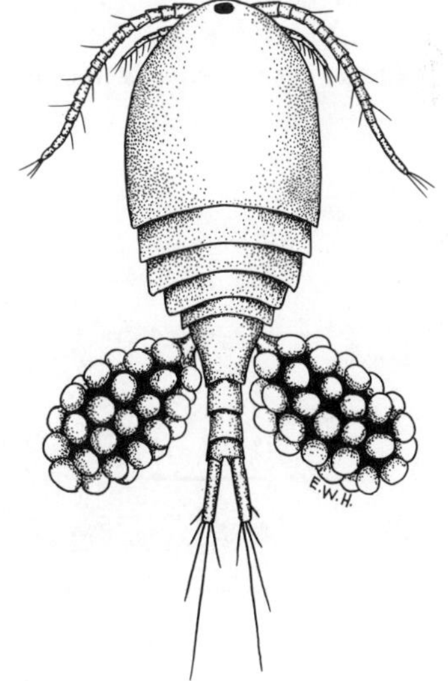

Fig. 30-4. A female copepod, *Cỳclops* sp.; 50 ×. Note the two egg sacs at the posterior end of the body.

length, and are very common in freshwater pools.

There are three groups of small crustaceans occurring in fresh water that have a bivalved carapace, and these groups are likely to be confused. The Ostrácoda (Figure 30-5) and Conchóstraca have the body completely enclosed in the carapace, whereas in the Cladócera (Figure 30-3) the head is outside the carapace. The Ostrácoda have only 3 pairs of thoracic legs; the Conchóstraca have 10 to 32 pairs.

SUBCLASS COPÉPODA:[7] Some of the copepods are free swimming and others are parasitic on fish; the parasitic forms are often peculiar in body form and quite unlike the free-swimming forms in general appearance. This group includes both marine and freshwater forms. The female of most copepods carries her eggs in two egg sacs located laterally near the end of the abdomen (Figure 30-4). The parasitic copepods are often called fish lice, and they live on the gills or skin or burrow into the flesh of their host; when numerous they may seriously injure the host. Some species serve as an intermediate host of certain human parasites [for example, *Diphyllobóthrium lātum* (Linn.)].

[7] Copépoda: *cope,* oar; *poda,* foot or appendage.

SUBCLASS OSTRÁCODA:[8] The ostracods have a bivalved carapace that can be closed by a muscle, and when the valves are closed, the animal looks like a miniature clam (Figure 30-5). When the valves of the carapace are open, the appendages are protruded and propel the animal through the water. Many species are parthenogenetic. Most of the ostracods are marine, but there are many common freshwater species.

SUBCLASS CIRRIPÈDIA: The best-known members of this group are the barnacles, the adults of which live attached to rocks, pilings, seaweeds, boats, or marine animals, and which are enclosed in a calcareous shell. A few species are parasitic, usually on crabs or molluscs. Most of the members of this group are hermaphroditic; that is, each individual contains both male and female organs. Some barnacles, such as the goose barnacle (Figure 30-6 A), have the shell attached to some object by means of a stalk; others, such as the rock barnacles (Figure 30-6 B), are sessile and do not have stalks.

SUBCLASS MALACÓSTRACA:[9] This subclass includes the larger and better known crustaceans; they differ from the preceding sub-

[8] Ostrácoda: from the Greek meaning shell-like (referring to the clamlike character of the carapace).

[9] Malacóstraca: *malac,* soft; *ostraca,* shell.

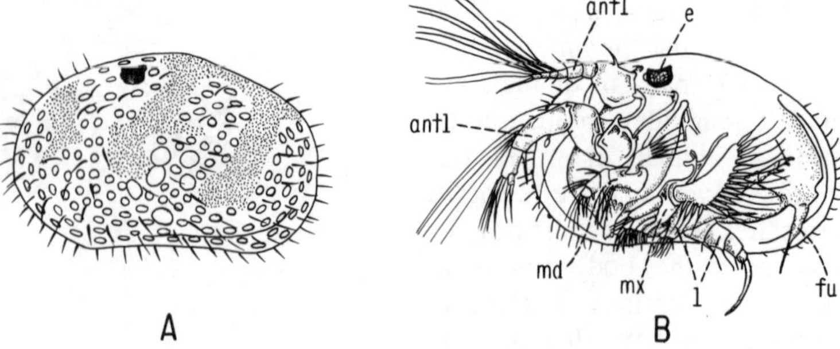

Fig. 30-5. An ostracod, *Cypridópsis* sp. **A**, lateral view; **B**, lateral view with the left valve of the carapace removed. *ant,* antenna; *antl,* antennule; *e,* eye; *fu,* furca; *l,* first and second thoracic legs; *md,* mandible; *mx,* maxilla. (B modified from Kesling.)

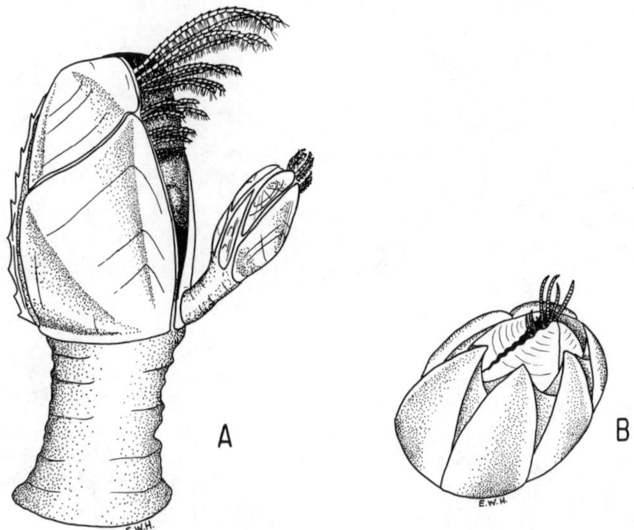

Fig. 30-6. Barnacles. A, a goose barnacle, *Lèpas* sp., 3 ×; B, a rock barnacle, *Balànus* sp., 2 ×. The basal stalk or peduncle of the goose barnacle is at the animal's anterior end; the biramous appendages protruding from the shell at the top of the figure are the posterior thoracic legs; a second small individual is shown attached to the first.

classes in having appendages (swimmerets) on the abdomen. There are typically 19 pairs of appendages, the first 13 being cephalothoracic and the last 6 abdominal. The leglike appendages on the cephalothorax are often clawlike. Only the more common orders in this group can be mentioned here.

ORDER **Amphípoda :**[10] The body of an amphipod is elongate and more or less compressed, there is no carapace, and seven (rarely six) of the thoracic segments are distinct and bear leglike appendages; the abdominal segments are often more or less fused, and hence the six or seven thoracic segments make up most of the body length (Figure 30-7). This group contains both marine and freshwater forms. Many of them, such as the beach fleas (Figure 30-7 B), live on the beach, where they occur under stones or in decaying vegetation. Most of the amphipods are scavengers.

ORDER **Isópoda :**[11] The isopods are similar to the amphipods in lacking a carapace, but are dorsoventrally flattened. The last seven thoracic segments are distinct and bear leglike appendages; the abdominal segments are more or less fused, and hence the thoracic segments (with their seven pairs of legs) make up most of the body length (Figure 30-8). The anterior abdominal appendages of the aquatic forms usually bear gills; the terminal abdominal appendages are often enlarged and feelerlike. Most of the isopods are small marine animals living under stones or among seaweed; away from the seacoast the most common species are the sowbugs—blackish, gray, or brownish animals usually found under stones, boards, or bark; some of the sowbugs (often called pillbugs) are capable of rolling up into a ball. In some areas, sowbugs are important pests of cultivated plants.

ORDER **Stomatópoda :**[12] The stomatopods are marine forms that can be recognized by the large abdomen, which is broader than

[10] Amphípoda: *amphi,* on both sides, double; *poda,* foot or appendage.

[11] Isópoda: *iso,* equal; *poda,* foot or appendage.

[12] Stomatópoda: *stomato,* mouth; *poda,* foot or appendage.

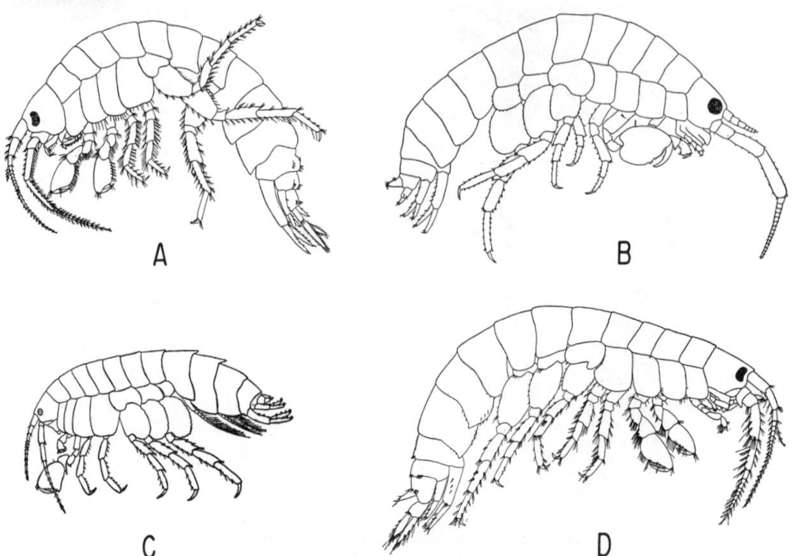

Fig. 30-7. Amphípoda. A, a common freshwater scud, *Dikerogámmarus fasciàtus* (Say), 10-15 mm in length; B, a sand flea or beach flea, *Orchéstia ágilis* Smith, abundant underneath seaweed along the coast near the high-tide mark; C, a common freshwater scud, *Hyalélla knickerbóckeri* (Bate), about 7 mm in length; D, a sea scud, *Gámmarus annulàtus* Smith, a common coastal form, about 15 mm in length. (Courtesy of Kunkle and the Connecticut State Geology and Natural History Survey; C, after Smith.)

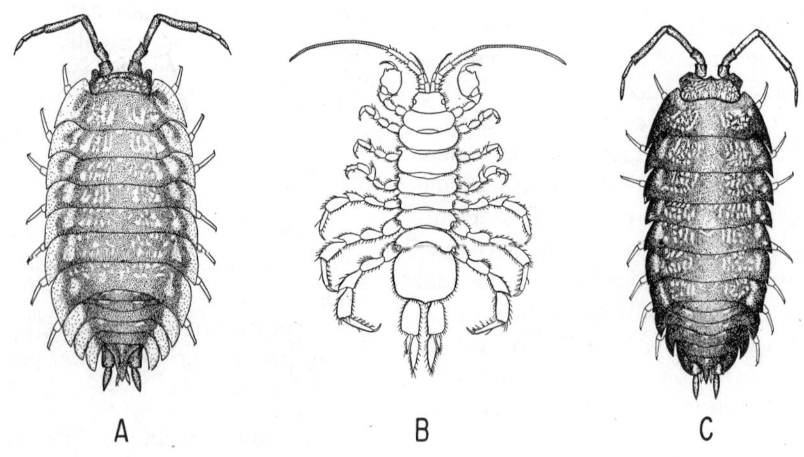

Fig. 30-8. Isópoda. A, *Oníscus asèllus* Linn., a common sowbug; B, *Asèllus commùnis* Say, a common freshwater isopod; C, *Cylísticus convéxus* (DeGeer), a pillbug capable of rolling itself into a ball. (Courtesy of the Connecticut State Geology and Natural History Survey. A and C, courtesy of Kunkle; after Paulmier. B, courtesy of Kunkle; after Smith.)

the cephalothorax. There are three pairs of legs, in front of which are five pairs of maxillipeds, one pair of which is very large and clawlike. The carapace does not cover the posterior thoracic segments. The stomatopods occur principally along our southern coasts; some are used as food.

ORDER **Decápoda**:[13] This order contains the largest and probably the best known of the crustaceans, the lobsters, crayfish (Figure 30-1), crabs (Figure 30-9), and shrimps. The carapace of a decapod covers the entire thorax; five pairs of the cephalothoracic appendages are leglike, and the first pair of these usually bears a large claw. The abdomen may be well developed (lobsters and crayfish), or it may be very much reduced (crabs). This is a very important group, for many of its members are used as food, and their collection and distribution provides the basis of a large coastal industry.

COLLECTING AND PRESERVING CRUSTACEA

The aquatic crustaceans must be collected by various types of aquatic collecting equipment. Most of them can be collected by a dip net. A white enameled dipper is the best means of collecting many of the smaller forms; the dipper is simply dipped into the water, and any small animals in the dipper can be easily seen. Forms so collected can be removed by means of an eye dropper or (if they are fairly large) by forceps. The smaller forms in ponds, lakes, and the ocean are often collected by means of a fine-mesh net called a plankton net, towed by a boat. Many of the larger forms are collected by traps; such traps (or "pots") are the standard means of collecting lobsters and crabs. The shore-dwelling and terrestrial forms can be collected by hand or forceps, or possibly (for example, beach fleas) with an aerial insect net. The larger forms with well-developed claws should be handled with care, for the claw may inflict serious injury; the safest way to pick up a large crayfish or lobster is from above, grasping the animal at the back of the carapace.

One must collect in a variety of places to obtain a variety of Crustàcea. When collecting in water, one should investigate

[13] Decápoda: *deca*, ten; *poda*, foot or appendage.

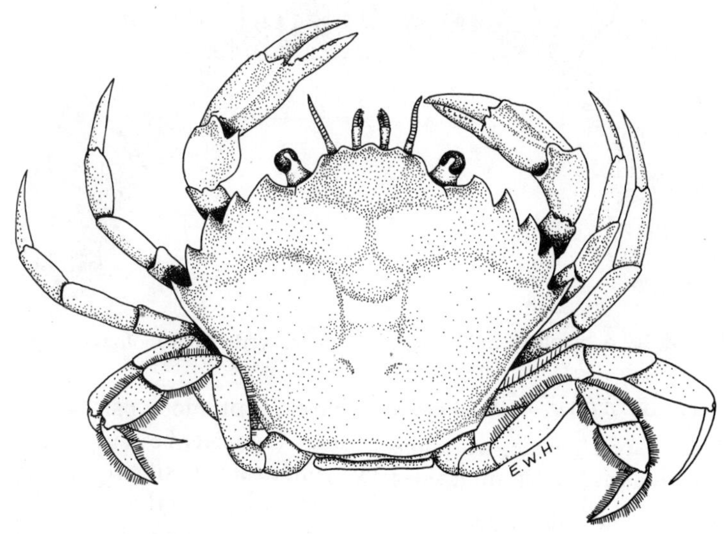

Fig. 30-9. A green crab, *Carcínides* sp.; $1\frac{1}{2}\times$.

every possible aquatic niche; some crustaceans are free-swimming, some burrow in the mud of the bottom, some occur under stones, and many are to be found on aquatic vegetation. The shore-dwelling forms are usually found under stones, debris, or decaying vegetation along the shore.

Crustaceans should be preserved in fluids (for example, 70 to 95 percent alcohol). Most of the smaller forms must be mounted on microscope slides for detailed study. Some of the smaller Malacóstraca can be preserved dry (for example, pinned), but specimens preserved in fluid are more satisfactory for study.

MYRIAPODS

The myriapods are terrestrial arthropods with nine or more pairs of legs and with the body elongate and wormlike. Of the four myriapod classes, the centipedes (Chilópoda) and millipedes (Diplópoda) are quite common and frequently encountered, but the Paurópoda and Sýmphyla are small or minute and are rarely seen by the general collector. The following key will serve to separate the four myriapod classes.

KEY TO THE CLASSES OF MYRIAPODS

1.	The legs evenly spaced on the body, usually one pair to a segment (Figures 30-12 and 30-14) 2	
1′.	The legs arranged in double pairs, most segments with two pairs (Figure 30-10) .... **Diplópoda**	p. 614
2(1).	Genital ducts opening near anterior end of body; body usually cylindrical; minute forms with 9 to 12 pairs of legs (Figure 30-14) 3	
2′.	Genital ducts opening near posterior end of body; body flattened, usually not minute, and with 15 or more pairs of legs (Figure 30-12) .. **Chilópoda**	p. 619
3(2).	Antennae branched; 9 pairs of legs (Figure 30-14 A) .... **Paurópoda**	p. 620
3′.	Antennae not branched; 10 to 12 pairs of legs (Figure 30-14 B) .. **Sýmphyla**	p. 620

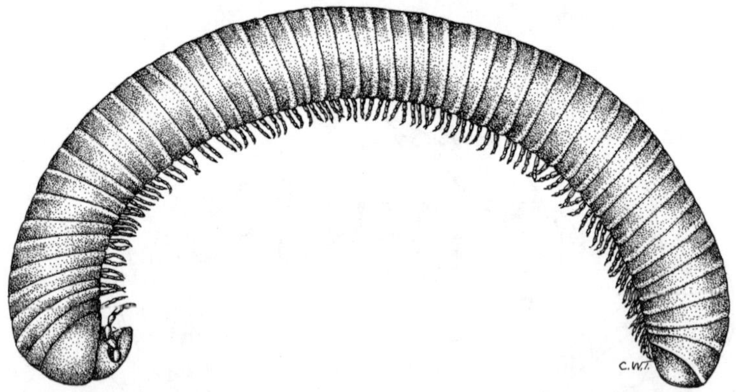

Fig. 30-10. A common millipede, *Nárceus* sp. (order Spirobóloda); $1\frac{1}{2}\times$.

CLASS DIPLÓPODA[14]—MILLIPEDES

The millipedes are elongate, wormlike animals with many legs; most millipedes have 30 or more pairs of legs, and most body segments bear two pairs. The body is cylindrical or slightly flattened, and the antennae are short and usually 7-segmented. The external openings of the reproductive system are located at the anterior end of the

[14] Diplópoda: *diplo,* two, or double; *poda,* foot or appendage (referring to the fact that most body segments bear two pairs of legs).

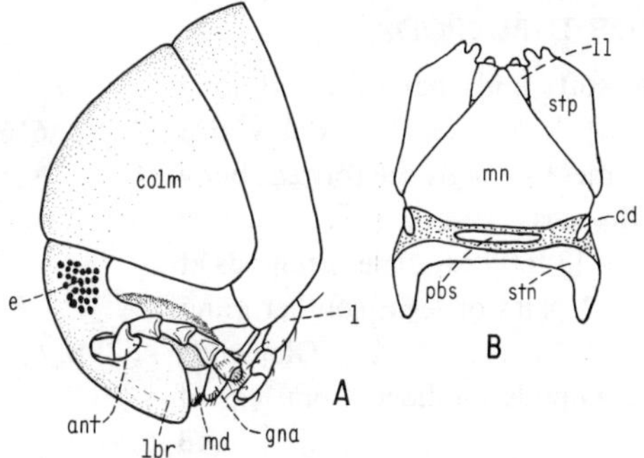

Fig. 30-11. Head structure in a millipede (*Nárceus*, order Spirobólida). A, lateral view of head; B, gnathochilarium. *ant*, antenna; *cd*, cardo; *colm*, collum, the tergite of the first body segment; *e*, eye; *gna*, gnathochilarium; *l*, first leg; *lbr*, labrum; *ll*, lamina lingualis; *md*, mandible; *mn*, mentum; *pbs*, prebasilare; *stn*, sternum of first body segment; *stp*, stipes.

body, between the second and third pairs of legs; one or both pairs of legs on the seventh segment of the male are usually modified into gonopods, which function in copulation. Compound eyes are usually present, each consisting of a group of ocelli. The first tergite behind the head is usually large and is called the collum (Figure 30-11 A).

The head in most millipedes is convex above, with a large epistomal area, and flat beneath; the bases of the mandibles form a part of the side of the head. Beneath the mandibles, and forming the flat ventral surface of the head, is a characteristic liplike structure called the gnathochilarium (Figure 30-11 B). The gnathochilarium is usually divided by sutures into several areas: a median more or less triangular plate, the mentum (*mn*); two lateral lobes, the stipites (*stp*); two median distal plates, the laminae linguales (*ll*); and usually a median transverse basal sclerite, the prebasalare (*pbs*), and two small laterobasal sclerites, the cardines (*cd*). The size and shape of these different areas differ in different groups of millipedes, and the gnathochilarium often provides characters by which the groups are recognized.

Millipedes are usually found in damp places—under leaves, in moss, under stones or boards, in rotting wood, or in the soil. Many species are able to give off an ill-smelling fluid through openings along the sides of the body; this fluid is sometimes strong enough to kill insects that are placed in a jar with the millipede, and it has an odor similar to cyanide. Millipedes do not bite man. Most millipedes are scavengers and feed on decaying plant material, but a few attack living plants and sometimes do serious damage in greenhouses and gardens, and a few are predaceous. These animals overwinter as adults in protected situations, and lay their eggs during the summer; some construct nestlike cavities in the soil in which they deposit their eggs; others lay their eggs in damp places without constructing any sort of nest. The eggs are usually white and hatch within a few weeks. Newly hatched millipedes have only three pairs of legs; the remaining legs are added at subsequent molts.

There are a number of arrangements of orders and families in this group; we follow the arrangement of Chamberlin and Hoffman (1958), which is outlined below (with alternate names or arrangements in parentheses).

Subclass Pselaphógnatha
  Order Polyxénida
Subclass Chilógnatha
  Superorder Pentazònia (Opisthándria)
    Order Glomérida
  Superorder Helminthomórpha (Olόgnatha, Eùgnatha)
    Order Polydésmida (Proterospermóphora)
    Order Chordeùmida (Nematóphora)
    Order Jùlida (Opisthospermóphora in part)
    Order Spirobólida (Opisthospermóphora in part)
    Order Spirostréptida (Opisthospermóphora in part)
    Order Cambálida (Opisthospermóphora in part)
  Superorder Colobógnatha
    Order Polyzonìida
    Order Platydésmida

KEY TO THE ORDERS OF DIPLÓPODA

1. Adults with 13 pairs of legs; integument soft; body hairs forming long lateral tufts; 2 to 4 mm in length........................**Polyxénida** p. 616

1′. Adults with 28 or more pairs of legs; integument strongly sclerotized; body hairs not forming long tufts; larger millipedes 2

2(1′). Body with 14 to 16 segments, and with 11 to 13 tergites; male gonopods at caudal end of body, modified from last 2 pairs of legs; southern and western United States.................................**Glomérida** p. 617

2′. Body with 19 or more segments; male gonopods modified from legs of seventh segment 3

3(2′). Body more or less flattened, or with lateral carinae; the number of body segments variable 4

3′. Body cylindrical or nearly so, without lateral carinae, and containing 26 or more segments 6

4(3). Body with 18 to 22 segments; eyes absent; head and mouth parts of normal size...**Polydésmida** p. 617

4′. Body with 30 to 60 (rarely 20, 26, or 28) segments; eyes usually present; head small, the mandibles usually much reduced 5

5(4′). Tergites with a median groove; gnathochilarium with most of the typical parts..**Platydésmida** p. 618

5′. Tergites without a median groove; gnathochilarium consisting of a single plate, or several indistinctly defined plates ....**Polyzoniida** p. 618

6(3′). Terminal segment of body with 1 to 3 pairs of setae-bearing papillae; collum not overlapping head; sternites not fused with pleurotergites.. .... **Chordeùmida** p. 617

6′. Terminal segment of body without such papillae; collum large, hoodlike, usually overlapping head; sternites usually fused with pleurotergites..7

7(6′). Stipites of gnathochilarium broadly contiguous along midline behind laminae linguales; third segment without legs ....**Jùlida** p. 617

7′. Stipites of gnathochilarium not contiguous, but widely separated by mentum and laminae linguales (Figure 30-11 B); third segment with legs 8

8(7′). Fifth segment with 2 pairs of legs; third segment open ventrally, the fourth and following segments closed 9

8′. Fifth segment with 1 pair of legs; third segment closed ventrally........ ....**Spirobólida** p. 618

9(8). Laminae linguales completely separated by mentum; both anterior and posterior pairs of gonopods present and functional, the posterior pair usually with long flagella ....**Cambálida** p. 618

9′. Laminae linguales usually not separated by mentum; posterior pair of gonopods rudimentary or absent, the anterior pair elaborate........ ....**Spirostréptida** p. 618

ORDER **Polyxénida**:[15] These millipedes are minute (2 to 4 millimeters in length) and soft-bodied, with the body very bristly. They are widely distributed, but are not common, and are usually found under bark. The order contains a single genus *Polýxenus,* in the family Polyxénidae.

[15] Polyxénida: *poly,* many; *xenida,* stranger or guest.

ORDER **Glomérida :**[16] Males of this group have the gonopods at the caudal end of the body, modified from the last two pairs of legs, which are clasperlike; the appendages of the seventh segment are not modified. These millipedes are relatively large, and the body can be contracted into a ball; they occur in southern and southeastern United States and in California. The United States members of this order are in the family Gloméridae.

ORDER **Polydésmida :**[17] The polydesmids are rather flattened millipedes, have the body keeled laterally, and the eyes are much reduced or absent. The tergites are divided, by a transverse groove a little anterior to the middle of the segment, into an anterior prozonite and a posterior metazonite; the metazonite is extended laterally as a broad lobe. The first and last two body segments are legless, segments 2 to 4 have a single pair of legs, and the remaining segments each bear two pairs of legs. The anterior pair of legs on the seventh segment of the male are modified into gonopods. The diplosomites (segments bearing two pairs of legs) are continuously sclerotized rings; there are no sutures between tergites, pleurites, and sternites. *Óxidus grácilis* (Koch), a dark-brown to black millipede 19 to 22 millimeters in length and 2.0 to 2.5 millimeters wide, is a common pest in greenhouses. This order is divided into ten families, and its members occur throughout the United States.

ORDER **Chordeùmida :**[18] The last tergite of these millipedes bears two or three pairs of hair-tipped papillae (spinnerets). The body is usually cylindrical, and composed of 30 or more segments; the head is broad and free and not overlapped by the collum. One or both pairs of legs on the seventh segment of the male may be modified into gonopods.

Three suborders of Chordeùmida occur in the United States. The suborder Chordeumídea, with nine families (in some classifications these millipedes are placed in a single family, the Craspedosomátidae), are small (mostly 4 to 15 millimeters in length), soft-bodied millipedes with 32 or fewer segments and no keels on the metazonites, and without scent glands; they are not very common. The suborder Lysiopetalídea, with one family, the Lysiopetálidae (=Callipódidae), contains larger millipedes with 40 or more body segments that are usually keeled; these millipedes can coil the body into a spiral. The secretions of the scent glands are milky white and very odoriferous. The suborder Striariídea, with one family (the Striarìidae), have 32 or fewer body segments, no scent glands, the anal segment three-lobed, and a high mid-dorsal carina on the metazonites; these millipedes are mostly southern and western in distribution.

ORDER **Jùlida :**[19] This order, together with the succeeding three, are combined by some authorities in the order Opisthospermóphora; the millipedes in these groups have the body cylindrical, with 40 or more segments; the collum is large and hoodlike and overlaps the head; either both pairs of legs on the seventh segment of the male are modified into gonopods or one pair is absent; scent glands are present; and the diplosomites are not differentiated into prozonite and metazonites. The millipedes in the order Jùlida have the stipites of the gnathochilarium broadly contiguous along the midline behind the laminae linguales. Segment 3 and the terminal segment are legless; segments 1, 2, and 4 have one pair of legs each; and the remaining segments (diplosomites) have two pairs of legs. The Jùlida are represented in the United States by five families arranged in two suborders.

[16] Glomérida: from the Latin meaning a ball of yarn (referring to the way these animals coil themselves into a ball).

[17] Polydésmida: *poly*, many; *desmida*, bands.

[18] Chordeùmida: from the Greek, meaning a sausage.

[19] Jùlida: from the Greek, meaning a centipede.

ORDER **Spirobólida:**[20] The millipedes in this order differ from the Jùlida in that they have the stipites of the gnathochilarium separated (Figure 30-11 B), and from the succeeding two orders in having one pair of legs each on segments 1 to 5. This group includes some of the largest millipedes in the United States; *Nárceus americànus* (Beauvois), which is dark brown and narrowly ringed with red, may reach a length of 4 inches (Figure 30-10).

ORDER **Spirostréptida:**[21] The members of this order have one pair of legs each on segments 1 to 4, and the posterior pair of gonopods on the seventh segment of the male is rudimentary or absent; the stipites of the gnathochilarium are separated, but the laminae linguales are usually contiguous. This order is represented in the United States by two families; most species occur in western and southern United States.

ORDER **Cambálida:**[22] These millipedes are very similar to the Spirostréptida, but have the laminae linguales separated by the mentum, and both pairs of legs on the seventh segment of the male are modified into gonopods. This order is represented in the United States by two families. One species in this group, *Cámbala annulàta* (Say), is known to be predaceous.

SUPERORDER COLOBÓGNATHA:[23] The members of this group have the head small and the mouth parts suctorial, and the body is somewhat flattened with 30 to 60 segments. The first pair of legs on the seventh segment of the male is not modified into gonopods. This superorder contains two orders, the *Platydésmida*[24] and *Polyzonìida*,[25] which may be separated by the characters given in the key; they are represented in the United States by one and two families, respectively. *Polyzònium bivirgàtum* (Wood), which reaches a length of about 20 millimeters, occurs in rotten wood.

[20] Spirobólida: *spiro,* spiral; *bolida,* throw.
[21] Spirostréptida: *spiro,* spiral; *streptida,* twisted.
[22] Cambálida: (derivation unknown).

[23] Colobógnatha: *colobo,* shortened; *gnatha,* jaws.
[24] Platydésmida: *platy,* flat; *desmida,* bands.
[25] Polyzonìida: *poly,* many; *zoniida,* belt or girdle.

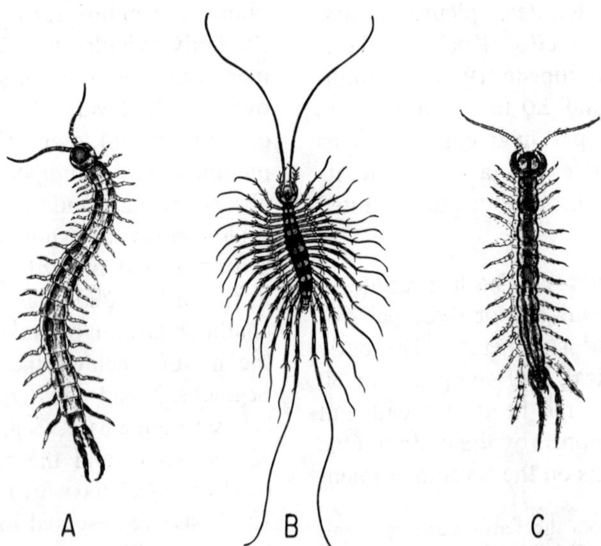

Fig. 30-12. Typical centipedes. A, a large centipede, *Scolopéndra obscùra* Newport, about ¼ natural size; B, a house centipede, *Scutígera coleoptràta* (Linn.), about ½ natural size; C, a small centipede, *Lithòbius erythrocéphalus* Kock, about natural size. (Courtesy of USDA.)

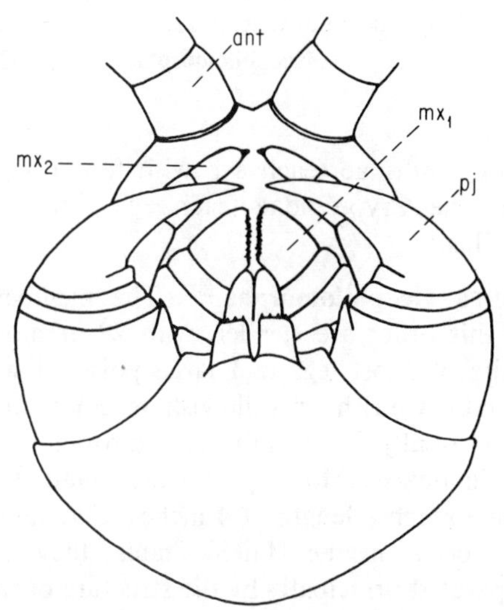

Fig. 30-13. Head of a centipede (*Scolopéndra*, order Scolopendromórpha), ventral view. *ant*, antenna; mx_1, first maxilla; mx_2, second maxilla; *pj*, poison jaw or toxicognath, a modified leg.

CLASS CHILÓPODA[26]—CENTIPEDES

The centipedes are elongate, flattened, wormlike animals with 15 or more pairs of legs. Each body segment bears a single pair of legs; the last 2 pairs are directed backward and are often different in form from the other pairs. The antennae consist of 14 or more segments. The genital openings are located at the posterior end of the body, usually on the next to the last segment. Eyes may be present or absent; if present, they usually consist of numerous ocelli. The head bears a pair of mandibles and 2 pairs of maxillae; the second pair of maxillae may be somewhat leglike in form, or short with the basal segments of the 2 maxillae fused together. The appendages of the first body segment behind the head are clawlike and function as poison jaws (Figure 30-13).

[26] Chilópoda: *chilo*, lip; *poda*, foot or appendage (referring to the fact that the poison jaws are modified legs).

Centipedes are found in a variety of places, but usually occur in a protected situation such as under bark or in rotten logs. They are very active, fast-running animals, and are predaceous; they feed on insects, spiders, and other small animals. All centipedes possess poison jaws with which they paralyze their prey; the smaller centipedes of the northern states are harmless to man, but the larger ones of the South and the tropics are able to inflict a painful bite. Centipedes overwinter as adults in protected situations and lay their eggs during the summer. The eggs are usually sticky and become covered with dirt, and are deposited singly; in some species the male will eat the egg before the female can get it covered with dirt.

The orders of centipedes occurring in the United States may be separated by the following key.

KEY TO THE ORDERS OF CHILÓPODA

1. Adults with 15 pairs of legs, the newly hatched young with 7 pairs (subclass Anamórpha) 2

1′. Adults and newly hatched young with 21 or more pairs of legs (subclass Epimórpha) 3

2(1). Spiracles unpaired, 7 in number, located on mid-dorsal line near posterior margin of tergites; antennae long and many-segmented; legs long (Figure 30-12 B); eyes compound . . . . **Scutigeromórpha** p. 620

2′. Spiracles paired and located laterally; antennae and legs relatively short (Figure 30-12 C); eyes not compound, but consisting of single ocelli or groups of ocelli, or absent . . . . **Lithòbiomórpha** p. 620

3(1′). Antennae with 17 or more segments; 21 to 23 pairs of legs; usually 4 or more ocelli on each side........................ **Scolopéndromórpha** p. 620

3′ Antennae 14-segmented; 29 or more pairs of legs; ocelli absent... **Geophilomórpha** p. 620

ORDER **Scutigeromórpha:**[27] This group includes the common house centipede, *Scutígera coleoptràta* (Linn.) (Figure 30-12 B), which is found throughout eastern United States and Canada. Its natural habitat is under stones and in similar places, but it frequently enters houses where it feeds on flies, spiders, and the like. In houses it often frequents the vicinity of sinks and drains; it is harmless to man. This order contains a single family, the Scutigéridae.

ORDER **Lithòbiomórpha:**[28] These are short-legged, usually brownish centipedes with 15 pairs of legs in the adults (Figure 30-12 C); they vary in length from 4 to about 25 millimeters. Some members of this order are quite common, usually occurring under stones or logs, under bark, and in similar situations. The order contains two families, the Henicópidae (4 to 11 millimeters in length, and the eyes consisting of a single ocellus each, or absent) and the Lithobìidae (10 to 25 millimeters in length, and the eyes usually consisting of many ocelli).

ORDER **Scolopéndromórpha:**[29] The scolopendrids are mainly tropical, and in the United States occur principally in the southern states. This group contains our largest centipedes, which reach a length of about 6 inches (Figure 30-12 A); some tropical species in this group are a foot or so in length. These are the most venomous of the centipedes; the bite of the larger species is quite painful. Two families in this order occur in the United States, the Scolopéndridae (each eye with four ocelli) and the Cryptópidae (each eye with one ocellus.)

ORDER **Geophilomórpha:**[30] The members of this order are slender, with 29 or more pairs of short legs and large poison jaws, usually whitish or yellowish in color, and they usually occur in the soil, in rotten logs, or in debris. Most species are small, but some reach a length of 4 inches. Five families occur in the United States; they are separated principally by the structure of the mandibles.

CLASS PAURÓPODA—PAUROPODS

Pauropods are minute, usually whitish myriapods 1.0 to 1.5 millimeters in length. The antennae bear three apical branches; the nine pairs of legs are not grouped in double pairs as in the millipedes; the head is small and is sometimes covered by the tergal plate of the first body segment (Figure 30-14 A). The genital ducts open near the anterior end of the body. Pauropods occur under stones, in leaf litter, and in similar places.

CLASS SÝMPHYLA—SYMPHYLIDS

The symphylids are slender, whitish myriapods, 1 to 8 millimeters in length, with 15 to 22 (usually 15) body segments and 10 to 12 pairs of legs (Figure 30-14 B). The antennae are slender and many-segmented, and the head is well developed and distinct. The genital openings are located near the anterior end of the body. The symphylids occur under stones, in decaying wood, and in other damp situations; one species, *Scutigerélla immaculàta* (Newport), is occasionally a pest in greenhouses.

[27] Scutigeromórpha: *scuti*, shield; *gero*, bear or carry; *morpha*, form.

[28] Lithòbiomórpha: *litho*, stone; *bio*, life; *morpha*, form.

[29] Scolopéndromórpha: *scolopendro*, centipede; *morpha*, form.

[30] Geophilomórpha: *geo*, earth; *philo*, loving; *morpha*, form.

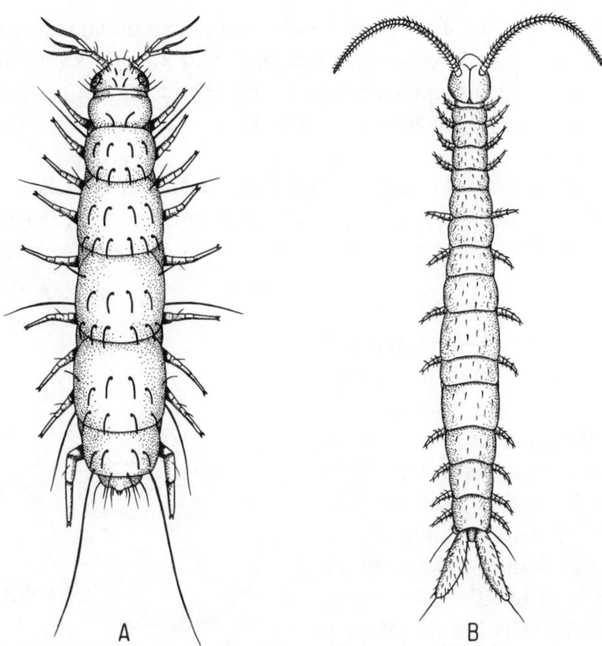

Fig. 30-14. A, a pauropod, *Pàuropus* sp., 95 ×; B, a symphylid, *Scolopendrélla* sp., 16 ×. (A, redrawn from Lubbock; B, redrawn from Comstock, after Latzel.)

COLLECTING AND PRESERVING MYRIAPODS

Myriapods may be killed in a cyanide bottle, but such specimens often become coiled or distorted; these animals are best killed and preserved in alcohol (about 75 percent) or in alcohol and glycerine (ten parts of alcohol to one part of glycerine). Millipedes may be picked up by hand or with forceps; except in the case of the smaller specimens it is well to handle centipedes with forceps, as the larger specimens can inflict a painful bite.

CHELICERATES

The five classes in this group may be separated by the following key; the Xìphosùra and Aráchnida are the only chelicerate classes likely to be encountered by the general collector.

KEY TO THE CLASSES OF CHELICERATE ARTHROPODS

1. Usually 7 pairs of appendages, with 5 pairs of legs; first pair of legs small, used by the male in holding the eggs; abdomen rudimentary; marine, spiderlike forms .... **Pycnogónida*** p. 622

1′. Six (rarely fewer) pairs of appendages, with 4 pairs of legs; abdomen usually well developed and constituting a distinct body region, occasionally fused with cephalothorax 2

2(1′). Abdomen with book gills; large (up to $1\frac{1}{2}$ feet in length) marine forms, the body oval and covered with a hard shell, and with a long spinelike tail (Figure 30-15) .... **Xìphosùra** p. 622

2′.	Abdomen without book gills; smaller forms, rarely over 3 inches in length, body not as above 3	
3(2′).	Minute forms, 1 mm in length or less, living in water or damp places; body elongate-oval and consisting of a head and 4 body segments; eyes, respiratory organs, and excretory organs absent; mouth parts reduced; legs unsegmented, each with several claws . . . . **Tardigràda***	p. 622
3′.	Not as above 4	
4(3′).	Adult legless and wormlike; internal parasites of vertebrates . . . . **Linguatùlida***	p. 623
4′.	Adult with legs, and usually not wormlike; free-living or parasitic forms . . . . **Aráchnida**	p. 623

CLASS PYCNOGÓNIDA[31]—SEA SPIDERS

The pycnogonids are marine, spider-like forms with long legs; they are occasionally found under stones near the low-tide mark, but usually occur in deep water. They are predaceous and have a sucking proboscis. The body consists principally of cephalothorax; the abdomen is very small. The sea spiders vary in length from one to several centimeters; little is known of their habits, for they are not common.

CLASS XÌPHOSÙRA[32]—KING CRABS OR HORSESHOE CRABS

The horseshoe crabs are marine forms and are quite common along the Atlantic Coast from Maine to the Gulf of Mexico. They are found in shallow water, and along sandy or muddy shores where they spawn. They feed chiefly on marine worms. Horseshoe crabs are easily recognized by the characteristic oval shell and the long spine-like tail (Figure 30-15).

CLASS TARDIGRÀDA[33]—WATER BEARS

The water bears are minute forms found in water (fresh or salt), moss, sand, or other damp places. Many species are able to withstand desiccation for several years. The taxonomic position of this group is debatable; it is usually grouped with the arachnids, but it may not belong there. Little is known of the habits of these animals.

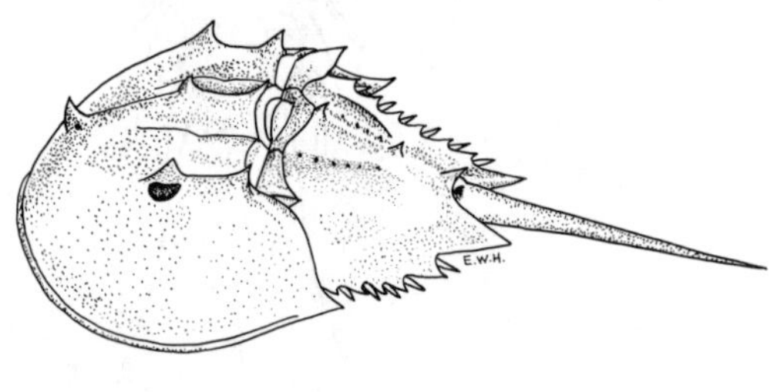

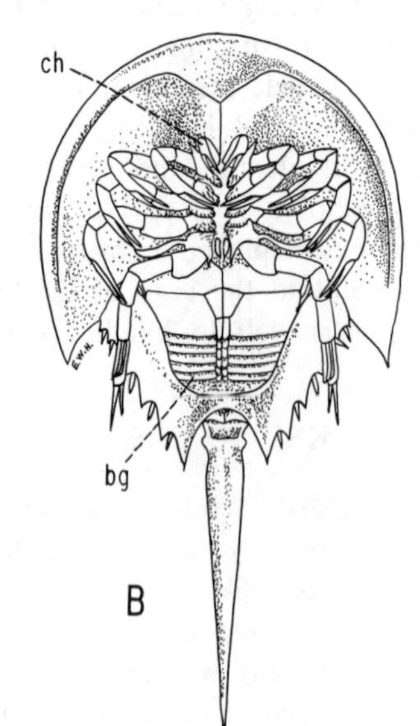

Fig. 30-15. A horseshoe crab, *Limulus* sp. (class Xiphosùra). A, dorsolateral view; B, ventral view. *bg*, book gills; *ch*, chelicera.

[31] Pycnogónida: *pycno*, thick or dense; *gonida*, offspring (referring to the eggs).
[32] Xiphosùra: *xipho*, sword; *ura*, tail.
[33] Tardigràda: *tardi*, slow; *grada*, walk.

CLASS LINGUATÙLIDA[34] (PENTASTÓMIDA)—TONGUEWORMS

Adult tongueworms are elongate, legless, and ringed, and there is no differentiation of head, thorax, or abdomen. The mouth is surrounded by two pairs of retractile hooks. The immature stages have four or six legs. The taxonomic position of these animals is debatable, but they are thought to be related to the arachnids.

Tongueworms are parasitic, and the adults usually occur in the mouth, nasal cavity, or respiratory tract of a carnivorous vertebrate. Some species have a complex life cycle that involves an intermediate host: eggs are discharged with mucus from the primary host (a carnivore), and hatch when eaten by a suitable intermediate host (usually a herbivorous vertebrate); the young on hatching in the intermediate host migrate to the liver, lungs, or other organs and become encysted; when the intermediate host (or the tissues of it containing these encysted tongueworms) is eaten by the primary host, the tongueworm leaves the cyst, migrates to the nose or respiratory tract of the primary host, and becomes an adult. Tongueworm infections, usually by the immature stages, occasionally occur in man.

CLASS ARÁCHNIDA[35]

[34] Linguatùlida: from the Latin, meaning tonguelike.

[35] Aráchnida: from the Greek, meaning a spider.

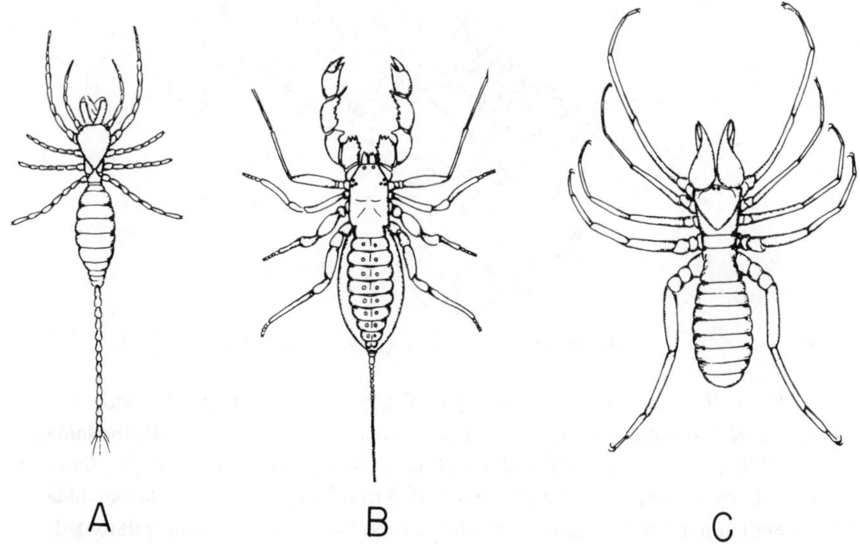

Fig. 30-16. Arachnids. A, a micro–whip-scorpion (order Microthelyphónida); B, a whip-scorpion (order Pedipálpida); C, a wind-scorpion (order Solpùgida). (Courtesy of the Institute of Acarology.)

The arachnids are divided into a number of orders, which may be separated by the following key; the orders marked with an asterisk are not likely to be encountered by the general collector.

KEY TO THE ORDERS OF ARACHNIDA

1. Abdomen unsegmented, or if segmented, then with spinnerets near middle of ventral side of abdomen.......................................2

1′. Abdomen distinctly segmented, with no spinnerets 3

2(1). Abdomen petiolate (Figures 30-32 to 30-37) . . . . **Aranèida** p. 632

2′. Abdomen broadly joined to cephalothorax (Figures 30-20 to 30-23 and 30-25 to 30-27) . . . . **Acarìna** p. 626

3(1′). Abdomen with a tail-like prolongation that is either thick and terminating in a sting (Figure 30-17) or thread- or whiplike without a sting (Figure 30-16 A, B); mostly tropical 4

3′. Abdomen without a tail-like prolongation 6

4(3). Abdomen ending in a sting (Figure 30-17); first pair of legs not greatly elongated; second ventral segment of abdomen with a pair of comblike organs . . . . **Scorpiónida** p. 625

4′. Abdomen not ending in a sting; first pair of legs longer than the other pairs (Figure 30-16 A, B); second ventral segment of abdomen without comblike organs 5*

5(4′). Pedipalpi slender, similar to the legs (Figure 30-16 A); minute forms, 5 mm in length or less . . . . **Microthelyphónida*** p. 625

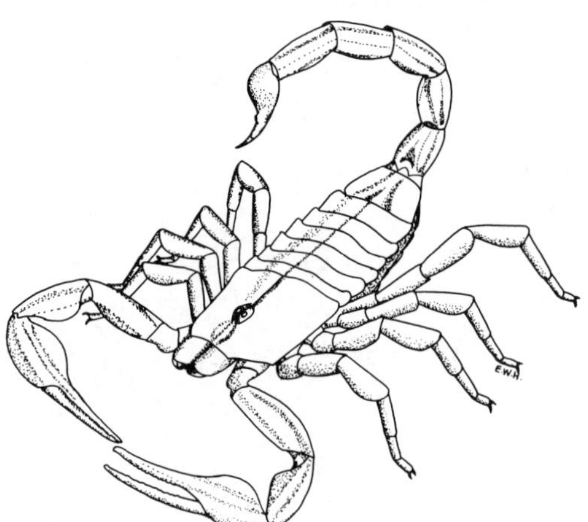

Fig. 30-17. A scorpion, *Centùrus* sp.; 2 ×.

5′. Pedipalpi much stouter than any of the legs (Figure 30-16 B); moderate-sized to large forms . . . . **Pedipálpida** p. 625

6(3′). Pedipalpi with pincerlike claws (Figure 30-18); abdomen not petiolate; body flattened and usually less than 5 mm in length . . . . . . **Chelonéthida** p. 626

6′. Pedipalpi usually without pincerlike claws; body not particularly flattened; abdomen and size variable 7

7(6′). Abdomen more or less petiolate; front tarsi very long and slender, much more so than the other tarsi 8*

7′. Abdomen broadly joined to cephalothorax; front tarsi similar to the other tarsi 9

8(7). Cephalothorax longer than broad, the lateral margins nearly parallel and with a transverse suture between second and third legs; abdomen with a very short terminal appendage; 4.5 to 7.5 mm in length; southern California . . . . **Schizopéltida*** p. 625

8′. Cephalothorax broader than long, the lateral margins rounded or arched, and without a transverse suture between second and third legs; abdomen without a terminal appendage; size variable; southern United States, from Florida to California .... **Amblypỳgi*** p. 625

9(7′). Legs extremely long and slender (Figure 30-19); cephalothorax not segmented; chelicerae small, not moving dorsoventrally; body robust, usually short and oval; common and widely distributed animals... **Phalángida** p. 626

9′. Legs moderately long; head distinct from the 3-parted thorax; chelicerae relatively large and moving dorsoventrally; body elongate, narrowed at base of abdomen (Figure 30-16 C); mostly nocturnal, desert forms.. **Solpùgida*** p. 626

ORDER **Microthelyphónida**[36] **(Palpigràda, Palpigràdi)** — Micro - Whip - Scorpions: These arachnids are tiny animals, 5 millimeters in length or less, with a long segmented tail; they are usually found under stones or in the soil. They are similar to the whip-scorpions in general form (Figure 30-16 A). This group is represented in the United States by only a few species occurring in the South and Southwest.

ORDER **Pedipálpida**[37] **(Thelyphónida, Holopéltida)**—Whip-Scorpions: The whip-scorpions are mainly tropical, and in the United States occur only in the southern states. They range in length from about $\frac{1}{2}$ to 4 or 5 inches. They are somewhat scorpionlike in appearance, but lack a sting at the end of the abdomen, and have a long whiplike tail (Figure 30-16 B). The whip-scorpions are nocturnal and predaceous; they are generally found under logs or other objects, or burrowing in sand. These arachnids are sometimes greatly feared, but they do not have poison glands. Some species when irritated give off a vinegarlike odor, and are called vinegarones.

ORDERS **Schizopéltida**[38] **(Pedipálida** in part) AND **Amblypỳgi**[39] **(Pedipálpida** in part)—Tailless Whip-Scorpions: These arachnids are similar to the Pedipálpida, but lack the long whiplike tail. The Schizopéltida are represented in the United States by a single species, *Trithỳreus pentapéltis* (Cook), which occurs in the desert regions of southern California; it is 4.5 to 7.5 millimeters in length, yellowish to reddish brown in color, and occurs under rocks or in leaf litter. The Amblypỳgi are represented in the United States by several species, occurring from Florida to southern California; the largest is about 2 inches in length.

ORDER **Scorpiónida**[40] — Scorpions: The scorpions are well-known animals that occur in the southern and western parts of the United States. They are fair-sized arachnids, varying in length up to 4 or 5 inches. The abdomen is broadly joined to the cephalothorax and is differentiated into two portions, a broad 7-segmented anterior portion, and a much narrower 5-segmented posterior portion that terminates in a sting (Figure 30-17). The pedipalps are large and claw-like.

Scorpions are largely nocturnal in habit, and during the day remain concealed in various protected places. When they run, the pedipalps are held forward, and the posterior end of the abdomen is usually curved upward. Scorpions feed largely on insects and spiders, which they capture with their pedipalps and kill with their sting. The young are born alive, and for a time after their birth are carried on the body of the

[36] Microthelyphónida: *micro,* small; *thely,* female; *phonida,* kill.
[37] Pedipálpida: *pedi,* foot; *palpida,* feeler.
[38] Schizopéltida: *schizo,* split; *peltida,* shield.
[39] Amblypygi: *ambly,* blunt; *pygi,* rump.

[40] Scorpiónida: from the Latin, meaning a scorpion.

mother. Scorpions grow slowly, and some species require several years to reach maturity.

The effect of a scorpion sting depends primarily on the species of scorpion involved. The sting of most species is painful and is usually accompanied by local swelling and discoloration, but is not dangerous. Of the forty-odd species of scorpions in the United States, two are very venomous and their sting may be fatal; these two are *Centruròides sculpturàtus* Ewing and *C. gértschi* Stahnke, and as far as known occur only in Arizona. These scorpions are slender and rarely exceed 2½ inches in length; *sculpturàtus* is a solid yellowish color, and *gértschi* is yellow with two irregular black stripes down the back. The venom of these two species is a neurotoxin. Scorpions do not ordinarily attack man, but will sting quickly if disturbed; in areas where scorpions occur, one should be careful in picking up boards, stones, and similar objects, and a scorpion found crawling on one's body should be brushed off rather than swatted.

ORDER **Solpùgida**[41] **(Solifùgae)**—Wind-Scorpions or Sun-Scorpions: These arachnids occur chiefly in desert regions; the one species that is found in eastern United States, *Ammótrecha cùbae* (Lucas), occurs in Florida. The body of a wind-scorpion may be an inch or more in length, and is somewhat constricted in the middle, and the chelicerae are very large (Figure 30-16 C). The large chelicerae give these animals a ferocious appearance, but they are relatively harmless; they do not possess venom glands. On each hind leg there are five racquet organs—short, broad, **T**-shaped structures (attached by the base of the **T**). The wind-scorpions are nocturnal in habit and very active and fast-moving; they are predaceous on other small animals.

[41] Solpùgida: from the Latin, meaning a venomous ant or spider.

ORDER **Chelonéthida**[42] **(Pseudoscorpiónida)**—Pseudoscorpions or Book Scorpions: The pseudoscorpions are small arachnids, seldom over 5 millimeters in length, and resemble the true scorpions in having large clawlike pedipalps, but the abdomen is short and oval and there is no sting (Figure 30-18); the body is very flat. The pseudoscorpions are found under bark, between the boards of buildings, between the pages of books, in moss, under leaves, and in similar situations. They often cling to and are carried about by large insects. They feed chiefly on small insects. They possess silk glands, the ducts of which open on the chelicerae; the silk is used in making a cocoon in which the animal overwinters. This group is small, but is widely distributed.

ORDER **Phalángida**[43] **(Opiliònes)**—Harvestmen or Daddy-Longlegs: These animals, which are perhaps better known by the name daddy-longlegs, are common in most parts of the country. They are easily recognized by the oval compact body and the extremely long slender legs (Figure 30-19). Harvestmen feed chiefly on plant juices or dead insects, but some species apparently feed chiefly on living insects. In the North, most species overwinter in the egg stage, but in the South, the adults usually overwinter. The eggs are laid in the ground, underneath stones, or in crevices in wood.

ORDER **Acarìna**[44] **(Acari)**—Mites and Ticks: The Acarìna constitute a very large group consisting principally of small to minute animals. The body is usually oval and compact, with little or no differentiation of cephalothorax and abdomen (Figures 30-20 to 30-23 and 30-25 to 20-27). Newly hatched young, called larvae, usually have only three pairs of legs (Figure 30-26) and acquire the

[42] Chelonéthida: *chelo*, claw; *nethida*, spin (referring to the spinning of silk from the chelicerae).

[43] Phalángida: from the Greek, meaning a finger or toe.

[44] Acarìna: from the Greek, meaning a mite.

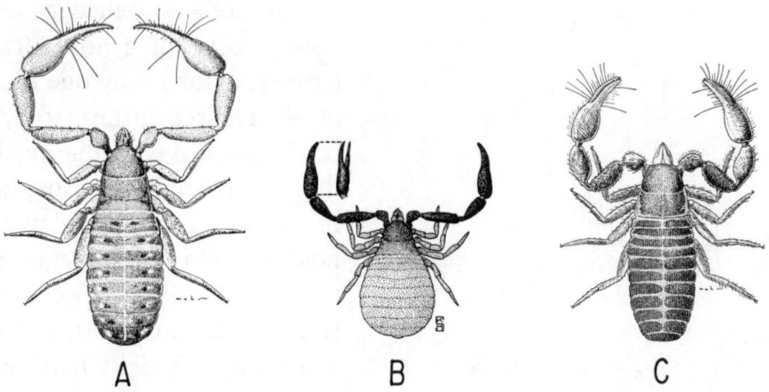

Fig. 30-18. Pseudoscorpions. A, *Dactylochélifer copiòsus* Hoff; B, *Lárca granulàta* (Banks); C, *Pselaphochérnes párvus* Hoff. (Courtesy of Hoff and Illinois Natural History Survey.)

fourth pair after the first molt. Instars between larva and adult are called nymphs.

The Acarìna rival the insects in number of species and in the variety of habits exhibited. The group includes both terrestrial and aquatic forms, and the aquatic forms occur in both salt and fresh water. They are abundant in soil and organic debris, where they usually outnumber other arthropods. Many are parasitic, at least during a part of the life cycle, and both vertebrates and invertebrates serve as hosts; most of the parasitic forms are external parasites of their hosts. Many of the free-living forms are predaceous, many are phytophagous, and many are scavengers. This group is one of considerable biological interest and economic importance.

The groups in the order Acarìna have been arranged differently by different authorities. The arrangement followed in this book may be outlined as follows:

Order Acarìna—mites and ticks
- Suborder Notostigmàta (Opílioacarìna)
- Suborder Parasitifórmes
  - Group I. Holothyrìna
  - Group II. Mesostigmàta—gamasid mites and others
  - Group III. Ixódides—ticks
- Suborder Acarifórmes
  - Group I. Acarídei—cheese, mange, itch, feather, and other mites
  - Group II. Tarsonemìni
  - Group III. Tetrapódili—gall mites
  - Group IV. Prostigmàta—spider, harvest, water, and other mites
  - Group V. Endeostigmàta
  - Group VI. Oribátei—oribatid mites

—Suborder *Notostigmàta*— The members of this group live under stones and in organic debris, and are predaceous. The legs are long and slender, and these mites are superficially somewhat similar to harvestmen.

—Suborder *Parasitifórmes*—Group I. Holothyrìna— This is a little-known group found mainly on islands in the Indian Ocean and in the Australian region; they are presumed to be predaceous.

—Group II. Mesostigmàta— This is the largest group in the suborder Parasitifórmes, and includes predaceous, scavenging, and parasitic forms. Members of this group are usually the dominant mite predators in leaf litter and soil. The gamasid mites are common representatives of this group. The parasitic mites in this group attack birds, bats, small mammals, snakes, and insects. One parasitic species, the chicken mite, *Dermanýssus gállinae* (DeGeer), is a serious pest of poultry; it hides during the day and attacks poultry and sucks their blood at

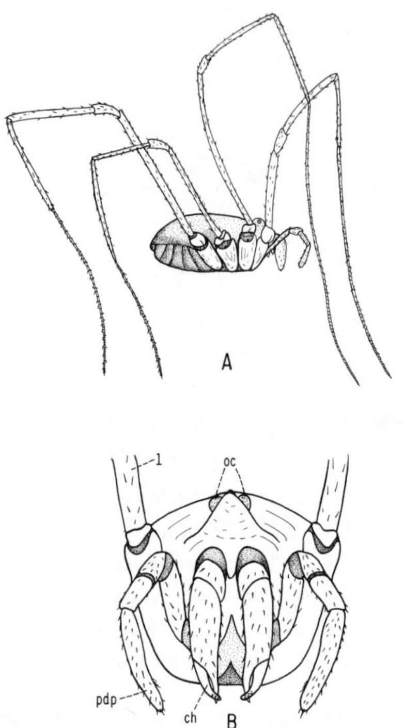

Fig. 30-19. A harvestman or daddy-longlegs (order Phalángida). A, lateral view; B, anterior view. *ch,* chelicera; *l,* front leg; *oc,* eyes or ocelli; *pdp,* pedipalp. The harvestmen typically have two eyes located on a tubercle and the chelicerae clawlike, as shown in B.

night; this species also causes a dermatitis in man.

—Group III. Ixódides—Ticks— Two families of ticks occur in North America: the Ixódidae or hard ticks, and the Argásidae or soft ticks. Ticks are larger than most mites and are parasitic, attacking chiefly mammals, birds, and reptiles. From man's point of view, they are annoying pests, and some species serve as the vectors of disease. Certain ticks, particularly engorging females feeding on the neck or near the base of the skull of their host (man or animals), inject a venom that produces paralysis; this paralysis may be fatal if the tick is not removed. The most important tick-borne diseases are spotted fever, relapsing fever, tularemia, and Texas cattle fever.

Ticks lay their eggs in various places, but do not lay their eggs on their host; the young seek out a host after hatching. The hard ticks take only one blood meal in each of their three instars; they remain on the host several days while feeding, but usually drop off to molt. The soft ticks usually hide in crevices during the day and feed on their host at night; each instar may feed several times. The hard ticks usually have only two or three hosts during their development, while the soft ticks may have many hosts; the cattle tick that transmits Texas cattle fever feeds on the same host individual during all three instars, and the protozoan that causes the disease is transmitted transovarially, that is, through the eggs to the tick's offspring. The hard ticks (Figure 30-20) possess a hard dorsal plate called the scutum, and they have the mouth parts protruding anteriorly and visible from above; the soft ticks (Figure 30-21) lack a scutum and are soft-bodied, and the mouth parts are ventrally located and not visible from above.

—*Suborder Acarifórmes*—Group I. Acarídei— This group includes the cheese, mange, itch, feather, and other mites, the most important of which are probably those that cause dermatitis in man or animals (the itch and mange mites). The most important mites causing dermatitis belong to three families: the Acáridae (=Tyroglýphidae), Sarcóptidae, and Psoróptidae. The family Acáridae is a very large group whose members are widely distributed; they live on all kinds of organic substances and often infest cheese, dried meats, flour, and seeds. They not only damage or contaminate these materials, but they often get on man and cause a dermatitis called grocer's itch or miller's itch. The Sarcóptidae include the itch or scab mites, which attack man and other animals and burrow into the skin; these mites cause severe irritation, and the resulting scratching often causes additional injury or leads to secondary infection. One of the best treatments for scabies (infection

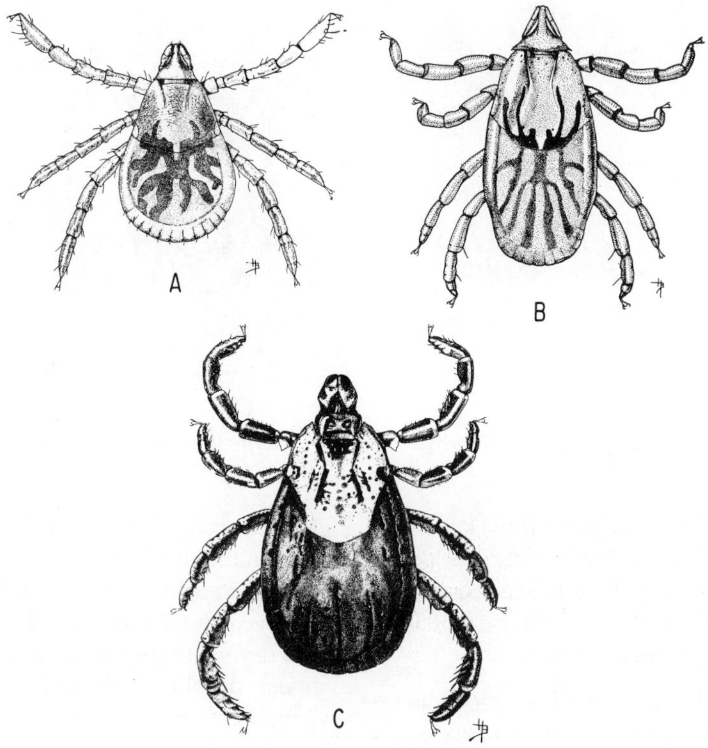

Fig. 30-20. The American dog tick, *Dermacéntor variábilis* (Say) (Ixódidae). A, larva; B, nymph; C, adult (unengorged) female. (Courtesy of USDA.)

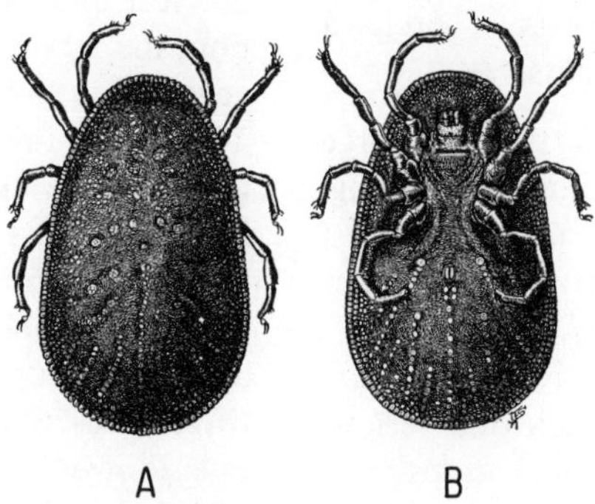

Fig. 30-21. The fowl tick, *Árgas pérsicus* (Oken), adult female. A, dorsal view; B, ventral view. (Courtesy of USDA.)

by these mites) is the application of a solution of benzyl benzoate. The Psoróptidae include the mange mites, which attack various domestic animals (Figure 30-22).

—Group II. Tarsonemìni— This group includes small mites associated with plants and some that are free-living or associated with insects. *Pyemòtes ventricòsus* (New-

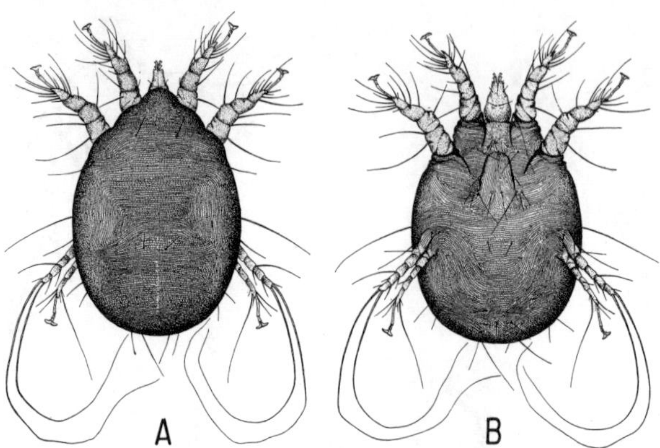

Fig. 30-22. The sheep scab mite, *Psoróptes équi òvis* (Hering), female. A, dorsal view; B, ventral view. (Courtesy of USDA.)

port) often causes a dermatitis known as "hay itch" in man, and sometimes occurs in grocery stores around discarded cereals; *Acaràpis woodi* (Rennie) causes "Isle of Wight" disease in honey bees.

—Group III. Tetrapódili—Gall Mites— The gall mites are elongate and wormlike and have only two pairs of legs (Figure 30-23). Some species form small pouchlike galls on leaves (Figure 30-24), some produce blisterlike galls on leaves, some produce a rusting of leaves, and still others attack buds. Many are serious pests of orchard trees or other cultivated plants.

—Group IV. Prostigmàta— This is a large group, containing predaceous, scavenging, plant-feeding, and parasitic forms; the best known mites in this group are the spider mites, harvest mites, and water mites.

The spider mites, or red mites, are plant feeders, and some species do serious damage to orchard trees, field crops, and greenhouse plants. They feed on the foliage or fruit and attack a variety of plants; they are widely distributed, and sometimes occur in tremendous numbers. The eggs are laid on the plant, and during the summer hatch in four or five days; there are four instars (Figure 30-25), and growth from egg to adult usually requires about three weeks. Most species overwinter in the egg stage. The immature instars are usually yellowish or pale in color, and the adults are yellowish or greenish (seldom red). Sex in these mites is determined by the fertilization of the egg; males develop from unfertilized eggs and females from fertilized eggs.

The harvest mites (also called chiggers or redbugs) are ectoparasites of vertebrates in the larval stage, whereas the nymphs and adults are free-living and predaceous on small arthropods and arthropod eggs. Harvest mites lay their eggs among vegetation; the larvae, on hatching, crawl over the vegetation and attach to a passing host. They insert their mouth parts into the outer layer of the skin, and their saliva partly digests the tissues beneath. The larvae remain on the host for a few days, feeding on tissue fluid and digested cellular material, and then drop off. These mites are small (Figure 30-26) and are seldom noticed; their bites, however, cause considerable irritation, and the itching persists for some time after the mites have left. On man, the mites seem to prefer areas where the clothing is tight. A person going into an area infested with chiggers can avoid being attacked by using a good repellent, such as dimethyl phthallate or diethyl toluamide; this material can be put on the clothing, or the clothing can be

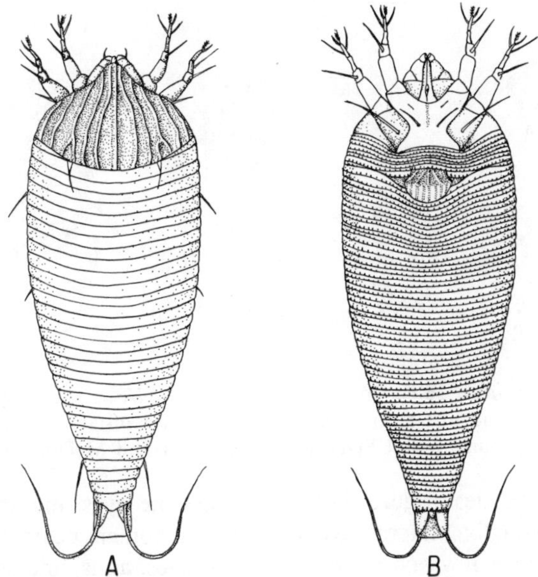

Fig. 30-23. A gall mite, *Phyllocóptes variábilis* Hodgkiss, a species attacking sugar maple; 460 ×. A, dorsal view; B, ventral view. (Redrawn from Hodgkiss.)

impregnated with it. A good material to reduce the itching caused by chiggers is tincture of benzyl benzoate. In the Orient, southern Asia, the Southwest Pacific, and Australia, certain harvest mites serve as vectors of scrub typhus or tsutsugamushi disease; this disease caused over 7000 casualties in the United States armed forces during World War II.

The water mites include a number of common and widely distributed freshwater species and a few marine forms; a few species occur in hot springs. The larvae are parasitic on crustaceans or aquatic insects, and most nymphs and adults are predaceous. Water mites are small, round-bodied, usually brightly colored (red or orange), and are often quite common in ponds; they crawl about over the bottom and over aquatic vegetation, and lay their eggs on the under sides of leaves or on aquatic animals. Water mite larvae (usually in the genus *Arrenùrus*) are often abundant on the bodies of dragonflies and damselflies; they crawl from the nymph to the adult when the latter emerges, and may remain there a couple of weeks, feeding on the body fluids of the insect and eventually dropping off and developing to the adult if they happen to get into a suitable aquatic habitat.

—Group V. Endeostigmàta— This is a small group of small to medium-sized free-living mites that are considered by some authorities to be very primitive. One species is known from the Devonian of England.

—Group VI. Oribátei—Oribatid Mites— The oribatids are small, oval mites that

Fig. 30-24. A mite gall on wild cherry caused by *Eriophỳes pádi* Nalepa. (Redrawn from Felt.)

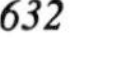

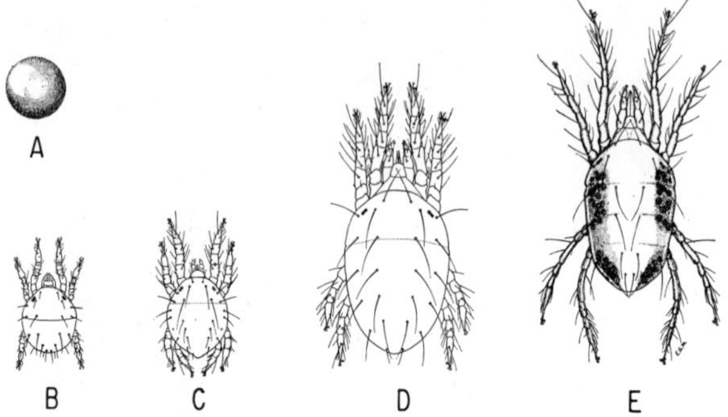

Fig. 30-25. The four-spotted spider mite, *Tetránychus canadénsis* (McGregor). A, egg; B, first instar, or larva; C, second instar, or protonymph; D, third instar, or deutonymph; E, fourth instar, adult female. (Courtesy of USDA, after McGregor and McDunough.)

superficially resemble beetles (Figure 30-27). Some species have winglike lateral extensions of the notum; in a few species these extensions, or pteromorphs, are hinged, contain veins, and are provided with muscles. Oribatid mites are found in leaf litter, under bark or stones, in moss and freshwater plants, and in the soil; they are apparently scavengers. They contain a large percentage of the soil fauna, and are important in promoting soil fertility through breaking down the organic matter. A number of species in this group have been found to serve as the intermediate hosts of certain tapeworms that infest sheep, cattle, and other ruminants.

ORDER **Aranèida**[45] **(Arànеае)**—Spiders: The spiders are a large, distinct, and widespread group; they occur in many types of habitats and are often very abundant. Many people have the idea that spiders are very venomous, but although they all have venom glands, they very rarely bite man; only a few species in the United States are dangerously venomous.

The body of a spider is divided into two regions, the cephalothorax and abdomen; the abdomen is unsegmented (in our species) and attached to the cephalothorax by a slender pedicel (Figures 30-28 A, B and 30-32 to 30-37). The cephalothorax bears the eyes, mouth parts, and legs, and the abdomen bears the genital structures, spiracles, anus, and spinnerets.

The cephalothorax is covered dorsally by the carapace and ventrally by the sternum; anterior to the sternum is a small sclerite called the labium (Figure 30-28 B, *lbm*). The eyes are simple and are located on the anterior end of the carapace (Figure 30-31); most spiders have eight eyes, but some have fewer; the number and arrangement of the eyes provide characters useful in distinguishing different families. The area

[45] Aranèida: from the Latin, meaning a spider.

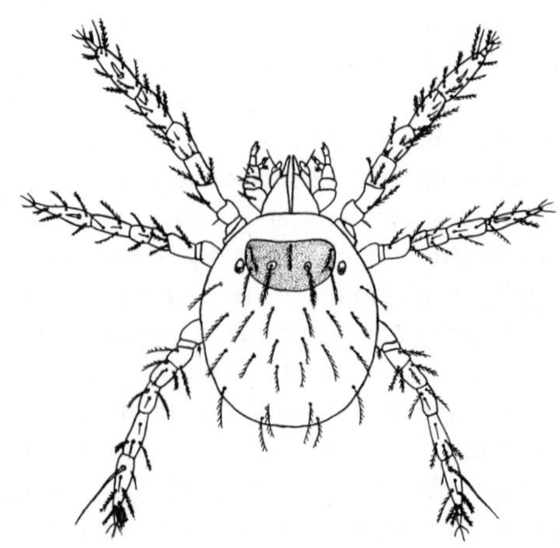

Fig. 30-26. A chigger, the larva of *Eutrombícula alfreddùgesi* (Oudemans); 215 ×. (Redrawn from a U.S. Public Health Service release.)

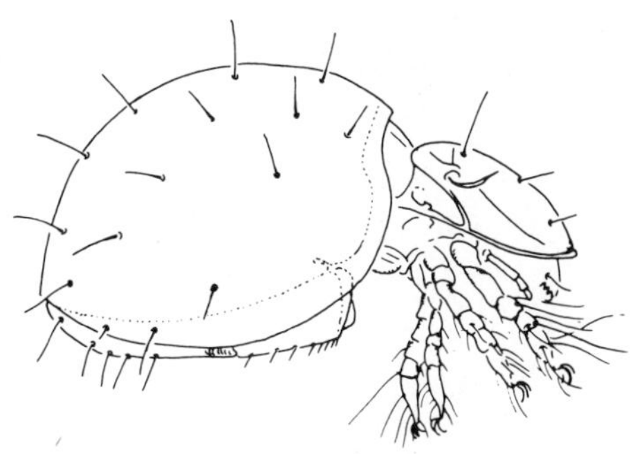

Fig. 30-27. An oribatid mite (family Phthiracáridae). (Courtesy of the Institute of Acarology.)

between the anterior row of eyes and the edge of the carapace is the clypeus.

The chelicerae are located at the anterior end of the cephalothorax, below the eyes, and are usually directed downward; they are 2-segmented, with the basal segment stout and the distal segment fanglike. Spiders have poison glands, and the ducts from these glands open near the tip of the fangs. The fangs move laterally in most spiders (suborder Labidógnatha), but move vertically in the tarantulas and trapdoor spiders (suborder Orthógnatha). The basal segment of the chelicerae sometimes bears a small, rounded lateral prominence (the boss) at its base. Some spiders have a filelike ridge on the lateral surface of the chelicerae; such spiders stridulate by stroking this ridge with the pedipalp to produce a soft sound.

The pedipalps, which are located behind the chelicerae and in front of the legs, are somewhat leglike or palplike; the basal segment, the endite (Figure 30-28 B, *cx*) is enlarged and functions as a crushing jaw. The labium lies between the two endites. The pedipalps are clubbed in male spiders; the terminal segment is modified into a copulatory organ (Figure 30-28 C).

The legs are 7-segmented (coxa, trochanter, femur, patella, tibia, metatarsus, and tarsus; Figure 30-28 E), and usually bear two or three claws at their apex. If there are three claws, two are paired and the third is a median claw; the median claw, when present, is usually small and difficult to see. The tip of the tarsus is usually provided with numerous hairs and bristles, which may obscure the claws. Bristles here that are thick, serrated, and somewhat clawlike are called spurious claws. Many spiders with only two claws have a dense tuft of hairs below the claws; this is the claw tuft (Figure 30-30 D, *clt*). The legs are often provided with hairs or bristles that are useful in separating families. The fine vertical hairs on the tarsi and metatarsi are called trichobothria (Figure 30-30 B, *trb*); these hairs are probably sensory in function. Spiders with a cribellum (a structure on the abdomen; see following paragraph) also have on the metatarsi of the hind legs a close-set series of heavy bristles, the calamistrum (Figure 30-30 B, *clm*); the calamistrum plays a part in the formation of the ribbonlike bands of silk spun by these spiders.

Near the anterior end of the abdomen on the ventral side is a transverse groove called the epigastric furrow (Figure 30-28 B, *ef*); the openings of the book lungs (Figure 30-28 B, spr_1) are located at the lateral ends of this furrow (book lungs are lacking in the Caponìidae), and the genital opening is located at the middle of this furrow. The book lungs are breathing organs consisting of saclike invaginations containing a series of sheetlike leaves. A few spiders have a second pair of book lungs, the openings of which are located laterally behind the epigastric furrow. Spiders also have tracheae, and there is usually a single spiracle, located on the midventral line of the abdomen anterior to the spinnerets (Figure 30-28 B, spr_2); this spiracle is often difficult to see.

Adult female spiders have a sclerotized structure, the epigynum, usually somewhat conical in shape, at the genital opening (Figure 30-28 B, *epg*); this structure varies considerably in different species and often provides good taxonomic characters. At the

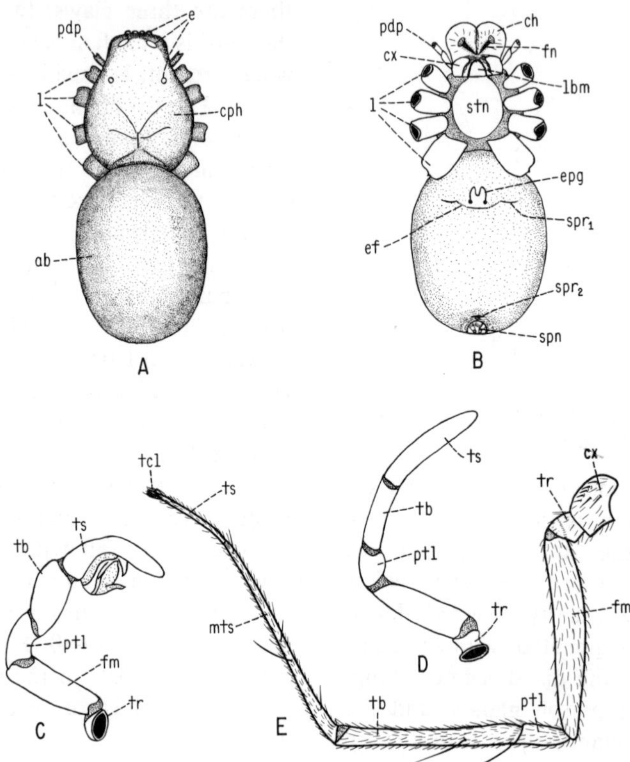

Fig. 30-28. Structural characters of spiders. A, dorsal view (generalized); B, ventral view (generalized); C, male pedipalp; D, female pedipalp; E, leg. *ab,* abdomen; *ch,* chelicera; *cph,* cephalothorax; *cx,* coxa (the coxa of the pedipalp, shown in B, is expanded to form the endite); *e,* eyes; *ef,* epigastic furrow; *epg,* epigynum; *fm,* femur; *fn,* fang of chelicera; *l,* coxae of legs; *lbm,* labium; *mts,* metatarsus; *pdp,* pedipalp; *ptl,* patella; *spn,* spinnerets; spr_1, book lung spiracle; spr_2, tracheal spiracle; *stn,* sternum; *tb,* tibia; *tcl,* tarsal claws; *tr,* trochanter; *ts,* tarsus.

posterior end of the abdomen on the ventral side are six (rarely two or four) fingerlike structures, the spinnerets, from which the silk of the spider is spun (Figures 30-28 B, *spn* and 30-29 B-E); at the apex of each spinneret are many (sometimes a hundred or more) spinning tubes, from which the silk emerges. Above (posterior to) the spinnerets is a small, variously developed tubercle, the anal tubercle, in which the anus is located. A few families of spiders (those in the section Cribellàtae) have a sievelike structure, called the cribellum, just anterior to the spinnerets (Figure 30-29 B, *crb*); this is an accessory silk-spinning organ. A few spiders that lack a cribellum have a small conical appendage, the colulus, between the bases of the anterior spinnerets; the function of this structure is not known.

Spiders undergo very little metamorphosis during their development; when hatched they usually look like miniature adults. If legs are lost during development, they can usually be regenerated. Spider eggs are generally laid in a silken sac; these egg sacs vary in their construction and are deposited in all sorts of places. Some are attached to leaves or twigs or bark, some are placed in crevices, some are placed in or near the web, and some are carried about by the female. The eggs usually hatch soon after they are laid, but if the eggs are laid

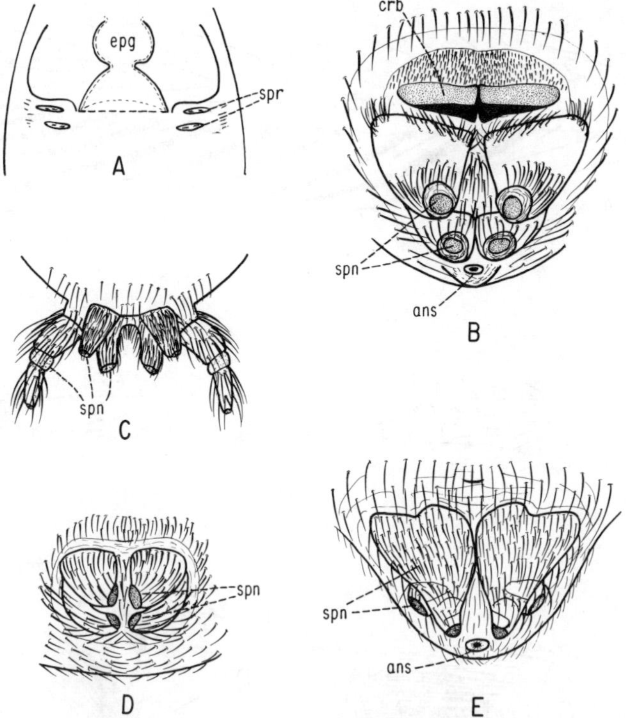

Fig. 30-29. Abdominal characters of spiders. A, base of abdomen of *Dýsdera* (Dysdéridae), showing the two pairs of spiracles; B-E, spinnerets, ventral view; B, *Amauròbius* (Amaurobìidae); C, *Tegenària* (Agelénidae); D, *Lycòsa* (Lycósidae); E, *Therídion* (Theridìidae). *ans,* anus; *crb,* cribellum; *epg,* epigynum; *spn,* spinnerets; *spr,* spiracle.

in the fall, the young spiders may remain in the sac until the following spring. The young spiders are sometimes cannibalistic, and fewer young may escape from the sac than there were eggs originally.

The two sexes of a spider often differ considerably in size, with the female being larger than the male. Mating is sometimes preceded by a more or less elaborate courtship performance, and in many cases is followed by the female killing and eating the male (hence the name black "widow" for one species of spider).

All spiders are predaceous and feed mainly on insects; some of the larger spiders may occasionally feed on small vertebrates. The prey is usually killed by the poison injected into it by the bite of the spider. Different spiders capture their prey in different ways; the wolf spiders and jumping spiders forage for and pounce on their prey, the crab spiders lie in wait for their prey on flowers—feeding on bees, flies, and other insects that frequent the flowers; the majority of spiders capture their prey in nets or webs. A few spiders are commensals; that is, they live in the web of a larger spider and feed on small insects not eaten by the larger spider.

Various types of silk are spun by spiders. Many spin a strand of silk almost wherever they go, the strand serving as a dragline. Some silk is covered with minute drops of a very sticky material, to which the spider's victims stick; in an orb web the spiral strands are viscous, and the radiating strands are simple silk. Many spiders wrap up in silk the insects caught in their web. Some silk, such as that of the hackled-band spiders, consists of flattened strands.

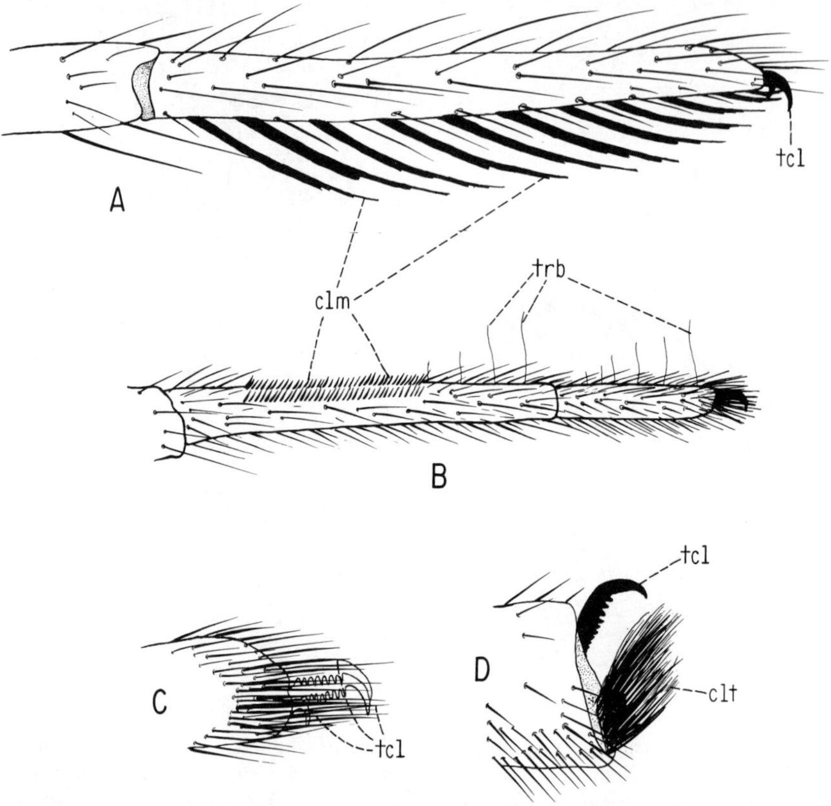

Fig. 30-30. Leg characters of spiders. A, hind tarsus of *Therídion* (Theridìidae); B, hind tarsus of *Amauròbius* (Amaurobìidae); C, tip of tarsus of a lycosid; D, tip of tarsus of a salticid. *clm,* calamistrum; *clt,* claw tuft; *tcl,* tarsal claws; *trb,* trichobothria.

The webs built by spiders are of several principal types; each species of spider constructs a characteristic web that is often as distinctive as the spider itself. The house spider and others build irregular nets, with the strands of silk extending in almost every direction. The sheet-web spiders make a closely woven, sheetlike, and usually horizontal web. The web of the funnel-web spiders is somewhat sheetlike, but is shaped like a funnel. Many spiders build orb webs consisting of radiating and spiral strands. The trap-door spiders and some of the wolf spiders construct tunnels. Some spiders construct leaf nests. Many spiders have a retreat of some sort close to or adjoining the web; they spend most of their time in this retreat and come out onto the web when it has caught something. The stimulus that brings out the spider is apparently the vibration of the web caused by the insect that is caught; a vibrating tuning fork held against the web will usually produce the same reaction by the spider.

Although spiders do not have wings, they often "fly." They get on top of a rock or post and spin out some silk. The wind catches this silk, and off "flies" the spider. If the wind is particularly strong, the silk may be torn off the spider; when many spiders are trying to fly on a windy day, large quantities of this silk ("gossamer") may be blown over the landscape. This flying of spiders is sometimes called "ballooning" or "parachuting," and it is usually young spiders that are involved.

Spiders play an important role in the general economy of nature, for they are quite numerous and their predatory habits serve to keep many other animals, particularly insects, in check. They are in turn preyed upon by various other animals, particularly wasps. Spider silk is used in the preparation of the cross-hairs in certain optical instruments. Many people dislike having spiders in the house because their webs are a nuisance (or simply because they dislike spiders), but spiders do not damage anything in the house and they may perform a service by destroying noxious insects. As we have pointed out above, the venomous nature of spiders is generally greatly exaggerated. Most spiders will not bite if handled carefully.

The order Aranèida is usually divided into two suborders, the Orthógnatha (Aviculariòidea) and the Labidógnatha (Argiopòidea), primarily on the bases of the structure of the chelicerae. The Labidógnatha is divided into two sections, the Cribellàtae and Ecribellàtae; the Cribellàtae have a cribellum and calamistrum, which are lacking in the Ecribellàtae. The majority of our spiders belong to the Ecribellàtae. The families occurring in the United States may be separated by the following key; groups marked with an asterisk are not likely to be encountered by the general collector.

KEY TO THE FAMILIES OF SPIDERS

1. Fangs of the chelicerae moving vertically or forward and backward; 2 pairs of book lungs; no cribellum; stout-bodied spiders, mostly western and tropical (suborder Orthógnatha) 2

1′. Fangs of the chelicerae moving laterally or in and out; usually only 1 pair of book lungs (if with 2, then a cribellum is present) (suborder Labidógnatha) 7

2(1). Anal tubercle well separated from spinnerets; abdomen with 1 to 3 sclerotized tergites 3

2′. Anal tubercle immediately adjacent to spinnerets; abdomen without sclerotized tergites 5

3(2). Endites well developed; labium fused to sternum; carapace with a transverse pit; widely distributed .... **Atýpidae** p. 643

3′. Endites weakly developed; labium not fused to sternum; carapace with a longitudinal pit or groove; mostly western United States 4

4(3′). Chelicerae with a group of apical teeth on mesal margin; labium about as long as wide; 4 spinnerets, the last segment of posterior pair a little longer than preceding segment .... **Antrodiaètidae*** p. 643

4′. Chelicerae without such teeth on mesal margin; labium much wider than long; 6 spinnerets, the last segment of posterior pair nearly twice as long as preceding segment .... **Mecicobothrìidae*** p. 643

5(2′). Tarsi with 2 claws and with claw tufts; large (40 mm or more in length), robust, hairy spiders, occurring in the South and West .. **Theraphósidae** p. 643

5′. Tarsi with 3 claws and without claw tufts; less than 30 mm in length 6

6(5′). Chelicerae with a group of apical teeth on mesal margin; anterior portion of carapace higher than posterior portion; anterior spinnerets separated by less than their own length; basal segment of posterior spinnerets as long as or longer than remaining segments combined; 15 to 28 mm in length .... **Ctenízidae** p. 643

6′. Chelicerae without such teeth on mesal margin; carapace flattened, the anterior part no higher than posterior portion; anterior spinnerets

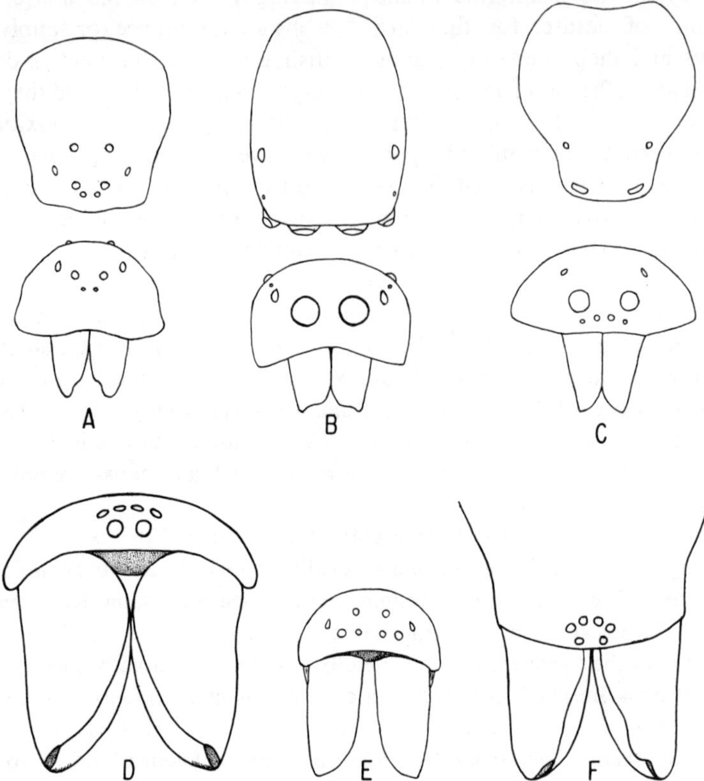

Fig. 30-31. Chelicerae and eye patterns of spiders; in A, B, and C the upper figure is a dorsal view and the lower figure is an anterior view; the other figures are anterior views. A, Oxyópidae; B, Saltícidae; C, Lycósidae; D, Dysdéridae (anterior view); E, Amaurobìidae (anterior view); F, Dysdéridae (dorsal view).

separated by at least their own length; the 3 segments of posterior spinnerets of about equal length; about 15 mm in length.... **Diplùridae** p. 643

7(1′). With 2 pairs of book lungs, or with 1 pair of book lungs and a pair of spiracles behind the book lungs, or without book lungs and with 2 pairs of spiracles 8*

7′. With 1 pair of book lungs, and a single spiracle (or none) between epigastric furrow and spinnerets 12

8(7). Book lungs lacking, and with 2 pairs of tracheal spiracles; 2 or 8 eyes; rare southwestern spiders .... **Caponìidae***

8′. One or 2 pairs of book lungs present; not more than 1 pair of tracheal spiracles 9*

9(8′). Eight eyes; 2 pairs of book lungs, the posterior pair about halfway between epigastric furrow and spinnerets; cribellum present; 5 to 10 mm in length; in southern mountains .... **Hypochílidae*** p. 643

9′. Six eyes or none; 1 pair of book lungs and a pair of spiracles (Figure 30-29 A); cribellum absent 10*

10(9′). Median eyes larger than lateral ones; minute spiders, about 1 mm in length .... **Oonópidae*** p. 644

10′. Median eyes not larger than lateral ones (Figure 30-31 F); 7 to 13 mm in length 11*

11(10′). Third legs directed backward; cephalothorax and legs reddish orange, abdomen dirty white; 12 to 13 mm in length; eastern United States........ **Dysdéridae*** p. 644

11′. Third legs directed forward; color brownish; 7 to 10 mm in length; widely distributed .... **Segestrìidae*** p. 644

12(7′). With a cribellum (Figure 30-29 B, *crb*) and a calamistrum (Figure 30-30 B, *clm*); if the cribellum and calamistrum are rudimentary (males of *Filastàta*), the eyes are all on a single raised tubercle and the pedipalps are longer than the body........ 13

12′. With neither a cribellum nor a calamistrum; eyes and pedipalps not as above 19

13(12). Anal tubercle large, 2-segmented, and fringed with long hair; 8 eyes in a compact group, the posterior median eyes triangular or irregular in shape; 2 to 4 mm in length........ **Oecobìidae*** p. 643

13′. Anal tubercle small, unsegmented, and without a conspicuous fringe of hair; arrangement of eyes variable, the posterior median eyes round.. 14

14(13′). Tarsi with 2 claws and with claw tufts; cribellum divided; eyes in 2 rows; rare southwestern spiders .... **Zorópsidae*** p. 643

14′. Tarsi with 3 claws and usually without claw tufts; cribellum and eyes variable 15

15(14′). Chelicerae fused together at base, each with an apical tooth, which with the fang forms a sort of claw; tracheal spiracle considerably anterior to spinnerets; labium fused to sternum; the 8 eyes in a compact group; 9 to 18 mm in length; southern United States .... **Filastátidae*** p. 643

15′. Chelicerae not fused together at base, and without an apical tooth; tracheal spiracle close to spinnerets; labium not fused to sternum.... 16

16(15′). Eight eyes, all light-colored (Figure 30-31 E); tarsi with trichobothria; cribellum divided; 4.5 to 12.0 mm in length .... **Amaurobìidae** p. 643

16′. Six or 8 eyes (if with 8, then some or all are dark-colored); tarsi usually without trichobothria; 1.7 to 8.0 mm in length........ 17

17(16′). Eight eyes, all dark-colored........ 18

17′. Either 8 eyes and only the anterior median ones dark, or 6 eyes and all pearly white; 1.7 to 6.0 mm in length .... **Dictýnidae** p. 643

18(17). Femora with trichobothria; eyes in 2 recurved rows; 2.4 to 8.0 mm in length .... **Ulobóridae** p. 643

18′. Femora without trichobothria; eyes in 2 or 3 rows, the first row of 4 eyes; posterior eyes often large .... **Dinópidae*** p. 643

19(12′). Tibiae and metatarsi of first and second legs with a series of long spines and a series of shorter spines between each 2 long ones; 5 to 8 mm in length .... **Mimétidae** p. 647

19′. Spines on first and second tibiae and metatarsi not as above........ 20

20(19′). With 6 spinnerets; widely distributed........ 21

20′. With 2 spinnerets (*Lùtica*, recorded from Oregon) .... **Zodarìidae***

21(20). Chelicerae fused together at base, each with an apical tooth, which with the fang forms a sort of claw 22

21′. Chelicerae not fused together at base, and without an apical tooth.... 26

22(21). Tarsi long, flexible, and with many pseudosegments; spiracle lacking; labium broader than long; 2 to 6 mm in length............**Phólcidae** p. 644

22′. Tarsi not greatly elongated, and without pseudosegments; spiracle present, and at least one-sixth the distance from epigastric furrow to spinnerets; labium longer than broad; mostly western spiders 23

23(22′). Eight eyes, in 2 rows; labium not fused to sternum; 3 tarsal claws; about 12.5 mm in length; western and southwestern United States.......... .... **Plectreùridae***

23′. Six eyes, in three groups of 2 each; labium fused to sternum; 2 to 3 tarsal claws 24

24(23′). Anterior row of eyes in a nearly straight line; carapace only two-thirds as wide as long; 3 tarsal claws; 5.6 to 9.5 mm in length; western United States ....**Diguétidae***

24′. Median pair of eyes distinctly anterior to lateral eyes; carapace more than two-thirds as wide as long; 2 to 3 tarsal claws; 3.5 to 15.0 mm in length; widely distributed 25

25(24′). Carapace flat, with a conspicuous median furrow in posterior portion; sternum pointed posteriorly; tarsi with 2 claws; 6.0 to 8.6 mm in length; southern and western United States...................**Loxoscélidae** p. 644

25′. Carapace much arched posteriorly and without a conspicuous median furrow; tarsi with 3 claws; 3.5 to 15.0 mm in length; widely distributed .... **Scytódidae** p. 644

26(21′). Tarsi with 2 claws and with or without claw tufts 27

26′. Tarsi with 3 claws and without claw tufts (Figure 30-30 C); spurious claws sometimes present...39

27(26). Tracheal spiracle immediately in front of spinnerets 28

27′. Tracheal spiracle well anterior to spinnerets, at least one-third the distance to epigastric furrow; 3 to 7 mm in length.............**Anyphaènidae** p. 644

28(27). Claw tufts present (Figure 30-30 D) 29

28′. Claw tufts absent 38

29(28). Eight eyes in 2 rows, 6 in first row; body flat; tropical spiders.......... .... **Selenópidae***

29′. Eyes in 2 to 4 rows; 2 or 4 in first row 30

30(29′). The anterior median eyes dark-colored; the other eyes light-colored....31

30′. All eyes dark-colored 32

31(30). Eyes in 2 rows of 4 each; tarsi with a dense row of short hairs beneath; anterior spinnerets normal; 4 to 15 mm in length........**Gnaphósidae** p. 644

31′. Eyes in 3 rows, of 4, 2, and 2; tarsi (except possibly the front tarsi) without a dense row of short hairs beneath; anterior spinnerets long and brush-like; southern United States ....**Prodidómidae***

32(30′). Hind coxae widely separated by the rounded sternum; a pair of spurious claws present; southwestern United States ....**Homalonýchidae***

32′. Hind coxae approximated; sternum oval or elongate; no spurious claws; widely distributed 33

33(32′). At least the first 2 pairs of legs laterograde, that is, turned so that the morphological dorsal surface is posterior and the anterior surface appears to be dorsal (Figure 30-32) 34

33′. Legs normal, not as above 35

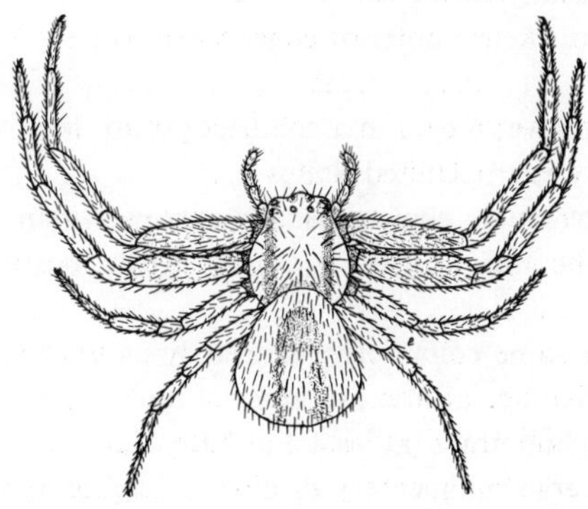

Fig. 30-32. A crab spider, *Misùmenops* sp. (Thomísidae).

34(33). Length 20 mm or more; colulus absent; apex of metatarsi with a soft trilobate membrane; southern United States .... **Sparássidae** p. 645

34′. Length 15 mm or less; colulus present but small; apex of metatarsi sclerotized, without a soft trilobate membrane; widely distributed.... .... **Thomísidae** p. 645

35(33′). Eyes in 4 rows of 2 each, the anterior eyes much larger than the others, and the eyes of the third row minute; 5 to 8 mm in length; southern and southeastern United States......................... **Lyssománidae*** p. 644

35′. Eyes in 2 or 3 rows 36

36(35′). Eyes in 3 rows (4-2-2), the anterior median eyes much larger than the others, the 2 eyes of the second row very small, and the 2 eyes in the third row medium-sized (Figure 30-31 B); body usually with scales.... .... **Saltícidae** p. 645

36′. Eyes not as above..37

37(36′). Eyes in 2 rows of 4 each; 3 to 15 mm in length........... **Clubiónidae** p. 644

37′. Eyes in 3 rows, usually 2-4-2, the eyes of the first row smaller than the eyes of the second row .... **Cténidae** p. 644

38(28′). At least the first 2 pairs of legs laterograde (see couplet 33).... **Thomísidae** p. 645

38′. Legs normal, not laterograde (see also couplet 51′).......... **Zodariidae***

39(26′). Spinnerets in a more or less transverse row; tracheal spiracle considerably anterior to spinnerets; 3.5 mm in length or less.......... **Hahnìidae** p. 645

39′. Spinnerets not in a single transverse row (Figure 30-29 C-E); size and location of tracheal spiracle variable..........................40

40(39′). Hind tarsi with a ventral row of strong, curved, serrated bristles forming a comb (Figure 30-30 A); 1 to 12 mm in length; spiders hanging in an inverted position in irregular webs..................... **Theridìidae** p. 646

40′. Hind tarsi without such a row of bristles 41

41(40′). Eyes in a hexagonal group, the anterior row recurved and the posterior row procurved (Figure 30-31 A); abdomen pointed apically (Figure 30-35 A); legs with prominent spines; 4 to 20 mm in length. . **Oxyópidae** p. 646

41′. Eyes not as above...42

42(41′). Tarsi with serrated bristles, forming at least 1 pair of spurious claws; tarsi usually without trichobothria 43

42′. Tarsi without serrated bristles, or at least none in the shape of spurious claws; tarsi usually with trichobothria 48

43(42). Labium with a thickened anterior edge; 8 eyes (rarely 6 or none); widely distributed 44

43′. Labium not as above; 6 eyes in a compact group; legs with short spines; cave spiders; western United States . . . . **Leptonétidae***

44(43). All eyes the same color; clypeus usually narrower than height of median ocular area (the area with the 4 median eyes); mostly builders of orb webs 45

44′. All eyes not the same color; clypeus usually as wide as, or wider than, height of median ocular area; mostly not building orb webs. 46

45(44). Femora with trichobothria (at least 1 at base of first and second femora); boss on chelicerae rudimentary or absent; chelicerae usually large and powerful; 3.5 to 9.0 mm in length. **Tetragnáthidae** p. 648

45′. Femora without trichobothria; boss on chelicerae usually present; chelicerae not unusually large; 1.5 to 30.0 mm in length. . . . **Aranèidae** p. 647

46(44′). Sternum broadly truncate posteriorly; anterior femora about three times as thick as posterior femora; legs without spines; pedipalp of female without a claw; chelicerae without a stridulating area; 1.6 to 2.7 mm in length; orb web weavers . . . . **Theridiosomátidae** p. 648

46′. Without the above combination of characters; web not an orb but an irregular net or modified sheet; lateral surface of chelicerae often with a stridulating area. 47

47(46′). Hind tibiae usually with 2 dorsal spines or bristles; tibiae of male pedipalp without an apophysis (a subapical pointed process); female pedipalp usually with a claw at apex of tarsus; 1.5 to 8.0 mm in length; sheet web spiders. . . . . **Linyphìidae** p. 648

47′. Hind tibiae with a single dorsal spine or bristle, or with none; tibiae of male pedipalp with at least 1 apophysis; female pedipalp without a claw; mostly less than 2 mm in length, and usually living in debris. . . . . **Micryphántidae** p. 648

48(42′). Chelicerae with a distinct boss. 49

48′. Chelicerae without a boss 51*

49(48). Trochanters with a curved notch along distal edge on ventral side; trichobothria numerous and in 2 rows or irregularly distributed; hind spinnerets not particularly lengthened (Figure 30-29 D); spiders not generally building webs. 50

49′. Trochanters not notched; tarsi with a single row of trichobothria; hind spinnerets very long (Figure 30-29 C); body with plumose hairs; spiders living in funnel webs; 2.5 to 20.0 mm in length. . . . . **Agelénidae** p. 645

50(49). Posterior row of eyes so strongly recurved that it might be considered as 2 rows, the 2 eyes in the middle row (or in the middle of the second row) usually much larger than the others (Figure 30-31 C); body hairs usually simple; anterior plate on pedicel rounded behind; 2.5 to 35.0 mm in length; egg sac carried attached to spinnerets, and young carried on back of mother. . . . . **Lycósidae** p. 646

50′. Posterior row of eyes only slightly recurved, the median eyes in this row little if any larger than the others; body with plumose hairs; anterior plate on pedicel emarginate or transverse behind; 9 to 26 mm in length;

egg sac held under cephalothorax, and young not carried about by mother .... **Pisaùridae** p. 645

51(48′). Body flat; posterior spinnerets very long; legs long and slender; anterior portion of carapace marked off by grooves and elevated above rest of carapace; rare tropical spiders, occurring in Texas........ **Hersiliidae***

51′. Body not flat; posterior spinnerets much shorter than anterior ones, often minute; hind legs normal or stout; carapace not as above (*Storèna*, recorded from Georgia) .... **Zodariidae***

—Suborder *Orthógnatha*— These spiders have large and powerful chelicerae that move in a plane more or less parallel to the median plane of the body; most species are heavy-bodied and stout-legged. The group is largely tropical; most United States species occur in the South and Southwest, but a few occur as far north as Massachusetts. The **Ctenízidae** includes the trap-door spiders, so called because they construct burrows in the ground that are closed by a door hinged with silk. The door fits snugly and is usually camouflaged on the outside. The tunnels may be simple or branched, or they may contain side chambers that are closed off from the main tunnel by hinged doors. These spiders occur in the South and West. The **Theraphósidae** (**Aviculariìdae**) includes the tarantulas, the largest of our spiders; these spiders are often greatly feared, but United States species are actually less venomous than the much smaller black widow spider. The **Diplùridae** includes the funnel-web tarantulas, so called because of the type of web they construct. The **Atýpidae** includes the purse-web spiders, whose webs are tubes of silk at the base of tree trunks and extending down into the ground; these spiders occur in the Northeast and in Florida. The **Antrodiaètidae,** which occur from Ohio west to the Pacific Coast, burrow in the ground, and their burrows are closed by double doors that meet in the middle of the opening. The **Mecicobothrìidae,** which occur along the West Coast, construct sheet webs similar to those of the funnel-web tarantulas.

—Suborder *Labidógnatha*— This group includes the vast majority of the spiders occurring in the United States. They differ from the Orthógnatha in having the chelicerae moving laterally, or in and out, rather than in a vertical plane, and they are generally smaller. This suborder is divided into two sections, the Cribellàtae and the Ecribellàtae, on the basis of the presence or absence of a cribellum.

—Section Cribellátae — Hackled Band Weavers— These spiders have a cribellum in front of the spinnerets (Figure 30-29 B, *crb*) and a calamistrum on the hind legs (Figure 30-30 B, *clm*). Their webs contain ribbonlike bands of silk, but the ribbonlike nature of these bands is usually visible only with considerable magnification. The **Hypochílidae,** or four-lunged spiders (so called because they have two pairs of book lungs), make irregular webs on the under side of overhanging ledges, usually along streams; these spiders occur in the mountains of the southeastern states. The **Amaurobìidae,** or white-eyed spiders, are widely distributed over the United States; they construct irregular webs under stones, in rock crevices, and in debris. The **Ulobóridae** construct orb webs or sectors of orbs; this group is widely distributed. The largest family in this section is the **Dictýnidae,** most species of which construct irregular webs on vegetation or on the ground. The other families in this section are the **Oecobìidae** (widely distributed), **Filastátidae** (southern states west to the Pacific Coast), **Zorópsidae** (rare spiders in the Southwest), and **Dinópidae.**

—Section Ecribellàtae— These spiders lack a cribellum and calamistrum. This group includes the majority of our spiders; it contains a large number of families, only the more important of which can be mentioned here.

FAMILY **Dysdéridae:** The dysderids are medium-sized spiders, 12 to 13 millimeters in length, with two pairs of spiracles at the base of the abdomen (Figure 30-29 A). They live under bark or stones, where they construct a retreat of silk, and hunt their prey from this retreat. These spiders occur from New England west to Nebraska and south to Georgia.

FAMILY **Oonópidae** — Minute Jumping Spiders: These spiders are only about a millimeter in length, and are most commonly found in buildings; they can often be recognized by their jumping habits. The oonopids occur in the eastern states.

FAMILY **Segestrìidae:** The segestriids have the three anterior pairs of legs directed forward and the hind pair directed backward. They are brownish in color, and 7 to 10 millimeters in length. They construct tubular retreats in crevices, under bark and stones, and in similar situations.

FAMILY **Lyssománidae:** These spiders are pale green in color, with some black around the eyes and some red scales on the anterior part of the carapace, and are 5 to 8 millimeters in length. They are usually found in low bushes, from the southeastern states west to Texas.

FAMILY **Scytódidae**—Spitting Spiders: The spitting spiders do not construct snares, but capture their prey by spitting out a mucilaginous substance that engulfs and traps the prey. These spiders generally occur in shaded places and in the dark corners of buildings.

FAMILY **Loxoscélidae:** These are light-colored spiders, 6.0 to 8.8 millimeters in length, that have the colulus large and conspicuous; they occur principally in the West. A few species in this family are quite venomous; one of these, *Loxoscèles reclùsus* Gertsch and Mulaik, is probably second in importance to the black widow in this respect. *L. reclùsus,* commonly known as the brown recluse, is slightly smaller than the black widow, and is light fawn to chocolate brown in color with a wide stripe of darker brown in the anterior part of the cephalothorax; it lives in cracks and crevices and occurs in Missouri, Arkansas, and Texas. A related species, *L. laèta* (Nicolet), is an important venomous spider in Chile.

FAMILY **Gnaphósidae (Drássidae)**—Hunting Spiders: These spiders are 4 to 15 millimeters in length; most species are uniformly dark-colored, but some species have a pattern of lines or spots. They construct a tubular retreat under stones and in debris, and hunt from this retreat.

FAMILY **Phólcidae**—Long-Legged Spiders: The pholcids are small (2 to 6 millimeters in length), with very long and slender legs; the tarsi are long and flexible, with many pseudosegments. They construct sheetlike or irregular webs, and usually hang upside down on the under side of the web. The egg sac is held by the female in her chelicerae.

FAMILY **Clubiónidae**—Two-Clawed Hunting Spiders: The clubionids are relatively common spiders, 3 to 15 millimeters in length, and occur on foliage or on the ground. They do not spin webs for the capture of prey, but construct a tubular retreat under stones or in rolled up leaves or folds of grasses. One species, *Chiracánthium inclùsum* (Hentz), is quite venomous; this spider is about 8 millimeters in length, greenish white in color, and occurs throughout the United States.

FAMILY **Anyphaènidae:** These hunting spiders are somewhat similar to the clubionids, but have the tracheal spiracle well anterior to the spinnerets, and the hairs of the claw tufts are somewhat flattened. They usually occur on foliage.

FAMILY **Cténidae**—Wandering Spiders: The wandering spiders are somewhat similar to

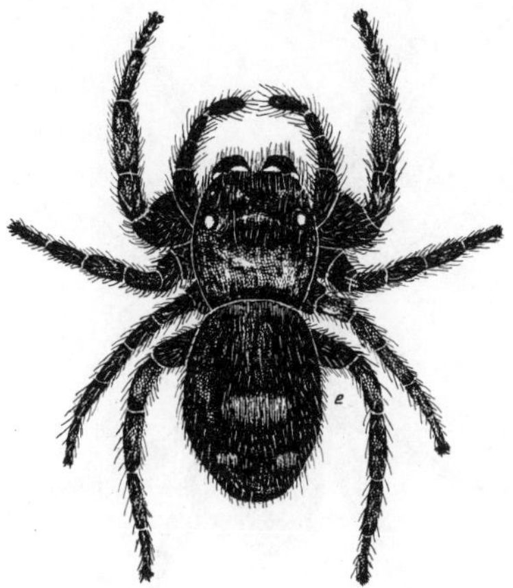

Fig. 30-33. A jumping spider, *Phidíppus àudax* (Hentz) (Saltícidae).

the clubionids, but have the eyes in three rows instead of two. They usually occur on foliage and are more common in the southern states.

FAMILY **Sparássidae (Heteropódidae)**—Giant Crab Spiders: These spiders are similar to the thomisids, but are larger and occur only in the southern states.

FAMILY **Thomísidae**—Crab Spiders: The crab spiders are somewhat crablike in shape, and walk sideways or backward; the two anterior pairs of legs are usually stouter than the two posterior pairs (Figure 30-32). These spiders spin no webs, but forage for their prey or lie in ambush for it. Many species lie in wait for their prey on flowers, and are able to capture flies or bees much larger than themselves. One of the most common species in this group is the goldenrod spider, *Misùmena vàtia* (Clerck), which is white or yellow with a light-red band on either side of the abdomen; this species can change color (over a period of several days), depending on the color of the flower.

FAMILY **Saltícidae (Áttidae)**—Jumping Spiders: These spiders are medium to small in size, stout-bodied and short-legged (Figure 30-33), with a distinctive arrangement of the eyes (Figure 30-31 B). The body is rather hairy and is often brightly colored or iridescent; some species are antlike in appearance. These spiders are hunters and pursue their prey; they construct silken retreats under stones and in debris.

FAMILY **Agelénidae**—Grass and Funnel-Web Spiders: These spiders build sheetlike webs, usually in grass; the webs are somewhat funnel-shaped and have a tubular retreat leading down into the grass. They are often very common, a fact that is most evident in the early morning when their webs are covered with dew.

FAMILY **Hahnìidae:** The hahniids are small spiders, 1.5 to 3.2 millimeters in length, that spin funnel webs similar to those of the Agelénidae but without the funnel-like retreats. The webs are located on or near the ground, usually in damp places, and are delicate and difficult to see unless covered with dew.

FAMILY **Pisaùridae**—Nursery-Web and Fishing Spiders: The egg sac in these spiders is carried by the female, under her cephalothorax and held by the chelicerae and pedipalps; before the eggs hatch, the female attaches the sac to a plant and ties leaves around it. The pisaurids are wandering spiders, and make webs only for the young. The female stands guard near this nursery web after the young hatch. Some spiders in

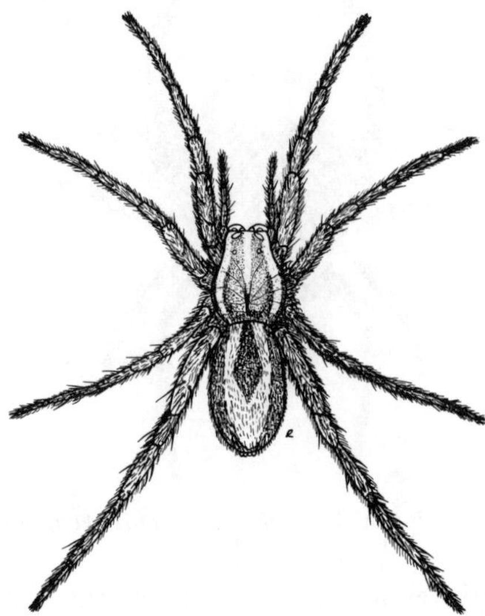

Fig. 30-34. A wolf or ground spider, *Lycòsa* sp. (Lycósidae).

this group, particularly the fishing spiders in the genus *Dolómedes,* are quite large, and may have a leg spread of 3 inches (Figure 30-35 B). The *Dolómedes* spiders live near water; they may walk over the surface or dive beneath it, and occasionally capture aquatic insects and even small fish.

FAMILY **Lycósidae**—Wolf Spiders or Ground Spiders: The wolf spiders are hunting spiders that chase their prey, and some are relatively large. Most of them are dark brown in color. The members of this group can usually be recognized by the characteristic arrangement of the eyes: four small eyes in the first row, two very large eyes in the second row, and two small or medium-sized eyes in the third row (Figure 30-31 C). The egg sac is carried about by the female, attached to her spinnerets; when the young hatch, they are carried about on the back of the female for a time. The lycosids are a large and widely distributed group, and many species are fairly common.

FAMILY **Oxyópidae**—Lynx Spiders: These spiders can usually be recognized by the arrangement of the eyes in a hexagonal group (Figure 30-31 A). The abdomen usually tapers to a point posteriorly (Figure 30-35 A). These spiders chase their prey over foliage with great rapidity; many can jump, and some ambush their prey at flowers. These spiders do not construct a web or a retreat; they occur among low vegetation and attach their egg sacs to foliage. The lynx spiders are more common in the southern states.

FAMILY **Theridìidae** — Comb - Footed Spiders: The webs of these spiders are an irregular network in which the spider usually hangs upside down; many live in buildings and other protected places. The cephalothorax is usually small, the abdomen large and rounded (some have the abdomen oddly shaped), and the legs are usually bent. The common name of the group is derived from the comb of serrated bristles on the hind tarsi (Figure 30-30 A); these combs are used in wrapping the prey in silk. One of the most important species in this group is the black widow spider, *Latrodéctus máctans* Fabricius, the most venomous spider in the United States; its bite is sometimes fatal. The female is about $\frac{1}{2}$ inch in body length, black and shining,

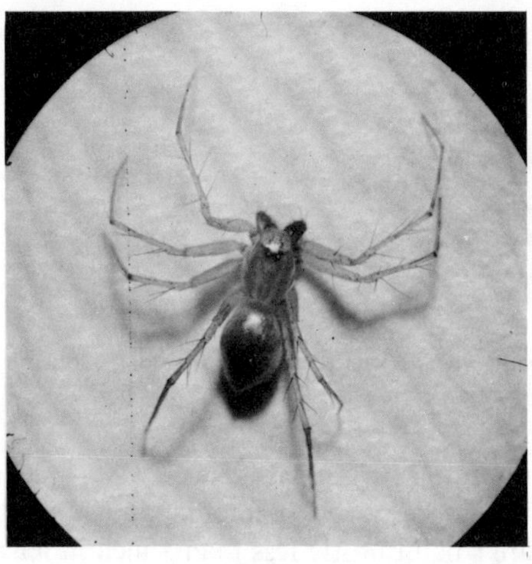

A

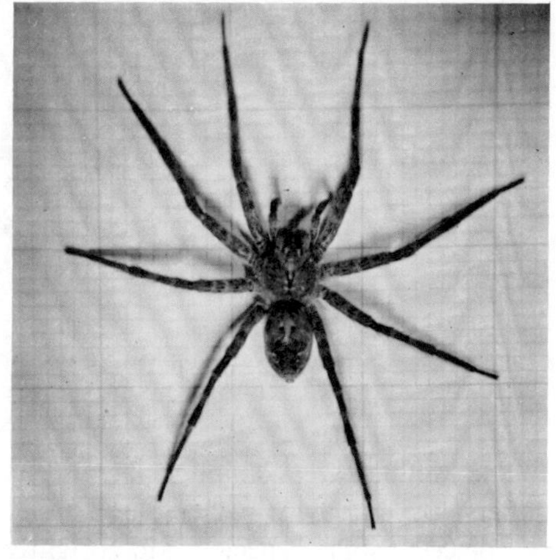

B

Fig. 30-35. A, a lynx spider, *Oxyòpes sálticus* Hentz; B, a fishing spider, *Dolómedes. tenebròsus* Hentz (the darker lines are 1 inch apart). (Courtesy of R. L. Snouffer.)

with a reddish-orange spot shaped like an hour glass on the ventral side of the abdomen (Figure 30-36); the male, which is less often seen because it is usually killed by the female after mating, is about $\frac{1}{4}$ inch in length and is marked like the female, but also has four pairs of reddish-orange stripes along the sides of the abdomen. Black widows are found under stones, about stumps, in holes in the ground, about outbuildings, and in similar places; they are widely distributed over the United States, but are more common in the southern states. Two other species of *Latrodéctus* that occur in the United States are quite venomous: the brown or gray widow, *L. geométricus* Koch, which occurs in southern Florida and southern California, and *L. bíshopi* Kaston, which occurs in southern Florida. Another common species in this family is the house spider, *Therídion tepidariòrum* (Koch).

FAMILY **Mimétidae** — Spider - Hunting Spiders: These spiders can generally be recognized by the spination of the tibiae and metatarsi of the first two pairs of legs: the larger spines are separated by a row of smaller spines. These spiders appear to feed largely, if not entirely, on other spiders; they do not construct a web for the capture of prey.

FAMILY **Aranèidae (Argiópidae, Epeìridae)** —Orb-Weavers: This is a very large and widely distributed group, and nearly all its members construct an orb web. There is a great deal of variation in size, color, and shape in this family, and the family is divided into several subfamilies, some of which are mentioned here.

The Gasteracanthìnae, or spiny-bellied spiders, are so called because of the spiny protuberances on the abdomen; these small spiders are usually found in woods, where their small orb web is suspended between two trees several feet apart.

The Nephilìnae, or silk spiders, are so called because of the large amount and great strength of their silk, which is sometimes used in the manufacture of fabrics. This group is largely tropical, but one species, *Néphila clávipes* (Linn.), is fairly common in the southern states; females are about 22 millimeters in length, the carapace is dark brown, the abdomen is dark greenish with several pairs of small light spots, and there are conspicuous tufts of hair on the femora and tibiae of the first, second, and fourth legs.

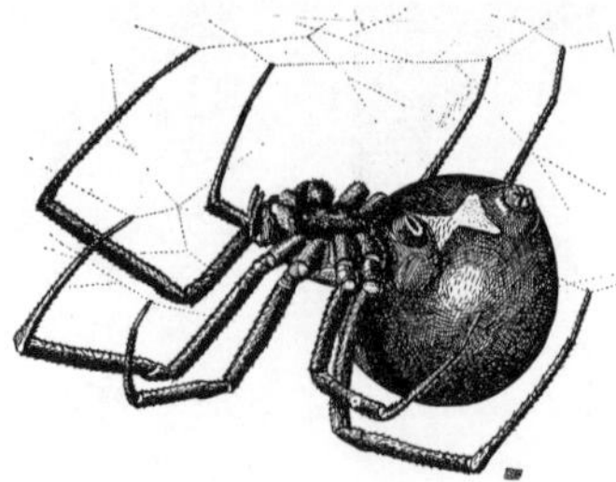

Fig. 30-36. The black widow spider, *Latrodéctus máctans* (Fabricius), female, hanging from its web. (Courtesy of Utah Agricultural Experiment Station.)

The Metìnae are a small group, and its members live in caves, ravines, and other dark places; some species are brightly colored.

The Argiopìnae, or garden spiders, are common in grassy places; they are often brightly colored, black and yellow or black and red (Figure 30-37). The web is constructed in grass and consists of an orb with a dense net of silk extending through the middle; the spider usually rests head downward in the center of its web.

The largest subfamily is the Araneìnae, or typical orb-weavers; the members of this group vary greatly in size and color.

FAMILY **Tetragnáthidae** — Four - Jawed Spiders: These spiders have very large and protruding chelicerae, especially in the males. Most species are brownish in color and rather long and slender, and the legs, especially the front pair, are very long. These spiders are usually found in marshy places.

FAMILY **Theridiosomátidae**—Ray Spiders: These small spiders (less than 3 millimeters in length) are usually found near streams or in other damp situations. The web is peculiar in that the radii unite in groups of three or four, and each group is connected to the center by a single thread. The web is drawn into a conical shape by a thread from the center to a nearby twig, where it is held taut by the spider; when an insect gets into the web the spider releases its line, allowing the web to spring back and entangle the insect.

FAMILY **Linyphìidae**—Sheet-Web Spiders: These are fairly common spiders, but they are small (mostly less than $\frac{1}{4}$ inch in length) and are not often seen. The webs, however, are often conspicuous, particularly when covered with dew; they are flat and sheetlike, sometimes bowl-shaped or dome-shaped, and usually with an irregular mesh of silk around or above the sheetlike part. The spider is usually found on the under side of the web.

FAMILY **Micryphántidae (Erigónidae)**—Dwarf Spiders: This is a very large group of small spiders, most of which are less than 2 millimeters in length. They are usually found on the ground in leaf litter and debris, and are seldom seen except by a careful collector.

COLLECTING AND PRESERVING CHELICERATES

To obtain a large collection of chelicerates, one needs primarily to collect in as many different types of habitats as possible. Chelicerates are frequently very abundant, often as abundant as insects or more so. The general collector of insects is likely to encounter more spiders and mites than any other types of chelicerates, so the following suggestions are concerned primarily with these groups.

Chelicerates occur in a great variety of situations and can often be collected with the same techniques and equipment used in collecting insects. Many may be taken by sweeping vegetation with an insect net;

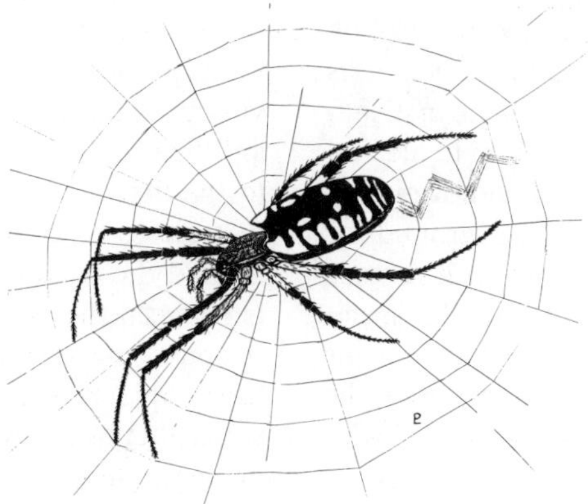

Fig. 30-37. A garden spider, *Argìope aurántia* Lucas.

many may be obtained with beating equipment, that is, using a sheet or beating umbrella beneath a tree or bush and beating the bush to knock off the specimens. The ground forms may be found running on the ground or under stones, boards, bark, or other objects. Many are to be found in the angles of buildings and similar protected places. Many of the smaller forms can be found in debris, soil litter, or moss, and are best collected by means of sifting equipment such as a Berlese funnel. Many are aquatic or semiaquatic and may be collected in marshy areas with aerial collecting equipment or in water with aquatic equipment. The parasitic species (various mites and ticks) must usually be looked for on their hosts.

Many chelicerates are nocturnal, and collecting at night may prove more successful than collecting during the day. Very few are attracted to lights, but may be spotted at night with a flashlight; the eyes of many spiders will reflect the light, and with a little experience one may locate a good many spiders at night by the use of a flashlight.

Chelicerates should be preserved in fluids rather than on pins or points; many forms, such as the spiders, are very soft-bodied and shrivel when dry. They are usually preserved in 70 to 90 percent alcohol; there should be plenty of alcohol in the bottle in relation to the specimen, and it is often desirable to change the alcohol after the first few days. Many workers preserve mites in Oudeman's fluid, which consists of 87 parts of 70 percent alcohol, 5 parts of glycerine, and 8 parts of glacial acetic acid; the chief advantage of this fluid is that the mites die with their appendages extended so that subsequent examination is easier. Alcohol is not suitable for preserving gall mites; such mites are best collected by wrapping infested plant parts in soft tissue paper and allowing them to dry. This dried material can be kept indefinitely, and the mites can be recovered for study by warming the dried material in Kiefer's solution (50 grams of resorcinal, 20 grams of diglycolic acid, 25 milliliters of glycerol, enough iodine to produce the desired color, and about 10 milliliters of water). Specialists on mites prefer specimens in fluid rather than mounted on permanent microscope slides, so that all aspects and structures can be studied.

Chelicerates may be collected by means of a net, forceps, vial, or a small brush, or they may be collected by hand. In the case of biting or stinging forms, it is safer to use some method other than collecting them in the fingers. Specimens collected with a net can be transferred directly to a vial of alcohol, or they may be collected in an empty vial and later transferred to alcohol. Since some species are quite active, it is sometimes preferable to put them first into a cyanide bottle and transfer them to alcohol after they have been stunned and are quiet. Specimens collected from the ground or from debris may be picked up with forceps or coaxed into a bottle, or the smaller specimens (and this applies to small specimens found in any sort of situation) may be picked up with a small brush moistened with alcohol.

Spider webs that are flat and not too large may be collected and preserved between two pieces of glass. One piece of glass is pressed against the web (which will usually stick to the glass because of the viscous material on some of the silk strands) and then the other piece of glass is applied to the first; it is often desirable to have the two pieces of glass separated by thin strips around the edge of the glass. Once the web is between the two pieces of glass, the glass is bound together with lantern-slide binding tape. Spider webs are best photographed when they are covered with moisture (dew or fog); they may often be photographed dry if illuminated from the side and photographed against a dark background.

GENERAL REFERENCES ON THE ARTHROPODA

Eddy, Samuel, and A. C. Hodson. 1950. Taxonomic keys to the common animals of the north central states exclusive of the parasitic worms, insects, and birds. Minneapolis: Burgess Publishing Co. 123 pp., 608 f.

Snodgrass, R. E. 1952. A textbook of arthropod anatomy. Ithaca, N.Y.: Comstock Publishing Associates. viii+363 pp., 88 f.

REFERENCES ON CRUSTACEANS

Crowder, William. 1931. Between the tides. New York: Dodd, Mead & Company, Inc. 461 pp., 451 f., 34 pl.

Edmondson, W. T. (ed.) 1959. Fresh-water biology. New York: John Wiley & Sons, Inc. xx+1248 pp.; illus. (Second edition of Ward and Whipple's "Fresh-water Biology.")

Miner, Roy W. 1950. Field book of seashore life. New York: G. P. Putnam's Sons. xv+888 pp., 251 pl.

Morgan, Ann H. 1930. Field book of ponds and streams. New York: G. P. Putnam's Sons. xvi+448 pp., 314 f., 23 pl.

Pennak, Robert W. 1953. Fresh-water invertebrates of the United States. New York: The Ronald Press Company. ix+769 pp., 470 f.

Ward, Henry B., and George C. Whipple. 1918. Fresh-water biology. New York: John Wiley & Sons, Inc. 1111 pp., 1547 f.

REFERENCES ON MYRIAPODS

Bailey, John W. 1928. The Chilopoda of New York State, with notes on the Diplopoda. N.Y. State Museum, Bull. 276:5-50; 15 f.

Chamberlin, Ralph V., and Richard L. Hoffman. 1958. Checklist of the millipedes of North America. U.S. Natl. Museum Bull. 212; 236 pp.

Johnson, Bert M. 1954. The millipedes of Michigan. Papers Mich. Acad. Sci., 39(1953): 241-252; 7 pl.

Keeton, Wm. T. 1960. A taxonomic study of the millipede family Spirobolidae (Diplopoda, Spirobolida). Entomol. Soc. Am., Mem. No. 17; ii+146 pp., 268 f.

Wood, H. C. 1865. On the Myriapoda of North America. Trans. Am. Phil. Soc., 13(7): 137-248; 61 f., 3 pl.

REFERENCES ON CHELICERATES

Atkins, J. A., C. W. Wingo, W. A. Sodeman, and J. E. Flynn. 1958. Necrotic arachnidism. Am. J. Trop. Med. and Hyg., 7(2): 165-184; 17 f.

Baker, Edward W., J. H. Camin, F. Cunliffe, T. A. Woolley, and C. E. Yunker. 1958. Guide to the families of mites. Contrib. No. 3 from the Institute of Acarology, Dept. Zool., Univ. Md., College Park, Md. ix+242 pp.; illus.

Baker, Edward W., and George W. Wharton. 1952. An introduction to acarology. New York: The Macmillan Company. xiii+465 pp., 377 f., 3 pl.

Bristowe, W. S. 1939-1941. The comity of spiders. London: The Ray Society. Two volumes. Vol. 1, 1939, x+228 pp., 19 pl., 16 text f. Vol. 2, 1941, x+229-560 pp., 3 pl., 81 text f.

Cloudsley-Thompson, J. L. 1958. Spiders, scorpions, centipedes, and mites. New York: Pergamon Press, Inc. xiv+228 pp., illus.

Comstock, J. H., and W. J. Gertsch. 1940. The spider book. New York: Doubleday & Company, Inc. xi+729 pp., 770 f.

Evans, G. O., J. G. Sheals, and D. Macfarlane. 1961. The terrestrial Acari of the British Isles. An introduction to their morphology, biology, and classification. Vol. 1, Introduction and biology. London: British Museum. vii+219 pp., frontis. +216 f.

Ewing, H. E. 1929. A manual of external parasites. Springfield, Ill.: Charles C Thomas, Publisher. xiv+225 pp., 96 f.

Hoff, C. Clayton. 1949. The pseudoscorpions of Illinois. Illinois Nat. Hist. Survey, Bull. 24(4):411-498; 51 f.

Hoff, C. Clayton. 1958. List of the pseudoscorpions of North America north of Mexico. Am. Museum Novitates, No. 1875; 50 pp.

Kaston, B. J. 1948. Spiders of Connecticut. Conn. State Geol. and Nat. Hist. Survey, Bull. 70; 874 pp., 6 text f., 144 pl.

Kaston, B. J., and Elizabeth Kaston. 1953. How to know the spiders. Dubuque, Iowa: William C. Brown Company, Publishers. vi+220 pp., 552 f.

Muma, Martin H. 1943. Common spiders of Maryland. Baltimore: The Natural History Society of Maryland. 173 pp., 15 pl.

Parrish, H. M. 1959. Deaths from bites and stings of venomous animals and insects. A.M.A. Arch. Internal Med., 104:198-207.

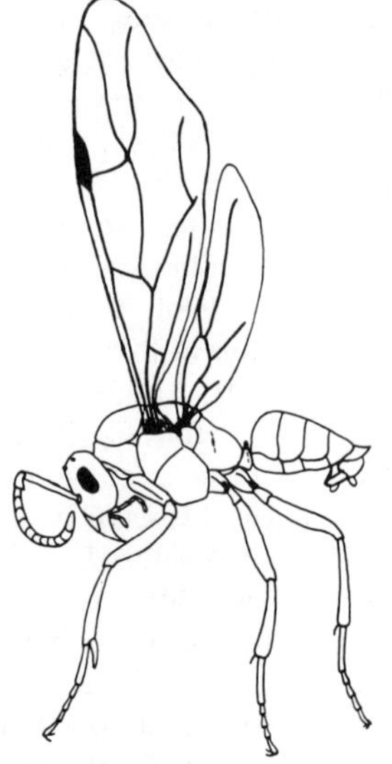

31

The Relation of Insects to Man

On the basis of their relation to man, insects may be classified into two general groups, beneficial and injurious. Many insects may be considered neutral because their numbers are so small that no direct effects are felt by man.

Man benefits from insects in many ways; without them, human society could not exist in its present form. Without the pollinating services of bees and other insects, we should have few vegetables, few fruits, little or no clover (and hence much less beef, mutton, and wool), no cotton, no coffee, no tobacco, few flowers—in fact, we should not have a great many of the things that are an integral part of our domestic economy and civilization. Insects provide us with honey, beeswax, silk, and many other useful products. Many species are parasitic or predaceous and are important in keeping the pest species under control; others help in the control of noxious weeds, and still others clean up refuse and make the world a little more pleasant. Insects are the sole or major item of food of many birds, fish, and other animals, including man in some parts of the world. Some species are used in the treatment of certain diseases. The study of insects has helped scientists solve many problems in heredity, evolution, sociology, stream pollution, and other fields. Insects also have aesthetic value; artists, milliners, and designers have made use of their beauty, and many people derive a great deal of pleasure from the study of insects as a hobby.

On the other hand, many insects are abnoxious or destructive. They attack various growing plants, including plants of value to man, and feed on them, injure or kill them, or introduce disease into them. They attack man's possessions, including his home, his clothing, and his food stores, and destroy, damage, or contaminate them. They attack man and animals and are annoying because of their presence, odors, bites, or stings, and many are agents in the transmission of some of the most serious diseases that beset man and animals.

Most people are much more aware of the injurious insects and their effects than they are of the beneficial insects, and the injurious species are probably better known than the beneficial ones. In spite of the excessive attention paid to injurious insects by the public in general and entomologists in particular, we believe that the good done by the beneficial insects outweighs the harm done by the injurious ones.

BENEFICIAL INSECTS

INSECTS AND POLLINATION

Sexual reproduction in the higher plants is made possible by the process of pollination. This process consists of the pollen (the male germ cells) being transferred from the stamens to the stigma; from the stigma a pollen tube grows down the style to the female germ cell. This process must take place in practically every case before the flower will bear seed; as the seed develops, the tissues around it swell and form the fruit.

A few of the higher plants are self-pollinating, but the majority are cross-pollinated; that is, the pollen of one flower must be transferred to the stigma of another. Pollen is transferred from one flower to another in two principal ways: by the wind and by insects. Wind-pollinated plants produce a large amount of dry pollen which is blown far and wide; such plants manage to reproduce because a few of the millions of pollen grains produced happen to land on the stigma of the right flower. Insect-pollinated plants produce smaller amounts of pollen, which is usually sticky and adheres to the bodies of insects that visit the flower; this pollen is later rubbed off the insect onto the stigma of another flower, in most cases more or less by accident as far as the insect is concerned.

Many flowers have peculiar features of structure that help to ensure pollination. Some, such as the iris, are so constructed that an insect cannot get to the nectar without collecting pollen on its body and cannot enter the next flower of this same kind without leaving some of the pollen on the stigma of that flower. Milkweeds have special pollen masses, the pollinia, which are arranged in such a way that when an insect alights on the edge of the flower, its legs slip into a fissure in the pollinia; the pollinia then become attached to the insect's leg and are carried to the next flower.

Some plants are dependent upon a single species or type of insect for pollination. Some of the orchids are pollinated only by certain long-tongued hawk moths. The Smyrna fig is pollinated by the fig wasp, *Blastóphagus psènes* (Linn.), and the yucca is pollinated solely by the yucca moth, *Tegetícula yuccasélla* (Riley). The Smyrna fig is peculiar in that all its flowers are female and produce no pollen; the pollen must come from a type of wild fig called the caprifig, which produces pollen but not edible fruit. The female wasp develops in a small gall at the base of the caprifig flower, and on emerging from this gall, becomes covered with caprifig pollen; she then flies to another fig to lay her eggs, and although she lays her eggs only on the caprifig, she occasionally visits the Smyrna fig flowers. Growers of Smyrna figs aid in the process of pollination by placing in their fig trees branches of the wild fig; when the fig insects emerge from the wild fig, they are almost certain to visit the flowers of the Smyrna fig and thus pollinate them. In the case of the yucca, the female yucca moth collects pollen from the yucca flowers, and immediately after laying her eggs in the ovary of a flower, she places the pollen she has collected on the stigma of that flower; this ensures the fertilization of the flower and the development of the seeds. The moth larvae feed on the seeds, but since more seeds develop than are eaten by the larvae, the perpetuation of the yucca is assured.

The plants that are wind pollinated and hence not dependent upon insects include corn, wheat, rye, oats, timothy, and other grasses; trees such as the willows, oaks, hickories, elms, poplars, birches, and conifers; and many wild plants such as ragweed and pigweed. On the other hand, such orchard fruits as apples, pears, plums, cherries, and citrus fruits; strawberries, raspberries, blackberries, cranberries, grapes; such vegetables as melons, cucumbers, pumpkins, squash, eggplant, peppers, and carrots; such field crops as the clovers, cotton, and tobacco; and many flowers—all are dependent upon insects for pollination.

The rosaceous plants (apple, pear, cherry, blackberry, strawberry) are dependent chiefly upon honey bees for pollination; the clovers are dependent upon various bees, chiefly honey bees and bumble bees. Many plants with strongly scented and conspicuous nocturnal flowers, such as honeysuckle, tobacco, and petunias, are pollinated not only by bees but also by certain moths. Umbelliferous plants like carrots and parsnips are pollinated chiefly by various flies, bees, and wasps. Pond lilies, goldenrod, and some other flowers are pollinated by bees and certain beetles.

Clover is an important farm crop in many parts of the country and is used as hay and forage and to enrich the soil. The average annual crop of clover seed in Ohio (250,000 bushels) would plant some 3 million acres in clover; this acreage would yield about 4.5 million tons of hay (worth about $90 million) and add about 273 million pounds of nitrogen to the soil (worth about $50 million). Red clover and alsike are entirely dependent on insects for pollination and seed production, and sweet clover and alfalfa, though somewhat self-pollinated, depend on insect pollination for profitable seed yields. The job of pollinating clover is tremendous; an acre of red clover, for example, contains about 216 million individual flowers, and every one of these must be visited by an insect before it will produce seed. Under normal field conditions (at least in Ohio) about 82 percent of the pollinating of red clover is done by honey bees and 15 percent by bumble bees. The average seed yields of red clover and alsike in Ohio are about 1.0 and 1.6 bushels per acre, respectively; with a dense honey-bee population in clover fields, these yields can be increased to 4 and 8 bushels per acre, and with maximum insect pollination, they can be increased to 12 and 20 bushels per acre.

Sheep may be raised on grasses that are wind pollinated, but a practical sheep raiser prefers clovers. Some years ago the sheep growers in New Zealand imported red-clover seed to improve their pastures. The clover grew all right, but produced no seed for the next year's crop because they were no suitable insects in New Zealand to pollinate the clover. After bumble bees were introduced there and had become established, thus making possible the pollination of clover, there was continuous good grazing for New Zealand sheep.

Orchard fruits, with the possible exception of sour cherries and most peaches, are largely or entirely insect pollinated, and this job is done chiefly by bees. Experiments involving the use of cages over orchard trees have shown that if bees are excluded from the tree when it is in bloom, the set of fruit is usually less than 1 percent of the blooms; if a hive of bees is caged with a tree, the set of fruit is increased, in some cases to as high as 44 percent of the blooms. Such experiments indicate that the fruit yields in orchards can be greatly increased by the use of bees. Although many factors complicate the problem of orchard pollination, a large number of growers obtain considerably increased yields of fruit by placing hives of bees in their orchards when the trees are in bloom.

The value to man of the pollinating insects is enormous; the annual yields of insect-pollinated plants in this country are valued at about $4½ billion. Of all the insects that pollinate plants, the most important is the honey bee; this insect is highly prized for its honey and wax, but for every dollar's worth of honey and wax it produces, 15 or 20 dollar's worth of pollinating services are rendered to agriculture.

COMMERCIAL PRODUCTS DERIVED FROM INSECTS

HONEY AND BEESWAX: The production of honey is a very old industry, dating back to the time of the Pharoahs. Honey bees are not native to the United States, but were introduced into this country about 1638. Several strains of this insect now occur here. Honey is used extensively as a food and in the manufacture of many products. Beeswax is used extensively by industry in making candles, sealing wax, polishes, certain types of inks, models of various kinds, and other products.

Beekeeping is a multimillion-dollar industry. California, the leading state in apiculture, has nearly half a million colonies of bees; Ohio is second, with about 375,000 colonies. There are about 6 million colonies of honey bees in the United States, which produce about 240 million pounds of honey and about 4½ million pounds of wax annually, a production worth about $50 million.

SILK: The silk industry is an ancient one, extending as far back as 2500 B.C. The rearing of silkworms and the processing and weaving of silk are principally an oriental industry, but they are practiced to some extent in a number of other countries, especially Spain, France, and Italy. Several types of silkworms have been utilized for the production of commercial silk, but the most important is *Bómbyx mòri* (Linn.), a domesticated species. Although silk is at the present time being replaced by various synthetic fibers, it is still a very important industry; the annual world production of silk is about 65 to 75 million pounds.

SHELLAC: Shellac is produced from the secretions of the lac insect, *Láccifer lácca* (Kern), a type of scale insect occurring on fig, banyan, and other plants in India, Burma, Indo-China, Formosa, Ceylon, and the Philippine Islands. These insects form encrustations ¼ to ½ inch thick on the twigs of the host plant. The twigs containing these encrustations are collected and ground; the "seed lac" so formed is melted and dried in sheets or flakes, which are shipped to a processing plant where the shellac is made. About $9 million worth of shellac is used annually in the United States.

DYES AND OTHER MATERIALS: Several insects have been used in the manufacture of dyes. The cochineal insect, *Dactylòpius cóccus* Costa, a scale insect somewhat similar to the mealybugs, is used for the production of cochineal dyes. These insects feed on *Opúntia* cacti (prickly pear) in the southwestern states and Mexico. The dye obtained from these insects is crimson in color and is produced from the dried bodies of the insects. This dye is now largely replaced by aniline dyes. Dyes have also been made from other types of scale insects and from certain cynipid galls. Some of the cynipid galls have also been used as a source of tannic acid, which is used in the manufacture of ink and for other purposes. Certain drugs, such as cantharidin—which is made from the dried bodies of a European blister beetle, the Spanish-fly *Lýtta vesicatòria* (Linn.)—have been made from insects. Many insects, such as hellgrammites, are often sold as fish bait.

PARASITIC AND PREDACEOUS INSECTS

Insects have a high reproductive capacity and are potentially able to build up tremendous populations, but they seldom do so—largely because of the many animals that feed on them. A considerable proportion of these entomophagous, or insect-eating, animals are insects. The check exerted upon insect pests by entomophagous insects is a very important factor in keeping down the populations of pest species; probably nothing that man can do in controlling insects by other methods will compare with the control exerted by entomophagous animals; yet the public has little knowledge or appreciation of this enormous benefit to man.

Entomophagous insects are of two general sorts, predators and parasites. The distinction between these two is not very sharp, but, in general, predators feed on smaller or weaker insects, usually using one or more for a single meal; they live apart from their prey, and often seek insects in different places for different meals; predators are usually active, powerful insects. Parasites live in or on the bodies of their host and live continuously with a single host during at least a part of their life cycle; they obtain successive meals from this host, and their feeding is at the expense of the host, but the host is not killed immediately (if at all). Parasites are smaller than their hosts, and often more than one parasite may live in or on the same host.

While we have here classified predaceous and parasitic insects as beneficial to man, it should be understood that their economic importance is determined by the insect they attack; if the species attacked is injurious, the entomophagous insect is considered beneficial, but if it attacks a beneficial species, it is considered injurious.

A great many insects are predaceous on other insects. Dragonflies and damselflies are predaceous during both nymphal and adult stages; the nymphs feed on a variety of aquatic insects, including mosquito larvae, and the adults feed on mosquitoes, many small moths, and other insects. Of the beetles, the ground beetles and tiger beetles are important predators, both as larvae and adults, and feed on a variety of insects. The ladybird beetles are important predators of aphids. Some of the wasps, particularly among the Véspidae and Sphècidae, are important predators of such insect pests as caterpillars and grasshoppers. Lacewings feed on aphids. Among the bugs (Hemiptera), a number of groups are predaceous; some of the stink bugs are predaceous on caterpillars, and many of the aquatic bugs prey on mosquito larvae. Mantids prey on many insects, including some injurious species. The important predators among the flies (Diptera) are the robber flies, dance flies, long-legged flies, and syrphid flies.

The majority of the entomophagous insect parasites are parasitic only during the larval stage. In the adult stage, the insect is usually active and free-living and only rarely feeds on the host of the larva; the adult usually locates the host and lays its eggs in, on, or near it. The eggs may be laid in or on the body of the host, or entirely apart from the host; in the latter case the host may be located and attacked by an active larval stage of the parasite, or the parasite eggs may be eaten by the host. The parasite larva may feed either internally or externally, depending on the species of parasite, and usually eventually kills the host. Entomophagous insect parasites may pupate inside the host, on the outside of it, or entirely apart from it.

Many entomophagous parasites are hyperparasites; that is, they parasitize another parasite. In such cases the parasite of a nonparasitic insect is termed a primary parasite, and the hyperparasite a secondary parasite. There are occasionally tertiary or even quaternary parasites, hyperparasites that attack another hyperparasite. These different degrees of parasitism complicate the relationship of a parasite to man; whether a hyperparasite is beneficial or injurious from man's point of view depends on what its host is.

Most of the parasitic insects that attack other insects belong to the orders Diptera and Hymenoptera. Among the Diptera the most important entomophagous parasites are the tachinid flies; other families containing important parasitic species are the Sarcophágidae, Pyrgótidae, Pipuncùlidae, Acrocéridae, and Bombylìidae. Among the Hymenoptera the most important parasitic groups are the Ichneumonòidea, Chalcidòidea, Proctotrupòidea, and Scoliòidea; these groups contain hundreds of parasitic species, many of which are valuable parasites of insect pests. Only a few insects in the other orders are entomophagous parasites; for example, the Melòidae and Rhipiphóridae among the beetles, and the Mantíspidae among the Neuroptera.

INSECTS AS SCAVENGERS

The insect scavengers are those that feed on decomposing plants or animals or on dung. Such insects assist in converting these materials into simpler substances which are returned to the soil where they are available to plants; they also serve to remove unhealthful and obnoxious materials from man's surroundings. Insects such as the wood-boring beetles, termites, carpenter ants, and other wood-feeders are important agents in hastening the conversion of fallen trees and logs to soil; the galleries of these insects serve as avenues of entrance for fungi and other decay organisms that hasten the breakdown of the wood. Dung beetles (Scarabaèidae, Histéridae, and others) and dung flies (principally various muscoids) hasten the decomposition of the dung. Carrion-feeding insects such as blow flies, carrion beetles, skin beetles (Derméstidae and Trogìnae), and others are of considerable value in the removal of carrion from the landscape. The insect scavengers are essential to maintaining a balance in nature.

THE IMPORTANCE OF SOIL INSECTS

Many types of insects spend a part of or all their lives in the soil. The soil provides the insect a home or nest, protection, and often food; it is tunneled in such a way that it becomes more aerated, and it is enriched by the excretions and dead bodies of the insects. Soil insects improve the physical properties of the soil and add to its organic content.

Soil insects vary in feeding habits. Many feed on humus or decaying plant materials; some feed on the underground parts of growing plants (and may be injurious); many are scavengers. Many feed above ground and use the soil only as a nest site; some of these, such as ants and digger wasps, bring food into the soil in connection with feeding the young.

Soil insects are often very numerous; the populations of springtails alone may be many millions per acre. Ants are sometimes extremely abundant; they generally nest in the soil and feed above ground. Other important soil-inhabiting insects are the mole crickets, cicadas (nymphal stages), termites, various burrowing bees and wasps, many beetles and flies (usually in the larval stage only), and some aphids.

INSECTS AS DESTROYERS OF UNDESIRABLE PLANTS

A large proportion of the insects feed on plants, but only a small number of these are considered pests; many of the others may be beneficial by destroying noxious weeds, cacti, or certain undesirable deciduous plants. It often happens that when a plant is introduced into a geographic area, it thrives to such an extent that it becomes a pest; in some cases plant-feeding insects have been introduced to bring this plant under control.

Prickly pear cacti (*Opúntia* spp.) were at one time introduced into Australia, and by 1925 had spread over some 25 million acres to form a dense, impenetrable growth. In 1925 a moth, *Cactoblástis cactòrum* (Berg), the larvae of which burrow in the cactus plants, was introduced into Australia from Argentina; as a result of the feeding of this moth, the dense cactus growth is now reduced to about 1 percent of the area it occupied in 1925.

A European species of St. Johnswort, *Hypéricum perforàtum* Linn., was introduced about 1900 into northern California; it became particularly abundant in the vicinity of the Klamath River, and is commonly called Klamath weed or goatweed. By the middle 1940's it had spread over about $2\frac{1}{3}$ million acres of range land in California and over extensive acreage in other western states. This plant is considered a serious pest because it replaces desirable range plants and is poisonous to livestock. Attempts to control it by chemicals were expensive and not entirely effective. From 1944 to 1948 a few species of European beetles (chrysomelids and buprestids) were imported into California to control Klamath weed; one of the chrysomelids, *Chrysolìna quadrigémina* (Rossi), proved particularly effective; the Klamath weed has been now reduced to about 1 percent of its former abundance, and more desirable plants on this range have increased.

It should be noted in this connection that weed-feeding insects are not always beneficial. In some cases an insect may feed on weeds early in the season and later invade cultivated crops; sometimes weeds may provide food on which large populations may be built up, later to attack crop plants. In other cases an insect may change its host from a wild to a cultivated plant; the Colorado potato beetle, for example, originally fed on wild species of *Solànum* (nightshade) and later changed to the potato.

INSECTS AS FOOD OF MAN AND ANIMALS

A great many animals utilize insects as food. Insectivorous animals may be important to man as food (for example, many fish, game birds, and mammals), they may have an aesthetic value (many birds and other vertebrates), or they may act as important agents in the control of insect pests. Man himself is sometimes insectivorous.

Many freshwater fish feed to a large extent on insects, particularly on such aquatic forms as the mayflies, stoneflies, caddisflies, mosquito larvae, midge larvae, and the larvae of various aquatic beetles. Although certain species of game fish prey upon smaller fish or on other aquatic animals, the insects are a basic item in the food chains leading to these game fish.

The birds that feed largely or entirely upon insects have an aesthetic value because of their interesting habits, and they often have a practical value by acting as important predators of insect pests. Birds that feed on insects consume large quantities of them; nestlings will often eat their weight in insects daily. Many examples might be cited of cases where birds have been instrumental in checking insect outbreaks; a particularly striking case is that of gulls checking a mormon cricket outbreak in Utah some years ago, an event now commemorated by a monument in Salt Lake City.

Many other vertebrates are insectivorous, and some of these have been of value in controlling insect pests. Toads, frogs, lizards, bats, skunks, moles, and shrews feed largely or entirely on insects.

Insects are utilized as food by man in many parts of the world. The Arabs eat locusts (Acrídidae); certain of the African natives eat ants, termites, beetle grubs, caterpillars, and grasshoppers; grasshoppers are frequently eaten by man in the Orient. In Mexico "Gusanos de Maguey" are considered a delicacy; these are the larvae of one of the giant skippers, which are collected from the fleshy leaves of the maguey plant. They are sold fresh in the market and are fried before eating; they may also be purchased in cans (Figure 31-1), already fried and ready to eat. The caterpillars are about $2\frac{1}{2}$ inches long when full grown. Cans of these and other edible insects are available in many places in the United States.

INSECTS IN MEDICINE AND SURGERY

Man has for centuries used insects or their products as therapeutic agents. Cantharidin, an extract from the bodies of blister beetles, has been used in the treatment of certain conditions of the urinogenital system. Bee venom has been used in the treatment of arthritis. Malaria has been induced in patients suffering from paresis, to produce high body temperatures.

One of the most striking roles of insects in medicine is the use of blow fly larvae in treating conditions involving decaying tissues. For centuries military surgeons have

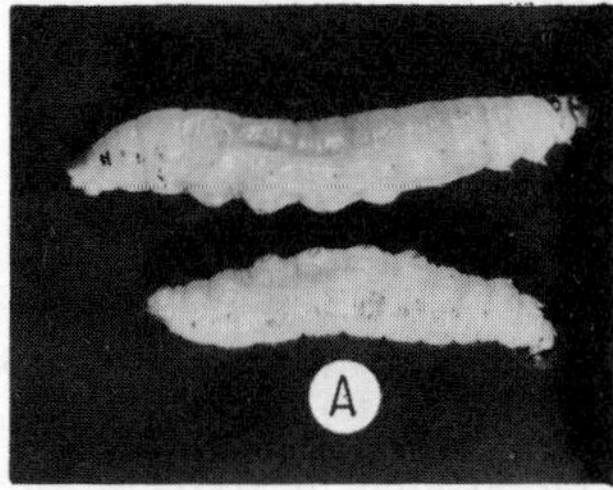

Fig. 31-1. "Gusanos de Maguey," edible caterpillars canned and sold in Mexico.

noticed that severe wounds which remained untreated for several days and became infested with maggots healed better when dressed than similar wounds that had not been infested. After World War I, this fact was investigated experimentally, and it was found that the fly larvae fed on the decaying tissues of such wounds and secreted something into the wound which promoted the healing process. From this experimental work, there was developed a technique of treating diseases such as osteomyelitis with blow fly larvae. The larvae were reared under aseptic conditions to avoid introducing additional infection, and were placed in the decaying tissues of the patient; there they were allowed to feed, and when full grown, were replaced by younger larvae. This treatment resulted in a less conspicuous scar afterward, and there were fewer recurrences than in the operative treatment formerly used. After further study of this process it was discovered that the excretion of the larvae that produced the curative effect was allantoin. At present, allantoin is used in the treatment of osteomyelitis and other deep-seated wounds in which there is decaying tissue. Thus, fly larvae have been instrumental in developing a modern medical treatment for a condition that was previously very difficult to cure.

THE USE OF INSECTS IN SCIENTIFIC RESEARCH

The processes of inheritance, variation, evolution, and the like are basically the same in all animals, and since many insects have a very short life cycle, they are frequently used in scientific studies of these processes. The little fruit flies, *Drosóphila* spp., which can easily be reared in large numbers, have been used extensively in genetic studies; much has been added to our knowledge of the basic principles of inheritance by the study of these flies.

Insects have been used as the experimental animal in studies of behavior, reaction to environmental factors such as temperature and moisture, and other biological phenomena. Studies of the social insects have provided much interesting and valuable information on social organization and behavior. In the development of insecticides, insects are regularly used as the experimental animal in tests of the toxicity of insecticidal materials.

Insect populations are often used as an index of ecological conditions. In studies of stream or lake pollution the degree of pollution can be determined by the type and amount of insect life present; similarly, the length of time an animal has been dead can often be determined by its insect fauna.

THE AESTHETIC VALUE OF INSECTS

Insects become fascinating animals when one begins to study them carefully. There are a great many people for whom insect study provides a stimulating hobby, one just as interesting as the study of birds, flowers, or other natural objects.

The beauty of insects has been utilized for patterns by artists, jewelers, and designers. Some of the butterflies, moths, and beetles have provided basic patterns in many types of art. A brilliantly colored tropical leafhopper, *Cardioscárta pulchélla* (Guérin), has a black, white, and red pattern that is frequently used in Mexican and Central American art. Insects are used in making jewelry, either by the use of all or part of actual specimens, or by using them as designs. Bracelets, necklaces, necktie pins, and scatter pins are often made in the design of an insect. In some tropical countries the natives make necklaces of "ground pearls," the wax cysts of female scale insects of the genus *Margaròdes*. The wings of *Mórpho* butterflies, brilliant bluish butterflies occurring in South America, are often mounted under glass and made into trays, pictures, and certain types of jewelry. Showy insects mounted in plastic or under glass are sometimes made into paperweights, book ends, and the like.

It is difficult to estimate in terms of dollars and cents the value of insects to man. The pollinating services of insects are worth at least $4½ billion annually, and commercial products derived from insects are worth about $144 million more. It seems safe to say that insects are worth nearly $5 billion annually.

INJURIOUS INSECTS

Man suffers tremendous losses from the feeding and other activities of insects. Many insects feed on plants that man cultivates; others feed on stored materials, clothing, or wood that are of value to man; still others feed on man and other animals directly.

INSECTS ATTACKING CULTIVATED PLANTS

Most types of plants, including all sorts of growing crops, are attacked and injured by insects. The injury is caused by insects feeding or ovipositing on the plant or serving as agents in the transmission of plant diseases; this injury may vary from a reduction in crop yields to the complete destruction of the plant. The damage to plants by insects has been estimated to amount to about $2 billion annually in this country.

PLANT INJURY BY FEEDING: One of the most noticeable types of plant damage is that caused by chewing insects feeding on the foliage. Such feeding results in leaves that are skeletonized, riddled with holes, eaten around the edges, or entirely consumed. This type of damage is caused principally by grasshoppers, the larvae of various moths and sawflies, and beetles. The smaller foliage feeders eat between the veins of the leaf and skeletonize it or chew many small holes in it; the larger feeders consume a part of or all the leaf. It is not uncommon for large areas of field crops or forest to be completely defoliated by this type of feeding.

Other insects feed on plants by sucking the sap from the leaves, stems, or other parts. Sucking insects feeding on leaves produce a characteristic spotting or browning of the leaves, or a curling and wilting (Figure 20-22); when feeding on the stems or twigs, they cause dwarfing or wilting. Damage is caused both by the removal of the sap and by actual injury to the plant tissues. This type of injury is produced by scale insects, aphids, leafhoppers, froghoppers, and various bugs. Scale insects are usually quite minute, but may occur in such numbers as to encrust the bark of a tree or the twigs or stems of a plant; these insects are able to kill orchard or shade trees. Aphids produce a curling of the leaves, and when feeding on fruit may cause stunted or misshapen fruits; in other cases aphid feeding may change the sugar content of the fruit and greatly impair its flavor.

Many types of insects feed inside plant tissues, as miners in the leaves or as borers in the stems, roots, or fruits. Leaf miners feeding between the upper and lower surfaces of the leaf may cause just as much defoliation as external foliage feeders. The mines are of various sorts, but each leaf-mining species produces a characteristic type of mine in a particular type of plant. There are some 500 leaf-mining species of insects in the United States, representing the orders Lepidoptera (about 400 species in 17 families), Diptera (65 species in 4 families), Hymenoptera (principally sawflies), and Coleoptera (about 40 species in the families Chrysomélidae, Bupréstidae, and Curculiónidae).

The species that tunnel in fruits include such pests as the codling moth, oriental fruit moth, apple maggot, plum curculio, and the nut weevils. Stalk and stem borers include the corn borer, wheat stem sawfly, squash vine borer, and many others. Insects that bore in the wood of living trees cause damage by weakening, deforming, or killing the trees. The most important wood borers are various beetles (chiefly in the families Cerambýcidae, Bupréstidae, Scolýtidae, and Curculiónidae), certain moths (Cóssidae and Aegerìidae), horntails, carpenter ants, and termites.

Many insects that feed on plant tissues inject a chemical into the plant which causes it to grow abnormally and produce a gall. Galls may be produced on various parts of a plant, but each species of gall insect produces a characteristic gall on a certain part of a particular type of plant. Each gall may harbor one or many gall insects. The stimulus to the formation of the gall is usually provided by the feeding stage of the insect; in a few cases the ovipositing female provides the stimulus when she lays her eggs in the plant. A plant gall may have an opening to the outside (for example, the galls of Homoptera and mites), or they may be entirely closed (for example, galls of larval insects). Five orders of insects contain gall-making species: the Diptera (principally the Cecidomyìidae, Tephrítidae, and Agromýzidae), Hymenoptera (Cynípidae, some Chalcidòidea, and some Tenthredínidae), Coleoptera (certain Curculiónidae, Bupréstidae, and Cerambýcidae), Lepidoptera (for example, the goldenrod gall moth, *Gnorimoschèma*), and Homoptera (various aphids, psyllids, and coccids). Other plant galls are caused by mites, roundworms, or fungi.

A great deal of damage to plants is caused by insects that live in the soil and attack the underground parts of the plant. Such damage is usually caused by the larval or nymphal stages of the insect. Wireworms (Elatéridae) and white grubs (Scarabaèidae) cause considerable losses to various field crops and grasses. Other insects that are root-feeding are the woolly aphids, the corn rootworm, and the onion and cabbage maggots.

Many insects build unsightly shelters in plants. Leaf rollers and leaf folders, chiefly small Lepidoptera, roll or fold the leaves and tie them with silk, feeding in the shelter so formed; leaf tiers and webworms tie several leaves together, or even entire branches, producing large silken webs or tents.

PLANT INJURY BY OVIPOSITION: A few insects injure plants when they lay their eggs, particularly when they oviposit in stems or fruits. The periodical cicada, in laying its eggs in twigs, usually injures the twig so much that the terminal portion dies; or weakens it so that it is easily broken at the point of oviposition. Tree crickets, treehoppers, and certain leafhoppers injure twigs in a similar manner. Insects that lay their eggs in fruit often cause the fruit to become misshapen.

INSECTS AND PLANT DISEASE: During recent years much has been learned of the role played by insects in the transmission of plant diseases. Some 200 plant diseases have been shown to have insect vectors. About three-fourths of these diseases are caused by viruses. A summary of the more important plant diseases transmitted by insects is given in Table 31-1.

TABLE 31-1 PLANT DISEASES TRANSMITTED BY INSECTS AND OTHER ARTHROPODS

A. VIRUS DISEASES

DISEASE	PATHOGEN	VECTOR	HOST	METHOD OF TRANSMISSION
Leaf roll	A virus	Aphids: *Mỳzus pérsicae* (Sulzer) and others	Potato	Inoculation by feeding
Bean mosaic	A virus	Aphids	Bean	Inoculation by feeding
Crucifer mosaic	A virus	Aphids: *Mỳzus pérsicae* (Sulzer) and *Brevicóryne brássicae* (Linn.)	Cabbage, mustard, turnip, and cauliflower	Inoculation by feeding
Sugarcane mosaic	A virus	Aphids: *Àphis màidis* Fitch, *Hysteroneùra setàriae* (Thomas), and *Toxóptera gráminum* (Rondani)	Sugarcane, sorghum, corn	Inoculation by feeding
Cucumber mosaic	A virus	Melon aphid, *Àphis gossýpii* Glover and cucumber beetles	Cucumber and other cucurbits	Inoculation by feeding
Beet mosaic	A virus	Aphid: *Àphis rùmicis* Linn.	Beet	Inoculation by feeding
Yellow dwarf	A virus	Aphids, many species	Onion	Inoculation by feeding
Spotted wilt	A virus	Thrips: *Thríps tabàci* Lindeman, *Frankliniélla* spp.	Tomato	Nymphs must feed on diseased plants
Yellow spot	A virus	*Thríps tabàci* Lindeman	Pineapple	Nymphs must feed on diseased plants
Aster yellows	A virus	Leafhoppers: *Macrostèles dívisus* (Uhler) and others	Many plants, especially flowers and vegetables	Pathogen introduced by feeding after incubation period
Curly top	A virus	Beet leafhopper, *Circùlifer tenéllus* (Baker)	Sugar beet, vegetables, ornamental and wild plants	Same
Streak disease of corn	A virus	Leafhoppers: *Cicadulìna* spp.	Corn	Same
Dwarf disease of rice	A virus	Leafhoppers: *Nephotéttix apicàlis* (Motschulsky) and *Deltocéphalus dorsàlis* (Motschulsky)	Rice and grasses	Pathogen introduced by feeding; passed to young through egg

DISEASE	PATHOGEN	VECTOR	HOST	METHOD OF TRANSMISSION
Clover club leaf virus	A virus	Leafhopper: *Agalliópsis novélla* (Say)	Clover	Inoculation by feeding; passed to young through egg
Rice stripe virus	A virus	Planthopper: *Delphacòdes striatélla* (Fallen)	Rice	Same
Hoja blanca disease	A virus	Planthopper: *Sogàta orizícola* Muir	Rice	Inoculation by feeding after an incubation period
Pseudo curly top	A virus	Treehopper: *Micrutàlis* sp.	Tomato, tobacco	Inoculation by feeding
Tobacco leaf curl	A virus	Whitefly: *Bemísia tabàci* (Gennadius)	Tobacco	Inoculation by feeding after an incubation period
Pineapple wilt	A virus	Mealybugs: *Dysmicóccus* spp.	Pineapple	Inoculation by feeding
Peach mosaic	A virus	Gall mite: *Eriophỳes insidiòsus* Keifer and Wilson	Peach	Nymphs must feed on diseased plants
Peach yellows	A virus	Plum leafhopper, *Macrópsis trimaculàta* (Fitch)	Peach	Pathogen introduced by feeding after incubation period
False blossom	A virus	Leafhopper, *Scleroràcus vacínii* (Van Duzee)	Cranberry	Pathogen introduced by feeding
Spindle tuber	A virus	Flea beetles, aphids, Colorado potato beetle, tarnished plant bug, grasshoppers	Potato	Same
		B. BACTERIAL DISEASES		
Stewart's disease	*Bactèrium stèwarti* Smith	Corn flea beetle, *Chaetocnèma pulicària* Melsheimer, corn rootworms, *Diabrótica* spp., and seed corn maggot	Corn	Pathogen winters in alimentary canal of vector, enters plant through feeding wounds
Cucurbit wilt	*Erwínia tracheíphila* (Erw. Smith)	Cucumber beetles, *Acalýmma vittàta* (Fabricius) and *D. undecimpunctàta howardi* Baker	Cucumber and other cucurbits	Pathogen winters in alimentary canal of beetle; enters with feces in wounds
Fire blight	*Erwínia amylóvora* (Burrill)	Various insects, especially bees and leafhoppers	Pear, apple, and quince	By nectar feeders, and from cankers to new growth by leafhoppers

DISEASE	PATHOGEN	VECTOR	HOST	METHOD OF TRANSMISSION
Bacterial soft rot	*Erwínia carotóvora* (Jones)	Fly maggots, *Hylemỳa brássicae* (Bouché) and *H. cilicrùra* (Rondani)	Potato, cabbage, and other vegetable crops	Pathogen persists in maggots to adult stage; spread by ovipositing flies
Olive knot	*Pseudómonas savastónoi* (Erw. Smith)	Olive fruit fly, *Dàcus òleae* (Gmelin)	Olive	Pathogen persists in maggot to adult stage; spread by ovipositing flies
Bacterial rot	*Pseudómonas melóphthora* Allen & Riker	Apple maggot, *Rhagóletis pomonélla* (Walsh)	Apple	Pathogen persists in maggot to adult stage; spread by ovipositing flies
		C. FUNGUS DISEASES		
Perennial canker	*Neofabraèa perénnans* (Zeller & Childs)	Woolly apple aphid, *Eriosòma lanígerum* (Hausmann)	Apple	Pathogen enters through punctures made by feeding aphids
Chestnut blight	*Endòthia parasítica* (Murrill)	Beetles	Chestnut	Spores carried by insects and birds; enters through beetle wounds
Dutch elm disease	*Ceratostomélla úlmi* (Schwarz)	Bark beetles, *Scólytus multistriàtus* (Marsh) and *Hylurgópinus rùfipes* (Eichhoff)	Elm	Spores enter cambium with beetles
Blue stain	*Ceratostomélla íps* Rumbold	Bark beetles: *Íps pìni* (Say) and *I. grandicóllis* Eichhoff	Red pine	Spores enter cambium as beetles lay eggs
Brown rot	*Sclerotínia fructícola* (Winter)	Plum curculio, *Conotrachèlus nénuphar* (Herbst)	Peach, cherry, plum	Pathogen enters through feeding or egg punctures
Potato scab	*Actinomỳces scábies* (Thaxter)	Potato flea beetle, *Épitrix cucùmeris* (Harris)	Potato	Pathogen enters with larva in tuber
Fusarium wilt	*Fusàrium oxyspòrum,* f. *vasinféctum* (Atkinson)	Grasshoppers	Cotton	Spores spread in fecal pellets
Downy mildew	*Phytóphthora phasèoli* Thaxter	Bees	Lima bean	Pathogen carried to flowers by bees
Blackleg	*Phòma língam* (Tode)	Cabbage maggot, *Hylemỳa brássicae* (Bouché)	Cabbage	Spores carried into plant on bodies of maggots

There are three ways by which insects cause plant pathogens to enter the plant:

1. The pathogen may accidentally gain entrance through egg or feeding punctures or openings through which the insect has entered the plant tissue. Certain molds and rots enter in this fashion.
2. The pathogen may be transmitted on or in the body of the insect from one plant to another. Bees pick up and spread the bacilli that cause fire blight in apple and pear. The fungus-causing Dutch elm disease is transmitted in this fashion by the elm bark beetle.
3. The pathogen may remain in the body of the insect for a time, often for long periods, and be inoculated into the plant by the feeding or feces of the insect. In some cases the pathogen passes a part of its life cycle in the insect, and may reproduce there. Cucurbit wilt disease is transmitted in this way by the striped and spotted cucumber beetles; the pathogen overwinters in the beetles, and the plants are infected in the spring by infected feces of the insect being dropped on the leaves and washed into the wounds of the plant. Stewart's disease of corn is transmitted in a similar manner by the corn flea beetle. In a few cases, such as the streak disease of corn, the pathogen may pass from the insect (a leafhopper) to its offspring through the eggs.

The virus diseases are caused by organisms that are too small to be seen; consequently, it has been difficult to determine some phases of their life cycle. Some can apparently be transmitted by almost any insect that feeds on the diseased plant; in other cases the pathogens appear to be transmitted by only one species of insect. The virus diseases are transmitted principally by insects in the order Homoptera.

The damage done by insect feeding alone may be severe, but a disease vector can, by a small amount of feeding, inoculate a plant with a disease that may reduce its productivity or even kill it. Two sugar beet leafhoppers per beet plant can cause in themselves comparatively little damage, but if they are carrying the pathogens of the curly-top disease, they may cause enormous losses.

INSECTS ATTACKING STORED PRODUCTS

After materials produced by plants and animals have been stored for use as food or clothing or have been utilized in buildings or fabrics, they may be attacked and damaged by insects. The damage is done by the insects feeding or tunneling in these materials, or contaminating them, and the possibility of insect attack greatly increases the expense of packing and storage. The annual insect damage to stored products in this country has been estimated to be about $850 million.

PESTS OF WOOD: All sorts of wooden structures, such as buildings, furniture, fence posts, telephone poles, and materials such as pasteboard and paper, are subject to attack by insects. One of the most widespread and destructive pests of wood and wood products is the termite. Termites eat out the interior portions of beams, sills, floors, and joists, and often build tunnels over or through foundations to reach the wooden parts of buildings. Timbers attacked eventually collapse. Powder-post beetles tunnel in dry posts and timbers and weaken them.

PESTS OF FABRICS AND CLOTHING: Most materials made from animal fibers, such as furs, clothing, blankets, rugs, and upholstering, may be attacked and damaged by insects. The amount of material actually eaten may be small, but the value of the materials attacked may be greatly reduced. The most important fabric pests are dermestid beetles and clothes moths.

PESTS OF STORED FOODS: Many types of stored foods, particularly meats, cheese, milk products, flour, meal, cereals, stored grain, nuts, and fruits, may be attacked by insects. Considerable damage may be done by the feeding or tunneling of the insects, or the actual damage may be slight and the effect of the insects mainly contamination. The important pests of this type are the Angoumois grain moth, Indian meal moth, Mediterranean flour moth, confused flour beetle, granary and rice weevils, saw-toothed grain beetle, and flour mites. Some of these attack whole grain, and others feed mainly on meal or flour. Bean and pea weevils tunnel in and may completely destroy stored beans and peas. Stored meats and cheese are attacked principally by the larder beetle, cheese skipper, and various mites. Drug store beetles attack a variety of vegetable products, including chocolate, pepper, and tobacco.

INSECTS ATTACKING MAN AND ANIMALS

Insects affect man and animals directly in four principal ways: (1) they may be merely annoying, (2) they may inject venom by their bites or stings, (3) they may live in or on man or animals as parasites, or (4) they may serve as agents in the transmission of disease. These types of damage by insects have been estimated to cost about $570 million annually in the United States.

ANNOYANCE OF INSECTS: Everyone has been bothered by insects that buzz around or crawl over one's body. Such effects are mainly psychological, but in some cases the "nuisance value" of annoying insects may be considerable. Bot flies and face flies, though they neither bite nor sting, cause great annoyance to cattle. Many insects annoy by their odors or secretions; others may get into one's eyes or ears.

VENOMOUS INSECTS: Many arthropods inject into man and animals toxins that cause irritation, swelling, pain, and sometimes paralysis. Those that inject a venom by their bite include various biting flies, bugs, mites, ticks, centipedes, and spiders; the bites of some of these are very painful, they often result in swelling or (for example, in the case of certain spiders) a necrotic ulcer, and in some cases may cause death; some tick bites result in paralysis. Those that inject a venom by their sting include the bees, wasps, and scorpions; such stings may be very painful and often cause considerable swelling; the sting of some scorpions may be fatal. Many people are particularly sensitive to bee or wasp stings and may suffer anaphylactic shock or even death as a result; probably more people in this country are killed by wasp or bee stings than by the bites of venomous snakes. A few caterpillars, such as the saddleback, flannel moth larvae, and the larvae of the io moth, have stinging hairs that produce a type of dermatitis. Some of the blister beetles have body fluids that are irritating to the skin. A few insects, such as rose chafers, are toxic when swallowed.

PARASITIC INSECTS: Many insects and other arthropods live in or on the bodies of man or animals as parasites and cause irritation, damage to tissues, and in some cases even death. The chewing lice are external parasites of birds and mammals, and feed on hair, feathers, dermal scales, and other external structures; they cause considerable irritation and a general run-down condition in the animal attacked. The sucking lice are external parasites of mammals and are blood-sucking; they cause irritation, and bad sores often result from the rubbing or scratching brought on by their bites. Fleas, bed bugs, and other biting forms cause similar irritation. The mange and scab mites, which burrow into the skin of man and animals, are often extremely irritating.

Many flies pass their larval stage as internal parasites of man and animals, causing a condition known as myiasis; these insects may cause serious damage, even death, to the animal affected. The larvae of the ox warble flies live under the skin of the host; they produce a general run-down condition in cattle, reduce milk production, and lower the value of the hides for leather. The sheep bot fly larva burrows in the nasal passages of its host. The screw-worm fly lays its eggs in wounds and other exposed tissues of man and animals, and the larvae feed on the living tissues of the host. The larvae of the horse bot flies develop in the alimentary tract of horses and cause irritation and damage to the mucous membranes there.

INSECTS AND DISEASE TRANSMISSION: The insects that attack man and animals do their greatest damage when they act as disease vectors. The bites and stings of venomous insects and the disturbance caused by parasitic insects may be severe, but are rarely fatal; many insect-borne diseases have a high mortality rate. Insects act as agents in the transmission of disease in two general ways: They may serve as mechanical vectors of the pathogen or they may act as biological vectors. In the latter case the insect serves as a host in the life cycle of the pathogen. There are some diseases, known to be transmitted by insects or other arthropods, in which the exact role played by the vector is not completely understood.

The insects of chief importance in the mechanical transmission of pathogenic organisms are the filth-inhabiting flies such as house flies and blow flies. These insects pick up the pathogens on their feet or on other parts of their body when feeding on fecal material or other wastes, or they may ingest the pathogens; later they contaminate man's food when they feed on it. These flies have the habit of regurgitating materials that were previously eaten, particularly on foods that are solid or semisolid, and so may contaminate human foods. Typhoid fever, cholera, and dysentery may be transmitted by flies in this way.

The arthropods that serve as a host of the pathogen as well as a vector are chiefly the blood-sucking forms; they pick up the pathogen when feeding on a diseased host and later infect another host. In such cases there is usually a period during which certain phases of the pathogen's life cycle are passed before the arthropod is capable of infecting another host. The host is usually infected either by the bite of the vector or by having the excretions or body fluids of the vector rubbed into the skin. In a few cases the vector must be swallowed before infection results.

—Malaria— This disease is a typical example of those in which an insect serves both as vector and host of the pathogen. Millions of people throughout the world are affected by it. Malaria is a disease characterized by rather regularly recurring paroxysms of chills and fever, and in which the red blood cells are destroyed by the pathogen. It is caused by Protozòa in the genus *Plasmòdium* and is transmitted by certain species of mosquitoes in the genus *Anópheles.* Three types of malaria are common in man: benign tertian malaria, caused by *P. vìvax* (Grassi and Feletti), which has wide distribution; malignant tertian malaria, caused by *P. falcíparum* (Welch), which is principally tropical, and is the most dangerous type of malaria; and quartan malaria, caused by *P. malàriae* (Grassi and Feletti), which is the least common of the three types.

A person normally acquires malaria only through the bite of an infective female *Anópheles* mosquito which has previously obtained the plasmodia from a malaria patient. When such a mosquito bites a person, large numbers of tiny spindle-shaped bodies (the sporozoite stage of the *Plasmòdium*) are injected into the blood stream with the mosquito's saliva (Figure 31-2). These leave the blood stream within a period of 30 or 40 minutes and enter the parenchymal cells of the liver. After one or more generations (the number depending on the species of *Plasmòdium*) of asexual reproduction in the liver cells,

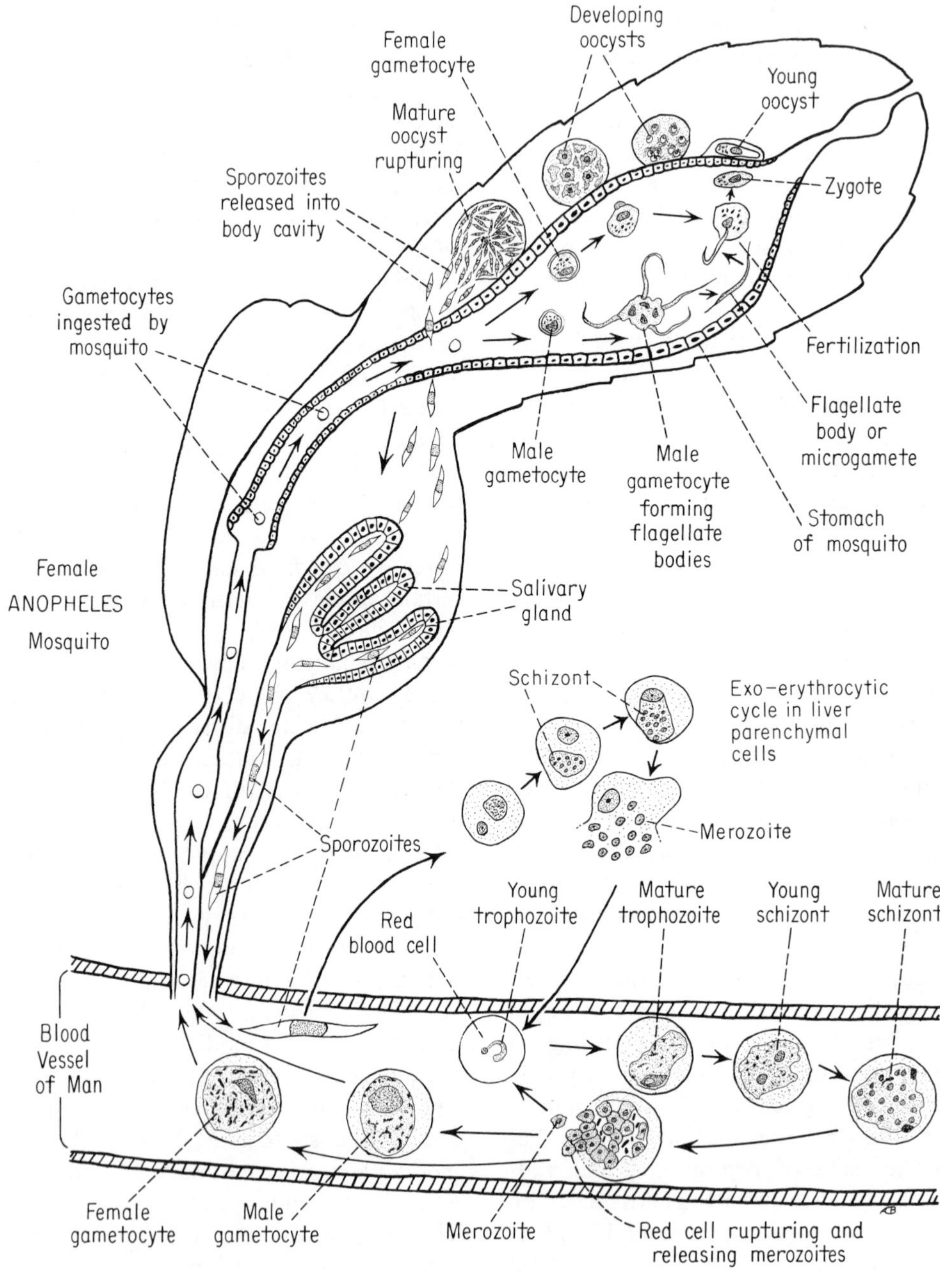

Fig. 31-2. Life cycle (diagrammatic) of the malarial parasite, *Plasmòdium vìvax* (Grassi and Feletti). For explanation, see text.

they enter the red blood cells. In a red blood cell the *Plasmòdium* is an irregularly shaped stage called a trophozoite, which feeds on the blood cell. When the trophozoite matures, its nucleus begins to divide and the trophozoite becomes a schizont. By successive nuclear divisions of the schizont, some 10 to 24 daughter organisms are formed; these products of schizont division are called merozoites. The red blood cell soon ruptures, and the merozoites are released into the plasma; they enter other red blood cells, and the process of feeding and asexual reproduction (which is here called schizogony) continues. The asexual cycle of *Plasmòdium* in the blood stream of man is repeated every 24 to 72 hours, the interval depending on the species of *Plasmòdium*; the release of the merozoites into the plasma coincides with the paroxysms of the disease.

After several generations of merozoites have been produced, sexual forms called gametocytes appear; these are of two types, male and female. The gametocytes develop no further until they are ingested by a suitable *Anópheles* mosquito. If the *Anópheles* mosquito bites a malarial patient and does not pick up any gametocytes, it does not become infective; if it picks up gametocytes, the parasite continues its cycle of development in the mosquito. Once in the stomach of the mosquito, the gametocytes undergo certain changes; the male gametocyte throws off flagellated bodies, and the female gametocyte throws off some of its chromatin material. The fusion of a flagellated body with a modified female gametocyte constitutes fertilization and results in the formation of a zygote. The zygote soon becomes elongated and motile, and burrows into the stomach wall and forms a cystlike structure known as an oocyst. Successive nuclear divisions in the oocyst result in the formation of a large number of elongate spindle-shaped bodies, the sporozoites. After some 10 to 15 days, depending on the temperature, the oocyst ruptures and releases the sporozoites into the body cavity of the mosquito; the sporozoites (or at least some of them) travel to and enter the salivary glands of the mosquito. From this time on, until the mosquito dies or until it hibernates, it is capable of infecting a person with malaria.

Some of the most serious diseases of man and animals are transmitted by insects and other arthropods, and the principal vectors are the biting flies, sucking lice, fleas, bugs, mites, and ticks. A summary of the more important diseases transmitted by arthropods is given in Table 31-2. The arthropods listed as "vectors" sometimes play a passive role in the transmission of the disease.

TABLE 31-2 DISEASES TRANSMITTED BY INSECTS AND OTHER ARTHROPODS

A. DISEASES CAUSED BY HELMINTHS (ROUNDWORMS AND FLATWORMS)

DISEASE	PATHOGEN	VECTOR	HOST	DISTRIBUTION
Tapeworms	*Dipylídium cànìnum* (Linn.)	Dog flea, *Ctenocephálides cànis* (Curtis)	Dog and man	World-wide
	Hymenólepis dimínuta (Rudolphi)	Rat flea, *Xenopsýlla cheòpis* (Rothschild)	Rat and man	World-wide
	Diphyllo-bóthrium látum (Linn.)	Water fleas (*Cỳclops* spp.) (Crustacea)	Man and animals	World-wide

DISEASE	PATHOGEN	VECTOR	HOST	DISTRIBUTION
	Thysanosòma ostiniòides Diesing	Psocids: *Liposcèlis* sp., *Rhyopsòcus* sp.	Sheep and other ruminants	North and South America
Lung fluke	*Paragònimus westermáni* (Kerbert)	Crabs and crayfish	Man	Far East, Africa, South and Central America, Mexico
Filariasis	*Wucherèria báncrofti* (Cobbold) and *Microfilària màlayi* (Brug)	Mosquitoes, principally in the genera *Aèdes, Cùlex, Anópheles,* and *Mansònia*	Man	World-wide in the tropics and subtropics
Onchocerciasis	*Onchocérca vólvulus* (Leuckart), a roundworm	Black flies, *Simùlium* spp.	Man	Mexico, Central America, equatorial Africa
Loaiasis	*Lòa lòa* (Cobbold), a roundworm	Deer flies, *Chrỳsops* spp.	Man	Africa
Guinea worm	*Dracúnculus medinénsis* (Linn.), a roundworm	Water fleas, (*Cỳclops* spp.) (Crustacea)	Man	Africa, Southern Asia, East Indies
		B. DISEASES CAUSED BY PROTOZÒA		
Malaria	*Plasmòdium vìvax* (Grassi and Feletti), *P. falcíparum* (Welch), and *P. malàriae* (Grassi and Feletti)	Mosquitoes in the genus *Anópheles*	Man	World-wide in tropical, subtropical, and temperate regions
African sleeping sickness	*Trypanosòma gambiénse* Dutton and *T. rhodesiénse* Stephens & Fantham	Tsetse flies, *Glossìna* spp.	Man and animals	Equatorial Africa
Nagana	*Trypanosòma brùcei* Plimmer & Bradford	Tsetse flies, *Glossìna* spp.	Wild and domestic animals	Equatorial Africa
Chagas disease	*Trypanosòma crùzi* Chagas	Assassin bugs, principally in the genera *Triátoma* and *Rhódnius*	Man and rodents	South America, Central America, Mexico, and Texas

DISEASE	PATHOGEN	VECTOR	HOST	DISTRIBUTION
Kala-azar	*Leishmània dónovani* (Laveran & Mesnil)	Sand flies, *Phlebótomus* spp.	Man	Mediterranean region, Asia, and South America
Espundia	*Leishmània braziliénsis* Vianna	Sand flies, *Phlebótomus* spp.	Man	South America, Central America, Mexico, North Africa, southern Asia
Oriental sore	*Leishmània trópica* (Wright)	Sand flies, *Phlebótomus* spp.	Man	Africa, Asia, South America
Texas cattle fever	*Babèsia bigémina* Smith & Kilbourne	Cattle tick, *Boóphilus annulàtus* (Say)	Cattle	Southern U.S., Central and South America, South Africa, Philippines
Amoebic dysentery	*Endamoèba histolýtica* (Schaudinn)	House fly, *Músca doméstica* Linn., various blow flies and flesh flies	Man and animals	World-wide

C. DISEASES CAUSED BY BACTERIA

DISEASE	PATHOGEN	VECTOR	HOST	DISTRIBUTION
Bubonic plague	*Pasteurélla péstis* (Lehmann & Newmann)	Various fleas, especially the rat flea, *Xenopsýlla cheòpis* (Rothschild)	Man and rodents	World-wide
Tularemia	*Pasteurélla tularénsis* (McCoy & Chapin)	Deer flies *(Chrỳsops* spp.); ticks, principally *Dermacéntor* spp. and *Haemaphysàlis,* spp.; fleas; and the body louse, *Pedículus humànus* Linn.	Man and rodents	United States, Canada, Europe, the Orient
Anthrax	*Bacíllus anthràcis* Cohn	Horse flies, *Tabànus* spp.	Man and animals	World-wide
Typhoid fever	*Bacíllus typhòsus* Zopf	House fly, *Músca doméstica* Linn., and various blow flies and flesh flies	Man	World-wide
Bacillary dysentery	*Bacíllus* spp.			
Cholera	*Víbrio cómma* (Schroeter)			

DISEASE	PATHOGEN	VECTOR	HOST	DISTRIBUTION
		D. DISEASES CAUSED BY SPIROCHAETES		
Relapsing fever	*Borrèlia recurréntis* (Lebert) and *B. dúttonii* (Breinl)	Ticks (*Ornithódorus* spp.), and the body louse, *Pedículus humànus* Linn.	Man and rodents	World-wide
Fowl spirochaetosis	*Borrèlia anserìna* (Sakharoff)	Fowl tick, *Árgas pérsicus* (Oken)	Chicken, turkey, goose	North America, Brazil, India, Australia, Egypt
		E. DISEASES CAUSED BY BARTONELLA AND RICKETTSIA ORGANISMS		
Verruga peruana or Oroya fever	*Bartonélla bacillifórmis* (Strong *et al.*)	Sand fly, *Phlebótomus* sp.	Man	Bolivia, Peru, Ecuador Chile
Epidemic typhus	*Rickéttsia prowazékii* da Rocha-Lima	Body louse, *Pedículus humànus* Linn., the rat flea, *Xenopsýlla cheòpis* (Rothschild) and the rat mite, *Liponýssus bàcoti* (Hirst)	Man and rodents	World-wide
Endemic or murine typhus	*Rickéttsia prowazékii mooseri* Monteiro	Rat flea, *Xenopsýlla cheòpis* (Rothschild) various other fleas, lice, mites, and ticks on rodents	Man and rodents	World-wide
Scrub typhus or tsutsugamushi disease	*Rickéttsia tsutsugamùshi* (Hayashi)	Harvest mites or chiggers, *Trombícula* spp.	Man and rodents	Japan, China, Formosa, India, Australia, East Indies
Spotted fever	*Rickéttsia rickéttsii* (Wolbach)	Various ticks, especially *Dermacéntor andersòni* Stiles	Man and rodents	North and South America
African tick fever	*Rickéttsia* spp.	Various ticks (Ixódidae)	Man	South Africa
Q fever				Australia, western United States
		F. DISEASES CAUSED BY VIRUS		
Yellow fever	A virus	Various mosquitoes, especially *Aèdes aegýpti* (Linn.)	Man, monkey, and rodents	American and African tropics and subtropics
Dengue	A virus	Mosquitoes in the genus *Aèdes,* principally *A. aegýpti* (Linn.) and *A. albopíctus* Skuse	Man	World-wide in tropics and subtropics

DISEASE	PATHOGEN	VECTOR	HOST	DISTRIBUTION
Encephalitis	Several virus strains	Various mosquitoes in the genera *Cùlex* and *Aèdes*	Man and Horse	United States, Canada, South America, Europe, and Asia
Pappataci fever	A virus	Sand fly, *Phlebótomus papatàsii* (Scopoli)	Man	Mediterranean region, India, Ceylon
Colorado tick fever	A virus	Various ticks	Man	Western United States

The annual losses in the United States due to insects have been estimated at about $3\frac{1}{2}$ billion (Metcalf *et al.*, 1962), which is less than the amount representing the benefits derived from insects. Thus, we may say that the good done by insects outweighs the harm they do; though the good is often less evident than the harm.

REFERENCES

Baker, E. W., T. M. Evans, D. J. Gould, W. B. Hull, and H. L. Keegan. 1956. A manual of parasitic mites of medical and economic importance. New York: National Pest Control Association, Inc. 170 pp., 59 f.

Beard, Raimon L. 1963. Insect toxins and venoms. Ann. Rev. Entomol., 8:1-18.

Bishopp, F. C., *et al.* 1952. Insects: U.S. Dep. Agr. Yearbook. xix+780 pp., illus.

Black, L. M. 1959. Biological cycles of plant viruses in insect vectors. In "The Viruses," 3 vol., ed. by F. M. Burnet and W. M. Stanley. Vol. 2. Pp. 157-185. New York: Academic Press, Inc.

Black, L. M. 1962. Some recent advances on leafhopper borne viruses. In "Biological Transmission of Disease Agents," ed. by K. Maramorosch. Pp. 1-9. New York: Academic Press, Inc.

Borror, Donald J. 1947. Insects and pollination. National Audubon Soc. Ser. 13, Bull. No. 9. 4 pp., illus.

Brittain, W. H. 1933. Apple pollination studies. Can., Dept. Agr., Publ., Bull. 162. 198 pp., 73 f.

Carter, Walter. 1962. Insects in relation to plant disease. New York: John Wiley & Sons, Inc. 705 pp., illus.

Chandler, Asa C., and Clark P. Read. 1961 (10th ed.). Introduction to parasitology. New York: John Wiley & Sons, Inc. xii+822 pp., f.258

DeLong, Dwight M. 1960. Man in a world of insects. Ohio J. Sci., 60(4):193-206.

Faust, E. C., P. C. Beaver, and R. C. Jung. 1962. Animal agents and vectors of human disease. Philadelphia: Lea & Febiger. 485 pp., 195 f.

Hermes, William B. 1961 (5th ed., revised by Maurice T. James). Medical entomology. New York: The Macmillan Company. xi+616 pp., 185 f.

Horsfall, William R. 1962. Medical entomology. Arthropods and human disease. New York: The Ronald Press Company. ix+467 pp., 90 f.

Hunter, George W., III, William W. Frye, and J. Clyde Swartzwelder. 1960 (3rd ed.). A manual of tropical medicine. Philadelphia: W. B. Saunders Company. xxx+892 pp., illus.

Markell, E. K., and Marietta Voge. 1958. Diagnostic medical parasitology. Philadelphia: W. B. Saunders Company. 276 pp., 115 f.

Metcalf, C. L., and W. P. Flint. 1962. (4th ed., revised by R. L. Metcalf). Destructive and useful insects. New York: McGraw-Hill Book Company, Inc. xii+1087 pp.; illus.

Peairs, Leonard M., and Ralph H. Davidson. 1956 (5th ed.). Insect pests of farm, garden, and orchard. New York: John Wiley & Sons, Inc. ix+661 pp., 577 f.

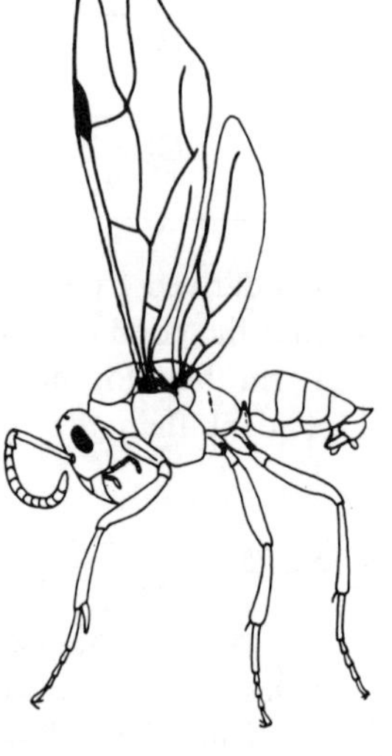

32

Collecting and Preserving Insects

One of the best ways to learn about insects is to go out and collect them; handling them and preparing collections will reveal to the student many things that he will not get from textbooks. Many people find the collection and study of insects an extremely interesting hobby, for it provides not only the satisfaction that comes from being in the field, but also the satisfaction of learning at first hand. The student will develop much more interest in insects by collecting and handling them than he will by merely looking at pictures or preserved specimens.

Since insects are so abundant, there is little likelihood that even extensive collecting will have much effect on their populations; the conservationist, therefore, need not worry about species being exterminated or about the balance of nature being upset by ordinary collecting.

WHERE TO COLLECT INSECTS

Insects can be found practically everywhere and usually in considerable numbers; the more kinds of places in which one looks for them, the greater the variety he will be able to collect. The best time to collect is in the summer, but insects are active from early spring until late fall, and many can be found in hibernation during the winter. The adults of many species have a short seasonal range; hence one should collect throughout the year if he wishes to get the greatest variety. Since different species are active at different times of the day, at least some kinds of insects can be collected at any hour. The best time to collect most species is during the daytime. Bad weather conditions, such as rain or low temperature, will reduce the activity of many insects, thus making it more difficult to find or collect them; but others are little affected and can be collected in any kind of weather. If one knows where to look, he can find insects in the average community at any hour of the day, any day in the year.

Many kinds of insects feed upon or frequent plants; hence plants provide one of the best places for collecting. Insects can be picked, shaken, or swept off the plant with a net. Different species feed on different kinds of plants; one should therefore examine all sorts of plants—grasses, flowers, weeds, shrubs, and trees. Every part of the plant may harbor insects; the majority will probably be on the foliage or flowers, but others may be on or in the stem, bark, wood, fruit or roots.

Various types of debris often harbor many kinds of insects. Some species can be found in the leaf mold and litter on the surface of the soil, particularly in woods or areas where the vegetation is dense; others can be found under stones, boards, bark, and similar objects; still others can be found in rotting or decaying material of all sorts, such as fungi, decaying plants or the bodies of dead animals, rotting fruits, and dung. Many of the insects in these situations can be picked up with the fingers or forceps; others can be obtained by sifting debris.

Many insects can be found in or around buildings, or on animals or human beings. Many use buildings, cavities under buildings, culverts, and similar places as a shelter, and some species are most easily collected in such situations. Other insects found in buildings feed on clothing, furniture, grain, food, and other materials. Insects that attack animals are usually to be found around those animals, and a person interested in collecting species that attack man can often get them with very little effort—by letting the insects come to him.

On warm evenings, insects from various sources are attracted to lights and can be collected at street or porch lights, on the windows or screens of lighted rooms, or at lights put up especially to attract them. In fact, this is one of the easiest ways of collecting many types of insects. Blue lights seem to be more attractive than red or yellow ones.

A great many insects—the immature stages only in some cases, and all stages in others—are found in aquatic situations. Different types of aquatic habitats harbor different species, and different insects can be found in different parts of any particular pond or stream. Some are to be found on the surface, others are free-swimming in the water, others occur on aquatic vegetation, others are attached to or are under stones or other objects in the water, and still others burrow in the sand or muck of the bottom. Many aquatic insects can be collected by hand or by means of forceps; others are most easily collected by various types of aquatic collecting equipment.

The adults of a great many species are best obtained by collecting the immature stages and rearing them. This involves collecting cocoons, larvae, or nymphs, and maintaining them in some sort of container until the adults appear. It is often possible to get better specimens by this method than by collecting adults in the field.

COLLECTING EQUIPMENT

The minimum equipment necessary to collect insects is one's hands, and some sort of container for the specimens collected. However, one can do much better with a net and killing jar, or better yet with some sort of shoulder bag containing some additional equipment. For general collecting it is best to have at least the following items:

1. Insect net
2. Killing jars
3. Pillboxes containing cleansing tissue
4. Envelopes, or paper for making envelopes
5. Vials of preservative
6. Forceps
7. Hand lens

The above items, with the exception of the first, sixth, and seventh, are most easily carried in a shoulder bag; the forceps and hand lens can be attached to a string around one's neck and carried in a shirt pocket. Strictly speaking, a hand lens is not a means of collecting, but it is very useful for examining insects in the field.

Other items of value for some types of collecting are as follows:

8. Aspirator
9. Beating umbrella or sheet
10. Sifter
11. Traps
12. Aquatic collecting equipment

THE INSECT NET

Insect nets can be purchased from a biological supply house, but they can be made fairly easily and much more cheaply at home. A homemade net may be made with the handle of a broom or mop, or a similar stick, a wire rim, and a cloth bag. The handle should be light and strong and about a yard long. Grooves are cut on opposite sides at one end of the handle, the groove being about 3 inches long on one side and about 2 inches long on the other; a hole is drilled about two-thirds through the handle at the end of each groove (Figure 32-1 A). The grooves and holes should be just large enough to accommodate the wire that forms the rim. The rim should be made of a stiff wire (from No. 6 to No. 8 gauge, depending on the sort of usage the net will receive), bent as shown (Figure 32-1 B), and fitted into the grooves and holes at the end of the handle. The rim is attached securely to the handle by means of wire (about No. 20 or No. 22 gauge) (Figure 32-1 C), which can be bound with friction tape to cover any rough wire ends. The net rim should have a diameter of about 12 inches.

The bag should be about twice as long as the diameter of the rim and rounded or tapered at the bottom. This bag should be made of two types of cloth; a heavy band of muslin or canvas around the rim, and a lighter material for the main part of the bag. A number of types of cloth are suitable for the bag; the choice will depend on the type of collecting for which the net will be used. The net should be light and strong for general collecting and have a sufficiently open mesh so that an insect can be seen through it. The best material for this sort of net is marquisette or scrim; cheesecloth is unsatisfactory because it snags too easily. An open bobbinet makes a good net if one is interested in collecting only the larger, fast-flying insects, but many of the smaller insects will escape through its meshes. For a net that will receive rough use, such as one to be used primarily for sweeping and from which even the smallest insects cannot escape, the best cloth is muslin.

The cloth for the bag can be cut into four pieces and sewed together or, if one wishes to make a net with as little sewing as possible, it can be made from a single piece cut as shown in Figure 32-1 E. The seams should be French seams so that the net can be used with either side out.

Some people may prefer an insect net that can be taken apart and carried inconspicuously. Such a net can be made from a collapsible frame known as a landing net, which can be bought from sporting-goods stores (Figure 32-2).

If used with care, an insect net will last a long time. It should be kept away from barbed wire and stout thorns, for most net material is easily ripped. Nets such as those just described should not be used to collect aquatic insects. They should be kept dry, for insects caught in a wet net are seldom fit for a collection. Moreover, moisture rots the fabric, making it tear more easily.

When collecting insects with a net, one may look for particular insects and then swing at them, or one may simply swing the net through vegetation (sweeping). The former method is usually used for collecting the larger insects, and often demands a certain amount of speed and skill; the latter method will produce the greater quantity

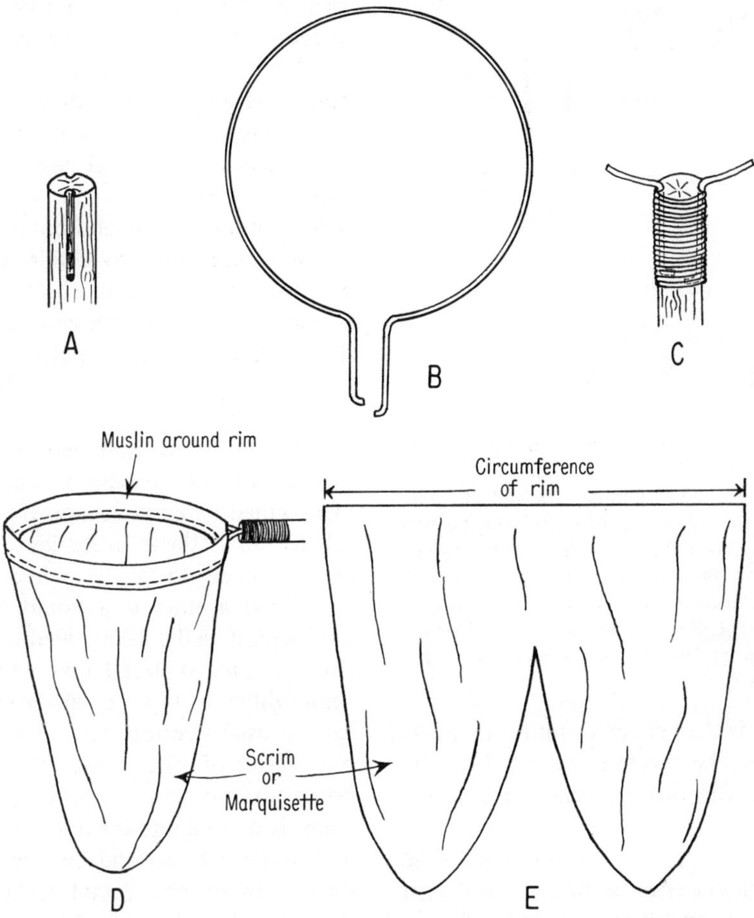

Fig. 32-1. The homemade insect net. Grooves and holes are cut in the end of the handle, as in A; the wire for the rim is bent, as shown in B, fitted into the holes and grooves, and held there with heavy cord or wire, C. The material for the bag is cut as in E, and the finished net is shown in D.

and variety of insects. When one catches a particularly active insect, he must use certain precautions to prevent the insect from escaping before it can be transferred to the killing jar. The safest method is to fold the net over, with the insect in the bottom of the net (Figure 32-3); the insect is then grasped through the net (provided it is not one that stings), and transferred to the killing bottle. If the insect is one that stings (when in doubt it is better to assume that it *does* sting), there are three methods of transferring it to the killing bottle: (1) The fold of the net containing the insect can be put into the killing bottle until the insect is stunned; then the insect can be picked out of the net and put into the bottle. (2) The insect can be grasped through the net with forceps, rather than with the fingers, and transferred to the bottle. (3) The insect may be gotten into a fold of the net and stunned by pinching (pinching the *thorax*), and then transferred to the killing bottle. The third method is the most efficient. After sweeping, to make sure that no desired individuals escape, the insects can be shaken into the bottom of the net, and this part of the net placed in the killing jar (a large-mouthed jar is needed for

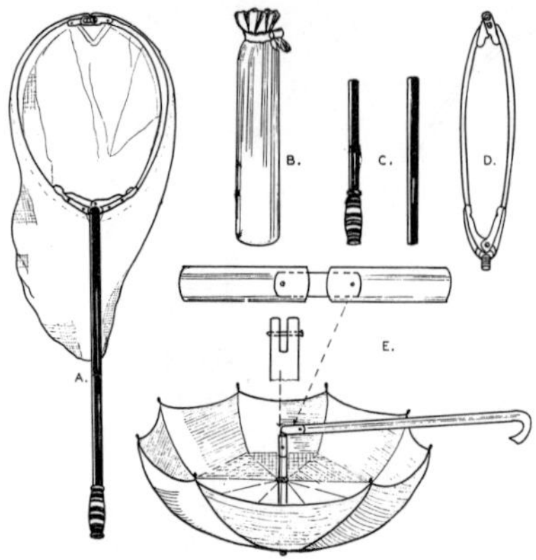

Fig. 32-2. The collapsible net and the beating umbrella. The net (A) may be collapsed (D), the handle removed and unjointed (C), and all these parts placed in a carrying bag (B). The beating umbrella (E) has a hinged joint in the handle and is held in the position illustrated when in use. (From DeLong and Davidson. Courtesy of the Ohio State University Press and the Department of Zoology and Entomology of the Ohio State University.)

this), which is then covered until the insects are stunned. The specimens desired, or the entire catch, can then be transferred to the killing jar.

KILLING BOTTLES

If the insect is to be preserved after it is captured, it must be killed, and killed in such a way that it is not injured or broken; this calls for some sort of killing bottle. Bottles of various sizes and shapes may be used, depending on the type of insects involved, and various materials may be used as the killing agent. It is desirable when in the field to have two or three bottles of different sizes for insects of different types. These should include at least one small bottle (perhaps an inch in diameter and 4 to 6 inches in length) for small insects, and one or more larger bottles for larger insects. Corked bottles are preferable to screw-capped bottles, but either type will do. Wide-mouthed bottles or jars are much better than narrow-necked ones. All killing bottles, regardless of the killing agent used, should be conspicuously labeled "POISON," and all glass bottles should be reinforced with tape to reduce the hazards of breakage.

The best materials to use in a killing bottle are ethyl acetate or cyanide. Bottles containing either of these materials will kill fairly quickly and will last a long time. Ethyl acetate (an ingredient of nail polish) is relatively safe to use, and bottles containing it can be used even by children; cyanide is extremely poisonous and bottles containing it must be handled with care. Ethyl acetate does not kill quite so quickly as cyanide, but insects once knocked out by it do not revive; cyanide kills more quickly, but specimens seemingly killed sometimes revive after they have been mounted. Specimens killed by ethyl acetate are much more relaxed than those killed by cyanide and are less likely to be discolored.

Ethyl acetate is a liquid, and bottles used with it as the killing medium must also contain some material that will absorb it. Many different types of absorbing material can be used—cotton, felt, or even paper—but plaster of Paris makes a longer-lasting bottle. A mixture of plaster of Paris and water is poured into the bottom of the bottle and allowed to set and become *completely* dry; a few drops of ethyl acetate added to the top of the plaster will be absorbed, and the bottle will be then ready for use. If the bottle is capped with a cork, cotton may be placed in a hole in the bottom of the cork and held there with a covering of cloth, and the ethyl acetate can be added to the cotton.

Cyanide bottles are of two types; those containing calcium cyanide, with a plug of cotton and cardboard to hold the cyanide in the bottle (Figure 32-4 A), and those containing sodium or potassium cyanide, with plaster of Paris holding the cyanide in the bottle (Figure 32-4 B). Small killing bottles made of a shell vial, plastic vial, or test tube are best made with calcium cyanide, larger bottles generally contain sodium cyanide and plaster of Paris.

A calcium cyanide killing bottle is prepared by putting a small quantity of cyanide

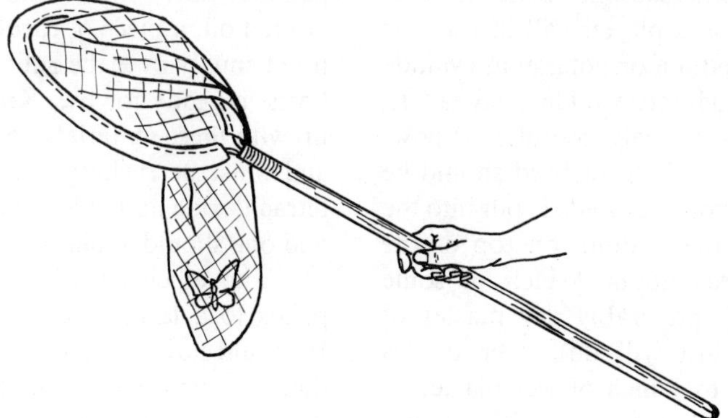

Fig. 32-3. An insect net turned to prevent the escape of captured specimens.

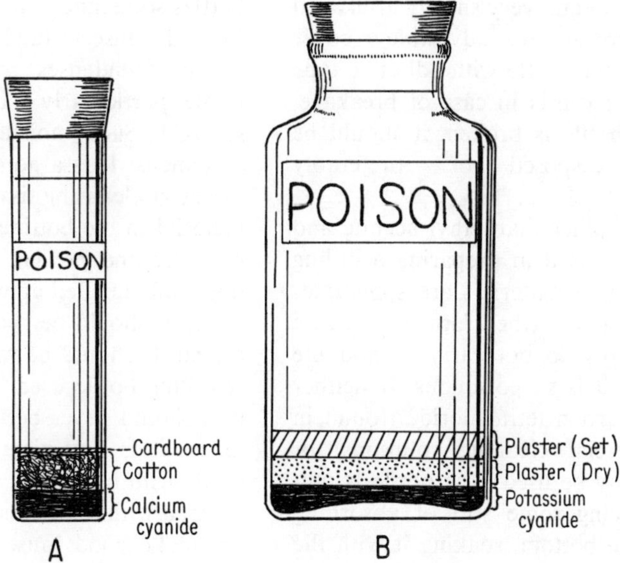

Fig. 32-4. Cyanide bottles. A, a small bottle made up with calcium cyanide; B, a large bottle made up with plaster of Paris.

in the bottom of the bottle and then adding a plug of cotton and a disc of cardboard (cut to fit snugly, and usually with a few pin holes in it). Bottles made of glass should have the bottom and the rim reinforced with adhesive tape to reduce the hazards of breakage. This type of bottle is ready for use as soon as it has been prepared. Calcium cyanide is a dark-gray powder that is often used as a fumigant; it is extremely poisonous, and should be handled with great care. Only persons familiar with its properties should use it; carelessness in its use may be disastrous.

If the killing jar is capped with a large cork, it is often more convenient to place the cyanide (calcium cyanide) in a hole in the bottom of the cork and keep it there by a plug of cotton and a covering of cloth.

A cyanide bottle with plaster of Paris takes longer to prepare but will last longer; a bottle made with calcium cyanide will last several weeks, whereas one made up with sodium cyanide and plaster will last a year or two. Either sodium or potassium cyanide may be used (sodium cyanide is cheaper), and should be in a finely granular or powdered form; the bottle to be used should be clean and dry. Enough cyanide is put into the bottle to cover the bottom; on top of the cyanide is poured about $\frac{1}{2}$ inch of some porous material, preferably dry plaster of Paris (fine sawdust will do); over this is poured about $\frac{1}{4}$ to $\frac{1}{2}$ inch of wet plaster of Paris, which is allowed to set. The bottle should be left uncorked, preferably outdoors, until it is thoroughly set and dried, usually from several hours to overnight; then it is corked, and very shortly afterward will be ready for use. It is advisable to cover the bottom of the bottle with adhesive tape to reduce the hazards in case of breakage. If a cyanide bottle is broken, it should be immediately disposed of — preferably buried.

Materials other than ethyl acetate and cyanide can be used in preparing a killing bottle. These two materials are sometimes difficult to obtain—the former because many drugstores do not carry it, and the latter because it is so poisonous. If neither is available, carbon tetrachloride (found in many commercial cleaning solutions) or chloroform may be used. The bottle is prepared by placing some sort of absorbing material in the bottom, soaking it with the killing agent, and then covering it with a piece of cardboard or screen. The absorbing material may be placed in a hole in the cork (if the bottle is capped with a cork), as described above for bottles made up with ethyl acetate or cyanide. Cotton makes a good absorbent. If chloroform is used, rubber bands or small pieces of rubber (for example, strips of an inner tube) are better than cotton. These are placed in the bottom of the bottle, chloroform is poured over them, and the bottle is corked and allowed to stand over night. By morning the rubber will have absorbed the chloroform and expanded; any excess chloroform is then poured off, a piece of cardboard or screen is fitted snugly over the rubber bands, and the bottle is ready for use. Killing bottles made up with these materials do not last very long and must be recharged frequently. Carbon tetrachloride and chloroform are poisonous, and one should avoid breathing the fumes.

The efficiency of a killing bottle depends to a large extent on how it is used. It should never be left uncorked any longer than is necessary to put insects in or take them out; the escaping gas reduces its strength, and an uncorked bottle (particularly one made up with cyanide) is a hazard. The inside of the bottle should be kept dry; bottles sometimes "sweat," that is, moisture from the insects (and sometimes from the plaster) condenses on the inside of the bottle, particularly if it is exposed to bright sunlight. Such moisture will ruin delicate specimens. It is a good idea to keep a few pieces of cleansing tissue or other absorbent material in the bottle at all times to absorb moisture and prevent the insects from getting badly tangled up with one another. This material should be changed frequently, and the bottle should be wiped out periodically. A killing bottle used for moths and butterflies should never be used for other insects unless it is first cleaned; insects put in a bottle with butterflies or moths will become covered with scales and look dusty, and will not make good museum specimens.

HANDLING THE CATCH

The collector must learn by experience how long it takes his killing bottles to kill an insect. He will learn that some insects are killed very quickly, while others, even in the same bottle, are very resistant to the killing agent. A mosquito in a strong cyanide bottle will be killed in a few minutes, whereas some of the snout beetles may remain alive in the same bottle for an hour or two. The catch should be kept in the killing bottle until the specimens are killed, but not much longer. Many insects will become discolored if left in too long, particularly in a bottle containing cyanide. It is advisable to remove the insects within an hour or two after they are killed.

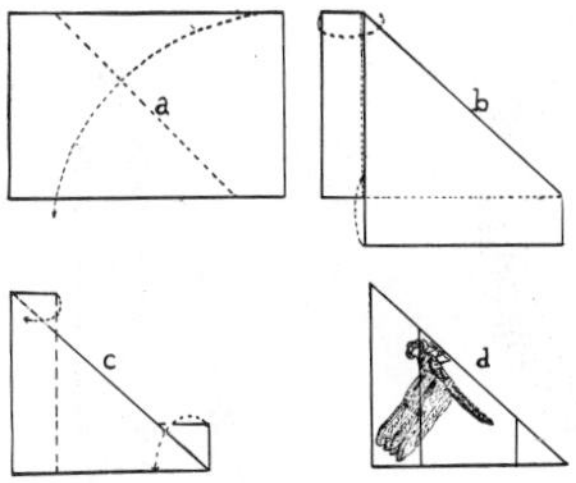

Fig. 32-5. A method of folding triangular paper envelopes for insect specimens. The paper is folded as illustrated in A, B, and C, to form the completed envelope D. (From DeLong and Davidson. Courtesy of the Ohio State University Press and the Department of Zoology and Entomology of the Ohio State University.)

Specimens removed from the killing bottle in the field may be placed in pillboxes or paper envelopes for temporary storage. The pillboxes should contain some sort of absorbent material, such as cleansing tissue, which will reduce the bouncing around of the specimens during transportation and will absorb excess moisture. Paper envelopes, either ordinary letter envelopes or triangular envelopes like that shown in Figure 32-5, are excellent for the temporary storage of large-winged insects such as butterflies, moths, or dragonflies. These triangular envelopes can be made quickly from a sheet of notebook paper, and specimens will remain in good condition in them; data on the collection can be written on the outside.

OTHER TYPES OF COLLECTING APPARATUS

Aerial nets such as those already described are standard collecting equipment for most work, but many other devices are useful in certain situations or for collecting certain types of insects. Some of the more important of these are described below. The collector who has a little ingenuity will be able to devise many others.

ASPIRATOR: This is a very useful device for capturing small insects, particularly if one wishes to catch them and keep them alive. Various forms of aspirators have been devised, but one of the simplest and easiest to handle is the vial type shown in Figure 32-6 A. Sucking through the mouthpiece will draw small insects into the vial, and a cloth over the inner end of the mouthpiece tube prevents the insects from being sucked into the mouth. If one has a series of vials to fit the cork of this type of aspirator, it is a simple matter to remove an insect-filled vial and replace it with an empty one. The insects caught in the vial may be killed by replacing the aspirator cork with a cork containing a killing agent.

An aspirator may also be made from a piece of Pyrex glass tubing, with the mouthpiece tube in one end and the intake tube in the other (Figure 32-6 B). This type, which does not involve any bending of the glass tubing and requires only one hole in each cork, is easier to make than the vial type of aspirator; however, it is a little more difficult to transfer insects out of this type of aspirator than out of the vial type. For killing the insects in the tube type of aspirator, a cyanide-filled cork, which can be used to replace the cork containing the mouthpiece tube, is best. Once the insects in the aspirator have been stunned, they can be transferred to another bottle.

BEATING UMBRELLA: Many insects that occur on vegetation feign death by dropping off the plant when it is jarred slightly. The collector can take advantage of this habit by placing a collecting device underneath a plant and then jarring the plant with a stick; the insects that fall onto the collecting device beneath may be easily picked up. The best device for this sort of collecting is a beating umbrella (Figure 32-2 E)—an umbrella frame covered with white muslin or light canvas. A white sheet, or

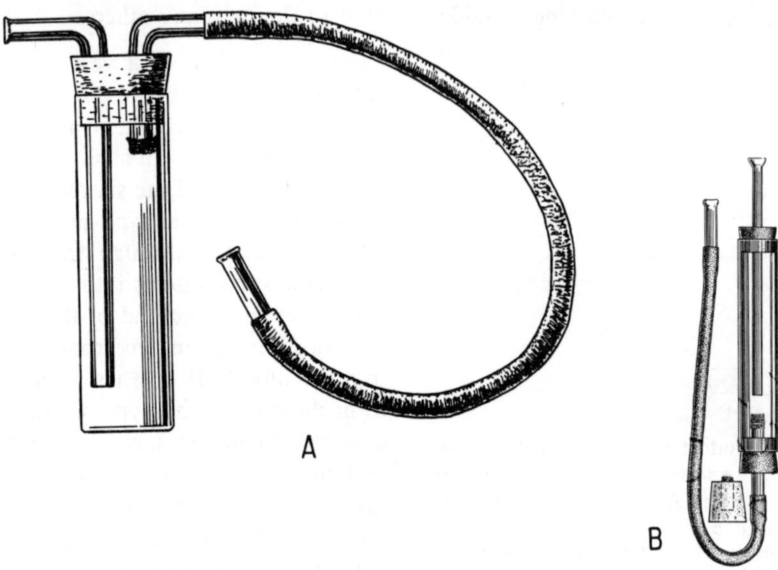

Fig. 32-6. Aspirators. A, the vial type; B, the tube type. (B, from DeLong and Davidson. Courtesy of the Ohio State University Press and the Department of Zoology and Entomology of the Ohio State University.)

even an open insect net, may also be used to catch insects jarred off a plant.

SIFTERS: Many small and unusual insects that occur in trash and leaf litter are most easily collected by some sort of sifting device; the insects that occur in such materials can often be collected in no other way. The simplest collecting procedure is to take a handful of the material and sift it slowly onto a large piece of white cloth, oilcloth, or cardboard; the tiny animals falling onto the white surface will reveal themselves by their movement, and can be picked up with an aspirator or a wet brush. The material may also be sifted onto a white cloth from a small box with a screen bottom.

Perhaps the simplest way of getting the insects and other animals out of soil, debris, or leaf litter, is to use a Berlese funnel (Figure 32-7). A Berlese funnel is an ordinary funnel containing a piece of screen or hardware cloth, with a killing jar or container of alcohol below it, and the material to be sifted placed on the screen. As the material dries—and this can be hastened by placing an electric light bulb above the funnel—the insects and other animals move downward and eventually fall into the container below the funnel, where they are killed. A Berlese funnel is the best device for collecting debris-inhabiting insects, mites, pseudoscorpions, and small spiders.

Anyone using a Berlese funnel will notice that many of the animals collected (for example, the springtails and many of the mites) remain on the surface of the alcohol. The fact that many soil- and debris-inhabiting animals will float on alcohol or water makes its possible to get many of these animals out of such materials by putting the materials in water; many animals come to the surface of the water, where they can be removed and placed in alcohol.

TRAPS: Traps are an easy and often very effective method of collecting many types of insects. A trap is any device containing something to which the insects are attracted, and which is so arranged that once the insects get into it, they cannot get out. The lure used and the general form of the trap will be determined by the type of insects one wants to collect. Space does not permit a description here of many types of traps, but the ingenious collector should be able to devise any that are not described. Some common types are shown in Figure 32-8.

A light trap such as that shown in Figure 32-8 C will catch a great many insects, but the specimens taken are often considerably battered. One can get specimens in better condition by simply waiting at a light and getting the insects directly into a killing bottle as they settle on something near the light (for example, a wall, screen, or sheet). Light traps are often useful in obtaining data on insect populations.

Traps of the type shown in Figure 32-8 A are useful for catching flies that are attracted to decaying materials such as meat and fruit; if the trap is visited frequently, the specimens it catches can be retrieved in good condition. Varying the bait will produce a more varied catch.

Traps of the type shown in Figure 32-8 B are useful for catching carrion beetles and other insects that do not fly readily. Such a trap may be made of a large tin can, preferably with a few holes punched in the bottom to prevent water from accumulating in it, and with some sort of screen over the bait to permit easy removal of the insects caught. The can is sunk in the ground with its top at ground level. Most of the insects attracted by the bait will fall into the can and be unable to get out. The bait may be a dead animal, a piece of meat that will eventually decay, fruit, molasses, or some similar material. Here again, varying the bait will yield a more varied catch.

Household insects that do not fly, such as silverfish and cockroaches, can be trapped by means of an open-topped baited box. A box 4 or 5 inches deep is placed on the floor, provided with a ramp from the floor to the top of the box, and baited with dog biscuits, crackers, or some similar materials.

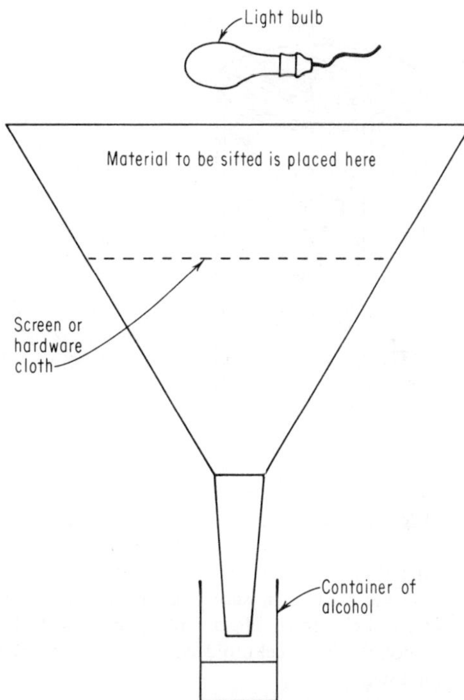

Fig. 32-7. A Berlese funnel. The funnel can be supported by a ringstand, or by three or four legs attached near the middle of the funnel. The light bulb can be that of an ordinary gooseneck lamp, or it can be in a metal cylinder placed over the top of the funnel. The material to be sifted is placed on the screen.

If the upper 2 or 3 inches of the box sides are coated on the inside with vaseline, the insects that get into the box will not be able to crawl out.

Many insects can be caught by "sugaring," that is, preparing a sugary mixture and spreading it on tree trunks, stumps, or fence posts. Various mixtures may be used, but one containing something that is fermenting is probably the best; it may be made with molasses or fruit juices and a little stale beer or rum.

AQUATIC COLLECTING EQUIPMENT: Many acquatic insects can be collected with one's fingers or with forceps when one is examining plants, stones, or other objects in the water, but many more can be collected by using a dip net, strainer, dipper, or other

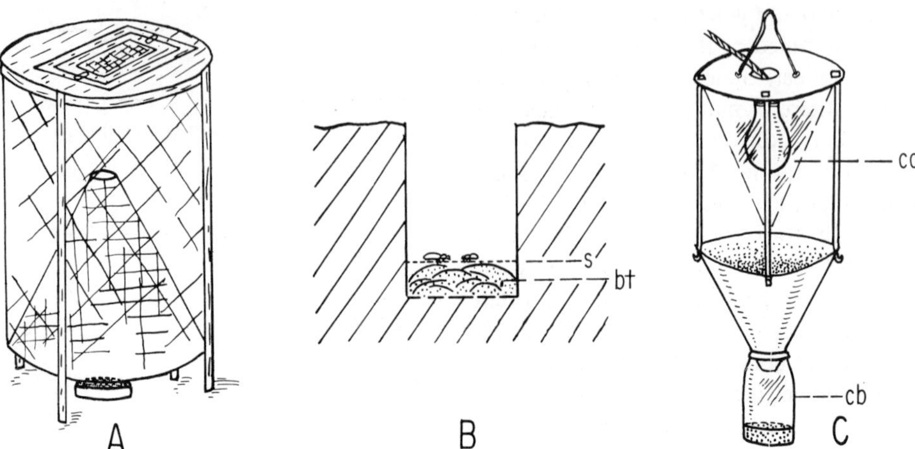

Fig. 32-8. Insect traps. A, a fly trap, a rectangular or cylindrical screen cage with a screen cone at the bottom; the bait is placed below the center of the cone, and the flies are removed through the door at the top of the cage. B, a beetle trap, consisting of a tin can set in the ground; *bt*, the bait; *s*, a screen over the bait, which facilitates removing the insects from the trap. C, a light trap; *cb*, a bottle to collect the specimens (a cyanide jar or a bottle containing alcohol); *cc*, a celluloid cone around the light, which serves to deflect specimens into the funnel below.

device. A dip net can be made much like an aerial net, but should be shallower (no deeper than the diameter of the rim) and much stronger. The handle should be heavy, and the rim should be made of $\frac{1}{4}$- or $\frac{3}{8}$-inch metal rod and securely fastened to the handle. The part of the bag that is attached to the rim should be of canvas, and it is desirable to have an apron of the same material extending down over the front of the bag. The rim need not be circular; many dip nets have the rim bent in the form of the letter D. The bag may be made of heavy marquisette or bolting cloth. Strainers of the tea-strainer type, with a rim from 2 to 6 inches in diameter, are useful for aquatic collecting if they are not subjected to too hard use. Dip nets or strainers can be used to collect free-swimming forms, forms on vegetation, and forms burrowing in the sand or muck of the bottom. A good catch can often be obtained in streams by placing the net or strainer at a narrow place in the current and then turning over stones or disturbing the bottom upstream from the net. Retrieving insects from the muck and debris collected in a net or strainer is not always easy, for most of them are not noticed until they move. A good way to locate them is to dump the contents of the net into a large white pan with some water; against the white background, the insects can be more easily located and picked out. The best device for collecting small free-swimming forms such as mosquito larvae or midge larvae is a long-handled white enameled dipper; small larvae are easily seen against the white background of the dipper and can be removed with an eye dropper.

The collector will often need a large heavy knife for prying up bark, cutting open galls, or digging into various materials. A vial of insect pins is useful for pinning together mating pairs before they are put into the killing bottle. A notebook and pencil should always be a part of the collector's gear. The collecting of certain types of insects often requires special items of equipment; the amount and type of equipment a collector uses will depend entirely on the sort of collecting he expects to do.

MOUNTING AND PRESERVING INSECTS

Insects can be mounted and preserved in various ways. Most specimens are pinned, and, once dried, will keep indefinitely. Specimens too small to pin can be mounted on "points," on tiny "minuten" pins, or on microscope slides. Large and showy insects, such as butterflies, moths, grasshoppers, dragonflies, or damselflies, may be mounted in various types of glass-topped display cases. Soft-bodied forms, such as nymphs and larvae and the adults of midges, caddisflies, mayflies, and stoneflies, should be preserved in fluids.

RELAXING

All insects should be mounted as soon as possible after they have been collected; if they are allowed to dry, they become brittle and may be broken in the process of being mounted. Specimens stored in pillboxes or envelopes for a long time must be relaxed before being mounted. Any wide-mouthed can or jar that can be made airtight can be used as a relaxing chamber; the bottom of the jar is covered with wet sand or cloth (preferably with a little carbolic acid added to prevent mold), the insects are put in the jar in open shallow boxes, and the jar is tightly closed. One must learn by experience how long it takes to relax an insect, but specimens are usually sufficiently relaxed to mount after a day or two in such a chamber.

PINNING

Pinning is the best way to preserve hard-bodied insects; pinned specimens keep well, retain their normal appearance, and are easily handled and studied. The colors often fade when the insect dries, but this is difficult to avoid; bright colors are generally better preserved if the specimens are dried rapidly.

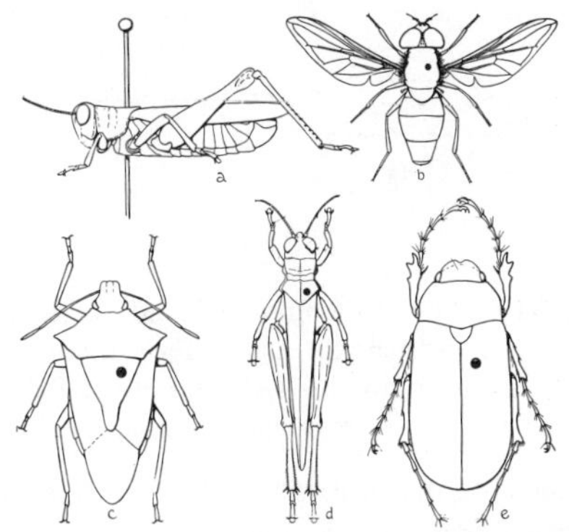

Fig. 32-9. Methods of pinning insects. A, specimen in lateral view showing method of pinning grasshoppers; the black spots in the other figures show the location of the pin in the case of flies (B), bugs (C), grasshoppers (D), and beetles (E). (Courtesy of the Illinois Natural History Survey.)

Common pins are undesirable for pinning insects; they are usually too thick or too short, and they rust. Insects should be pinned with a special type of steel pin known as an insect pin. These pins are longer than common pins, they can be obtained in various sizes (thicknesses), and they do not rust. Insect-pin sizes range from 00 to 7; the smaller sizes (that is, smaller in diameter) are too slender for general use, for which sizes 2 and 3 are the best. These pins may be obtained from various supply houses (see list at the end of this chapter).

Insects are usually pinned vertically through the body as shown in Figures 32-9 and 32-10. Forms such as bees, wasps, flies, butterflies, and moths are pinned through the thorax between the bases of the front wings; with flies and wasps it is desirable to insert the pin a little to the right of the midline. Bugs are pinned through the scutellum (Figure 32-9 C), a little to the right of the midline if the scutellum is large. Grasshoppers are pinned through the posterior part of the pronotum, just to the right of the midline (Figure 32-9 D). Beetles should be pinned through the right elytron, about halfway between the two ends of the body (Figure 32-9 E); the pin should go

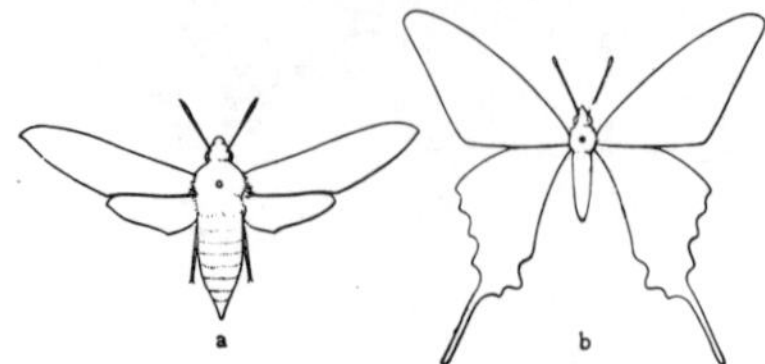

Fig. 32-10. Method of pinning Lepidoptera. These insects are pinned through the center of the thorax, in both moths (A) and butterflies (B). (Courtesy of the Illinois Natural History Survey.)

through the metathorax and emerge through the metasternum (see Figure 22-2) so as not to damage the bases of the legs. Dragonflies and damselflies are best pinned horizontally through the thorax, with the left side uppermost; this reduces the space necessary to house the collection, and a specimen so pinned can be studied just as easily as one pinned vertically. If the specimen does not have the wings together above its back when it dies, the wings should be so placed and the specimen put into an envelope for a day or so until it has dried enough for the wings to remain in this position; then it is carefully pinned through the upper part of the thorax, below the base of the wings.

The easiest way to pin an insect is to hold it between the thumb and forefinger of one hand and insert the pin with the other. All specimens should be mounted at a uniform height on the pin—about an inch above the point. Uniformity (and this applies to the position of labels on the pin as well as to the position of the insect) can be obtained with a pinning block. Pinning blocks are of various types (Figure 32-11), but a common type (Figure 32-11 A) consists of a block of wood in which are drilled three small holes of different depths, usually 1, $\frac{5}{8}$, and $\frac{3}{8}$ inches, respectively.

If the abdomen sags when the insect is pinned, as it sometimes does, the pinned specimen may be stuck on a vertical surface with the abdomen hanging down, and left there until it dries. If the insect is pinned on a horizontal surface, a piece of stiff paper or cardboard may be placed on the pin beneath the insect to support it until it dries. Another method of supporting a sagging abdomen is by means of crossed pins, with the abdomen resting in the angle of the cross.

A sheet of cork, balsa wood, or other soft material is very useful for the temporary storage of pinned insects until they can be sorted and put into boxes.

MOUNTING SMALL INSECTS

Insects too small to pin may be mounted on a card point (Figure 32-12 A-C), on a "minuten" pin (Figure 32-12 D), or on a microscope slide, or they may be preserved in liquid. Most small specimens are mounted on points.

Points are elongated triangular pieces of light cardboard or celluloid, about 8 or 10 millimeters long and 3 or 4 millimeters wide at the base; the point is pinned through the base, and the insect is glued to the tip of the point. Points can be cut with scissors or a razor blade, or they can be cut with a special type of punch (obtainable from

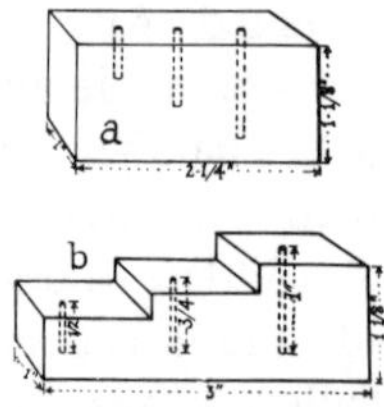

Fig. 32-11. Pinning blocks. These may be a rectangular piece of wood containing holes drilled to different depths (A), or a block shaped like a stair step, with holes drilled to the bottom (B). The block of the type shown in A usually has the holes drilled to depths of 1 in., $\frac{5}{8}$ in., and $\frac{3}{8}$ in. After a specimen or label is placed on the pin, the pin is inserted into the appropriate hole until it touches bottom—into the deepest hole for the specimen, the middle hole for the label bearing locality and date, and the last hole for any additional label. (From DeLong and Davidson. Courtesy of the Ohio State University Press and the Department of Zoology and Entomology of the Ohio State University.)

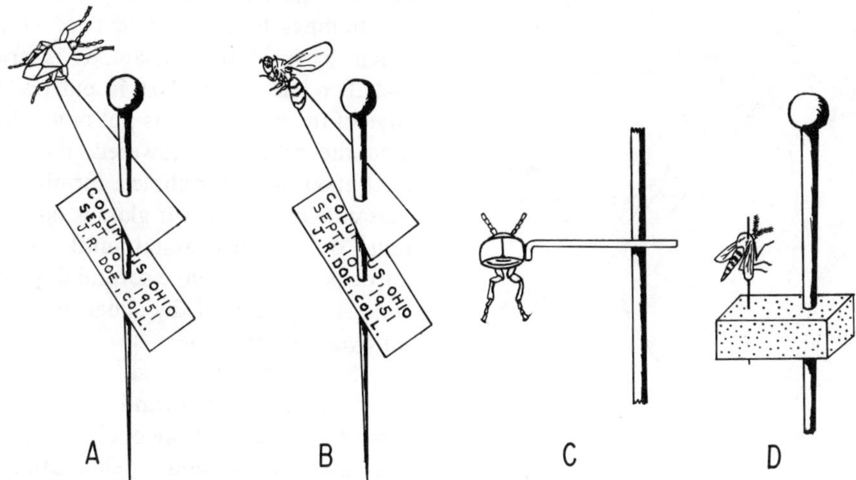

Fig. 32-12. Methods of mounting minute insects. A, bug on point, dorsal side up; B, fly on point, left side up; C, beetle mounted dorsal side up, attached by its side to the bent-down tip of the point; D, mosquito mounted on a minuten pin.

supply houses), or they can be obtained directly from supply houses.

Putting an insect on a point is a very simple process. The point is put on the pin, the pin is grasped by the pointed end, and the upper side of the tip of the point is touched to the glue and then touched to the insect. One should use as little glue as possible (so that body parts are not covered by it), and the specimen should be correctly oriented on the point. The standard positions of an insect mounted on a point are shown in Figure 32-12 A and B; the point should extend to the left of the pin, and if the specimen is mounted dorsal side up (Figure 32-12 A), the head should be pointing forward (away from the observer); if it is mounted on its side, the head should be directed to the left (away from the pin), with the left side of the insect uppermost (Figure 32-12 B). It is important that body parts which have to be examined when the insect is being identified should not be imbedded in glue. Beetles mounted on points should always have the ventral side of the body visible; flies, wasps, and other insects in which the wings are extended above the body are best mounted on their side.

The glue used in mounting insects on points should be quick-drying and should be quite hard when it sets. A good type of glue to use is a commercial glue (not paste or mucilage) or household cement. Glue is also useful in repairing broken specimens and replacing broken-off wings or legs.

MOUNTING ON MICROSCOPE SLIDES

Many insects that are too small to pin, particularly soft-bodied forms that cannot be properly preserved on points, and often such structures as genitalia, are mounted on microscope slides. Specimens so mounted are usually killed and preserved in fluids (see page 700) until they can be mounted. The procedure followed in mounting a specimen on a microscope slide will vary somewhat, depending on the insect and on the type of mounting medium used. Some insects, particularly dark-colored or thick-bodied specimens, and such structures as genitalia, must be cleared before mounting.

If it is necessary to clear a specimen, the clearing is usually done with a solution of potassium hydroxide (KOH); many small or thin-walled specimens make good mounts without clearing. If KOH is used, the speci-

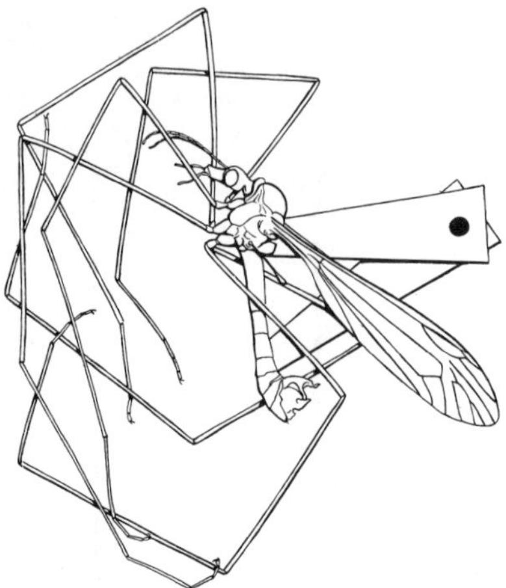

Fig. 32-13. Method of mounting crane flies and other insects that are elongate and too small to pin. These insects should be mounted on a double point mount, with the legs mounted away from the pin. (Courtesy of the Illinois Natural History Survey.)

men is either soaked or boiled in a 10 to 15 percent solution. Clearing a specimen by soaking it in cold KOH usually requires from several hours to a day or so; the same specimen can be cleared in a few minutes by boiling in KOH, but it is sometimes distorted by the boiling process, especially if it is lightly sclerotized.

Many different media are suitable for mounting small insects on microscope slides, some requiring more preliminary treatment of the specimen than do others. Space does not permit a detailed discussion here of all the possible types of mounting media, but we may mention three common types: Canada balsam, gum Arabic, and diaphane.

Specimens mounted in balsam must be dehydrated before they are put into the balsam; if they are put into balsam directly from 70 percent alcohol, the medium will become clouded. Dehydration involves running the specimen successively through increasing concentrations of alcohol (70, 95, and 100 percent), then through xylol, and finally into the balsam on the slide. The length of time the specimen is left in each solution before moving it to the next depends on its size; the time may vary from a few minutes to an hour or two. When the specimen is in the balsam, it is oriented, and then the cover glass is put on. If one edge of the cover glass is put down first and then the other side lowered, there is less likelihood of air bubbles forming in the balsam. Once the cover glass is on, the slide must be kept horizontal until the balsam hardens. This may take several days, but the time is shortened if the slides are placed in an oven or slide drier.

Specimens mounted in gum Arabic or diaphane medium can be moved directly from the preserving alcohol to the mounting medium without dehydration. This medium is particularly useful for mosquito larvae and other insects that require little or no clearing; the medium itself has some clearing action. Gum Arabic requires a little longer to harden than does balsam.

A number of different types of mounting media, including those just mentioned, may be obtained from supply houses. The balsam can be obtained ready to use, or the dry material may be obtained and dissolved in xylol to make a medium of the desired consistency. The gum Arabic medium is made up of the following ingredients:

Gum Arabic	30-40 g
Chloral hydrate	50 g
Glycerine	20 ml
Distilled water	50 ml
Cocaine hydrochloride	0.5 g

It is not absolutely necessary to add the cocaine; insects like mosquito larvae can be put into this medium alive and mounted, and in such cases the cocaine hastens the killing of the larvae. There are various formulas for gum Arabic mounting media; another formula, often called Hoyer's mounting medium, is similar to that given above, but omits the cocaine and calls for 200 grams instead of 50 grams of chloral hydrate.

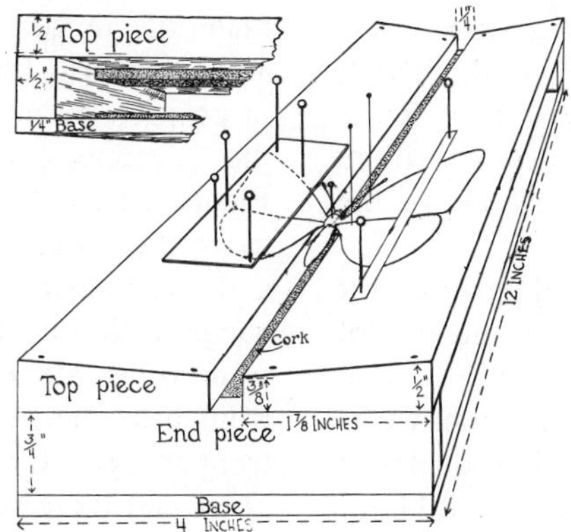

Fig. 32-14. The spreading board, showing dimensions, details of construction (inset), and a spread specimen. The wings of the specimen may be held in place by a single broad strip of paper as shown on the left wings, or by a narrower strip and pins as shown on the right wings. (Courtesy of the Illinois Natural History Survey.)

This type of medium is made up by first putting the gum Arabic in water and allowing it to dissolve (which takes about 24 hours at room temperature), then adding the chloral hydrate and allowing the solution to stand until all is dissolved, and then adding the glycerine. If the resulting material is not absolutely clear, it should be filtered once or twice through glass wool. It should be stored in glass-stoppered bottles.

In some cases (for example, scale insects), it may be desirable to stain the insect before it is mounted. A number of different stains are suitable for this purpose, but one very commonly used is acid fuchsin. The following procedure is followed when this stain is used:

1. Clear the specimen in KOH.
2. Wash in two or three changes of distilled water to remove the KOH.
3. Transfer from water to 95 percent alcohol, for at least 10 minutes.
4. Transfer to acid fuchsin, for 20 to 40 minutes.
5. Wash out the excess stain in 95 percent alcohol, for no more than a few minutes.
6. Clear in carbolxylol (3 parts xylol and 1 part melted crystals of carbolic acid).
7. Mount in balsam.

The acid fuchsin stain is prepared from the dry material (obtainable from a supply house) according to the following formula:

Acid fuchsin	0.5 g
10% hydrochloric acid	25.0 ml
Distilled water	300.0 ml

SPREADING INSECTS

It does not greatly matter about the position of the legs or wings of most insects when the specimen is pinned, as long as all parts can be easily seen and studied. With moths and butterflies and possibly some other insects, and in the case of insects mounted in display boxes (see below), the wings should be spread before the insect is put into the collection. The method of spreading will depend on whether the specimen is mounted pinned or unpinned, and the position into which the wings should be put depends on the type of insect.

An insect that is to be a part of a pinned collection is spread on a spreading board (Figure 32-14). Spreading boards can be obtained from a supply house or they can be made at home. An insect to be mounted under glass, as in a Riker or glass mount, may be spread on any flat surface such as a piece of corrugated cardboard or a sheet of cork or balsa wood. An insect spread on a spreading board is ordinarily spread dorsal side up, and the pin is left in the insect; one spread on a flat surface for a Riker mount is spread in an upside-down position, and the pin is *not* left in the body of the insect.

There are certain standard positions for the wings of a spread insect. In the case of butterflies and moths (Figure 32-10) and mayflies, the rear margins of the front wings should be straight across, at right angles to the body, and the hind wings should be far enough forward that there is no large gap at the side between the front and hind wings. With grasshoppers, dragonflies, damselflies, and most other insects, the front margins of the hind wings should be straight across, with the front wings far enough forward that they just clear the hind wings. The front and hind wings of a butterfly or moth are always overlapped, with the front edge of the hind wing *under* the rear edge of the front wing; in other insects the wings are usually not overlapped.

The actual process of spreading an insect is relatively simple, though it requires a little practice to acquire any degree of proficiency. One must be very careful not to damage the specimen in the spreading process. Butterflies and moths must be handled with particular care in order not to rub off the scales on the wings; these insects should always be handled with forceps. If the specimen is to be mounted on a spreading board, it is first pinned (like any other pinned insect), and the pin inserted in the groove of the spreading board until the wings are flush with the surface of the board. If the specimen is to be spread upside down on a flat surface, the pin is inserted into the thorax from underneath, and the insect is pinned on its back on some flat surface. It is often advisable to place a pin along each side of the body to prevent it from swinging out of line.

The steps in spreading a butterfly are shown in Figure 32-15. The wings are held in position by strips of paper or other material pinned to the board; the antennae and other structures are oriented and held in position by means of pins. Starting with the specimen in the position shown in Figure 32-15 A, proceed as follows: Remove the lower pin on the right-hand strip and, holding the strip fairly tight over the wings with one hand, carefully raise the front wing. Maneuver the wing with a pin from near the base of the wing, along the front margin; the veins are heavier at this point and there is less likelihood of tearing the wing. Do not put the pin through the wing if it can be avoided. Raise the front wing to the standard position, pin the strip down just in front of the wing, then replace the pin at the bottom of the right-hand paper strip (B). Repeat the process with the other front wing (C). Now raise the hind wing on the right side to the desired position and pin the strip immediately behind the hind edge of the wing (D). Repeat this process with the other hind wing (E). With larger or stiff-winged forms, it may be desirable to add additional strips at the steps shown in B and C to prevent the wings from slipping back; or it may be necessary to take several steps to get the front wings into position, advancing the right wing a little way, then advancing the left wing. If it seems necessary, or if the wings are not perfectly flat at the edges, additional strips may be used. With specimens mounted upside down (as in Figure 32-15), it is desirable to have the specimen securely held down. Once the wings are in position, the antennae can be properly oriented and held in place by crossed pins (F). With a specimen mounted upside down on a flat surface, the final step is removing the pin from the body of the insect; this is done by holding the body down with forceps and carefully withdrawing the pin (G).

The length of time it takes a spread specimen to dry will depend on the size of the specimen and such other factors as temperature and humidity. No general state-

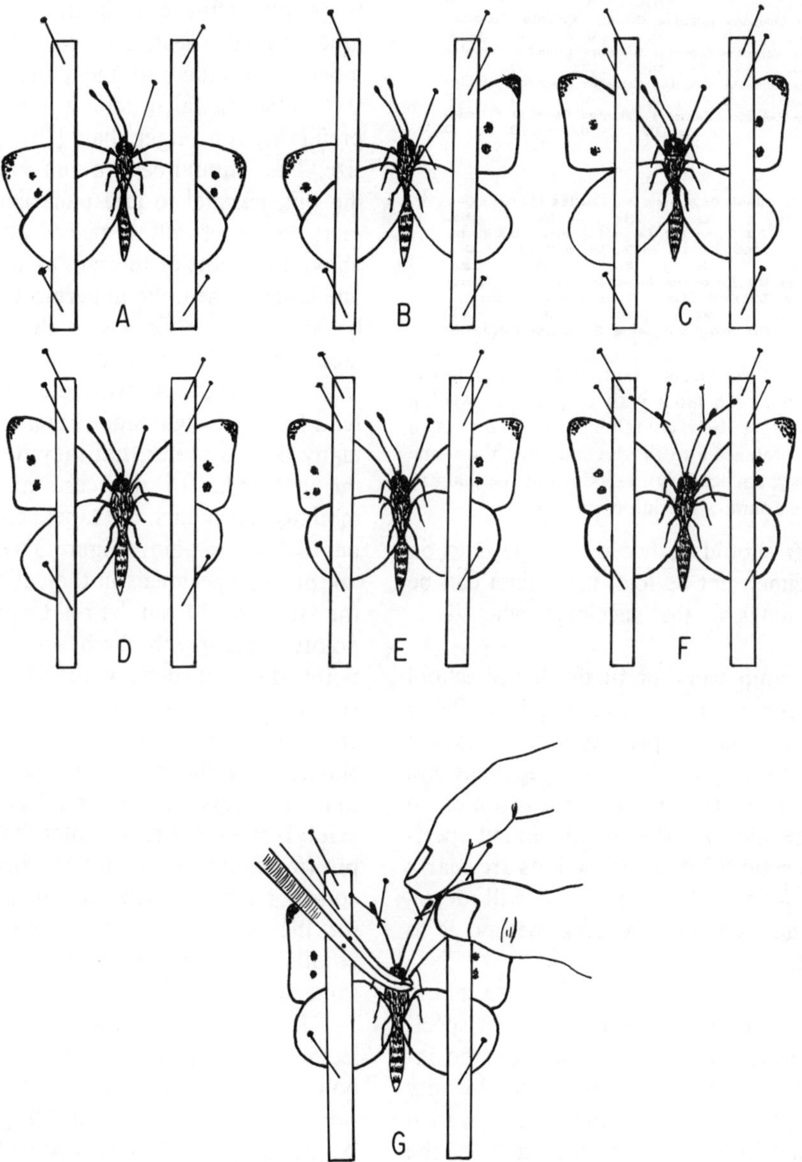

Fig. 32-15. Steps in spreading a butterfly upside down on a flat surface. A, position before starting to raise the wings; B, front wing on one side raised; C, front wing on the other side raised, with hind margin of front wings in a straight line; D, hind wing on one side raised; E, hind wing on the other side raised; F, antennae oriented and held in position by pins; G, removing the pin from the body of the butterfly.

ment of the time required can be made; the student will have to learn this by experience. To determine whether the specimen is ready to be removed from the spreading board, touch the abdomen gently with a needle; if the abdomen can be moved independently of the wings, the specimen is not yet dry; if the body is stiff, the specimen can be removed. Some of the larger moths may take a week or more to dry thoroughly. In every

Columbus Columbus Columbus Columbus Columbus Columbus

O. O. O. O. O. O.

Columbus Columbus Columbus Columbus Columbus Columbus

O. O. O. O. O. O.

Columbus Columbus Columbus Columbus Columbus Columbus

O. O. O. O. O. O.

Columbus Columbus Columbus Columbus Columbus Columbus

O. O. O. O. O. O.

Columbus Columbus Columbus Columbus Columbus Columbus

O. O. O. O. O. O.

Lincoln Co., Lincoln Co., Lincoln Co., Lincoln Co., Lincoln Co.,

Me. Me. Me. Me. Me.

D.J. Borror D.J. Borror D.J. Borror D.J. Borror D.J. Borror

Lincoln Co., Lincoln Co., Lincoln Co., Lincoln Co., Lincoln Co.,

Me. Me. Me. Me. Me.

D.J. Borror D.J. Borror D.J. Borror D.J. Borror D.J. Borror

Lincoln Co., Lincoln Co., Lincoln Co., Lincoln Co., Lincoln Co.,

Me. Me. Me. Me. Me.

D.J. Borror D.J. Borror D.J. Borror D.J. Borror D.J. Borror

Fig. 32-16. Two sheets of printed locality labels (actual size), each label with a space for writing in the date. Labels containing the name of a town are preferable to those containing the name of a county, particularly in sections of the country where the counties are large.

case care should be taken that the data on the specimen not be lost; these data can be noted alongside the specimen when it is spread.

In camp work or in the lower school grades, for example, mounting in a Riker or similar mount is preferable to spreading the specimen pinned; such specimens are more easily displayed and are less subject to breakage. On the other hand, spread specimens in good scientific collections are nearly always pinned. Circumstances will determine what type of spreading method is to be used.

LABELING

The scientific value of an insect specimen depends to a large extent on the information regarding the date and locality of its capture, and to a lesser extent on such additional information as the name of the collector and the habitat or food plant on which the specimen was collected. The beginning student may look upon such labeling as an unnecessary chore, but the time will always come when data on a specimen are indispensable. An insect collector should *always* label his specimens with date and locality; this is the minimum amount of data for a specimen; additional data are desirable, but optional.

The appearance of an insect collection is greatly influenced by the nature of the labels. Small, neat, and properly oriented labels add much to the collection. They should be on fairly stiff white paper, and preferably not larger than $\frac{1}{4}$ by $\frac{3}{4}$ inches in size. They should be at a uniform height on the pin, parallel to and underneath the insect; one label only is placed about $\frac{5}{8}$ inch above the point of the pin, or if more than one label is used, the uppermost one should be at this distance above the point. The labels should be oriented so that all are read from the same side; we prefer that they be read from the right side (Figure 32-21), but many people prefer that they be read from the left side. In the case of specimens mounted on points, the label should extend parallel to the point (Figure 32-12 A, B). If the pinned specimens in the collection have the labels read from the right, specimens on points placed with them should have the point directed downward; if the pinned specimens have the labels read from the left, specimens on points placed with them should have the point directed upward (so that all labels can be read from the same side). If there are two or more labels on the pin (for example, one for locality, date and collector, as in Figure 32-16, and another for the host plant), the labels should be parallel and arranged to be read from the same side.

Labels indicating locality, date, and collector may be printed by hand with a fine-pointed pen or they may be obtained partly printed from a supply house (Figure 32-16). A number of labels may be typed on a sheet of plain paper and photographed, and the labels cut from a print made of the photograph; the size of the print will determine the size of the labels.

The above discussion applies to labels containing data concerning the locality, date, and collector and not to labels identifying the insects. Identifying labels are discussed below, under "Arrangement and Care of the Collection."

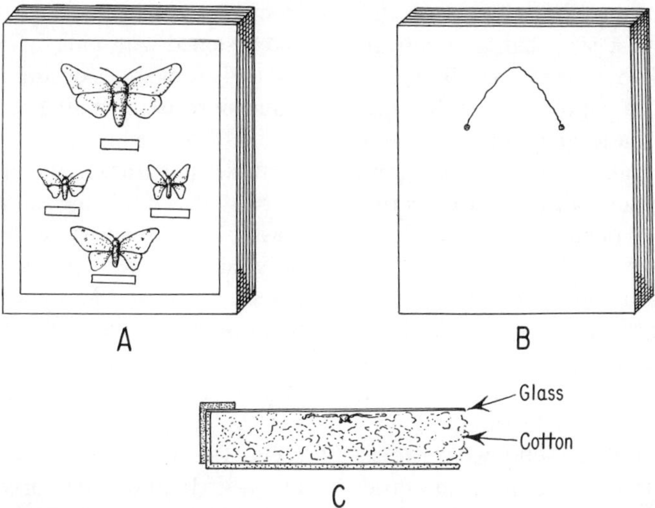

Fig. 32-17. The Riker mount. A, front view; B, back view; C, sectional view showing a specimen in place under the glass on the cotton.

BOXES FOR PINNED INSECTS

Pinned insects should be kept in boxes having a soft bottom that will permit easy pinning. Several types of insect boxes may be purchased from supply houses; the most commonly used type is a wooden box about 9 by 13 by 2½ inches in size with a tight-fitting lid and with an inner bottom of sheet cork; such boxes usually cost from $3.50 to $12.00; the better boxes of this type are called Schmitt boxes. Large collections in institutions are frequently kept in cabinets containing drawers similar in construction to Schmitt boxes. Homemade boxes are quite practical for the beginning collector, and can be made of cigar boxes (if deep enough to take an insect pin) lined with sheet cork, balsa wood, or a soft corrugated cardboard. The material lining the bottom should either be glued to the bottom of the box or be cut so that it fits very tightly in the box. A heavy cardboard box lined in the bottom with corrugated cardboard makes a good temporary box. The corrugated cardboard should be soft enough to take an insect pin easily; otherwise, the pin may be bent as it is put into the box.

DISPLAY MOUNTING

Many collectors may wish to keep their collection in containers where the insects can be easily displayed. Several types of mounts are useful for this purpose. A pinned collection may be easily displayed if it is mounted in glass-topped boxes or in glass-doored wall cabinets; in the latter case the back of the cabinet should be covered with a material that will permit easy pinning. Butterflies, moths, and many other insects may be displayed in Riker mounts—boxes in which the insects are directly under the glass top and on cotton (Figure 32-17). Cases somewhat similar to Riker mounts, but without the cotton and with glass on the top and bottom (Figure 32-18 A and 32-19 A), are useful for displaying one or a few specimens (that is, one or a few in each mount). It is also possible to enclose specimens between sheets of plastic, or to embed specimens in plastic.

RIKER MOUNTS: A Riker mount (Figure 32-17) is a cotton-filled cardboard box with most of the lid removed and replaced with glass, and with the glass top holding the insects in place on the cotton. Riker mounts may be of almost any size (12 by 16 inches is about the largest size that is practical), and are about $\frac{3}{4}$ to 1 inch deep. They can be purchased from supply houses, but they are very easily made at home; all that is required is a box, glass, cotton, and binding tape. Almost any sort of cardboard box may be used; if it is too deep, it can be cut down. Cardboard is most easily cut with a razor blade held in a holder; such holders can be purchased from any hardware store or "five-and-ten" for about 25 cents. A section of the lid is cut out, leaving a margin around the edge of the lid about $\frac{1}{4}$ to $\frac{3}{8}$ inches. A piece of glass (windowpane thickness will do) is then cut to fit on the inside of the lid. Anyone who can use a glass cutter can cut the glass himself, often from discarded pieces; otherwise, he can buy the glass and have it cut at a hardware store. Before the glass is put into the lid, it is well to cover the lid with binding tape. This will greatly improve the appearance of the box, particularly if the box originally had printing on it. Black tape makes the best-looking boxes, but ordinary brown gummed paper, which comes in rolls, will do. A little practice will enable one to cover a homemade box neatly. The glass is held in the lid with strips of gummed paper or masking tape on the four sides, each strip as long as that side of the glass. The cotton used should be of a good grade, with a smooth surface; it should be thick enough to extend a little way above the sides of the box before the lid is put on, and should be cut a little small and stretched to fit the box. If one wishes to hang up this sort of mount, two brass fasteners can be put into the bottom (from the under side, and reinforced on the inside with gummed paper) and a piece of string or wire tied between the two fasteners (Figure 32-17 B). One should be careful to place the insects in the box so that they will be right side up when the box is hung. When large-bodied insects are placed in a Riker mount, a little hole should be teased in the cotton with forceps for the body of the insect. After the specimens are in the box, the lid is put on and fastened with pins or tape.

It is sometimes desirable to mount individual insects in small Riker mounts. Such mounts may be made in any small box (for example, a pillbox), and if the box is not more than 2 or 3 inches wide, a sheet of plastic (which can be cut with scissors) can be used in place of glass.

GLASS MOUNTS: Mounts similar to Riker mounts, but without the cotton and with glass on the top and bottom (Figures 32-18 A and 32-19 A), are excellent for displaying individual moths, butterflies, or other insects. They are made in two general ways: all glass (Figure 32-18) or with a cardboard frame (Figure 32-19). The size will depend on the size of the specimen(s) to be mounted; one should allow a margin on all four sides of the mount, and the mount should be deep enough to accommodate the body and legs of the specimen. Mounts for large-bodied insects such as sphinx moths will be fairly heavy if made entirely of glass, and for such insects a mount with a cardboard frame may be preferable; for smaller insects the all-glass mounts are preferable because they are easier to make.

The only materials needed to make an all-glass mount are glass, a transparent cement, and binding tape. One can obtain scrap window glass free at most hardware stores, and cut it himself. A commercial household cement, which is fast-drying and easily applied, is a suitable cement. Many tapes are suitable, but the best is probably an electrical tape (black, $\frac{3}{4}$ inch wide).

Glass cutting is easy to learn, safe, and much cheaper than having the glass cut professionally. One needs a glass cutter, a perfectly flat surface, a straightedge (for example, a yardstick or ruler), and some way of holding the straightedge firmly against the glass when using the cutter. The glass is scratched *with a single stroke* of the cutter; with practice, one can learn the pressure necessary to make this scratch. The

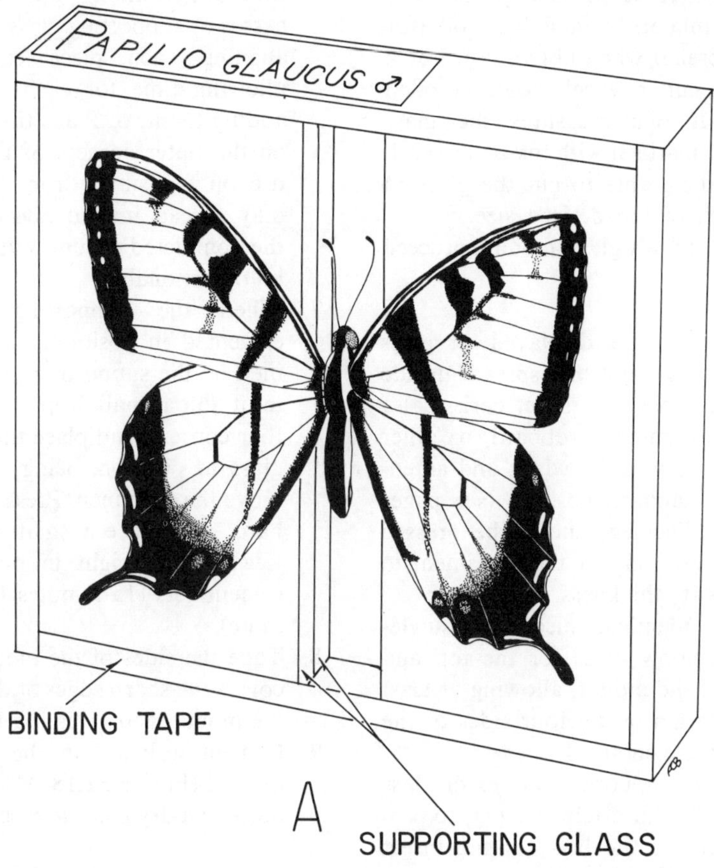

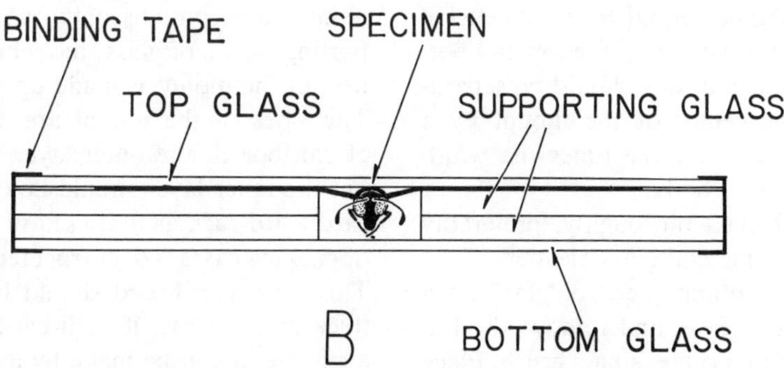

Fig. 32-18. The all-glass mount. A, the completed mount; B, a sectional view of the mount.

glass is broken by pressing *away from* the scratch. Pieces can be broken in the hands or at the edge of a table; narrow pieces should be turned over and tapped firmly (with the reverse end of the cutter) along the scratch line until the glass breaks. The narrower the piece to cut off, the more skill necessary to cut it evenly.

A glass cutter keeps its edge longer if the wheel is immersed in a light oil (for example, kerosene) when not in use. For a better cut, the cutter wheel should be oiled during use. If one measures the glass accurately and marks it with ink before each cut, he should be able to cut the glass to within $\frac{1}{32}$ inch of the desired size.

To make an all-glass mount, proceed as follows:

1. Specimens to be displayed in glass mounts must first be spread upside down on a piece of sheet cork, balsa wood, corrugated cardboard, or other flat surface, with the wings and antennae in a standard position (see pages 689-692). The legs should be pressed close to the body of the specimen, to minimize its thickness.
2. Cut two identical pieces of single-weight window glass for the top and bottom of the mount, allowing at least $\frac{1}{4}$ inch margin on all four sides of the spread specimen(s).
3. Cut enough supporting pieces of glass (single weight or double weight) to provide room for the body of the insect (Figure 32-18 B). These supporting pieces should all be the same size; their length should equal one dimension (usually the shorter) of the top and bottom pieces, and they should be separated in the center of the mount by a distance two or three times the width of the insect's body.
4. Clean all glass thoroughly, preferably with a commercial glass cleaner.
5. Place the bottom piece of glass on a clean flat surface, and remove the lint from it with a camel's-hair brush. Place a small drop of cement on the corners of one end. After removing the lint from one of the supporting pieces, press the piece down in place with the end of the brush handle, line it up with the edges of the bottom piece, and remove any excess cement that oozes out.
6. Continue building up needed thicknesses of supporting glass on each side, aligning each piece carefully, and allowing time for each to set before adding the next. Place the cement only on the outer corners of the glass, and use only a small drop. Some cement may spread inward and be visible in the completed mount, but this will not be objectionable.
7. When the supporting pieces are cemented in position, place the specimen on the supporting pieces and center it. Put a small drop of cement on the four corners, and place the top piece of glass in position, being careful not to move the specimen. Press the top down hard, and place a small weight on it. Leave this weight in place until the cement sets (15 minutes to an hour or more).
8. Tape the sides of the mount. The tape covers the sharp edges of the glass, seals the mount, and gives it a finished look.
9. Cement a label on the top edge, if desired (Figure 32-18 A).
10. Store in a dry place to discourage mold.

A glass mount with a cardboard frame (Figure 32-19) is very similar to the all-glass mount, but contains only one pair of supporting pieces of glass; the remaining thickness of the mount is made up by the frame. The sides of the mount are of two layers of cardboard; the outer layer may be thin, but the inner layer should be of very heavy cardboard such as that used in certain types of packing cases (*not* corrugated cardboard). This inner cardboard should be at least as thick as the glass; if such cardboard is not available, it can be made by cementing two or more thicknesses of ordinary cardboard together. The width of the cardboard strips forming the inner layer of the sides will determine the depth of the mount and the amount of space available for the body and legs of the insect. A good mount of this type requires considerable care in cutting and

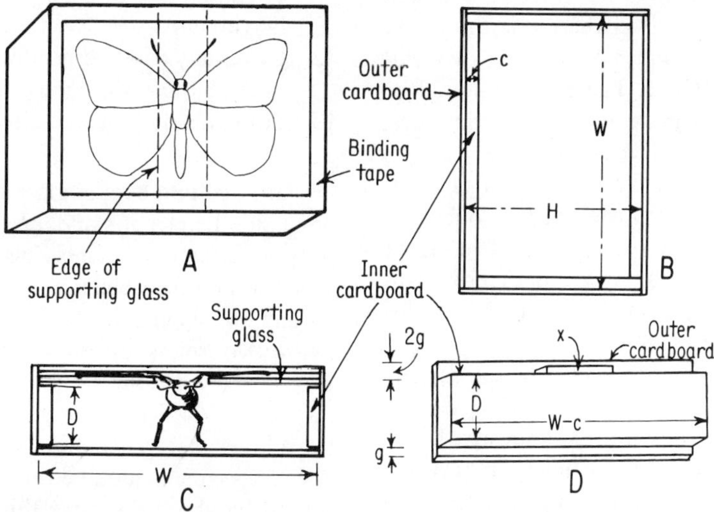

Fig. 32-19. Construction of a glass mount. A, the completed mount; B, top view of the frame, showing the construction of the corners; C, sectional view; D, view from inside of one section of the frame (top or bottom), showing how the two layers of cardboard are put together. *c*, thickness of inner cardboard; *D*, width of inner strip of cardboard; *g*, thickness of glass; *H*, height of case; *W*, width of case; *x*, a cardboard wedge to prevent the supporting glass from slipping sideways.

fitting the parts; the glass and cardboard must be measured and cut very exactly.

To construct a glass mount with a cardboard frame, proceed as follows:

1. Specimens are first spread, as described above for all-glass mounts.
2. Measure the thickness of the spread insect (or of the thickest specimen if more than one is put into the same mount) to determine the depth of the mount; add at least $\frac{1}{8}$ inch for clearance. Let us call this measurement *D*. The inner cardboard layer of the sides will consist of strips having a width of *D*. Mounts with $D = \frac{5}{8}$ inch will accommodate most specimens.
3. Cut two identical pieces of single-weight window glass for the top and bottom of the mount, allowing at least $\frac{1}{4}$ inch margin on all four sides of the spread specimen(s). Let us represent the measurements of this glass as follows: W = its width, H = its height (for most specimens *W* will be greater than *H*), and g = its thickness (single-weight window glass is $\frac{3}{32}$ inch thick; a thicker glass may be used if desired).
4. Cut two pieces of single-weight window glass to support the specimen in the mount. These pieces should be separated in the center of the mount by a distance two or three times the width of the insect's body; they will have a height of *H* and a width of something less than $\frac{1}{2}$ *W*.
5. Measure and cut the cardboard strips that will form the sides of the mount. The outer strips (of ordinary cardboard) will have a width of $D + 3g$ (assuming that all the glass is of the same thickness); the length of each strip will be *W* or *H* (depending on whether it goes at the side, top, or bottom) plus the thickness of the cardboard. It is better to cut these pieces a little long; then they can be cut down to the right length when the frame is put together. Two of the inner strips (heavy card-

board) will have a width of D and a length of $W - c$ (where c is the thickness of the inner strip) and two will be D by $H - c$. These strips should be cut perfectly straight along the sides, preferably with a razor blade.

6. Glue together the two pieces of cardboard that form each of the four sides of the frame (thin outer strip, thick inner strip), as shown in Figure 32-19 D. The left ends of each pair of strips should be even.
7. Put the four sides together, the corners fitted as shown in Figure 32-19 B, and fasten them with an adhesive cellophane tape; any protruding ends of the outer strip are cut off before the frame sections are taped together. Any labels to be placed in the mount are put in at this point.
8. Glue in position the two small pieces labeled x (Figure 32-19 D). These are pieces of the same cardboard that forms the inner layer of the frame; they have a width equal to g and a length equal to the space in the center of the mount between the two supporting pieces of glass. They will prevent the supporting glass from slipping sideways.
9. Clean all glass thoroughly, preferably with a commercial glass cleaner.
10. Place the two supporting pieces of glass in position, and remove the lint from them with a camel's-hair brush. Lay the specimen on these pieces of glass and center it; after removing the lint from the top piece of glass, place it in position on top of the specimen. The top piece of glass is then fastened on with tape; the top glass should be pressed down tightly when it is taped so that the specimen will be held tightly against the supporting glass. Many tapes are suitable, but the best is probably a photographic binding tape (black, $\frac{3}{8}$ inch wide) or an electrical tape (black, $\frac{3}{4}$ inch wide).
11. Remove the lint from the bottom piece of glass, place it in position, and fasten it with tape.
12. Cover any exposed portions of the sides of the mount with tape.
13. Store in a dry place to discourage mold.

If large numbers of glass mounts are to be made, the use of standard sizes will simplify glass cutting, displaying, and storing. Two or more specimens can be put in a mount by placing them in a vertical row (with two series or pieces of supporting glass), and (or) side by side (with at least three series or pieces of supporting glass, the lateral ones being narrower than the middle ones). Specimens mounted in a vertical row should be about the same thickness; if one is thicker, the thinner one may slip. The specimens are held in position by the top piece of glass; hence it is important that this piece be pressed down tightly against the specimen.

PLASTIC MOUNTS: Butterflies, moths, and other insects may be mounted for display between two sheets of a fairly thick transparent plastic; each sheet is bulged out (the plastic can be so shaped when it is heated) where the body of the insect will be. The two sheets are put together, with the insect between, and sealed around the edges with acetone or some other sealing material. Such sheets can be obtained, all ready for use, from some supply houses.

Many types of insects may be embedded in bioplastic. This is a rather involved process, and space does not permit describing it in detail here. The materials needed, together with instructions for their use, can be obtained from supply houses. Ward's Natural Science Establishment has recently prepared a booklet entitled, *How to Embed in Bioplastic,* which is a complete manual on the subject.

The above are only a few of the possible types of mountings useful for displaying insects; an ingenious collector should be able to devise many additional types.

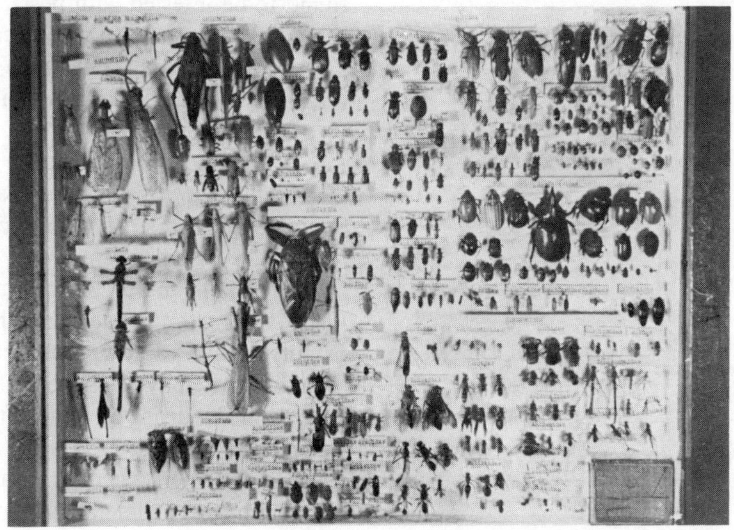

Fig. 32-20. A synoptic insect collection.

ARRANGEMENT AND CARE OF THE COLLECTION

The arrangement of an insect collection and the method of handling the identification labels will depend largely on the size of the collection and the extent to which the collector is able to get it identified. For a small collection that is housed in one or a few boxes, an arrangement similar to that in Figure 32-20 is suggested. It is unlikely that anyone except the specialist will have the material in his collection identified further than to family, and for many collectors, particularly the beginner, it will be difficult enough to carry the identification that far. The simplest arrangement, therefore, is to have the specimens arranged by order and family, with the order label (containing order name and common name) on a separate pin, and the family label (containing family and common names) either on a separate pin or on the pin of the first insect in the row of specimens in that family. There are various ways of arranging the specimens in a small collection, but the arrangement should be neat and systematic and the labels should be easily seen.

In larger collections, such as those of specialists or those in museums, where the specimens are identified to species, the species determination is usually put on a plain white or bordered label about $\frac{1}{2}$ by $1\frac{1}{4}$ inches in size, and the label placed low on the pin against the bottom of the box. This label contains the complete scientific name (genus, species, subspecies if any, and the name of the describer), the name of the person making the determination, and the date the determination was made (Figure 32-21). In large collections where the specimens are kept in trays in cabinets, each tray contains several cork-bottomed boxes, with specimens of just one species in each box (Figure 32-22).

All insect collections are subject to attack by dermestid beetles, ants, and other museum pests, and if the collection is to last any length of time, certain precautions must be taken to protect it from these pests. Various materials may be used for this purpose, but one material commonly used is naphthalene (in flake or ball form). Naphthalene flakes can be put into a small cardboard pillbox that is firmly attached to the bottom of the insect box (usually in one

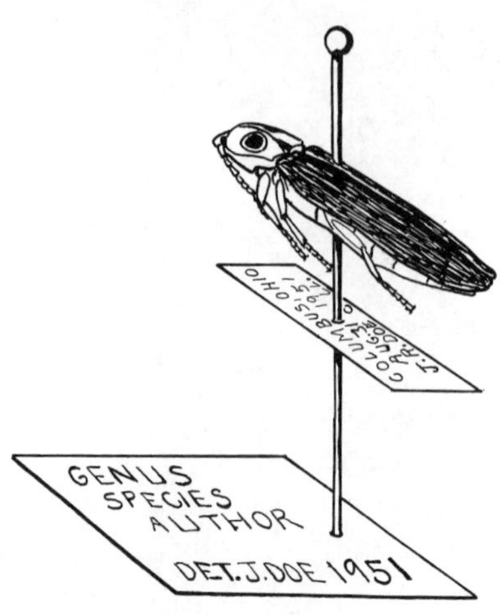

Fig. 32-21. The identification label, giving the scientific name of the insect and the name of the person identifying the specimen.

corner), and has a few pin holes in it. Paradichlorobenzene can also be used, but it volatilizes more rapidly than naphthalene and must be renewed at more frequent intervals. To protect specimens in Riker mounts, naphthalene flakes should be sprinkled under the cotton when the mount is being made. A collection should be checked periodically to make sure that plenty of repellent is present. If a box is found to be infested with pests, it should be fumigated (for example, with carbon bisulfide). Many good collections have been ruined by pests because the collector failed to protect them.

The collector will soon realize that when an insect dries, it becomes very brittle and is easily broken. All insect specimens must be handled with extreme care if they are to be kept intact. A specimen that has lost its legs, antennae, or other parts is usually of little value. If a part of a specimen breaks off, it may be fastened back on by means of a drop of glue or household cement. In the case of insects with a long slender abdomen, such as damselflies and dragonflies, it is sometimes advisable to reinforce the abdomen with a slender bristle (for example, a brush bristle) or a small-sized insect pin.

PRESERVATION OF INSECTS IN FLUIDS

Any type of insect can be preserved in fluid. Insects may be preserved in fluid temporarily until one has an opportunity to pin them, and many collectors prefer to store their collection in fluid rather than dried in envelopes or pillboxes. However, specimens preserved in fluids are usually not so easily examined as those on pins or points, and in general any insect that *can* be pre-

Fig. 32-22. A drawer of a large insect collection.

served dry should be mounted on a pin or point.

Some insects cannot be pinned and must be preserved in fluids. All soft-bodied adult insects, such as mayflies, stoneflies, caddisflies, aphids, and the like, should be preserved in fluids; if pinned, they shrivel and become distorted. Most insect nymphs, particularly the soft-bodied ones, should be preserved in fluids. All larvae (except those that are to be inflated) should be preserved in fluid; the smaller larvae are usually mounted on microscope slides for study. Most arthropods other than insects (myriapods, crustaceans, and arachnids) should be preserved in fluid. Many minute insects, such as springtails, lice, fleas, and minute flies, are usually preserved in fluid until they are mounted on microscope slides.

For small hard-bodied insects such as lice and fleas, for such nymphs as those of dragonflies, damselflies, and mayflies, and for soft-bodied adult insects, probably the best killing and preserving fluid is ethyl alcohol. Insects may be killed in 95 percent alcohol, and after a day or so transferred for permanent preservation to a 70 or 75 percent solution; if the specimens are very small in proportion to the amount of alcohol used, they may be killed and preserved in 75 or 80 percent alcohol.

Alcohol is satisfactory as a preservative for insect larvae, but is usually unsatisfactory as a killing agent. Improper killing methods will result in larvae that are discolored, shrunken, inflated, or distorted. The two principal methods of killing larvae are by chemicals or by heat. Several chemical solutions may be used, but the most important ones are as follows:

X. A. Mixture:

Xylene	1 part
95% ethyl alcohol	1 part

Larvae killed with this mixture should be transferred to 75 percent alcohol after 24 hours and preserved in the alcohol.

KAAD Mixture:

Kerosene	1 part
95% ethyl alcohol	7 to 10 parts
Glacial acetic acid	2 parts
Dioxane	1 part

If this mixture is used, the amount of kerosene should be reduced for such soft-bodied larvae as maggots. Commercial isopropyl alcohol (rubbing alcohol) may be used in place of the ethyl alcohol; the dioxane is added only to make the kerosene miscible, and may be omitted. Larvae killed in this mixture are ready for transfer to alcohol for storage after from ½ to 4 hours; they become somwhat clear if left in this mixture too long. Specimens killed in this mixture are best preserved in 95 percent alcohol.

Isopropyl alcohol is ordinary rubbing alcohol and is the best material for killing larvae if the above materials are not available.

Any of these killing agents are likely to remove the bright colors of larvae, especially greens, yellows, and reds. All known killing and preserving fluids are likely to destroy some colors.

If living larvae can be brought into the laboratory, many collectors prefer to kill them with heat. The living larva is dropped into hot water (180 degrees Fahrenheit to boiling) and left there until the water cools; some larvae, such as white grubs, may darken after they are placed in preserving alcohol unless they are boiled for a short time. Most larvae killed in hot water should be preserved in 75 percent (or stronger) ethyl alcohol.

Most larvae are preserved in 75 to 80 percent ethyl alcohol, but several other preservatives may be used. The following are the combinations most often used:

1.	95% ethyl alcohol	100 parts
	Distilled water	100 parts
	Formaldehyde	13 parts
	Glacial acetic acid	5 parts
2.	95% ethyl alcohol	55 parts

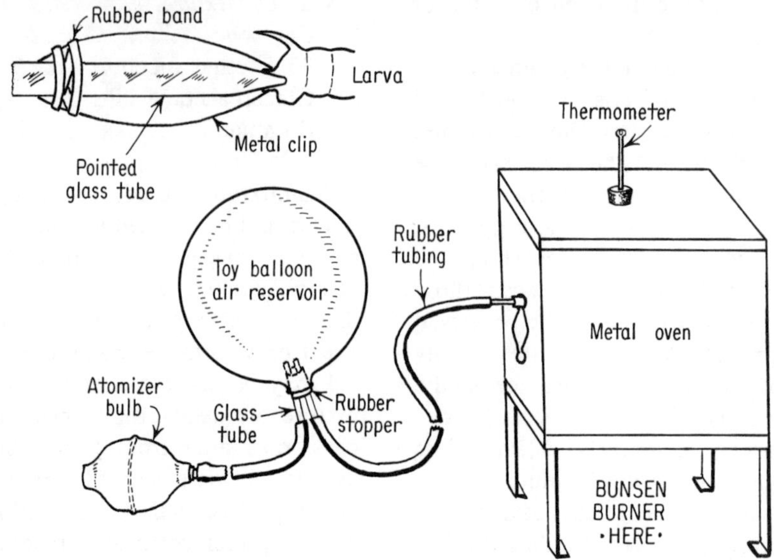

Fig. 32-23. Device for inflating insect larvae. A toy rubber balloon is used as an air reservoir and is maintained full by pressing the atomizer bulb; the air tube from the reservoir is attached to the posterior end of the caterpillar by means of metal clips, as shown in the upper drawing. The caterpillar is held in a heated metal oven while being inflated, and kept there until dried.

	Distilled water	35 parts
	Formaldehyde	5 parts
	Glacial acetic acid	5 parts
3.	95% ethyl alcohol	15 parts
	Formaldehyde	6 parts
	Glacial acetic acid	2 parts
	Distilled water	30 parts

(This mixture is called Kahle's solution.)

A problem always encountered when specimens are preserved in fluids is the evaporation of the fluid. Rubber corks are preferable to ordinary corks, and it is often advisable to use oversized corks that do not extend very far into the bottle. All vials should be well filled with fluid, and should be examined at least once or twice a year so that evaporated fluid may be replenished. Evaporation may be retarded by covering the corks with some sort of sealing material such as paraffin or petroleum jelly; another method is to place a number of alcohol-filled stoppered vials in a large jar, fill the jar with alcohol, and seal the jar with a rubber gasket.

INFLATING LARVAE

The most satisfactory method of preserving the natural colors of larvae, particularly in caterpillars, is by inflation. This is not a simple process, and not many collectors take the trouble to preserve their larvae this way. Larvae that are starved a day or so before inflating make better specimens, for starvation rids the intestine of newly consumed food that might produce a dark streak in the inflated specimen. A larva to be inflated is killed in a killing bottle and is removed as soon as it appears dead. It is then placed on a piece of absorbent paper, and pressure is applied by means of a glass tube near the head until the intestine starts to protrude from the anus. The protruded portion should then be punctured, and the body contents squeezed out by pressing the glass tube back along the body. When the specimen has been completely deflated, the tip of a glass inflating tube (coated with oil or vaseline so that it will not stick to the dried specimen) is inserted into the posterior end of the larva and fastened there with a clamp (Figure 32-23). Air is then applied through this tube until the larva is inflated. The inflated larva is placed in a small oven, and the air pressure in the larva is maintained until the larva has become completely dry, which takes from 10 minutes to an hour. Excessive heat should be avoided because it may injure the specimen. When the specimen is dry, the inflating tube is removed. The specimen may be mounted in various ways; one method is to attach it with household cement to an artificially colored dry leaf reinforced underneath with stiff paper. Inflated specimens are very fragile and must be handled with care.

PACKING AND SHIPPING INSECTS

We are concerned here with the transporting or shipping of *dead* insects; before transporting or shipping living insects, one should check with the quarantine officials and the postal authorities.

One may transport an insect collection by automobile or ship it by mail without damage if certain precautions are taken. Since all students of insects may eventually have occasion to transport or ship insects, and since many that are shipped arrive in a damaged condition, we are offering here some suggestions that may help prevent damage to material that is transported or shipped.

Pinned specimens should be inserted firmly into the bottom of the insect box, preferably with pinning forceps; the bottom of the box should be of a material that will hold the pins firmly. Large specimens should be braced with extra pins to prevent them from swinging around and damaging other specimens; long appendages, or a long abdomen, should be braced and supported by extra pins. A sheet of cardboard cut to fit the inside of the box (with a slot cut out to facilitate removal) should be placed over the top of the pinned specimens, and the space between this and the lid of the box should be filled with cotton, cellucotton, or a similar material. One should *never* include in a box of pinned specimens vials of insects preserved in fluid, regardless of how firmly the vials may appear to be fastened in the box; the rough handling the average box gets when going through the mail may dislodge even the most "firmly" attached vial and ruin the specimens.

When specimens preserved in fluids are to be shipped, measures should be taken to protect the specimens in the containers. The containers should be completely filled with fluid, and it is sometimes desirable to add cotton or some similar material in the container to prevent the specimens from bouncing about. Small and delicate larvae, such as mosquito larvae, should be in vials so completely filled with fluid that there is not even an air bubble in the vial. One method of accomplishing this is to use glass tubes stoppered with rubber stoppers. The vial containing the specimens is filled to the brim, a hypodermic needle is put through the stopper, and the stopper is carefully inserted into the end of the tube. The excess fluid comes out through the hypodermic needle, and when the needle is removed, the stopper seals and (if the process is carefully done) there is no air bubble inside the tube.

If two or more containers of insects in fluid are packed in the same box, they should be wrapped in wide strips of cellucotton or some similar soft material so that no two vials are in contact.

Insects in glass or Riker mounts can ordinarily withstand considerable jolting without damage, but care should be taken that the glass of these mounts does not get broken. Such mounts should be packed in an abundance of soft packing material, and no two of them should touch each other in the box.

Insect material mounted on microscope slides should be shipped in wooden or heavy cardboard slide boxes, preferably boxes in which the slides are inserted into grooves and are on edge in the box. Strips of a soft material should be placed between the slides and the lid of the box, so that the slides do not bounce about.

Dried specimens in envelopes or pillboxes should be packed in such a way that the specimens do not bounce around inside the box. Pillboxes should be padded inside with cellucotton to immobilize the specimens, and boxes containing envelopes should be filled with cotton or cellucotton.

Boxes containing pinned insects, insects in fluids, microscope slides, or dried specimens in envelopes or pillboxes that are to be sent through the mail should be packed inside a larger box (a wooden box or strong carton), surrounded by at least 2 inches of packing material. Insects preserved in fluid should be particularly well packed and in strong containers. Most types of insect specimens can be sent through the mail without damage if well packed; pinned specimens, particularly large or relatively fragile specimens, are most likely to be damaged in shipment, and particular care should be taken in packing them.

Whenever material is shipped through the mail, an accompanying letter should be sent to the addressee, notifying him of the shipment. Packages of dead insects sent through the mail are usually marked "Dried (or Preserved) Insects for Scientific Study," and are sent by parcel post. It is well to mark such packages for gentle handling in transit, though this does not always ensure that they will not get rough treatment. Material shipped to points inside the United States should be insured, though it may be difficult to place an evaluation on some material. The statement "No Commercial Value" on a box shipped from one country to another will facilitate the box getting through customs.

ENTOMOLOGICAL SUPPLIES

Most of the supplies needed for making an insect collection can be obtained from supply houses. The leading biological supply houses in the United States are as follows:

Bio Metal Associates, Box 346, Beverly Hills, Calif.

Braun-Knecht-Heimann Co., 1400 Sixteenth Street, San Francisco 19, Calif.

Carolina Biological Supply Co., Burlington, N. C.

W. H. Curtin & Co., 4220 Jefferson Ave., Houston, Texas.

General Biological Supply House, Inc., 8200 S. Hoyne Ave., Chicago 20, Ill.

Robert G. Wind Co., 702 Ocean View Ave., Monterey, Calif.

Ward's Natural Science Establishment, Inc., 3000 Ridge Road East, Rochester 9, N. Y.

A great many concerns throughout the country handle optical equipment such as microscopes and lenses, laboratory supplies, and scientific instruments. Some of the leading suppliers of such equipment (many of whom also handle entomological supplies) are as follows:

American Optical Co., Box A, Buffalo 15, N. Y.

Bausch and Lomb Optical Co., 635 St. Paul Street, Rochester 2, N. Y.

Braun-Knecht-Heimann Co., 1400 Sixteenth Street, San Francisco 19, Calif.

Carpocapsa, 375 Lehigh Ave., East Liberty Station, Pittsburgh, Pa.

Central Scientific Co., 1700 Irving Park Road, Chicago 13, Ill.

Clay-Adams Co., 44 East Twenty-third Street, New York 10, N. Y.

A. Daigger and Co., 159 West Kinzie Street, Chicago 10, Ill.

Dennoyer-Geppert Co., 5235 Ravenwood Avenue, Chicago, Ill.

Fisher Scientific Co., 711 Forbes Street, Pittsburgh 19, Pa.

General Scientific Equipment Co., 2706 West Huntingdon Street, Philadelphia 32, Pa.

The Kauffman-Lattimer Co., 263 North Front Street, Columbus 15, Ohio.
E. Leitz, Inc., 304 Hudson Street, New York 13, N. Y.
New York Scientific Supply Co., 28 West Thirtieth Street, New York 1, N. Y.
Standard Scientific Supply Corp., 34 West Fourth Street, New York 12, N. Y.
W. M. Welch Scientific Co., 1515 Sedgwick Street, Chicago 10, Ill.

REFERENCES ON COLLECTING AND PRESERVING INSECTS

Beirne, B. P. 1955. Collecting, preparing, and preserving insects. Can. Dept. Agri., Entomol. Div. Publ. 932; 133 pp., 108 f.

Borror, Donald J., and Arthur C. Borror. 1961. Glass mounts for displaying Lepidoptera. Turtox News, 39(12):298-300; 2 f.

DeLong, D. M., and R. H. Davidson. 1936. Methods of collecting and preserving insects. Columbus, Ohio: Ohio State University Press. 20 pp., 11 f.

Edwards, J. Gordon. 1963. Spreading-blocks for butterfly wings. Turtox News, 41(1): 16-19; 3 f.

Klotz, Alexander B. 1932. Directions for collecting and preserving insects. Rochester, N.Y.: Ward's Natural Science Establishment, Inc. 29 pp., 30 f.

Mansuy, Margaret C. 1929. Collection and preservation of insects for use in the study of agriculture. U.S. Dep. Agr., Farmers' Bull. No. 1601; 19 pp., 18 f.

Oldroyd, Harold. 1958. Collecting, preserving and studying insects. New York: The Macmillan Company. 327 pp., 135 f., 1 map, 15 pl.

Oman, P. W., and Arthur D. Cushman. 1948. Collection and preservation of insects. U.S. Dep. Agr., Misc. Pub. No. 601; 42 pp., 42 f.

Peterson, Alvah. 1948. Larvae of insects. An introduction to nearctic species. Part I. Lepidoptera and plant infesting Hymenoptera. Ann Arbor, Mich.: J. W. Edwards. 315 pp.; illus. (Data on collecting and preserving larvae, p. 4-10.)

Peterson, Alvah. 1953 (7th ed.). A manual of entomological techniques. Ann Arbor, Mich.: J. W. Edwards, Publisher, Inc. v+367 pp., 182 pl.

Ross, H. H. 1941. How to collect and preserve insects. Illinois Nat. Hist. Survey, Cir. 39. 48 pp., 53 f.

Valentine, J. Manson. 1942. On the preparation and preservation of insects, with particular reference to Coleoptera. Smithsonian Inst. Misc. Collections, 103(6):1-16; 5 f.

Wagstaffe, Reginald, and J. Havelock Fidler (ed.). 1955. The preservation of natural history specimens. Vol. I. Invertebrates. New York: Philosophical Library, Inc. xiii+205 pp., 129 f.

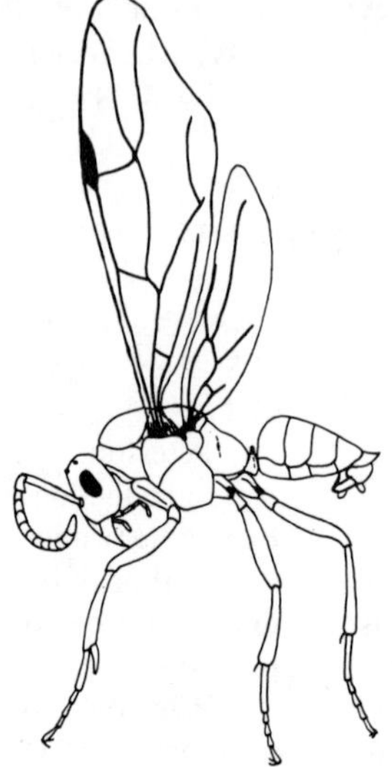

33

Activities and Projects in Insect Study

There are almost innumerable things to do in studying insects; some can be done by almost anyone, but others require particular facilities and a background of training. Activities with insects can be geared to any grade level and they constitute an essential part of the learning process; some may serve as group or class projects.

COLLECTIONS

Collecting is the first step in getting acquainted with insects. The suggestions given in the preceding chapter for collecting insects need not be repeated here, but we may suggest some types of collections that a student may make.

SYNOPTIC COLLECTIONS: A synoptic collection is one in which many different types of insects are represented and the specimens are arranged systematically (Figure 32-20). The beginning student usually makes this sort of collection. A synoptic collection that is fairly complete is useful to a teacher in providing him with specimens of many types of insects. The completeness with which a synoptic collection is labeled will depend primarily on its size and the use to which it is put. Small collections need to be labeled only to order and family (including common names); large collections may be labeled to species.

COLLECTIONS OF SHOWY INSECTS: Many beginning or amateur collectors may be interested principally in collecting the larger and more showy insects in order to have a more attractive or striking collection. Such collections are of value, but the collector will miss most of the insects if he pays no attention to the smaller or less striking species. The various methods of preparing insects for a collection have been discussed in Chapter 32; additional suggestions are given below under "Displays."

COLLECTIONS OF SPECIAL TAXONOMIC GROUPS: Many people who collect insects eventually become interested in a particular order or family and concentrate their efforts on that group. In this way one becomes acquainted with individual species and their taxonomy, identification, distribution, and habits. By concentrating his efforts on a particular group, and by contacts and exchanges with other collectors interested in that group, a collector may build up a sizeable collection and be in a position to contribute to our knowledge of that group by his publications. Everyone interested in entomology, regardless of the field in which he is primarily interested, should concentrate on a particular taxonomic group; a certain satisfaction comes with a thorough knowledge of even a small group of animals, and such a study can prove to be a very interesting hobby for the person whose major interest or occupation is in another field.

ILLUSTRATIVE COLLECTIONS: Collections made to illustrate various things about insects can be very useful to a teacher. A collection of the life stages of different insects will illustrate life history and metamorphosis. A collection of insects beneficial to man, or of insects injurious to man, will emphasize the economic importance of these animals (Figure 33-1). A collection of insects peculiar to a specific habitat (for example, wood-borers, aquatic insects, flower-frequenting insects, gall insects, and the like), or with particular habits (for example, predators, parasites, or scavengers) will point out certain aspects of insect ecology. A collection might be made up to illustrate mimicry or protective coloration in insects. A series of many specimens of a particular species will illustrate the phenomenon of variation.

DISPLAYS

Displays involving insects may range from an incidental or temporary exhibit to a more or less elaborate insect zoo or museum, and they serve primarily as teaching devices. Good displays may get across certain information or arouse interest, but in many cases they are of value chiefly to those who prepare them. The subject of

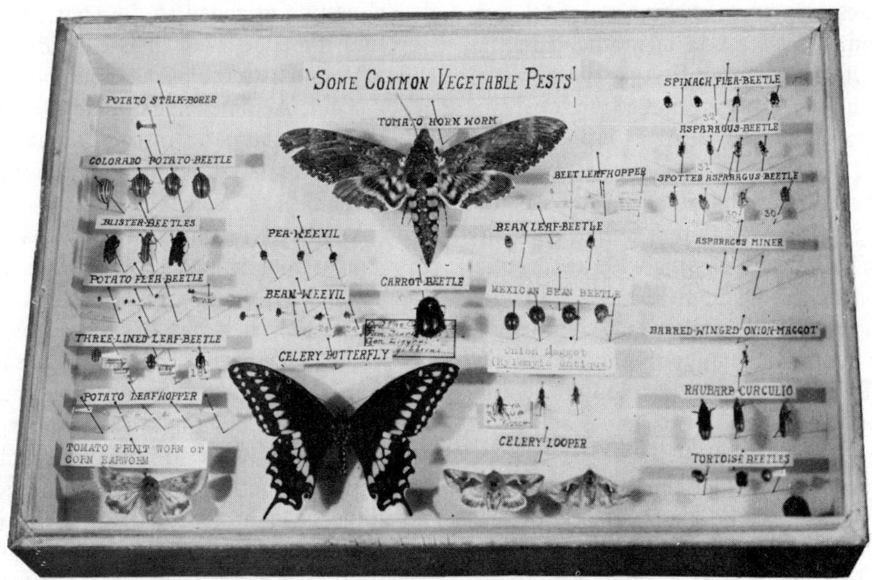

Fig. 33-1. An illustrative collection showing some common insect pests of vegetables.

displays is likely to be of more interest to the teacher or camp counselor than to the student.

DISPLAY COLLECTIONS

Collections make excellent displays, especially if they are attractively arranged and adequately labeled. Various methods of mounting insects for display have been discussed in Chapter 32 (under Display Mounting, page 693). One who wishes to prepare an attractive display will do well to study the techniques used in stores, museums, and fairs; there are many tricks to attract attention.

A collection set up in such a way that looking at it requires manipulation by the observer will attract more attention than it would otherwise. Small pinned insects, for example, can be mounted on a rotating disc in a closed box, with the disc turned by a crank or dial on the outside of the box, and arranged so that a turn of the disc brings one insect at a time into view through an opening in the top of the box. An even better effect is achieved if a magnifying glass is set in this opening and the insects so placed that, as the disc is turned, they come into sharp focus under a light designed to illuminate the specimen. A magnifying glass may be mounted over a box of mounted insects so that it can be moved along the box and placed above any specimen the observer wishes to see.

CHARTS

Charts are standard visual aids in the teaching of many different subjects. Many types of wall charts dealing with insects may be obtained from supply houses, but it is often a better teaching technique to have one or more students prepare the charts. Students with a flair for art should be particularly helpful in preparing displays of this sort.

Charts may be made in black and white or color, and may be diagrammatic or pictorial, or both. They may also be made by using a combination of drawing and lettering together with actual specimens; specimens can be attached to a chart in vials or in glass-topped mounts.

One may get ideas for charts by examining textbooks or supply-house catalogues. Charts showing anatomical characteristics of insects, such as the parts of the body (Figure 2-1), wing venation (Figure 2-8), types of antennae (Figure 2-9), and the like, are very useful in teaching. Many charts do not require great artistic ability. Charts depicting life histories are very useful and can be made to show what the different stages look like, where they are found, what they do, and the time of year they occur. Such charts can often be improved by adding to them actual specimens of the various stages, together with materials in which the insects have lived or on which they have fed.

A type of chart that is seldom available from a supply house is one showing the habitat relationships of insects. A chart made to show the insects living on a particular species of plant might consist of a central drawing of that plant, with various types of insects included in the drawing (insects occurring on the different parts of the plant) and adequately labeled. Actual specimens of these insects, suitably mounted for display, can be attached to the chart, possibly around the edge, with lines extending from the specimens to the part of the plant where they occur. A somewhat similar chart might be made for aquatic insects, showing just where in an aquatic habitat the various types of insects occur.

Another type of insect chart that is seldom available from supply houses is one depicting food chains involving insects. A food chain is a series of organisms, each of which feeds on the next one in the chain. A chart showing this sort of thing could be fairly specific, depicting a particular species of plant (the basic link in the chain), a few species that feed on it (including, for example, a caterpillar), a few species that feed on each of these (for example, a ground beetle that is predaceous on the caterpillar and an ichneumon that is parasitic on it),

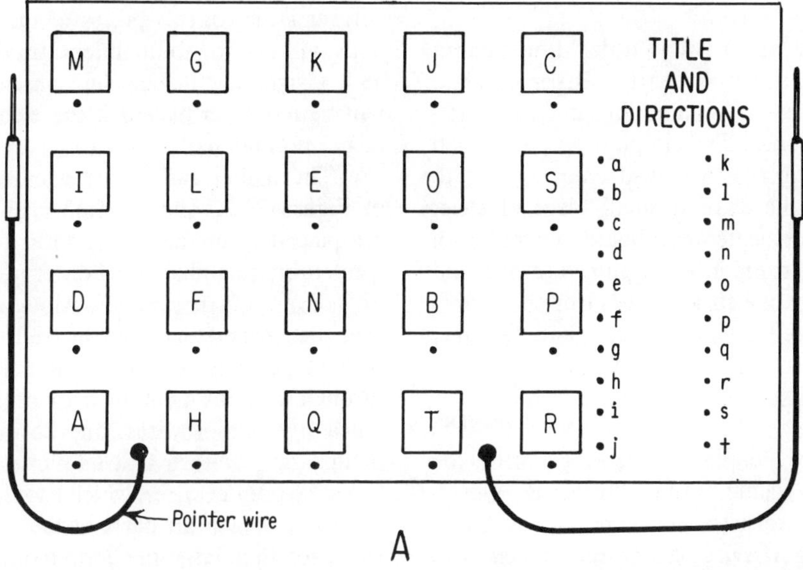

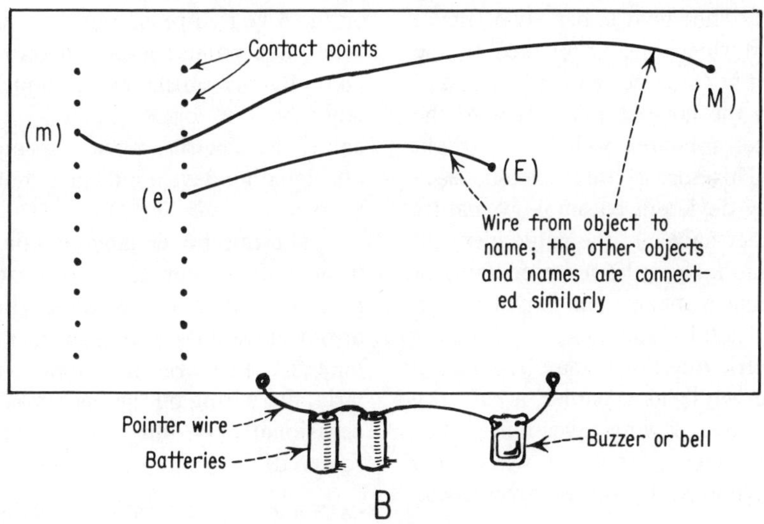

Fig. 33-2. Diagram of a namer. A, front view; B, rear view. *A-T,* pictures or specimens of the objects to be named; *a-t,* names of the objects on the board; the dots represent contact points.

others that feed on these (such as insects or other animals that prey upon or parasitize the ground beetle and the ichneumon), and so on. On the other hand, the chart could be more general and show only certain categories, such as plant-feeding insects, parasitic insects, predaceous insects, and scavenging insects, with arrows on the chart to indicate the food relationships. Such charts could contain the names or drawings of the insects involved in the chains, or actual specimens of the insects could be attached to the chart.

There is usually little difficulty in attaching to a wall chart a Riker or glass mount or a vial containing an insect preserved in fluid. The simplest way to attach a pinned insect to a wall chart is first to fasten to the chart a small piece of sheet cork or corrugated cardboard covered with white paper; the insect is pinned to this, and a small boxlike structure of clear sheet plastic is placed over the insect and fastened to the sheet of cork or cardboard.

ELECTRIC QUESTIONERS

Many people are familiar with the children's game called "Electric Questioner." It consists of a large display board containing a series of pictured objects with the names in a mixed order at the bottom. On the board are a number of electric contact points, one by each picture and one by each name. The board has two metal pointers, and when one is touched to the contact point next to one of the pictures and the other to the contact point next to the correct name, a buzzer sounds or a light flashes on. This sort of thing can be used as a teaching device in entomology, nature study, or other subjects; the game element, the manipulation, and the noise or lights of these questioners make them popular with children and adults alike.

An electric questioner may be made in one of three ways: as a namer, a category questioner, or a keying questioner. The general arrangement and the wiring are somewhat different in these three questioners.

NAMERS: Namers can be used with insects or with such other things as birds, fish, plants, minerals, or maps. The materials needed are a board (a piece of heavy cardboard, pressed wood, or plywood), objects to be named (pictures or specimens), labels with the names of the objects on the questioner, contact points (stove bolts or brass paper fasteners), insulated bell wire, two dry cells (or a transformer, if house current is used), two pieces of metal (large nails will do) for the pointers, friction tape, and a signaling device. Such a questioner will be more permanent if the electric contacts are soldered.

The namer can be arranged as shown in Figure 33-2. The specimens or pictures are placed in mixed order, with the names (preferably in alphabetical order) at the side or bottom of the board. Alongside each specimen or picture, and at each name, a contact point is inserted in a hole drilled through the board. On the back of the board are a number of wires, one between each picture or specimen and its name.

The pointer wires, which should be long enough to reach all parts of the board, are run through holes at the bottom of the board and attached to the batteries and the signaling device. The signaling device may be a light bulb, buzzer, or bell that will operate on the 6-volt current from the two dry cells. When one pointer is placed on the contact point by the object to be named and the other on the contact point by the correct name, the electric circuit is completed and the signaling device indicates that the name is correct.

The questioner may contain anywhere from half a dozen to many dozen objects. It is often desirable to attach the pictures or objects and the names in such a way that they can be changed from time to time; similarly, the wiring on the back may be shifted occasionally (if the connections are not soldered).

CATEGORY QUESTIONERS: This type of questioner indicates into which of two or more categories any particular object should be placed. It might be designed, for example, to indicate whether an insect is beneficial or harmful to man, whether it is predaceous or plant-feeding, or in what order it is classified. Such a questioner has many possibilities and can be made with many objects besides insects.

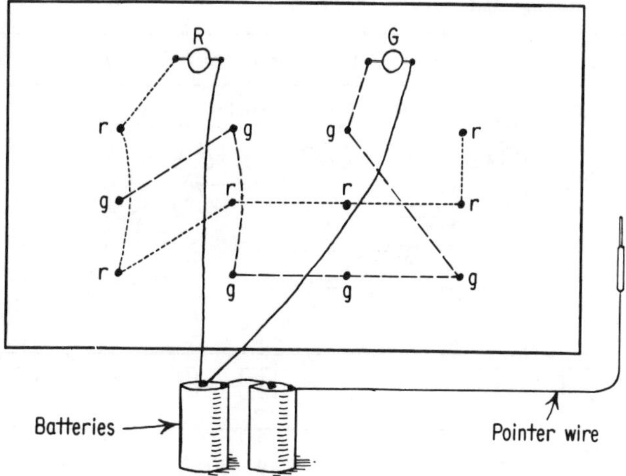

Fig. 33-3. Diagram of a category questioner. *G*, green light bulb (for one category); *R*, red light bulb (for another category); *g*, contact points of the objects in category *G*; *r*, contact points of the objects in category *R*.

The best signaling device here is a series of colored lights, one color for each category. In a questioner involving beneficial and harmful insects, a red light might be used to indicate a harmful insect and a green light a beneficial insect. The other materials needed for this type of questioner are much the same as for a namer except that there will be only one pointer wire, and a different light bulb (and socket) will be used for each category.

On the back of the board (Figure 33-3) a wire is run from one terminal of the red bulb (if red is used for a particular category) to the contact points of all the objects that fall into this category; another wire is similarly connected for each additional signal bulb, from one terminal of the bulb to the contact points of all the objects falling into that category. From the other terminal of each bulb a wire is run to one pole of the batteries; the pointer wire is attached to the other pole of the batteries. When the pointer is placed on the contact point of any object on the board, a light will flash on, indicating the category into which the object falls.

KEYING QUESTIONERS: Any relatively simple analytical key (for example, to the major orders of insects, the major groups in the animal kingdom, or the trees in the school yard) can be set up on an electric questioner. Names, pictures, or specimens of the forms to be keyed out can be placed at the top or around the border of the board and the key plotted at the bottom or in the center of the board. A plan for a questioner of this type is illustrated in Figure 33-4.

Contact points are placed at each object to be keyed out and also on the key diagram. At each forking of the key diagram, there is a different contact point for each form or group that is reached by going out along that line. The key characters may be written along the lines of the diagram or printed on a piece of paper pasted on the board.

In the wiring of this type of questioner, there is a separate wire for each group or form keyed out. The contact points of the objects in each group are connected to one another and to a set of points on the key diagram. The pointers are connected as in a namer, so that when one pointer is touched to the contact point of the form to be keyed out and the other pointer is touched to the correct contact point at each fork in the key diagram, the signal will operate.

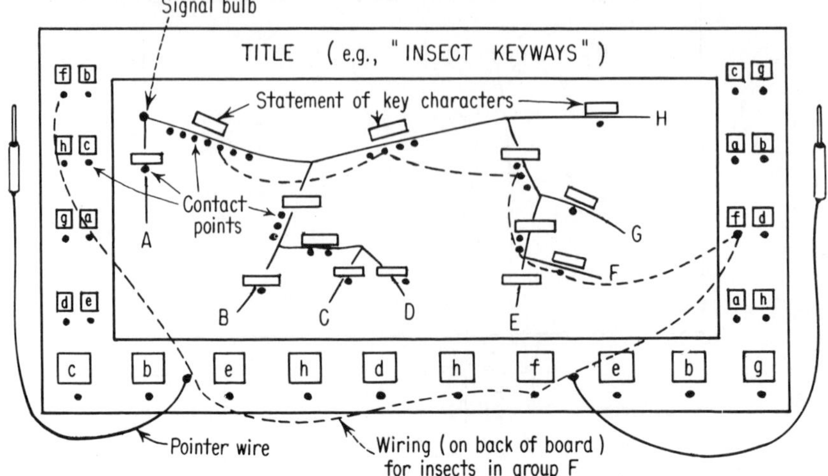

Fig. 33-4. Diagram of a keying questioner.

THE WORK OF INSECTS

Displays consisting of objects showing the work of insects will illustrate the ways in which insects are important to man, and also illustrate the apparent ingenuity and engineering skill many insects exhibit. Such displays could be classified as insect damage, the beneficial work of insects, and insect homes, but no sharp line should be drawn between these categories.

INSECT DAMAGE: Most insect damage is done by feeding, and since insects feed in various ways and on a great many different things, the possibilities are almost endless for displaying objects that have been fed upon by insects. Leaf-feeding insects damage the leaf in different ways: Some chew from the edge of the leaf and may either remove large pieces or consume the entire leaf; some chew holes in the leaf; some mine between the two surfaces of the leaf, and some insects suck the sap from the leaf, causing a yellowing or browning of the leaf or causing it to wilt and curl. Most insects' style of feeding on a leaf is quite characteristic, and a collection of leaves fed upon by different insects makes a very instructive type of display. Different wood-boring insects vary in the types of tunnels they make: Some bore in or just under the bark, and many excavate a rather elaborate system of galleries; others bore into the wood of trees or logs, making galleries of different sizes and shapes; still others bore into seasoned wood. The galleries of bark beetles (Scolýtidae), long-horned wood-boring beetles, metallic wood-boring beetles, powder-post beetles, carpenter ants, termites, and others make very interesting displays. The work of insects attacking household goods can be demonstrated by clothing or carpeting that has been attacked by clothes moths or carpet beetles, meal or flour infested with various moths or beetles, or books that have been damaged by book lice or termites. Insect galls make interesting displays. Twig injury by the egg laying of such insects as cicadas or treehoppers illustrates this type of insect damage.

THE BENEFICIAL WORK OF INSECTS: Insects benefit man in many different ways, and displays can be made to illustrate how these benefits are provided. In the case of the products of commercial value derived from insects (such as honey and beeswax from bees, silk from the silkworm, shellac from certain scale insects, or tannic acid from certain insect galls), displays can be made up to show how these various products are obtained. Displays illustrating the role of insects in pollinating plants can be made by using a combination of actual materials and charts; for example, the insects and plants concerned, and comparative yields of fruits with and without insect pollination. Specimens of caterpillars or other insects that have been attacked by parasitic insects will illustrate the role of some insects in keeping others under control. These are but a few of the displays that will emphasize the benefits man derives from insects.

INSECT HOMES: This category overlaps to some extent that of insect damage. For any sort of boring insect, whether it bores into a leaf, stem, wood, fruit, or other material, the gallery it makes serves as its "home," at least during a part of its life cycle. Similarly, galls provide a home for insects, not only for those that originally induced the gall growth in the plant, but often for many others also, after the original inhabitants have left. The tent caterpillar, webworms, and others make a nest by tying leaves together with silk. Cocoons provide a "home" for insect pupae. Many wasps construct fairly elaborate nests of mud or a papery material. Many caterpillars roll or fold up a leaf and live inside the roll or fold. Many insects (bagworms, certain leaf beetles, caddisflies, and others) construct cases in which the larva lives. All these things and many others provide excellent objects for a display of insect homes.

MISCELLANEOUS DISPLAYS

Several other types of displays, which do not readily fall into the categories discussed above, may be mentioned here. A classroom display, for example, may include a bulletin board for pictures, photographs, clippings, and the like, a bookshelf for reference books and pamphlets of special interest, and a "What is it?" shelf. The latter could display a recent or interesting find, with the question asked, "What is it?" Some sort of special recognition could be given the first person identifying it; once it is identified, or after it has been displayed for a certain period, a placard should be placed beside it to identify it and tell something about it.

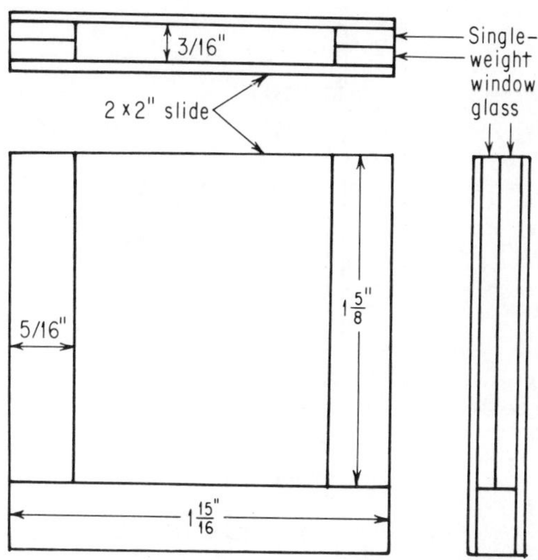

Fig. 33-5. Water cell for lantern-slide projection of small living aquatic insects.

Any display that is changed at regular intervals (for example, a "What is it?" display) might be made the responsibility of particular individuals in a class.

DISPLAYS OF LIVING INSECTS

A display of something alive and moving invariably attracts more attention and arouses more interest than an inanimate display, and the bigger and more active the animal that is displayed, the better. Living insects can be displayed in cages or by means of projection.

Caged insects might be displayed for a short period only (for example, a day or two), they might be displayed as they develop from immatures to adults, or they might be displayed throughout all stages of their life cycle. Almost any sort of insect can be kept alive for a short period, and no elaborate cages are necessary; more care is required for maintaining the insect through a part of or all its life cycle. The

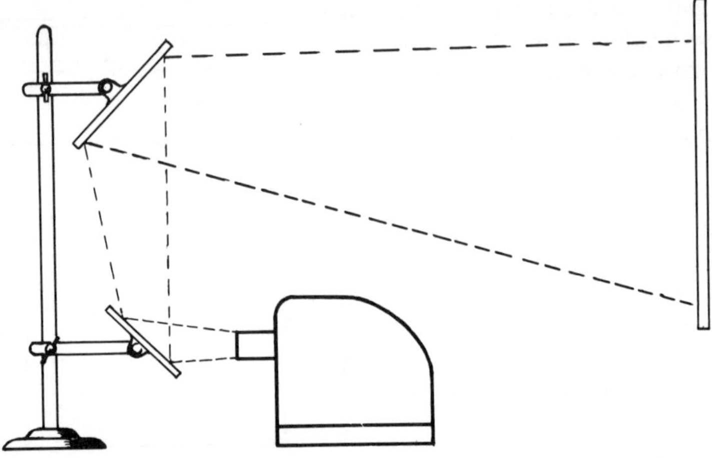

Fig. 33-6. Diagram showing the use of the projection cell.

subject of keeping insects in captivity is discussed in greater detail in the following section (page 716).

A slide-sized water cell (Figure 33-5), the materials in which cost about five cents, can be used with almost any slide projector to project alive small insects or other aquatic organisms, and the result is like a motion picture. Such a cell can be made with two 2 by 2 inch slides (actually 50 millimeters, or about $1\frac{15}{16}$ inches, square), which can be purchased at any photographic supply store, and narrow strips of single-weight window glass. These strips are cut $\frac{5}{16}$ inch wide, with the strips at the bottom $1\frac{15}{16}$ inches long and those at the sides $1\frac{5}{8}$ inches long. The sides and bottom of the cell are made of two thicknesses of this glass, making inside of the cell $\frac{3}{16}$ inch thick. Any good waterproof cement (for example, household cement) may be used in putting the cell together. The trick in making a cell of this sort is to make it watertight; hence the pieces should be cemented together carefully. A strip of wood could be used in place of the strips of glass, or the entire cell could be made of plastic instead of glass, but glass is the preferred material.

If the slide carriage of the projector will not take this cell (and it probably won't), remove the carriage and insert a narrow strip of thin wood or heavy cardboard into the bottom of the slide carriage aperture; the cell will rest on this strip. The cell is filled to about $\frac{1}{4}$ inch from the top with water, the organisms to be projected are added, and the cell is inserted into the projector. In some projectors this cell will heat up after 10 or 15 minutes of use; hence it is advisable to have one or two extra cells that can be used alternately, to avoid overheating. The image on the screen will be upside down, but this is a minor detail; if one desires it right side up, it can be inverted by means of mirrors (Figure 33-6).

Insects that are mounted on microscope slides (permanent mounts) can be projected by means of a 2 by 2-inch projector if a special carriage (Figure 33-7) is made for the slide. Such projection is not satisfactory unless the specimen on the slide is at least $\frac{1}{4}$ inch long.

Living aquatic insects in a watch glass or petri dish and insects mounted on microscope slides can be projected for small groups or for drawing by means of a photographic enlarger.

Elaborate and expensive microprojectors for projecting minute organisms on microscope slides are available from supply houses handling optical equipment, but a fairly satisfactory microprojector can be

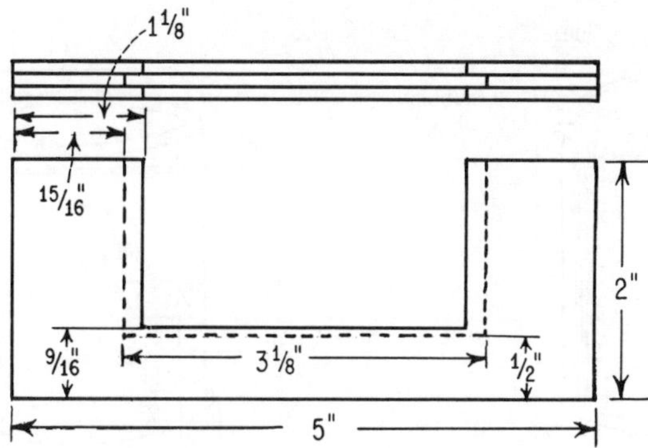

Fig. 33-7. Lantern-slide carriage for microscope slides.

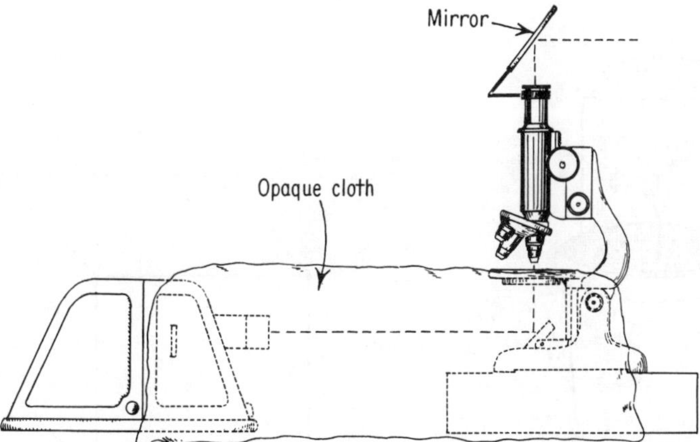

Fig. 33-8. Diagram of a homemade microprojector. The opaque cloth is fastened tightly around the projector and around the base of the microscope to prevent the escape of the light.

made with a microscope, a projection lantern with a strong bulb (300 to 500 watts), some opaque cloth, and a mirror. A diagram of such a microprojector is shown in Figure 33-8. The cloth is used over the space between the projector and the substage of the microscope and around the substage, to prevent the escape of light. Such a setup will give a fairly clear field up to 3 feet or more in diameter, and in a well-darkened room magnifications up to 100 times can be used. A somewhat more elaborate homemade microprojector is described by H. S. Seifert in Turtox News, 29(1): 30-33, 1951.

Any thin and transparent or translucent insect or insect structure can be mounted between 2 by 2-inch slides and projected. This is an ideal method of displaying and demonstrating insect wings, and the slide can also be used as a negative to make photographic prints of insect wings. The wings are removed, preferably from a dried specimen, and mounted dry; for most wings half an inch or more in length, one-half of a Kodak 35-millimeter mask provides a frame for the slide and is just about the right thickness for the wing to be held in place by the glass without danger of being crushed; for smaller wings no mask of any sort need be used. If the wings are not flat when they are removed from a dried insect, they should be placed in 95 percent alcohol

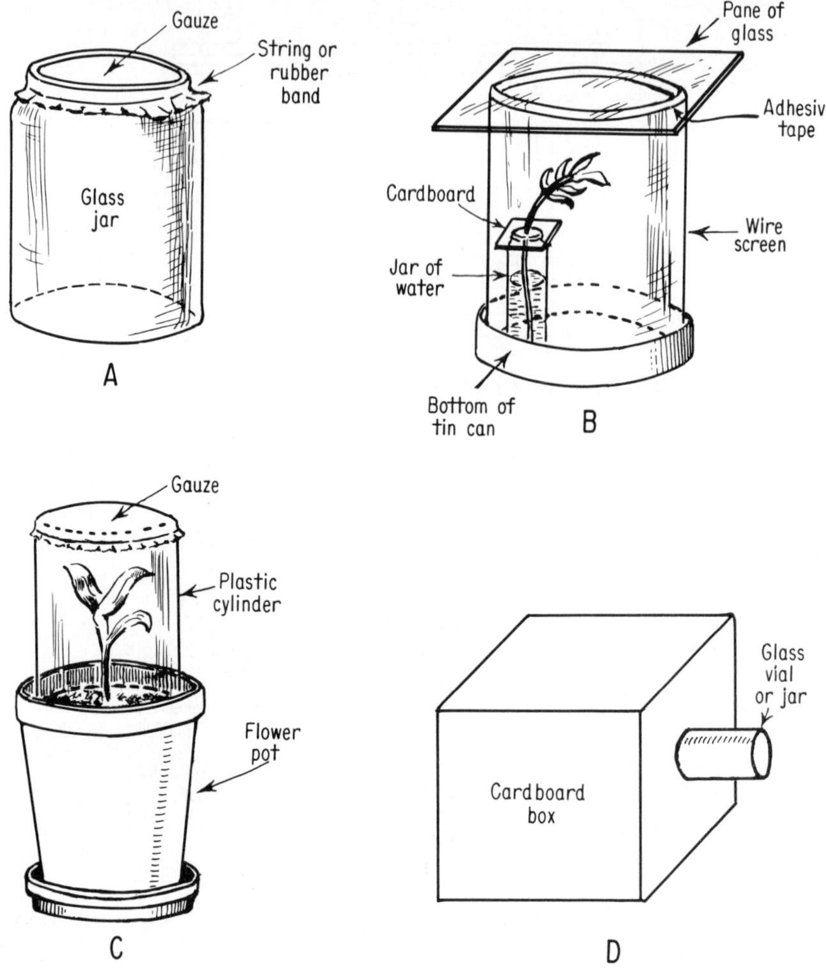

Fig. 33-9. Some types of insect cages. A, jar cage; B, cylindrical screen cage; C, "flowerpot" cage; D, emergence box.

to soften them so that they can be flattened without tearing; they are then put wet on the slide, oriented, and allowed to dry before the mask and cover slide are added and the slide bound. Wings so mounted can be projected directly onto a blackboard, where the venation can be labeled on the projected image.

KEEPING LIVING INSECTS IN CAPTIVITY

Relatively little equipment or attention is required to keep an insect alive in captivity for a short period; insects can be brought in from the field, kept in a cage of some sort for a day or so, and then released. On the other hand, rearing adult insects from their immature stages or maintaining cultures of insects through one or more generations usually requires more equipment and attention. However, there are many types of insects that are fairly easy to rear or culture.

Rearing adult insects from immature stages is an excellent way to learn about their habits and life histories. The activities of insects in cages can generally be more easily observed, and certainly observed to a greater extent, than insects in the field. Many insects collected as immatures and reared will be found to be parasitized, and the parasites will emerge rather than the host insect; this is particularly true of gall insects and caterpillars.

CAGES FOR INSECTS

Almost anything will serve as a suitable cage for keeping insects in captivity a short time or for rearing some types of insects. The simplest type of cage is a glass (or clear plastic) jar of some sort covered with gauze held in place with a string or rubber band (Figure 33-9 A); the jar may vary in size from a small vial up to a large (1-gallon or larger) jar, depending on the size and numbers of the insects. In some cases food, water, or other materials necessary to the well-being of the insects can simply be placed in the bottom of the jar. Such containers are also suitable for aquaria; mosquitoes, for example, can be reared in vials that hold only a few cubic centimeters of water.

Cages suitable for rearing some types of insects or for display can be made of cardboard, gauze, and clear plastic. Any small cardboard box can be used; its size will depend on the size of the insect it is to contain. Holes cut in the ends and covered with gauze will provide ventilation; clear plastic or glass in the front will provide visibility; the top may be covered with either glass, clear plastic, or an opaque lid.

A more permanent type of cage can be made of window screen with a wood or metal framework. The bottom inch or so of a large tin can with a cylinder of screen inserted in it (Figure 33-9 B) makes a good cage. Cages of wood and screen can be made with the opening at the top, like a lid, or with a door on one side. If the cage is to be used for fairly active insects and it is necessary to get into the cage frequently, it should be provided with a sleeve (Figure 33-10 A).

When one is rearing a plant-feeding insect, and the plant upon which it feeds is not too large, the insect can be reared in a "flowerpot" cage (Figure 33-9 C). The plant is planted in a flowerpot or a large tin can, and a cylinder of glass, plastic, or screen is placed around the plant and covered at the top with gauze.

An emergence box such as that shown in Figure 33-9 D works well for rearing adults from larvae living in debris, soil,

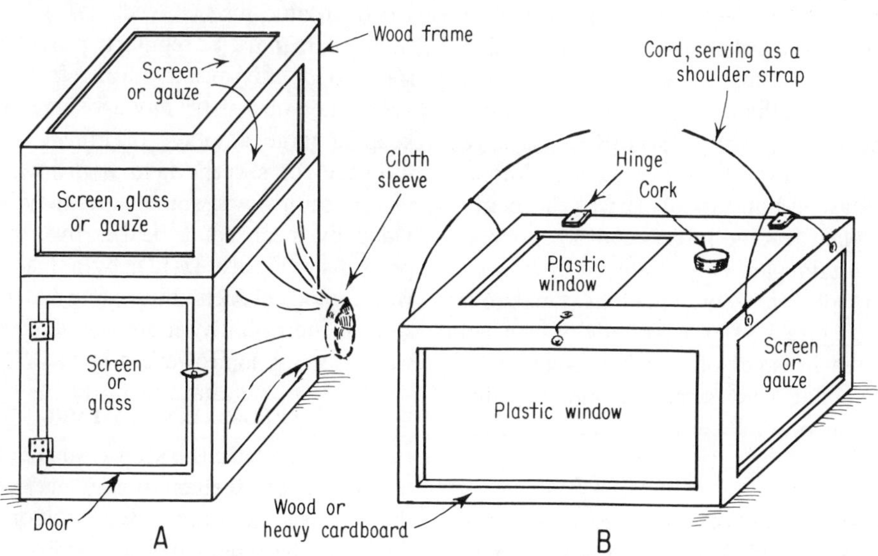

Fig. 33-10. Insect cages. A, sleeve cage; B, a field carrying cage.

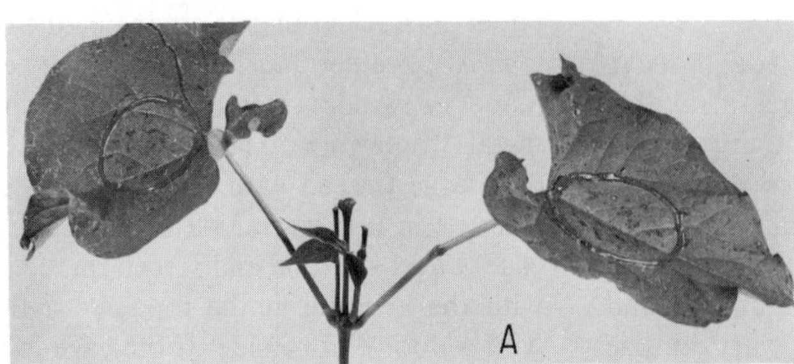

Fig. 33-11. Methods of caging insects in the field. A, tanglefoot barrier on leaf for small non-flying leaf-feeding insects; B, a cage of plastic and gauze for caging insects on their food plant. (A, courtesy of Davidson.)

excrement, and other materials. The material containing the larvae is placed in the box, which is then closed tight. When the adults emerge, they are attracted by the light coming into the box through the vial, and go into the vial.

The best way to rear some insects is to leave them in their habitat in the field and cage them there. Many types of cages can be constructed around an insect in the field. In the case of a plant-feeding insect, a cage consisting of a roll of clear plastic or fine screen, with gauze at each end, may be placed around that part of the plant containing the insect (Figure 33-11 B), or a cage made of window screen on a wooden framework may be built about part of the plant. Many plant-feeding insects can be confined on a certain part of a plant by means of barriers of some sort, such as tanglefoot bands (Figure 33-11 A). Aquatic insects can be reared in cages of screen submerged in their habitat; the screen should be fine enough to prevent the escape of the insect but coarse enough to allow food material to enter.

Cages made of heavy cardboard or wood, gauze, and plastic can easily be fitted with a shoulder strap and used to bring living material from the field into the laboratory or classroom. With a carrying cage such as the one shown in Figure 33-10 B, large materials can be put into the cage by lifting the lid, or single insects may be put into the box through the hole in the lid.

When one is rearing insects indoors, he must usually make sure that the conditions of temperature and humidity are satisfactory and that sufficient food and water is provided. Many insects, such as leaf-eating caterpillars, must be regularly provided with fresh food; this means adding fresh leaves every day or so, or having some way of keeping large amounts of foliage fresh in the cage for several days at a time. If the insect requires water, the water may be provided by means of a beaker inverted in a petri dish (Figure 33-12); by a vial full of water, plugged with cotton, and lying on its side in the cage; by a sponge soaked with water; or by some similar means.

SOME INSECTS EASILY REARED

INSECTS INFESTING FLOUR OR MEAL: Some of the easiest insects to rear indoors are those that normally live indoors; for example, the insects that attack flour, meal, and other stored food products (see page

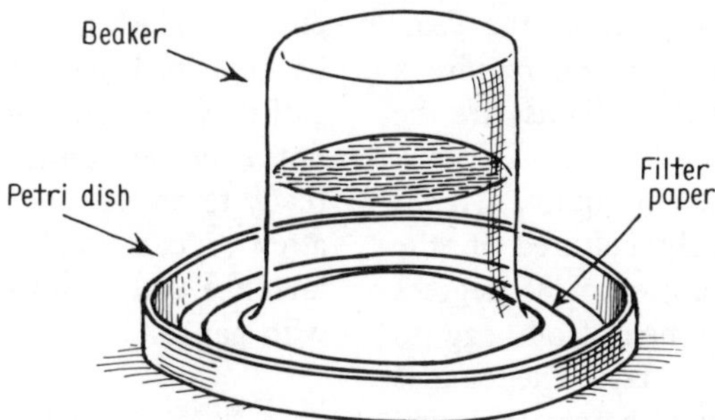

Fig. 33-12. A method of providing water for caged insects.

665). They may be kept and reared in the original container of the food material, or in a glass jar covered with fine gauze. It is usually not necessary to provide these insects with moisture. The various stages of the insect can be obtained by sifting the meal, and some of these can be added to fresh meal to keep the culture going.

COCKROACHES: Cockroaches are excellent insects for rearing, since they are fairly large and active, most people are familiar with them, and in most parts of the country they are abundant and easily obtained. A culture may be started by trapping some adults (page 682). Cockroaches can be reared in various types of containers, a large glass or plastic jar covered with gauze, or even an open box, provided the box is several inches deep and the upper 2 or 3 inches of the sides are smeared with vaseline so that the roaches cannot climb out. These insects are practically omnivorous, and many different types of material will serve as suitable food. Dog biscuits make a good food. Plenty of water should be provided.

AQUATIC INSECTS: Many types of insects that have aquatic immature stages can be reared easily from the immature to the adult stage. The type of aquarium needed will depend on the type of insect being reared; small forms feeding on organic debris or microorganisms can be reared in containers as small as vials; larger ones, particularly predaceous forms, require larger containers. Larvae or pupae of mosquitoes, for example, can be kept in small containers in some of the same water in which they were found, with a cover over the container to prevent the escape of the adults; when vials are used, the simplest cover is a plug of cotton. In many cases it is necessary to simulate the insect's habitat in the aquarium (for example, have sand or mud in the bottom and have some aquatic plants present), and in the case of predaceous insects, such as dragonfly nymphs, smaller animals must be provided as food. The water must be aerated for some aquatic types. In maintaining an aquarium, one should strive to keep all the conditions in the aquarium as near as possible to the conditions in the animal's normal habitat.

When one is attempting to maintain aquatic insects generation after generation in the laboratory, special provision must be made for the different life-history stages. The different stages frequently require special food, space, or other conditions. Since mosquitoes are easily cultured in the laboratory, suggestions for culturing these insects are given in the following paragraph.

MOSQUITOES: The species of mosquito selected for culturing in the laboratory should be one that does not require a period of dormancy in the life cycle; many species, particularly the species of *Aèdes* (which have a single generation a year), are difficult or impossible to rear continuously without subjecting the eggs to a period of refrigeration. Species that breed continuously throughout the warmer parts of the year, and in which the adults do not require a large space for their mating flights, are the best for culturing.

The yellow fever mosquito, *Aèdes aegýpti* (Linn.), is easily cultured in the laboratory;[1] at a temperature of 85 degrees Fahrenheit the development from egg to adult requires only 9 to 11 days. The females must obtain a blood meal before they will produce eggs; a person's arm can provide this meal, but a laboratory animal such as a rabbit (with the hair shaved from a portion of its body) is better. The adults are allowed to emerge in cages of about 1 cubic foot capacity; a solution of honey in the cage will provide food for the males (which do not feed on blood) and for the females before their blood meal.

A small dish of water is placed in the cage for egg laying; if wooden blocks or paper are placed in this water, the eggs will be deposited on these at the margin of the water as it recedes. These eggs will usually hatch within 10 to 20 minutes after they are placed in water at room temperature, even after months of desiccation. If the larvae are reared in large numbers, they are best reared in battery jars; as many as 250 larvae can be reared in a 6-inch battery jar half filled with water. The larvae can be fed ground dog biscuit, which is sprinkled on the surface of the water daily; for first instar larvae, 30 to 35 milligrams should be used daily. This amount should be increased for successive instars up to 140 to 150 milligrams daily for fourth instar larvae. Pupation of the fourth instar larvae takes place 7 to 9 days after the eggs hatch, and the adults emerge about 24 hours later.

GALL INSECTS: It is usually fairly easy to rear adult insects from galls; the important thing in rearing most gall insects is to keep the gall alive and fresh until the adults emerge. The plant containing the gall can be kept fresh by putting it in water, or the gall may be caged in the field. If the gall is not collected until the adults are nearly ready to emerge (as determined by opening a few), it can simply be placed inside a glass jar, in a vial of water, and the jar covered with gauze.

[1] Since this species is an important disease vector, special precautions should be taken to prevent the escape of any individuals reared.

LEAF MINERS: The procedure described for gall insects will work for leaf miners that pupate in the leaf; if the leaf miner pupates in the soil (for example, certain sawflies), the plant containing the insect should be grown in a flowerpot cage.

WOOD-BORING INSECTS: If the insect bores into drying or dried wood, the wood containing the larvae can be placed in an emergence box like that shown in Figure 33-9 D; if it bores only into living wood, the adults can be obtained by placing some sort of cage over the emergence holes (in the field).

TERMITES: Termite cultures are easily maintained in the laboratory and are of value in demonstrating the social behavior and the wood-eating and fungus-cultivating habits of these insects. Various types of containers can be used for a termite culture, but the best for demonstration purposes is either a battery jar or a glass-plate type of container. A termite colony will last quite a while without queens in either type of container, but will prove more interesting if queens or supplemental queens are present.

If a battery jar is used, $\frac{1}{4}$ inch or so of earth is placed in the bottom of the jar and a sheet of wood is placed on either side of the jar; balsa wood is the best because the termites become established in it quickly. Thin, narrow strips of a harder wood are placed on each side between the balsa wood and the glass, and pieces are placed between the sheets of balsa wood to hold them in place. Termites placed in such a container become established in a few hours; they tunnel through the earth and the wood and

Fig. 33-13. A glass-plate type of container for rearing termites.

build fungus "gardens" (which are apparently an important source of nitrogen and vitamins) between the wood and the glass. The wood will be destroyed in a few weeks and must be replaced. Water must be added every few days. This can be done by thoroughly moistening a pad of cotton and putting it between the glass and the wood at the top on each side.

A glass-plate type of container is somewhat similar to the ant nest described below, but has a metal rather than a wood frame (Figure 33-13). The container should be about a foot wide, a foot high, and about $\frac{1}{2}$-inch thick, and should have a pan at the base to hold it upright. No earth need be used in this type of container. A piece of balsa wood is placed in the container, with narrow strips inserted between it and the two glass plates (front and rear). The termites are placed in the space between the wood and the glass. A thin pad of cotton batting is placed over the top of the wood, between the two glass plates, and this is thoroughly soaked with water about twice a week. The fungus gardens are maintained here as in the battery-jar culture.

CATERPILLARS: The chief problem encountered in rearing caterpillars is that of providing suitable food. Many caterpillars feed only on certain species of plants; hence it is necessary to know the food plant of a caterpillar one wishes to rear. Caterpillars may be reared in almost any sort of cage, provided the cage is cleaned and fresh food is provided regularly. Plant food can be kept fresh longer if it is put in a small jar of water inside the cage; a cover on the top of the water jar, around the stem of the plant, will prevent the caterpillars from falling into the water. If the caterpillar is one that requires special conditions for pupation, the conditions must be provided. Butterfly larvae will usually pupate on the leaves or on the sides or top of the cage; most moth larvae will pupate in the corner of the cage or under debris of some sort. Some moth larvae (for example, the larvae of sphinx moths) pupate in the ground; they should be reared in a cage containing several inches of soil.

HATCHING OVERWINTERING COCOONS: Many of the larger moths pupate in the fall and emerge as adults in the spring, and their cocoons can be collected in the fall. If these cocoons are brought indoors in the fall, they may dry out or the adults may emerge in the middle of the winter (though this may not be objectionable). The drying out can be prevented by putting the cocoons in a jar that has an inch or so of dirt in the bottom, and sprinkling the dirt and cocoon with

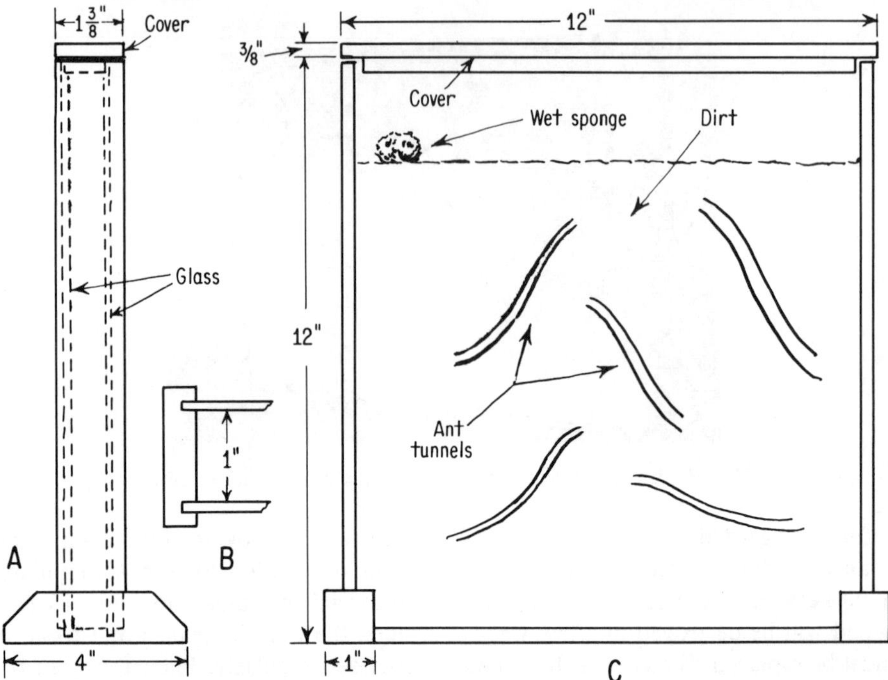

Fig. 33-14. The vertical type of ant cage. A, end view; B, top view of one end showing cage construction; C, front view.

water about once a week. To keep the cocoons from emerging in the middle of the winter, they may be kept in screen cages (preferably cages containing some dirt or debris) outdoors (for example, on the outside window sill of a room). If the emerging moth is a female and it emerges at a time when other moths of its kind are on the wing, it will often attract male moths from a considerable distance if kept in an outdoor cage.

ANTS: Because of their social behavior, ants make very interesting animals to maintain in indoor cages. The simplest type of ant cage, particularly for display, is a narrow vertical cage with a wooden framework and glass sides (Figure 33-14). This is filled with an ant-dirt mixture obtained by digging up an ant hill, preferably a small one under a stone or board; this mixture should contain all stages and castes if possible. The queen can usually be recognized by her larger size. The glass sides of the cage should be darkened by covering them with some opaque material; otherwise all the tunnels the ants make will be away from the glass and not visible. Food and moisture must be provided. Food can be provided by putting a few insects into the cage from time to time, or by putting a few drops of diluted molasses or honey on a small sponge or wad of cotton in the cage. Moisture can be provided by keeping a wet sponge or wad of cotton on the under side of the lid or on top of the dirt.

HONEY BEES: An observation bee hive makes an excellent class demonstration. It can be set up inside a classroom window, and the bees can come and go at will, yet all that goes on inside the hive can be observed. Space does not permit a detailed description of how an observation bee hive is constructed, but the accompanying illustration (Figure 33-15) shows what it is like. One who wishes to set up an observation bee hive

Fig. 33-15. An observation bee hive.

should get in touch with a local beekeeper and ask for his help and suggestions.

BLOW FLIES: Blow flies are abundant in all sections of the country and are an interesting type of insect to maintain in cultures. Blowfly cultures are useful for demonstration or experimental purposes, and both adults and larvae can be used as food for other animals. To maintain a culture of blow flies, one needs a sleeve cage for the adults (preferably one of about 1 cubic foot capacity), tubes or small jars for rearing the larvae, and a larger jar for pupation. A culture can be started by placing lean meat out in the open where flies can oviposit in it; if more than one species is obtained at the start, they can be sorted out in the pupal or adult stage.

The larvae are reared in large test tubes or small jars; the eggs are placed with some meat in a test tube and the tube is plugged with cotton (Figure 33-16 A). Before the larvae are ready to pupate, the plug is removed and the tube is placed in a larger jar that has sand or crumpled paper in the bottom (Figure 33-16 B). The larvae migrate out of the tube and pupate in the sand or paper; the pupae are then recovered, placed in a small dish, and put into the cage to emerge. The adult flies should be provided with water and food. The food should consist of lump sugar in a small dish and fresh lean meat in another dish. The sugar may be left in the cage for a considerable period, but the meat should be changed about every other day. The flies begin to lay eggs on the meat a few days after their first feeding on meat. Some of these eggs can then be placed in the rearing tubes and the culture continued.

FRUIT FLIES: Fruit flies (*Drosóphila*) are small brownish flies that are often seen around decaying fruit; they are too small to be of much value as a display insect, but the ease of rearing them and their rapid rate of

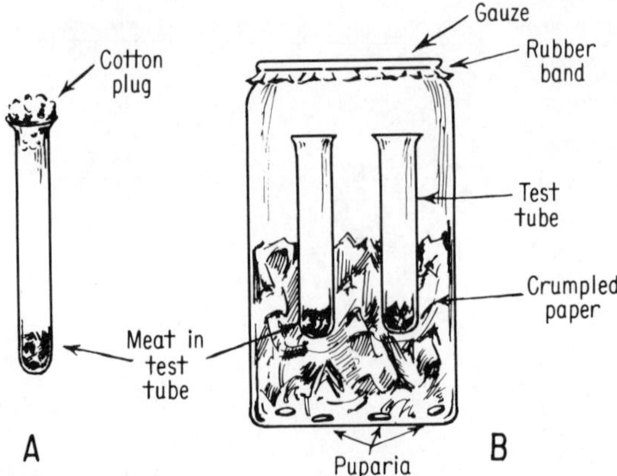

Fig. 33-16. A method of rearing blow flies. A, culture tube containing lean meat and fly eggs; B, a chamber for pupation.

reproduction make them ideal for the study of hereditary processes. Cultures may be started by placing a mashed ripe banana in the open and allowing the flies to oviposit on it; special stocks of flies for genetic work can be obtained from supply houses. Fruit flies reared for genetic studies are usually reared in half-pint bottles on a special medium. The adult flies are usually anaesthetized with ether before they are handled.

There are a number of formulas for media suitable for culturing *Drosóphila,* but the following is a very satisfactory one:

Corn meal	95 g
Agar	15 g
Brewer's yeast	5 g
Tegosept (1 g/10 ml alcohol) ...	10 ml
Karo (preferably dark)	75 ml
Molasses	75 ml
Water	850 ml

The solids are weighed and poured into a pot, and then the Tegosept, Karo, and molasses are added and stirred; water is then added and the mixture is heated, with constant stirring, until the boiling point is reached. The mixture is allowed to simmer a while and then is poured into the half-pint culture bottles, about an inch deep in each bottle. This recipe provides enough medium for about 20 bottles. After the medium is put into the culture bottles, a piece of paper toweling is inserted into the medium along one side of the bottle; this absorbs and serves as a base for the medium. The bottles are then allowed to cool and can be stored in a refrigerator until ready for use. Once flies are introduced into a culture bottle, the medium should last at least a few weeks. When the flies are introduced, the bottles are stoppered with a cotton plug. Discarded culture bottles should be cleaned as soon as possible and sterilized.

The Tegosept is added to the medium to reduce or prevent the growth of fungus. It can be obtained from the Goldschmidt Chemical Corporation, 153 Waverly Place, New York 14, N. Y.

OTHER SUGGESTIONS FOR REARING INSECTS: There are a number of insects that will prove interesting to rear or maintain for a short time in captivity. Singing insects such as crickets, katydids, or cicadas may be kept caged for a time with relatively little difficulty. If case-making insects are caged, it will often be possible to observe how the cases are made, and perhaps special materials (such as colored bits of glass for caddisworms usually using sand grains) may be provided for the case. Caging predaceous insects with their prey (particularly mantids), or parasitic insects with their hosts, will demonstrate these interrelationships. With a little knowledge of a species' food habits and habitat requirements, the ingenious student can usually devise methods of rearing almost any type of insect.

SPECIAL STUDIES

Once the student has acquired a little background of knowledge about insects, his curiosity may be aroused and he may wish to make some sort of special study of insects. The possibilities of such studies are enormous; to discuss all the types of special studies to be made with insects would involve a survey of practically the whole field of biology. We wish to discuss here briefly a few types that may be adapted to students of various grade levels. Some of these may be used as group projects for a camp or elementary school group, while others may be suitable for a doctoral research program; still others may be adapted to intermediate grade levels.

SURVEYS

A detailed study of a particular field area is valuable in providing information about field populations—their numbers, their interrelationships, and the factors affecting them. Such a study usually involves three principal types of field work: (1) a study of the topographic features, soil, vegetation, and other characteristics of the area, and the preparation of one or more maps; (2) a study of the temperature, rainfall, humidity, evaporation, wind, and other environmental conditions in the area; and (3) periodic censuses in the area of the populations of insects and other organisms. The field work is followed by compilation and analysis of the data obtained and by the drawing of conclusions.

The thoroughness of a study of this sort will depend on several factors, particularly the purpose of the study, the training of the person or persons making the study, the equipment available, and the nature of the area. The study may vary from a rather cursory survey of the available insect populations to a project in which special techniques are used to get data on populations and environmental conditions and in which careful analyses are made of the data obtained.

It may be of value to discuss briefly some of the field procedures and techniques used in surveys of this type.

MAPPING: Maps are useful in many types of field studies. It is often possible to secure maps from various local or governmental agencies (state or county surveyors, U.S. Geological Survey, and other agencies), but in many studies the investigator must make his own maps. There are four ways of preparing a map of a field area: by freehand sketching, by compass and pacing, by means of a plane table and alidade, and from an aerial photograph.

A freehand sketch of an area, made from a vantage point from which the entire area can be seen, may not be an accurate map, but it may be valuable for some purposes. Such a map is useful for charting the principal features of an area that will be mapped more accurately later by another method.

A compass and pacing survey is the most practical method of mapping if one needs a fairly accurate map but lacks special mapping equipment. The only equipment necessary to make a map by this method is a compass with which one can sight and obtain a bearing on a distant object. To make a map by this method, one usually makes first a freehand sketch map; then distances are measured by pacing, directions are determined by compass readings, and the sketch map is redrawn—more accurately and to scale—from the data obtained.

Mapping by means of a plane table and alidade gives a more accurate map than either of the two methods described above, particularly if distances are measured with a tape rather than by pacing. A plane table is a sketching board attached to a tripod in such a way that it can be leveled and locked in any desired position. An alidade is a device that is placed on the sketch board and along which one sights a distant object; it has a straightedge at its base parallel with the line of sight. A triangular ruler will serve as an alidade if a regular sighting alidade is not available. By this method the map takes form as the survey progresses; directions are determined by sighting along the alidade, distances are measured (by pacing or tape), and points are plotted on the map in the field.

The simplest and most accurate method of mapping an area is to prepare the map from an aerial photograph that has been taken with the camera pointing straight down. The map is made by simply tracing off the desired details. The scale can be determined by comparing the measured distance between two points on the area with the distance between these two points in the photograph. The average student or teacher does not have the means of taking aerial photographs, but a great deal of the country has been photographed from the air by various governmental agencies and many of these photographs are available to the public at a nominal cost. Aerial photographs of many areas can be obtained from the local office of the Agriculture and Marketing Administration of the U.S. Department of Agriculture; photographs of coastal areas may sometimes be obtained from the U.S. Coast and Geodetic Survey.

All maps should contain a title identifying the area, a statement of when and by whom the map was made, the mapping method used, the scale (usually expressed as 1 inch equals so many yards, feet, or miles), a line indicating north, and a legend identifying the symbols used.

MEASURING ENVIRONMENTAL FACTORS: A detailed discussion of this subject is beyond the scope of this book; suffice it to say that there are instruments with which temperature, humidity, evaporation, wind, and many other factors can be measured and recorded. Such instruments should be used in detailed surveys by advanced students. Local weather-bureau data are inadequate for studies of insects, because insects are small and live in small niches, and in an area such as a field or woods, two insects only a few inches apart may be in quite different conditions of such factors as temperature and humidity. The study of climatic factors affecting these animals involves a study of what are called microclimates.

CENSUSES OF INSECT POPULATIONS: It is seldom practical to make a census of an insect population in a field area by counting every insect; most field studies involve some method of estimating the population from samples. Sampling techniques can be designed to estimate the total population in a given area, or they can be designed to indicate comparative populations. The former involves making accurate counts on sample areas that are representative of the entire area studied, and the latter involves using some standard sampling procedure that, when used at different times or in different places, gives information on population trends or differences. The particular method used in any given case will depend on the nature of the area chosen for census and the species in which the investigator is interested.

In cases where the total population in an area such as a field is to be estimated, the insects in a number of small sample areas are collected and counted. A cylinder covering an area of about 1 square foot is put down over the vegetation, and a fumigant is introduced into the cylinder to stun or kill the insects caught there. Then, all the materials inside the cylinder, together with the soil below it to some standard depth, is taken to the laboratory and examined, and the insects (and perhaps other animals as well) are carefully counted. The total popu-

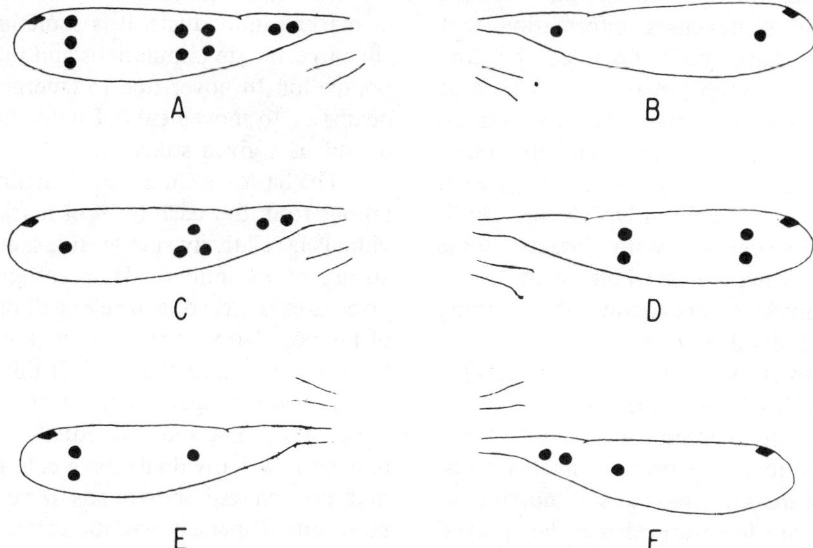

Fig. 33-17. A method of marking damselfly wings. Dots may be placed at three locations on the wing; proximal to the nodus (one or two dots); just distal to the nodus (one to four dots), and just proximal to the stigma (one to three dots). Each insect marked has an identifying number consisting of two letters (indicating which wing is marked) and three digits (indicating the number of dots in each of the three locations on the wing). The specimens shown here are identified as follows: A, LF243; B, RF101; C, LF231; D, RF022; E, LH012; F, RH210.

lation of the area is calculated from several such samples. The accuracy of this method depends on the number and the representativeness of the samples; the number of samples taken will usually depend on the amount of time the investigator has for this study.

Most of the methods used to estimate field populations, particularly in cases where the investigator is interested in only one or a few species, involve procedures designed to count a standard percentage of the population. This percentage may be unknown, but it is possible to determine population trends or to compare the populations of different areas by this method. The sampling techniques used will depend largely on the habits of the species concerned. A common method of sampling the populations on low vegetation is to take a given number of standard sweeps with an insect net and count the catch. For other insects the investigator may count the insects (or points of insect injury) on a certain number of plants, fruits, or leaves. Traps may be used in some cases to determine population trends or differences. Many different sorts of counting techniques may be used in studies of this sort, and in any given study, the technique must be adapted to the characteristics of the species being studied; the aim in each case is to count a uniform percentage of the population.

In some cases it may be possible to obtain a fairly accurate estimate of the total population of a given species in a given area by means of marking. This technique is discussed in the following section.

MARKING INSECTS

The practice of marking animals so that individuals or groups can be subsequently recognized has been used in studies of many kinds of animals and has yielded a great deal of information about the animals marked, in some cases information that could not have been obtained by any other method. With larger animals such as birds (by banding), mammals (by tagging, tattooing, ear marking, and by other methods), and fish (by gill tagging), each animal is marked differently and can be individually recognized. With insects, some methods involve the marking of mass lots of individuals; others involve the marking of insects individually.

The small size of most insects makes it impractical to mark them with any sort of numbered tag; consequently most of the marking of insects, especially small insects, consists of marking mass lots of individuals. Flies that are live-trapped may be sprayed with various dyes (acid fuchsin, eosin, methylene green, and others) and released; the use of different colors serves to mark lots released from different points or at different times. Some insects can be marked with radioactive materials by feeding the adults or larvae with these materials; the marked individuals are identified by means of special instruments designed to detect radioactivity.

Some types of insects can be marked so that individuals can be recognized. Insects such as bees can be marked on the thorax with dots of different colored enamel, the color or position of each dot representing a particular digit; others, such as moths, dragonflies, damselflies (Figure 33-17), and the like, can be marked with dots on the wing. The dots, of a fast-drying material like nail polish or India ink, are put on with a fine brush or a pointed stick. Individual insects may also be marked by cutting off certain sections of certain legs, or by cutting characteristic notches in the wings.

A great deal can be learned about the habits and behavior of an insect by the use of marking techniques: for example, length of life, mating habits, territorial behavior, movements and flight range, and changes in color or habits with increasing age of the adult. With adequate data on the recaptures of marked individuals, it is sometimes possible to estimate populations and the rate of population turnover due to emergence and deaths or to movements of individuals into or out of a given study area.

The basic formula for calculating populations from the recaptures of marked individuals is relatively simple. If a sample consisting of M individuals is collected in a given area, marked, and released, then M/P of the population is marked (where P is the total population on the area). If this population is sampled again later, assumming that none of the marked individuals has died, that no new individuals have emerged, and that the marked individuals have become uniformly dispersed over the sampling area, then the proportion of the second sample that is marked is the same as it was when the marked individuals were first released. If the total number in the second sample is represented by C, and the number of marked individuals in this sample is represented by M', then the proportion of the second sample that is marked is M'/C.

Thus,

$$\frac{M}{P} = \frac{M'}{C}$$

Therefore

$$P = \frac{M \times C}{M'}$$

or

$$\text{Total population} = \frac{(\text{number marked}) \times (\text{total number recaptured})}{\text{number of marked individuals recaptured}}$$

In most ecological studies of a particular insect, some technique of marking can be used to advantage. A high school biology class, camp nature-study class, or a similar group might undertake a study involving marking as a group project; there are many insects in every neighborhood that could be marked either in mass lots or individually. Such a project would not only arouse considerable interest, since many people would be on the lookout for the marked insects, but a great deal of information about the insect might be obtained from the study.

EXPERIMENTS WITH LIVING INSECTS

The possibilities of experiments with living insects are almost endless and can be discussed only briefly here. A great deal of present-day research on insects involves such experiments. These may be concerned with the reactions of the insect to various environmental conditions—odors, chemicals, temperature, humidity, or wind; its food habits, to determine what a particular insect eats, or the effects of different foods; patterns of locomotion, such as how the insect flies, walks, or runs; its life history, including the details of the life history and how the insect's development may be affected by various environmental factors; the enemies of a particular species—parasites, predators, or competitors—what they are and how they operate; social behavior, in such insects as ants, bees, wasps, or termites; heredity, using some rapidly reproducing insect such as *Drosóphila*; or testing the effectiveness of insecticides. Such experiments may involve work in the laboratory or in the field, or both.

Many types of experiments, such as those designed to test insecticides, involve the use of controls and replication. If, for example, a particular chemical is to be tested for its insecticidal action, several similar lots of an insect will be treated with the chemical, and some (the controls) will be treated in as nearly as possible the same way but without the chemical. Replication, or repeating the tests with several lots of the insect, makes possible more definite conclusions from the data obtained. Statistical procedures will frequently be used to analyze the data obtained in the experiments, and the validity of the conclusions will be determined by the results of these statistical procedures.

PHOTOGRAPHING INSECTS

Photographing insects will test the skill and ingenuity of the photographer and may yield pictures that are very striking and of considerable educational value. Volumes have been written about photographic techniques, so we need not go into the subject in detail, but we may make some suggestions to the amateur photographer who wishes to photograph insects.

With most insects and most cameras, the chief problem of the photographer will be to get a picture in which the insect is big enough to show up well. Most insects are too small to show up in a picture taken from a distance of 3 feet, the minimum for most cameras without special lenses. The first prerequisite in photographing insects is to have equipment with which small objects can be photographed. A few cameras, such as the AF model Argus and the Practiflex, will photograph from 15 inches without supplementary lenses; with a copying lens these cameras can photograph from about $9\frac{1}{2}$ inches, and from these distances good pictures can be obtained of a great many insects. Considerable enlargement can be obtained by using a camera normally taking pictures larger than 35-millimeter size, with a double-extension bellows and a 35-millimeter adapter. Various telephoto lenses may also be used to get the enlargement necessary for good insect pictures. It is possible to photograph through a binocular microscope and get pictures of very small insects. In taking pictures of insects, as in photographing anything else, an understanding of one's equipment is more important than the price paid for that equipment; it is possible to get excellent pictures with inexpensive equipment.

To photograph insects through a binocular microscope, a suitable adapter can be made out of a simple cylinder of cardboard, such as a pillbox of the right size with the top and bottom cut out (Figure 33-18). Before attempting this sort of photo-

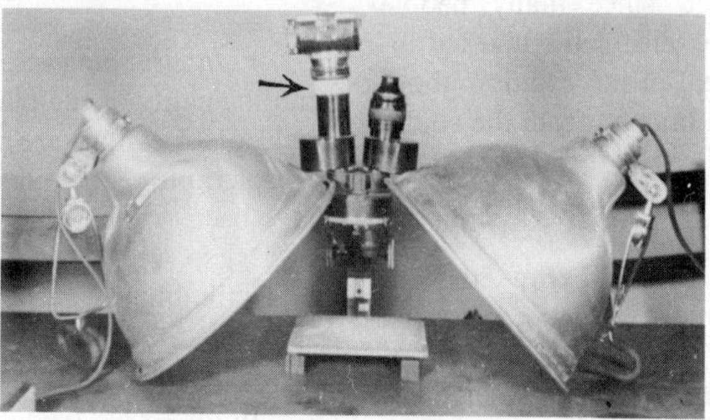

Fig. 33-18. A method of taking photographs through a binocular microscope. The camera, with the front lens element removed, is placed on the adapter ring (indicated by arrow) over one eyepiece of the microscope; the adapter ring is simply a circular cardboard pillbox with the top and bottom removed. With this equipment, using a No. 2 blue photoflood bulb in each reflector, the exposure time for outdoor Kodachrome at a magnification of 12.5 is about 2 seconds at *f*.11.

graphy the photographer should make sure of just what he is getting on the film. If a camera is used that projects onto a ground glass the same image that will appear on the film, this is no problem; with any other type of camera that has a removable back, the photographer can determine what he is getting by removing the back of the camera and placing a ground glass on the film track. What appears in focus to one looking through the microscope may not necessarily be in focus on the film, or only the center of the film may be exposed. It may be necessary in some cases to remove all or part of the camera lens. The exposures in this type of photography usually have to be determined by trial and error. One can obtain some very striking pictures of insects by photographing them through a binocular microscope, once the problems of focus and exposure have been solved.

Pictures of dead or mounted insects may be useful for some purposes, but pictures of living insects, or at least of insects that *look* alive and are in a natural pose, are far better. Unfortunately, an insect will not always pose as the photographer would like it to, and he may have to use various tricks to get the picture he wants. Some insect pictures can be made in the field, but one can often get better pictures if the insect is brought indoors where it can be photographed under controlled conditions. Insects that refuse to stand still may be slowed down by chilling them for a time in a refrigerator or by stunning them in a killing jar. Knowledge of the insect's habits is essential in photographing insects in the field. One can often get an excellent picture by training the camera on a spot where the insect will eventually alight and then waiting for the insect to alight there; pictures of bees, wasps, or butterflies can be obtained by aiming the camera at a flower and photographing the insects when they come to the flower.

One can get pictures of considerable entomological value without photographing any insects at all; insect nests or cocoons, damaged leaves or other objects, woodborer tunnels, and similar objects make excellent photographic material and are usually much easier to photograph than living insects.

DRAWINGS OF INSECTS

The student will sooner or later have occasion to make drawings of insects or insect structures, either for his personal notes as a part of a laboratory exercise or as part of a research prepared for publication. One need not be a natural artist to prepare good drawings of insects; the aim

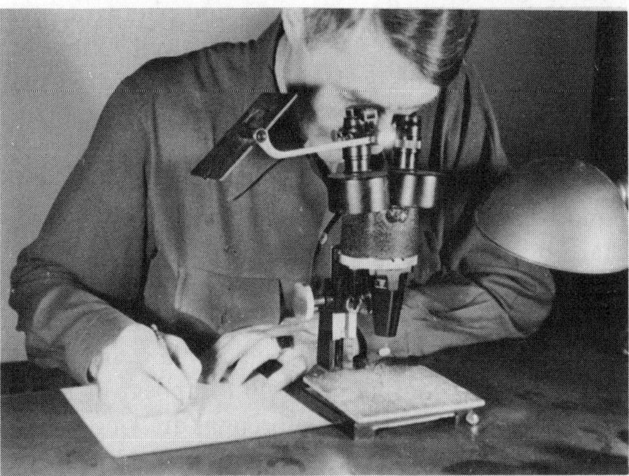

Fig. 33-19. The camera lucida in use.

of entomological drawing is accuracy rather than artistry, and simple line drawings often serve better than elaborately shaded or wash drawings.

The student should strive primarily for accuracy in drawings of insects or insect structures. A gifted artist can make a freehand drawing that is fairly accurate, but most people require some sort of mechanical aid to secure accuracy. There are several devices and techniques by which one can turn out an accurately proportioned drawing with a minimum of effort; these include the camera lucida, projection apparatus, the use of crosshatching, and careful measurements of the specimen to be drawn.

A camera lucida (Figure 33-19) is a device that fits over the eyepiece of a microscope; it contains a system of prisms and mirrors so arranged that, by looking through it, the observer sees both the object under the microscope and the paper on which the drawing is to be made, and can draw exactly what he sees through the microscope. It takes a little practice to learn how to use a camera lucida, but once one gets the knack of it, he can turn out accurate drawings rather rapidly. A camera lucida is a rather expensive piece of equipment and is likely to be available only in well-equipped university or research laboratories.

Any insect or insect structure that is fairly flat and translucent can be drawn by projection. The object to be drawn is projected by means of a photographic enlarger, projection lantern, or other projection apparatus onto a sheet of paper, and the drawing is traced over the projected image. This is the ideal method of making drawings of insect wings, which can be mounted between two glass slides. Elaborate projectors can be obtained which will give magnifications from four or five up to several hundred, but they are rather expensive. Photographic enlargers or projection lanterns can be used if one does not want too much magnification.

The crosshatching principle can be used for making drawings from specimens and for copying drawings at a different scale. The object to be drawn is observed through a grid of crossed lines and drawn on coordinate paper, the detail of the object being put in one square at a time. For drawing a macroscopic object, a grid made of crossed threads can be set up in front of the object; for microscopic objects, a transparent disc on which fine crosslines are scratched is put into the eyepiece of the microscope. For copying a drawing at a different scale, a grid of one scale is put over the drawing to be copied and the details of the drawing are copied one square at a time on coordinate paper that has a different scale.

A wall chart or any greatly enlarged drawing can be made from a text figure either by projection or by the crosshatching method. Text drawings can be projected by an opaque projector and traced, or they can be enlarged on a chart by using the grid principle described in the preceding paragraph.

If one does not have any of these mechanical aids, he can achieve a considerable degree of accuracy by carefully measuring the specimen to be drawn and then making the drawing agree with these measurements. Measurements of small objects should be made with dividers.

The simplest way to obtain a symmetrical drawing, when one is drawing an animal that is bilaterally symmetrical, is to make only the right or left half of the drawing from the specimen and then to make the other half from the first half.

When one is preparing a drawing for publication, he should keep in mind the method by which his drawing will be reproduced and the character of the publication in which his drawing will appear. Most printed illustrations are reproduced either by a zinc etching, a halftone, or by lithoprinting. The zinc process is used for line drawings in a printed publication; it reproduces only black and white, and the original must be made with India ink. Any shading desired in such a drawing must be done by stippling (small dots, or by using stippleboard drawing paper), or by various types of lines. Wash drawings or photographs that are reproduced in a printed publication are reproduced by means of halftones; a halftone plate is made by photographing through a screen the picture to be reproduced, and the printed illustration is made up of a series of tiny dots. The lithoprinting process involves making a plate, and the printed page is reproduced by offset printing; in this process, black-and-white drawings and photographs are reproduced about equally well. Fine lines in a black-and-white drawing are usually reproduced better by lithoprinting than by a zinc etching. Drawings prepared for publication are ordinarily made about twice the size at which they will be reproduced, sometimes larger; the resulting reduction tends to eliminate minor irregularities in the original drawing. If the reduction is very great, particularly in a zinc reproduction, the fine lines will disappear or lines close together on the original drawing will appear run together in the printed drawing.

The student who wishes to learn how to prepare good drawings should study the better drawings in textbooks and research papers. By studying carefully the details of such drawings, he will learn some of the tricks of giving an effect of contour with a minimum of shading, and he will learn the methods of shading that are the best to produce the desired effects. He will also learn something of the preferred style of arranging and labeling drawings.

SOURCES OF INFORMATION AND MATERIALS

Information on insects is available in the form of literature published by various federal and state organizations, from various private organizations such as supply houses, museums, and societies, and from a great mass of books and periodicals. Much of this literature will be available in a good library, and a good bit of it can be obtained at little or no cost by the student or teacher. Information is also available from contacts with other people who are interested in insects—amateurs and workers in universities, museums, and experiment stations. Materials such as entomological equipment or visual aids such as slides, movies, and exhibits are available from supply houses, museums, and often from various state or private agencies.

GOVERNMENT PUBLICATIONS

Many government publications are available to the public free of charge, and others can frequently be obtained free through a senator or congressman. The publications that are sold are sold at a nominal cost. There is a wealth of literature on insects available from the government.

Information on the publications of various governmental agencies can be obtained from the Superintendent of Documents, Government Printing Office, Washington 25, D.C. This office publishes a number of lists of publications (one is on insects), which are available without cost. Most government publications on insects are published by the U.S. Department of Agriculture, and information on the publications of this department may be obtained from the following sources: (1) from List No. 11, *List of the Available Publications of the U.S. Department of Agriculture* (which is revised about every year or so), available from the Office of Information, U.S. Department of Agriculture, Washington 25, D.C.; (2) from various indexes published by the USDA; (3) from indexing journals, such as the *Agricultural Index* and *Bibliography of Agriculture*; and (4) from the *Monthly List of Publications and Motion Pictures,* formerly published monthly but now published every two months (this is available free from the Office of Information, USDA).

The federal government has many publications dealing wholly or in part with insects. These include several serial publications, such as the *Journal of Agricultural Research* (semimonthly, discontinued since 1949), *The Experiment Station Record* (monthly, discontinued since 1946), and *Bibliography of Agriculture* (monthly). Some publications, such as the USDA *Yearbooks* and various annual reports, appear once a year. Publications of a great many series appear irregularly; among those of the USDA that frequently deal with insects are the *Bulletins, Farmers' Bulletins, Technical Bulletins, Circulars,* and *Miscellaneous Publications.*

STATE PUBLICATIONS

Many of the publications of state agencies are available free to residents of that state. In some states there are several agencies whose publications would be of interest to the student or teacher of entomology—particularly the state agricultural experiment station, the state extension service, the state departments of education and conservation, the state biological or natural history survey, and the state museum. Information on the publications available from these agencies can usually be obtained by writing to the agencies directly. The publications of various state agencies are listed in the *Monthly Check List of State Publications,* which is published by the Library of Congress.

Many state agricultural experiment stations are closely associated with the state agricultural college and are located in the same town; the state extension service is nearly always a part of the state agricultural college. State departments of education or conservation are usually located in the state capital; state museums are usually located either in the state capital or in the same town as the state university. Most state universities have museums that contain insect collections and which often publish papers on insects. State biological surveys are usually associated with the state university or the state agricultural college.

The locations of the agricultural experiment station and the state agricultural extension service in the various states are given below; these addresses generally include the location of the state university or agricultural college.

TABLE 33-1 LOCATION OF STATE AGRICULTURAL EXPERIMENT STATIONS AND EXTENSION SERVICES

STATE	LOCATION OF STATE AGRICULTURAL EXPERIMENT STATION	TITLE AND ADDRESS OF STATE AGRICULTURAL EXTENSION SERVICE
Alabama	Auburn	Extension Service, Ala. Polytechnic Inst., Auburn
Alaska	College	
Arizona	Tucson	Extension Service, College Agr., Univ. Arizona, Tucson
Arkansas	Fayetteville	Extension Service, Univ. Ark., Little Rock
California	Berkeley	Calif. Agr. Extension Service, Berkeley
Colorado	Fort Collins	Extension Service, Colo. Agr. College, Fort Collins
Connecticut	New Haven (State Station) Storrs (Storrs Station)	Extension Service, Univ. Conn., Storrs
Delaware	Newark	Division of Agr. Extension, Univ. Delaware, Newark
Florida	Gainesville	Agr. Extension Service, Univ. Florida, Gainesville
Georgia	Experiment (State Experiment Station) Tifton (Coastal Plain Experiment Station)	Agr. Extension Service, Univ. Georgia, Athens
Hawaii	Honolulu	Agr. Extension Service, Univ. Hawaii, Honolulu
Idaho	Moscow	Extension Division, Univ. Idaho, Moscow
Illinois	Urbana	Extension Service in Agr. and Home Economics, Coll. of Agr., Univ. Ill., Urbana
Indiana	Lafayette	Dept. Agr. Extension, Purdue Univ., Lafayette
Iowa	Ames	Extension Service, Iowa State College Agr. and Mech. Arts, Ames
Kansas	Manhattan	Division of Extension, Kansas State Univ., Manhattan
Kentucky	Lexington	Extension Division, Coll. Agr. Univ. Ky., Lexington
Louisiana	University Station, Baton Rouge	Extension Division, La. State Univ. and Agr. and Mech. College, Baton Rouge
Maine	Orono	Extension Service, Coll. Agr., Univ. Maine, Orono
Maryland	College Park	Extension Service, Univ. Maryland, College Park

STATE	LOCATION	TITLE AND ADDRESS
Massachusetts	Amherst	Extension Service, Univ. Mass., Amherst
Michigan	East Lansing	Extension Division, Michigan State College, East Lansing
Minnesota	University Farm, St. Paul	Extension Division, Coll. Agr., Univ. Minn., St. Paul
Mississippi	State College	Agr. Extension Dept., Miss. State Coll., State College
Missouri	Columbia (College Station) Mountain Grove (Fruit Station and Poultry Station)	Agr. Extension Service, Coll., Agr., Univ. Missouri, Columbia
Montana	Bozeman	Extension Service, Montana State College, Bozeman
Nebraska	Lincoln	Extension Service, Coll. Agr., Univ. Nebraska, Lincoln
Nevada	Reno	
New Hampshire	Durham	Extension Service, Univ. New Hampshire, Durham
New Jersey	New Brunswick	Division of Extension, Rutgers Univ., New Brunswick
New Mexico	State College	Extension Service, New Mexico State Univ., University Park
New York	Geneva (State Station) Ithaca (Cornell Station)	Extension Service, N. Y. State Coll. Agr. at Cornell Univ., Ithaca
North Carolina	Raleigh	Agr. Extension Service, North Carolina State Coll., Raleigh
North Dakota	Fargo	Extension Dept., North Dakota Agr. Coll., Fargo
Ohio	Wooster	Extension Service, Ohio State Univ., Columbus
Oklahoma	Stillwater	Extension Division, Okla. A. and M. Coll., Stillwater
Oregon	Corvallis	Extension Service, Oregon State Coll., Corvallis
Pennsylvania	State College	Dept. Agr. Extension, Pa. State Univ., State College
Puerto Rico	Mayaguez (Federal Station) Rio Piedras (College Station)	Agr. Extension Service, Univ. Pto. Rico, Rio Piedras
Rhode Island	Kingston	Extension Dept., Rhode Island State Coll., Kingston

STATE	LOCATION	TITLE AND ADDRESS
South Carolina	Clemson	Extension Division, Clemson Agr. Coll., Clemson
South Dakota	Brookings	Extension Division, S.D. State Coll. Agr. and Mech. Arts, Brookings
Tennessee	Knoxville	Division of Extension, Coll. Agr., Univ. Tenn., Knoxville
Texas	College Station	Extension Service, Texas A. and M. Coll., College Station
Utah	Logan	Extension Division, Utah State Agr. Coll., Logan
Vermont	Burlington	Extension Dept., Coll. Agr., Univ. Vt., Burlington
Virginia	Blacksburg (College Station) Norfolk (Truck Experiment Station)	Division of Extension Work, Va. Polytech. Inst., Blacksburg
Washington	Pullman (College Station) Puyallup (Western Washington Station)	Agr. Extension Service, State Coll. Wash., Pullman
West Virginia	Morgantown	Extension Dept., W. Va. Univ., Coll. Agr., Morgantown
Wisconsin	Madison	Extension Division, Coll. Agr., Univ. Wisc., Madison
Wyoming	Laramie	Extension Service, Univ. Wyoming, Laramie

MISCELLANEOUS AGENCIES

Biological supply houses are useful sources of equipment, material, and often of publications of interest to an entomologist. All supply houses publish catalogues, and their catalogues are sent free or at a nominal cost to teachers and schools. These catalogues are of value in indicating what can be obtained from the supply houses, and many of their illustrations will suggest to the ingenious student or teacher things that he can prepare himself.

A list of the supply houses handling entomological equipment and supplies is given on page 704. Some of these (for example, General Biological, Ward's, and Carolina Biological Supply) put out a monthly publication that is sent free to teachers. These publications often contain articles of a technical nature as well as suggestions for the teacher. General Biological Supply House also publishes a series of leaflets called Turtox Service Leaflets, which cover a variety of subjects, and many of them are of value to the student or teacher of entomology.

Many societies, museums, and research institutions publish material that is useful to the entomologist. Entomological societies (see below), state biological survey organizations, and organizations such as the National Audubon Society (1130 Fifth Ave., New York 28, N. Y.), will send lists of their publications on request.

DIRECTORIES OF ENTOMOLOGISTS

Anyone interested in insects will find it profitable to become acquainted with others who have similar interests. If he is located near a university or museum or experiment station, he should become acquainted with the workers there who are interested in insects. Persons throughout the country who are interested in various phases of entomology can often be located by consulting the membership lists of the various entomological societies, which are usually published at intervals in the societies' journals, or various directories. Some of the most useful directories of people working in entomology and other biological fields are mentioned below; they are usually available in a good public or university library.

Naturalists' Directory. This is published every few years by the Cassino Press, Salem, Massachusetts. The entries include the name, address, and special interests, and are arranged alphabetically under the various states, Canadian provinces, and many foreign countries.

Directory of Zoological Taxonomists of the World. This was published by the Society of Systematic Zoology in 1961. It contains (1) a detailed classification of the animal kingdom, with a list of the specialists working on each group, and (2) an alphabetical list of the specialists, with their addresses. It is particularly valuable in locating someone who is an authority on a particular group of animals.

Directories of the U.S. Department of Agriculture: *Directory of Organization and Field Activities of the U.S. Department of Agriculture;* USDA Agric. Handbook No. 76 (1960). *Workers in Subjects Pertaining to Agriculture in Land-Grant Colleges and Experiment Stations, 1961-62;* USDA Agric. Handbook No. 116 (1962). These directories are revised every year or so, and are particularly useful for determining who is located at a particular university or experiment station.

American Men of Science. Volume 2 of the tenth edition (1960) covers the biological sciences; the entries are listed alphabetically and include a biographical sketch.

Who Knows—and What. This is a biographical directory of authorities in various fields; the entries include a biographical sketch, and there is a detailed classification of subject matter fields, with reference to the authorities in each.

Entoma. This book, which is published every few years by the Entomological Society of America, is not primarily a directory of entomologists, but of various entomological services and products; it contains a great deal of information regarding entomological equipment and supplies, sources of insecticides, and the like.

ENTOMOLOGICAL SOCIETIES

There are a great many entomological societies in this country, membership in which is generally open to anyone interested in entomology. The dues vary, but are generally $5.00 or more per year. Members receive the publications of the society, notices of meetings, and news letters. The national societies usually have meetings only once a year; smaller local societies may have meetings at more frequent intervals.

A list of the entomological societies in the United States and Canada may be found in *Entomol. News,* 42(4): 126-130 (1931), and a list of the entomological societies of the world may be found in *Bull. Ent. Soc. Am.,* 2(4): 1-22 (1956). Some of the better known entomological societies in the United States and Canada, with their addresses and principal publications, are as follows:

American Entomological Society. Academy of Natural Sciences, Philadelphia, Pennsylvania. *Transactions of the American Entomological Society;* quarterly. *Entomological News;* monthly, except August and September.

Brooklyn Entomological Society. Brooklyn,

New York. *Bulletin of the Brooklyn Entomological Society;* five times yearly. *Entomologica Americana;* quarterly.

Cambridge Entomological Club. Harvard University, Cambridge, Massachusetts. *Psyche;* quarterly.

Entomological Society of America. 4603 Calvert Road, College Park, Maryland. *Annals of the Entomological Society of America;* quarterly. *Journal of Economic Entomology;* bimonthly. *Bulletin of the Entomological Society of America;* quarterly.

Entomological Society of Ontario. Guelph, Ontario. *Canadian Entomologist;* monthly (since 1953 published jointly by the Entomological Society of Ontario and the Entomological Society of Canada).

Entomological Society of Washington. Washington, D. C. *Proceedings of the Entomological Society of Washington;* monthly, except July, August, and September.

Florida Entomological Society. Gainesville, Florida. *The Florida Entomologist;* quarterly.

Kansas Entomological Society. Manhattan, Kansas. *Journal of the Kansas Entomological Society;* quarterly.

New York Entomological Society. New York. *Journal of the New York Entomological Society;* quarterly.

Pacific Coast Entomological Society. San Francisco, California. *The Pan-Pacific Entomologist;* quarterly.

USE OF A LIBRARY

Small public libraries seldom have much reference material on insects, but large university libraries or the libraries of museums and research institutions usually contain a great deal. Since the average student knows very little about how to use a library, it seems worth while to discuss this subject briefly here.

Large libraries are usually staffed with well-trained workers, and it will be to the student's advantage to become acquainted with the staff of a library he plans to use. It will also be to his advantage to learn something of the general layout of the library—where the books on particular subjects are kept, where the card catalogues are located, and how the books in the library are classified.

There are two principal systems of library classification in use; most large libraries use either the Library of Congress System or the Dewey Decimal System. Whatever the system, each book is marked with a catalogue number that indicates something of the book's content, and the books are arranged on the shelves according to the catalogue number. If one understands the system used, it will take much less time to locate any particular book. In the Library of Congress System, letters are used to designate the main classifications, and numbers are used for subordinate categories; for example, Q represents scientific books, with QK for botany, QL for zoology, QR for bacteriology, and so on. In the Dewey Decimal System, numbers alone are used, with each digit in the number representing a particular classification; for example, the digit 5 of a 500 number indicates a book on natural science, with 590 for zoology, 595 for insects and certain other invertebrates, 595.7 for insects, and 595.76 for beetles.

Every library contains a card catalogue, with one or more cards for each book and periodical, and the cards are arranged alphabetically. Each book is listed by author, by title, and one or more times by subject. The card for each book contains the author's name, the name of the book, the number of pages and figures, when and where the book was published, and often a brief outline of its contents; the card also contains a catalogue number, which tells anyone familiar with the system of classification and the arrangement of the books in the library where to look for that particular book.

Below is a list of important general references, usually available in a large library, which will help one locate a particular book, periodical, or other reference:

A World Bibliography of Bibliographies. Three editions are now out, 1939-1940, 1947-1949, and 1955, the last consisting of four volumes. This covers most separate bibliographic works published in European languages since 1470; it is general in scope and stronger in the humanities than in technical fields.

Bibliographic Index. This is a journal, published quarterly; it is a bibliography of bibliographies classified by subjects arranged alphabetically.

The United States Catalogue and the Cumulative Book Index. This is published monthly, with cumulations at intervals. All books and pamphlets printed in English are listed alphabetically by author, title, and subject. This reference is a useful source of information on current or recent books.

Document Catalogue. This is a journal, published monthly; it lists all government publications, alphabetically by author and subject, and is a comprehensive list of all government publications.

Monthly Check List of State Publications. Publications are listed in this journal by states and departments, with an annual index by author, title, and subject. This reference is useful as a source of information on the publications of such state agencies as experiment stations, universities, wildlife departments, and the like.

Concilium Bibliographicum. This contains bibliographic references printed on 3 by 5 cards, one reference to a card; it was published from 1896 to 1940. The cards are arranged according to a classification number (the system of classification is similar to the Dewey Decimal System), and each card contains the complete citation. The classification is quite detailed, and references on any particular subject are easy to locate.

Zoological Record. This is a bibliography of the world literature on zoology and has been published annually since 1864. It contains titles of papers, books, and the like, arranged alphabetically by author under some 19 major headings; each of the 19 sections contains a subject index and a systematic index (to orders, families, and so forth).

Agricultural Index. This index is published monthly; it is a detailed index, alphabetically arranged by subject, to some 150 American and English periodicals and to government publications.

Bibliography of Agriculture. This is published monthly; it lists references, alphabetically by subject, on subjects pertaining to agriculture from all over the world; it contains a section on entomology.

Bibliography of the More Important Contributions to American Economic Entomology. Parts 1 to 5 were by Samuel Henshaw, 1890-1896, and Parts 6 to 8 were by Nathan Banks, 1898-1905.

Index to the Literature of American Economic Entomology. This was published from 1917 to 1962, the first several volumes about every five years, and more recent volumes yearly; Volume 18 (1962), which covers the literature of 1959, is the last in this series. This is a very valuable index for entomologists; the entries in each volume are arranged alphabetically by author and subject, and the subject classification is quite detailed. The more recent volumes cover the literature from North America, Hawaii, and the West Indies.

Review of Applied Entomology. This is published monthly in two series: A, agricultural entomology, and B, medical and veterinary entomology; it is an abstracting journal of the world literature on applied entomology. The entries are not arranged in any special sequence, but each volume contains an author and a detailed subject index.

Biological Abstracts. This is an abstracting journal, published monthly, with the papers arranged in each issue under a number of major subject matter headings. Each volume is fully indexed. This is a very useful reference in all fields of biology.

REFERENCES

Borror, Donald J. 1934. Ecological studies of *Argia moesta* Hagen (Odonata) by means of marking. Ohio J. Sci., 34(2):97-108; 17 f., 2 graphs.

Borror, Donald J. 1948. Analysis of repeat records of banded white-throated sparrows. Ecol. Monographs, 18(3):411-430; 4 f.

Borror, Donald J. 1958. A projection cell for small aquatic organisms. Turtox News, 36(2):50-51; 1 f.

Brower, A. E. 1930. An experiment in marking moths and finding them again (Noctuidae). Entomol. News, 41(1):10-15; 41(2):44-46; pl. II.

Chamberlin, W. J. 1946. Entomological nomenclature and literature. Ann Arbor, Mich.: J. W. Edwards, Publisher, Inc. xvi + 135 pp.

Cruickshank, Allan D. (ed.) 1957. Hunting with the camera. New York: Harper & Bros. 215 pp., frontis. (color) + 41 f. Chapter 4, Insects, by Edward S. Ross; pp. 108-134, f. 23-29.

Demerec, M., and B. P. Kaufman. 1945. Drosophila guide. Washington: Carnegie Inst. Wash. Publ. 44 pp., 14 f.

Hillcourt, William. 1950. Field book of nature activities. New York: G. P. Putnam's Sons. 320 pp., illus.

Kalmus, Hans. 1948. Simple experiments with insects. London: William Heinemann, Ltd. xii + 132 pp., 39 f.

Kinne, Russ. 1962. The complete book of nature photography. New York: A. S. Barnes & Company, Inc. 191 pp., illus.

Lindquist, A. W., W. W. Yates, R. A. Hoffman, and J. S. Butts. 1951. Studies of the flight habits of three species of flies tagged with radioactive phosphorus. J. Econ. Entomol., 44(3):397-400.

Miller, D. F., and G. W. Blaydes. 1962 (2nd ed.). Methods and materials for teaching biological sciences. New York: McGraw-Hill Book Company, Inc. x + 453 pp., illus.

Mueller, Justus F. 1935. A manual of drawing for science students. New York: Rinehart & Company, Inc. xiv + 122 pp., 90 f.

Needham, J. G., *et al.* 1937. Culture methods for invertebrate animals. Ithaca, N.Y.: Comstock Publishing Co., Inc. xxxii + 590 pp., 84 f.

Peterson, Alvah. 1953 (7th ed.). A manual of entomological techniques. Ann Arbor, Mich.: J. W. Edwards, Publisher, Inc. v + 367 pp., 182 pl.

Ridgway, John L. 1938. Scientific illustration. Stanford University, Calif.: Stanford Univ. Press. xiv + 173 pp., 23 f., 22 pl.

Smith, Roger C. 1958 (5th ed.). Guide to the literature of the zoological sciences. Minneapolis: Burgess Publishing Co. xi + 203 pp.

Trelease, Sam F. 1947. The scientific paper—how to prepare it—how to write it. Baltimore: The Williams and Wilkins Company. 152 pp., 8 f.

Zweifel, Frances W. 1961. A handbook of biological illustration. Chicago: University of Chicago Press. xv + 131 pp., 61 f.

Glossary

Abdòmen—the posterior of the three main body divisions (Fig. 2-1, *ab*).

Accéssory cell—a closed cell in the front wing of Lepidoptera formed by the fusion of two branches of the radius, usually the R_3 cell (Fig. 26-15, *acc*).

Accessory vein—an extra branch of a longitudinal vein (indicated by a subscript *a*; for example, an accessory of M_1 is designated M_{1a}); the most posterior vein in the anal area of the front wing of certain Hymenoptera (Fig. 29-1, *ac*).

Acróstichal bristles—one or more longitudinal rows of small bristles along the center of the mesonotum (Diptera; Fig. 27-5, *acr*).

Acùlea (pl., **acùleae**)—minute spines on the wing membrane (Lepidoptera).

Acùleate—with aculeae (Lepidoptera); with a sting (Hymenoptera).

Acùminate—tapering to a long point.

Acute—pointed; forming an angle of less than 90°.

Adfrontal areas—a pair of narrow oblique sclerites on the head of a lepidopterous larva (Fig. 26-3, *adf*).

Adventítious vein—a secondary vein, neither accessory nor intercalary, usually the result of a number of cross-veins lined up to form a continuous vein.

Aèdeàgus—the male intromittent organ; the distal part of the phallus.

Aestivation—dormancy during a warm or dry season.

Agámic—reproducing parthenogenetically, that is, without mating.

Alinòtum—the notal plate of the mesothorax or metathorax of a pterygote insect (Fig. 2-4, *AN*).

Álula (pl., **álulae**)—calypter (see).

Ametábolous—without metamorphosis.

Anal—pertaining to the last abdominal segment (which bears the anus); the posterior basal part (for example, of the wing).

Anal area of the wing—the posterior portion of the wing, usually including the anal veins.

Anal cell—a cell in the anal area of the wing; cell 1A (Diptera; Fig. 27-3 B, A).

Anal crossing—where vein A branches posteriorly from Cu + A (Odonata, Fig. 8-2, *Ac*).

Anal lobe—a lobe in the posterior basal part of the wing.

Anal loop—a group of cells in the hind wing of dragonflies, between Cu_2, 1A and 2A, which may be rounded (Fig. 8-4 B), elongate (Fig. 8-4 C), or foot-shaped (Fig. 8-2, *alp*).

Anal veins—the longitudinal veins posterior to the cubitus, usually three in number (Fig. 2-8 A).

Annulated—with ringlike segments or divisions.

Anteápical—just proximad of the apex.

Anteapical cell—a cell in the distal part of the wing (leafhoppers; Fig. 20-1, table).

Anteclýpeus—an anterior division of the clypeus (Fig. 8-6, *aclp*).

Antecóxal sclerite—a sclerite of the metasternum, just anterior to the hind coxae.

Antenna (pl., **antennae**)—a pair of segmented appendages located on the head above the mouth parts, and usually sensory in function (Fig. 2-9).

Antennal club—the enlarged distal segments of a clubbed antenna (Fig. 22-3, *acl*).

Antennal fossa—a cavity or depression in which the antennae are located (Fig. 27-4, *af*).

Antennal groove—a groove in the head capsule into which the basal segment of the antenna fits (Fig. 22-3, *agr*).

Anténnule—the first antennae of Crustacea (Fig. 30-1, *antl*).

Antenòdal cross-veins—cross-veins along the costal border of the wing, between the base of the wings and the nodus, extending from the costa to the radius (Odonata; Fig. 8-2, *an*).

Antepenúltimate—the second from the last.

Anterior—front; in front of.

Anterior cross-vein—the r-m cross-vein (Diptera; Fig. 27-3 B, *acv*).

Anterodorsal—in the front and at the top or upper side.

Anteromésal—in the front and along the midline of the body.

Anteroventral—in the front and underneath or on the lower side.

Ànus—the posterior opening of the alimentary tract (Fig. 2-17, *ans*).

Àpical—at the end, tip, or outermost part.

Apical cell—a cell near the wing tip (Figs. 20-1, table; 27-3 B, *SM*; 29-1, 29-3, *AP*).

Apical cross-vein—a cross-vein near the apex of the wing (Plecoptera, Fig. 11-6, *apc*; Homoptera, Fig. 20-1, table).

Apodeme—an invagination of the body wall that forms a rigid process that serves for muscle attachment and for strengthening the body wall (Fig. 2-2, *apd*).

Apóphysis (pl., **apóphyses**)—a tubercular or elongate process of the body wall, either external or internal (Fig. 2-2, *apo*).

Appendículate marginal cell—with the vein forming the posterior side of the marginal cell extending a short distance beyond the apex of the cell (Hymenoptera; Figs. 29-66, 29-68, *ap*).

Appendix—a supplementary or additional piece or part (of the homopteran wing, see Fig. 20-1, *ap*).

Ápterous—wingless.

Aptérygote—belonging to the subclass Apterygòta (see Chap. 6).

Aquatic—living in water.

Arcuate—bent like a bow, or arched.

Árculus—a basal cross-vein between the radius and the cubitus (Odonata; Figs. 8-2 to 8-4, *arc*).

Àreole—an accessory cell (see also basal areole).

Arèolet—a small cell in the wing; in the Ichneumonidae, the small submarginal cell opposite the second recurrent vein (Fig. 29-21 A, *are*).

Arista—a large bristle, usually dorsally located, on the apical antennal segment (Diptera; Fig. 27-4, *ar*).

Arístate—bristlelike; with an arista; aristate antenna, Figs. 2-9 J and 27-14.

Aròlium (pl., **aròlia**)—a padlike structure at the apex of the last tarsal segment, between the claws (Orthoptera; Fig. 9-4 D, *aro*); a padlike structure at the base of each tarsal claw (Hemiptera; Figs. 19-1, 19-3 A, *aro*).

Articulation—a joint, as between two segments or structures.

Aspirator—a device with which insects may be picked up by suction (Fig. 32-6).

Asymmetrical—not alike on the two sides.

Àtrium (pl., **àtria**)—a chamber; a chamber just inside a body opening.

Attenuated—very slender and gradually tapering distally.

Átrophied—reduced in size, rudimentary.

Auricle—a small lobe or earlike structure (Hymenoptera; Fig. 29-79, *au*).

Auxílary vein—the subsosta (Diptera; Fig. 27-3 B, *av*).

Axílla (pl., **axíllae**)—a triangular or rounded sclerite laterad of the scutellum, and usually just caudad of the base of the front wing (Hymenoptera; Fig. 29-4, *ax*).

Áxillary cell—a cell in the anal area of the wing (Diptera, Fig. 27-3 B, *axc*; Hymenoptera, Fig. 29-1, *ax*).

Axillary vein—a vein in the anal area of the hind wing (Hymenoptera, Sýmphyta; Fig. 29-1, *axv*).

Band—a transverse marking broader than a line.

Basad—toward the base.

Basal—at the base; near the point of attachment (of an appendage).

Basal anal cell—an anal cell near the wing base; a cell at the base of the wing between 1A and 2A (Plecoptera; Fig. 11-4, *BA*).

Basal areole—a small cell at the base of the wing; the cell at the base of the wing between *Sc* and *R* (Lepidoptera; Figs. 26-23 to 26-25, *BA*).

Basal cell—a cell near the base of the wing, bordered at least in part by the unbranched portions of the longitudinal veins; in the Diptera, one of the two cells proximal to the anterior cross-vein and the discal cell (Fig. 27-3 B, *B*); Hymenoptera, see Figs. 29-1 and 29-3.

Basal vein—a vein in about the middle of the front wing, extending from the median vein to the subcostal vein (Hymenoptera; Figs. 29-1 and 29-3, *bv*).

Basement membrane—a noncellular membrane underlying the epidermal cells of the body wall (Fig. 2-2, *bm*).

Basistérnum—that part of the sternum anterior to the sternacostal suture.

Beak—the protruding mouth-part structures of a sucking insect; proboscis (Figs. 2-11 to 2-13, *bk*).

Bìfid—forked, or divided into two parts.

Bilateral symmetry (see symmetry).

Bilobed—divided into two lobes.

Bipectinate—having branches on two sides like the teeth of a comb.

Biràmous—with two branches; consisting of an endopodite and an exopodite (Crustacea).

Bisexual—with males and females (insects).

Bituberculate—with two tubercles or swellings.

Bivalved—with two valves or parts; clamlike.

Book gill—the leaflike gills of a horseshoe crab (Fig. 30-15, *bg*).

Book lung—a respiratory cavity containing a series of leaflike folds (spiders).

Borrow pit—a pit formed by an excavation, where earth has been "borrowed" for use elsewhere.

Boss—a smooth lateral prominence at the base of the chelicera (spiders).

Brace vein—a slanting cross-vein; in Odonata, a slanting cross-vein just behind the proximal end of the stigma (Fig. 8-4 F, *bvn*).

Brachýpterous—with short wings that do not cover the abdomen.

Bridge cross-vein—a cross-vein above the bridge vein (Odonata; Fig. 8-2, *bcv*).

Bridge vein—the vein that appears as the basal part of the radial sector, between M_{1+2} and the oblique vein (Odonata; Fig. 8-2, *brv*).

Brood—the individuals that hatch from the eggs laid by one mother, individuals that hatch at about the same time and normally mature at about the same time.

Búcca (pl., **búccae**)—a sclerite on the head below the compound eye and just above the mouth opening (Diptera; Fig. 27-4, *buc*).

Búccula (pl., **bucculae**)—one of two ridges on the under side of the head, on each side of the beak (Hemiptera; Figs. 2-11, 19-1, *buc*).

Caècum (pl., **caèca**)—a saclike or tubelike structure, open at only one end.

Calamístrum—one or two rows of curved spines on the metatarsus of the hind legs (spiders; Fig. 30-30, *clm*).

Cállus (pl., **cálli**)—a rounded swelling.

Calýpter—one of two small lobes at the base of the wing, located just above the haltere (Diptera; Fig. 27-3, *cal*). (Also called alula or squama.)

Camera lùcida—a device enabling one to make accurate drawings of objects seen through a microscope; when it is attached to the eyepiece of the microscope (Fig. 33-19), the observer can see the object under the microscope and his drawing paper at the same time.

Campániform sensíllum—a sense organ consisting of a dome-shaped cuticular area into which the sensory cell process is inserted like the clapper of a bell.

Campodèiform larva—a larva shaped like the thysanuran *Campòdea* (Fig. 6-4 A), that is, elongate, flattened, with well-developed legs and antennae, and usually active.

Cannibalistic—feeding on other individuals of the same species.

Capitate—with an apical knoblike enlargement; capitate antennae, Fig. 2-9 F.

Càrapace—a hard dorsal covering consisting of fused dorsal sclerites (Crustacea; Fig. 30-1, *crp*).

Cardo (pl., **cardines**)—the basal segment or division of a maxilla (Fig. 2-10 A, *cd*); one of two small laterobasal sclerites in the millipede gnathochilarium (Fig. 30-11 B, *cd*).

Carìna (pl., **carìnae**)—a ridge or keel.

Càrinate—ridged or keeled.

Carnivorous—feeding on the flesh of other animals.

Caste—a form or type of adult in a social insect (termites, see Fig. 10-2; ants, see Fig. 29-56).

Caterpillar—an eruciform larva; the larva of a butterfly, moth, sawfly, or scorpionfly.

Caudad—toward the tail, or toward the posterior part of the body.

Caudal—pertaining to the tail or the posterior part of the body.

Caudal filament—a threadlike process at the posterior end of the abdomen.

Cell—a unit mass of protoplasm, surrounded by a cell membrane and containing one or more nuclei or nuclear material; a space in the wing membrane partly (an open cell) or completely (a closed cell) surrounded by veins.

Céphalad—toward the head or anterior side.

Cephálic—on or attached to the head; anterior.

Céphalothòrax—a body region consisting of head and thoracic segments (Crustacea and Arachnida; Fig. 30-28, *cph*).

Cercus (pl., **cerci**)—one of a pair of appendages at the end of the abdomen (Fig. 2-1, *cr*).

Cervical—pertaining to the neck or cervix.

Cervical sclerite—a sclerite located in the lateral part of the cervix, between the head and the prothorax (Fig. 2-4, *cvs*).

Cervix—the neck, a membranous region between the head and prothorax (Fig. 2-4, *cvx*).

Chaètotáxy—the arrangement and nomenclature of the bristles on the exoskeleton (Diptera; Figs. 27-4 and 27-5).

Cheek—the lateral part of the head between the compound eye and the mouth (see *gena*).

Chèlate—pincerslike, having two opposable claws.

Chelícera (pl., **chelícerae**)—the anterior pair of appendages in arachnids (Fig. 30-28, *ch*).

Chèliped—a leg terminating in an enlarged pincerslike structure (Crustacea; Fig. 30-1, *chp*).

Chìtin—a nitrogenous polysaccharide with the formula $(C_{32}H_{54}N_4O_{21})_x$, occurring in the cuticula of arthropods.

Chordotònal organ—a sense organ the cellular elements of which form an elongate structure attached at both ends to the body wall.

Chrýsalis (pl., **chrýsalids or chrysálides**)—the pupa of a butterfly (Fig. 26-4 A, B).

Class—a subdivision of a phylum or subphylum, containing a group of related orders.

Clàval suture—the suture of the front wing separating the clavus from the corium (Hemiptera; Fig. 19-1, *cls*).

Claval vein—a vein in the clavus (Hemiptera, Homoptera, Fig. 20-6, *clv*).

Clàvate—clublike, or enlarged at the tip; clavate antenna, Fig. 2-9 D, E.

Clàvus—the oblong or triangular anal portion of the front wing (Hemiptera and Homoptera; Figs. 19-1, 19-4, *cl*).

Claw tuft—a dense tuft of hairs below the claws (spiders, Fig. 30-30 D, *clt*).

Cleft—split or forked.

Closed cell—a wing cell bounded on all sides by veins and not reaching the wing margin.

Closed coxal cavity—one bounded posteriorly by a sclerite of the same thoracic segment (front coxal cavities, Coleoptera, Fig. 22-4 B), or one completely surrounded by sternal sclerites and not touched by any pleural sclerites (middle coxal cavities, Coleoptera, Fig. 22-4 D).

Clubbed—with the distal part (or segments) enlarged; clubbed antennae, Fig. 2-9 D-F, L. M.

Clýpeus—a sclerite on the lower part of the face, between the frons and the labium (Fig. 2-3, *clp*).

Coárctate larva—a larva somewhat similar to a dipterous puparium, in which the skin of the preceding instar is not completely shed but remains attached to the caudal end of the body; the sixth instar of a blister beetle, also called a pseudopupa (Fig. 22-45 H).

Coarctate pupa—a pupa enclosed in a hardened shell formed by the next to the last larval skin (Diptera; Fig. 3-7 F.).

Cocoon—a silken case inside which the pupa is formed.

Cóllophore—a tubelike structure located on the ventral side of the first abdominal segment (Collembola; Fig. 6-5, *co*).

Cóllum—the tergite of the first body segment (Diplopoda; Fig. 30-11 A, *colm*).

Còlon—the large intestine; that part of the hindgut between the ileum and the rectum (Fig. 2-17, *cn*).

Cólulus—a slender pointed structure lying just anterior to the spinnerets (spiders).

Commensalism—a living together of two or more species, none of which is injured thereby, and at least one of which is benefited.
Compound eye—an eye composed of many individual elements or ommatidia, each of which is represented externally by a facet; the external surface of such an eye consists of circular facets that are very close together, or of facets that are in contact and more or less hexagonal in shape (Fig. 2-1, *e*).
Compressed—flattened from side to side.
Cóndyle—a knoblike process forming an articulation.
Cónnate—fused together or immovably united.
Constricted—narrowed.
Contíguous—touching each other.
Convergent—becoming closer distally.
Corbícula (pl., **corbículae**)—a smooth area on the outer surface of the hind tibia, bordered on each side with a fringe of long curved hairs, which serves as a pollen basket (bees; Fig. 29-79, *cb*).
Corium—the elongate, usually thickened, basal portion of the front wing (Hemiptera; Fig. 19-4, *cor*).
Cornea—the cuticular part of an eye.
Cornicle—one of a pair of dorsal tubular processes on the posterior part of the abdomen (aphids; Fig. 20-3, *crn*).
Córonal suture—a longitudinal suture along the midline of the vertex, between the compound eyes (Fig. 2-3, *cs*).
Corpus allatum—one of a pair of small structures immediately behind the brain.
Cósta—a longitudinal wing vein, usually forming the anterior margin of the wing (Fig. 2-8, C).
Cóstal area—the portion of the wing immediately behind the anterior margin.
Costal break—a point on the costa where the sclerotization is weak or lacking or the vein appears to be broken (Diptera; Figs. 27-22 A, B and 27-23 C-E, *cbr*).
Costal cell—the wing space between the costa and the subcosta.
Coxa (pl., **coxae**)—the basal segment of the leg (Fig. 2-5, *cx*).
Coxópodite—the basal segment of an arthropod appendage.
Crawler—the active first instar of a scale insect (Fig. 20-28 B).
Cremáster—a spinelike or hooked process at the posterior end of the pupa, often used for attachment (Lepidoptera; Fig. 26-4, *cre*).
Crénulate—wavy, or with small scallops.
Cribéllum—a sievelike structure lying just anterior to the spinnerets (spiders; Fig. 30-29 B, *crb*).
Crochets (pronounced **croshàys**)—hooked spines at the tip of the prolegs of lepidopterous larvae (Fig. 26-3, *cro*).
Crop—the dilated portion of the foregut just behind the esophagus (Fig. 2-17, *cp*).
Cross-vein—a vein connecting adjacent longitudinal veins.
Crùciate—crossing; shaped like a cross.
Ctenídium (pl., **ctenídia**)—a row of stout bristles like the teeth of a comb (Psocoptera, Fig. 14-3 F, *ct*; Siphonaptera, Fig. 28-1, *gc*, *prc*).
Cùbito-anal cross-vein—a cross-vein between the cubitus and an anal vein (Fig. 2-8, cu-a).
Cùbitus—the longitudinal vein immediately posterior to the media (Fig. 2-8, Cu).
Cùneus—a more or less triangular apical piece of the corium, set off from the rest of the corium by a suture (Hemiptera; Fig. 19-4 A, *cun*).
Cursorial—fitted for running; running in habit.
Cutícula (or **cùticle**)—the noncellular outer layer of the body wall of an arthropod (Fig. 2-2, *cut*).
Cyst—a sac, vesicle, or bladderlike structure.

Deciduous—having a part or parts that may fall off or be shed.
Decumbent—bent downward.
Deflexed—bent downward.
Dentate—toothed, or with toothlike projections.
Denticulate—with minute toothlike projections.
Depressed—flattened dorsoventrally.
Deùtonymph—the third instar of a mite (Fig. 30-25 D).

Diapause—a period of arrested development or suspended animation.
Dichóptic—the eyes separated above (Diptera).
Dièclous—having the male and female organs in different individuals, any one individual being either male or female.
Dilated—expanded or widened.
Discal cell—a more or less enlarged cell in the basal or central part of the wing (Homoptera, the *R* cell, Fig. 20-1; Lepidoptera, Fig. 26-6, *D*; Diptera, Fig. 27-3 B, *D*).
Discal cross-vein—a cross-vein behind the discal cell (Diptera; Fig. 27-3 B, *dcv*).
Discoidal cell—a cell near the middle of the front wing (Hymenoptera; Figs. 29-1 and 29-3, *D*).
Discoidal vein—the vein forming a continuation of the median vein beyond the end of the transverse median vein, and extending along the posterior margin of the first discoidal cell (Hymenoptera; Figs. 29-1 and 29-3, *d*).
Distad—away from the body, toward the end farthest from the body.
Distal—near or toward the free end of an appendage; that part of a segment or appendage farthest from the body.
Diurnal—active during the daytime.
Divaricate—extending outward and then curving inward or toward each other distally (divaricate tarsal claws, Fig. 22-10 A).
Divergent—becoming more separated distally.
Dormancy—a state of quiescence or inactivity.
Dorsad—toward the back or top.
Dorsal—top or uppermost; pertaining to the back or upper side.
Dorsocentral bristles—a longitudinal row of bristles on the mesonotum; just laterad of the acrostichal bristles (Diptera; Fig. 27-5, *dc*).
Dorsolateral—at the top and to the side.
Dorsomésal—at the top and along the midline.
Dorsoscutellar bristles—a pair of bristles on the dorsal portion of the scutellum, one on each side of the midline (Diptera).
Dorsoventral—from top to bottom, or from the upper to the lower surface.
Dorsum—the back or top (dorsal) side.

Écdysis (pl., **écdyses**)—molting; the process of shedding the exoskeleton.
Ectoparasite—a parasite that lives on the outside of its host.
Ejaculatory duct—the terminal portion of the male sperm duct.
Elatériform larva—a larva resembling a wireworm, that is, slender, heavily sclerotized, with short thoracic legs, and with few body hairs (Fig. 22-30 B).
Elbowed antenna—an antenna with the first segment elongated and the remaining segments coming off the first segment at an angle (Fig. 2-9 N).
Élytron (pl., **élytra**)—a thickened, leathery, or horny front wing (Coleoptera, Dermaptera, some Homoptera; Coleoptera, Fig. 22-1, *el*).
Emarginate—notched or indented.
Embòlium—a narrow piece of the corium, along the costal margin, separated from the rest of the corium by a suture (Hemiptera; Fig. 19-4 C, *emb*).
Emergence—the act of the adult insect leaving the pupal case or the last nymphal skin.
Empòdium (pl., **empòdia**)—a padlike or bristlelike structure at the apex of the last tarsal segment, between the claws (Diptera; Fig. 27-2, *emp*).
Endite—the basal segment of the spider pedipalp, which is enlarged and functions as a crushing jaw (Fig. 30-28, B, *cx*).
Endocutícula—the innermost layer of the cuticula.
Endoparasite—a parasite that lives inside its host (for example, Fig. 27-85 B).
Endópodite—the mesal branch of a biramous appendage.
Endoptérygote—having the wings developing internally; with complete metamorphosis.
Endoskeleton—a skeleton or supporting structure on the inside of the body.
Entire—without teeth or notches, with a smooth outline.
Epicrànium—the upper part of the head, from the face to the neck (Lepidoptera; Fig. 26-3, *epcr*).
Epicutícula—the very thin, nonchitinous, external layer of the cuticula.

Epidermis—the cellular layer of the body wall which secretes the cuticula (Fig. 2-2, *ep*).

Epigastric furrow—a transverse ventral suture near the anterior end of the abdomen, along which lie the openings of the book lungs and the reproductive organs (spiders; Fig. 30-28 B, *ef*).

Epígynum—the external female genitalia of spiders (Fig. 30-28 B, *epg*).

Epimèron (pl., **epimèra**)—the area of a thoracic pleuron posterior to the pleural suture (Fig. 2-4, *epm*).

Epipharynx—a mouth-part structure attached to the inner surface of the labrum or clypeus; in chewing insects a median lobe on the posterior (ventral) surface of the labrum or clypeus.

Epíphysis (pl., **epíphyses**)—a movable pad or lobelike process on the inner surface of the front tibia (Lepidoptera).

Épiphyte—an air plant, one growing nonparasitically upon another plant or upon a nonliving object.

Epipleùra (pl., **epipleùrae**)—the bent-down lateral edge of the elytron (Coleoptera).

Epipleùrite—a small sclerite in the membranous area between the thoracic pleura and the wing bases (Fig. 2-4, *epp*).

Epiproct—a process or appendage situated above the anus and appearing to arise from the tenth abdominal segment; actually the dorsal part of the eleventh abdominal segment (Fig. 2-1, *ept*).

Epistérnum (pl., **epistérna**)—the area of a thoracic pleuron anterior to the pleural suture (Fig. 2-4, *eps*).

Epístomal suture—the suture between the frons and the clypeus (Fig. 2-3, *es*).

Épistome—the part of the face just above the mouth; the oral margin (Diptera).

Erùciform larva—a caterpillar; a larva with a more or less cylindrical body, a well-developed head, and with both thoracic legs and abdominal prolegs.

Esóphagus—the narrow portion of the alimentary canal immediately posterior to the pharynx (Fig. 2-17, *eso*).

Eustérnum—the ventral plate of a thoracic segment, exclusive of the spinasternum.

Evagination—an outpocketing, or saclike structure on the outside.

Eversible—capable of being everted or turned outward.

Exarate pupa—a pupa in which the appendages are free and not glued to the body (Fig. 3-7, C-E).

Excavated—hollowed out.

Exocutícula—the layer of the cuticula just outside the endocuticula, between the endocuticula and the epicuticula.

Exópodite—the outer branch of a biramous appendage.

Exoptérygote—with the wings developing on the outside of the body, as in insects with simple metamorphosis.

Exoskeleton—a skeleton or supporting structure on the outside of the body.

Exserted—protruding or projecting from the body.

External—the outside; that part away from the center (midline) of the body.

Exùviae (always used in the plural)—the cast skin of an arthropod.

Eye-cap—a structure overhanging or capping the compound eye (Lepidoptera; Fig. 26-28 B, *ec*).

Eye, compound (see compound eye).

Eye, simple (see ocellus).

Face—the front of the head, below the frontal suture (Diptera; Fig. 27-4, *fa*).

Facet—the external surface of an individual compound-eye unit or ommatidium.

Family—a subdivision of an order, suborder, or superfamily, and containing a group of related genera, tribes, or subfamilies. Family names end in *-idae.*

Fastígium—the anterior dorsal surface of the vertex (grasshoppers).

Fèces—excrement, the material passed from the alimentary tract through the anus.

Fèmur (pl., **fémora**)—the third leg segment, located between the trochanter and the tibia (Fig. 2-5, *fm*).

Filament—a slender threadlike structure.

File—a filelike ridge on the ventral side of the tegmen, near the base, a part of the stridulating mechanism in crickets and long-horned grasshoppers (Fig. 9-2).

Filiform—hairlike or threadlike; filiform antenna, Fig. 2-9 B.

Flábellate—with fanlike processes or projections; flabellate antenna, Fig. 2-9 L.

Flabéllum (pl., **flabélla**)—a fanlike or leaflike process (Hymenoptera; Fig. 29-15, *flb*).

Flagéllum (pl., **flagélla**)—a whiplike structure; that part of the antenna beyond the second segment (Fig. 2-9, N, *fl*).

Follicle—a minute cavity, sac, or tube.

Fontanélle—a small, depressed, pale spot on the front of the head between the eyes (Isoptera; Fig. 10-3, *fon*).

Foràmen magnum—the opening on the posterior side of the head, through which pass the internal structures that extend from the head to the thorax (Fig. 2-3, *for*).

Foregut—the anterior portion of the alimentary tract, from the mouth to the midgut.

Fossorial—fitted for or with the habit of digging.

Frass—wood fragments made by a wood-boring insect, usually mixed with excrement.

Frénulum—a spine or group of spines arising at the humeral angle of the hind wing (Lepidoptera, Fig. 26-6, *f*).

Frons—the head sclerite bounded by the frontal and epistomal sutures and including the median ocellus (Fig. 2-3, *fr*).

Front—that portion of the face between the antennae, eyes, and ocelli; the frons.

Frontal bristles—bristles above the antennae, away from the edge of the compound eye (Diptera; Fig. 27-25 B, *fb*).

Frontal lùnule—a small crescent-shaped sclerite located just above the base of the antennae (Diptera; Fig. 27-4, *frl*).

Frontal suture—one of two sutures arising at the anterior end of the coronal suture and extending ventrad toward the epistomal suture (Fig. 2-3, *fs*); a suture shaped like an inverted **U**, with the base of the **U** crossing the face above the bases of the antennae, and the arms of the **U** extending downwards on each side of the face (Diptera; Fig. 27-4, *fs*).

Frontal vitta—an area on the head between the antennae and the ocelli (Diptera; Fig. 27-4, *fv*).

Fronto-orbital bristles—bristles along the front next to the compound eyes (Diptera; Fig. 27-4, *fob*).

Furca—a fork or forked structure; a forked apodeme arising from a thoracic sternum.

Furcula—the forked springing apparatus of the Collembola (Fig. 6-5, *fur*).

Gàlea—the outer lobe of the maxilla, borne by the stipes (Fig. 2-10 A, *g*).

Gall—an abnormal growth of plant tissues, caused by the stimulus of an animal or another plant.

Ganglion (pl., **ganglia**)—a knotlike enlargement of a nerve, containing a coordinating mass of nerve cells (Fig. 2-17, *gn*).

Gaster—the rounded part of the abdomen posterior to the nodelike segment or segments (ants).

Gèna (pl., **gènae**)—the part of the head on each side below and behind the compound eyes, between the frontal and occipital sutures (Fig. 2-3, *ge*); the cheek.

Gènal comb—a row of strong spines borne on the anteroventral border of the head (Siphonaptera; Fig. 28-1, *gc*).

Generation—from any given stage in the life cycle to the same stage in the offspring.

Genículate—elbowed, or abruptly bent; geniculate antenna, Fig. 2-9 N.

Genitàlia—the sexual organs and associated structures; the external sexual organs (Figs. 2-6 and 2-7).

Genovertical plate—an area on the head above the antenna, next to the compound eye (Diptera; Fig. 27-4, *gvp*).

Gènus (pl., **género**)—a group of closely related species; the first name in a binomial or trinomial scientific name. Names of genera are Latinized, capitalized, and when printed are italicized.

Gill—evaginations of the body wall or hindgut, functioning in gaseous exchanges in an aquatic animal.

Glàbrous—smooth, without hairs.

Glòbose, Glóbular—spherical or nearly so.

Glossa (pl., **glossae**)—one of a pair of lobes at the apex of the labium between the paraglossae Fig. 2-10 C, *gl*). (In bees, see Fig. 29-15.)

Gnathochilàrium—a platelike mouth-part structure in the Diplopoda, representing the fused maxillae and labium (Fig. 30-11).

Gonapóphysis—a mesal posterior process of a gonopod, in the female forming the ovipositor (see Figs. 2-7 and 6-2).

Gonopod—a modified leg that forms a part of the external genitalia.

Gonopore—the external opening of the reproductive organs.

Gregarious—living in groups.

Grub—a scarabaeiform larva; a thick-bodied larva with a well-developed head and thoracic legs, without abdominal prolegs, and usually sluggish (Fig. 22-59).

Gùla—a sclerite on the ventral side of the head between the labium and the foramen magnum (Fig. 22-2, *gu*).

Gular sutures—longitudinal sutures, one on each side of the gula (Fig. 22-2, *gs*).

Gynándromorph—an abnormal individual containing structural characteristics of both sexes.

Haltère (or **hálter**)—a small knobbed structure on each side of the metathorax representing the hind wings (Diptera; Fig. 5-3, *hal*).

Hámuli (sing., **hámulus**)—minute hooks; a series of minute hooks on the anterior margin of the hind wing, with which the front and hind wings are attached together (Hymenoptera).

Haustellate—formed for sucking, the mandibles not fitted for chewing.

Haustellum—a part of the beak (Diptera; Figs. 2-13 and 2-14, *hst*).

Head—the anterior body region, which bears the eyes, antennae, and mouth parts (Fig. 2-1, *hd*).

Hemélytron (pl., **hemélytra**)—the front wing of Hemiptera (Fig. 19-4).

Hemimetábolous—having a simple metamorphosis like that in the Odonata, Ephemeroptera, and Plecoptera.

Herbívorous—feeding on plants.

Hermáphrodític—possessing both male and female sex organs.

Heterodynamic life cycle—a life cycle in which there is a period of dormancy.

Heterógamy—alternation of bisexual reproduction with parthenogenetic reproduction.

Heterómerous—the three pairs of tarsi differing in the number of segments (Coleoptera; for example, with a tarsal formula of 5-5-4).

Hibernation—dormancy during the winter.

Hindgut—the posterior portion of the alimentary tract, between the midgut and anus.

Holometábolous—with complete metamorphosis.

Holóptic—the eyes contiguous above (Diptera).

Homodynamic life cycle—a life cycle in which there is continuous development, without a period of dormancy.

Hòmonym—one or the same name for two or more different things.

Honeydew—liquid discharged from the anus of certain Homoptera.

Hornworm—a caterpillar (larva of Sphíngidae) with a dorsal spine or horn on the last abdominal segment (Fig. 26-42).

Horny—thickened or hardened.

Host—the organism in or on which a parasite lives; the plant on which an insect feeds.

Hùmeral—pertaining to the shoulder; located in the anterior basal portion of the wing.

Humeral angle—the basal anterior angle or portion of the wing.

Humeral bristles—bristles on the humeral callus (Diptera; Fig. 27-5, *hb*).

Humeral callus—one of the anterior lateral angles of the thoracic notum, usually more or less rounded (Diptera; Fig. 27-5, *hc*).

Humeral cross-vein—a cross-vein in the humeral portion of the wing between the costa and the subcosta (Fig. 2-8, *h*).

Humeral suture—the mesopleural suture (Odonata; Fig. 8-1, pls_2).

Humeral vein—a branch of the subcosta that serves to strengthen the humeral angle of the wing (Neuroptera, Fig. 21-4, *hv*; Lepidoptera, Fig. 26-26, *hv*).

Humerus (pl., **humeri**)—the shoulder; the lateral angle of the pronotum (Hemiptera).

Hyaline—like glass, transparent, colorless.

Hypermetamorphosis—a type of complete metamorphosis in which the different larval instars represent two or more different types of larvae (Fig. 22-45).

Hyperparasite—a parasite whose host is another parasite.

Hypodermis—the epidermis (see).

Hypógnathous—with the head vertical and the mouth parts located ventrally (for example, as in Fig. 2-3).

Hypopharynx—a median mouth-part structure arising postorally and anterior to the labium (Figs. 2-10, 2-12, 2-15, *hyp*); the ducts from the salivary glands are usually associated with the hypopharynx, and in some sucking insects (for example, Figs. 2-12 and 2-15) the hypopharynx is the mouth part structure containing the salivary channel.

Hypopleùral bristles—a more or less vertical row of bristles on the hypopleuron, usually directly above the hind coxae (Diptera; Fig. 27-5, *hyb*).

Hypopleùron (pl., **hypopleùra**)—the lower part of the mesepimeron; a sclerite on the thorax located just above the hind coxae (Diptera; Fig. 27-5, *hypl*).

Ileum—the anterior part of the hindgut (Fig. 2-17, *il*).

Imàgo (pl., **imàgoes** or **imágines**)—the adult or reproductive stage of an insect.

Inclinate—bent toward the midline of the body.

Inferior appendage—the lower one (Anisoptera) or two (Zygoptera) of the terminal abdominal appendages, used in grasping the female at the time of copulation (male Odonata; Fig. 8-1, *iap*).

Infraepistérnum—a ventral subdivision of an episternum (Fig. 8-1, *iep*).

Inner vertical bristles—the more mesally located of the large bristles on the vertex, between the ocelli and the compound eyes (Diptera; Fig. 27-4, *ivb*).

Inquiline—an animal that lives in the nest or abode of another species.

Instar—the stage of an insect between successive molts, the first instar being the stage between hatching and the first molt.

Instinctive behavior—unlearned stereotyped behavior, in which the nerve pathways involved are hereditary.

Integument—the outer covering of the body.

Intelligence—the capacity to modify behavior as a result of experience.

Interantennal suture—a suture extending between the bases of the two antennae (Siphonaptera; Fig. 28-3, *ias*).

Intercàlary vein—an extra longitudinal vein that develops from a thickened fold in the wing, more or less midway between two pre-existing veins (Ephemeroptera; Fig. 7-5, ICu_1).

Intercostal vein—the subcosta (Hymenoptera; Fig. 29-1, *ic*).

Intersternite—an intersegmental sclerite on the ventral side of the thorax; the spinasternum.

Interstitial—situated between two segments; (interstitial trochanter of Coleoptera, Fig. 22-5 D, *tr*); coincident (the ends of two veins meeting).

Intra-alar bristles—a row of two or three bristles situated on the mesonotum above the wing base, between the dorsocentral and the supra-alar bristles (Diptera; Fig. 27-5, *iab*).

Invagination—an infolding or inpocketing.

Iteropàrous—a type of life history in which the animal reproduces two or more times during its lifetime.

Johnston's organ—a sense organ similar to a chordotonal organ, located in the second antennal segment of most insects; functions in sound reception.

Joint—an articulation of two successive segments or parts.

Jùgal lobe—a lobe at the base of the wing, on the posterior side, proximad of the vannal lobe (Hymenoptera; Figs. 29-13 and 29-14, *jl*).

Jùgum—a lobelike process at the base of the front wing, which overlaps the hind wing (Lepidoptera; Fig. 26-5, *j*); a sclerite in the head (Hemiptera and Homoptera; Figs. 2-11 and 19-1, *j*).

Keeled—with an elevated ridge or carina.

Labéllum—the expanded tip of the labium (Diptera; Figs. 2-13 and 2-14, *lbl*).

Làbial—of or pertaining to the labium.

Labial palpus (pl., **labial palpi**)—one of a pair of small feelerlike structures arising from the labium (Fig. 2-10, *lp*).

Labial suture—the suture on the labium between the postmentum and the prementum (Fig. 2-10 C, *ls*).

Làbium—one of the mouth-part structures: the lower lip (Figs. 2-3, *lbm*, and 2-10 C).

Làbrum—the upper lip, lying just below the clypeus (Fig. 2-3, *lbr*).

Labrum-epipharynx—a mouth part representing the labrum and epipharynx.

Lacínia (pl., **lacíniae**)—the inner lobe of the maxilla, borne by the stipes (Fig. 2-10 A, *lc*).

Lamélla (pl., **laméllae**)—a leaflike plate.

Lámellate—with platelike structures or segments; lamellate antenna, Figs. 2-9 M and 22-9 C, D.

Lámina linguàlis—one of two median distal plates in the millipede gnathochilarium (Fig. 30-11 B, *ll*).

Lanceolate—spear-shaped, tapering at each end.

Lanceolate cell—a cell in the anal area of the wing (Hymenoptera; Fig. 29-1, *L*).

Larva (pl., **larvae**)—the immature stages, between the egg and pupa, of an insect having complete metamorphosis; the six-legged first instar of Acarina (Figs. 30-25 B and 30-26); an immature stage differing radically from the adult.

Larviform—shaped like a larva.

Laterad—toward the side, away from the midline of the body.

Lateral—on or pertaining to the side (that is, the right or left side).

Laterotérgite—a tergal sclerite located laterally or dorsolaterally.

Lateroventral—to the side (away from the midline of the body) and below.

Leaf miner—an insect that lives in and feeds upon the leaf cells between the upper and lower surfaces of a leaf.

Lígula—the terminal lobes (or lobe) of the labium, the glossae and paraglossae (Fig. 2-10 C, *lg*).

Linear—linelike, long and very narrow.

Longitudinal—lengthwise of the body or of an appendage.

Looper—a caterpillar that moves by looping its body, that is, placing the posterior part of the abdomen next to the thorax and then extending the anterior part of the body forward; a measuringworm.

Lòrum (pl., **lòra**)—the cheek; a sclerite on the side of the head (Hemiptera and Homoptera; Figs. 19-1 and 20-1, *lo*); the submentum in bees (Fig. 29-15, *smt*).

Luminescent—producing light.

Lunule, frontal (see frontal lunule).

Maggot—a vermiform larva; a legless larva without a well-developed head capsule (Diptera; Fig. 3-6 A).

Malpighian tubules—excretory tubes that arise near the anterior end of the hindgut and extend into the body cavity (Fig. 2-17, *mt*).

Mandible—jaw; one of the anterior pair of the paired mouth-part structures (Fig. 2-10, *md*).

Mandibulate—with jaws fitted for chewing.

Marginal cell—a cell in the distal part of the wing bordering the costal margin (Diptera, Fig. 27-3 B, *MC*; Hymenoptera, Figs. 29-1, 29-3, *MC*).

Marginal vein—a vein on or just within the wing margin; the vein forming the posterior side of the marginal cell (Hymenoptera; Figs. 29-1, 29-3 and 29-16 B, *mv*).

Margined—with a sharp or keel-like lateral edge.

Maxílla (pl., **maxíllae**)—one of the paired mouth-part structures immediately posterior to the mandibles (Fig. 2-10, *mx*).

Máxillary—on or pertaining to the maxilla.

Maxillary palpus (pl., **maxillary palpi**)—a small feelerlike structure arising from the maxilla (Fig. 2-10 A, *mxp*).

Maxílliped—one of the appendages in Crustacea immediately posterior to the second maxillae.

Mèdia—the longitudinal vein between the radius and the cubitus (Fig. 2-8, M).

Medial cross-vein—a cross-vein connecting two branches of the media (Fig. 2-8, m).

Median—in the middle; lying along the midline of the body.

Median cell—a cell between the subcostal and median veins at the base of the wing (Hymenoptera; Figs. 29-1 and 29-3, *MD*).

Medio-cubital cross-vein—a cross-vein connecting the media and cubitus (Fig. 2-8, m-cu).

Membrane—a thin film of tissue, usually transparent; that part of the wing surface between the veins; the thin apical part of a hemelytron (Hemiptera; Fig. 19-4, *mem*).

Mémbranous—like a membrane; thin and more or less transparent (wings); thin and pliable (cuticula).

Mental setae—setae on the mentum (Odonata; Fig. 8-8, *mst*).

Mentum—the distal part of the labium, which bears the palpi and ligula (Fig. 2-10 C, *mn*); a median, more or less triangular plate in the millipede gnathochilarium (Fig. 30-11 B, *mn*).

Meropleùron (pl., **meropleùra**)—a sclerite consisting of the meron (basal part) of the coxa and the lower part of the epimeron.

Mésad—toward the midline of the body.

Mésal—at or near the midline of the body.

Mesénteron—the midgut, or middle portion of the alimentary tract (Fig. 2-17, *mg*).

Mesepimèron (pl., **mesepimèra**)—the epimeron of the mesothorax (Figs. 2-4 and 22-2, epm_2).

Mesepistérnum (pl., **mesepistérna**)—the episternum of the mesothorax (Figs. 2-4 and 22-2, eps_2).

Mesinfraepistérnum—a ventral subdivision of the mesepisternum (Fig. 8-1, iep_2).

Méson—the midline of the body, or an imaginary plane dividing the body into right and left halves.

Mesonòtum—the dorsal sclerite of the mesothorax (Fig. 2-1, n_2).

Mesopleùral bristles—bristles on the mesopleuron (Diptera; Fig. 27-5, *mpb*).

Mesopleùron (pl., **mesopleùra**)—the lateral sclerite(s) of the mesothorax; the upper part of the episternum of the mesothorax (Diptera; Fig. 27-5, pl_2).

Mesoscutellum—the scutellum of the mesothorax (Fig. 2-4, scl_2).

Mesoscùtum—the scutum of the mesothorax (Fig. 2-4, sct_2).

Mesosternum—the sternum, or ventral sclerite, of the mesothorax.

Mesothorax—the middle or second segment of the thorax (Fig. 2-1, th_2).

Métamère—a primary body segment (usually referring to the embryo).

Metamorphosis—change in form during development.

Metanòtum—the dorsal sclerite of the metathorax (Fig. 2-1, n_3).

Metapleùron (pl., **metapleùra**)—the lateral sclerite(s) of the metathorax (Fig. 19-8, pl_3).

Metascutéllum—the scutellum of the metathorax (Fig. 2-4, scl_3).

Metastérnum—the sternum, or ventral sclerite, of the metathorax.

Metatarsus (pl., **metatarsi**)—the basal segment of the tarsus (Fig. 30-28, *mts*).

Metathorax—the third or posterior segment of the thorax (Fig. 2-1, th_3).

Metazònite—the posterior portion of a millipede tergum, when the tergum is divided by a transverse groove.

Metepimèron (pl., **metepimèra**)—the epimeron of the metathorax (Fig. 2-4, epm_3).

Metepistérnum (pl., **metepistérna**)—the episternum of the metathorax (Fig. 2-4, eps_3).

Metinfraepistérnum—a ventral subdivision of the metepisternum (Fig. 8-1, iep_3).

Midgut—the mesenteron, or middle portion of the alimentary tract (Fig. 2-17, *mg*).

Millimeter—0.001 meter, or 0.03937 inch (about 1/25 inch).

Minùte—very small; an insect a few millimeters in length or less would be considered minute.

Mirror—a membrane in the sound-producing organs of a cicada (Fig. 20-10, *mr*).

Molt—a process of shedding the exoskeleton; ecdysis; to shed the exoskeleton.

Monècious—possessing both male and female sex organs, hermaphroditic.

Moniliform—beadlike, with rounded segments; moniliform antenna (Fig. 2-9 C).

Morphology—the science of form or structure.

Myiàsis—a disease caused by the invasion of dipterous larvae.

Naìad—an aquatic, gill-breathing nymph.

Nasùtus (pl., **nasùti**)—an individual of a termite caste in which the head narrows anteriorly into a snoutlike projection (Fig. 10-2 B).

Nocturnal—active at night.

Node—a knoblike or knotlike swelling.

Nodiform—in the form of a knob or knot.

Nodus—a strong cross-vein near the middle of the costal border of the wing (Odonata; Figs. 8-2 to 8-4, *nod*).

Notàulix (pl., **notàulices**)—parapsidal suture (see).

Notopleùral bristles—bristles on the notopleuron (Diptera; Fig. 27-5, *nb*).
Notopleùral suture—a suture between the notum and the pleural sclerites (Fig. 22-2, *npls*).
Notopleùron (pl., **notopleùra**)—an area on the thoracic dorsum, at the lateral end of the transverse suture (Diptera; Fig. 27-5, *npl*).
Nòtum (pl., **nòta**)—the dorsal surface of a body segment (usually used when speaking of the thoracic segments).
Nymph—an immature stage (following hatching) of an insect that does not have a pupal stage; the immature stages of Acarina that have eight legs.

Oblique vein—a slanting cross-vein; in Odonata, where Rs crosses M_{1+2} (Fig. 8-2, *obv*).
Obtect pupa—a pupa in which the appendages are more or less glued to the body surface, as in the Lepidoptera (Figs. 3-7 A, B, and 26-4).
Occipital suture—a transverse suture in the posterior part of the head which separates the vertex from the occiput dorsally and the genae from the postgenae laterally (Fig. 2-3, *os*).
Occiput—the dorsal posterior part of the head, between the occipital and postoccipital sutures (Fig. 2-3, *ocp*).
Ocellar bristles—bristles arising close to the ocelli (Diptera; Fig. 27-4, *ob*).
Ocellar triangle—a slightly raised triangular area in which the ocelli are located (Diptera; Fig. 27-4, *ot*).
Océllus (pl., **océlli**)—a simple eye of an insect or other arthropod (Fig. 2-3, *oc*).
Ommatídium (pl., **ommatídia**)—a single unit or visual section of a compound eye.
Onísciform larva—platyform larva (see).
Oothèca (pl., **oothècae**)—the covering or case of an egg mass (Orthoptera).
Open cell—a wing cell extending to the wing margin, not entirely surrounded by veins.
Open coxal cavity—one bounded posteriorly by a sclerite of the next segment (front coxal cavities, Coleoptera, Fig. 22-4 A), or one touched by one or more of the pleural sclerites (middle coxal cavities, Coleoptera, Fig. 22-4 C).
Opérculum (pl., **opércula**)—a lid or cover.
Oral—pertaining to the mouth.
Oral vibrissae—a pair of stout bristles, one on each side of the face near or just above the oral margin, and larger than the other bristles on the vibrissal ridge (Diptera; Fig. 27-4, *ov*).
Orbital plate—a sclerite on the head next to the compound eye (Diptera; Fig. 27-24 C, *orp*); also called genovertical plate.
Order—a subdivision of a class or subclass, containing a group of related families.
Osmetèrium (pl., **osmetèria**)—a fleshy, tubular, eversible, usually **Y**-shaped scent gland at the anterior end of certain caterpillars (Papilionidae; Fig. 26-3, *osm*).
Óstiole—a small opening.
Óstium (pl., **óstia**)—a slitlike opening of the insect heart.
Outer fork—the fork of R_{4+5} (Ephemeroptera; Figs. 7-4 and 7-5, *of*).
Outer vertical bristles—the more laterally located of the large bristles on the vertex, between the ocelli and the compound eyes (Diptera; Fig. 27-4, *ovb*).
Ovary—the egg-producing organ of the female (Fig. 2-17, *ovy*).
Oviduct—the tube leading away from the ovary through which the eggs pass (Fig. 2-17, *ovd*).
Ovíparous—laying eggs.
Ovipósit—to lay or deposit eggs.
Ovipositor—the egg-laying apparatus; the external genitalia of the female (Figs. 2-1, 2-7, 8-1 E, 29-5, *ovp*).

Paèdogénesis—the production of eggs or young by an immature or larval stage of an animal.
Palp—palpus (*qv*).
Palpifer—the lobe of the maxillary stipes which bears the palpus (Fig. 2-10, A, *plf*).
Palpiger—the lobe of the mentum of the labium which bears the palpus (Fig. 2-10 C, *plg*).
Palpus (pl., **palpi**)—a segmented process borne by the maxillae or labium (Fig. 2-10, *lp, mxp*).
Papílla—a small nipplelike elevation.
Paraglóssa (pl., **paraglóssae**)—one of a pair of lobes at the apex of the labium, laterad of the glossae (Fig. 2-10 C, *pgl*).
Pàraproct—one of a pair of lobes bordering the anus lateroventrally (Fig. 2-1, *ppt*).

Parápsidal suture—a longitudinal suture of the mesonotum separating the median area from the lateral area (Hymenoptera; Figs. 29-4 and 29-17). (Also called parapsidal furrow or notaùlix.)

Parápsis (see scapula).

Parasite—an animal that lives in or on the body of another living animal (its host), at least during a part of its life cycle.

Parasitic—living as a parasite.

Parthenogénesis—reproducing by eggs that develop without being fertilized.

Patélla—a leg segment between the femur and tibia (arachnids; Fig. 30-28, *ptl*).

Paurometábolous—with simple metamorphosis, the young and adults living in the same habitat, and the adults winged.

Pecten—a comblike or rakelike structure (Hymenoptera; Fig. 29-79, *pr*).

Pectinate—with branches or processes like the teeth of a comb; pectinate antenna, Fig. 2-9 H; pectinate tarsal claw, Fig. 22-6 B.

Pedicel—the second segment of the antenna (Fig. 2-9 N, *ped*); the stem of the abdomen, between the thorax and the gaster (ants).

Pedipalps—the second pair of appendages of an arachnid (Figs. 30-19 and 30-28, *pdp*).

Pelagic—inhabiting the open sea; ocean-dwelling.

Penultimate—next to the last.

Péristome—the ventral margin of the head, bordering the mouth.

Peritròphic membrane—a membrane secreted by the cells lining the midgut; this membrane is secreted when food is present, and forms an envelope around the food; it usually pulls loose from the midgut, remains around the food, and passes out with the feces.

Pétiolate—attached by a narrow stalk or stem.

Pétiole—a stalk or stem; the narrow stalk or stem by which the abdomen is attached to the thorax (Hymenoptera).

pH—a measure of the acidity or alkalinity of a medium. A pH value of 7.0 indicates neutral; lower values indicate acid and higher values indicate alkaline.

Phallus—the male intromittent organ, including any processes that may be present at its base.

Pharynx—the anterior part of the foregut, between the mouth and the esophagus (Fig. 2-17, *phx*).

Phrágma (pl., **phrágmata**)—a platelike apodeme or invagination of the dorsal wall of the thorax.

Phỳlum (pl., **phỳla**)—one of the dozen or so major divisions of the animal kingdom.

Phytóphagous—feeding on plants.

Pictured—with spots or bands (wings; for example, Fig. 27-69).

Pílifer—one of a pair of lateral projections on the labrum (Lepidoptera; Fig. 26-2, *pf*).

Pìlose—covered with hair.

Planídium larva—a type of first instar larva in certain Diptera and Hymenoptera which undergo hypermatamorphosis; a larva that is legless and somewhat flattened.

Platyform larva—a larva that is extremely flattened, as the larva of the Psephenidae (Fig. 22-37). (Also called onisciform larva.)

Pleùral—pertaining to the pleura, or lateral sclerites of the body; lateral.

Pleural suture—a suture on a thoracic pleuron extending from the base of the wing to the base of the coxa, which separates the episternum and epimeron (Figs. 2-1 and 2-4, *pls*).

Pleurite—a lateral or pleural sclerite.

Pleuron (pl., **pleura**)—the lateral area of a thoracic segment.

Pleurotérgite—a sclerite containing both tergal and pleural elements.

Plumose—featherlike; plumose antenna, Fig. 2-9 I.

Point—A small triangle of stiff paper, used in mounting small insects (Fig. 32-12).

Pollen basket—(see corbicula).

Pollen brush—a brush of short stiff hairs used in collecting pollen (bees; Fig. 29-79, *pbr*).

Pollen rake (see pecten).

Polyembryony—an egg developing into two or more embryos.

Porrect—extending forward horizontally; porrect antennae, Fig. 27-24 G.

Postabdomen—the modified posterior segments of the abdomen, which are usually more slender than the anterior segments (Crustacea, Fig. 30-3, *pa*; see also the postabdomen in the scorpion, Fig. 30-17).

Posterior—hind or rear.

Posterior callus—a rounded swelling on each side of the mesonotum, between the base of the wing and the scutellum (Diptera; Fig. 27-5, *pc*).

Posterior cell—one of the cells extending to the hind margin of the wing, between the third and sixth longitudinal veins (Diptera; Fig. 27-3 B, *P*).

Posterior cross-vein—a cross-vein at the apex of the discal cell (Diptera; Fig. 27-3 B, *pcv*).

Postgèna (pl., **postgènae**)—a sclerite on the posterior lateral surface of the head, posterior to the gena (Fig. 2-3, *pg*).

Posthùmeral bristle—a bristle on the anterolateral surface of the mesonotum, near the margin of the humeral callus (Diptera; Fig. 27-5, *pb*).

Postmarginal vein—the vein along the anterior margin of the front wing, beyond the point where the stigmal vein arises (Chalcidoidea; Fig. 29-16 B, *pm*).

Postmentum—the basal portion of the labium, proximad of the labial suture (Fig. 2-10 C, *pmt*).

Postnòdal cross-veins—a series of cross-veins just behind the costal margin of the wing, distad of the nodus, and extending from the costal margin of the wing to R_1 (Odonata; Figs. 8-2, 8-3, *pn*).

Postnòtum (pl., **postnòta**)—a notal plate behind the scutellum, often present in wing-bearing segments (Fig. 2-4, *PN*).

Postoccípital suture—the transverse suture on the head immediately posterior to the occipital suture (Fig. 2-3, *pos*).

Postócciput—the extreme posterior rim of the head, between the postoccipital suture and the foramen magnum (Fig. 2-3, *po*).

Postscutéllum—a small transverse piece of a thoracic notum immediately behind the scutellum; in Diptera, an area immediately behind or below the mesoscutellum (Fig. 27-17, *pscl*).

Postvertical bristles—a pair of bristles behind the ocelli, the hindmost of the pairs of bristles in this location, and usually situated on the posterior surface of the head (Diptera; Fig. 27-4, *pv*).

Preápical—situated just before the apex; preapical tibial bristle of Diptera, Fig. 27-26 B, *ptbr*.

Prebasilàre—a narrow transverse sclerite, just posterior (basal) to the mentum, in the gnathochilarium of some millipedes (Fig. 30-11 B, *pbs*).

Predàceous—feeding as a predator.

Predator—an animal that attacks and feeds on other animals, usually animals smaller or less powerful than itself.

Pregenital—anterior to the genital segments of the abdomen.

Prementum—the distal part of the labium, distad of the labial suture, on which all the labial muscles have their insertions (Fig. 2-10 C, *prmt*).

Preoral—anterior to or in front of the mouth.

Prepéctus—an area along the anteroventral margin of the mesepisternum, set off by a suture (Hymenoptera; Fig. 29-4, *pp*).

Prepupa—a quiescent stage between the larval period and the pupal period; the third instar of a thrips (Fig. 18-1 B).

Presutural bristles—bristles on the mesonotum immediately anterior to the transverse suture and adjacent to the notopleuron (Diptera; Fig. 27-5, *psb*).

Probóscis—the extended beaklike mouth parts (Fig. 27-32, *prb*).

Proclinate—inclined forward or downward.

Proctodaèum—the hindgut, or the hindmost of the three major divisions of the alimentary tract, from the Malpighian tubules to the anus.

Produced—extended, prolonged, or projecting.

Proepimèron—the epimeron of the prothorax (Fig. 22-2, epm_1).

Proepistérnum—the episternum of the prothorax (Fig. 22-2, eps_1).

Profile—the outline as seen from the side or in a lateral view.

Prógnathous—having the head horizontal and the mouth parts projecting forward.

Proleg—one of the fleshy abdominal legs of certain insect larvae (Fig. 26-3, *prl*).

Prominence—a raised, produced, or projecting portion.

Prominent—raised, produced, or projecting.

Pronòtal comb—a row of strong spines borne on the posterior margin of the pronotum (Siphonaptera; Fig. 28-1, *prc*).

Pronotum—the dorsal sclerite of the prothorax (Figs. 2-1 and 2-4, n_1).

Propleùral bristles—bristles located on the propleuron (Diptera; Fig. 27-5, *ppb*).
Propleuron (pl., **propleura**)—the lateral portion, or pleuron, of the prothorax (Fig. 27-5, pl_1).
Propòdeum—the posterior portion of the thorax, which is actually the first abdominal segment united with the thorax (Hymenoptera, suborder Apocrita; Fig. 29-4, *prd*).
Propupa—the instar preceding the pupa, in which the wing pads are present and the legs are short and thick (Thysanoptera; Fig. 18-1 B). (Sometimes also called the prepupa.)
Prosòma—a term referring to the anterior part of the body, usually applied to that part of the head anterior to the mouth; the anterior part of the cephalothorax.
Prostérnum—the sternum, or ventral sclerite, of the prothorax.
Prothorax—the anterior of the three thoracic segments (Fig. 2-1, th_1).
Protonymph—the second instar of a mite (Fig. 30-25 C.).
Proventrículus—the posterior portion of the foregut; the gizzard (Fig. 2-17, *prv*).
Proximad—toward the end or portion nearest the body.
Proximal—nearer to the body, or to the base of an appendage.
Prozònite—the anterior portion of a millipede tergum, when the tergum is divided by a transverse groove.
Prùinose—covered with a whitish waxy powder.
Pseudaròlium (pl., **pseudaròlia**)—a pad at the apex of the tarsus, resembling an arolium (Hemiptera; Fig. 19-3, *psa*).
Pseudocùbitus—a vein appearing as the cubitus, but actually formed by the fusion of the branches of M and Cu_1 (Neuroptera; Fig. 21-1 C, *pscu*).
Pseudomèdia—a vein appearing as the media, but actually formed by the fusion of branches of Rs (Neuroptera; Fig. 21-1 C, *psm*).
Pseudopupa—a coarctate larva; a larva in a quiescent pupalike condition, one or two instars before the true pupal stage (Coleoptera, Meloidae; Fig. 22-45 H.)
Pteropleural bristles—bristles on the pteropleuron (Diptera; Fig. 27-5, *ptb*).
Pteropleuron (pl., **pteropleura**)—a sclerite on the side of the thorax, just below the base of the wing, and consisting of the upper part of the mesepimeron (Diptera; Fig. 27-5, *pt*).
Pterostigma—a thickened opaque spot along the costal margin of the wing, near the wing tip (also called the stigma) (Odonata; Figs. 8-2 and 8-3, *st*).
Ptérygote—winged; a member of the sub-class Pterygota (see Chap. 6).
Ptilìnum—a temporary bladderlike structure that can be inflated and thrust out through the frontal suture, just above the bases of the antennae, at the time of emergence from the puparium (Diptera).
Pubéscent—downy, covered with short fine hairs.
Pulvílliform—lobelike or padlike; shaped like a pulvillus; pulvilliform empodium, Fig. 27-2 B, *emp*.
Pulvíllus (pl., **pulvílli**)—a pad or lobe beneath each tarsal claw (Diptera; Fig. 27-2, *pul*).
Punctate—pitted or beset with punctures.
Puncture—a tiny pit or depression.
Pùpa (pl., **pùpae**)—the stage between the larva and the adult in insects with complete metamorphosis, a nonfeeding and usually an inactive stage (Fig. 3-7).
Pupàrium (pl., **pupària**)—a case formed by the hardening of the next to the last larval skin, in which the pupa is formed (Diptera; Fig. 3-7 F).
Pupate—transform to a pupa.
Pupíparous—giving birth to larvae that are full grown and ready to pupate.
Pygídium—the last dorsal segment of the abdomen.

Quadrangle—a cell immediately beyond the arculus (Odonata, Zygoptera; Fig. 8-3, *q*).
Quadrate—four-sided.

Radial cell—a cell bordered anteriorly by a branch of the radius; the marginal cell (Hymenoptera; Fig. 29-6, *MC*).
Radial cross-vein—a cross-vein connecting R_1 and the branch of the radius immediately behind it (Fig. 2-8, *r*).
Radial sector—the posterior of the two main branches of the radius (Fig. 2-8, Rs).
Radius—the longitudinal vein between the subcosta and the media (Fig. 2-8, R).

Raptorial—fitted for grasping prey; raptorial front legs, Figs. 9-4 F, 19-2.
Réclinate—inclined backward or upward.
Rectum—the posterior region of the hindgut (Fig. 2-17, *rec*).
Recurrent vein—one of two transverse veins immediately posterior to the cubital vein (Hymenoptera; Figs. 29-1 and 29-3, *rv*); a vein at the base of the wing between the costa and subcosta, extending obliquely from the subcosta to the costa (Neuroptera; Fig. 21-4, *hv*).
Recurved—curved upward or backward.
Réniform—kidney-shaped.
Retículate—like a network.
Retina—the receptive apparatus of an eye.
Retractile—capable of being pushed out and drawn back in.
Rhabdom—a rodlike structure formed of the inner surfaces of adjacent sensory cells in the ommatidium of a compound eye.
Riker mount—a thin, glass-topped exhibition case filled with cotton (Fig. 32-17).
Rostrum—beak or snout.
Rudimentary—reduced in size, poorly developed, vestigial.

Scape—the basal segment of the antenna (Fig. 2-9 N, *scp*).
Scápula (also called **parápsis**) (pl., **scápulae**)—one of two sclerites of the mesonotum immediately laterad of the parapsidal sutures (Hymenoptera; Fig. 29-4, *sca*).
Scarabaèiform larva—a grublike larva, that is, one with the body thickened and cylindrical, with a well-developed head and thoracic legs, without prolegs, and usually sluggish (Fig. 3-6 B.).
Scavenger—an animal that feeds on dead plants or animals, on decaying materials, or on animal wastes.
Scent gland—a gland producing an odorous substance.
Scientific name—a Latinized name, internationally recognized, of a species or subspecies. The scientific name of a species consists of the generic and specific name and the name of the describer of the species, and that of a subspecies consists of generic, specific, and subspecific names and the name of the describer of the subspecies. Scientific names (excluding authors' names) are always printed in italics.
Sclerite—a hardened body wall plate bounded by sutures or membranous areas.
Sclerotized—hardened.
Scólytoid larva—a fleshy larva resembling the larva of a scolytid beetle.
Scòpa (pl., **scòpae**)—a pollen-collecting apparatus, either a corbicula (which see) or a brush of hairs on the ventral side of the abdomen (bees).
Scópula (pl., **scópulae**)—a small, dense tuft of hair.
Scraper—the sharpened anal angle of the front wing (tegmen) of a cricket or long-horned grasshopper, a part of the stridulating mechanism.
Scròbe—a groove or furrow (antennal scrobe, Fig. 22-78 J, *agr*).
Scutéllum—a sclerite of a thoracic notum (Fig. 2-4, *scl*); the mesoscutellum, appearing as a more or less triangular sclerite behind the pronotum (Hemiptera, Homoptera, Coleoptera).
Scùtum—the middle division of a thoracic notum, just anterior to the scutellum (Fig. 2-4, *sct*).
Sebàceous glands—glands secreting fatty or oily material.
Sectorial cross-vein—a cross-vein connecting two branches of the radial sector (Fig. 2-8, *s*).
Segment—a subdivision of the body or of an appendage, between joints or articulations.
Semelpàrous—a type of life history in which the animal reproduces only once during its lifetime.
Semiaquatic—living in wet places, or partially in water.
Seminal vesicle—a structure, usually saclike, in which the seminal fluid of the male is stored before being discharged.
Sense cone or **sense peg**—a minute cone or peg, sensory in function (Figs. 14-5 F and 18-3, *scn*).
Serrate—toothed along the edge like a saw; serrate antenna, Fig. 2-9 G.
Sessile—attached or fastened, incapable of moving from place to place; attached directly, without a stem or petiole.
Sèta (pl., **sètae**)—a bristle.
Setàceous—bristlelike; setaceous antenna, Fig. 2-9 A.

Sètate—provided with bristles.

Sètulose—bearing short blunt bristles.

Sigmoid—shape like the letter **S**.

Simple—unmodified, not complicated; not forked, toothed, branched, or divided.

Spátulate—spoon-shaped; broad apically and narrowed basally, and flattened.

Species—a group of individuals or populations that are similar in structure and physiology and are capable of interbreeding and producing fertile offspring, and which are different in structure and (or) physiology from other such groups and normally do not interbreed with them.

Spermathèca (pl., **spermathècae**)—the saclike structure in the female in which sperms from the male are received and often stored.

Spinastérnum—an intersegmental sclerite of the thoracic venter which bears a median apodeme or spina, associated with or united with the sternal sclerite immediately anterior to it; also called the intersternite.

Spindle-shaped—elongate and cylindrical, thickened in the middle and tapering at the ends.

Spine—a thornlike outgrowth of the cuticula.

Spinneret—a structure with which silk is spun, usually fingerlike in shape (Figs. 30-28 B and 30-29 B-E, *spn*).

Spinose—beset with spines (a spinose costa in Diptera, Fig. 27-22 H).

Spiracle—an external opening of the tracheal system; a breathing pore (Figs. 2-1 and 2-18, *spr*).

Spirácular bristle—a bristle very close to a spiracle (Diptera; Fig. 27-21, *spbr*).

Spiracular plate—a platelike sclerite next to or surrounding the spiracle.

Spur—a moveable spine; when on a leg segment usually located at the apex of the segment.

Spùrious claw—a false claw; a stout bristle that looks like a claw (spiders).

Spurious vein—a veinlike thickening of the wing membrane between two true veins; an adventitious longitudinal vein between the radius and the media, crossing the r-m cross-vein (Diptera; Fig. 27-11, A-C, *spv*).

Squàma (pl., **squàmae**)—a scalelike structure; a calypter; the palpiger (Odonata; Fig. 8-5, *plg*).

Stadium (pl., **stadia**)—the period between molts in a developing insect.

Stalked—with a stalk or stem; with a narrow stemlike base; fused together to form a single vein.

Sternacóstal suture—a suture of the thoracic sternum, the external mark of the sternal apophysis or furca, separating the basisternum from the sternellum.

Sternàuli (pl., **sternàulices**)—a longitudinal furrow on the lower part of the mesopleuron (Hymenoptera).

Sternéllum—the part of the eusternum posterior to the sternacostal suture.

Sternite—a sclerite on the ventral side of the body; the ventral sclerite of an abdominal segment (Fig. 2-1, *stn*).

Sternopleùral bristles—bristles on the sternopleuron (Diptera; Fig. 27-5, *stb*).

Sternopleuron (pl., **sternopleura**)—a sclerite in the lateral wall of the thorax, just above the base of the middle leg (Diptera; Fig. 27-5, *stpl*).

Stígma (pl., **stígmata**)—a thickening of the wing membrane along the costal border of the wing near the apex (Figs. 8-2, 8-3, 14-3, *st*).

Stigmal vein—a short vein extending posteriorly from the costal margin of the wing, usually a little beyond the middle of the wing (Chalcidoidea; Fig. 29-16 B, *sv*).

Stìpes (pl., **stípites**)—the second segment or division of a maxilla, which bears the palpus, the galea, and the lacinia (Fig. 2-8 A, *stp*); lateral lobes of the millipede gnathochilarium (Fig. 30-11 B, *stp*).

Stomodaèum—the foregut.

Strìa (pl., **strìae**)—a groove or depressed line.

Strìate—with grooves or depressed lines.

Strídulate—to make a noise (chirp or creak) by rubbing two structures or surfaces together.

Stripe—a longitudinal color marking.

Stylate—with a style; stylelike; stylate antenna, Fig. 2-9 K.

Style—a bristlelike process at the apex of the antenna (Fig. 2-9 K, *sty*); a short, slender, fingerlike process (Fig. 6-2, *sty*).

Stylet—a needlelike structure; one of the piercing structures in sucking mouth parts.

Stylus (pl., **styli**)—a short, slender, fingerlike process (Thysanura; Fig. 6-2, *sty*).

Subantennal suture—a suture on the face extending ventrally from the base of the antenna (Figs. 2-3 and 29-12, *sas*).

Subápical—located just proximad of the apex.

Subbasal—located just distad of the base.

Subclass—a major subdivision of a class, containing a group of related orders.

Subcosta—the longitudinal vein between the costa and the radius (Fig. 2-8, Sc).

Subdiscal (or **subdiscoidal**) **vein**—the vein forming the posterior margin of the third discoidal cell (Hymenoptera, Figs. 29-1 and 29-3, *sd*).

Subequal—approximately, or almost, equal in size or length.

Subesophágeal ganglion—the knotlike swelling at the anterior end of the ventral nerve cord, usually just below the esophagus (Fig. 2-17, *segn*).

Subfamily—a major subdivision of a family, containing a group of related tribes or genera. Subfamily names end in *-inae*.

Subgènal suture—the horizontal suture below the gena, just above the bases of the mandibles and maxillae, a lateral extension of the epistomal suture (Fig. 2-3, *sgs*).

Subgénital plate—a platelike sternite that underlies the genitalia.

Subgènus (pl., **subgénera**)—a major subdivision of a genus, containing a group of related species. In scientific names, subgeneric names are capitalized and placed in parentheses following the genus name.

Subimàgo—the first of the two winged instars of a mayfly after it emerges from the water.

Submarginal cell—one or more cells lying immediately behind the marginal cell (Hymenoptera; Figs. 29-1 and 29-3, *SM*).

Submarginal vein—a vein immediately behind and paralleling the costal margin of the wing (Chalcidoidea; Fig. 29-16 B, *sm*).

Submedian cell—the cell behind the median cell, in the basal posterior portion of the wing (Hymenoptera; Figs. 29-1 and 29-3, *SMD*).

Submentum—the basal part of the labium (Fig. 2-10 C, *smt*).

Subocular suture—a suture extending ventrally from the compound eye (Fig. 2-3, *sos*).

Suborder—a major subdivision of an order, containing a group of related families.

Subphỳlum (pl., **subphỳla**)—a major subdivision of a phylum, containing a group of related classes.

Subquadrangle—a cell immediately behind the quadrangle (Odonata, Zygoptera; Fig. 8-3, *sq*).

Subspecies—a subdivision of a species, usually a geographic race. The different subspecies of a species are ordinarily not sharply differentiated and intergrade with one another and are capable of interbreeding.

Subtriangle—a cell or group of cells proximal to the triangle (Odonata, Anisoptera; Fig. 8-2, *str*).

Successions—groups of species that successively occupy a given habitat as the conditions of that habitat change.

Súlcate—with a groove or furrow.

Superfamily—a group of closely related families. Superfamily names end in *-oidea*.

Superior appendage—one of the two upper appendages at the end of the abdomen, a cercus (Odonata; Fig. 8-1, *sap*).

Supplement—an adventitious vein formed by a number of cross-veins being lined up to form a continuous vein, located behind and more or less parallel to one of the main longitudinal veins (Odonata; Fig. 8-2, *mspl, rspl*).

Supraalar bristles—a longitudinal row of bristles on the lateral portion of the mesonotum, immediately above the wing base (Diptera).

Suture—an external linelike groove in the body wall, or a narrow membranous area between sclerites (Fig. 2-2, *su*); the line of juncture of the elytra (Coleoptera).

Swimmeret—an abdominal appendage that functions as a swimming organ (Crustacea; Fig. 30-1, *sw*).

Sýmbiont—an organism living in symbiosis with another organism.

Symbiòsis—the living together, in a more or less intimate association, of two species, which benefits both.

Symmetry—a definite pattern of body organization; bilateral symmetry, a type of body organization in which the various parts are arranged more or less symmetrically on either side of a median vertical plane; that is, where the right and left sides of the body are essentially similar.

Synonyms—two or more names for the same thing.

Systematics—taxonomy (*q.v.*).

Taenídium (pl., **taenídia**)—a circular or spiral thickening in the inner wall of a trachea.

Tandem—one behind the other, the two connected or attached together.

Tarsal claw—a claw at the apex of the tarsus (Fig. 2-5, *tcl*).

Tarsal formula—the number of tarsal segments on the front, middle, and hind tarsi, respectively.

Tarsus (pl., **tarsi**)—that part of the leg beyond the tibia, consisting of one or more segments or subdivisions (Fig. 2-5, *ts*).

Taxís (pl., **taxes**)—a directed response involving the movement of an animal toward or away from a stimulus.

Taxonomy—the science of classification into categories of varying rank, based on similarities and differences, and the describing and naming of these categories.

Tégmen (pl., **tégmina**)—the thickened or leathery front wing of an orthopteran.

Tégula (pl., **tégulae**)—a small scalelike structure overlying the base of the front wing (Fig. 29-4, *tg*).

Telson—the posterior part of the last abdominal segment (Crustacea).

Tenáculum—a minute structure on the ventral side of the third abdominal segment which serves as a clasp for the furcula (Collembola).

Téneral—a term applied to a recently molted, pale, soft-bodied individual.

Tentorial pits—pitlike depressions on the surface of the head that mark the points of union of the arms of the tentorium with the outer wall of the head. There are usually two tentorial pits in the epistomal suture (Fig. 2-3, *atp*) and one at the lower end of each postoccipital suture (Fig. 2-3, *ptp*).

Tentorium—the endoskeleton of the head, usually consisting of two pairs of apodemes.

Tergite (the *g* has the soft or *j* sound)—a sclerite of the tergum; the dorsal surface of an abdominal segment (Fig. 2-1, *t*).

Tergum (pl., **terga**)—the dorsal surface of any body segment.

Terminal—at the end; at the posterior end (of the abdomen); the last of a series.

Terrestrial—living on land.

Testis (pl., **testes**)—the sex organ in the male that produces sperm.

Thorax—the body region behind the head, which bears the legs and wings (Fig. 2-1, *th*).

Tibia (pl., **tibiae**)—the fourth segment of the leg, between the femur and the tarsus (Fig. 2-5, *tb*).

Tibial spur—a large spine on the tibia, usually located at the distal end of the tibia.

Tórmogen cell—an epidermal cell associated with a seta; it forms the setal membrane or socket.

Tóxicognáth—a poison jaw (centipedes; Fig. 30-13, *pj*) (a modified leg).

Tràchea (pl., **tràcheae**)—a tube of the respiratory system, lined with taenidia, ending externally at a spiracle, and terminating internally in the tracheoles (Fig. 2-18).

Tracheòles—the fine terminal branches of the respiratory tubes.

Translucent—allowing light to pass through, but not necessarily transparent.

Transverse—across, at right angles to the longitudinal axis.

Transverse costal vein—a cross-vein in the costal cell (Hymenoptera; Fig. 29-1, *tc*).

Transverse cubital vein—a transverse vein connecting the marginal and cubital veins (Hymenoptera; Figs. 29-1 and 29-3, *tcb*).

Transverse marginal vein—a cross-vein in the marginal cell (Hymenoptera; Fig. 29-1, *trd*).

Transverse median vein—a cross-vein between the median or discoidal vein and the anal vein (Hymenoptera; Figs. 29-1, 29-3, *tm*).

Transverse radial vein—same as transverse marginal vein (which see).

Transverse suture—a suture across the mesonotum (Diptera; Fig. 27-5, *trs*).

Triangle—a small triangular cell or group of cells near the base of the wing (Odonata, Anisoptera; Figs. 8-2 and 8-4, *tri*).

Tribe—a subdivision of a subfamily, containing a group of related genera. Names of tribes end in *-ini.*

Trichobóthria—minute sensory hairs on the tarsi (spiders; Fig. 30-30 B, *trb*).

Tríchogen cell—the epidermal cell from which a seta develops.

Trígonal brace—a strong forked vein in the basal part of the wing, formed by the fork of Cu_1 in the front wing and of M_{3+4} in the hind wing (Neuroptera, Ascalaphidae, and Myrmeleontidae; Fig. 21-3, *trbr*).

Trigonal vein—the vein forming the anterior fork of the trigonal brace (Neuroptera, Ascalaphidae, and Myrmeleontidae).

Tripectinate—having three rows of comblike branches.

Triúngulin larva—the active first instar larva of the Strepsiptera and certain beetles that undergo hypermetamorphosis (Figs. 22-45 A and 23-1 F).

Trochánter—the second segment of the leg, between the coxa and the femur (Fig. 2-5, *tr*).

Trochántin—a small sclerite in the thoracic wall immediately anterior to the base of the coxa (Coleoptera; Fig. 22-5 B, *tn*).

Tròpism—the orientation of an animal with respect to a stimulus, either positive (turning toward the stimulus) or negative (turning away from the stimulus).

Truncate—cut off square at the end.

Truss cell—the cell immediately behind the point of fusion of Sc and R_1 (Neuroptera; Fig. 21-3, *trc*).

Tùbercle—a small knoblike or rounded protuberance.

Tỳlus—the clypeal region of the head (Hemiptera; Fig. 19-1, *ty*).

Týmbal—a sclerotized plate in the sound-producing organ of a cicada (Fig. 20-10, *tmb*).

Týmpanal hood—one of a pair of tubercles or rounded prominences on the dorsal surface of the first abdominal segment (Lepidoptera).

Týmpanum (pl., **týmpana**)—a vibrating membrane; an auditory membrane or eardrum (Fig. 2-5 D, *tym*).

Types—forms designated when a species or group is described to be most representative or typical, to serve as the reference if there is any question about what the species or group includes. The type of a species or subspecies (the holotype) is a specimen, the type of a genus or subgenus is a species, and the type of a tribe, subfamily, family, or superfamily is a genus.

Unisexual—consisting of or involving only females.

Uropod—one of the terminal pair of abdominal appendages, usually lobelike (Crustacea, Fig. 30-1, *ur*).

Vagìna—the terminal portion of the female reproductive system, which opens to the outside (Fig. 2-17, *vag*).

Válvifers—the basal plates of the ovipositor, derived from the basal segment of the gonopods.

Valvùlae—the three pairs of processes forming the sheath and piercing structures of the ovipositor.

Vánnal lobe—a lobe in the anal area of the wing, immediately distal to the jugal lobe when a jugal lobe is present (Hymenoptera; Fig. 29-68, *vl*).

Vás déferens (pl. **vàsa deferéntia**)—the sperm duct leading away from a testis.

Vein—a thickened line in the wing.

Venter—the ventral side.

Ventrad—toward the ventral or under side of the body; downward.

Ventral—lower or underneath; pertaining to the under side of the body.

Vermiform larva—a legless wormlike larva, without a well-developed head (Fig. 3-6 A).

Vertex—the top of the head, between the eyes and anterior to the occipital suture (Fig. 2-3, *ver*).

Vesicle—a sac, bladder, or cyst, often extensible.

Vestigial—small, poorly developed, degenerate, nonfunctional.

Vibrissae, oral—(see oral vibrissae).

Vitta (pl., **vittae**)—a broad stripe.

Vivíparous—giving birth to living young, not egg-laying.

Vulvar lamina—the posterior margin (usually prolonged posteriorly) of the eighth abdominal sternite (female Odonata).

Wireworm—an elateriform larva; a larva that is slender, elongate, heavily sclerotized, with a few hairs on the body, with thoracic legs but without prolegs; the larva of a click beetle (Fig. 22-30 B).

Y-vein—two adjacent veins fusing distally, forming a **Y**-shaped figure (for example, the anal veins in the front wing of Fig. 26-30 B).

REFERENCES

Borror, Donald J. 1960. Dictionary of word roots and combining forms. Palo Alto, California. N-P Publications. v + 134 pp.

Brown, Roland W. 1954. Composition of scientific words. Washington, D.C.; published by the author. 882 pp.

Carpenter, J. R. 1938. An ecological glossary. London: Kegan Paul, Trench, Trubner & Co. Ltd. ix + 306 pp., 12 app. of maps and tables.

Dorland, W. A. Newman. 1932 (16th ed.). The American illustrated medical dictionary. Philadelphia, Pa.: W. B. Saunders Company, 1493 pp., illus.

Hanson, Donald R. 1959. A short glossary of entomology with derivations. Published by the author, Los Angeles, Calif., 83 pp.

Henderson, I. F., and W. D. Henderson, 1939 (3rd ed., rev. by J. H. Kenneth). A dictionary of scientific terms. London: Oliver & Boyd Ltd. xii + 383 pp.

Jardine, N. K. 1913. The dictionary of entomology. London: West, Newman & Co. ix + 259 pp.

Smith, John B. 1906. Explanation of terms used in entomology. Brooklyn, N.Y.: Brooklyn Entomological Society. 154 pp., 3 pl.

Snodgrass, R. E. 1935. Principles of insect morphology. New York: McGraw-Hill Book Company, Inc. ix + 667 pp., 319 f.

Torre-Bueno, J. R. de la. 1937. A glossary of entomology. Lancaster, Pa.: Science Press. x + 336 pp., 9 pl.

Tuxen, S. L. (ed.). 1956. Taxonomist's glossary of genitalia in insects. Copenhagen: Ejnar Munksgaard. 284 pp., 215 f.

Tweney, C. F., and L. E. C. Hughes (ed.). 1940. Chambers's technical dictionary. New York: The Macmillan Company. viii + 957 pp.

Abbreviations Used in the Figures

The following list includes all the abbreviations used in the original figures in Chapters 2 through 30. The abbreviations used on wing drawings for the veins and cells (using the Comstock-Needham terminology) are not listed in the figure legends, but are included in the following list. Subscript numerals are used to designate branches of the longitudinal veins. Such numerals are often used to designate the particular thoracic segment on which a structure is located (1 designating the prothorax; 2, the mesothorax; and 3, the metathorax). Subscript numerals are occasionally used to designate the particular abdominal segment on which a sclerite is located.

a, anal vein
A, anal vein; anal cell
ab, abdomen
ac, accessory vein
Ac, anal crossing
acc, accessory cell
acl, antennal club
aclp, anteclypeus
acr, acrostichal bristles
acv, anterior cross-vein
adf, adfrontal area
aed, aedeagus
af, antennal tossa
agr, antennal groove
al, anal lobe
alp, anal loop
an, antenodal cross-veins
AN, alinotum
anc, anal cleft
anp, anal plate
anr, anal ring
ans, anus
ant, antenna
antl, antennule
ao, dorsal aorta
ap, appendix; appendiculate marginal cell
AP, apical or posterior cell
apc, apical cross-vein
apd, apodeme
apo, apophysis
ar, arista
arc, arculus
are, areolet
aro, arolium
art, articulation
as, antennal suture
asp, apical spur
aspr, anterior spiracle
at, alimentary tract
atb, anal tube
atp, anterior tentorial pit
au, auricle
av, auxiliary vein
aw, anterior wart
ax, axilla
AX, axillary cell
axc, axillary cell
axv, axillary vein

B, basal cell
BA, basal areole; basal anal cell
bcv, bridge cross-vein
bg, book gill
bk, beak, rostrum
bm, basement membrane
bp, brood pouch
br, brain
brv, bridge vein
buc, bucca; buccula
bv, basal vein
bvn, brace vein

c, costal vein
C, costa; costal cell
cal, calypter
cb, corbicula
cbr, costal break
cd, cardo
cec, circumesophageal connective
ch, chelicera
chp, cheliped
cl, clavus
cla, clasper
clm, calamistrum
clp, clypeus
cls, claval suture
clv, claval vein
cm, caecum
cn, colon
co, collophore
colm, collum
com, commissural trachea
con, connective
cor, corium
cp, crop
cph, cephalothorax
cr, cercus
crb, cribellum
cre, cremaster
crn, cornicle
cro, crochet
crp, carapace
cs, coronal suture
csp, cusp
ct, ctinidium
cu, cubital vein
Cu, cubitus; cubital cell
cun, cuneus
cut, cuticula
cvs, cervical sclerite

cvx, cervix
cx, coxa
cxc, coxal cavity
cxg, coxal groove
cxp, coxopodite

d, discoidal vein
D, discal cell; discoidal cell
dc, dorsocentral bristles
dcv, discal cross vein
dg, dorsal gonapophysis
do, dorsal ostioles
dtra, dorsal trachea

e, compound eye
ec, eye cap
ef, epigastric furrow
el, elytron
emb, embolium
emp, empodium
ep, epidermis
epcr, epicranium
epg, epigynum
eph, epipharynx
epm, epimeron
epp, epipleurite
eps, episternum
ept, epiproct
es, epistomal suture
eso, esophagus
ex, exuvia

f, frenulum
fa, face
fb, frontal bristles
fc, food channel
fl, flagellum
flb, flabellum
fm, femur
fmb, femoral bristle
fn, fang
fob, fronto-orbital bristles
fon, fontanelle
for, foramen magnum
fr, frons or front
frclp, frontoclypeus
frl, frontal lunule
fs, frontal suture
fu, furca
fur, furcula
fv, frontal vitta

g, galea
gc, genal comb
ge, gena
gen, genitalia
gi, gill
gl, glossa
gls, gland spines
gn, ganglion
gna, gnathochilarium
gr, gill remnant
gs, gular suture
gu, gula
gvp, genovertical plate

h, humeral cross-vein
hal, haltere
hb, humeral bristles
hc, humeral callus
hd, head
ho, horn
hr, heart or heart chambers
hst, haustellum
ht, humeral tooth
hv, humeral vein
hyb, hypopleural bristles
hyp, hypopharynx
hypl, hypopleuron

iab, intra-alar bristles
iap, inferior appendage
iar, interantennal ridge
ias, interantennal suture
ic, intercostal vein
ICu, cubital intercalary vein
iep, infraepisternum
il, ileum
ivb, inner vertical bristles

j, jugum
jl, jugal lobe

l, leg
L, lanceloate cell
lbl, labellum
lbm, labium
lbr, labrum
lc, lacinia
le, labrum-epipharynx
lg, ligula
lgp, lateral gonapophysis
ll, lamina lingualis
lo, lorum
lp, labial palpus
ls, labial suture
lst, lateral setae
ltra, longitudinal trachea

m, medial cross-vein
M, media, medial cell
MC, marginal cell
mcf, median caudal filament
m-cu, medio-cubital cross-vein
md, mandible
MD, median cell
mdu, microduct
mdv, median vein
mem, membrane
mf, fork of media
mg, midgut or mesenteron
mh, movable hook of palpus
ml, median lobe
mm, marginal macroducts
mn, mentum
mo, mouth
mp, mouth parts
mpb, mesopleural bristles
mpo, marginal 8-shaped pores
mr, mirror
msl, mesosternal lobe
mspl, medial supplement
mst, mental setae
mt, Malpighian tubules
mts, metatarsus; first tarsal segment
mv, marginal vein
mx, maxilla
mxl, maxillary lobe
mxp, maxillary palpus

n, notum
nb, notopleural bristles
nc, ventral nerve cord
n_1l, pronotal lobe
nod, nodus
npl, notopleuron

o, opening
ob, ocellar bristles
obv, oblique vein
oc, ecellus or simple eye
ocp, occiput
ocs, ocular suture
of, outer fork
omg, outer margin of coxal cavity
op, operculum
orp, orbital plate
os, occipital suture
osm, osmeterium
ot, ocellar triangle
ov, oral vibrissae
ovb, outer vertical bristles
ovd, oviduct
ovp, ovipositor
ovy, ovary

p, palpus
P, posterior cell
pa, postabdomen

pb, posthumeral bristle
pbr, pollen brush
pbs, prebasilare
pc, posterior callus
pclp, postclypeus
pcv, posterior cross-vein
pdp, pedipalp
ped, pedicel
pf, pilifer
pg, postgena
pgf, pygofer
pgl, paraglossa
phx, pharynx
pj, poison jaw
pl, pleuron
pla, plate
plf, palpifer
plg, palpiger
pls, pleural suture
plw, posterolateral wart
pm, postmarginal vein
pmt, postmentum
pn, postnodal cross-veins
PN, postnotum
po, postocciput
pos, postoccipital suture
pp, prepectus
ppb, propleural bristles
ppt, paraproct
pr, pollen rake
prb, proboscis
prc, pronotal comb
prd, propodeum
prl, proleg
prmt, prementum
pro, prosoma
prv, proventriculus
ps, parapsidal suture
psa, pseudarolium
psb, presutural bristles
pscl, postscutellum
pscu, pseudocubitus
psl, paired second lobe
psm, pseudomedia
psp, posterior spiracle
pt, pteropleuron
ptb, pteropleural bristles
ptbr, preapical tibial bristles
ptl, patella
ptp, posterior tentorial pit
ptsp, preapical tibial spur
pul, pulvillus
pv, postvertical bristles
pvp, perivalvular pores
pwp, pleural wing process
py, pygidium

q, quadrangle

r, radial cross-vein
R, radius; radial cell
rec, rectum
r-m, radio-medial cross-vein
Rs, radial sector
rspl, radial supplement
rv, recurrent vein

s, sectoral cross-vein
sa, sensory area
sap, superior appendage
sas, subantennal suture
sc, salivary channel
Sc, subcosta; subcostal cell
sca, scapula
scb, scutellar bristles
scl, scutellum
scn, sense cone; sense peg
sco, scopula
scp, scape
scr, scar
sct, scutum
scv, subcostal vein
sd, subdiscoidal or subdiscal vein
sec, secretion of adult
segn, subesophageal ganglion
sgl, salivary glands
sgo, scent gland opening
sgs, subgenal suture
sh, shell
sld, salivary duct
sm, submarginal vein
SM, submarginal vein
SMD, submedian cell
smm, submedial macroducts
smml, submarginal macroducts
smt, submentum
sos, subocular suture
sp, spine or spur
spb, supraalar bristles
spbr, spiracular bristle
spn, spinneret
spr, spiracle
spth, spermatheca
spv, spurious vein
sq, subquadrangle
st, stigma
stb, sternpleural bristles
stg, prosternal groove
stn, sternite or sternum
stp, stipes
stpl, sternopleuron
str, subtriangle
stra, spiracular trachea
sty, style, stylet, or stylus
su, suture
sv, stigmal vein
sw, swimmeret

t, tergite or tergum
tb, tibia
tbr, tergal bristles
tc, transverse costal vein
tcb, transverse cubital vein
tcl, tarsal claw
tg, tegula
th, thorax
thap, thoracic appendages
tl, transverse lanceolate vein
tm, transverse median vein
tmb, tymbal
tn, trochantin
tnt, tentorium
tr, trochanter
trb, trichobothria
trbr, trigonal brace
trc, truss cell
trd, transverse radial vein
tri, triangle
trs, transverse suture
ts, tarsus
tsp, tibial spur
tub, tubercle
ty, tylus
tym, tympanum

ur, uropod

va, valve
vag, vagina
vc, ventral circulus
ver, vertex
vf, valvifer
vg, ventral gonapophysis
vl, vannal lobe
vlv, valvula
vtra, ventral trachea
vu, vulna

w, wing
wb, base of wing

y, young

INDEX

Numbers in italics refer to pages bearing illustrations; numbers in bold face indicate the most important page references. Italicized letters in parentheses are abbreviations used in labeling the figures. Names in capitals are taxonomic groups larger than a genus. A number of items not in this index may be found in the glossary (p. 741).